Matthew Fontaine Maury
Scientist of the Sea

Matthew Fontaine Maury
Scientist of the Sea

by

FRANCES LEIGH WILLIAMS

RUTGERS UNIVERSITY PRESS

New Brunswick   *New Jersey*

This book was manufactured with the assistance of
a grant from The Ford Foundation

Manufactured in the United States of America by
Quinn & Boden Company, Inc., Rahway, New Jersey

Grateful acknowledgment is made to Houghton Mifflin
Company for permission to quote from *The Year of
Decision* by Bernard De Voto and *Recollections of a
Rebel Reefer* by James Morris Morgan.

To the memory of
my parents
Francis Deane Williams
Mary Mason Anderson Williams
who kindled my interest in history
and
Douglas Southall Freeman
who introduced me to the joys and
disciplines of historical research

Preface

The U.S. Navy continues to bestow its commendation "well done" on Matthew Fontaine Maury for services rendered more than a century ago. Each of the pilot charts issued monthly by the U.S. Naval Oceanographic Office bears the words "Founded upon the researches made in the early part of the nineteenth century by Matthew Fontaine Maury, while serving as a lieutenant in the United States Navy."

First superintendent of the U.S. Naval Observatory and Hydrographical Office, Maury spent years of intensive study of the ocean—its currents, its tides, depths, salinity, temperatures—and the winds above it. This work enabled him in 1847 to begin publication of his revolutionary *Wind and Current Charts* of the oceans of the world, soon followed by his *Sailing Directions,* which explained the shorter, safer sailing routes revealed by his studies.

Maury early became convinced that adequate scientific knowledge of the sea could be obtained only through international co-operation. He proposed that the United States invite the maritime nations of the world to a conference to establish a "universal system" of meteorology, and he was the leading spirit of that pioneer scientific conference when it met in Brussels in 1853. Within a few years, nations owning three fourths of the shipping of the world were sending their oceanographic observations to Maury at the Naval Observatory, where the information was evaluated and the results given worldwide distribution.

The first accurate, systematic deep-sea soundings, made under his direction, led to the discovery of the "telegraphic plateau" in the Atlantic. Further studies made it possible for Maury to contribute knowledge of major importance to the successful laying of the Atlantic Cable and to the exploration of the Arctic and the Antarctic.

Crusading articles written by Maury while recovering from an accident played a significant role in the establishment of the bureau system for naval administration and the U.S. Naval Academy. He was also the author of a textbook on navigation that became required study for midshipmen.

Maury's major publication was *The Physical Geography of the Sea* (first published in 1855), a work in which he so effectively recorded the facts then known about the sea, the results of his research, and his theories about the phenomena of the sea that the book came to be recognized as the first textbook of modern oceanography. It was widely read, in addition, because it was one of the first books containing scientific information written in language a layman could understand.

Maury used his influence to secure navigation of the Amazon River for the ships of the world. He fought for a national weather service that would predict as well as report the weather, that would supply crop reports to farmers.

Maury travelled no easy path to success. His life was a series of the most dramatic obstacles and challenges. His theories and actions—and successes—not only brought him international acclamation—honors from universities and nearly fifty learned societies, decorations from emperors, kings, and Pope Pius IX—they aroused controversy and earned him powerful enemies. When, at the peak of his career, Virginia seceded from the Union, Maury did not hesitate to act. Fully aware he was giving up all that he had worked and hoped for—enlarged scientific activity, his beloved Navy, the financial security and education of his family— Maury resigned his United States commission to serve his native state. Maury devised a system of torpedo defense for southern harbors, perfected his electric torpedoes, and went to England to purchase and outfit Confederate cruisers. Upon the collapse of the Confederacy, he conceived a plan whereby war-stricken Confederates might make a new start in the undeveloped lands of Mexico, and he became Imperial Commissioner of Colonization under Maximilian to put his plan into effect. As soon as it appeared safe for him to return to the United States, Maury began to work for the rebuilding of the South while serving as professor of physics at the Virginia Military Institute and superintendent of the Physical Survey of Virginia.

Why, then, is Maury so little known today except by specialists of the fields in which he worked?

The greatest single reason is that his whole colorful story has never been told. There has been no fully documented Maury biography based on research in depth from primary sources.

Of the books about him the best have been *A Life of Matthew Fontaine Maury, U.S.N. and C.S.N.*, compiled by his daughter, Diana Fontaine Maury Corbin, and *Matthew Fontaine Maury: The Pathfinder of the Seas* by Charles Lee Lewis, associate professor of the U.S. Naval Academy.

The Corbin work, published in London in 1888, was the only life of Maury available for 54 years after his death. This memoir continues to provide an interesting picture of Maury in the midst of his family. But because the publisher failed to give the author the opportunity to correct proofs, the book contains numerous errors that have been repeated by other authors who did not check the original letters, speeches, and other materials in the Manuscript Division of the Library of Congress, the Maury Collection of the Alderman Library of the University of Virginia, the Navy and Military Service Branch of the National Archives, or in smaller collections owned by individuals or libraries.

A good general view of Maury's career was presented in the biography by Charles Lee Lewis published in Annapolis in 1927. However, certain significant phases of Maury's work were not adequately covered, there was scant study of Maury the man, and only the most limited documentation provided. Encouragement to search out and correct errors in previously published material was given me in full measure by Professor Lewis, and I wish to pay him tribute for his scholarly, generous, and heartening attitude.

Out of respect for my predecessors, I want to say that no previous statements have been controverted without unequivocal proof. Research in original sources has enabled me to correct errors of varying degrees of significance, beginning with the wrong date of Maury's birth and ranging through incorrect assertions about his professional and personal life to the wrong date of his burial. Necessary corrections proved so numerous that I have described most of them in the Notes rather than in the body of the text.

I had the extreme good fortune of finding material that throws new light on various phases of Maury's life. This material fills in gaps in knowledge about his forebears, his early home life, his years at sea, and the difficulties that caused him to ask to be relieved as astronomer of the Navy's South Seas Exploring Expedition. Court records supplied additional information on the stagecoach accident in which Maury was crippled, on the homes in which he lived. The hitherto unused abstract of the Court of Inquiry before which Maury appeared is the basis for my account of that ordeal through which Maury passed so successfully. A wide variety of sources made it possible for me to report in detail personal relations and background developments that were of great significance in Maury's life. Of this type, none is more important than the story of the well-disguised but unrelenting opposition that Maury encountered in Washington from rival scientists Alexander Dallas Bache, superintendent of the U.S. Coast Survey, Joseph Henry, secretary of the Smithsonian Institution, and their scientific friends, as well as opposition from certain fellow officers of the Navy. Recent books on Bache and Henry barely mention Maury—and then either faintly intimate their antagonism to Maury or suggest that all was friendly between the three scientific leaders in Washington in the two decades before the Civil War. I have endeavored to present not only an accurate but a balanced account of this highly significant feud. For the reader who desires more details on Maury's antagonists, the Notes and Bibliography provide information on their writings and on articles and books about them.

It is my hope that I have cut a clear path for the reader through the labyrinth of oft-repeated given names of the Fontaines, Maurys, Minors, and Herndons. Matthew Fontaine Maury pronounced his last name Mawry, as is the custom among the Virginia Maurys. Maury is, however, generally pronounced Murray in Tennessee; and I have learned that Maury's own nephew, Maj. Gen. Dabney Herndon Maury, pronounced Fontaine as if it were written Fountain. I have followed family usage in writing Jean de la Fontaine, rather than Jean de La Fontaine as recommended by some authorities.

In the chapters describing Maury's years at sea, I have used nautical terms and the system of stating time found in the logs, ships' journals, officers' journals of the day, or in letters or published writings of Maury and his contemporaries. In many cases, these terms differ from those in present use by seafarers. In his writings Maury used "the" before the name of a ship, and I have done the same. In official communications Maury employed the military or European style of writing a date, but in general writing he made use of the American style. For ease of reading, I have followed the latter style. Quotation marks are used with the name of a plantation the first time it is mentioned in the text but not thereafter. Maury wrote the name of plantations without quotation marks.

Wherever a choice of terminology had to be made, I used the term employed either by Maury or by the official body that handled the subject under discussion. My use of Navy Retiring Board, rather than Naval Retiring Board, is based on Maury's usage; the latter title was generally used in the stormy congressional debates on the work of this board and so appears in the quotations in this book from those debates. The tragic conflict of 1861-1865 is called the Civil War in this book because Maury used that term rather than War Between the States, the name preferred by many Southerners. I also decided in favor of *Merrimac,* rather than the technically correct spelling *Merrimack,* because the Governor's Advisory Council, of which Maury was a member, used this spelling when they voted to raise the vessel for ironplating.

In my effort to give an authoritative account of each phase of his work I have, whenever possible, let the story be told in Maury's words (as in the account of the commencement of astronomic work at the Naval Observatory) or in those of a contemporary expert (as in the explanation of how Maury created his wind and current charts and discovered shorter sailing routes, which is told as presented to the House of Lords by Baron Wrottesley, the distinguished British astronomer and scientific leader).

Notes providing both documentation and supplementary material are at the back of the book to prevent intrusion on the reader's pleasure. The Bibliography includes the location of manuscript sources. I have also prepared and included a bibliography of Maury's publications.

Maury was a man whose scientific work has special relevance in our time, when oceanography is daily becoming more important to the national defense and to the increasing population of the world. It has been my aim to provide a book that gives the full story of Maury, both for the specialists of the fields in which he worked and for the general reader who wants to become acquainted with the accomplishments and life of one of the most controversial and neglected figures in the history of America and science.

FRANCES LEIGH WILLIAMS

Acknowledgments

(Titles listed are those of positions held at the time of my research.)

I want first to express my gratitude to Maury's granddaughter, Mrs. N. Montgomery Osborne of Norfolk, Virginia, for aiding me in the early phases of my research with insight into Maury family traditions and *esprit*. My warmest thanks go also to another member of the family, Mrs. Anne Fontaine Maury Hirschfeld of Lantana, Florida, for the loan of her copy of the Genealogical Chart of the Fontaine and Maury families begun by her great-great-aunt, Ann Maury of New York, and especially for arranging for me to have unlimited study of the letters from Matthew Fontaine Maury to her grandparents, Commander and Mrs. William Lewis Maury and to Matthew, Ann, and Rutson Maury of New York—letters that are regularly on loan to the Alderman Library, University of Virginia. I am indebted to Greenhow Maury, Jr., of Richmond for family data and for permitting me to have copies made of early pencil drawings of the Fontaines; to the late Mrs. Martha R. Upshur of Richmond for information on Maury's wartime stay in the home of her grandfather, Robert Henry Maury, and for interpretation of some of the intricacies of Maury genealogy; to Maury's great-granddaughter, Mrs. Mary Maury Fitzgerald McKeon of Amherst, Massachusetts, for encouragement in my research; to Miss Lucy Herndon Ewin of Biloxi, Mississippi, for information on Ann Herndon; to Herndon Maury Gatewood of Richmond for making available to me the Bible in which Richard and Diana Maury recorded the baptismal sponsors of their children and other family data, the Bible in which Matthew Fontaine Maury and his wife Ann Herndon Maury recorded the births of their children, as well as other books and pictures that belonged to Maury.

For advice on naval matters, I am particularly indebted to Rear Admiral James C. Shaw, USN (Ret.) Cos Cob, Connecticut, and Dr. John

Acknowledgments

Lyman of the National Science Foundation, Washington, for a critical reading of the entire manuscript; Commander Robert H. Maury, USN (Ret.), Weems School of Navigation, Annapolis, for a reading of the chapters describing Maury's years at sea, those of Matthew's brother John, and for correcting technical errors therein; Captain F. Kent Loomis, USN (Ret.), Office of the Chief of Naval Operations, Washington, for information about ships in which Maury sailed; Rear Admiral John D. Hayes, USN (Ret.), of Annapolis, for a clarification of points about naval rank prior to 1861; Mrs. Marjorie S. Clopine, Librarian, U.S. Naval Observatory, Washington, for reading and offering helpful comment on the portion of the manuscript describing the founding of the Naval Observatory; Col. Floyd M. Johnson, Jr., USMC, Quantico, Virginia, for securing information on the Navy's present use of the original U.S. Naval Observatory building and for accompanying me on a highly instructive visit to the historic structure; William G. Watt, Director, Maritime Safety Division, Vincent T. Miscoski, Technical Assistant to the Director of Technical Production Department, and Oscar L. Martin, Navy Specialist, Pilot Chart Section, Maritime Safety Division, U.S. Naval Oceanographic Office, Washington, for arranging an examination of that office's complete collection of Maury's Wind and Current Charts, for explaining them, for assisting in making the best selection for reproduction, and for checking my bibliography of Maury's charts; Captain W. J. Murphy, USN, Director, Litigation and Claims Division, Office of the Judge Advocate General, for explaining the procedure of the court of inquiry held on Maury; Captain Wade DeWeese, USN (Ret.), Director, United States Naval Academy Museum, Annapolis, for information on Maury Hall at the Naval Academy and assistance in securing pictures; Lieutenant Commander D. M. Cooney, Head, Magazine and Book Branch, Office of Information, Department of the Navy, for locating additional pictures.

For extremely generous assistance in manuscript repositories, libraries, and museums, I want to express gratitude to Elbert L. Huber, Chief, Navy and Military Service Branch, National Archives; Dr. C. P. Powell, John de Porry, Dr. Elizabeth G. McPherson, Manuscript Division, Library of Congress; Legare H. B. Obear, Chief of the Loan Division, Library of Congress; Milton Kaplan and Miss Virginia Daiker, Prints and Photographs Division, Library of Congress, Edward N. MacConomy, Merwin C. Phelps, Legislative Reference Service, Library of Congress, Charles E. Deatley, Archivist, Smithsonian Institution; Mrs. Fowler Wahl and Mrs. Margarette de Andrade of the Brazilian Embassy; Mme. Avenel, Librarian, French Embassy, all of Washington, District of Columbia;

Acknowledgments

to Milton C. Russell, Head, Reference and Circulation Section, General Library Division, Mrs. Bertie Craig Smith, Assistant Head and their associates of the Reference and Circulation Section, General Library Division, Virginia State Library; John W. Dudley, Assistant Archivist, Virginia State Library; Miss India Thomas, House Regent, The Confederate Museum; Miss Elizabeth J. Dance, Curator of Prints, The Valentine Museum; Col. Catesby ap Catesby Jones, Executive Secretary, and James A. Fleming, Curator of Printed Books, Virginia Historical Society; all of Richmond, Virginia;

to Francis L. Berkeley, Jr., Curator of Manuscripts, Miss Anne Freudenberg, Robert E. Stocking, Assistants in Manuscripts, Alderman Library, University of Virginia; Robert W. Jeffrey and Joseph Presbrey, who have served successively as Director of Public Relations, Virginia Military Institute, Lexington; Seymour Robb, Librarian, Carol M. Newman Library, Virginia Polytechnic Institute, Blacksburg, Mrs. Thomas V. Brabrand, Curator of Prints, Albert M. Barnes, Assistant Curator of Exhibits, The Mariners Museum, Newport News; Parke S. Rouse, Jr., Executive Director, Jamestown Commission, Jamestown Island, all of Virginia;

to Dr. Dan M. Robison, State Librarian and Archivist, State of Tennessee, Robert T. Quarles, Assistant Archivist, Tennessee State Library and Archives, and President of the Tennessee Historical Society, Nashville; to the late Mrs. O. N. Torian, Archivist, University of the South, Sewanee; Arthur Ben Chitty, Jr., Historiographer of the University of the South, and his wife Elizabeth, all of Tennessee;

to William S. Powell, Librarian, North Carolina Collection, University of North Carolina, Chapel Hill, North Carolina;

to Thomas Graham, Secretary-General, Descendants of the Signers of the Declaration of Independence, Mrs. Dorothy Charlton Hauck, The Historical Society of Pennsylvania, both of Philadelphia;

to Miss Elizabeth E. Roth, First Assistant, Print Room, New York Public Library, Mrs. H. A. Downing, Secretary, American Society of the French Legion of Honor, both of New York;

to Miss Dorothy A. Brockhoff, Reference Librarian, Missouri Historical Society, St. Louis, Missouri.

Acknowledgments

In my search for primary source material in the Spotsylvania-Fredericksburg, Virginia, area where Maury was born and later lived for some years, I received valuable assistance from Oscar Fitzallen Northington, Jr., Superintendent of the Fredericksburg and Spotsylvania National Park, who took me to the site of the house in which Maury was born, explained the few facts known about the original dwelling and supplied me with many answers on soil conditions, iron furnaces, and churches of the area; from Ralph Happel, Park Historian, who added valuable information on the roads traveled by the Maurys on their journey to Tennessee; from George H. S. King, genealogist of Fredericksburg, who provided facts on churches and early ministers of Spotsylvania County; from Mrs. Maria Herndon Morton and Mrs. Marguerite M. Morton of "Maple Hill," Post Oak, Spotsylvania County, who gave me clear information on the numerous Herndon homes in the county; from Joseph Savage, Jr., attorney of Fredericksburg, who checked a court record that included a deposition by Maury on the house he rented in Fredericksburg; and from Mrs. Wistar Braxton, who made me welcome in her home so that I might become personally acquainted with the house in which Maury spent many happy prewar hours with his Minor cousins, and in which Maury's family lived during the first months of the Civil War.

In my research in Tennessee, where Maury spent his youth, I met with generous assistance at every turn. I am particularly indebted to Captain Thomas P. Henderson, attorney of Franklin, who made available to me his wealth of knowledge about that community and the whole of Williamson County, interpreted legal records in the Franklin Court House, took me to visit the site of Harpeth Academy as well as "Tree Hill," originally the home of Abram Maury, and through the courtesy of its owner, Will Reese, Sr., to make a study of the gravestones in the family burying ground on the estate. Captain Henderson also showed me other landmarks familiar to Maury in his youth, and took me to meet Mr. and Mrs. Harry A. Ormes, the owners of the 200-acre farm of Richard and Diana Maury. To Mr. and Mrs. Ormes I am deeply grateful for answering endless questions, for taking me over the central portion of the farm, explaining the lay of the whole farm, the soil and its degree of productivity, and the water supply, for aiding me in the examination of the chimney ruins of the Richard Maury log home and the gravestones of Maury's brother and sister, for permitting me to study the abstract of their property that led me to long-searched-for information on Richard and Diana's possession of the land; to Mrs. Ewing Roberts Green of Franklin for permission to have copied her photostat of the grant to her great-grandfather Alexanderia Ewing of land on which Richard Maury temporarily settled his family on reaching Tennessee.

Many other individuals have assisted me generously in the preparation of this book. I want especially to thank Mrs. Mary Wells Ashworth, Richmond, author, for reading the first portion of the manuscript and for wise and generous counsel; Lundie Weathers Barlow, then of Boston, for ascertaining facts about manuscripts in the Houghton Library, Harvard University; the Rev. George MacLaren Brydon, D.D., Historiographer of the Diocese of Virginia, for information on Episcopal clergymen who officiated in Spotsylvania County, Virginia, during Maury's early childhood years; the late Robert Hill Carter of "Redlands," Carter's Bridge, Virginia, for facts about Maury's friend and fellow naval officer, Robert Carter of Shirley; Major Robert T. Fallon, USA, Instructor of English, U.S. Military Academy, West Point, New York, for a critical reading of the manuscript; James R. Gilliam, Jr., of Lynchburg, Virginia, for lending me valuable items from his Maury collection; the Rt. Rev. Frederick D. Goodwin, Bishop of Virginia, for assistance in my search for facts on Maury's baptism; Mrs. Jane Bell Gladding, Dean of Women and Associate Professor of Chemistry, Richmond Professional Institute, Richmond, Virginia, for securing out-of-date chemical information; Mrs. Alice Rogers Hager of Arlington, Virginia, author and former Foreign Service Officer, U.S. Information Agency, for a reading of the manuscript with special reference to the international aspects of Maury's work; Maj. Gen. Henry Winston Holt, of Richmond, then Assistant Adjutant General for Air, Virginia, for securing data on the militia services of Maury's forebears; Mrs. Betty Lou Holt of Richmond for bibliographical assistance; Mrs. Amanda Bryan Kane of New York for the gift of a valuable Maury pamphlet; the Rev. Stiles B. Lines, Ph.D., Rector of St. Paul's Church, Delray Beach, Florida, for facts on early church history, Miss Jackie Martin of Washington for making available her photographic knowledge in the selection of Maury's charts for reproduction in this book; to Dr. Robert Douthat Meade, Head of the History Department, Randolph-Macon Woman's College, Lynchburg, Virginia, for information about the Rev. James Maury; the Rt. Rev. Robert C. Mortimer, Bishop of Exeter, England, for facts about confirmation records in England; Lewis F. Powell, Jr., attorney of Richmond, for interpreting obscure phrases in early Maury deeds and for reading the chapters in which legal instruments played a significant role in Maury family life; Colonel Kenneth Purdie, then Associate Professor of Mathematics, Virginia Military Institute, for facts on Lexington and Goshen Pass, Virginia; to Mrs. Mary Harding Ragland of Richmond for invaluable assistance in making it possible for me to study in her home the collection of Maury letters to her great-grandfather General William Giles Harding of "Belle Meade," Nashville—letters regularly on loan to Vanderbilt University Library, Nashville; Miss Marie Sauer, Washington editor, for a critical reading of the manuscript and much appreciated suggestions of needed changes; Dr. Earl Gregg Swem, then of Williamsburg, Virginia, for scholarly and helpful advice on involved points of research; Dr. Harry J. Warthen of Richmond for a modern surgeon's interpretation of the contemporary descriptions of the injuries suffered by Maury in his stagecoach accident and of his terminal illness; J. Harvie Wilkinson, Jr., banker of Richmond, for securing authoritative information on currency values in the late eighteenth century; the Rev. John Page Williams, Dean of Church Schools in the Diocese of Virginia, for assistance in my search for the date of Maury's confirmation in London; Mrs. Rebecca Yancey Williams of Richmond, author, for aid in securing information on contemporaries of Richard Maury.

For diligence and unfailing patience in typing the four complete drafts of this manuscript, I am grateful to Mrs. Betsey Mullen Hathaway, Mrs. Doris McFarland Davison, Mrs. Norma Kruger, Mrs. Helen H. Quinn, Mrs. Mary K. Kahr, Miss Mary Mason Holt, Mrs. Cathryn Vaden, and Mrs. Sophie Whitworth.

Thanks of a particular order are due Philip Van Doren Stern of Brooklyn, New York, for scholarly generosity in sending me information on Matthew Fontaine Maury, Matthew and Rutson Maury, from the Public Record Office, London, and for his advocacy of a completely documented work on Maury.

I want to pay a personal tribute to my aunt, Mrs. Kathleen Anderson Bourland, for the sustaining encouragement she has given me from the autumn day in 1955 when I first discussed with her a tentative outline of this biography. Her unflagging interest and moral support have been of immeasurable value to me.

My deepest thanks of all go to my friend and business partner, Winifred Hanigan. Her unfaltering belief in this work has, in Maury's words, "strenthened my hands" and made possible the long sustained effort.

Contents

Contents

Matthew Fontaine Maury
Scientist of the Sea

CHAPTER I

A Challenging Heritage

No wind from the sea blew across the winter-drab fields of Spotsylvania County, Virginia, on January 14, 1806,[1] when Matthew Fontaine Maury was born. Nor did any other omen of the child's future hover over the home of his parents, Richard and Diana Maury, on their small plantation in Spotsylvania's Wilderness area,[2] more than a hundred miles inland from the surf-pounded coast. True, the town of Fredericksburg, ten miles to the east, possessed wharves from which ships found their way down the Rappahannock River into Chesapeake Bay and on into the Atlantic Ocean. But small Matthew was to have no such trip nor sight of the sea for years to come.

Westward, not eastward, his parents would take him before he reached his fifth birthday. His trouble-beset father would pack wife, children, and chattels into wagons, cross the tree-topped Blue Ridge and Allegheny Mountains, and then push down into Tennessee to settle near the town of Franklin. When seven, Matthew would move with his parents and his numerous brothers and sisters into a log house on their farm in a narrow valley in Williamson County. There he would often watch the clouds that sailed high overhead. But those were the only sailing objects that he would see, for there were no ships on the nearby West Harpeth River—it was scarcely wider than a creek.

Yet this boy of the land, whose father wanted him to be a farmer, would at nineteen turn his face toward the sea. He would go not only for action and adventure but because of a hunger for knowledge that burned within him. He would secure a midshipman's warrant in the hope that the Navy would give him the knowledge of mathematics and science that he coveted. He would go to sea, learn about ships, and absorb all that the Navy, not yet possessing an academy, could teach him aboard a man-of-war. But, even more, this nature-observing youth would study the Sea and her ways. He would give her the devotion of

1

close attention, and eventually she would reveal to him secrets she had until then withheld from all.

What peculiar ability and quality were met in Matthew Fontaine Maury to open his eyes to that which others had not perceived? From what source did he gain the mind and energy needed to investigate and systematize knowledge of the sea until a science was born?

Environment played its part, but Maury was to a marked degree the product of his heritage.

In France, about 1535, a young aristocrat, Jean de la Fontaine, an officer in the household of Francis I,[3] was converted to Protestantism. Jean's allegiance to the new and unpopular Huguenot faith was known at court, but his abilities were so valued that he was retained in royal service through the reigns of Henry II, Francis II, and the first two years of Charles IX's minority. His high position provided a safeguard against persecution and enabled him to assist fellow Huguenots.

When the Edict of Pacification was pronounced on January 17, 1562, Jean believed that persecution would cease, and he resigned his court post to take up residence on his estate near Le Mans in the province of Maine. He had, however, underestimated the hatred felt by the Catholic populace toward Huguenots. One night a little more than a year later a band of zealous anti-Protestants bludgeoned their way into his house and murdered him, his wife, and his valet.[4]

During the noisy confusion of the attack, Jean's 14-year-old son, Jacques, led his younger brothers out of the house and, with them, made his way on foot to La Rochelle, the Protestant stronghold on the coast. There a shoemaker took Jacques in and taught him how to make and mend shoes. He supported his brothers from his meager wages. In early manhood Jacques established his own business and prospered. In 1603 he married, and at the end of that year his wife bore him a son, Jacques II. When his first wife died, Jacques remarried. His second wife attempted to poison him, apparently to inherit his fortune. His life having been saved by prompt medical attention, Jacques tried to hush up the poison attempt, but this proved impossible. His wife was carried to prison, tried, and condemned to death. Henry IV happened to be at La Rochelle at the time, and Jacques applied to him for a pardon for her. The King of France said he must see the husband Madame de la Fontaine had been so anxious to get rid of; he wanted to judge from the man's appearance whether there was any excuse for her act. When Jacques appeared before the King, Henry IV cried out, "Let her be hanged, let her be hanged. He is the handsomest man in my kingdom." Jacques died in 1633 and left his family 9,000 livres.[5]

Jacques II early showed aptitude for study, was tutored by a Protestant clergyman in La Rochelle, studied at the College of Saumur, and at the Protestant Theological Seminary in that city on the Loire River. Before entering the ministry he traveled as tutor to a young nobleman and during his travels learned several foreign languages. In 1641 Jacques II married Marie Chaillon, a handsome brunette from the village of Rue au Roy, near the town of Pons, in Saintonge. Marie, having brought a good dowry to the marriage, persuaded her husband to buy a small estate called "Jenouille" and the nearby manor of Jaffé, located near the little town of Royan, which faces the Atlantic Ocean at the mouth of the Gironde. Jacques was as ardent a Huguenot as his father and grandfather had been. His religious beliefs led him to decide that, in the practice of humility, he and his family should drop the aristocratic prefix *de la* from their name. He served as pastor of the united Protestant churches of Vaux and Royan, preaching in one village in the morning and in the other in the afternoon. When his church at Royan was pulled down, as a part of the persecution of Huguenots, he continued to preach in the ruins until forced to stop. Foreseeing an intensification of persecution, he prepared his congregations for the trials ahead, turning down a call to a large church at La Rochelle to stay with his people. He died at his home in 1666.[6]

His son, Jacques III, was born at Jenouille on April 7, 1658. While he was a baby, his nurse dropped him. To hide her carelessness she took him to be examined by an ignorant doctor who failed to observe that his right leg was broken below the knee. The fractured bone knitted irregularly and made him lame for life. He was, however, handsome of face and "was of a very lively and inventive turn." The boy early showed marked intellectual ability and went on to secure a master's degree from the college of the province of Guyenne. He successfully managed both of the paternal estates that he inherited and, being a candidate for the ministry, served as pastor to his father's congregations, whose churches had been destroyed. His ministry, carried on in secret, was first halted by imprisonment and then terminated by the Revocation of the Edict of Nantes, issued in October, 1685. Jacques refused to obey the order to abjure his Huguenot faith and left the country to avoid the death penalty decreed by Louis XIV for any Protestant pastor remaining in France fifteen days after announcement of the Revocation. Jacques also smuggled his fiancée, her sister, and his niece onto a fishing vessel bound for England. After eleven days on the water, they landed at Appledore, in Devon, on the Bristol Channel, and went up the Taw River to the town of Barnstaple. Jacques and his fellow Huguenot refugees were taken into

3

the homes of sympathetic English people, and Jacques adopted the English version of his Christian name, being thenceforth known as James Fontaine.[7] Meanwhile in France his estates had been confiscated and awarded to his nearest of Roman Catholic kin.

James Fontaine and his fiancée Anne Elizabeth Boursiquot were married in the parish church in Barnstaple on February 8, 1686.[8] They settled in Taunton, the trade center of Somersetshire, where James Fontaine struggled to make a living. At first James worshipped in the Church of England parish church but was disturbed by the Established Church's persecution of Presbyterians and lack of charity to Huguenots. He therefore presented himself to the Presbyterian Synod assembled at Taunton in 1688, was examined, and received holy orders from that body on June 10, 1688.[9] He served as minister to impoverished fellow Huguenots and established a small cloth-weaving business to earn a living for himself and refugee French weavers. Devising a method by which he wove a greatly superior calimanco cloth, James became such a successful competitor to English weavers that they forced him to retire from business and leave Taunton.[10]

The much-beleaguered man moved his family to Ireland in December of 1694.[11] There at Bear Haven on the coast of Cork he developed a fishing business so profitable it attracted the attention of French privateers, who considered Huguenots fair prey. Fortunately one of the Fontaines had a dream warning that they were about to be attacked, and so the family was prepared and able to drive off a first privateer attack. The Frenchmen, however, returned in greater force, seized all the fishing boats, gear, and nets and destroyed the work shacks.[12]

Realizing that further effort in this isolated spot was pointless, James Fontaine moved his wife and eight children to Dublin, where he leased a house on St. Stephen's Green and established a preparatory school. The school proved very successful and enabled James Fontaine to give both his sons and daughters an excellent preparatory education.[13]

With funds derived from his school he sent three of his sons to college. Two of them, Peter and Francis, decided to become clergymen.[14] John, desiring action, became an ensign in Lord Shaw's Regiment of the British Army and participated in the fighting in Spain in the Spanish War of Succession.[15] On returning home he resigned his commission and, after futile efforts to secure employment in Ireland, agreed with his father that the future of the young Fontaines lay across the Atlantic, where a new land offered opportunity. The matter was discussed by all, for they were an extraordinarily close-knit family, given to acting as a unit. It was decided that John should go first to America to see if he could buy a tract on which his brothers and sisters could settle. He arrived in Virginia in May, 1715.[16]

Not long after John's departure, his sister Mary Anne, living with her parents in Ireland, became engaged and was married in Dublin on October 20, 1716, to Matthew Maury. Matthew was warmly welcomed into the Fontaine family because he was the son of devout Huguenots, Abraham and Marie Fourquereau Maury, who had fled from their home, Castel Mauron in Gascony, following the Revocation of the Edict of Nantes.[17]

Matthew and Mary Anne soon decided they also would like to make their life in the New World. These two young people, who were to be the great-grandparents of Matthew Fontaine Maury, waited impatiently in Dublin for word from John as to whether he had found land on which they could settle. Infrequent letters brought news from John of his warm welcome to Virginia by His Majesty's lieutenant governor and commander in chief of the royal colony, Alexander Spotswood,[18] and by numerous planters of distinction. John had been on several tours within the colony to look at land for sale, but instead of reporting facts about land he told them he had been included by Governor Spotswood in his transmontane expedition to claim the western lands for the King of England. John mentioned that they could eventually read the journal he had kept on this journey and reported that at the conclusion of the trip he and his companions had each received from the Governor a small commemorative golden horseshoe, a gift that was to earn the group the title Knights of the Golden Horseshoe.[19]

At last word came that John, after looking over lands in Virginia and other middle Atlantic colonies, had located and purchased a suitable tract. Matthew Maury could not immediately take Mary Anne across the wintry Atlantic, for she was pregnant; yet he felt he could not wait longer to determine whether or not they would make Virginia their future home. He sailed without her and was as captivated by Virginia and the warm welcome extended him on his arrival there in late March, 1718, as had been John. He decided to purchase a portion of the property that John had acquired on the north side of the Pamunkey River in King William County. Anxious to get back to Mary Anne, Matthew Maury hired artisans to build a house on his property and sailed for Ireland.

In Dublin a joyous Mary Anne greeted her husband by placing in his arms a son, James. As soon as the infant was strong enough for travel, Matthew and Mary Anne Maury said farewell to the family in Ireland and set sail with James, arriving in Virginia in the autumn of 1719.[20]

They named their new home "Fontainebleu" [21]—pretentious, perhaps, but understandable in a couple newly come into the pride of possessing the first land of their own. It was on this plantation that Matthew Fontaine Maury's grandfather, James Maury, spent his youth.

On adjoining acres Mary Anne's brother James Fontaine and his wife were settled. Mary Anne also saw other brothers each June 1, when all the Fontaines who had emigrated to Virginia met for a religious service to commemorate the anniversary of the family's deliverance from French privateers.[22]

This service was led by Mary Anne's brother, the Reverend Peter Fontaine, who had first served as minister to Huguenots settled at Manakin, above the falls of the James River, and then had become rector of Westover Parish in Charles City County.[23]

Another participant in the annual Fontaine thanksgiving service was the Reverend Francis Fontaine, who also first served as rector of King William Parish, church of the Huguenot settlement at Manakin, before going on to become professor of Oriental languages at the College of William and Mary and rector of York-Hampton Parish.[24]

Mary Anne and Matthew Maury gave their son James a sufficiently good preparatory education for him to do very well at the College of William and Mary and to become an instructor in the college's grammar school. In February, 1742, James Maury was recommended by the college's president, the Reverend James Blair, to the Bishop of London for ordination in the Church of England. Back across the Atlantic went 24-year-old James to be examined and to receive holy orders, as had so many of his family before him.[25] Soon after returning to Virginia he married on November 11, 1743, Mary Walker, the 19-year-old daughter of King and Queen County's prominent physician, James Walker, and his wife, Ann Hill Walker.[26] James Maury began his ministry in King and Queen and within eight years was called to be rector of Fredericksville Parish,[27] in a section of Louisa that not long afterwards was annexed to Albemarle County in a straightening of county and parish lines.[28]

Like his grandfather, the Reverend James Fontaine, James Maury found it necessary to add to his clergyman's salary, for he and his wife had thirteen children, of whom twelve lived to maturity. Maury, being a superior Latin and Greek scholar, built a schoolhouse in the yard of his home and ran a classical school for boys.[29] In this way he secured enough income to support his large family and to have funds to invest in the Loyal Company, which was second in importance only to the Ohio Company in its development of western land.[30]

Possibly one of James Maury's greatest services was the inspiration he gave to young Thomas Jefferson, who came to board in the home of the "parson," a term he and most other Virginians of the period used in addressing a clergyman of the Established Church of England. Jefferson was drilled mercilessly in Latin and Greek,[31] and stimulated by his pedagogue's discourses on the western land. Parson Maury talked with great enthusiasm about the Mississippi and its recent exploration, and he spoke often of the need for men to press on beyond and explore the other great river that the Indians called the Missouri. At this time was possibly sown in the mind of Thomas Jefferson the idea that eventually grew into his sending the Lewis and Clark Expedition to explore the far northwest.[32]

Jefferson's close friend Dabney Carr also boarded with the Maurys, as did another of the parson's ablest students, James Madison, later to become president of William and Mary College and first bishop of Virginia,[33] not to be confused with his cousin who became United States President James Madison. Parson Maury frequently permitted his son, James II, to go home with Tom Jefferson for weekends. It was only a 14-mile ride to "Shadwell." The friendship of the junior Maury and Jefferson was to endure, and it was Jefferson who later urged George Washington to send his friend as the new republic's first consul at Liverpool.[34]

The Reverend James Maury had an unusually large library for a man of his means.[35] He was a constant student of the physical world and was particularly interested in the possibilities of coal that came from the soil of Virginia.[36] He had a huge zest for life and the physical energy to match his drive, but withal he was a man of heart "beloved by his parishioners." [37]

James Maury was the plaintiff in the famous "Parson's Cause," which came to trial in November, 1763, in Hanover County Court House. He sought to have his back salary, as clergyman of the Established or Anglican Church, paid in tobacco as stipulated by the royal laws of the Virginia colony. Popular resistance to payment of these salaries in tobacco when "the weed" was bringing a high price had been agitated in the colony chiefly by the growing number of those who refused to conform to the requirements in doctrine or discipline of the Church of England. These Dissenters,[38] religious skeptics, and some dissatisfied planters had brought great pressure against the General Assembly of the colony, which had passed the Two Penny Acts permitting the salary of Established clergy to be paid on the basis of twopence in place of each pound of tobacco.[39] To defend their action in paying their rector less than he was entitled to by the colony's royal law, the collectors of the levies for Maury's parish hired a young country lawyer, Patrick Henry.[40] When the hearing of the case got under way, Patrick Henry created a sensation in the courtroom by contending that "royal misrule" had "dissolved the political compact," and he branded as "enemies of the community" the Established clergy who sought their salary in tobacco. There were shouts of treason, but Henry was carried from the court as a hero. Maury wrote to the Reverend John Camm that Patrick Henry came to him afterwards to apologize for remarks about him.[41]

James Maury felt he had not been given a trial by his peers and that the number of Dissenters on the jury had prejudiced his case.[42] However, he opposed the senseless persecution of Dissenters that had been carried on in Virginia. In a printed address he stated that he would feel it an "honor and happiness" to promote the spiritual good of "any one honest and well disposed person of whatever persuasion," admitting that, while he preferred his own church, he thought he saw errors in it as well as in the others. He volunteered to assist in the correction of these.[43] A man of probity, piety, and highly developed mental power, the Reverend James Maury was widely respected throughout Virginia.

To the Reverend James Maury and his wife, Mary Walker Maury, at their home "Rock Spring," Albemarle County, was born on May 19, 1766, their twelfth child, Richard Maury.[44] Only three when his father died, Richard was taught by his eldest brother, the Reverend Matthew Maury, who succeeded to their father's church and classical school.[45] However, there were no funds for Richard to receive the college education that had been available for his older brothers. He therefore turned to farming and became a plantation overseer, but this in no way kept him from the social life to which his birth entitled him.[46] Genial and attractive in an easy, friendly way, Richard was welcome in the leading homes of Albemarle and nearby Louisa and Caroline counties.

In Richard Maury coursed the blood of men and women who had paid for their religious convictions with their fortunes and their lives. His Huguenot forebears had been officers of high position at court, clergymen, and teachers, but men not ashamed to work at a trade when necessity compelled. They had possessed ability, the will to overcome difficulties, and a strongly independent spirit. Mingled with Richard's French blood was that of the English-descended Walkers and Hills, who were Virginia planters and physicians—men accustomed to private success and public service. This was the heritage Richard Maury transmitted to his son, Matthew Fontaine Maury.

On January 18, 1792, Richard Maury married 24-year-old Diana Minor of "Topping Castle" plantation in Caroline County, Virginia.[47]

The founder of the Minor family [48] in Virginia had been a Dutch sea captain named Maindort Doodes, who between 1639 and 1650 came so much under the spell of Virginia that he decided to become a planter instead of a seafarer. He first settled near the port of Norfolk.[49] He must have quickly made himself liked by Virginians for he was not molested when England and her colonies were at war with Holland from 1652 to 1654. By the time the next Dutch war was in progress, a decade later, Maindort had moved away from the coast to Lancaster County.[50] He and his wife, Mary, had had a son born in 1640 who dropped his father's given name, Maindort, and called himself Doodes Minor, or the younger Doodes. The fact that Virginians pronounced Maindort as Minor influenced the son to take that as the family name.[51] The father and son, having become fully Virginian in feeling and commitment, were naturalized on September 20, 1671, at a "grand assembly holden at James Cittie" (Jamestown) and given all rights of natural-born Englishmen.[52]

The ability and industry of the father, Maindort Doodes, was evidenced by the sizable amount of property left by a will he wrote in 1677.[53] His high moral sense was revealed in the stipulation that his slaves and their issue should gradually be freed after his death.

Doodes Minor married Elizabeth (Cocke?),[54] a Virginia girl, and they had six children, of whom one was Garritt Minor. Doodes did well as a small planter and left considerable property by the will that was proved at Saluda, Virginia, on May 27, 1695.

Garritt Minor, who was baptized April 13, 1679,[55] soon ran into nearly as much trouble with the spelling of his Christian name as had his grandfather, Maindort Doodes. Virginians spelled it seven different ways but most often Garrett. On October 17, 1706, Garrett Minor married Diana Vivian, the daughter of Captain John Vivian and Margaret Smith Vivian of Middle Plantation (Williamsburg). The couple lived in Middlesex County, where Garrett was a planter and a justice of the county court.[56] To them was born a son, John, on June 29, 1707.

A young man of great promise, John Minor [57] married Sarah Carr, the daughter of Mary Dabney and Thomas Carr,[58] who had patented 5,000 acres of good Virginia land. John and Sarah were the maternal great-grandparents of Matthew Fontaine Maury.

Sarah had grown up at her parents' plantation, Topping Castle,[59] on the North Anna River in Caroline County, but after marriage she moved with her husband to a plantation he owned and to which he had given the name "Minor's Folly." John early became an influential man in Caroline, a great planter [60] and a justice of the county court. His energy and good management enabled him to increase his holdings, which

9

were located in four different counties. Among his many children his son John most closely resembled him.

John Minor II,[61] the grandfather of Matthew Fontaine Maury, had been born November 18, 1735. He early married Elizabeth Cosby, the daughter of Ann Overton and David Cosby, a planter of Louisa County.[62]

John inherited Topping Castle and to this he added other holdings. He had so much territory to cover that he transacted business while riding at a canter a strong black cob with a bobbed tail. Successful as a great planter, he also managed the Hanover property of General Thomas Nelson, Governor of Virginia,[63] was a vestryman of his church, county magistrate, member of the Caroline County Committee of Correspondence and of the Committee of Safety. An active champion and defender of colonial rights, John Minor drilled a company of Caroline's militia and fought in the War for Independence, during which he became a major. He was present at the siege of Yorktown,[64] as was his son John III. To avoid confusion with his son of the same given name, the father was known as Major John Minor after the Revolution. He lived until March 21, 1800, leaving many children, of whom one was his daughter Diana.

Diana Minor was the descendant of men who possessed a talent for acquiring property, the ability to administer and to command. From Dutch sea captain Maindort Doodes through successive generations of Minors, her paternal forebears had been men of moral force, mental and physical energy. They had occupied positions of trust in their communities, administering the business of the church and justice in the courts, as had also the Carrs and the Cosbys. They had been men of property who had not hesitated to risk losing it by active leadership in the cause of winning independence from Great Britain. Diana Maury passed on to her son Matthew a tradition of personal achievement and loyal public service.

The birth of Matthew Fontaine Maury was the cause of no unusual excitement in Richard and Diana's home, for he was their seventh child. Their two eldest, Mary and John, had been born before they had moved to their Spotsylvania County property and, since its acquisition their family had been enlarged by the arrival of Walker, Matilda, Betsy, and Richard Launcelot.[65] The couple had, in fact, proved more productive than their acres.

The land had looked very promising to Richard Maury on the last day of August, 1797, when he had signed the contract to acquire it from General Henry (Light-Horse Harry) Lee and his wife Ann of Westmoreland County. Richard and Diana had longed for a place of their own, and it had seemed providential to Richard that his brother Matthew that year sold a big farm their father had owned in Albemarle.[66] Richard had hoped to buy a larger place with his share of the money from his father's property but had decided he was fortunate to have the 66 pounds and 19 shillings, current money of Virginia, that Lee asked for 103 acres of the mine tract he had acquired from General Alexander Spotswood.[67] The land was partially fenced, and on it stood a house and some cabins for slaves. Lee, the master of "Stratford" on the other side of Fredericksburg,[68] had also permitted Richard to lease 323 acres for a rental of "1,000 pounds of crop tobacco and cash" (amount not specified [69]) to be paid each year by Christmas Day. The bargain had seemed a good one, for 426 acres formed a small plantation and, when additional slaves had come to Diana following her father's death in 1800, Richard had thought their prospects equaled their dreams.

But by January of 1806 Richard Maury wasn't so sure about the potential of his land. As a boy he had heard often of his great-uncle John Fontaine's ride through this section with the Knights of the Golden Horseshoe as they made their way to Governor Spotswood's nearby iron mines.[70] There was iron ore in the soil on his land, too.[71] Perhaps that had something to do with his crops not being as abundant as he had thought they would be; perhaps it didn't, and possibly he had agreed to pay too much tobacco as rent; maybe he had fields under cultivation that shouldn't have been.[72] At any rate, Richard's acres didn't grow sufficient tobacco to be rewarding.

While tobacco, Virginia's "golden weed," was the crop on which Richard Maury relied for cash, he also raised hogs and some cattle for meat, corn for the cattle and horses as well as a supply to be ground into corn meal for family use. Potatoes were grown in quantity, and cultivation of a vegetable garden was not neglected. In late fall and winter the woods rang with the sound of axes because open fires had to be fed constantly to keep the family warm. Long lengths of wood had to be cut for the giant kitchen fireplace.

Cook and kitchen, situated in a small building just outside the house, fell under the direction of Diana, as did the hen house and the springhouse, where the milk and cream were kept and the butter churned. At hog-killing time, after the weather had turned cold, Diana directed the proper hanging of hams and sides of bacon for curing in the smokehouse and preparation of the sausage according to the recipe used at Topping Castle. She had inherited the great energy of her father, Major John Minor, and like him, kept her children and servants busy from dawn to dusk. However, to both she was confidante and comforter, for she had a

11

sensitivity of feeling as well as a keen intelligence. Diana was firm but not harsh in the training of her children.

They, however, felt that their father was severe.[73] They wearied of his frequent reminder that they were not supposed to speak to their elders until spoken to. Little could the young Maurys realize how many problems Richard was trying to work out in his head, nor that their prattle about things they wanted touched on a sore nerve.

By the time Matthew was two years old his mother was already well along toward term with another baby, but it was not this addition to his family that was distressing Richard. Both he and Diana came of very large families and considered them normal and right. What worried him was a haunting sense that he was failing as a provider. He couldn't understand why. Each year he had believed he would do better with his crops the next, but each year he had failed to make what he needed to meet his obligations. His intention to pay had never been questioned and his creditors had, at first, been courteous and patient. Of late, though, they had grown clamorous, insistent, and dreadfully worrisome. Richard was frustrated and distressed. He knew that Diana was more grieved than she would admit because she could not make available to him the money left her by her father at his death in 1800. Major Minor had carefully protected her inheritance by leaving it in trust with her brothers John and Launcelot as administrators.[74]

When the year 1808 began and Richard was unable to clear up his debts, his creditors bluntly announced that the time for promises was over; they wanted payment. Husband and wife shut the door of their bedchamber against the children and discussed their plight. Reluctantly they agreed there was nothing to do but sell some of the land they had so proudly bought eleven years before. Their thoughts were somber indeed on February 13 as they signed an agreement to part with 24 acres of the land they held in fee simple plus 55½ acres of the tract they had leased from the Lees. They got only $155, but this was evidently the fair market value, for the purchaser was their friend Edward Herndon [75] of "Laurel Hill," who was soon to marry Richard's sister Elizabeth.[76]

Richard Maury used the $155 to pay his most pressing obligations and started his next crop of tobacco with renewed hope that he could pull out of the economic difficulties and keep the rest of his farm holdings. But the weather was not helpful, worms and bugs were troublesome, and his acres refused to produce the bumper crops he needed. He was confronted with the fact that the natural products of that soil were weeds, briers, honeysuckle, and thickets of scrub-growth trees. With carefully managed crop rotation and sufficient fertilizer Richard Maury might have made the land pay.[77] Instead he further depleted the soil by planting tobacco year after year to meet the terms of his lease and to produce a surplus to sell for ever-needed cash. He was not the canny business manager his clergyman father had been.

On May 21 the Maury household again heard the squalls of a new-born infant who was promptly named Charles. Among the visitors who came early that summer to see the new baby and Diana was her brother Brigadier General John Minor, who had a highly successful law practice in Fredericksburg, where he had built "Hazel Hill," [78] a large, rambling home set in 50 acres of ground. Skilled in the handling of affairs, General Minor saw little promise that Richard could manage any better in the future than he had in the past. The General's worry for the future of his sister and her children made him feel he again had to discuss the situation with his brother-in-law. To Richard, talks with Diana's prosperous brother rubbed salt in the wounds he already bore from the harassment of debt and the even deeper fear of failure. John Minor, who liked Richard as a human being, tried to be as considerate as he could, but he was explicit on the point that creditors had certain legal recourses that they might feel impelled to use.

Hard pressed as he was, Richard held out a while longer. But on August 1 he sadly admitted that others could protect the future of his family better than he could, and he signed an indenture placing all his holdings in trust. He designated William G. Maury, John M. Herndon, and General Minor as trustees to handle his affairs.[79] Each of these men was related either to Diana or to Richard, and they found the transaction embarrassing. To Richard Maury it was a humiliation.

Almost immediately the trustees made a move that Richard had avoided—they sold his slave Isaiah and used the proceeds to satisfy creditors. Then they considered how to secure an education for John Maury. The boy showed real promise. His uncle, John Minor, suggested that steps be taken that would lead to a service commission. A friend of President Thomas Jefferson's, General Minor persuaded the President to grant a Navy appointment to the grandson of the Chief Executive's old teacher, the Reverend James Maury.

Thirteen-year-old John Maury could scarcely contain his excitement on March 8, 1809, when he received an appointment as acting midshipman in the United States Navy.[80] Richard's feelings were mixed; he was proud that his son was to become an officer but concerned that one of his children was going away from him, for his family often seemed all that he had. Diana was even more distressed. Her first-born son, named for her father, was very dear to her, and she dreaded the long separations that a naval career meant, as well as having John exposed to the rough ways of seafaring men.

John, however, had no qualms. With a near-bursting pride he read over and over the official communication. Sitting down immediately he wrote to Robert Smith, the Secretary of the Navy, accepting the appointment: "I will report in person to the commanding officer of Frigate *United States* as soon as I can procure a little necessary apparel, which will be in a very few days." John signed the oath and sent off his acceptance.[81] A short while afterwards John told the family goodbye and left to join his ship. Following his departure, letters were eagerly awaited, and when they came they were read aloud to the whole family. Little Matthew listened carefully, for his oldest brother had been his hero and he missed him badly.

The Richard Maurys continued short on money but never on relatives, for Spotsylvania County was full of their kinspeople, as was also the town of Fredericksburg. It was important to Richard and Diana that their children know their kin and be known by them; all Virginians felt that way. Visits were frequently made between the homes. Each Sunday presented an opportunity for a get-together after church, when there was an exchange of family news. If Richard Maury had not received a letter from his brother James at his consular post in Liverpool, then one had come to his brother Fontaine or to his brother Abraham, both of whom lived in Fredericksburg. The Maurys were proud of James's success and wealth.[82]

Another favorite topic of talk was their cousin Abram Maury. This son of their uncle Abraham [83] had left Lunenburg County, Virginia, and established himself on the frontier of Tennessee by 1793. There he had purchased land and laid out a town called Franklin, which was made the seat of Williamson County. The Virginia Maurys had all rejoiced when a new county was cut off in 1807 from Williamson and named Maury County in recognition of Abram's [84] services to the state. Richard was very proud of his family and his heritage, but his children did not just meet and hear of Maurys; their mother's people, the Minors, also were a constant influence.

The greatest single influence in the Maury home, however, was religion. Richard carried on in his household his family's tradition of holding a worship service every morning and every evening. Diana was as devout as her husband. Both were members of the Protestant Episcopal Church, formed after the War for Independence as the American offspring of the Church of England,[85] in which both had been baptized. On Sundays, except when weather made the roads impassable, when there was sickness in the house, or when their church lacked a rector, they drove ten miles into Fredericksburg to attend service at St. George's. Matthew was baptized before he was eleven months old.[86]

While life in these years was full of economic strain for Richard and Diana, their children had a happy time of it, none more so than Matthew. He was a fine-looking child with a handsome head covered with light-brown ringlets. His blue eyes usually twinkled with friendliness. Matthew—or Matt, as he was sometimes called—never had to worry about playmates; he and Dick, two years his senior, were inseparable. As soon as Charles could toddle he followed his older brothers like a devoted spaniel. Not that there weren't dogs around the Maury home. Like any other Virginia gentleman of the period, Richard kept several hunting dogs and some well-trained hounds that doubled as pets for the children.

The ownership of twelve slaves was a part of the paradox of Richard Maury's life.[87] Their possession gave the appearance of wealth that he did not have and could not make. A part of Diana's inheritance, the slaves were absolutely essential to her husband in rural Virginia, where no hands were available for hire. Their upkeep was a burden, but if he were to give up this labor force he would be giving up any possible chance he had of making a living from farming. Richard's creditors understood this dilemma, but it didn't make them any less impatient to be paid.

In spite of every effort, Richard's income continued less than he needed for maintenance of family and property. His creditors were adamant; no extension of time could be granted him. Like many another hard-pressed American of the time, Richard Maury's thoughts turned westward, and he thought what a relief it would be to leave all this behind and start afresh. Abram Maury and his brother Philip were living well in middle Tennessee. Their letters indicated that there was still acreage to be had, land that had not been worn out. Richard came to believe that if he could just farm some soil that hadn't been depleted by tobacco he could make a good living. When Diana began to recover her strength from the birth, on May 23, 1810, of their ninth child, Catharine Ann, Richard told his wife of his growing inclination to leave Virginia and join the other Maurys in the southwest.

The thought of giving up their home and going to what she considered the frontier was frightening to Diana, who was used to having her wise brothers nearby for counsel. Perhaps that was part of Richard's trouble and he thought he could do better far from the successful Minors. Diana loved her husband too deeply not to realize how family conferences about his economic plight grated on his spirit. But now this possibility of a major move would have to be discussed. Some of her family questioned whether there would be decent schooling for the children in Tennessee. She worried over how John could ever come that far for his shore leaves. Richard chafed under the endless discussions of the pros and cons of the move. It was all very well for everyone to debate the issue, but he was the one from whom his creditors demanded action. Finally he made the decision. He would make the trip; he would find new opportunity.

The first step was to persuade the trustees to dissolve the trust in which he and Diana had placed their property two years earlier. The relatives-trustees eventually agreed that Richard might be right; perhaps he could do better in Tennessee. It was September 15 before the three men signed a relinquishment of trust [88] and thus set the Maury property free to be put on the market. Richard wanted a quick sale and let it be known he would sell at a modest price. The bait worked. In less than a week he had a buyer, and on September 22, 1810, Richard and Diana sold to Nathaniel Gordon the 79 acres remaining of the original 103 they had purchased in fee simple. However, for this land, their dwelling, their barn, slave cabins, and other improvements the couple received only $300.[89]

When the deed of sale was taken to court to be recorded, the magistrate was not wholly satisfied because Diana had inscribed her name on the legal instrument at home. The reason given for her not coming before the court was that it was not convenient for her to travel the dozen miles from their home to Spotsylvania Court House. This statement apparently puzzled the magistrate, who had before him the relinquishment of trust that stated "the said Richard Maury is about to remove out of this state with his family and wishes to carry with him a part of the property conveyed by said deed of trust."

The court pondered this question: if Diana Maury was able to accompany her husband to Tennessee, had she stayed at home because she did not wholeheartedly approve of the sale of their property and did not wish to reveal her feelings? The court felt sufficient doubt on the point to take action on September 24, when it issued to three prominent citizens of Spotsylvania County an order that concluded with these words: "We do therefore command you that you do personally go to the said Diana and receive her acknowledgement of the same, and examine her privately and apart from the said Richard Maury, her husband, whether she doth the same freely and voluntarily without his persuasion or threats." [90] Whatever emotions and desires may have been churning within her, Diana was much too loyal and devoted a wife not to back Richard. When the representatives of the court came to the house and asked to see her alone, she assured them that she fully approved of her husband's plan and was agreeable both to the sale and to their move to Tennessee.

Diana possessed great physical stamina, but she was forty-two and had borne nine children, the last only a few months before. She could only have dreaded the approaching 700-mile wagon trip across mountains in autumn weather. But the obligation to face realities was a part of her code and of the code she taught her children. She would trust God to protect her baby, Catharine Ann, and see them all through safely.

At last they were ready. Early one crisp fall day Richard gave the order for the little cavalcade to start [91] down their lane and turn left on the narrow road leading to the stagecoach road. Once they turned westward on that thoroughfare between Fredericksburg and Orange, the Maurys' journey to a new life had begun in earnest. But it was not until they reached Salem that the arduous portion of the trip began. This was the gateway to southwest Virginia, a rugged section with some mountains that exceeded 5,000 feet in height. At Salem parties about to subject their wagons to mountain travel paused to check and, if necessary, to repair wheels, brakes, and harness, as well as to have their horses freshly shod. Even families like the Maurys, who had to save money whenever possible, took this opportunity to enjoy a night's lodging, or at least a meal, in one of the town's comfortable hostelries, such as the Globe Tavern.[92]

From Salem the road snaked its way uphill and down. Progress was slow, twelve miles a day often proving an exhausting journey. Late each afternoon the Maurys camped close by a stream or mountain spring. Richard and Diana both believed that children should work, so all but the smallest had their assigned tasks. Matthew was fully capable of gathering dried leaves and twigs to be used as kindling for starting the nightly fire. The Maury cook grumbled over the strangeness of it all but produced a good supper of smoke-cured bacon from home, hoecakes of corn meal cooked in the hot ashes, and sometimes a rabbit just shot or fish freshly caught. To Matthew and his brothers this all seemed like a grand adventure; but the nightly encampment, the autumn cold, the alternate combinations of wind and dust or rain and mud, and the long days of jolting travel were hard on Diana and her infant daughter and not easy on any of the party.

Small for his age, Matthew was allowed to ride in a wagon most of the time. On steep grades up mountains the little boy was expected to walk as did everyone who could, the wagon loads having to be lightened as much as possible to spare the horses. The four-year-old's short legs wearied quickly, however, and his sympathetic older sister Matilda often came to his rescue. Trying to turn his weariness into a joke, she would crouch down by the side of the road and order him to climb aboard her shoulders. He was not heavy, and she was strong enough to carry him piggyback until she could chaff him into getting back on his own

17

feet.[93] Matilda's kindness set up a special bond between her and Matthew, a bond he was later to acknowledge in tangible form.

Down the stagecoach road between the Middle and North Forks of the Holston River the Maurys moved until they crossed from Virginia into Tennessee.[94] At last they reached Nashville, on the Cumberland River. Settled as a western outpost by the intrepid James Robertson and eight men in 1779, Nashville was in 1810 still a small town in spite of having been proudly incorporated as a city. The Maurys barely paused in Nashville; they were anxious to press on to their destination, 18 miles to the south.

Richard Maury's hopes soared when he saw the bluegrass that grew lushly in the fields of the rolling country between Nashville and Franklin. The look of fertility convinced him that he had done right to come, that here he would surely succeed as had his kinsmen who had preceded him. He was all eagerness as he crossed into Williamson County and at last reached Franklin,[95] proud to tell his children that this was the community their cousin Abram Maury had laid out. A courthouse stood in the center of a cluster of frame houses, small stores, and a blacksmith shop.

Two miles beyond town they reached journey's end, Abram Maury's home "Tree Lawn," a substantial house set on a slight elevation that dropped off to fields and meadows.[96] The welcome to the newcomers from Virginia was warm, for there was an intense feeling of family loyalty among the Maurys, stemming from the time of persecution suffered by their Huguenot forebears. Abram's wife, born Martha Worsham of Amelia County, Virginia, greeted the tired travelers with true plantation cordiality.

Abram Maury had for years carried on an extensive business in buying and selling land in middle Tennessee,[97] and Richard could not have had a better adviser on what good farm land was available. However, because there had been debts to settle before leaving Spotsylvania and it had been necessary to lay out cash for supplies for the trip and expenses incurred on the road, Richard had little left of the $300 gained from the sale of his Virginia property. As he looked over Williamson County, Richard discovered that, although the area was sparsely settled and might be termed backwoods by those from the long-settled eastern seaboard, land itself carried a good value. Big tracts had earlier been assigned as grants to men who had fought in the Revolution, and these men or their assignees were now selling portions of their land at prices ranging from $4 an acre upward; [98] there was no free land to be picked up. Finding that his capital was insufficient for a purchase, Richard resolved the problem, early in 1811, by leasing from Alexanderia Ewing a portion of his farm about two miles southeast of Franklin.[99] The Maurys moved into a simple house on the property, and Diana set to making it homelike.

Shortly after they were established in this rented house, Diana started Matthew on home lessons. She drilled him orally, teaching him chiefly to memorize verses of psalms and hymns. He was a rapid learner and soon could take part in daily family worship when, divided into two groups, the Maurys read or said the Psalms antiphonally. This practice was to give Matthew such a knowledge of the Psalms that he could quote them throughout his life.[100]

Richard worked at farming the rented land but felt he would do better when he was able to have his own acres. Diana longed for a place of their own and wrote her brothers to that effect; but as trustees of her inheritance they were in no hurry to release money after Richard's difficulties in Virginia. In 1813, however, a good farm some six miles from Abram Maury's home came up for sale, 200 acres for $1,000. Abram knew it well, for he had witnessed its sale twelve years earlier to William Sloan, then living in North Carolina. Sloan had decided to go farther west to Missouri and was willing to part with this property. A letter was sent off to General John Minor and Launcelot Minor recommending that this farm be bought. Since Abram Maury's judgment could be trusted, Diana's brothers agreed to pay the required sum and signed the agreement of purchase.[101]

The Minor brothers, anxious for their sister, her husband, and her children to have a permanent home, had taken no chances on the new property's being lost through mismanagement on Richard's part. The indenture began: "Whereas Major John Minor, late of Topping Castle, Caroline County, in the State of Virginia, by his last will and testament, bequeathed a certain distributive share of his personal estate to John and Lancelot [Launcelot] Minor, his executors, in trust for the benefit of Richard Maury and Anna [Diana] his wife, and their children out of which, in pursuance of said trust, the said Executives have applied the sum of one thousand dollars to the purchase of the tract of land hereinafter described." The indenture went on to stipulate that the property was to be held in trust for the Maury children by Diana's brothers, who were to allow their sister and her husband "to occupy, cultivate and use said tract of land." [102]

It was one more humiliation for Richard, but it seemed worth it to him in order to own property again. Diana shared his view and encouraged him to start construction of a home as rapidly as possible. He, his older sons, and slaves cut trees and built a log house on a point of high ground on the farm, which lay a little over six miles northwest of

Franklin. Diana was pleased that the dwelling gave them a view of the dirt road through the narrow valley that connected Boyd's Mill on the north with Leiper's Fork on the south, where Widow Benton had a homestead of 2,560 acres. Her son, Thomas Hart Benton, supervised the cultivation of this holding in addition to practicing law in Franklin.[103]

The Richard Maury's new farm was described, in the legal instrument, as "lying on the waters of West Harpeth River in Williamson County and State of Tennessee." [104] In hot summers to come the boys of the family must have wished this were true, but it was a long walk to the river and there was no stream of any size on the farm—nothing but a spring from which flowed a small meandering brook.

The great difference for Richard Maury in his Tennessee farming was that his main crop was cotton instead of the tobacco he had grown in Virginia. Also he had fewer slaves, as debt had forced him to sell some before leaving Virginia. Therefore, all the boys had to help in the fields and even at seven Matthew was expected to do his share.

Soon after the Maurys settled in their permanent home in 1813, Dick was sent to a nearby "old field school," which provided elementary education for the children of the area. As soon thereafter as he could persuade his father to pay the extra cost of enrolling him, Matthew entered this school. Like the other pupils he carried his lunch in a tin bucket and stayed all day. The school had one teacher, a man whose salary was paid by the parents' contributing according to the number of children they sent. The teacher was severity incarnate, but small Matthew had no trouble because he was accustomed to giving absolute obedience to his father. In addition, he liked to learn and was an apt student.

Nimble-minded Matthew soon learned what Dick was studying as well as his own beginner's lessons. He listened with interest to the lessons in elementary geography and the chant of the names of the rivers, seas, and continents of the world "sung" by the older students. But Matthew's biggest thrill came when the schoolmaster handed him Webster's *Elementary Spelling Book*—the "Blueback," as it was called. It was the first book he had ever been allowed to hold in his hands, and to him it was such an unforgettable experience that he told of it years later.[105]

The Maury home contained the Bible, the Episcopal prayer book and hymnal, probably a guide to home medicine, and Bradford's *Tennessee Almanac,* but few other books. Matthew was book-hungry during his early years. As one result, he spent a great deal of time observing nature. Whenever he could get out of the chores required of him, he and Dick roamed the fields and woods, watching birds and following the tracks of animals. They watched strange cloud formations in the skies and looked for natural springs. In warm weather they waded in streams, and before long they learned to swim in the West Harpeth River. Both boys became good swimmers, and Matthew also developed into a competent horseman. Besides hunting nuts and berries, they searched for wild honey stored in hollow trees. This supplied them with a sweet, an item of diet of which they had little. Sugar, tea, coffee, and molasses had to be bought at a store in Franklin.

Money was always scarce, and most of what the Maurys ate was produced on the farm, which supplied an ample, if not fancy, table. Cows were kept to furnish the needed milk and butter, chickens and hogs for meat. Occasionally there was beef. Vegetables were grown, and their own field corn and wheat were taken to nearby Boyd's Mill to be ground for table consumption. Their old cook from Virginia baked fluffy batter bread, crisp corn-meal cakes, light bread, and beaten biscuits, made mouth-watering by inserting a scrap of home-cured ham. About the only luxury kept in the household was whiskey, which Richard Maury had on hand for visitors.[106] He might be living in a log house, but he never forgot who he was nor the Virginia tradition in which he had been reared. He and Diana were both hospitable, and guests received the best they had to offer. Silver spoons and some other table silver brought from Virginia were used, and not just when there was company.

Matthew was thus early exposed to a pattern of contradictions. The log house was larger than a cabin but far from spacious. The warm, cheering open fire in the main room did little in winter to relieve the cold in the garret rooms where the older children slept. The furniture was made on the property as there had been little room in the crowded wagons for Diana's home pieces. Diana herself worked endlessly at the spinning wheel or the loom. Yet the Maurys were accustomed to the service of slaves who cooked and brought the food in from the outside kitchen, who washed the clothes and did much of the heavy labor.[107] But it took more than their three men slaves to clear land by cutting trees, raise cotton, and do general farming on 200 acres. Matthew and all his brothers were expected to let their lessons suffer, if necessary, to labor in the fields.

Matthew was normally an obedient child but on one occasion, when very small, he dared his father's wrath because of his dislike for working in the cotton field. According to a story later told on him by his brother Charles, Matthew and he had been told to pick cotton but Matthew was anxious to go into the woods on some adventure of his own. In a fit of childish rebellion he suggested to Charles that they pick off the whole cotton bolls and stuff them into a hollow stump that stood in the field. It was a stupid little scheme but all that the child could think of as a protest. Richard Maury caught the boys in the act of hiding the cotton and whipped them soundly, so effectively that both boys long remembered, just as their father had intended.[108]

Yet Richard was no sterner with his children than many other fathers of large families of the day, and his severity was tainted by no cruelty. His children knew that he cared about them, and they respected him. He might lack power in the councils of men, but in his home he had authority. Richard was strong on the moral law, Old Testament style. Diana supplied the young people with the further step of understanding and compassion taught in the New Testament. The fabric of their teaching was in very truth straight out of the Bible. There was in the parents' minds a serene conviction that he who lived by the Bible was rich without other belongings, and this belief Richard and Diana passed on to their children.

Richard told them often of their Huguenot heritage. He enjoined them that they must live out the religion for which their forebears had given their lives or suffered exile. This was all a part of Diana and Richard's efforts to see that their children had as full a religious training as was possible. They disliked their children growing up without hearing the teachings of the Episcopal Church or being confirmed at the proper age, but as yet their denomination had no church in all of Tennessee. In 1811 the Reverend Gideon Blackburn, a Presbyterian minister, came to Franklin, and thereafter the Maurys had a choice of hearing his staunchly Christian and often lengthy sermons or worshipping with the small local Methodist congregation.[109] They were able to familiarize their children with the Episcopal prayer book by its daily use at home.

But all the talk in the Maury home was not religious or instructive, for conversation was the family's chief entertainment, especially in the long winter evenings. The children loved to hear their parents reminisce about Virginia and relatives there, but their favorite subject continued to be their brother John. From late in 1811 all talk of John had taken on a new seriousness. At that time a letter had come to Richard and Diana with news not calculated to please the parents of any 16-year-old boy. John had reported that, in accordance with a Navy custom he had secured a long furlough to serve as first officer in a 300-ton merchant vessel, the *Pennsylvania Packet,* on a trading voyage to the far Pacific and Canton.[110] The youth had explained that this opportunity had come to him through Lieutenant William Lewis,[111] under whom he had been serving in the frigate *United States.* John had proudly reported that this ship, of which he would be second in command, would be manned by a crew of 25 and would mount 6 small guns.

All the Maurys had been excited over the adventurous trip their

22

brother was to have. Richard had felt great pride that his son, after only two years and nine months as a midshipman, had been offered such a responsible billet. Fatherly pride, however, was offset by concern over the risks the boy would face, a concern which Diana fully shared. Heartsick as she was over this unexpected development, Diana sought to console her husband with the fact that their eldest son was serving under a man whose good character and ability were known to them. Lieutenant Lewis, a native of Spotsylvania County, had taken a bachelor of arts degree at the College of William and Mary, studied medicine for a period, and read some law before entering the Navy as a midshipman in 1802.

After John sailed, his parents tried to reconcile themselves to the fact that they would receive few if any letters from him. But they did not anticipate that his life for the next years would be completely altered by an international tension that would result in war. The United States had long remonstrated officially with England over her impressment of American nationals for duty on her ships and for highhanded search of American vessels at sea. In the first five months of 1812 the American people took action. Mass protest meetings were held, and even in landlocked Tennessee men talked of having to teach England, once and for all, to respect America. Late in June, Nashville newspapers announced that the United States had on June 18 formally declared war on Great Britain. In "the old southwest," as elsewhere, President James Madison's appeal was made for volunteers to fight what some termed the second war for independence.

The declaration of war filled Richard and Diana Maury with anguish. Now to all the risks they had previously dreaded for John was added the possibility that he might be captured by the British or killed in action at sea. Hungrily they sought out copies of the *Clarion and Tennessee Gazette* and the Nashville *Examiner,* both of which carried accounts of the fighting on land and sea.

However, Richard and Diana felt new hope when they read, in the November 23, 1813, issue of the Nashville *Examiner* news of successes won in the Pacific by the U.S. frigate *Essex,* 32 guns, commanded by Commodore David Porter. Throughout that long winter Matthew and all the young Maurys joined with their parents at family prayers, held before breakfast and after supper, to ask God's protection for John.

It was in May, 1814, that the Maurys at last received word of John —the news they had longed to hear. He was safely back in the United States, at a far southern port, having returned in the *Essex Junior,* 20,[112] one of the ships captured and converted by Commodore Porter before his defeat in the *Essex.* John wrote that he was anxious to see all of them, but had orders that would take him to Norfolk to report for duty in the *Epervier,* 32. The family's disappointment was soon ended by a letter reporting that a slow trip up the coast had caused John to miss the *Epervier,* which had sailed without him,[113] and that he would soon arrive in Tennessee on a short leave.

Matthew was eight and a half years old when his weather-bronzed brother came home that summer of 1814. John brought a story of such exciting adventure that no boy, particularly a younger brother, could help but regard him as a hero.

John's commanding officer, William Lewis, after delivering his American cargo in China had sailed back across the Pacific to the Washington Islands (renamed Marquesas in 1842). Captain Lewis had left John and four sailors on Nukuhiva Island to secure a cargo of sandalwood pending his return in two months. John quickly made friends with Gattenewa, chief of the Happa tribe of Nukuhivan cannibals. But after losing three of his men in raids by the Happas' rival tribe, the Typees (Taipii), John decided to secure himself and his remaining sailor by building a tree hut high off the ground. There they lived while weeks slipped into months and a year and a half had passed. John lost hope of ever being rescued. But one day, scanning the horizon from his hut perched high in the coconut palms, he spied the sails of a square-rigged ship. To his great delight the frigate broke out an American flag as she entered the harbor. Behind her trailed a number of smaller vessels.

John Maury and his sailor, Baker, dropped their rope ladder and raced to the beach. There they seized a canoe and started paddling toward the frigate that had come to anchor, but they were not allowed to board the ship.

It was with great difficulty that John, with his sun-baked skin, long beard and unkempt hair, was able to persuade the Americans that he was actually a midshipman of the U.S. Navy. John was able to establish his identity only by encountering a former shipmate, Stephen Decatur McKnight, when that young officer came ashore with a landing party.

From McKnight John learned that the United States had been at war with England since the middle of June, 1812, and that the *Pennsylvania Packet* had undoubtedly been bottled up in a Chinese harbor by the British. He also learned that the frigate in the harbor was the *Essex,* 32, commanded by Commodore David Porter and that the other ships were prizes he had captured.

Once John had established his identity with Commodore Porter, he was able to render valuable service in persuading Chief Gattenewa to co-operate in supplying and refitting the American ships. When Porter's fleet finally sailed from Nukuhiva, the young midshipman found himself the executive officer of the *Essex Junior*. This was the refitted *Atlantic*, largest and fastest of the prizes Porter had captured, commanded by Lieutenant John Downes.

Young Matthew sat engrossed as John told of his later adventure, of the cruise to the South American coast, of the sea battle between the *Essex* and a superior British force that had ended in defeat of the gallant Porter, and of the parole that had brought him and the surviving Americans home in the *Essex Junior*.[114]

Matthew persuaded John to tell the story over and over, so that the details would not be forgotten. John spoke with pride of serving in the Navy and praised the type of officers with whom he was associated. Matthew was as proud as his older brothers and sisters when John left to report to Commodore Thomas Macdonough and to fight the British on Lake Champlain.[115]

The visit of his brother was over, but its effect on Matthew had just begun. The boy was to remember that all the exciting things that had happened to John had come about because he was an officer of the United States Navy.[116]

CHAPTER II

Education—A Burning Desire

Matthew's curiosity was aroused. What was the meaning of those little marks and figures that had been made on the new half-soles of his well-scuffed shoes? Telling later of this curiosity, he said, "It was about this time that my first ambition to become a mathematician was excited by an old cobbler, Neil by name, who lived not far from my father's house, and who used to send the shoes home to his customers with the soles all scratched over with little x's and y's. The example of that man first awakened in my breast the young spirit of emulation; for my earliest recollections of the feelings of ambition are connected with the aspiration to emulate that man in mathematics." [1]

The elderly shoemaker must have been delighted to try to explain mathematics to one so full of questions. He told Matthew that the symbols were not a mystery but tools for men to use in working out difficult problems. The boy immediately wanted to learn how to use the little x's and y's, but he could not pursue this study at the elementary old field school. In fact, he had already absorbed all that his schoolmaster knew how to teach. Matthew begged his father to send him to Harpeth Academy, where Dick was studying.

Probably because of the expense, Richard refused his son's request, declaring that he needed the boy on the farm. Through an accident, however, Matthew achieved his desire to go on with his education. Having climbed up 45 feet in a forest tree, he lost his hold and plummeted to the ground. Dick, who was with him, ran in alarm to get men to carry Matthew to the house. On first seeing the still body of the boy, the rescuers thought him dead. Matthew was still breathing but had nearly bitten off his tongue when he struck the earth, and he had seriously injured his back. He lay at home for long weeks. Finally the doctor advised Richard Maury that, when the boy recovered, he should not attempt farm work for some time, if ever. This was welcome news to Matthew, and he pressed his advantage with his father. Relieved that his son would recover, Richard said Matthew could go to the academy as soon as he was able to ride, twice daily, the six miles to the school.[2]

In 1818, at twelve years of age, Matthew entered Harpeth Academy to begin the only formal education he was ever to receive. The school was situated across the road from Tree Lawn, the home of Abram Maury, who was one of the academy's trustees. Harpeth was the most famous of the academies that had been authorized by the Tennessee legislature between 1805 and 1807. Its high educational standards were made possible by the teaching ability of the men who served as its principals and supervised its curriculum.[3] The school had opened in 1811 under the direction of the Reverend Gideon Blackburn, who had come to Franklin after serving the federal government as superintendent of schools in the Cherokee Nation, the confederation of Indians living in some fifty villages located on rivers in Georgia, Tennessee, and North Carolina. Blackburn had also worked among the Cherokees as a Presbyterian missionary. His intimate knowledge of Indians was probably more fascinating to Matthew and the other boys than the long sermons that he preached on Sundays.[4]

Blackburn personally started Matthew in the study of Latin grammar, through which the new pupil was said to have "marched with seven league boots in only seven days."[5] Though this was an obvious exaggeration, Matthew did early show promise of an ability to learn languages that was to prove useful to him in later years. At the academy Matthew's closest friends were William C. S. Ventress, whom he called Ven, and Alex C. Maury, a cousin whose first name was pronounced Ellick in the Southern manner.[6] Matthew, at this period, was shy and usually silent with adult strangers but experienced no difficulty in making friends with the boys attending the academy. Like schoolboys anywhere, they let off steam after classes by wrestling and horseplay.

On December 19, 1821, Dr. Blackburn left Harpeth Academy to devote his time to preaching and to the development of other educational institutions. A most able successor took over immediately—James Hervey Otey, a man both kind and purposeful. Born twenty-one years earlier in Liberty, Bedford County, Virginia, Otey had already obtained his bachelor's degree from the University of North Carolina.[7] When his appointment as principal of Harpeth Academy was announced in the newspaper, Otey took the opportunity to disclose that he was making few changes in the textbooks used, which he listed as follows:

Latin Grammar (Rudalman's), *Sacra Historia,* Aesop's *Fables, Viri Romae,* Man's *Introduction,* Caesar's *Commentaries,* Ovidii *Expurgata Latin Prosody* [sic], *Virgil, Greek Grammar* (Westonhall's),

27

Greek Testament, Graeca Minora, Sallust (Editio Expurgata), Homer's *Iliad*, 4 books, *Elements of Ancient and Modern Geography, English Grammar* (Murray's), Hutton's *Mathematics*, Day's *Navigation, Surveying,* Cavano's *Natural Philosophy,* Witherspoon's *Moral Philosophy,* Hedge's *Logic,* Blair's *Lectures, Chronology, Philosophy of the Human Mind,* by Stewart.[8]

These were the textbooks Matthew studied at Harpeth. He did well in his work and was liked by his instructors including Principal Otey. Matthew, in turn, formed a lasting admiration for Otey, to whom he referred as his "preceptor." [9] A well-balanced, happy man who without priggishness lived up to his own high moral code, Otey was personally convinced that there was great satisfaction to be derived from doing a job right, and he had the gift of getting this idea across to young people. As a teacher, he was not afraid to encourage a student with praise, and Matthew learned from him what an incentive this could be.

Outside of school, however, Matthew was full of pranks, fond of games, horseback riding, and long walks in the woods. He and Dick hunted squirrels, rabbits, raccoons, and possums. In the hot Tennessee summers Matthew spent as much time as he could swimming in the river.[10] He, Dick, Ven, and Ellick knew all the families around and were invited to occasional gatherings in their homes. Probably the most impressive Tennessee home that Matthew visited was that of his father's cousin Abram Maury, to whom the boy was so devoted that he called him Uncle Abram.[11] Matthew went often to Tree Lawn with Ellick, the son of Abram Maury's brother. There Matthew also saw something of his cousin A. P. Maury, who had spent a year as a cadet at the U.S. Military Academy but had found the emphasis on mathematics, science, and drilling at West Point not to his literary taste and had returned to Tennessee in 1819 to study law and edit a paper in Nashville.[12] A.P. was only four years and one month older than Matthew but was already considered to have a political career ahead of him. At Tree Lawn Matthew probably met two political figures who were to help him later. One was Nashville lawyer John Bell, who came for meetings as a trustee of Harpeth Academy. Bell was soon to go to Congress and eventually to the United States Senate. The other man was Samuel Houston, the future leader of Texas, already admired for the bravery he had shown when fighting under Jackson at Horseshoe Bend, and recently elected as the representative to Congress from this, the 9th District of Tennessee.[13]

By this year of 1823 Matthew had developed into a serious student. Hungry for learning, he was frustrated not only by the lack of books in his own home but particularly by the scarcity of works on scientific subjects among the volumes owned by Harpeth Academy. He found a few scientific titles in the library of Abram Maury, who invited his young relative to stay at his home when severe winter weather made too difficult the boy's long ride or walk to and from school. At Tree Lawn Matthew could find maps to pore over and, even more to his interest, a *Dictionary of Arts and Sciences,* Ferguson's *Astronomy,* Pinkerton's *Geography,* and Morse's *Abridged Geography.*[14]

Matthew had still not grown very tall, but he had recovered from his back injury; and at seventeen he was required to do his full share of the farm work, his father obviously expecting him to make this his future. This idea did not coincide at all with the boy's desire for further education, a wish with which his mother was sympathetic because she had seen the difference college training had made in the lives of her brothers and might have made in that of her husband. Besides, Diana had already observed that this son already possessed "great decision of character," an attribute that was hers to a marked degree according to one of Richard's nephews.[15] She must also have been pleased to observe that Matthew exhibited the unflagging energy of her father and the intellectual bent of her brothers.

Richard, however, having been only three when his father died, may not have realized in how many ways Matthew resembled the Reverend James Maury. Like the parson, Matthew was short of stature, fascinated by nature, and possessed of an insatiable curiosity about the formation of dew, the clouds and rainfall, the progress of a storm, the qualities of a curious-looking rock, and filled with a constant desire to add to his knowledge. The youth resembled his grandfather also in his friendly response to people as well as in his reverence for God. However, his faith Matthew also held in common with his father. While Richard Maury did not develop the power to overcome difficulties that religion gives to many men, he strove zealously to keep God central in his life and that of his family.

It may be that some physical deficiency, rather than indolence of will, was the cause of Richard's often casual direction of the work on his farm. Instead of going to the fields to supervise his hands, he frequently stood on the knoll in front of the house and shouted his orders to his distant workers. This ability to project his voice so that he could be heard at an extraordinary distance was the one unusual talent that Richard possessed.[16] Matthew took boyish pride in it.

Another cause for Matthew's pride in his father was the fact that Richard was known in the neighborhood for his amiability. But it could only have distressed Matthew when his father's ingenuousness led others to take advantage of him in a trade.[17]

As for Richard's view of Matthew—he had affection for him and considered him normally an obedient son. He did not, however, place a high value on the boy's superior work at school and was irritated by his endless eagerness for more education. Matthew's talk of education seemed sheer stubbornness to Richard, since his older boys, Walker and Dick, did not plague him with such proposals and were content with the prospect of becoming farmers.[18]

In June, 1823, James Hervey Otey left Harpeth Academy. Matthew would have been low in spirits over this development had not Otey's place been filled by William C. Hasbrouck, who was promoted to acting principal.[19] Hasbrouck, an able young teacher and recent graduate of Union College, was interested in seeing his student Matthew reach his full potential.

All talk of Matthew's future, however, was abruptly halted in July when a letter reached the Maurys' log home informing Richard and Diana that their eldest son, John, had died on June 23 and been buried at sea as his ship, the *Decoy,* approached the Virginia Capes. John had been en route to Norfolk to secure supplies for the squadron of Commodore David Porter, assigned to the duty of eradicating piracy from the West Indies.[20] Twenty-eight years old and a lieutenant by statutory rank, John had been serving Porter as "Captain to the Squadron" and was bearing a report from his commodore to the President when he died of yellow fever contracted in the line of duty.[21]

Diana and Richard were overwhelmed with grief. John's earlier safe return from the dangers among island cannibals had lulled them into a false sense of safety for their son. Richard found the loss almost more than he could take and bemoaned the fact that his boy had been able to spend only one leave with them in his fourteen years in the Navy.[22] In addition to the sorrow that filled her heart, Diana was concerned about the future of John's delicate young widow, Eliza, and his boys, five-year-old William and one-year-old Dabney—all of whom would have to live on a Navy widow's pension.

Richard lengthened the daily prayers as the family unitedly sought the consolation of religion. Try as he would to shake it off, the bereaved father found himself engulfed by his sense of loss.

This was Matthew's first acquaintance with grief. It was hard for him to accept that anyone as alive as John could be dead. John, his hero from his earliest years, would return no more—the hurt went deep. To almost anyone the death of a healthy young person is sad; to Matthew, John's going seemed a horrible waste—a life left unfinished. What resolves he made at that time were not then recorded but his later actions gave evidence of them.

A serious, thoughtful Matthew entered the fall term at Harpeth Academy in 1823. His diligent application to his studies won him the further respect of Acting Principal Hasbrouck, to whom he confided his wish to study more mathematics and science. William C. Hasbrouck had grown up in Newburgh, New York, a town about eight miles from West Point, and he told Matthew of the superior training in mathematics that could be obtained at the U.S. Military Academy. By the time Matthew entered his senior year at Harpeth in 1824 the suggestion had taken root in his mind. Concerning this he was to state, "I was anxious to enter the Military Academy at West Point. But the bare mention of the wish put my father in a rage. I abandoned the idea, therefore." [23] Richard had formed a bad opinion of West Point when Abram's son A.P. returned full of dislike for the academy after serving only one year as a cadet. But it was mainly grief about John that made Richard unwilling to contemplate having another son leave home for a service career.[24]

Hasbrouck continued to urge his pupil to seek a college education. Matthew later told of it in this way:

> I had at school been called on by the teacher to hear first one class, and then another, until I became a regular amateur assistant. This was being useful and I was proud of the occupation, though it seriously interfered with my own studies. The teacher, who was a poor young man from New York (he is now a lawyer of property at Newburgh), finding that I was to be taken from school to follow the plough, offered in the fullness of his heart to send me to one of the northern colleges. He had just drawn $500 in a lottery, and like Gil Blas with his "ducats" he thought there would be no end to his $500 prize. And no doubt in my eyes, also, the $500 seemed like the old woman's empty barrel of meal in the Bible, perfectly inexhaustible. But pride or unwillingness to lay myself under such obligations prevented the acceptance of the good Dominie's offer.[25]

Matthew had been tempted to accept Hasbrouck's extremely generous proposal. He so badly wanted the chance at even one year of college; but, in the end, his determination to stand on his own feet was stronger.

It was an unhappy period for the boy as he struggled to figure some way out of his dilemma. Everything in him revolted at the idea of being permanently confined to the narrow valley where his parents lived, limited forever to the life of a small farmer. Matthew had to get out into a larger world of action and thought. The urge to learn was a compulsion, a gnawing hunger within him. His father had forbidden him the free education available at the Army's academy. Then should he not follow John's course and become a midshipman? Even though the Navy had no academy, he would be taught mathematics, navigation, and astronomy on board ship. He understood his father's feeling against his going into uniform, but he believed it wrong to give in to this. Besides, if he went into the Navy he might be more like John, whom Commodore Porter had declared "an officer of extraordinary merit." [26]

Merit appealed to Matthew. He had thought a great deal about the news from North Carolina that James Hervey Otey was going into the Episcopal ministry. His admiration for his preceptor deepened, and the need to decide what he himself was going into drummed in Matthew's head. Endlessly he discussed his Navy idea with Ellick and the other boys at school as the first half of his senior year drew to a close in December, 1824.

The new year of 1825 began, and on its second day Abram Maury died.[27] All the many Maurys residing in middle Tennessee gathered for the funeral. The talk about how well Abram had used his life reinforced Matthew's private resolution, which was, he reported, "to make myself a useful man." [28]

The pressure of time was working in him. In less than two weeks he would be nineteen. Soon he would complete his course at Harpeth Academy. He decided he must act.

Never before had he gone against his father's will in a matter of any consequence. But wasn't it his father who had so often read to the family the Bible parable of the talents? If he could secure an appointment to the Navy and have it actually in hand, maybe he could induce his father to agree with him that a naval career was right for him. But, right or wrong, it was something he had to do. Of the step he took he later said, "I . . . secretly set about, through the agency of a friend (at that time a shop-boy or, as we say in the West, a store-boy), to obtain a warrant in the Navy, for my prospects, as I thought, had become exceedingly gloomy." [29]

Full of excitement and boyish enthusiasm, Matthew reported his action in a letter written on January 6 to his closest friend, Ven, whose family had recently moved from Tennessee to Mississippi:

> Ventress! What do you think? I don't know what you think but I know what I think and I'll wager my old beaver, you can't guess. Try: You are going to study medicine? No; that is one trial, and you're not to have but one more: (Ellick [Alex C. Maury] is going to set up a printing office?) No: that is two guesses. A-n-d . . .

t-h-r-e-e! Me and Ellick are going to the Na-na-na-vy; it sounds large now don't it? but it is a fact; we will soon expect our commissions as our petitions will have been gone four weeks next Tuesday; now it is a fact.

Mr. F. [Frank] Owen has written for me to his brother George and Samuel Houston. My Dad and Mom say I shall *not* go; but you can guess whether I will or not. I am as determined as ever for you know I always intended going.

[Ellick] Maury has told you of the death of Uncle Abram.

Write immediately or I may be gone to the Navy.[30]

Having set his course, Matthew's spirits now soared with assurance. Naturally sanguine of temperament, he apparently did not doubt that Samuel Houston would promptly grant his request.

The congressman did just that. The simply worded application, although seconded by no distinguished citizen and made with no pressure, must have interested rugged Sam Houston, who well remembered the difficulties of his own boyhood. He took to the sound of this youth of proper ambition who, like himself, had been born on a farm in Virginia and moved to Tennessee. Of course, the applicant's being one of the Maurys of Williamson County was not overlooked by the astute politician. Houston recommended that the application be granted. In almost the time he had predicted, Matthew received an official communication that bore at the top the magic heading: "Washington, D.C., February 1, 1825."[31] It advised the 19-year-old that he had been accepted as an acting midshipman in the United States Navy.

Matthew was overjoyed. He wanted to tell everyone of his good fortune. But first he must go home and tell his father what he had done. It was the hardest task Matthew had ever had. As soon as he began to think about the prospect he realized how false had been his hope of converting his stern parent to approval of his becoming a midshipman.

Richard Maury was very angry and gravely disappointed in his son; he sought to hide neither emotion. Describing his father's reaction, Matthew later said, "It disturbed the family very much and my father expressed his disapprobation of my conduct in strong terms. And, as I had proceeded without consulting him, he determined to leave me to my own resources."[32]

Diana was no more pleased than Richard over Matthew's secret move, and she dreaded his going to sea. However, she recognized that her boy's mind and spirit were committed and that he could not be deflected from his purpose. A loving mother, possessed of "a mighty tender conscience,"[33] Diana tried to understand what had compelled Matthew to defy his father. She struggled to make peace between them; but Richard was implacable and Matthew stuck to his determination to go.

If the father thought his refusal to supply money for the trip would keep Matthew at home he really was blind to the nature of his son. Even at nineteen Matthew posessed the power of persuasion; he talked neighbor Sanford G. Allen into selling him a mare on his word to remit the price, $75, when he reached his destination. Matthew was relieved when provision for his means of transportation had been made. His wardrobe was scant, but the weather was warming up. He would make out with what he had. As for the lack of cash, he decided he would have to risk starting without it.

In early April, 1825, Matthew satisfactorily concluded his course at Harpeth Academy. He was now extremely impatient to start for Washington to report to the Navy. Yet when the moment of departure came, the boy found it difficult to tell the family goodbye. He realized how much he was going to miss his understanding mother, his brothers Walker, Dick, and Charles as well as his sisters Matilda, Betsy, and Catharine Ann.[34] His eldest sister, Mary, was not present for the farewells as she was away traveling with her husband, Noah Miller Ludlow, actor and part owner of a repertory company.[35] Up until the very end of this leave-taking, Matthew hoped his father would relent and forgive him before he went away. But when Matthew resolutely mounted the gray mare Fanny and called out his final goodbye, no response came from his father, who turned his back in disapproval. There was nothing for Matthew to do but accept this as the price of his decision and ride off.

"The bitterest pang I felt on leaving home," he later declared, "was parting with my brother Dick, two years my senior. We two had hitherto been inseparable." Matthew continued: "I set out from home without a cent in my pocket, intending to trust to luck and, if necessary, stop on the road and work out my bills when I got to [a] town. However, (Sunday morning) I found that the faithful Dominie had left thirty dollars for me."[36] This money had been left with a friend in Franklin to be given Matthew as he rode through town. It was from William C. Hasbrouck for Matthew's teaching assistance at Harpeth Academy and was to be his total capital for the 750-mile trip to Washington.

At an inn in eastern Tennessee Matthew met two merchants, Read and Echols, en route from Huntsville, Alabama, to Baltimore to purchase goods. The men took a liking to the youth and suggested that he join them. When they crossed from Tennessee into Virginia, Matthew learned one of the unpleasant economic facts of life of the time: the Tennessee currency he was using had to be converted into Virginia currency or federal dollars. As Matthew wrote: "Mine host (at an inn) in-

formed me that thence forward my Tennessee money 'would not go' and
he offered 'as it was me' to give me $20 for what I had left. I thought
him very kind and accepted his offer." [37] The inexperienced youth received an inordinately poor rate of exchange, so much so that he realized
he would have to husband every penny if he was to complete his trip,
the largest portion of which lay ahead. Observing the boy's natural dismay, each of the merchants took him aside and offered him money,
which he politely but firmly declined.[38]

Matthew was traveling back over the route by which he and his
family had journeyed to Tennessee fourteen and a half years earlier. Although he was an experienced rider, it was still not easy for him to
spend all the daylight hours in the saddle day after day. One way to forget weariness was to remind himself that he was riding toward his desired future. Each 25 to 30 miles that was covered daily took him that
much nearer naval training and the mathematical and scientific instruction he desired.[39] Besides, it was spring, and Matthew always responded to the beauty nature created in such abundance. When the
three travelers reached Fincastle, a church-studded hamlet in Botetourt
County, Virginia, Matthew and the merchants parted company, for
Read and Echols were to proceed down the valley of Virginia to Win-
chester and thence into Maryland. Matthew rode on alone to Albemarle
County.

His destination was "Piedmont," the home of his father's first cousin
Reuben Maury. It was situated near Charlottesville, a community proud
of its new University of Virginia, the last great dream of Jefferson, who
was nearing death at "Monticello." Reuben Maury, "steady, prudent,
liberal-hearted," [40] closely oversaw his plantation and his two mills and
had a comfortable home. In the best tradition of the Maury family,
Reuben gave his young kinsman a cordial welcome and gathered other
relatives to have a meal with Matthew.

The newly arrived youth was engaged in answering questions about
the family in Tennessee when he was served a deep saucer of a "curious
cream colored" concoction.[41] He took a spoonful and emptied it on his
plate thinking it some new type of spread. His relatives explained that
this was vanilla ice cream and that the whole saucer was for him. Everyone laughed and Matthew blushed at his own ignorance. Not even
Reuben's gay-hearted brother Tom Maury meant to embarrass the boy
with laughter, but it had that effect.[42] Matthew resolved he would fill
the gaps in his social knowledge; courtesy and good manners were his
already by instinct and parental training.

From Charlottesville Matthew headed for Spotsylvania County, where
he had been born. There he visited at Laurel Hill,[43] the home of his

father's sister Elizabeth, who had married Edward Herndon.[44] This couple, though well up in their sixties, had temporarily taken into their home Edward's niece and nephew, Ann Hull Herndon and Brodie Herndon, who had just been orphaned.[45]

Ann was an engagingly pretty girl nearing her fourteenth birthday.[46] Their difference in age seemed to make no difference to Matthew, and he had no difficulty in making friends with Ann.[47] He liked the way her auburn hair caught glints of the sun and admired her neatly molded nose and well-shaped mouth. Seeing the sadness of her expression, he tried to take her mind off her sorrow. She had lost her mother, Elizabeth Hull Herndon, only a few weeks before;[48] and the death of her father, Dabney Herndon, cashier (chief executive officer) of the Farmer's Bank in Fredericksburg, had occurred the preceding December.[49] Matthew was a good storyteller, and Ann proved a willing listener to his tales about Tennessee. In fact, the young girl was full of admiration for this newly met cousin whose mother, Diana Minor Maury, was the niece of her grandmother, Mary Minor Herndon. Ann found him very handsome with his wavy brown hair, highly colored cheeks, and alert blue eyes, often merry with laughter. He was only five feet six, but he had broad, square shoulders and a well-developed chest. His strong neck supported a fine-looking head. His hands were small but powerful. Later, when asked what she thought of him at this first meeting, Ann replied, "The young shepherd David straight from the fold." [50]

Matthew's arrival in Spotsylvania was the cause for much visiting around among the Maurys and Minors, all of whom wanted to see how Richard and Diana's son had developed since he left Virginia. The senior member of the family was Abraham Maury, Richard's brother, who had served as an officer in the Revolution.[51] The preceding autumn Colonel Maury had been one of the committee to welcome the Marquis de Lafayette to Fredericksburg. The town still rang with praise of the graciousness of General Lafayette when he made their community an early stop on his extended tour of the United States, now nearing its completion.[52]

Enjoyable as Matthew found the comfortable hospitality and friendliness of his relatives, he was eager to go on to Washington. Having reached Spotsylvania with only 25 cents left in his pocket, he knew this would not take him and Fanny, his mare, on to the capital city. Besides, he must discharge his obligation to his trusting friend back in Tennessee. Edward Herndon agreed to sell the mare for the needed $75. Matthew was happy when this sum was promptly remitted and his promise had been kept.[53]

While he had been too proud to take money from the strangers with whom he had traveled, Matthew now had to face the fact that his future opportunity in the Navy was more important than his pride. Besides, he found it much easier to accept help from his kindly aunt Elizabeth and her generous husband. With coins again jingling in his pockets, Matthew left Fredericksburg for Washington, proceeding almost certainly by the combination stage and steamboat line, which had just reduced the fare to $3.50. Never having traveled on a boat, the boy surely could not have resisted the chance to go by stage to Potomac Creek, board the steamboat at 6 P.M., and sleep aboard while being transported to Washington City for arrival there at 3 A.M.[54] Early on a June morning, Washington's famous miasma shrouded the marshy Potomac flats. It meant nothing to Matthew then, but it would in years to come.

Washington, with its many undeveloped areas, a population of 15,000 persons, and city streets that whirled with summer dust, would not have impressed a foreign visitor that June day in 1825, but to Matthew it was the metropolis it called itself. Carriages and hacks were numerous, people were well dressed.[55] The homespun of most of the country people he knew in Tennessee was not the garb of the city dwellers.

Government officials and bankers in Washington talked of the Industrial Revolution that was transforming England, and to a lesser degree the Continent, from a society and economy based on agriculture and commerce to industrialism. More generally heard, however, was discussion about westward expansion in the United States. A few months earlier a charter had been granted to the Chesapeake and Ohio Canal Company, and men speculated on what changes the canal would bring when it connected Washington with the "west." The Erie Canal was nearing completion. In the autumn the canal would link New York with Buffalo, and immigrants would go west that way. The new President, John Quincy Adams, was known to favor internal development.[56]

Washingtonians were also full of talk about General Lafayette, who was in Boston but expected back in Washington early in August prior to sailing to France from the capital city.

The copper-covered, low, half-bowl dome of the Capitol glittered in the June sun and could be seen at a distance because of the commanding position on which the seat of Congress had been built. Along Pennsylvania Avenue the four rows of poplars that bordered the wide street rustled in the summer breeze.[57] Matthew noted all that he saw because that was his habit, but he had come a long way and he had but one immediate purpose—to get to the office of the Secretary of the Navy and report.

To reach the Navy Department building the youth had to pass close to "the President's House." [58] The mansion had been rebuilt and painted white after severe damage by the British in the War of 1812. John Quincy Adams had been voted into the Presidency the preceding February by the House of Representatives. The election had gone to the House after votes for William H. Crawford and Henry Clay had prevented either Adams or his chief opponent, Andrew Jackson, from having a majority in the electoral college. There had been much criticism in Tennessee over the fact that, while Jackson had won 99 electoral votes to 84 for Adams, it was Adams who had been given the Presidency by the House.[59] Matthew was not politically minded, but he possessed an ever-alert curiosity and certainly scrutinized the entrance and grounds of the Executive Mansion in the hope of catching a glimpse of the President of the United States.

To the west of the residence of the Chief Executive stood Matthew's goal—the Navy Department. The structure was not overly large, being about 55 by 165 feet; but it had a good plain façade of classic appearance and was identical to its immediate neighbor, used by the Army, and to the buildings of the State Department and Treasury on the east of the Executive Mansion.[60]

Once across the threshold of the Navy Building and his eyes adjusted to the relative darkness of the long central hall, Matthew's first act was surely to ask in which room he would find Richard B. Maury. Before leaving Fredericksburg he had learned, to his surprise and pleasure, that his uncle Fontaine's son was on the Navy Department's small staff of clerks and was soon to be made Register.[61]

Neither Richard B. nor any other of the department's small staff of thirty men, amused though they may have been, dissuaded Matthew from his determination to report to the Secretary of the Navy in person. Matthew, sublimely oblivious to the protocol observed toward a Cabinet officer, was fully capable of presenting himself to the Secretary, but it seems likely that Richard B. accompanied his young kinsman to make the introduction.

To reach the Secretary's office, Matthew had to pass, on the first floor, the auditors' office, a place he was to come to know as the source of his pay. Upstairs he went past Number 8, the office of the enormously powerful three Navy commissioners, whose $3,500 each per year far exceeded the pay of their fellow senior captains. But the next room was of more interest to a 19-year-old, for there were kept the models of Navy ships and there men worked to design the vessels to be built in the future.[62]

At last he was in Room Number 1, the office of the Secretary of the Navy. After a short delay he was presented to Samuel Lewis Southard, the impressive-looking $6,000-a-year civilian chief of the department.[63]

The Secretary was courteous in his welcome and took time to talk to Matthew at some length.

Southard was aware of the youth's background. In his own early manhood he had gone to Virginia as a tutor and there become a friend of James Monroe under whom he had studied law in Fredericksburg, where he had known the Maurys and Minors.[64]

The officers' corps of the Navy then being extremely small, it is probable that Southard had heard of the career of Matthew's brother John. In the files were two letters that had reached the department shortly before Southard took office in 1823. In them Commodore David Porter had urged that "Lieutenant Maury, acting as Captain to the Squadron" be granted the pay of a captain. Discussing John's handling of the assignment, Porter stated, "I can with safety say, without disparagement to anyone, that no officer in the Navy, whatever may be his rank, could have filled it more to my satisfaction or to his own credit." [65]

If Southard did not know of the record John had achieved before his death, Richard B. Maury may have mentioned it to him as an indication that the Navy could expect well of Matthew.

The preliminary courtesies over, Southard asked Matthew why he had come to Washington before being ordered to do so, since the letter that had been sent him was a notification of appointment to serve but not authorization to report. The Secretary, fortunately, was neither pompous nor severe and at thirty-eight years of age could still understand the boy's impetuous mistake. He informed Matthew that the department would reimburse him at the rate of 15 cents a mile for his trip from Franklin.[66] He did, however, caution Matthew that his pay would not begin until his orders to active duty were issued and that his pay would be $19 a month, plus one ration a day.[67] In dismissing his young visitor, the Secretary stressed that it would be up to Matthew whether he would make good in his first six months of sea duty and after that receive his official warrant as a midshipman.

Matthew hadn't the slightest worry in the world about making good—he was bubbling over with certainty. He was going to receive a travel reimbursement of over $100, more money than he had ever had in his life. He could imagine himself in the uniforms he would buy.

Once the Secretary had received him, Matthew felt already in the Navy and wanted to learn facts about the service. Available at the department was the latest edition of the official *Navy Register,* which answered many of his questions. It showed that at the end of the previous year, 1824, there were in the Navy 24 captains, 29 master commandants, and 172 lieutenants. There were also 69 young men with the title of passed midshipman, which meant that they had passed an examination and had been promoted to a rank in which they would serve until they were made lieutenants. Of midshipmen there were 310. Matthew learned that, aside from the three Navy commissioners, the highest ranking captain of a vessel of 32 guns or upward received $100 per month plus 8 rations per day. The captain of a ship of from 20 to 32 guns received $75, a master commandant $60, a lieutenant-commanding $50, and a lieutenant only $40 a month with 3 rations per day. It was fortunate that Matthew's aim was not money, for this was meager compensation even for the times. Of course, the higher ranking officers did not consume all their rations and could receive the small monetary equivalent of those they did not draw.

Then there was the question of rank. Matthew recalled that when his brother John had told his adventures in the Pacific he had spoken of his commander as Commodore Porter. Now Matthew learned that there was no such fixed rank in the Navy, but that the title commodore was used to designate a captain commanding more than one ship, and that such an officer was called commodore as a matter of courtesy. The highest statutory rank in the U.S. Navy was captain. The legislators had consistently ignored proposals to establish the ranks of commodore, rear admiral, vice-admiral, and admiral, such as existed in the navies of other nations. The reason given was that such titles did not suit a republic, but this argument failed to satisfy the Navy. Honesty would have required admission by the congressmen that the higher pay necessary to such ranks was the chief drawback to their establishment.[68]

The golden age of the Navy, the War of 1812, was long over, and in the intervening decade the Navy had been required to cut expenditures. As a result of the peacetime move, a number of Navy ships had been laid up "in ordinary" (mothballs) though some of the older vessels were being replaced by new construction. The total fleet in 1825 consisted of only 7 ships of the line; 6 frigates, first class, including the new *Brandywine;* 3 frigates, second class; 7 sloops of war, 7 schooners (including 1 galliot) and a few other smaller craft.[69]

During the next weeks, while he was awaiting orders, Matthew had further opportunity to gain information about the Navy from Richard B. Maury. It was at Richard B.'s home that Matthew became acquainted with Eliza, the widow of his Navy brother John, and her two little boys, who had come from Fredericksburg for a summer visit.[70] From Eliza Matthew learned more facts about John's Navy career.

Sightseeing was as popular in Washington then as now. After nearly thirty years of work, the Capitol was nearly completed although neither the massive columns of the portico nor the outside front stairs leading to the main floor were yet in place. Visitors still had to enter through the basement, where John Marshall presided over the Supreme Court. A stairway led directly to the great rotunda. Off the rotunda the semi-circular Senate chamber, with seats for the forty-eight senators, was of striking classic design but not nearly so large as the marble-columned Hall of the House of Representatives, whose arching ceiling rose to a cupola sixty feet above the floor.[71] Like any other young American, Matthew was undoubtedly impressed by the building, but he would have found it more exciting had Congress been in session and perhaps a debate in progress.

To Matthew, though, the sight of greatest interest in Washington was to be observed at the Navy Yard located about one mile from the city on the Anacostia River, a branch of the Potomac, where he saw a ship that had been launched on June 16—the *Brandywine, 44.* The frigate, designed by William Doughty, had been laid down in the yard in 1821 and was now being rushed to completion because she had been designated by the President as the vessel to carry the Marquis de Lafayette home at the termination of his tour. In honor of the Marquis, the vessel had been named for the Revolutionary battle in which he had been wounded while serving with Washington.[72]

The *Brandywine,* "hauled alongside the Navy Yard"[73] to be fitted for sea, was the first ship of any size that Matthew had ever seen and a beauty to behold. She measured 175 feet between the perpendiculars, molded beam of 45 feet, depth in hold 14½ feet, 1,726 tons displacement. Matthew was to learn that she had cost $825,000 to build.[74]

On July 1 the mechanics "hung the rudder" and four days later the intricate work of rigging the ship began.[75]

July 9, 1825, was a date Matthew was never to forget. On that day he received a liver-colored envelope bearing his eagerly awaited orders. Ripping it open he read and reread the slip from the Navy Department, dated "8 July, 1825, Washington City" and addressed to "M. F. Maury, *Present.*" The orders, written in standard form, read: "Proceed to Washington and report to Captain T. Tingey for duty on board the *Brandywine.*"[76] Matthew could hardly contain himself. He would be on the *Brandywine* when she carried Lafayette back to France.

Matthew's heritage had stood him in good stead, for each midshipman and officer had been selected for this duty, in so far as possible, from descendants of men who, like Lafayette, had served in America's War for Independence.[77] The difference in Matthew's case was that his mother and father had not made a move to secure him this opportunity, while the parents of most of the other "young gentleman of the steerage" with whom he was to serve had brought influence to bear on the Secretary of the Navy to have their sons sail on this historic cruise. In any event, he was to have his first duty with a hand-picked group of men. The assignment was a happy omen for Matthew's future in the Navy.

Now that he had orders he could have his uniforms made, both full dress and undress. Most important was his short Navy dress jacket, of blue wool cloth with six brass buttons on each lapel and a standing collar with a diamond formed of gold lace on each side. Full dress required a plain chapeau (cocked hat), half boots, and a cut-and-thrust sword, sharpened on both sides and at the tip for the thrust into an enemy's body. He also had to have both blue trousers and white, to suit the seasons, white vests, and collars that would show above the jacket collar. Two regulation black cravats must be purchased, and a heavy coat was essential for winter deck duty. A quadrant and a copy of Bowditch's *American Practical Navigator* also were required items.[78]

Matthew was shocked when he learned the cost of his outfit. The idea of going in debt was distasteful to him, but he had no choice. The only question was where he could get that much money. He couldn't ask his father. He did not feel he could take more from his relatives in Virginia, and he was anxious not to impose on newly married Richard B. Maury, whose Navy Department salary was small. Finally Matthew thought of his friend Ventress, whose family had comfortable means. Feeling sure that Ven would help him if he could, Matthew reluctantly wrote his former schoolmate and asked for a loan of the necessary $200,[79] hoping that a reply and a check would arrive before his orders did.[80]

The suspense of waiting for Ven's answer only added to Matthew's keen anticipation of his first duty in the United States Navy.

CHAPTER III

The Navy Gains
a Midshipman

It was August 13, 1825. Glistening in the summer sun, the new frigate *Brandywine* rode at anchor in the Potomac, off Greenleaf's Point. A light-yellow band along her gun ports set off her black hull. Her lower masts and topmasts were smartly painted in black, matching her freshly tarred standing rigging. The frigate carried more than her rating of 44 guns, as did most men-of-war of the period.[1] Because her supplies and equipment were not yet stowed in her hold, she rode high in the water, and the copper sheathing on her bottom could be seen when a passing vessel sent its wake against her sides.

In a boat alongside the frigate, Matthew Fontaine Maury waited his turn among the seven officers, one boatswain, and twelve other already warranted or acting midshipmen who were to join the ship that day.[2] He was naturally excited but also serious, so much so that during the wait he made a resolution: "I will make everything bend to my profession." [3] It was a resolution that was to be kept.

Dressed in regulation white ducks, white vest, and navy-blue pea jacket properly decorated with brass buttons and midshipman's insignia, and wearing a visored cap and a dirk attached by a gilt chain to the blue webbing belt around his waist—he felt a little strange, but proud.[4] The uniform was itself a symbol of achievement.

At last his turn came, and he climbed over the ship's side, to stand for the first time on the holystoned deck of a warship. At that moment past limitations were sloughed off—for Maury the future had begun.

He reported to the lieutenant in temporary command of the ship [5] and was promptly turned over to a passed midshipman, who took him from the upper, or spar, deck down a companionway to the main, or gun deck, then down to the berth deck to a bulkheaded area 20 feet in length, running the width of the ship. This was the steerage, assigned as quarters for midshipmen, both warranted and acting, the latter soon learning that the qualifying prefix was not regularly used before their title.

It had been hot on deck; below decks it was stifling. The steerage was ventilated by only two ports, 8 by 12 inches in size, located just above the water line. The sickening odor, the newly arrived midshipman was told, was caused by bilgewater in the ship, though she had been in the water less than two months. Far away were the sweet smells of country fields and shaded woods, and equally as far the freedom of space—a frigate imposed its own limitations and nowhere more so than in the steerage. Further limiting the available space was equipment. Each of the midshipmen was assigned a two-foot-square wooden locker, painted black, in which to keep his clothes and possessions, a campstool, and a hammock of hempen cloth. Also provided were two crude washstands and basins to serve all "the young gentlemen," [6] as the midshipmen were most frequently called.

Maury and another midshipman named William F. Irving struck up a friendship. The two youths soon discovered they had a common interest—books. Maury was further stimulated when he learned that his friend from New York was the nephew of the popular author Washington Irving. A more immediately valuable acquaintance was Samuel Barron, who, though not yet sixteen, had already seen nearly five years of sea duty. Maury found out that, like himself, Barron had been born in Virginia and was the son of the late Commodore Samuel Barron. More surprising was the fact that Sam had been appointed a midshipman on January 1, 1812, when only two years old, to ensure the child's being able to follow in the Navy footsteps of his father.[7]

Other midshipmen with whom Matthew discovered the bond of Virginia birth were William Francis Lynch, with whom he formed a friendship that was to last; John W. Willis, who enjoyed talking about his home town, Fredericksburg; and young William Radford, whose stepfather was the distinguished General William Clark. The General, who had explored the northwest with Meriwether Lewis, was at that time chief of Indian Affairs and lived in St. Louis, where he had recently entertained Lafayette. Young Radford could report on Lafayette from firsthand experience; in return, Maury could chat with Radford about Fincastle, Radford's birthplace, where Maury had stopped on his ride from Tennessee.[8]

Some days before sailing the number of midshipmen more than doubled.[9] To honor Lafayette and to satisfy influential parents, the Secretary of the Navy had ordered twenty-six midshipmen to the *Brandywine* instead of the normal complement of eleven, and there was scarcely room left to stand in the steerage.[10] It was fortunate for Maury that physical comfort was not his first consideration. Far more important to him was being thrown with people of intelligence and ability. This he had in the *Brandywine.*

New arrivals in the steerage relayed accounts they had read in the papers of Lafayette's activities in these last days before his departure from the country. After arriving in Washington and paying a short visit to President Adams, the General had proceeded by carriage to make his farewells to Jefferson, Madison, and Monroe at their Virginia homes. His return to Washington was imminent.[11]

On board the *Brandywine* all hands worked feverishly to complete preparations for sea. The sides of the hold were whitewashed, the "bright ware" polished, the guns blacked, their carriages oiled, and the decks stoned to a sparkling white.

Shipboard terms had to be quickly learned by Maury and the other newcomers in the steerage. Experienced midshipmen like Sam Barron lost no time in teaching them to use Navy language and to tell time by the ship's bell. One expression they had no trouble learning was scuttle-butt.[12] In the below-decks heat and general discomfort the boys frequently wanted a drink of water and went to the scuttlebutt, a giant cask with the top off and a shelf holding tin cups. Here gossip was exchanged. If an officer appeared while the midshipmen were there, the youths were required to work the cask's pump, which brought up water from a larger vat in the hold.

Maury and his fellow novices were given a rapid training in the rudiments of shipboard behavior. One of the first requirements impressed on the youths was the respect due to all officers—and especially to the quarter-deck, as the seat of authority. The need of absolute obedience to any command was stressed. The transition from home life to the authoritarian regime of a warship was not overwhelming for Maury because his father had not permitted the questioning of an order and his parents had insisted he show deference to persons older than himself.[13]

Instruction was given as to the correct manner of saluting an officer and climbing the rigging. The basic elements of handling the ship, battle stations, and gun mechanisms were explained to the midshipmen. In addition, they were taught the proper way to give a command to a sailor.

A midshipman in the United States Navy in 1825 was in a peculiar position. He was outranked by the ship's carpenter, gunner, boatswain, master's mate, and sailing master, yet Navy Regulations of 1818, still in effect when Maury began his training, stated clearly: "The commanding officers will consider the midshipmen as a class of officers, meriting in an especial degree their fostering care."[14] Their status was more clearly defined in the 1920 Regulations: "Midshipmen are by law officers in a qualified sense. They are classed as being of the line." [15] These regulations, issued nearly one hundred years apart, show that while the midshipmen of 1825 were trained in a ship at sea and those in 1920 at Annapolis, all were considered officers—but officers carefully limited in power.

The indoctrination of the *Brandywine*'s new midshipmen continued on August 14, when the anchor was hauled in and the ship towed by two steamboats from her position off Greenleaf's Point across stream to anchorage off Alexandria, and again the next day when she was towed down the Potomac to drop anchor off Sandy Point. On August 16 the small steamboats were discharged after they had successfully maneuvered the frigate to a mooring in the Potomac close to the point where the river empties into Chesapeake Bay.[16] In the following days, as he scurried about on his new duties, Maury had an opportunity to observe the great quantity of stores and water that had to be taken on board. Doubtless it seemed to him that the loading was taking forever.

A marine, Miles Collier, died in the *Brandywine* on August 21, and Maury had his first experience of a naval burial. The ship's chaplain not having yet reported, the service was read by a young civilian named George Jones assigned to the ship as schoolmaster. Sailors "each with a red jacket, small straw hat, white pantaloons and shirt with blue collar" went ashore ahead of the coffin, and behind it marched "two midshipmen with side arms." [17]

That same day furniture was received on board the *Brandywine* for the cabin of the nation's guest, General Lafayette. Ensigns and pennants [18] with which to dress ship were brought on board, as were other objects of particular interest to young Maury—charts, some books on navigation, and six *Nautical Almanacs,* those British Admiralty guides essential to the navigator, which provided not only tables and calculations of the tides, data on eclipses and other phenomena but also a three-year forecast of the position of the sun, moon, and planets at a given latitude and longitude at any hour.

At last, on September 5, Captain Charles Morris,[19] who was to have the honor of commanding the ship taking Lafayette back to France came on board and took over from executive officer, Lieutenant Francis H. Gregory. As conversation never lagged among the midshipmen until the master at arms appeared at 9 P.M. to "douse the glim," there must have been much talk that evening about their distinguished captain. When a midshipman, Morris had been the first of Stephen Decatur's boarding party to cut down a Tripolitan pirate in Decatur's famed destruction of the U.S. *Philadelphia,* which the pirates had captured and were holding in the harbor of Tripoli. And Sam Barron could tell them how Morris, as a lieutenant, had given the orders for Captain Isaac Hull that proud day in 1812 when the *Constitution* had shot down every mast on Britain's *Guerrière* and forced Captain James R. Dacres to surrender his ship. Morris had been made a captain in reward for his part in achieving that spectacular victory.

On September 7 Captain Morris gave the long-awaited word—all hands were to be in full dress the next day to welcome Lafayette, beloved of all Americans. And still supplies were received on the ship, the final items being two log books, six thermometers, and 2,000 quills. The paper work had to go on!

At 10:30 sharp on the morning of September 8 a commodore's launch could be seen approaching the *Brandywine*. All hands, assembled on the deck of the frigate, watched the progress of the craft as she was rowed from the steam vessel *Mount Vernon*. For Maury and every other midshipman it was a moment of intense excitement when their eyes made out the figure of General Lafayette. By the General's side was his official host of the day, Secretary of the Navy Southard. The guns of the frigate roared out a salute. Seventeen times the salvos sounded, the first such ear-splitting experience for Maury. In spite of high wind and rain, the yards were manned, and on deck the marines were drawn up at attention. As the barge drew alongside, Lafayette was cheered repeatedly by the men aloft.

Seated in a specially constructed and ornamented boatswain's chair, General Lafayette was hoisted up and over the side to be welcomed by Captain Morris. The 68-year-old French nobleman was alert and affable but showed the wear of his 12-month tour of the United States in which he had been feted everywhere by a grateful people. The General was accompanied by his son, George Washington Lafayette, and his secretary, Auguste Levasseur.

Distinguished citizens who had escorted Lafayette from the capital now came on board. Included were the Commander in Chief of the Army; the generals of the militia of the District of Columbia; the mayors of Washington, Georgetown (then a separate town), and Alexandria; Commodore William Bainbridge, who in the *Constitution* had captured the British frigate *Java* in 1812; and George Washington Parke Custis, stepgrandson of George Washington reared at Mount Vernon.

A group of Revolutionary heroes had cruised down Chesapeake Bay from Baltimore in a steamboat to add their farewell to the man who had been their fellow officer. Their small streamer- and flag-bedecked steamboat and other craft from Washington anchored near the *Brandywine* and added color to this historic scene of farewell. At 1 P.M. the officers

47

of the *Brandywine* were presented to Secretary of the Navy Southard, who met them on the quarterdeck. The "grand collation" was served at 3 P.M. to Lafayette, Secretary Southard, and the other distinguished guests. Wine flowed freely, for toasts were numerous. Music was supplied by the ship's band. At 4:30 the festivities concluded, the Secretary of the Navy left the ship to the cheers of the crew high overhead and to another salute of 17 guns. One by one the other guests followed the Secretary off the ship and were rowed to their steamers.[20]

Also going ashore was one who had been expected to sail in the *Brandywine*—the chaplain, who had reported for duty only that morning. That worthy had been so frightened by the booming of the guns and the orderly but noisy confusion of the day that he had immediately tendered his resignation.[21] The proffer had been equally as promptly accepted, the captain deciding that the ship's company would manage somehow without the challenge to courageous living that the chaplain might have made.

At 5:30 A.M., September 9, the *Brandywine* weighed anchor, and Maury started on his first Navy cruise. At seven o'clock she passed the lightboat off Smith's Point and by eight she was standing down Chesapeake Bay with all sail drawing.[22] It was a sight and an experience that must have thrilled the land-reared Maury. The ship's performance certainly charmed the conservative *Daily National Intelligencer* of Washington, which, a few days later, reported: "The frigate *Brandywine* passed the Capes of Virginia to sea on Friday at 2 o'clock with a fine breeze from the North. She must have gone down the river and bay with prodigious rapidity as she reached the Capes some hours before the quick steamboat *Mount Vernon* performed little more than half the distance on her return back to the city." [23]

The *Brandywine* was the scene of rejoicing from quarter-deck to steerage. She was going to be a fast sailer. She was making 11 knots as she sped between Cape Henry and Cape Charles into the Atlantic. But the pounding waves were to throw a damper on the enthusiasm of both officers and crew. Early the next morning the ship was found to be leaking. Captain Morris ordered more than 2,000 pounds of iron shot heaved overboard. The lightened ship rose sufficiently for sailors to locate the leak, close to the water line but below the berth deck.

Fully aware of his responsibility to return Lafayette safely to France, Captain Morris decided to report the situation to his illustrious guest and ask him to decide whether the *Brandywine* should turn back. As the ship was already both pitching and rolling, Lafayette was suffering from seasickness. He managed to listen courteously to Morris, inquired carefully into the location of the leak, and then advised the captain that he

48

wished to continue the voyage.[24] Brave, brave man. To risk a leak is one thing, but to vote to do so when in the grip of *mal de mer* is heroism.

Captain Morris had undoubtedly counseled Lafayette that the ship's planking would swell and greatly reduce the leak, while the pumps would be manned to control any further intake of water.

Meanwhile the Atlantic had had the same effect on the new midshipmen as it had on General Lafayette. According to Schoolmaster Jones, "The steerage was strewed with its inmates and twelve of the midshipmen were lying around in the cockpit. Old tars sympathized with them and offered them 'salt water with fat bacon and molasses as a grand specific.' "[25] This observer also reported some water coming into the steerage "as the main deck including forward cabin is flooded." In fact, the ocean was so rough that even some experienced sailors were ill.

By September 16 Lafayette had recovered and appeared on deck. His attitude toward the junior officers was one of "paternal friendship,"[26] and they listened with interest as well as respect as he talked of George Washington and the Revolution.

Diana Maury Corbin, in describing her father's first voyage, stated: "The gallant Marquis frequently noticed the studious little Middy, and had many a kind talk with him."[27] With his well-known courtesy, General Lafayette surely asked the youth's name and recognized it as French in origin. Perhaps Lafayette recalled Maury's uncle, Colonel Abraham Maury, who had been one of those to welcome him the preceding fall at Fredericksburg. Whatever was discussed, the main thing that stuck in Maury's mind was that greatness did not preclude kindness.

Maury now received his first training in gunnery as Captain Morris had the guns exercised, going through the evolutions of a real engagement, though no powder was used. The *Brandywine* mounted 30 long guns, 32-pounders, on her main deck, and, on the upper deck, 24 carronades, 32-pounders, for a total of ten guns in excess of her rating. The boy from a peaceful Tennessee farm quickly learned that there were twelve men in a gun crew, eight or ten guns in a division, and over each division was a lieutenant assisted by two or three midshipmen.[28] When good weather prevailed, the captain ordered that Quarters be held each afternoon. Before sunset the ship's band was ordered up, the drummers sounded a steady beat, and every man had to dress, lash his hammock in the nettings, and report promptly to his battle station. The roll of each gun crew was called by a midshipman, and the sailors answered the role assigned to them, such as "first loader" or "powder boy."[29]

One part of Maury's naval education was temporarily postponed. This was the need to harden himself to the sight of a sailor's being flogged. In deference to Lafayette's presence aboard ship, a lighter kind of punishment was meted out to erring crew members. A "half a dozen" or more on the bare back with "the colts," a rope of about two feet long and a half inch thick, was ordered instead of flogging with the cat-o'-nine-tails. This special dispensation did not last once the General had left the ship, for on October 15 Maury saw sailors, charged with drunkenness, their backs bared, and their wrists tied to the bulwark, receive half a dozen with the cats.[30] The terror of the victims, their screams as the cat cut into their flesh, and their pleas for mercy were things that no man liked to remember. However, Maury was to learn that most of the good sailors believed flogging necessary to the maintenance of discipline.

But during Lafayette's trip all was made as pleasant as possible, with the exception of one thing important to all young men. William Radford declared "the food was very bad." [31] In a midshipman's mess in the days of sail, meals were always starchy and monotonous, but on this maiden voyage of the *Brandywine* an accident made them even less palatable than usual. During the rough weather encountered in the first few days out, a steward who was cleaning tar from an officer's uniform placed a large opened bottle of turpentine on a barrel of sugar belonging to the midshipmen's mess. A sudden pitch of the ship turned over the bottle, and the contents seeped through a crack into the sugar. Thereafter Maury and his comrades had coffee, tea, and bread pudding strongly flavored with turpentine.[32]

The most colorful event of each week was General Muster, held on Sunday with all hands in dress uniform. The rules and regulations for the better government of the Navy were read. Church service was held and, in the absence of the chaplain, the ship's well-educated and deeply religious schoolmaster was called on to officiate.[33] He read a service from the Episcopal *Book of Common Prayer*. Listening to those familiar words, Maury must have found his thoughts straying from worship to his family back home.

On October 3 England was sighted, and on the 4th the coast of France was in view. At 2 P.M. that day a pilot was taken on board.[34] Now fell to Captain Morris a maneuver of diplomacy that brought to Maury's attention the fact that a United States naval officer in command of a vessel often had to handle matters of a diplomatic nature as well as the sailing and fighting of a man-of-war.

Captain Morris had anchored just off the harbor of Le Havre. On October 5 he received on board the American consul, who informed him that, though Charles X had replaced Louis XVIII as the King of France since Lafayette's departure from his homeland, the consul believed that Lafayette could land without objection from the new regime. Captain Morris decided to take no chance of discourtesy to his distinguished passenger and sent Lieutenant David Farragut ashore to check with the authorities. Farragut learned that there was no governmental objection to Lafayette's returning to his native soil, and he made arrangements for a steamboat to go out to the frigate for the General.[35]

Meanwhile, Lafayette was enjoying a reunion on board the *Brandywine* with his daughter-in-law, Mme. George Washington Lafayette, her children, and his son-in-law, M. de Lasteyrie, and his children, who had come with the American consul. The *Brandywine* fired a salute of 21 guns to the city of Le Havre, and this was returned by the city one hour later.[36] In farewell, General Lafayette received the officers in his cabin and, when offered anything they could give, he asked for the flag of the ship as a memento of his voyage. The midshipmen requested that they might be allowed to send him "a durable mark of their filial attachment." This sentiment took shape in a handsomely engraved silver urn, which was subsequently made in Paris under the direction of the American consul and sent to Lafayette at his home.[37] But now departure time had come. Lafayette saluted the sailors, seated himself in a bosun's chair, and was lifted over the bulwarks and lowered to the waiting steamboat below, which then circled the *Brandywine* as the men manned the yards and cheered.

Lafayette was escorted ashore by Captain Charles Morris and Captain George C. Read. The two officers were to accompany Lafayette to Paris, as a final courtesy from the American people, and then to go on an official tour of French naval dockyards.[38]

The *Brandywine* sailed immediately, crossed the English Channel, and proceeded in a gale of wind to Cowes on the Isle of Wight. After anchoring there on October 8, the ship received a thorough calking to end the danger of leaks. While she was being worked on, Maury and the other midshipmen were allowed to visit nearby points of interest—Carisbrooke Castle, where Charles I had been confined, and Portsmouth, whose harbor was full of men-of-war, including two brand-new 120-gun ships. Most interesting to the boys was the *Victory*, flagship of Lord Nelson at the battle of Trafalgar. Now a receiving ship, the *Victory* was marked by a brass plate on the spot where Nelson had received his fatal wound. The inscription read: "England expects that every man will do his duty." [39]

But youthful Maury reported other visits that pleased him even more. Writing to his friend William Ventress, in Mississippi, he said, "We laid off Cowes two weeks during which time we were visited by all the lords, ladies etc. . . . but none like one little girl and how I delight to talk of her. She is the pretty daughter of Sir Jno. Bailey, one of the 12 . . . Judges of the King's Bench, by whom I was treated like a son; another midshipman and myself were invited by Sir Jno. to dine, without his knowing so much as our names, I having paid great attention to his daughter, Meg, as he called her." [40] He went on to tell how Meg had invited him to visit them in London if he ever could. For one who considered himself shy with the fair sex, Maury was successful enough in his first meeting with a girl from another country.

It had been an unforgettable privilege to Maury to meet the great Lafayette and to be on this historic cruise, and like any 19-year-old he also wanted to have as much fun as possible. But he had not lost his desire to learn. He had already discovered that Bowditch's *Practical Navigator* lacked much that he wanted to know. In Cowes he browsed in a bookshop until he found a secondhand copy of Norie's *Epitome of Navigation,* which he purchased and bore back to the steerage of the *Brandywine* to study.[41] There were times, though, when study was impossible, for talking, shouting, and singing were almost constant in the midshipmen's quarters. The youths vented their unspent energies in noise, wrestling, and rough play they called skylarking. In the midst of the hullabaloo Maury often thought of home and longed for news of his family. He wrote to Ventress: "I have only heard from Tennessee twice since I left it," and urged his friend to send him a letter in Gibraltar.[42] In the lonely night watches, he had time to speculate on when and if his father would get over being angry with him for going into the Navy. He also wondered how long it would be before his family would realize that letters did eventually catch up with a Navy man. He hoped that thence they would be willing to write him more often.

Captain Morris having left the ship, the *Brandywine* was under the temporary command of her executive officer, Lieutenant Francis H. Gregory. On October 22 the trumpeted call could be heard through the ship, "All hands weigh anchor, ahoy." The sails were quickly spread, the anchor was aweigh, and the *Brandywine* set course for the Mediterranean.[43]

By now Maury was beginning to get used to his new life. The sailors wore wide-bottom canvas trousers, which they rolled to the knees for deck work, and clubbed their hair in a pigtail doubled up at the nape of the neck. They smelled of tar because they tarred the pigtail, of whiskey because of their daily grog, and of perspiration because each man had only a gallon of water a day for all purposes and many didn't use much of that to bathe. But the tars weren't so different from some of the rough, rugged, independent countrymen Maury had known in Tennessee. Many sailors were twice and even three times his age, but Maury and the other midshipmen were taught to lead them aloft on the foremast to reef the topsails and to give them other commands.

The nimble-footed midshipmen were proud of this dangerous duty and usually referred to themselves as reefers.

Maury learned from Sailing Master Elisha Peck the basic elements of navigation, from the boatswain seamanship, and from the gunner ordnance.[44] Midshipmen were kept busy ten hours out of the twenty-four. Eight of these hours were spent on deck keeping watch, while two more were consumed, Maury later stated, by "casual interruptions for duty, such as exercising great guns and small arms—going to Quarters—attending to the duties of his division—reefing topsails & C. [*sic*]"[45] Had Maury gone into detail rather than using that abbreviation he might have described a duty that he, as an acting midshipman, was often given—supervising a crew of six sailors as they sprinkled the deck with sand and holystoned it clean—or another duty that fell to an older midshipman in charge of the holds—that of being present when liquor was pumped and guarding it against theft. This "young gentleman" also had to make sure that none of his detail carried a lighted candle in the spirit room, where the liquor was kept, for fire was a dreaded hazard in wooden ships.

Following this drawing of the liquor, the sweepers were piped every morning at 11:30, the mechanics knocked off from work, the small cask of whiskey was brought up to the main deck and poured into a large tub. An equal amount of water was added, and at noon each sailor received a half pint of this half-and-half "grog," drank it, and proceeded to dinner, his main meal of the day. The same ritual was gone through again before supper, and thus each seaman received his daily ration of a half pint of whiskey.[46] Doubtless this assisted them in spinning the long yarns of shipwrecks and battles with which they regaled each other when off duty.

Hope for better food rose as the ship neared the Mediterranean, where the mess steward could buy fruits and vegetables at a very low cost. As the *Brandywine* sailed down the northeast coast of Spain, the air grew balmy. The moon was full. A midshipman played sentimental tunes on his flute.[47] The reefers talked constantly about what they would do on their coming liberties in Mediterranean ports.

Schoolmaster Jones had lost hope of carrying on any systematic instruction of the midshipmen. He wrote disconsolately: "We had a school in the *Brandywine* and the forward cabin for it after leaving Havre but its rules were not sufficiently strict and it did not amount to much."[48] He added, "Larking got the better of *Bowditch* and study."[49]

The course in which Jones would have instructed the boys, had a regular time been strictly enforced for study, was navigation. The text-

book he mentioned was *The American Practical Navigator* by Nathaniel
Bowditch. Of this he wrote:

> Let us examine this book, the one put as a text book into their
> hands and used in their examination for promotion and therefore
> placed before them as the great perfection of a navigator's knowl-
> edge. It is an excellent *practical* work, and does not pretend to more
> than this, but it is intended chiefly for Captains of merchantmen
> and he who uses it, wanders blindfolded through its labyrinths for
> there is little attempt at explanation except what is absolutely nec-
> essary. A little geometry at the beginning and an exhibition of the
> principles of sailing so blind that no officer, I have yet met with,
> could understand from it, the two last and most important—this is
> the book, the height of an officer's attainments, who, when they have
> finished it, cannot even tell why they count half degrees for whole
> ones from their sextants at the meridian observation. It has been
> hinted too that it matters little how ignorant they are, as long as
> they fight our battles well.[50]

Maury was profoundly disappointed in the amount of schooling he
was being given in the *Brandywine*. He shared with young Mr. Jones
the opinion that Bowditch's work left much to be desired as a textbook
for midshipmen.[51]

On November 2 the *Brandywine* reached the harbor of Gibraltar,
where the American squadron rode at anchor. The guns roared out a
salute to Commodore John Rodgers and then the frigate took station
a short distance from his flagship, the *North Carolina,* 74. This ship of
the line, also designed by William Doughty, had been launched in 1820.
However, the midshipmen of the *Brandy,* as they already called their
ship, did not think the heavier vessel had "the dark proud look" of
their fast-flying frigate.[52]

The *Brandywine*'s midshipmen were given shore leave in Gibraltar.
Boats took them to the northern end of the town. For Maury this was
a stimulating experience. He could see numerous soldiers on sentry duty
in protection of this British bastion. Among those pacing the walls were
the kilted members of the Scottish regiment called the "Forty-Twos."
On the docks were dark-skinned men in the white garments of the Arab
world and Spaniards in velvet suits, their hats decorated with beads. In
the crowded streets there were officers and sailors of many nations.[53]
Maury's purchases at Gibraltar included a Spanish dictionary and a
Spanish textbook on navigation.[54]

The most exciting adventure at Gibraltar for the midshipmen, of
course, was climbing "the Rock." The British had given permission for

the officers of the American squadron to make the ascent.[55] From high up on that carefully fortified rock the midshipmen looked westward to the Atlantic from which they had come and eastward to the Mediterranean, sea of the ancient world, about which they had studied.

After two weeks at Gibraltar the *Brandywine,* in company with the *North Carolina,* 74, the *Constitution,* 44, and the sloop-of-war *Erie,* 18, sailed for Port Mahon on the island of Minorca.[56] This was the winter rendezvous for American naval vessels on duty in the Mediterranean at that time. Mahon was reached on November 28. On December 3 the first liberty party of fifty sailors went ashore.[57] Matthew was told they would return to the ship drunken and exhausted, many of them battered from fights. This he was to see come true, as the sailors spent their time in Mahon getting drunk on the *vino negro* of the island, dancing the fandango with the native women, and making love hard and fast. As the pattern was repeated in nearly every port, liberty was granted the sailors only four times a year.

For Maury, as a midshipman, the situation was very different. In port he was on duty two days and off one, which was his "liberty day," when he was free to leave the ship. On shore the *Brandywine* midshipmen soon discovered a sport not too expensive for their means—they could rent donkeys and ride out on the ancient road through the island.[58] They saw the natives busy cultivating *zulla* as fodder for animals but were far more interested in trying to secure figs and almonds for their taste-starved palates. To Matthew, accustomed to the ample farmlands of America, the Minorcans' need to terrace and cultivate the hills to their summit must have been startling. The youths visited the rocks where remains of early pagan altars could still be seen. The island had been conquered successively by Carthaginians, Romans, Moors, and Spaniards, by the Corsairs under Barbarossa and Piali, by the British and the French. It had been retaken by the British and finally had been acquired by the Spanish in 1802 under the Treaty of Amiens.[59]

At Port Mahon Maury watched the frequent religious processions through the streets. One was "led by a boy, with a lantern on a long pole, and a bell which he rang at intervals; next came four monks, carrying a canopy, under which was another one with the host. They were attended by two soldiers and passed rapidly on chanting a solemn hymn." [60] The Minorcans took off their hats and knelt in the streets as the procession passed. The United States naval officers did neither and, as a result, were scowled at by the residents.

Captain Daniel Todd Patterson took command of the *Brandywine* on December 5 and set all hands to putting the frigate into first-class shape.[61] The midshipmen were kept so busy that, by January 21, George Jones abandoned all effort to hold school on the ship. He moved ashore to a rented room and came on board only to report and remain on the payroll.[62] Matthew doggedly pursued his own private effort to study navigation and Spanish. But he felt cheated as these words of his reveal: "The first ship I sailed in had a schoolmaster; a young man from Connecticut. He was well qualified and well disposed to teach navigation, but not having a schoolroom, or authority to assemble the midshipmen, the cruise passed off without the opportunity of organizing his school. From him, therefore, we learned nothing." [63]

On liberty days that winter, when the winds "beat fierce from the North," the midshipmen had no place to go in Port Mahon except the local taverns. These offered entertainment at their monte tables, and gambling fever seized some officers and even some of the midshipmen. Standing orders had been issued by Commodore Rodgers against gambling at monte, but this did not stop it.[64] Monte was no problem to Matthew, for he had assigned half of his $19 monthly pay to his sister Matilda.[65] She had helped him on the long trek to Tennessee and throughout his early years and now, because of family reverses, she needed financial assistance. He was also restrained from extravagance by recollection of the bill he had run up in Washington for uniforms.

Any spare money Maury preferred to spend with his friends in securing a decent meal. The favorite delicacy was red-legged partridge from the 100-mile-distant African coast. But when going to or from the taverns, the midshipmen had to proceed with great caution for fear of running into Commodore Rodgers, a strict disciplinarian who did not hold with complete freedom for the young midshipmen. The squadron commander would arbitrarily order any luckless midshipmen he met in the streets to fall in and follow him about Mahon until the youth's liberty was at an end.[66]

On Thursday, February 16, 1826, the 12-gun schooner *Porpoise* beat her way into the harbor of Mahon with mail from the United States.[67] The next day it was revealed that the *Brandywine* had been ordered home. The midshipmen were in a frenzy of excited talk as they cleaned their uniforms that Sunday for inspection by Commodore Rodgers. On February 21 Captain George C. Read, having completed his tour of French dockyards, came on board the *Brandywine* to relieve Captain Patterson, who was to remain in the Mediterranean in command of the *Constitution*.[68] Final preparations to put to sea were made. At daybreak of February 26, Captain Read hove up the anchor from the lower harbor of Port Mahon and by 9 A.M., with moderate breezes from the northeast, the *Brandywine* "got underweigh under topsails, top gallant sails and royals." [69]

March 8 found the *Brandywine* "working up to the anchorage at Gibraltar." [70] There was no visiting the Rock now, for all speed was to be observed in taking on stores. The next day the frigate sailed for the return voyage to the United States.

It was a rough trip marked by gales, squalls, and heavy seas. But even this April weather did not dampen the spirits of the homeward-bound midshipmen, who were no longer bothered with any schoolroom assignments. Schoolmaster Jones had been transferred to the *Constitution* with Captain Patterson and remained in the Mediterranean.

Maury tried to continue his own system of learning something. "If I went below only a moment or two and could lay hands upon a dictionary or any book, I would note a sentence, or even a word, that I did not understand, and fix it in my memory to be reflected upon when I went on deck." [71]

Excitement mounted throughout the ship's company as the *Brandywine* neared Sandy Hook on April 17. A pilot was taken on board that day, and the wait for the tide to take her over the bar seemed endless. At 11 A.M. of April 18 the frigate, abreast of Staten Island, was visited by the port's health officer and received permission to proceed. The sun was at the meridian on April 18, 1826, when the ship ended her long maiden voyage. She came to in the North River, in seven fathoms of water, and promptly furled sail. [72]

But now, for the men on the *Brandywine*, it was a question of "so near and yet so far." All about was the bustle of the port of New York; sounds of Manhattan Island floated out to them. Among the men there was disappointment over not getting ashore. Liberty was given sparingly. One by one the few officers and midshipmen who were to be transferred to other ships left the *Brandywine*. [73] The sailors whose time was up muttered among themselves, but they and the mechanics were kept busy. Midshipmen talked of nothing but home and when their leaves would be issued. Finally, on April 26, the mayor of the city of New York came on board for an official visit, and was saluted with 13 guns. The next day the *Brandywine* "backed and filled out of the North River," and came to off Governor's Island, lying close to Castle William. It was not until April 30 that she reached anchorage off the Navy Yard, located in Brooklyn, almost opposite Corlears Hook at the tip of Manhattan. [74]

The next day the sailors whose term of service had expired were at last allowed to go ashore. The sails were unbent and sent on shore to the Navy Yard. Mechanics were set to repairing damage from the stormy Atlantic crossing. Ship's stores were replenished and the issuance of leaves began. [75]

Maury sat down to write a letter to Secretary of the Navy Southard.

He headed it "U.S.F. *Brandywine,* New York, May 2, 1826," and began, "I acknowledge receipt of my warrant with pleasure." [76] He had just received, in care of Commodore Isaac Chauncey, commanding officer of the New York Navy Yard, the official warrant, dated April 27, stating that he had satisfactorily completed his term of trial as an acting midshipman and was warranted a midshipman as of February 1, 1825. In the information Maury was required to send the Navy Department at this time, he reported himself as "Born in Virginia, Appointed from Tennessee, Citizen of Virginia." [77]

Midshipman Maury had completed his first cruise and received his first "well done" from the Navy.

CHAPTER IV

Around the World by Sail

Maury's first leave had proved, in the tradition of service vacations, both pleasant and frustrating. The natural excitement he had experienced on May 18, when his leave had been issued, had been considerably reduced by the realization that the two weeks' absence it gave him did not provide enough time for a trip to Tennessee to see his parents, brothers, and sisters.[1] For the first time he understood, as his father and mother had understood before he became a midshipman, that in entering the Navy he had made a decision that had cut him off from his closest kin.

The next best thing was to spend his leave with other relatives. Matthew informed his commanding officer that he would go to Washington and probably on to Virginia.[2]

In Washington Richard B. Maury set Matthew's mind at rest that the money he had requested from Ven had arrived after his departure in the Brandywine and had been dispensed according to the instructions he had left.[3] Matthew was also able to learn from Richard B. that his cousin and schoolmate at Harpeth Academy, Ellick (Alex C.) Maury, had received an appointment as acting midshipman and had left Franklin, Tennessee, on April 30 to report in Norfolk to the Macedonian, 38, which was about to sail for South America.[4] A letter from his brother Dick informed Matthew that Dick had become engaged and that his family plans included a son to be called Mat.[5]

After a brief stay with the Richard B. Maurys, Matthew apparently journeyed the 60 miles beyond Washington to visit his aunt Mrs. Edward Herndon and her husband at Laurel Hill. On the plantation he could ride horseback, swim, see his Spotsylvania kinfolk, and get his fill of food cooked especially to please a young man just home from the sea.

On June 1, in compliance with his orders, Maury returned to New York and again reported for duty in the Brandywine.[6]

In 1826 maritime commerce had already made New York a city of nearly 200,000 inhabitants. Men were conscious of the sea and its importance to them. The lower part of Manhattan Island was girded by slips and shipyards. In the harbor, in the rivers, in the slips, there were ships—sailing ships and steamboats, merchantmen and men-of-war, ferryboats and smaller craft such as the new Erie Canal boats and the sloops that brought hay from upstate farms to feed the work horses of New York.[7]

From the *Brandywine,* as Maury supervised the holystoning of the deck, he had a panoramic view of much of this marine activity that had made New York a major port. On his liberty days he had no trouble reaching Manhattan. The Navy Yard ferry took him across the East River from the yard in Brooklyn to the end of Walnut Street in Manhattan, where the air was filled with the strange echoing noises that he easily recognized as the sound of calkers at work on the ships in the civilian yards.[8]

Wherever he wanted to go in Manhattan Maury went on foot because he had used up his small funds on his leave. Even at the end of the month, June 30, 1826, when the *Brandywine* closed a fiscal period, he had no balance coming to him. At that time he had completed 11 months and 22 days of active service for a total credit in pay and rations of $298.43; but the rations had been devoured and his half of the pay used up, the balance having gone to his sister.[9] Fortunately Maury did not need funds with which to see most of the things in which he was interested.

A walk along Water Street would bring the midshipman from the ferry dock to South Street, a place of endless fascination to the ship-minded. The bowsprits of ships tied up in the slips protruded into the street, and spars were as numerous as trees in a forest. On the land side of the street were shops and shipping offices, with sailmakers at work upstairs. Maury had seen sailors from many lands in the ports he had visited in France, England, and the Mediterranean, but in South Street he saw a concentrated cross section of salt-bitten mariners rubbing shoulders with black-broadclothed merchants. Here he could stand and gaze into the windows of the shops that sold navigational instruments—quadrants, compasses, chronometers, which provided extremely accurate time to seafarers, and barometers, which measured atmospheric pressure. In the windows were plentiful displays of "long glasses" (telescopes) and the brass trumpets through which commands were shouted in blowing weather. The hundreds of articles offered by the ship chandleries were, by now, commonplace to Maury. Far from common, though, was the opportunity to see woodcarvers creating figureheads and scrollwork that would adorn ships soon to sail the seas.[10]

Whitehall Slip terminated South Street, and from there it was but a short walk to the Battery, where the promenade offered a superlative view of ships coming in from the outer harbor. Jutting off from the Battery was Castle Garden, which had served as Fort Clinton during the War of 1812 but was of more interest to Maury as the place where General Lafayette had been entertained on arrival in New York two years before. Of peculiar interest to midshipmen was a flagstaff at the Battery operated as a signal station to report departure or arrival of a ship. It was the final station of a chain of communications that, using bright buntings on extremely high poles spaced at distances that permitted visibility except in fog or heavy snow, ran out to Sandy Hook. When the "telegrapher" at the Battery in Manhattan saw the bunting run up across on Staten Island, he raised his signal and owners, insurers, and the curious flocked to the waterfront to take part in the excitement of welcoming a ship to port.[11]

On board the *Brandywine* the laborious task of readying the ship for a three years' cruise had begun.[12] Having been in the water only a year, the frigate did not require major repairs, but all the decks had to be scraped, the gun deck calked, the rigging overhauled, the ship painted, lime sprinkled throughout the hold, and the casks whitewashed. Under the eagle eye of the sailing master the stowing of the ship's hold went on as provisions and stores were hoisted on board, checked for condition, and carefully stowed with one consideration in mind—"That the ship might be at all times properly trimmed for her best qualities under sail."[13] Men wrestled with paper work, for all records had to be brought up to date. Maury was glad that he and his good friends William Irving and John Willis still had their names on the muster roll when the new period began July 1; a good many of their fellow midshipmen had been transferred to other ships.[14]

In July and August they were joined by many new shipmates as men appeared on board daily to build the ship's company to full strength, 480 officers and sailors. When newly appointed acting midshipmen reported, Maury had the pleasure, as an "old hand," of indoctrinating them in the ways of the steerage.

There were no prouder midshipmen in the U.S. Navy than those of the *Brandywine* when they heard the news that their frigate was to be the flagship of Commodore Jacob Jones, ordered to the Pacific to relieve Commodore Isaac Hull in command of the squadron of naval vessels on duty in the Pacific Ocean. Word filtered down from the quarterdeck that the newly launched sloop-of-war *Vincennes* would sail in company with the *Brandy*. In the Pacific the *Brandywine* would relieve the frigate *United States*, 44, while the *Vincennes*, 20, Master Commandant

William Bolton Finch, would relieve the sloop-of-war *Peacock*, 18, Master Commandant Thomas ap Catesby Jones.[15]

Late in August Commodore Jones arrived from Washington, where he had been one of the three powerful Navy commissioners. A crack officer, trained by the redoubtable Edward Preble in the Navy's early wars, Jones carefully inspected the two vessels that made up his little squadron. He was much displeased by the number of men that had been crowded into each ship. This situation was caused by the need to send out officers and sailors to permit men on the Brazil and Pacific stations to return to the United States. Jones remonstrated with the authorities in Washington, but the Navy Department ordered him to ignore the crowding and take his ships to sea as fast as possible. All hands were keyed up for departure on August 26 when a final inspection of the hold of the *Brandywine* revealed serious trouble. Water had leaked from a large number of the water casks while others were found to be entirely empty. New casks had to be secured and filled. By the time this was completed, the wind had died. The commodore waited hopefully for the wind to rise but could not long delay his departure, and so he engaged steamboats to tow the two sailing vessels from the East River into the North River.[16]

Finally, on the morning of August 31, the wind was co-operative. The *Brandywine* hoisted the broad blue pennant that marked her as the flagship of Commodore Jones, was saluted by the *Vincennes* with 13 guns, and answered with 7. Jones spoke to his ranking lieutenant (executive officer) and the order was given, "Up anchor." A bandsman played the fife to encourage the seamen. Around and around went the capstan. Up came the anchor of the *Brandywine* from the bottom of the North River. A strong breeze from north northeast gave the *Brandywine* and *Vincennes* a brisk departure from New York City.[17]

After a fast passage to New York's outer harbor, the ships suffered another maddening wait for winds to take them over the bar and to sea on September 3, 1826.[18] Matthew Fontaine Maury was off on his second cruise—a midshipman in the *Brandywine*—not in the *Macedonian* as has been erroneously stated by several biographers.[19]

Maury soon became acquainted with the frigate's new schoolmaster, Inocencia De Soto, of whom he later wrote:

> The dominie was a Spaniard and, being bound to South America, there was a perfect mania in the steerage for the Spanish language. In our youthful impetuosity we bought books, and for a week or so, pursued the study with great eagerness. But our spirits began to flag, and the difficulties of *ser* and *estar* finally laid the copestone

for us over the dominie's vernacular. The study was exceedingly dry. We therefore voted both teacher and grammar a bore, and committing the latter to the deep, with one accord, we declared in favor of the Byronical method—"'Tis pleasant to be taught in a strange tongue by female lips and eyes" and continued to defer our studies till we should arrive in the South American vale of paradise, called Valparaiso.[20]

The winds were very light, the weather fair, and the youths wished to enjoy the cruise to Rio. Maury thought little of the schoolteacher but continued his own studies and presently had a small vocabulary with which to pursue "the Byronical method" once he got to South America.

Though Commodore Jones was in command of the *Brandywine*, Maury and his fellow midshipmen received commands more often from the ranking lieutenant, John H. Aulick, and the other lieutenants, John Cross, Cornelius K. Stribling, and Thomas A. Dornin, as well as from Sailing Master Mallaby.[21]

In view of the pride of the *Brandy*'s crew, it was a good thing they could not peer over their commodore's shoulder and see him write the Secretary of the Navy:

> Altho' I do not consider the *Brandywine* as sailing fast in her present trim, being unavoidably too much by the head, we have run 854 miles in the 5 days that we have been out.
>
> This ship outsails the *Vincennes* if the breeze is more than 6 knots [sic]—under that she outsails us. The *Brandywine* is remarkably tight, leaking not more than 6 inches in the 24 hours.
>
> I am much pleased with all the officers and we have a good crew.[22]

After several weeks at sea the bread, stocked in the midshipmen's mess at New York, was beginning to mold; the fresh meat and vegetables were long since used up. The meals were based on the standard ration, which was "a daily proportion of the following weekly total: one half pound of suet, 5½ lbs. of beef, 1 lb. of flour, 2 ozs. butter, 4 ozs. tea, 1 pint rice, ½ pint vinegar, 6 ozs. of cheese, 3 lbs. of pork, 98 ozs. bread, 7 ozs. sugar, 1 pint of peas, 7½ pints of spirits."[23]

While at sea the beef issued was not only salted but invariably tough and hard to digest. The midshipmen's favorite dish was dried peas or beans cooked with salt pork to a soupy consistency. The best way to eat the stale, moldy bread, they found, was to persuade the cook to mix sugar and butter with it and bake it. On holidays some of the whiskey ration was used as a sauce for this concoction.[24]

The spirit ration, though, was considered by Commodore Jones responsible for the deaths of two young sailors on this passage from New York to Rio. After one jumped overboard one night and another fell from the mizzentop, the commodore stopped half the whiskey allowance to the younger men.[25] This led to much dissatisfaction among the crew, but discipline was strictly maintained. It was already a custom in the Navy when a ship crossed the equator for Neptune to hold a court of misrule to initiate the "first timers." [26] But captains dreaded the drunken revelry that often accompanied the horseplay, and there is no record of Neptune's having boarded the *Brandywine,* in spite of the invitation of her name.

As the son of a farmer Maury had early been conscious of the role of weather. His brief sea experience had already greatly intensified that awareness, and on this trip he observed the way the atmosphere became humid, even oppressive, as they approached the equator. Then he noticed improvement as they sailed south of the line, the air seeming to become rarefied.

The stars were brilliant overhead, and Maury became interested in studying two luminous bodies high in the heavens and another less brilliant formation at a lower level. He learned that these were the Magellanic Clouds. Soon he was to become familiar with the Southern Cross.[27] Due to his interest in observing the southern skies, deck watch at night was no longer drudgery.

On Wednesday, October 25, Maury caught his first sight of the lofty, mist-covered summit of Cape Frio, landmark for all mariners sailing to Rio de Janeiro. For two days the wind blew out of the harbor, but Friday morning found the *Brandywine* standing in for Rio, and Maury saw the picturesque bay fringed by palms at the water's edge. Thirty miles to the south stood the rock formation British sailors had named "Lord Hood's Nose," while Sugar Loaf, rising 1,270 feet, was to be seen nearer at hand.[28]

On October 28 the *Brandywine* moored in the harbor of Rio, the *Vincennes* coming to anchor on her starboard quarter.[29] The following day, Sunday, Commodore Jones paid official visits to the British and French admirals whose flagships were in harbor. He then went ashore and doubtless Maury and his fellow midshipmen were anxious to do the same. However, they were occupied for the next days in the pomp and ceremony of honoring the admirals who returned their commodore's visits. By November 1 watering the ship and receiving fresh provisions had begun, and liberties were granted.[30] Matthew got ashore during the first two weeks of their stay in the harbor.

He had a personal cause for rejoicing on November 8 when the frigate *Macedonian,* 38, sailed in and saluted the *Brandywine* with 13 guns. The

Macedonian, which had been captured from the British in 1812, was flying the broad pennant of Commodore James Biddle as flagship of the United States squadron assigned to protect American interests on the east coast of South America.[31] Maury was able to visit his cousin and schoolmate, Ellick Maury, acting midshipman in the *Macedonian,* as small boats plied back and forth between the American ships in harbor.[32]

On November 14 a tense situation developed for the Americans. Maury and the other midshipmen of the *Brandywine* had been told that their government was patrolling the east coast to protect American shipping during the war then going on between Brazil and Argentina for the control of Uruguay (Banda Oriental). They also heard that the Uruguayans desired independence from both countries.

On November 14 the United States chargé d'affaires in Rio de Janeiro, Condy Raguet, received a communiqué from the Brazilian Secretary of State for Foreign Affairs, the Marquis of Inhambupé, stating "that the welfare and security of the state require that the port of this Capital should be shut until new orders." [33] Raguet rushed a messenger with the news to Commodore Jones who was readying both *Brandywine* and *Vincennes* to sail. Back went a note acknowledging receipt of advice concerning the embargo of the port and this sea-dog reply: "I have to inform you that I shall go to sea tomorrow, if the weather will permit; and altho' it is known to the Brazilian Government, that I intended to sail immediately, upon having watered our ships, I will thank you, should you deem it necessary to repeat the information." [34]

Raguet reminded Jones that Brazil was headed by an emperor, Dom Pedro, whose power had been curtailed by a constitution but who still had power to act precipitately. At the same time Chargé Raguet sent a strong remonstrance to Inhambupé "concerning the treatment of ships of war of a friendly and neutral power" that led Brazil's foreign secretary to ask for a moderation of the Emperor's orders.[35] Commodore Jones reluctantly agreed to remain in port with his squadron for three days. He and his officers were extremely annoyed, especially after Raguet warned that the forts would almost surely fire on the American vessels if Jones tried to put to sea.[36] Finally, on November 17th, Chargé Raguet sent word to Commodore Jones that the Emperor would allow him to leave the port. Raguet added: "I have no hesitation in expressing my belief that the determined stand which you took upon this occasion and which met (with) my most entire approbation, was the means of settling this question between our Government and that of the Brazil but (there) may be further refusal to grant a similar favor later." [37]

Maury had watched the messengers hurrying back and forth. He had seen an international incident successfully resolved by a combination of a firm stand on the part of the Navy and prompt, intelligent, diplomatic negotiation. It was a lesson he was not to forget.

On November 18 the *Brandywine* and *Vincennes*, in company, put to sea, and began their cruise down the long east coast of South America. The weather worsened on November 30, when the ships encountered strong gales and alternate rain and hail. The hatches were covered with tarpaulins to protect the men on the berth deck. The sails were handled with even greater care, and the midshipmen were repeatedly sent aloft to take another reef in the sails. As the ships neared the Falkland Islands, Commodore Jones gave orders to prepare ship for the ordeal ahead.[38]

Maury was to write later in his "Navigation of Cape Horn":

> From the time Sir Francis Drake was driven off Cape Horn till the present day the boldest navigators have approached it with caution. They never venture in the latitude of it until each has prepared his vessel for the rough weather to be expected in rounding it; for this, no precaution is omitted. Men of war strike part of their armament into the hold; get their anchors between decks; send up stump masts; bend the storm sails; and secure their spars with preventer rigging, as they get near the tempestuous regions. In the roughness of the passage, the crew is liable to much exposure . . . the tempest, the sea and the iceberg assume their most terrible character. . . . The gales, frequently accompanied with hail and sleet, are proverbial among seamen for their unremitting severity, and the length of their duration.[39]

In describing this doubling of Cape Horn late in 1826, Maury said: "The U.S.S. *Brandywine* . . . found the winds varying from N.W. to S.W., she ran up the usual *westing* without crossing the parallel of 57° 30'. When the winds freshened so that she could not beat to windward, she lay to with her head to the south, giving the land a wider berth." [40] Often the *Brandywine* seemed on her beam ends: "The waves run to a height which, in other seas, they seldom attain. In the calm they cause no less damage than in the gale, by distressing the ship with labor. In that succeeding a storm, vessels sometimes roll their masts away." [41]

At last, after a passage of seventeen days, the *Brandywine* and *Vincennes* safely rounded the Horn.[42] The crews were tired, and more were sick than usual, but the thrill of navigation through such perils had gripped Maury's mind, and he began to give serious thought to the difficulties involved.

Christmas Eve and Christmas Day, 1826, were happy ones on board the *Brandywine* for all hands were employed in getting the guns up from below, securing them on their carriages, and getting the anchors off the bow in preparation for reaching Valparaiso. On December 26 the *Brandywine* and the *Vincennes,* in company, stood in for the Chilean port and came to anchor in the nearly semicircular bay.[43] Perhaps American officers called Valparaiso "the vale of Paradise" because it seemed just that after the bleakness and violence of Cape Horn. On the south of the bay Maury could see the city rising from a narrow strip of beach up steep slopes and valleys of hills more than a thousand feet in altitude. The rocky promontory jutted into the Pacific and gave protection to the bay from both south and west.[44]

The officers of the *Brandywine* and the *Vincennes* were disappointed not to find the United States Pacific Squadron in the harbor. However, they celebrated New Year's Day of 1827 by welcoming on board the *Brandywine* the captain and some officers of His Britannic Majesty's ship *Cambridge*. On the 6th, the frigate *United States,* 44, flagship of Commodore Isaac Hull, sailed in, came to an anchor, saluted with 13 guns and hoisted the red pennant. Two days later, Commodore Jones sent a party of calkers to Commodore Hull to expedite work on the 1797 frigate *United States*.[45] The sight of this frigate must have made Maury think of his brother John, who had served long in the *United States*.

On Tuesday, January 9, "Mr. Maury with 6 men went to work on board the *Columbia*."[46] This was an American brig on duty in the Pacific. She needed calking and either Matthew or another *Brandywine* midshipman directed the work each day until it was finished. Friday was an unpopular day with seamen of the age of sail, but all in the *Brandywine* and *Vincennes* were pleased with Friday, January 19. On that day the U.S. schooner *Dolphin,* 12, Lieutenant Commanding Beverley Kennon, arrived from Callao, and the relieving officers for that ship were sent to her and a crew of men to the *United States,* ending the crowded living conditions of Jones's two vessels. Five days later the *Brandywine* got under way in company with the *United States,* followed by the *Vincennes* and *Dolphin*. The ships anchored in the harbor of Callao, Peru, on February 9.[47]

As soon as possible the midshipmen went ashore and took one of the coaches that ran twice daily the eight miles from Callao to Lima.[48] On shipboard they had heard much of Lima and her graceful ladies, noted for their small feet and hands and beautifully arranged hair. Now the "young gentlemen" found that their best view of the Limans was to be had in the Alameda, a plaza made pleasant by fountains and tree-shaded walks. There were stone seats where Maury and his friends could sit and watch the passers-by. Many pretty women wore the native *saya y manto* to advantage, drawing the black silk hood so that only one eye was revealed, while others draped their shoulders with French shawls. The Peruvian men puffed constantly on *cigarillos*.[49]

A more exciting pastime was to go to the Chingano to see the Peruvian *samacueca* performed. On the stage, dancers went through the graceful and amorous movements of the dance to instrumental and vocal music that was a blend of Spanish and Indian tunes. While they watched the performance the midshipmen sipped refreshments purchased from booths that surrounded the ampitheater.[50]

"After arriving on that station [Callao]," Maury wrote later, "the commander, who had often expressed his wish that we should learn to speak Spanish, sent down for all 'the young gentlemen,' as the middies were called, and commenced to ask us one by one—'Can you speak Spanish?' 'No, sir.' 'Then you are no gentleman.' . . . But always receiving the same answer, he sent us out of the cabin as a set of blackguards. As he was as ignorant on the subject as any of us, we included him among the number and thought it an excellent joke. Thus ended our scholastic duties on that ship." [51]

Actually some of the *Brandywine*'s midshipmen knew a little Spanish; but, sticking together as they always did, no one would admit this to the commodore. As soon as possible Maury carried out his earlier plan of learning Spanish from daughters of prominent Peruvian families who invited the United States officers into their homes.[52]

On March 9 a piece of good fortune came to Maury in the form of orders to transfer to the *Vincennes*. He reported next day on board the graceful sloop-of-war.[53] Smaller than the *Brandywine*, the *Vincennes* was variously rated at 18 or 20 guns, but actually mounted 24. Designed by Samuel Humphreys, chief constructor of the Navy, she had been built at the New York Navy Yard and launched shortly before she sailed in company with the *Brandywine*. The *Vincennes* was 127 feet long between the perpendiculars and 33 feet 9 inches in the beam, with a 15 foot 6 inch depth of hold.[54] She had been designed for speed in cruising and maneuverability in fighting and, while still on her maiden voyage, was already called "the most beautiful vessel of her class and . . . the fastest sailer in the Navy." [55]

Maury was now under the command of William Bolton Finch, master commandant, the original title adopted in the U.S. Navy for officers ranking after captain and before lieutenant, changed to commander in 1837.[56] As the commanding officer of a ship, Finch was addressed as captain. An accomplished officer, of superior intelligence, Finch required high efficiency of performance but was amiable of temperament, and men liked to serve under him. A chaplain assigned to the *Vincennes* wrote:

"The Cabin is quite a pavilion of elegance, and the ward room as neat and comfortable as a parlor at home." [57] A great satisfaction to Maury was the fact that there were fewer midshipmen in the steerage and that he could study with less distraction. His main cause for pleasure, however, was the rumor that when the *Vincennes* could be spared from patrolling the west coast of South America, she would be sent on a long and adventurous cruise.

Meanwhile the *Vincennes* was very much occupied in her patrol duties. Maury always liked to know the facts behind every situation, and he busied himself finding out the reason why the United States was maintaining so large a squadron to protect whalers and other North American merchantmen in the Pacific waters. He learned that the countries on the west coast of South America in 1827 were in a state of political turmoil because of the difficulties inherent in the effort to establish republican governments after their long war for independence from Spain. Recent years had seen Simón Bolívar's great victory against the Spanish viceroy at Junín, Antonio José de Sucre's conclusive battle at Ayacucho, a constitutional convention in Peru, and the formation of the Republic of Bolívar (Bolivia). Sucre had succeeded Bolívar as president of the Republic of Bolívar, but native leaders were now resisting his leadership. They feared that the constitution Bolívar had written for them was more idealistic than practical.[58]

In his effort to become informed about South American politics Maury also learned that each of the republics had a pro-Bolívar and an anti-Bolívar group. He was told that tenure of authority was precarious, and war was considered imminent as there were grave tensions between the various countries. Each leader spoke much of "liberty," a word that always stirred Maury, descended as he was from people who had fought first for religious freedom and later for freedom from England. He observed developments with interest and was much amused by the fickleness and bravado of some of the participants in the political drama.[59]

Maury's hopes of getting any real schooling were again thwarted. "The schoolmaster," he later wrote in an article on Navy education, "was a young lawyer who knew more about *jetsam* and *flotsam* than about lunars and dead reckoning—at least, I presume so, for he never afforded us an opportunity to judge of his knowledge on the latter subjects. He was not on speaking terms with the reefers, ate up all the plums for the duff, and was finally turned out of the ship as a nuisance." [60]

While young Matthew Maury did not learn anything from this teacher, he was continuing his own education and evidently had access in the *Vincennes* to Riddle's *Investigations of the Rules and Principles of Lunar and Other Observations* as well as to Riddle's *Spherical Trigo-*

nometry. He developed a system of chalking problems in spherical trigo-
nometry on the round shot in the rack on deck and working out solu-
tions as he paced back and forth on watch.[61] He also became experienced
in shipboard duties, improved his Spanish when on shore, and enjoyed
his on-the-scene study of the people, history, and geography of South
America.

From 1827 to 1829 the *Vincennes* patrolled constantly on the west coast
of that continent. Maury wrote an account of this period to James H.
Otey, who after ordination had returned to Franklin, organized the first
Episcopal church in Tennessee, and resumed as principal of Harpeth
Academy.

> My cruising has been very interesting since I joined this ship, and
> particularly for the last eight or ten weeks. Owing to the unsettled
> state of affairs in Guayaquil [Ecuador], we were compelled to stay
> there, as long as affairs wore a doubtful aspect, in order to protect
> our commerce against any outrages that might have been committed.
> On the 10th of last month we were alarmed by the cry of *"Viva la
> patria! Viva Guayaquil!"* and on going on shore to find from
> whence these exclamations came, we found the whole city in arms
> and drawn out in order of battle, one party headed by the brother
> of the other's leader. . . . After a little bloodshed one party de-
> clared in favor of the LIBERTADOR [Bolívar] and permitted the other,
> called the rebels, to leave the country: they have since joined the
> Peruvians. A wise piece of policy, indeed, for it is expected that
> . . . so soon as Bolívar shall quell all disturbances in Colombia
> . . . unless Peru will make proper concessions, he will adopt meas-
> ures to unite Peru and Colombia under the government of the
> latter.[62]

Maury's interest in international relations was an instructive one and
was to be a keystone of his later work.

Writing on February 18, 1829, Maury thanked his former principal,
the Reverend Mr. Otey, for a letter received only recently, though it had
been mailed from Tennessee twelve months earlier, "which is the latest
date I have heard from any part of the United States." [63] This lack of
mail from home, the appallingly long delays in transit that meant a
letter was out of date long before it was received, worried Maury greatly.

Some months later, after a cruise southward to Peruvian waters, he
revealed his feelings to his friend Ven in a letter written from Callao
on June 18, 1829: "I received your favor of May 28 one year minus four
days after date." But cut off as he was, Maury still felt close to his friend

and rejoiced with Ven over the happy news of his having become engaged. He declared about Ven's fiancée, "She is no doubt all that is feminine," [64] and asked if she would pick out a girl for him for his return home within a year or two. However, he hastened to let his friend know that he wasn't doing too badly in the romance department: "I pass my time quite pleasantly here among the Spanish ladies and, of late years, have made it a general rule not to visit a port without falling in love with some of them; of late days my life has been almost as fruitful in adventures as was that of the student of Salamanca, though it not infrequently happens that the declaration commences on the other side, I am yet a *bashful youth.*" [65]

Maury undoubtedly thought these remarks very humorous but the truth was he was still in no financial position to pay serious court to anyone. In addition to sending the allotment to his sister Matilda, he used a good amount of money for sightseeing. The writing in his geographies for young people, published decades later, shows how closely he observed the places he visited in Chile, Bolivia, Peru, and Ecuador. Maury was to return to these countries again, but he carried with him from this first experience a love of the people and an unfading memory of the majesty of the Andes.

As late as mid-June of 1829 Matthew was writing in a letter that the *Vincennes* was expected to sail across the Pacific and return home via the Cape of Good Hope. He commented: "I think it quite probable that I shall go that way in an Indiaman [general term used for merchant ships trading with the Orient] in case this vessel does not." [66] The remark was typical of his determination.

In late June the danger of war between the nations on the west coast of South America had abated sufficiently for the *Vincennes* to be released from her patrol of those waters and ordered to proceed across the Pacific to Canton, sail through the South China Sea into the Indian Ocean, and thence continue around South Africa into the Atlantic and back to the United States. If the *Vincennes* successfully completed this voyage, she would be the first American warship to circumnavigate the globe. The *Congress* had preceded her across the Pacific but had returned to South America.[67] Preparations for the long cruise were rushed to completion.

It was customary then in the American Navy for a commanding officer to designate the officers he preferred to have serve under him. Finch was fortunate in being able to have transferred to the *Vincennes* an extremely capable group of men. There were four lieutenants, and of these one was to become Maury's lifelong friend—Thomas A. Dornin. Another appointment to the *Vincennes* that proved fortunate for Maury was that of the Reverend Charles S. Stewart as chaplain. A man of culture as well as of faith, Stewart had traveled widely and had served as a missionary in the Sandwich Islands. He liked Matthew Maury's interest in new sights and people, and his fine powers of observation, and was to include him on all the side excursions for which the young midshipman could secure permission to leave the ship. To Stewart the world is indebted for his colorful two-volume account of this historic cruise, *A Visit to the South Seas in the U.S. Ship Vincennes During the Years 1829, 1830 and 1831.*

Every man in the American squadron of ships in Callao harbor was excited on July 4, 1829. The *Vincennes* was scheduled to sail at noon, and the crews of the remaining vessels were ready to give the war-sloop a hearty send-off in keeping with the important mission on which she was ordered. At noon, however, the wind was too light for the ship to get out of the harbor, and there was nothing to do but wait for the breeze. Finally, at sunset, the momentous order to weigh anchor was given, and the *Vincennes* set sail to the cheers of sailors manning the yards of the three American warships in the harbor. The *Vincennes'* band played the nostalgic strains of "Home, Sweet Home." [68] But few on board were thinking of home, for they were headed for adventure such as sailing men dreamed of.

On the broad sweep of the Pacific the midshipmen were kept busy as sail was crowded on for speed. On that voyage each of the *Vincennes* midshipmen learned to master every trick a reefer should know.

The ship's first destination was the cluster of islands called the Washington Group (now the Marquesas). When the *Vincennes* approached Nukuhiva, one of the group's northernmost and largest islands that Commodore David Porter had claimed for the United States, Captain Finch issued strict orders to be observed by the men during their stay among the Nukuhivans.[69] The ship was to be *tabu*, forbidden to the native women, and the sailors were ordered to behave in a way that would convince the Polynesians "of the moral worth of Americans." [70] The *Vincennes* had been sent on this cruise to achieve specific objectives that would be negated if the crew indulged in the licentious behavior that had sometimes been the rule during warship visits among the peoples of the Pacific Islands.

No one on board the war-sloop was more interested in this particular port of call than Maury. It was a piece of great good fortune to him to come here for Nukuhiva was the island where his oldest brother, John Minor Maury, had been stranded from early in 1812 to December, 1813.

On July 28 the *Vincennes* anchored in the harbor of Taiohae, Nuku-hiva Island,[71] and the next day the chief of the local Happa tribe and his family visited the ship. Maury reported later "I . . . set about studying the language that I might learn something about my brother's history there." [72]

From the ship he could watch the almost naked Happas, whose harbor this was, skillfully paddling their canoes, and he could see clusters of palm trees on shore similar to the ones in which John had lived in his well-hidden platform hut.

When the first party went ashore at Nukuhiva, Maury was unable to go because of his duties on shipboard, but he received an interesting account from his friend Irving. Maury was on the next expedition, a visit to the Valley of Taioa. The party was headed by Chaplain Stewart, whose knowledge of the Hawaiian language enabled him to understand some of the Nukuhivan speech.

The guide for the trip was Taua, a prominent native "wizard" of the Happa tribe, and their interpreter was an Englishman, William Morrison, who had long lived on the island as a collector of sandalwood. Stewart took along members of the ship's band and had the French horn and Kent bugle played while his group ate their picnic lunch. The music brought out the natives, and the visitors had a chance to observe them at close hand. Maury, who was particularly responsive to the beauties of nature, must have been enchanted by the scenery he saw that day. Stewart described it in this way: "I have gazed on much beautiful and noble scenery in various parts of the world . . . but must unhesitatingly proclaim triumph to the glen of Taioa over everything of the kind I ever beheld." [73] The group visited a native home and a temple, and Maury, for the first time, saw the idols worshiped by these cannibal people.

On another trip Stewart took Maury and four other officers on an expedition to the coastal settlement at Hakapaa. They set off by small boat, again guided by Taua. Landing at a distant point, they were proceeding up a lush tropical valley when they saw a party of Typee warriors on the ridge of a steep cliff, some 600 feet directly above them. The Typees, who were the inveterate enemies of the Happas, were equipped for battle. On their heads were tall bonnets of feathers, over their shoulders were light mantles, and they brandished spears. They tossed their tufted war clubs in the air as a gesture of defiance to the enemies below. Maury doubtless expected fighting to start at any moment, but Stewart learned from Taua that this kind of belligerent demonstration was made whenever non-Typees came near that tribe's portion of the island. [74]

On a later trip with the chaplain and other officers into the interior of Nukuhiva Island, Maury partook of a native feast. Among the familiar foods served were pork, sugar cane, coconuts, and bananas. The Americans found less to their liking the natives' favorites—raw fish, sour breadfruit, and a root like a yam called taro. Chaplain Stewart certainly had the midshipmen in his party avoid drinking the intoxicating liquor made from the kava root, with which the Nukuhivans befuddled themselves.

During these expeditions Maury concentrated hard on learning the Happa speech. By the end of the stay, thanks to his ear for languages and his good memory, he had mastered a small working vocabulary. He was hoping he might be able to converse with someone who had known his brother John. He wrote of the results in these words:

> The Happas and Typees were at war. The latter having just captured three children from the former, we went to the rescue and recovered two, the third had been eaten. When we returned to the Happa Valley from the expedition—it was the valley where dwelt my brother—the men had liberty and the old Happa chief remained on board as a hostage, for his subjects were all a set of savages and the women literally in the fig leaf state. Finch felt it necessary to hold the chief to ensure the safe return of his seamen.
>
> At night, when all the men had come off safe and sound, and a few days only before we left, I was sent to take the old fellow ashore. Going ashore, I made myself known to him. He was the firm and fast friend of my brother. Had saved his life. He was then old. He it was that offered me his scepter, his own wife and the daughter of a neighboring chief if I would remain.[75]

Maury did not report precisely how he managed to decline Gattenewa's generosity.

The exploring parties had been in some danger on land, but it was on a final cruise to Typee waters that every man on board came near to losing his life. Finch had Happa chiefs on the *Vincennes* at the time, and this added to the seriousness of the near catastrophe. Of this experience Stewart wrote:

> On August 11, 1829, in endeavoring to get from the bay of Oomi, we were becalmed while under the influence of a tremendous current, setting dead on shore, in water too deep to let go an anchor. The ship was carried irresistibly by the swell of the sea, against the cliffs at the base of Tower Bluff—till, it can only be said, that her keel did not touch the rocks. She went stern foremost into the very breakers and was prevented from striking, only by spars thrust from the poop deck against the cliffs.
>
> To have touched must have been inevitable shipwreck against a bare-faced rock several hundred feet in height with a depth of

water below, which would have left the mast heads alone above the surface. For several minutes each heave of the sea was expected to be followed by the tremendous concussion.

Every face was pale with agitation and the silence of the grave hung over the ship. The chiefs from Taiohae were in great consternation and Telpu, the warrior, catching the young prince Moana in his arms—tears in eyes—burst out, "Destroyed! Utterly! is the great man-of-war canoe!" adding a doleful foreboding that we would all be devoured by the Typees.

And when by a breath of air from the land, topsails were filled for a moment—carried once more to a situation of hope—soon afterwards by a trade wind [we were] borne to open sea." [76]

When the *Vincennes* returned to her former anchorage at Taiohae, in the Happas' portion of Nukuhiva Island, the ship's supply of water and wood was quickly replenished, and preparations were made for departure. On the last night in Chief Gattenewa's village, there was a ceremonial presentation of gifts to Gattenewa and the other Happa chiefs with strong injunctions to promote peace on the island. Then a grand exhibition of fireworks was set off on board as a farewell treat to the natives lining the shore. At daybreak the American sloop-of-war weighed anchor. [77]

The *Vincennes* enjoyed fine breezes as she sailed toward Tahiti in the Society Islands. The 700-mile passage was accomplished in five days. Soon after their arrival at Papeete on August 17, Maury went ashore with a party to visit the capital town of Tahiti. On this island paradise he first saw Christian missionaries at work among a primitive people. Tahiti's 18-year-old ruler, Queen Pomaré, who had succeeded her brother to the throne, had been converted to Christianity. She welcomed Captain Finch, who brought her a message from President Andrew Jackson, and accepted an invitation to visit the *Vincennes*. On coming on board, she was terrified by the firing of the guns in her honor but soon recovered from her fright. Pomaré was shown over the ship, and the guns were explained to her.

The *Vincennes* had been ordered to visit Tahiti because each year about twenty American whaling vessels anchored in Papeete harbor for long stays. It was known that men were occasionally left behind because of sickness, that some deserted to stay with island beauties, and there had even been cases of merchant captains placing recalcitrant seamen in rowboats and cutting them adrift at sea on the chance that they might reach these islands.

Queen Pomaré fully assented to Finch's request on behalf of the

75

United States government that she protect American nationals, and gave him a gracious letter for President Jackson assuring him of her desire to co-operate.[78]

After a month's stay in Tahitian waters the *Vincennes* sailed for the group Captain Cook had named the Sandwich Islands but which, on arrival, Finch learned Americans should call the Hawaiian Islands if they were to please the natives.[79] As they approached the island of Hawaii, which the Americans spelt Owhyhee, Maury saw silhouetted against the sky the volcano Mauna Loa.

Maury's only interesting expedition on the island of Hawaii was to the falls of the Wailuku River, called the Cascade of the Rainbow. It was a relief to him and his friends William Irving and Stephen Rowan, whom he called Darby, to get off the ship and accompany Chaplain Stewart on the climb to this secluded and beautiful falls.[80]

When the *Vincennes* anchored in the harbor of Honolulu, island of Oahu, in mid-October, Finch went ashore with Stewart to call on the chaplain's former associates, the Protestant missionaries, the Reverend and Mrs. Hiram Bingham, who had reached Hawaii in 1820, and Dr. and Mrs. Gerrit P. Judd, who had come soon after.

Finch asked Mr. Bingham to act as his interpreter, and a formal audience with the King was arranged.[81] King Kamehameha III (Kauike-aouli), who was only sixteen years of age, was governing under a regent, the strong-willed Kaahumanu, "favorite wife" of the king's late father, the great Kamehameha I.[82] When Finch was received at court, letters from President Jackson and Secretary of the Navy John Branch were delivered to the King with a present consisting of a handsome pair of gauntlet gloves. The regent, Dowager Queen Kaahumanu, was given a silver vase, and two silver goblets were presented to the king's sister, Princess Nahienaena.

Finch then excused himself and went with Bingham for a private conference with Kamehameha and Boki, the governor of Oahu. Mr. Bingham translated for Finch, who explained that he had been asked by American merchants and shipowners on the island to try to secure sums long owed them by the native government. These debts, incurred principally by the preceding King of Hawaii, Liholiho (Kamehameha II), and Kaumualii of Kauai prior to their deaths, had been outstanding for years. Previous efforts at collection had failed. Finch was much impressed by the dignity and businesslike attitude of the young King and his regent, who called the native chiefs into conference on the matter the next day.

An investigation of accounts resulted and, after much conferring, Finch was able to get $50,000 of the claims acknowledged and a pledge from the chiefs that the debt would be liquidated in nine months. The chiefs agreed to prorate the obligation among the various islands of the Hawaiian group, whose people would make payment in sandalwood. Finch's settlement of this irksome matter was a great relief to United States Consul John C. Jones, Jr.

Finch was highly popular during his stay except with one group of merchants who considered him too friendly with the missionaries. These critics informed Finch that Kamehameha III and his government were being dictated to by the missionaries, but Finch reported to the Secretary of the Navy that he did not consider this charge to be true.

Finch also succeeded in arranging to have several deserters from American merchant ships turned over to him to be taken back to the United States. In addition, he ascertained for the Navy Department that about 100 whalers and some 25 American merchantmen visited the Hawaiian Islands annually. He reported to the department that the value of those vessels' cargoes was estimated at approximately $5,270,-000.[83] During this stay Maury observed once again that naval officers could play a role in international affairs as well as navigate a ship.

Before final departure, Finch gave a gala party on the *Vincennes*. Of the royal guests Maury found most impressive the young Princess Nakienaena, who conducted herself with both grace and dignity. In a farewell conference with the King, Finch secured the promise that deserting American merchant seamen would not be secreted nor rewards demanded when sick sailors were turned over to the consul or to the agents for their ships. With that achieved, he ordered the *Vincennes* to weigh anchor and continue her voyage across the Pacific to Canton.[84]

On December 19 the *Vincennes* passed the northernmost of the Ladrone Islands (now the Marianas), and Christmas Eve was spent battening down the ship's hatches in anticipation of a storm. For days the sea was rough, and the war-sloop pitched and tossed through the Bashi Channel. On the 29th one of the marines suffered a fate dreaded by seafaring men. He became caught in some gear, and his leg was torn almost off. The ship's surgeon was forced to amputate. Grog was the only anesthetic available.[85]

On the last day of 1829 the *Vincennes,* not far out in the China Sea from Macao, was rammed by two fishing junks; but none of the vessels was badly damaged, and the American warship proceeded to anchor off the small rocklike island of Loo-Chow. On New Year's Day, 1830, "after a tedious voyage of 39 days," she dropped anchor in the roads of Macao.[86]

From the deck of the *Vicennes* Maury had a good view of the walled Portuguese city, which extended up a hillside overlooking the bay.

Established in 1557, Macao was the oldest European outpost in the Orient. It was located on a strip of land about three miles long and a mile wide, for which the Portuguese authorities paid rent to the Chinese. Here all European and American merchants doing business in Canton, the chief center of Western trade with China, maintained houses to which they retired for the hot months from March to September, when trading was suspended. Their wives lived in Macao the year round, for Tao Kuang, Emperor of China, did not permit women at the Occidental factories, or houses of trade, located on the outskirts of Canton. Macao's wide main street, the Praya Grande, extended in the shape of a crescent. The many colors of the buildings and palm trees gave the city an exotic tropical appearance.[87]

Upon anchoring Captain Finch dispatched a letter to United States Consul John S. Grosvenor at Canton, 70 miles up Pearl River, stating the purposes of his visit. At the same time Finch wrote to Messrs. J. P. Sturgis, Samuel Russell, J. R. Latimer, and W. H. Low, leading American merchants in Canton, requesting information on the amount and condition of trade between the United States and China and asking their opinion as to the advisability of periodic visits by American warships to Chinese waters. The merchants replied that more naval vessels should be sent to China on goodwill missions, and thus increase respect for the American flag. They advised that there were often 40 to 50 American merchantmen in port with no armed protection and that "American trade centering in the port of Canton fluctuates from five to seven millions of dollars annually, with like exports." The merchants also reported that they were subject to "many local grievances and impositions by local Mandarins in contravention of known laws of the Empire."[88]

While fulfilling his orders in securing this information Finch stayed ashore in Macao as a guest in the residence of J. R. Latimer. Chaplain Stewart was entertained by Dr. Robert Morrison, who was for many years the only Protestant English-speaking missionary in China and Chinese interpreter for British and American residents. Maury and his fellow midshipmen were included in the attentions showered on the officers of the *Vincennes* by the American merchants and especially by "the chief representative of the British East India Company, Mr. Plowden."[89]

January was the height of the business season for the Canton merchants. Upon receiving an invitation from Charles N. Talbot, acting consul at Canton in the absence of Grosvenor, Captain Finch decided to visit the American factories there. He picked a group of officers to accompany him, and Maury was one of the thirteen chosen. A permit to make the trip to the restricted city was secured from the Chinese custom house near Macao. Because of imperial laws governing foreign warships, as well as shallow water in the approaches to Canton, Captain Finch engaged a Chinese craft for the trip. After an interesting 55-mile passage to Whampoa, the group of American officers saw many foreign merchantmen riding at anchor there. Some of the ships were unloading goods onto Chinese junks and sampans for transportation up the remaining 10 or 12 miles of shallow river to the foreign factories located just outside the walls of Canton.

Above Whampoa the Pearl River narrowed to such an extent that Maury could see details of the pagodas on either side as well as hear the temple bells. He also saw women wading where the tide had receded at the edge of the river. They had babies slung on their backs and were busy gathering shellfish. Because of the density of traffic on the river, the pilot of Finch's chartered craft had to maneuver carefully as he approached the wharves of the factories, or hongs, of the foreign merchants. These hongs on the outskirts of the city were as far as the group from the *Vincennes* went, for no foreigners were allowed within the walls of Canton, a metropolis of about one million people. The naval officers were told that the laws of the Chinese Empire did not permit the foreign merchants to stay the whole year at their own factories. In the off-season for trade they were required to go to Macao.

At the factories Maury, along with the *Vincennes'* other officers, learned that Americans at Canton traded goods brought from the States and sandalwood from Pacific islands for rice, tea, silks, cassia, cinnamon, nankeens, rhubarb, vermilion, chinaware, even straw matting and rattan chairs. There was some trading in furs and bêche-de-mer (sea slugs). The factories were really warehouses and Maury saw the wide variety of goods that made the China trade so profitable for Americans.

The American merchants supplied Captain Finch with the type of information about trade that he had been sent to secure for the United States government. It had been a long time, the merchants pointed out, since the *Congress,* 36, had visited China in 1819. She had been the only warship of the United States ever to come there. Finch promised to report their request that men-of-war be sent more often to Chinese waters. The party of naval officers returned to Macao on January 18 and rejoined their ship.[90] The *Vincennes* sailed from Macao Roads on January 22.[91]

The island of Luzon was sighted after a passage of eight days. After coasting the shore for two days the *Vincennes,* on January 29, 1830, passed Corregidor Island and came to anchor in Manila Bay.

The dark, moss-covered stone walls that surrounded the oldest part of the city virtually hid it from view save for its red-tiled roofs and the tower and domes of the cathedral and churches. Around the walls ran a broad moat, across which were eight drawbridges that were raised nightly from 11 P.M. to 4 A.M. The trading section of Manila was set on one side of the Pasig River, which emptied into the bay. But the homes of the major portion of the population were across the river, where the streets were muddy and the houses mostly of light bamboo construction, with roofs thatched with nipa palm.[92]

Maury and some of his friends went ashore at the first opportunity and hired a carriage pulled by very small horses. They saw the palace of the Captain General and Governor of the Philippines, where Captain Finch had been received by Mariano Rocafuerte, the representative of His Catholic Majesty, King Ferdinand VII of Spain. Opposite the palace the midshipmen saw the state prison, the government buildings, and the huge cathedral on the west of the plaza.[93]

Maury's most enjoyable experience in Manila was a tour he made with some other midshipmen and Chaplain Stewart. After having midday dinner in the city, they hired carriages and drove through Santa Magdalena parish and along the bay to the outer port of Cavite. On the drive they saw native Philippine people driving their high, two-wheeled carts called *carromatos,* pulled by slow, plodding water buffaloes. On their way back to the main section of Manila the group stopped to visit the handsome dome-topped Pantheon at Manila's Campo Santo. This elaborate burying place must have seemed unusual to Maury, who was accustomed to a small graveyard near a family home or in an unpretentious churchyard.

The afternoon's trip terminated at the Calzada, a wide, tree-shaded avenue encircling one section of the city and located just outside the old moat. There, as the cool of the evening approached, the midshipmen could see the prominent people of Manila enjoying their daily drive. Governor General Rocafuerte took the air in a handsome coach pulled by four matching horses, attended by many outriders. At sunset, when the bells of the cathedral and other churches reminded the faithful that it was time for vespers, carriages halted and the devout stood facing the city and crossed themselves. As the tones of the Angelus ceased, the carriages quickly whirled into motion again. Maury undoubtedly watched for the phaetons in which rode pretty young girls, dressed in full evening costume without hat or mantilla to hide their jet-black hair. But the señoritas were closely guarded by their mother or some older woman of the family. The carriages were driven at a smart clip but not too fast to permit the city's fashionable citizens to see each other, their main enjoyment obviously being to see and be seen.

On the public parade ground near the bay about 2,000 men drilled late each afternoon to the strains of two full military bands. The musicians were all natives of the islands, as were the soldiery, though both were commanded by Spanish officers. The completion of the drill and the music ended the evening promenade on the Calzada.[94]

While Maury was observing the ways of Manila and its people, his captain was busy conferring with G. W. Hubbell, consular agent of the United States, American merchants doing business there, and Captains Chever and Benjamin, in command of two American merchantmen in port at that time. Finch was to report later to Washington that Americans in the Philippines also felt that further visits from their country's men-of-war would be advantageous.[95]

On February 9 the *Vincennes* sailed from Manila, cruised down the South China Sea, and passed between the Malay Peninsula and Borneo en route to the Strait of Sunda. They raised Java Head and entered the narrow passage that separates Java from Sumatra. Finch anchored the *Vincennes* for two days to water the ship for the long voyage ahead. Here Maury had a chance to observe the efficiency of the Dutch, who controlled Java, and from whom both water and supplies for the ship were purchased.[96]

Once in the Indian Ocean the *Vincennes* had ahead of her weeks of continuous sailing. These were the monotonous periods on long cruises, when the character and temperament of officers and men were of paramount importance. It was during this tedious passage that the following incident, recounted by Maury's daughter, Diana, took place:

> While in the *Vincennes,* he [Matthew Maury] became a great favorite with the Captain who used frequently to invite him to dine in the cabin. On one such occasion, when the Captain had taken a glass or so too much, he insisted that Maury should drink more than the moderate quantity he allowed himself and which he never exceeded. He firmly and politely declined; but when his superior officer insisted, and, rising from his seat, approached, glass in hand, to push him yet further, he dashed the glass to the floor, and, turning on his heel, left the cabin.[97]

Maury must indeed have been a favorite to be forgiven such behavior, however merited the young man may have felt it to be. Perhaps Finch decided to ignore the impetuous action since the midshipman was obviously only trying to stick to his rule of life.

Maury's captain was well aware of the studying the youth was doing in his off-duty hours. "It was during this period," a fellow officer, William Leigh, later reported, "that, without assistance, he went through a course of study commencing with the rudiments of Euclid and extend-

ing to the higher mathematics of La Place [now written Laplace]." [98]
Maury also started work on a set of lunar tables at this time.

Doubling the Cape of Good Hope on April 7, the *Vincennes* reached
Capetown the next day, 56 days from Manila.[99] The ship rode at anchor
less than a mile from the city. All hands could enjoy a fine view of Table
Mountain. The South African city proved most hospitable. The representative of the British government cordially received Finch and his officers, as did both Dutch and British residents. In this city of 20,000 inhabitants the midshipmen saw the old castle dating from about 1666
and visited the beautiful gardens that had formerly belonged to the
Dutch East India Company. The Americans were impressed by this 120-
acre park "immediately adjacent to the most compact part of town."
Most of the officers took a popular carriage ride out along a road that
led north from Capetown to the Constantia vineyard already famous for
the sweet wine produced there.[100]

The *Vincennes* left her anchorage in Table Bay on April 19 and set
sail for St. Helena, lying some 200 miles off the west coast of Africa and
about 15° south of the equator. The island was sighted on May 1, and
officers went ashore the next day and were entertained by the Honorable Brigadier General Dallas, the British Governor. Maury and his mess-
mates were undoubtedly fascinated by their visit to Longwood House,
which looked much the same, they were told, as when Napoleon had
died there nine years before. From Longwood the officers went to visit
the tomb where Napoleon's body was still interred, far from his native
Corsica and from the France he had led to glory and defeat. The tomb
was surrounded by a double enclosure, the outer one of wooden poles,
enclosing four willow trees. A plain iron railing guarded an inner area
of 12 square feet. There, raised only a few inches above the ground,
under three large uninscribed flagstones of granite lay the remains of
the Emperor of the French.[101]

On the evening of May 5 the *Vincennes* began the last leg of her voyage. By this time cockroaches had multiplied in the steerage and there
was an endless battle to kill the smelly hardshells on the ceiling and
knee beams. No matter how often the casks were whitewashed and the
hold was limed, both bugs and smells multiplied in the bowels of the
ship. The odor of bilgewater was nauseous and made life unpleasant in
the steerage. But the ship was homeward bound at last.

Once the *Vincennes* had crossed the equator and thus reached the
North Atlantic, the spirits of even the most weary of the crew began to
rise. Men became positively merry when, after 32 days at sea, they sighted
the distant New Jersey shore.

June 8, 1830, was a thrilling and crowded day. The *Vincennes* received a pilot on board, and at noon there sprang up a fine breeze that took the ship to the quarantine station by 4 P.M. Finch had observed the strictest sanitary regulations aboard, and these now paid off in the inspectors' giving a clean bill of health to the much-traveled sloop-of-war. The topsails soon filled, and within an hour the *Vincennes,* in all her glory, was standing in to upper New York harbor as the first vessel of the United States Navy to have circumnavigated the globe.

As she approached her anchorage "the news collector" came off to her in one boat and two steamboats loaded with cheering friends of the ship's officers and other well-wishers circled the *Vincennes.* The rattle of the anchor being paid out was drowned as the band struck up a salute to America, "Hail, Columbia! happy land!" [102]

New York was a happy sight to Maury. He had been away from the United States almost four years. He had been around the world and had probably learned more about it and his fellow man than any college could have taught him in the same period. He had observed many of the procedures involved in the conduct of international relations, had earned the respect of his commanding officer and of his shipmates, and had made several close friendships that would last. He had learned, in widely differing climates, the role that weather plays in the life of man and the supreme importance to the mariner of the winds and currents of the sea. He had also gained a knowledge of practical seamanship and had studied as much as his limited free time and the very scanty supply of books on board the *Vincennes* had permitted. But his studies had all been self-directed. He wanted more than this. He longed for training in advanced mathematics and navigation, and he hoped the Navy would give him this instruction on shore.

CHAPTER V

Climbing the Rungs
of the Ladder

When sailing ships of war returned from such a long cruise as had the *Vincennes,* the crew was promptly paid off, the officers were given three months' leave, and the ship was temporarily dismantled.

Maury received his leave on June 12, 1830.[1] First he wanted to see as many of his family and friends as he could and then he planned to prepare himself to take the examination required of midshipmen at the end of their first five years of service.[2] In six more months he would be twenty-five, and he felt it was time to climb off the bottom rung of the ladder and show some progress in his chosen career.

His country, Maury found, had changed much in the years he had been away. The population had soared to nearly thirteen million. Andrew Jackson was making his weight felt as President. Talk about the West had increased greatly. So many immigrants had moved westward over the Erie Canal and so much produce had been shipped eastward over that waterway, in its first five years, that a canal craze was sweeping the East.[3] Canal boosters weren't in the least alarmed by the fact that the Baltimore and Ohio Railroad had in May started hauling passengers on railcars pulled by horses or that New York's well-known industrialist Peter Cooper was about to try out the "Tom Thumb," a steam locomotive he had had built.[4]

New York was bigger, busier, and more crowded than when Maury had sailed in the *Brandy,* but he did not dally for sightseeing. He was officially attached to the New York Navy Yard and would be returning there after his leave. He set out for Washington, where he went to stay in Georgetown [5] at the home of his cousin Richard B. Maury, who had become register of the Navy Department.[6] From Georgetown Maury wrote to his brother Dick on July 3, "I have not got myself to rights since leaving the ship." [7] He was doubtless referring to a post-cruise struggle to extract from the fourth auditor some small sum still due him by the Navy Department. He was definitely short of funds.

84

"I shall take a tour in a few days," he continued, "among our old Virginia relatives where in all probability I shall not remain longer than the first of August."[8] Then he was going home. After five years, he was finally to see his parents, brothers, and sisters once again.

He made the trip to Tennessee by stagecoach in company with his sister-in-law, Eliza, her two young sons, and their Negro nurse.[9] Richard and Diana Maury had wanted so much to see for the first time the two sons of their son John, as well as to welcome his widow. It was an exciting homecoming for all concerned.

For Maury the greatest joy was to be back on happy terms with his father, who had forgiven him for entering the Navy. Richard had become reconciled in 1826 after receiving reports from officers of the *Brandywine* that his son showed promise of developing into an officer of merit.[10] Maury had approximately a month's visit in the familiar log home in Tennessee. Certainly one of his first calls was to his former schoolmaster, the Reverend James H. Otey, who had been so good about writing him during his long absence. Dick rode with Maury whenever he could get away from his farming and the two enjoyed their old sport of swimming their horses across Harpeth River.

In September Maury and his traveling companions returned by stage to Virginia, where they visited at Laurel Hill, in Spotsylvania, once again enjoying the hospitality of the Edward Herndons.[11] While visiting there Maury saw Ann Hull Herndon, whom he had first met in 1825 on his way to join the Navy. He found her a radiant 19-year-old whose auburn hair set off her very fair skin. For Maury, one of her chief charms was her soft, gentle voice. She sang Scotch ballads, and he told her stories of his experiences at sea, watching her blue eyes sparkle when she grew excited.[12]

Laurel Hill was a well-run plantation and a fine place to visit.[13] It was especially so for Matthew in the early fall of 1830, and not only because Ann lived nearby with an aunt. He still hadn't had his fill of good home-cooked meals nor of the restfulness he found in just being with his kindly affectioned relatives. He probably rode over to nearby Caroline County to see his mother's family, the Minors. Mrs. John Minor, the widow of his uncle, the general, was, that summer of 1830, in residence at Topping Castle, where Maury's mother had grown up.[14]

On October 6, 1830, Maury reported to the school maintained for the instruction of midshipmen at the New York Navy Yard.[15] This school, however, was not well organized, disciplined, or staffed, as most senior officers in the United States Navy in 1830 placed a low value on formal naval education.[16] Some of these older officers were well-educated men like Jacob Jones, Maury's commander in the *Brandywine* in 1826-1827;

Commodore Jones had studied some law and medicine before he went into the Navy.[17] But most of the senior captains and commodores had gone to sea as midshipmen and gained their knowledge of navigation through shipboard experience. They had practiced what they proudly termed a "rough and ready" navigation of their ships in the War of 1812, and the glory of the Navy's achievements in that struggle against a superior naval power had strengthened their conviction that the old methods should be continued.[18]

At the school Maury set himself to study in earnest for the examination for promotion. The subjects on which he would be examined were Bowditch's *Navigator,* Playfair's *Euclid* Books 1, 2, 3, 4, and 6, McClure's *Spherics,* Bourdon's *Algebra,* mental and moral philosophy, Spanish or French (he chose Spanish), and seamanship.[19]

For recreation during this stay at the New York Navy Yard Maury took the ferry to Manhattan. In the harbor he saw more small steamboats than he had four years before, but the seagoing ships were still all proud beauties of sail. Not as handsome but just as colorful were the "coasters," which came and went frequently, their captains navigating by their knowledge of headlands and by constant sounding with the lead.

A place of which Maury heard much among men interested in ships was the Tontine Coffee House, on the northwest corner of Wall and Water streets, where merchants and brokers met daily from 11 A.M. to 2 P.M. to transact business. Insuring of ships and cargo was transacted there as it was at Lloyd's in London. The other great center of marine trade was on Wall Street—the Merchants' Exchange, which had been completed in 1827. Here was located the terminus of the chain of signal stations which in 1826 had ended at the Battery. The signal station was on the roof of the Exchange.[20]

Lower Manhattan was more thickly studded than before with shipyards, for in 1830 the great upsurge of merchant shipbuilding was well under way.

All these evidences of the importance of shipping may have further irritated Maury with the limited amount of knowledge he was gaining about navigation. In any event, he was dissatisfied with the teaching at the New York Navy Yard school and decided he could do better by studying on his own. Doubtless he was also tired of the endless skylarking of his fellow midshipmen, of solely male companionship, of Navy Yard life, and longed to be in a home and surrounded by some family life. He went to his superiors and explained his belief that he could better prepare for his examination through private study. On December 22 he was detached from the school and granted an unlimited leave.[21]

He went to Washington and moved in with the Richard B. Maurys. In return for the hospitality he taught his brother John's son, young Dabney Maury, who was also staying in the household.[22] Matthew daily put in long hours of concentrated work on the course of study he had begun in the *Vincennes* and, at this time, progressed to advanced study in the works of the French astronomer and mathematician, La Place. Scientific rules and reasons increasingly occupied his mind.

His whole time, however, was not devoted to books, for pretty Ann Hull Herndon arrived to visit in Georgetown. Maury was a young man who had little trouble deciding what he liked and, once he was clear on that point, he poured out his devotion in unstinted fashion. This was his pattern in work, and it proved to be so in romance. He fell in love and wooed the Virginia girl with ardor.

Ann had thought him fascinating the day she met him. Now, five and a half years later, she was twenty and he twenty-five, and both were sufficiently mature to care very deeply. In those winter days of 1831 Maury went to call on Ann every night but always left before 10 P.M., when a watchman blew a horn as a signal for lights to be put out in Georgetown.[23]

Maury had not forgotten his resolve "to bend all to my profession." He did not confine himself to the study of the required textbooks but read and studied everything available. The more he studied the more fascinated he became with the theory behind mathematics and its use in the science of navigation. He also coached other midshipmen who were in Washington preparing to take the examination.[24]

Maury was ordered to appear on March 3, 1831, before the Examining Board then in session in Washington.[25] The examiners were officers who had gone to sea before Fulton launched the steamboat which they had, at the time, probably joined in calling his folly. They were old-line captains concerned with the practical navigation of a sailing vessel.

Maury later told of this ordeal in an article he wrote for the *Southern Literary Messenger*:

> The midshipman who seeks to become learned in the branches of science that pertain to his profession and who before the Examining Board should so far stray from the lids of Bowditch as to get among the isodynamic and other lines of a magnetic chart would be blackballed as though he were to clubhaul a ship for the Board in the Hebrew tongue. . . . Midshipmen, turning to Bowditch, commit to memory the formula of his first and second method for "finding the longitude at sea by a lunar observation." Thus crammed or "drilled," as it is called, they go before the Board of Examination,

where, strange to say, there is a premium offered for such qualification. He who repeats "by heart" the rules of Bowditch, though he does not understand the mathematical principles involved in one of them, obtains a higher number from the Board than he who, skilled in mathematics, goes to the blackboard and, drawing his diagrams, can demonstrate every problem in navigation.[26]

William O. Stevens and C. Alphonso Smith, of the English Department of the Naval Academy at Annapolis, described the situation when Maury "was questioned as to the lunar problem. Instead of repeating the Bowditch formulas, after immemorial custom, he had the audacity to step to the blackboard and work out the question as a problem in spherical trigonometry. The 'Professor of Mathematics' conducting the examination got lost in trying to follow him, and brazenly declared the demonstration wrong. The midshipman insisted. The officers of the examining board, knowing still less than the schoolmaster, decided after an embarrassed consultation to support him on general principles. Accordingly they looked as wise as possible, informed the midshipman that he was all wrong and bade him go to sea again and learn his business. Under this decision Matthew Fontaine Maury lost two years in promotion." [27]

Maury's foolhardy display of knowledge may have satisfied his youthful pride but, as Professors Stevens and Smith stated, it placed him low on the list and was to make his next promotion two years later than was necessary. Maury passed the examination but was rated 27th in a class of 40 when he could have been at the top. The midshipmen whom he had drilled passed with a high rating.[28] Perhaps his low placement on the list taught him the folly of showing off his knowledge, for there is no record of any later similar episode in his naval career.

The fact that Maury had passed the examination meant that he would be promoted to passed midshipman. This was an officer's grade that was warranted rather than commissioned, and Maury was to receive his warrant as a passed midshipman on June 24, 1831, to take rank as of June 4.[29]

Meanwhile, once Maury had passed the examination he was free to pursue his own plans until he received orders to report for active duty. Being very much in love, he went from Washington to Fredericksburg to press his suit with Ann.

"The old 'burgh," as Maury was fond of calling it, was a pleasant place in springtime, especially for young lovers. He spoke of "the very yellow jasmine which made the bower under which I fell in love with my gentle Nannie," as he often called Ann.[30] He was never to forget it and later asked that a slip from that jasmine be planted on his grave. Maury was intense and ardent; he was handsome in his uniform [31] and Ann soon said yes. Matthew described his condition in a belated letter to Dick apologizing for his long silence. "I was too much in love, alias crazy, to write letters." [32]

Having proposed and been accepted, Maury doubtless asked consent for their engagement from his fiancée's older brother, John Minor Herndon, who had headed the family since the death of both mother and father, and from Ann's uncle, Edward Herndon, who was devoted to his niece. Maury admitted that he was financially unable to afford marriage at that time, and made it clear that Ann might have a long wait before his prospects improved. But all the relatives were pleased by the engagement, for Ann and Matthew were distant cousins, both being great-grandchildren of John Minor (I) and Sarah Carr Minor.[33] Ann's father, Dabney Herndon, and Matthew's older brother, John, had been close friends. Both Ann and Matthew had been reared in the Episcopal Church and placed an emphasis on religion. They had both been taught a sense of responsibility and the importance of courtesy in human relations. Both enjoyed parties but preferred a family circle to other society.

In all that Maury wrote to or about his Ann he most frequently praised her charming femininity and graciousness of manner. In commenting on the relationship between man and woman he was to observe: "Our greatest happiness often depends upon a word, the glance of an eye, the tone of the voice, or what is more expressive, but more undescribable still, the manner." [34]

Maury had found and won a girl who pleased him in every way. Now, like most Navy men, he began to dread the months he would be separated from her. As a result he made some inquiries about the possibility of securing work on land. He was anxious to marry but not to leave the Navy, as is evidenced by his account to Dick: "I thought if I could be employed as surveyor or anything of that sort by a state, I would try a hand at it but I believe that I have too many notions and that after all Uncle Sam will have the selling of my bones to the Doctors." [35]

Even romance could not make Maury forget his determination to continue his studies and to make use of his mind in professional achievement—aims that he called his "notions."

Maury, however, was delighted that his orders were slow in coming. This was the rule rather than the exception in 1831 because the United States was at peace and most of the large vessels of the Navy were in ordinary. Officers often had to wait many months for a berth on the small number of ships in active service.

But when Maury finally received his orders he was pleased with them. He was to report on June 11 to the sloop-of-war *Falmouth*, 18, as acting sailing master,[36] a billet that would give him opportunity to show his ability.[37] Good as the news was, it in no way changed the necessity for his waiting to be married, for the *Falmouth*, launched only two years before, was scheduled for a cruise—around the Horn into the Pacific, to join the American squadron there in patrolling the west coast of South America. This meant another three or four years' absence from the United States. The prospect was a gloomy one for both Matthew and Ann, but somewhat more bearable to Matthew as he would be carrying out new and exciting responsibilities, while his fiancée would just have to sit at home and wait for his return.

Before leaving to report to his ship, Maury purchased a seal and had it engraved with the one word, *Mizpah*. This was his gift to his betrothed, and their agreement was that Ann would use it only for sealing her letters to him. As it had to others throughout the centuries, the single Biblical word expressed the full meaning of the verse, "The Lord watch between thee and me when we are absent one from another." [38]

The parting from Ann in early June was a distressing wrench, but at last Maury was on his way to New York. From his years of sea service he knew exactly what was required of the sailing master of a vessel. The sailing master directed the officer of the watch what course to steer and the amount of sail to be carried and, in questions of navigation, acted as the spokesman of the captain. The official title of sailing master was commonly shortened to the term "master," and this shorter term was to be officially adopted in the Navy in another six years, and changed to lieutenant junior grade in 1883.[39] Maury's statutory rank of passed midshipman was, of course, not altered by the fact that he had been assigned to carry out the duties of sailing master of the *Falmouth*. On June 11, 1831, Maury reported to the *Falmouth* as acting sailing master.[40] The position entailed real responsibility, and Maury resolved to use the weeks before sailing to gain information on the winds and currents that others had encountered on the route the *Falmouth* would sail. He felt sure he could find printed information on the subject because so many Navy and merchant vessels were making the voyage around Cape Horn. In those June weeks, although he hunted widely in New York, he was unsuccessful in his effort to secure definite information on winds and currents.[41]

Maury was delighted with his new assignment, for he was serving with officers whom he knew and admired. Like her twin vessel, the *Vincennes*, the sloop-of-war *Falmouth* was commanded by an officer with the rank of master commandant,[42] Francis H. Gregory, under whom Maury had served in the *Brandywine*. The "first," as Maury and his contemporaries spoke of the ranking lieutenant of a ship, was Lieutenant Thomas A. Dornin. The other lieutenants were Elisha Peck, who had been sailing master of the *Brandywine* in 1825, William H. Glendy, Charles W. Chauncey, and Charles M. Armstrong. The surgeon was William W. S. Ruschenberger, a man of charm and culture, whom Maury had come to know in the *Brandywine* when that frigate and the *Vincennes* had sailed in company to Valparaiso in 1826.[43]

When he went on board Maury discovered that much of the preparatory work had already been accomplished, for Dornin had joined the *Falmouth* on April 1 to ready her for sea, and by June 6 most of the officers and crew had come on board. Captain Gregory [44] hoped to sail on June 30, but, as was so often the case in those days, business and navigation had to wait for nature to co-operate. On July 2 the *Falmouth* proceeded from New York to Sandy Hook, where the winds again tried the patience of the new acting sailing master. On July 5, 1831, the *Falmouth* got across the bar, discharged the harbor pilot, and was under way.[45]

Maury had no problem in becoming familiar with the *Falmouth*. She was almost identical to the *Vincennes* and handled much the same. She had been laid down in the New York Navy Yard in 1826, under plans drawn by Samuel Humphreys, and had been launched in 1828. Her original rating of 18 guns was often later given as 20, for, as was customary, she always mounted more than the listed rating.[46]

There were "232 souls aboard" as the *Falmouth* cruised southward in warm July weather. Maury took his responsibility very seriously, as well he might, for he was head of a department of the ship and, as such, answerable only to the captain. Due to the importance of his duties as navigation officer, he was exempt from standing sea watches.[47]

Maury was perpetually inspecting the sail rooms and giving orders for repairs when needed, visiting the cable tiers, checking to see that no more than the proper amounts of water, wood, or provisions were brought up daily from the hold, and reporting on their expenditure to the captain. He had to keep the keys to the afterhold and the "spirit room" and weekly examine the accounts of the boatswain and carpenter. He had detailed reports to make on items from masts to slop clothes, from decayed provisions to a lost flag. Inspection of both standing and running rigging was his to perform regularly. He was in charge of the compasses, hourglasses, and other timepieces and had to compare them frequently to prevent errors in computation. The lead lines and log lines were under his supervision.[48]

Of great interest to Maury were his recordings in the logbook concerning the course steered, distance run, the set and velocity of currents, the direction of the wind, the state of the weather, results of astronomical observations made to determine the ship's location, and the variation of the compass. He also had to record the longitude of any place the ship visited and describe all coasts with emphasis on peculiarities that would serve as points for future recognition. A study of the tides, their direction, rise, and fall, also was expected, and he was to examine all coastal charts and report on any inaccuracies. His duties went on and on.[49] Maury set himself to keeping clear and precise records on the winds and currents encountered, to learning at first hand that information not available on paper to help him.

The first port of call was Rio de Janeiro, where once again Maury found himself gazing up at Sugar Loaf. He enjoyed the social entertainment extended by hospitable Brazilians to the officers of the *Falmouth*,[50] but as a newly engaged man he certainly found himself wishing he could have the companionship of Ann.

As the *Falmouth* sailed down the long southeast coast of South America Maury was preparing himself for his first real test as master—he was about to navigate a ship around the Horn. He described the voyage in this way:

> The U.S.S. *Falmouth* and H.B.M.S. *Volage* doubled Cape Horn in October 1831; the latter had thirty-eight, the former twenty-four days from the Cape to the latitude of Talcahuana. Both of them took a westerly gale off the pitch of the Cape. The *Falmouth* stood down on the starboard tack to 62° 5′ S. and found the winds more favorable. The *Volage*, persisting in the attempt to gain the "inshore" passage, lay to on either tack, to preserve her relative position with regard to the latitude of the Cape, and was drifted off to the eastward. When this gale abated, she stood up to the Cape again, and took another, in which she was also driven to the eastward. In the third attempt, she succeeded in doubling the Cape. She put into Talcahuana to repair the damages which she had sustained while riding out the gales from the westward. The *Falmouth* arrived in Valparaiso in excellent order.[51]

During this experience the germ thought of Maury's great future work had been born. He had searched unsuccessfully for guides to a navigator making this voyage. He knew now how much it would mean to have accurate wind and current information plus reliable sailing directions. He determined that he would record the detailed observations he had made and evaluate them. In the *Falmouth* he had a tiny stateroom to himself, just slightly larger than his bunk, but it gave him a place to write.

In this little cubbyhole he sorted his notes and wrote his first scientific paper, "On the Navigation of Cape Horn." In it he recorded not only his own account just quoted but records of various passages by navigators. He noted: "The fact that winds with *westing* are more prevalent than those with *easting,* in them, is established from the circumstance that the return is less dreaded and shorter than the outward bound passage. The ratio of winds with westing in them to those with easting is as *three* to *one.*" [52]

After providing an adequate basis for his deductions, Maury advised the best course to follow, stating that, "The 'inshore passage' is to be pursued always, when the winds are favorable, keeping close into the land, never passing to the southward of Diego Ramírez, more than 10 or 12 leagues." [53] He pointed out, however, that, "Common practice teaches that good passages are more frequently made by those vessels, which finding contrary gales off the Cape, stand boldly to the south, than by those that lie to in them, keeping near the parallel of the Cape." [54]

He gave specific sailing directions for each course, and his observations on the phenomenon of the erratic action of the barometer were to prove of interest to scientists in the United States as well as to mariners. Of this he said, in part:

> The barometer has not been found to be of much practical utility off Cape Horn, how useful soever it may be in middle latitudes, by indicating the approach of hurricanes; it is no index to the winds in the high latitudes to the south of Cape Horn.
>
> Here the mercury, below the mean height of lower latitudes, becomes very unsteady, falling and rising several inches in a few hours. During the strength of a gale, sometimes it is observed to rise, at other times it falls or remains in *statu quo.* Its mean height south of the latitude of Cape Horn is 29.03 inches. [55]

When Maury finished this article, written in any snatches of free time he had in the *Falmouth,* he mailed it to the outstanding scientific publication of the United States at that time—the *American Journal of Science and Arts,* published in New Haven, Connecticut. When this article finally reached the desk of the journal's editor, Benjamin Silliman, it was read with great interest. Although the author was unknown to him and was only a passed midshipman in the United States Navy, Dr. Silliman recognized that the facts had been systematically gathered and presented, that there was new information in the article, and he decided it was worthy of publication. It was to appear in the July, 1834, issue of the journal and was to mark the launching of Maury's writings on the subjects of navigation and meteorology.

Meanwhile, when the *Falmouth* reached Valparaiso, Maury and his friend Thomas Dornin called on the Monte Rallas family and renewed other acquaintanceships from their visits there between 1827 and 1829.[56] Maury, however, was a far more serious young man than he had been on his earlier cruise and was thinking of his future. In a frank letter to his brother Dick, married and farming in Tennessee, Maury wrote on November 17:

> Between ourselves, Dick, I should leave Uncle Sam and his Navy if I had any other means of making my way decently through the world. My pay now is nearly $700 and in two or three years more will be $960 but if I had a respectable situation on shore that would yield me a genteel sufficiency I would not, with the present prospect of promotion in the Navy, remain for five times the sum. I find promotion slower every year; in fact the inducements held out are not calculated for a man of ordinary talent and enterprise, spiced with a little ambition. Money, with me never was of primary consideration. At a moderate calculation, I will not be a Captain (things continuing the same) for 25 years.
>
> As for turning my attention wholly and entirely to money matters [that] is what I shall never do.[57]

In this complaint of poor pay and slow advancement Maury was but expressing the sentiments of all Navy officers of the day. Their other chief criticism concerned the length of time it took the Navy to send their mail to distant stations. Because of these and other unsatisfactory conditions, many able officers left the service, and others obtained long furloughs during which they could engage in civilian pursuits that would bring in more money.

Also there were, of course, problems of the frictions that inevitably developed where so many men were cooped up in small ships, or on faraway stations, for such long stretches of time. The lack of entertainment or relaxation caused boredom. Homesickness was especially severe among officers and crew at a holiday period associated with family celebrations back home. This was true in the *Falmouth* in December, 1831, as the men on board knew that they would be on duty with the Pacific Squadron for two or three years. The political state of the countries on the west coast of South America was still so unsettled that the United States Navy maintained its patrol from Concepción to Guayaquil to ensure safety for American merchant vessels and citizens doing business in those countries. In view of these facts, it is not surprising that Maury wrote home, just before Christmas of 1831: "We are not at this time by any means the merriest set of sailors that you ever saw together." [58]

In Callao, in an effort to be sociable, Maury went to pay his respects to the "Doña Gertrudes," as Maury called a young lady whom he had met on his previous cruise. He found the girl's mother playing cards in the same room and in the same place where he had told her good-bye two and a half years earlier. From experience, Maury suspected this meant only one thing—the attractive daughter was nearby, and Mamma was keeping her usual watch. The Peruvian dowager murmured a greeting but never looked up from her cards, so Maury knew he was not supposed to interrupt her game. He continued on to the adjoining room in search of the daughter. There he found her "rigged in the North American costume" and having a flirtatious talk, "by flickering candlelight," with a redheaded Englishman. Maury was sufficiently informed as to the etiquette of courting to make a rapid exit. He learned that the young lady left Callao the next day for Lima, whether in retreat from him or the Englishman he evidently did not know nor care too much. On December 14, when writing of this, he dryly commented, "I have not been very punctual in renewing my visit." [59] It was typical of Maury's sense of humor.

One of the duties of the sailing master, when it seemed "to the interest of the service," was to ask permission of the ship's captain for boats to survey a coast or a harbor or to investigate a possible hazard to navigation.[60] One survey Maury conducted from the *Falmouth* while patrolling the west coast of South America was described by Midshipman William B. Whiting:

> I encountered some ridicule from my messmates for predicting that Maury would be a distinguished man. I asserted that there was that in him which could not be kept down. . . . In a survey of San Lorenzo Island while attached to the *Falmouth* I was an assistant to Maury, and he displayed that perseverance and energy undismayed by difficulty, when he had once determined upon accomplishing a result, which ever marked his career.
>
> In prosecuting the survey of the Boca del Diables he scaled rocks and crept around the corners of cliffs where I was almost afraid to follow him, but the attainment of his object seemed to be with him the only subject of his thoughts.
>
> He landed on the Labos Rocks to the westward of San Lorenzo to make some astronomical and trigonometrical observations while I remained in the boat. When he landed it was almost a dead calm,

and the sea comparatively smooth; but by the time he had finished his observations a fresh wind had sprung up from the southwards, the tide had risen, and the sea was raging so as to forbid the near approach of the boat, one minute receding from the rock so as to leave a yawning gulf of twenty or thirty feet depth, then rushing up again with an irresistible force.

Calling on me to approach as near as I dared, Maury ascended to the highest point of the rock, took off his jacket, and with a string which he found in his pocket tied in it his watch and sextant, and then threw it with all his might into the sea toward the boat, while the bowman of the boat stood ready to seize it with his boathook before the water had time to penetrate the wrapping. Maury then, watching the culmination of a wave, sprang from the rock himself and, being a good swimmer and possessed of much youthful strength, reached the boat in safety, but it was a fearful leap.[61]

While this was an exciting adventure, there were long weeks in which there were no events to break the monotony of routine coastal patrol. It was then, of course, that the thoughts of men in the *Falmouth* turned largely to friends and family back home. January of 1833 was such a period for Maury. At that time he wrote to Ven, whom he had not seen for nine years, "It is twelve months since my latest from home." Then, as if ashamed of complaining, he added, "of the subject upon which all are most fluent and few agreeable 'self,' I shall say only that the present incumbent is as gay as in the halcyon days when he shouldered his satchel and that he is a Lieutenant pro tem in Uncle Sam's service." [62]

In spite of this bravado, other letters that Maury wrote during this long period of duty reveal how depressed he was about his financial condition and the fact that he had tied a girl to him but saw no way of marrying her, even when he returned to the States in eighteen or twenty months. Like many another young man in this embarrassing and frustrating position, he grew afraid that relatives would try to persuade him "to resign, turn preacher, schoolmaster, merchant or something of the sort—none of these things suit me. . . . If on my return to the U.S. . . . I am not promoted, I think I shall go . . . right off to sea again." [63]

The knowledge that there was little he could do to change his situation was the cause of Maury's greatest worry. He described his feelings in these words: "All of us have to fight what I call the battle of life, for the period when a young man, who has to work for his living, first sets out in life to the time when he begins to secure a living is always a gloomy one, and at such a time a youth will oftentimes feel his heart sink within him from the mere weight of despondency. This is a time when the wisdom of the saw ''Tis wise and brave to hope the best' is needed." [64] The struggle through which he passed created in him a vast sympathy and understanding of youth, as well as a lasting antipathy to long engagements.[65]

The strain Maury suffered during these years of separation from Ann was known by her. She later wrote of it most feelingly, when her son wished to become engaged while at college, and warned him of what a long engagement does to a man.[66]

The best evidence of the tension in Maury at that time is the fact that he allowed himself to become involved in the only known personal argument he ever had with a fellow officer. He and another passed midshipman were playing billiards one evening in a saloon in Lima when they got into a highly emotional dispute. Maury managed to cool off fairly quickly, but not so the other officer, who thereafter bore Maury a grudge.[67]

But, even though disturbed by his own problems, Maury did not forget the needs of his brothers. He had earlier become convinced that an Army career presented the best opportunity for his younger brother Charles. Probably through the influence of his benefactor Samuel Houston, who had become governor of Tennessee in 1827, Maury had secured the promise of a West Point appointment for Charles. Charles had refused the opportunity, but Maury had continued his interest in the boy's education and corresponded with the principal of Harpeth Academy about it.[68]

His brother Dick was experiencing financial difficulties, as his family included a wife and three children and he had made only $300 the preceding year. Maury promptly wrote the fourth auditor of the United States, Amos Kendall, who handled naval officers' pay, to send the $300 that he had on account with the department to his brother Richard L. Maury. He advised Dick, for safety's sake, to communicate with the auditor as well.[69]

Maury's greatest pleasure in this period came from friendships he made with South Americans like the Roca Fuerte family of Guayaquil and with various members of the diplomatic set stationed in the ports visited by the *Falmouth*.[70]

These years that Maury spent on the west coast of South America, although discouraging to him on the personal level, were to prove the springboard for some of his most creative work. On board the *Falmouth,* in 1833, he began work on ideas for a new textbook on navigation, which he considered badly needed for use by midshipmen. His first schoolmaster in the *Brandywine* had once said to another midshipman, "I go on the supposition that you wish to be more than a smatterer in an important part of your profession, and that you will not suffer yourself, in anything, to be led blindly on, groping and feeling your way at every step. This you will do if you study Bowditch only, an excellent book of its kind, but not fitted for the study of a naval officer." [71] This was an opinion that came close to being one held by Maury.

The text criticized had come into being when Nathaniel Bowditch, of Salem, Massachusetts, a port in which all men were interested in navigation, had seen the need of modernizing *The Practical Navigator* written by John Hamilton Moore and published in London in 1784. Bowditch had begun to do a revision of Moore's work but found so many errors in it that in 1802 he wrote his own book and called it *The New American Practical Navigator*. This text had become like Holy Writ to the Navy.[72] Maury dreamed of a textbook that would so clearly present both the practice *and* the theory of navigation that a midshipman could truly understand it and not just learn the rules by rote as was then done. He had, however, too little free time in the *Falmouth* to do more than preliminary work.[73] The serious effort would have to wait for shore leave.

In mid-April, 1833, Maury indicated the extent of his shipboard responsibility when he wrote Dick, "I am and have been for the last year, doing the duties and receiving the pay of a lieutenant." [74] Maury undoubtedly mentioned his increase in pay to prevent Dick from worrying about having borrowed from him. Actually the $300 Matthew had lent Dick to tide him over a serious situation had taken all that Maury had been able to save toward getting married. Even on a lieutenant's pay he was receiving less than $700 a year (including rations), and he had been on that pay for only one year.

In Callao, that August 21, Maury was transferred from the *Falmouth*, which was shortly to return to the United States, to the schooner *Dolphin*, 12, to serve as her executive officer.[75] He was not to remain long on duty in that small ship.

On October 27, 1833, there arrived in Callao harbor the *Potomac*, 44, a frigate of the first class, under command of Captain John Downes.[76] The *Potomac* had joined the American squadron patrolling the west coast of South America in October, 1832, after making history at Quallah Battoo, on the west coast of Sumatra. There Downes had landed a force of 282 men, captured three forts, and burned the town to avenge the plundering of the ship *Friendship*, of Salem, and the slaughter of her crew, after which Downes had extracted a pledge that the Sumatrans would not again molest an American ship.[77]

Shortly after the *Potomac* reached Callao, Maury was transferred to that frigate, a sister ship to his much-loved *Brandywine.*[78] This was a fortunate development for him, as the 1,750-ton *Potomac* was scheduled to return to the United States to complete her circumnavigation of the globe.[79] Maury was extremely anxious not only to be with his fiancée but somehow to work out a way to improve his financial situation and be able to marry.

On November 22 the *Potomac,* with a complement of 400 men, stood out of Callao Roads for Valparaiso, where she anchored on December 17.[80] It was ironic that at this juncture, when every nerve in Maury's body was straining in anticipation of a reunion with Ann, there occurred an episode of a romantic nature that was completely disconcerting to him and was the only one of its kind that he ever experienced. The event was recorded in some detail by his shipmate William Whiting.

On February 9, 1834, the night before the *Potomac* was to leave Valparaiso for the homeward voyage, a young Chilean army officer came on board and sought out Passed Midshipman Maury. The South American was in great anguish of spirit, for he had that day proposed to the lady of his choice, Señorita Manuela Poma, only to be told by her that she had given her affections to an American naval officer. The Chilean officer informed Maury that he was the American she had named. This was news indeed to Maury, who was utterly astonished as well as very much embarrassed. The young Chilean kept asking why Maury had blighted his happiness. Maury, who had met Señorita Poma on an earlier visit to Valparaiso, protested his respectful admiration for the young lady but assured the officer that nothing of a romantic nature had occurred between them. He told of his own serious love for Ann Herndon and of his betrothal to her. The Chilean officer left the ship apparently somewhat comforted, but his visit had shaken Maury badly, and as the *Potomac* sailed the next morning, February 10, before dawn,[81] Maury had no chance to take any action. But the conscientious young American asked himself questions. Had he overdone his effort at the flowery Latin compliment? Had his quiet but friendly "Southern" manners led the dark-eyed girl to think he cared for her?

Maury was so distressed that as soon as ship duties permitted he sat down and wrote a long letter to Manuela. This he sent back to her by a ship returning to Valparaiso.[82]

It was probably fortunate for Maury that he had to turn his thoughts from this personal matter and concentrate on his shipboard duties when the *Potomac* ran into real danger on the voyage around the Horn and past the Falkland Islands. On March 10 the *Potomac* was buffeted by strong gales, and very early the next day encountered the first of many icebergs. From 8 A.M. until meridian the frigate threaded her way carefully between great pieces of floating ice while managing to escape contact with five massive bergs. Four of these menaces were sighted on March 12, and twice that number were seen the following day. On March 13 the danger was so grave that the crew was kept at quarters from 4 A.M. to 6 A.M. Skillful navigation, however, averted collisions up until afternoon, when all hands heard the dreaded noise of wood crunching against ice; in spite of every navigational precaution the *Potomac* had struck a berg. By good fortune, however, the wooden ship escaped from this collision without serious damage.

The *Potomac* thereupon proceeded with even greater caution, as the fog on the 14th was so thick as to reduce visibility to zero. The crew was kept at quarters throughout the day. Finally, on the 16th the frigate sailed into "pleasant weather," and this fact was joyfully entered in the log.[83]

The navigational hazards experienced on this passage were to be remembered by Maury and to prove useful to him in his later work.

The *Potomac* anchored in the harbor of Rio de Janeiro on March 27. Damage done on the rough voyage was quickly repaired, the ship was watered, and fresh provisions received on board.[84] The frigate sailed for the United States on April 9 and came to off the Charlestown Navy Yard in Boston, Massachusetts, on Saturday afternoon, May 24. Soon afterwards 268 members of the crew went ashore with hammocks and bags swinging in every direction.[85] They had completed the term of service for which they had signed on.

Not long after arrival in Boston, Maury received a letter informing him that the Valparaisan girl, Manuela Poma, had died of tuberculosis, of which she had been very ill when telling her fanciful story about Maury and rejecting her Chilean suitor.[86] Maury probably decided that Manuela had told her story deliberately to try to prevent her suitor's getting hopelessly involved with a dying person. She had certainly not expected to see Maury again, and may have thought he had already sailed and could not be harmed by use of his name.

On May 27, 1834, Maury received a leave of absence of three months.[87] He had been on sea duty, far from home, for the better part of nine years and had been engaged to be married for a third of that time. His plans and his hopes were numerous but so were his uncertainties. He was frustrated to the point of humiliation that he was still short of funds. But the important thing was to go to Fredericksburg as fast as possible and see Ann.

CHAPTER VI

Marriage, a Scientific Book, and an Accident

The trip from Boston to Fredericksburg, Virginia, seemed very long to Maury in early June of 1834. He was in a blaze of impatience to reach Ann. Three years had been too long a time to be separated from his fiancée. Impatience, however, was but one of the emotions that assailed him on this tedious journey. His spirits alternated between joyful anticipation of the coming reunion and nagging anxiety about his insufficiency of funds. He thought of the $300 accumulated pay he had assigned to Dick, but he did not regret that help to his favorite brother nor the money that had gone to Matilda. Instead he calculated the amount of pay that was still due him by the Navy Department; it would come through eventually. But, figure it as he would, he was forced to acknowledge that the amount was far from adequate for marriage.

Once he and Ann were reunited, however, Maury's uncertainty and worry were over. He decided that there was no way further delay could add to his funds and that, with or without money, they would be married at once.

Ann brought no personal fortune to their marriage because her father, Dabney M. Herndon, had died nine years earlier, and his modest estate had been used to bring up his six children.[1]

Matthew described Ann as "my first and only love," [2] and said that when he was courting her she called him "Cousin" and "lent all the enchantment of young love's dream to the word." [3] Cousins they were but distant cousins.[4] Years later, when asked to write a sketch of his life for a German publication, Maury wrote this simple passage: "In July, 1834, he married Miss Ann H. Herndon, a beautiful and accomplished lady of Virginia." [5]

The wedding took place on July 15 at Laurel Hill, the Edward Herndons' home about 12 miles southwest of Fredericksburg where bride and groom had first met.[6] In the parlor of this comfortable old Virginia plantation dwelling, the two young people pledged themselves in the solemnly beautiful service of the Episcopal Church.[7] Maury's parents were in Tennessee and Ann's were dead; but her brother Dr. Brodie S. Herndon came from Culpeper to join her other brothers and sister who were present for the ceremony.[8] Relatives of the bride and of the groom who lived nearby in Spotsylvania County or in Fredericksburg also came to see Matthew and Ann married.

The officiating clergyman was the Reverend Edward C. McGuire, rector of St. George's Church in Fredericksburg. Excited and jubilant, Matthew gave the minister the last $20 he had in his wallet. Mr. McGuire must have look startled, for Matthew afterwards remarked that it was evidently the largest marriage fee the clergyman had ever received.[9]

As fine a wedding present as Maury could ask was the publication in the July, 1834, issue of the *American Journal of Science and Arts* of the article he had written on board the *Falmouth*, "On the Navigation of Cape Horn." [10]

Matthew and Ann, carrying out the custom of the time in Virginia, spent the weeks after their marriage in visits to various relatives in their country homes.[11] While enjoying plantation hospitality and all the fine food that that included, Maury had no need of money, but he knew he soon would have, so he wrote the Navy Department requesting that his back pay be sent on.

When Maury returned to Fredericksburg on September 25 he found himself in a dilemma. Amos Kendall, the fourth auditor, had, as Maury put it, "disallowed $450 of my just claim." [12] This difficulty was probably caused by a difference in calculation of how long Maury had been on lieutenant's pay as distinct from that of his actual rank of passed midshipman. There may also have been some issue of half pay, as Maury had renewed his three-month leave.[13] Whatever the cause, Matthew was in serious need of money. He reluctantly wrote Dick to request the return of the principal of a loan he had made some years before. He advised: "Ann and her sister Mary and myself returned here yesterday. We go into winter quarters taking board with Mrs. [Willia G.] Gregory, a daughter of Uncle Abram's [who lived in Fredericksburg]. From Uncle Herndon's we went on a visit to Uncle Minor's in Louisa where we spent ten or twelve days very pleasantly." [14]

Fortunately Dick sent the money promptly, plus partial interest on it. The interest bothered Maury who returned it, saying, "You have beat me in generosity all hollow. I beg you will buy Mat a hat with the balance you speak of." [15]

The acceptance by the *American Journal of Science and Arts* of his first writing, and in the same issue a description and drawing of an invention he had conceived entitled "Plan of an Instrument for Finding the True Lunar Distance" [16] encouraged Maury to seize fate by the fore-lock and concentrate all his energies on completing the navigation text he had conceived and begun while acting sailing master of the *Fal-mouth*. It was a gamble. Even if he finished the book to his own satis-faction, would it sell? It should, he reasoned, because he was convinced he could write a text that would make it possible for midshipmen to understand the mathematical principles behind the formulas for finding longitude at sea by lunar observation. He outlined the plan for his book. It would include sections on algebra, geometry, logarithms, plane trigo-nometry, spherics, nautical astronomy, and navigation. The 28-year-old officer had carefully studied the works of Bonnycastle, Colburn, Hutton, Legendre, Davies, Bowditch, Lardner, Hassler, Kelly, Keith, and La Place and he made acknowledgment to those mathematicians and scientists in his text.[17]

"It is not pretended," he wrote in the preface, "that new theories are set forth or that new principles are established in this work; but it is believed that those which have already been established are here em-bodied in such a form that the means of becoming a theoretical as well as a practical navigator are placed within the reach of every student." [18]

In their rented bedroom, with Ann tidying up around him or sitting at her sewing beside him, Maury worked away at his sheaf of papers. Thinking always of the midshipman, he sought to expound "the theory and most simple methods of finding time, latitude and longitude by chronometers, Lunar Observations, Single and Double Altitudes" as well as "a new and easy plan for finding Different Latitudes . . . Course and Distance." [19] It was a bold course that the young officer had set him-self, and relatives wondered why he did not seek some more practical form of employment while he waited for naval orders.[20] Matthew tried to explain: "I do not expect much direct profit from it though it may be of some collateral advantage in making my name known to the [Navy] Department and to my brother officers in a favorable manner." [21]

Engrossed as he was in his writing, late each afternoon Maury put away his papers and turned his attention to his bride. Some evenings he and Ann were invited out to "tea," the very pleasant supper that Virginians served. A frequent evening diversion was a walk, followed by an impromptu call at the Caroline Street home of Maury's aunt, Mrs. John Minor, where he liked to gather with his cousins, red-haired lawyer John Minor III, Mary and her husband, William Matthews Blackford.[22] The Minors talked often of their work with the Coloniza-tion Society and its program of freeing slaves and transporting them to Liberia for settlement.[23] They discussed the act passed in August by which the British Parliament outlawed slavery,[24] and Maury may have raised the question of whether such a decree could ever be made wholly effective.

More important to Maury was to learn what had transpired in the United States during his absence on foreign duty. From William Blackford, editor of a local newspaper, the *Political Arena,* Maury was able to obtain details of the Nullification Controversy, which had rocked the country. Following the enactment by Congress in 1828 and 1832 of tariff acts that favored the manufacturing and shipbuilding North at the expense of the agricultural South, South Carolina had declared the high tariff acts null and void. In that state a strong Unionist group, led by men like Joel R. Poinsett, had bitterly fought the nullification movement, led by John C. Calhoun, but the Nullifiers had proved stronger and declared that South Carolina would leave the Union if the national government used force to make the state pay the tariff. Disunion or war had been averted only by a compromise tariff, which Congress had voted in 1833.[25]

With the promise of a gradual reduction in the protective tariff South Carolina had repealed her Nullification Ordinance.[26] However, the clash had built a mighty fire, and the embers still smoldered. Maury heard the issue discussed repeatedly; men recalled that Kentucky and Virginia had earlier resisted the Alien and Sedition Acts of Congress, that Georgia and Alabama had prevented the execution of federal laws and court decrees relative to the Indians within their borders and that United States laws relating to embargo, nonintercourse, and Army enlistments had been nullified by state action in New England states between 1809 and 1815.[27] The sovereignty of a state and the rights reserved to it by the federal Constitution continued as favorite topics of conversation in Fredericksburg. The rise of sectionalism was deplored by the moderate-minded.[28]

Another frequent subject of interest was President Andrew Jackson, whose aggressive political leadership was evoking strong reactions, favorable and unfavorable. In the circle in which Maury moved at that time he heard criticism of Jackson's personal actions but even stronger critical comment concerning his wholesale removal from office of all previous political appointees. Among the victims of the President's clean sweep had been Maury's uncle James Maury, who had been replaced by a Jackson appointee in Liverpool late in 1829.[29] The old gentleman, his sons, and daughter Ann had returned home from England, made an extended tour of the United States, and settled in New York.[30]

Fredericksburg, a river port, stagecoach junction, and trading center with a population of 3,500,[31] seemed a place well suited to a young man wrestling with big ideas and trying to mobilize them into usefulness for others and advancement for himself. Others had gone through the same process in this community. There had been George Washington, who had, as a boy, lived at nearby Ferry Farm, been initiated into the Masonic lodge at the town's "Lodge No. 4, A.F. & A.M.," and later paid his filial visits to his mother at the home he had bought her at 1200 Charles Street and to his sister Betty Washington Lewis and Fielding Lewis at "Kenmore." [32]

James Monroe had started the practice of law there in 1786 and had become a member of the town council.[33] In his youth seafaring John Paul Jones had come there to visit his brother William Paul.[34] President James Madison had been born at Port Conway,[35] just 20 miles down the river from Fredericksburg, and Fredericksburg was the closest town for the Lees of Stratford, some 40 miles distant on the Potomac. The town had often heard the opinions of Richard Henry and Francis Lightfoot Lee, who had put their names to the Declaration of Independence. Nor had General Henry (Light-Horse Harry) Lee been a stranger to Fredericksburg.[36]

In the first year of marriage, Maury had no alternative to boarding in a relative's home. He was still a passed midshipman on leave "awaiting orders" and, therefore receiving only $40 a month.[37] But he longed for a better living arrangement, one that would give Ann and him more privacy. He later stated: "I attach great consequence to the manner and place of life for the first year or two after marriage: It is then that the domestic mould for domestic happiness is cast; it is then that true character and disposition develop themselves on both sides and that is the time for assimilation to take place, each accommodating and moulding one's self to the other." [38]

That Maury took marriage very seriously and placed full value on it is indicated by his comment made later to a daughter on the verge of marriage: "The step you are about to take is *the* step of life—with a woman it certainly is such." [39] This observation was unusual for a man whose mind was preoccupied with scientific studies. Unlike most men of the nineteenth century, Matthew Maury believed a wife was the equal in marriage of her husband; he freely used the word "partner." He also felt that Ann was his very dear "friend" and "companion," as well as his sweetheart and permanent "love." [40] He believed that in marriage "there is no trait perhaps more winning than that of a generous confidence . . . confidence begets confidence." [41]

One great bond between Ann and Matthew was their Christian faith. He was much pleased when, after she had read her religious paper, Ann suggested she would like to mail it to his mother in Tennessee.[42] On Sundays they went together to hear Mr. McGuire at St. George's Episcopal Church in the heart of Fredericksburg. Maury's religion was, however, not primarily institutionally centered. He had not yet sought confirmation in his own church, nor was he given to expounding religious ideas to others. In November, 1834, he heard that his brother Dick had left the family faith and joined the Church of the Disciples (Campbellites), later named the Christian Church.[43] On the 16th Matthew sat down to share his personal concepts with Dick:

> I do not regret that you have turned away from worldly things. Persons professing to be Christians are very apt to make the conduct of their brother-professors around them a standard for their own conduct towards God. This may, without knowing it, and unless one keeps a watchful eye upon his own heart tend, more or less, to lead us to regard unduly the opinions of the world, and prompt us to do what an untrammeled conscience would condemn. Learn your duties, Dick, from the Bible. There you have them laid down in example, law and precept. I love to see Christians *after* the Bible and according to their own consciences and not according to the opinions of other men. I hope, Dick, whatever persuasion you join that you will be a Christian according to the Bible as you understand it. [He went on to urge Dick to use his] own good sense, sound judgements and reason and never to adopt a sort of *easy* religion, a newly devised way of getting to Heaven without the trouble of repenting for, and imploring the divine forgiveness of past sins.[44]

Maury worked long hours on the preparation of the textbook. By late fall of 1834 he had made sufficient progress to hope that he could complete the work in the following spring "provided my labours be not interrupted by a call into active service for the Navy Department." [45]

At this time he was anxious to go to Tennessee to see his mother and father but could not figure out a way to do it in view of his concentration on the book and his lack of funds. So he kept himself resolutely at his self-imposed task. Finally, on April 30, 1835, he completed the book and signed the preface.[46] Soon afterwards he sent the manuscript to Philadelphia publishers Key and Biddle.

After what seemed a long wait Maury heard from the publishing house. They had accepted his manuscript. They suggested that they send proofs on for him to correct in Fredericksburg.[47]

This suited Maury perfectly. He wished to stay close to Ann and their first child, who had been born on June 25. The girl had been named Elizabeth and promptly nicknamed Betty.[48]

Matthew was also busy helping Ann set up housekeeping in a clapboard house he had rented from George and Sarah Ellis.[49] The plain, two-storied building stood in the center of Fredericksburg, on the south side of Charlotte Street, halfway between Princess Anne and Prince Edward streets.[50] Maury was pleased that there was a yard at the back where the baby could be put out for air and that Ann could have her younger sister Mary and brother Charles live with them. He also invited his brother John's widow, and her boys, William and Dabney, to share the home. This would be advantageous to all, for such a move would mean that Eliza Maury's pension, as a naval officer's widow, would help with the rent and groceries, and that her sons would have a man to assist in their upbringing.[51]

By the time early autumn brought relief from the summer's heat, Ann had regained her strength, and the various members of the household had adjusted to their life together.

Maury, however, was restless over Key and Biddle's slow progress in publishing his book. Like many another novice author, he suspected the firm's delay was caused by lack of enthusiasm over the prospects of an unknown writer. In mid-October he decided he would have to take action if the delay was to be ended. Disregarding a much-too-lean wallet, he took the stagecoach from Fredericksburg to Philadelphia on October 19.[52] In that large, prosperous city the most that Maury could afford was a small garret chamber, and he lived on cheese and crackers while trying to expedite the publishing of his book.[53] After ten days of this, he poured out his dreams and ambitions to his boyhood confidant, his brother Dick:

> Without wishing to excite your expectations, I will let you into the secret of my plans, which I wish you to preserve as a secret in order that, if I should not succeed in what I undertake, my friends and family may not feel the effects of disappointment. You must bear in mind that this is the first nautical work of science that has ever come from the pen of a naval officer and upon its merits I intend to base a claim for promotion. Such a case has no precedent. Therefore, you must look upon it as an experiment in which I may, or I may not, be successful. If I succeed, I shall be put over the heads of many who are now above me. You see in this another motive for secrecy for many of those over whose heads it is likely I would be placed would, if they knew I contemplated such a thing would use every exertion to prevent it.
>
> I shall ask to be made a lieutenant of ten years' rank. If this is done (of which I am by no means sanguine), besides the advantage of making me old in rank, it will entitle me (I think) to back pay,

as though I had been a lieutenant for these ten years; and this back pay will amount to some $4,000 or $5,000.

I shall be promoted next March at any rate, and my object is to get the book out and present my claim before that time, which, by being presented before I receive any promotion, will be doubly strong. I wish to impress upon you that I am not sanguine of success but am resolved to try every honorable means to accomplish the object and to take the most favorable time for it. The book, I hope, will be out in about six weeks. One hundred pages are printed; there are about 300 more. Negotiations for having 150 of the latter stereotyped [sic] (they are tables) are on foot.

. . . I shall be here about six weeks, I expect.[54]

It is the frank letter of an ambitious 29-year-old anxious for promotion and some material success. The years of poverty, his marriage, and now the birth of his child had made money much more important to him. Maury had confidence that he had something valuable to give the Navy, a great desire to give it, and a natural hope of being suitably rewarded for so doing. He was not without encouragement. Nathaniel Bowditch wrote him: "A work of the kind you are preparing for the press, containing the demonstrations of the formulas of Nautical Astronomy, would be very useful to those who have a taste for the subject and would like to examine the demonstration of the rules." [55] Even more heartening were the words of Philadelphia's distinguished professor Alexander Dallas Bache, who had consented to give the text a critical reading. Bache advised:

My opinion is that such a work will be valuable to them (the younger officers of the Navy) and will meet with favor among them, supplying as it does, the mathematical principles involved in the studies of their profession in a sufficiently condensed form. Coming from one of their profession, especially, I should anticipate that the work would be received among them, even without the injunction of the authorities, who would, however, I think find it to the interest of the service to sanction it.

Allow me to say that I consider the work fully to sustain the high character for scientific attainment which I have always heard attributed to its author.[56]

Bache had evidently heard of Maury from his two midshipmen brothers, Richard and George M. Bache, the latter having served in the *Brandywine*.[57]

Returning to Fredericksburg in early December, 1835, Maury worked at proofreading the body of the text. He also planned the course of studies he would next undertake. The proofs on the 174 pages of mathematical tables that were to be carried in the back of the text were slow in reaching him, but by January 12, 1836, he was nearly through with this tedious work. On that date he wrote his first cousin Ann Maury at her father's new home on Fourth Street in New York: "I sometimes tremble for the fate of my 'exploit,' as a lady termed it, and in my desponding moods, wish the printers had never seen it. But I suppose this feeling is common to every budding author." [58]

In spite of this uneasiness, Maury, after finishing the proofs, began studying mineralogy and geology, and followed the course he had worked out for himself. He found the days all too short for these fascinating subjects. [59] Books on these sciences were available in Fredericksburg because of the iron and gold mining that was carried on in the surrounding county, though on a small scale. [60] At this time Maury tried to teach himself drawing and sketching as well. [61] This long stay on shore by a naval officer seems strange today. But it was common in that period when the Navy had more officers than ships at sea and often kept an officer on half pay for three or four years before offering him another berth afloat. [62]

Finally on April 29, 1836, Key and Biddle applied for copyright to the Eastern District of Pennsylvania on the title *"A New Theoretical and Practical Treatise on Navigation* by M. F. Maury, passed midshipman, U.S. Navy." [63]

When Maury received the first volume he would have been less than human had he not turned quickly to the title page to look at his name and the motto of Lafayette, which he had adopted for himself—"Cur non?" With those two words "Why not?" he stated to the world his basic attitude—why not try?—effort was worth the risk of failure—achievement was more to be desired than ease.

In the hope of carrying out his promotion plan, Maury went to Washington to tackle that doughty Tennessean, President Andrew Jackson, and Secretary of the Navy Mahlon Dickerson. He saw the President personally. [64] Such an appointment was not then too difficult an achievement for a Navy appointee from Tennessee who was a young relative of the man for whom Tennessee's Maury County had been named.

Maury again reported his Washington activities to his sympathetic cousin, Ann Maury, who, with her brothers Mat and Rutson, was greatly interested in his scientific writing:

I have been spending several weeks in Washington upon the very *modest* business of claiming promotion out of my rank, which claim

—you must not be shocked when I tell you—was founded upon the merits of book-making.

The President said—I had deserved it; and said that the Secretary of the Navy ought, moreover, to reimburse me out of the contingent fund for all the expenses which I have incurred in publishing: the latter I declined.

Now the Secretary is an old bachelor—tell Mat, no offense—and a very old granny. The case was referred to him, and he overruled by saying the work brought with it its own reward, consequently he very wisely withheld what was acknowledged to be a just reward.[65]

The publication of Maury's book created a stir. One of the earliest and most perceptive reviews was written by Edgar Allan Poe in the *Southern Literary Messenger,* June, 1836. Poe, editor of the publication, concluded his critique with this paragraph:

The spirit of literary improvement has been awakened among the officers of our gallant Navy. We are pleased to see that science is also gaining votaries from its rank. Hitherto, how little have they improved the golden opportunities of knowledge which their distant voyages held forth and how little have they enjoyed the rich banquet which nature spreads for them in every clime they visit! But this time is coming when, imbued with a taste for science and a spirit of research, they will become ardent explorers of the regions in which they sojourn. Freighted with the knowledge which observation only can impart, and enriched with collections of objects precious to the student of nature, their return after the perils of a distant voyage will then be doubly joyful. The enthusiast in science will anxiously await their coming, and add his cordial welcome to the warm greetings of relatives and friends.[66]

The imaginative Poe had painted a word picture of Maury's future, but the critic was not to live to see his prediction become fact rather than vision.

Perhaps more valued by Maury at the time was the praise that poured in from Navy officers like Cadwalader Ringgold, G. J. Pendergrast, O. H. Perry, Samuel F. Du Pont, and William B. Shubrick.[67] Maury's former commander, Captain Francis H. Gregory, wrote, "It illustrates with clearness and simplicity the principles on which navigation is founded," and Commander Irving Shubrick declared it "far superior as a book of instruction" to Bowditch.[68] Among the book's most ardent supporters were the men who since 1831 had been designated professors of mathematics in the Navy, especially John H. C. Coffin and Joseph T. Huston. The professors were assigned to teach midshipmen on shipboard and at the inadequate Navy Yard schools.[69]

Maury had dedicated his book to Professor Benjamin Silliman, who had spurred him to complete the text by publishing his first scientific articles in the *American Journal of Science and Arts*. In the July, 1837, issue of that publication appeared a highly laudatory review of the book. It ended with these words: "The style of the *Treatise* deserves much praise; it unites fullness of statement with brevity and precision. The estimation in which the work is held among those best qualified to appreciate its worth, may be inferred from the fact that a copy has been ordered to be placed on board all our national vessels. It cannot fail to be of important service to the interests of nautical science." [70]

Of course, some of the old sea dogs who had navigated "by guess and by God" [71] thought it fantastic that a mere passed midshipman should have written a scientific book, and there must have been critical reaction on the part of jealous contemporaries. More important to the needy young officer was that the book, with its 216 pages of text, 174 pages of tables, and 9 plates, sold well at $4 a copy in bookshops or $2.50 from the publishers.[72]

Later, Maury's *Navigation*, under a general order signed September 4, 1844, by Secretary of the Navy John Y. Mason, largely replaced Bowditch's work as the standard textbook for midshipmen of the Navy and was so used for many years.[73]

No orders came in the winter and spring months of 1836, and the young officer continued the study of mineralogy and geology and started on astronomy.[74] In an address before the Geological and Mineral Society of Fredericksburg on May 15, Maury first mentioned in public his thoughts about God and science. After urging a mineral survey of the United States, Maury spoke of how students of geology could read "sermons written in the stones by the finger of God." [75]

Maury was busy cataloguing specimens in "a fair collection of Minerals" [76] when he received a notice from the Navy Department, dated June 21, advising that as of June 10, 1836, he was a lieutenant.[77] The long-awaited promotion had come at last.

But, although Maury was a lieutenant, still no "liver colored envelope" arrived with orders to active duty.

Ann's health wasn't too good, and she was exceedingly thin. Maury decided that a lessening of financial strain was the medicine she needed. He secured a temporary job as superintendent of the United States Gold Mine, located some 12 miles west of Fredericksburg on the Rappahannock River. The mine, privately owned and operated, was less than three miles from Maury's birthplace.[78] He moved his whole household to the simple frame house at the mine provided for him by the company.

There Ann's health improved. After his daily work, Maury played with his nephews and his 13-month-old Betty. He was extremely proud of his little girl and in describing her to a relative declared, "She is a great pet." [79]

The mine property covered 450 acres of land through which ran three veins of quartz lying between layers of rock. Maury worked a crew of fifty men, including ten Cornish miners, on the job of sinking a new shaft through the rock. A steam engine was used for draining the mine. A fourth vein was opened on the property that summer, and in this a foot-wide vein of quartz was located in clay. The gold was found "in metallic spangles and points disseminated in the quartz, often visible to the naked eye; pieces rarely large, and more generally concealed entirely in the quartz." [80]

The gold-bearing quartz was crushed by Chilean mills, great wheels of wood covered with iron and powered by water. The crushed quartz was then placed with mercury in receptacles known as Tyrolese or Hungarian bowls to be agitated. Distillation decomposed the amalgam, the gold was thus removed, and some of the mercury was recovered for re-use. Maury, however, declared: "The metallurgical process of obtaining gold in Virginia is by no means perfect, in every stage through which it passes, from the stamps to the 'blowing off' of the quicksilver, there is a wasteful loss of both metals." [81] He promptly began designing an alembic that would eliminate this loss.[82]

At the end of the summer Maury was offered a salary of $1,200 a year to start in as an engineer, and the mine president promised him promotion as the company was tripling its work force for 1837 and had plans for further expansion.[83] Maury, however, was not impressed at the prospect, as 100 pounds of the quartz averaged only one pennyweight of gold and the maximum yield of gold per week throughout the summer had been $600. In fact, he considered that local brown hematite iron ore might prove better mining than the gold.[84]

This brief experience with metallurgical engineering had given Maury a taste of administering a scientific project, and out of it came one valuable contact in the scientific world. On August 30 Dr. Benjamin Silliman came from Yale to visit the United States Mine. Maury was delighted at the privilege of showing the mine to this distinguished man to whom he had dedicated his book. Silliman was on a tour of inspection of "the gold region of Virginia," which included Spotsylvania, Louisa, Culpeper, and Goochland counties.[85] Maury doubtless discussed with Dr. Silliman his ideas for the new alembic, for they subsequently corresponded about it and Maury's article on the subject was published in the *American Journal of Science and Arts*.[86]

Maury returned to Fredericksburg in early September, 1836, with a determination to persuade the Navy to give him active duty. He had been on shore two and a third years and felt it was time to go to sea. It did not comfort him to know that such a tried and tested officer as David Farragut, with whom he had served in the *Brandywine,* was cooling his heels in Norfolk, as were scores elsewhere.[87] When only one ship of the line and often only three frigates were in commission, some officers could be utilized in the Navy yards and some could secure temporary assignment with the Coast Survey; but for the rest there was nothing to do but wait for the few berths available on the war-sloops, schooners, or brigs.[88]

Partially to alleviate this situation and utilize its trained naval officers, but also to win honor for the United States, a naval exploring expedition had been proposed as early as 1828. Many Americans felt embarrassed that their nation was playing no role in the exploration of the uncharted areas of the world. Great Britain was adding to her prestige by exploration of the arctic and search for the Northwest Passage.[89] It had taken eight years, however, to persuade Congress to pass an act, which it did on May 18, 1836, authorizing the United States Navy to send an expedition to explore and survey "The South Sea," the term then used for the southern portion of the Pacific Ocean. From the start there had been political bickering about the expedition, its cost, and its purpose. The contention was to continue.[90]

In 1834 Mahlon Dickerson of New Jersey, former successful iron manufacturer, state supreme court judge, governor and U.S. senator, had been appointed by Andrew Jackson to serve as Secretary of the Navy. Having himself backed Van Buren for the White House, Dickerson was not a wholehearted admirer of the President.[91] In 1834-1835 Jackson championed the exploring expedition, and his Navy Secretary brought up arguments against it. Once the expedition was authorized, President Jackson appointed a very able Navy officer, Captain Thomas ap Catesby Jones to the command.[92]

Immediately friction developed between Secretary Dickerson and Jones. Commodore Jones demanded a privilege then usually accorded the commander of a squadron by selecting Josiah Tattnall, Charles H. Bell, Thomas A. Dornin, and A. B. Pinkham to command the smaller vessels of his expedition. The selection did not please the Secretary, who looked with favor on the desire of Alexander Slidell and Charles Wilkes to have two of the commands. The Secretary went so far as to consult some of the old captains about Jones's opinion of Wilkes and Slidell and reported this to the commodore. Jones, however, stood his ground, remarking, "that I differ from some of the old captains on more subjects than one is very true. There are, however, some of them whose opinions have great weight with me." [93]

Among the first of the officers Jones asked to serve under him was newly promoted Lieutenant Matthew Maury. In the summer of 1836 Maury had had a short visit with Commodore Jones, whose home was near Prospect Hill, Virginia. At that time the commodore extracted, Matthew reported, "a partial promise to accompany him." [94] As a result, Maury applied to the department for sea duty, and Jones then formally requested him as one of the officers of the expedition. As soon as Thomas A. Dornin was given command of the storeship *Relief,* he asked the department to assign Matthew as his executive officer.[95]

Dornin had previously reported that Tennessee friends were trying to get the President to have Maury command one of the ships. The Bishop of Tennessee, the Right Reverend James H. Otey, had personally petitioned Jackson to do this on the merits of the young officer's textbook on navigation; [96] but Maury himself had no hope of receiving a command, for, as he said, "the Honorable Secretary and I have had almost too many sparrings for those western friends to be gratified." [97] In fact Maury felt almost an unwillingness to take part in the expedition as he feared it would "be a bungling concern . . . founded upon the very awkward mistake of sending out for such service so large and unwieldy a ship as a frigate . . . an encumbrance." [98] The amount of friction about the expedition also disturbed Maury for he knew the power of the old captains who opposed the undertaking chiefly because of the scientific objectives it was supposed to achieve.

In spite of his misgivings, Maury set to work to help Dornin line up the best possible officers for the *Relief.* He sent Dornin a list of passed midshipmen who were worth considering. He put behind their names the following respective evaluations "clever, smart, ugly and selfish," "said to be smart," "very clever," "pretty clever—sings," and "he is much beloved by his shipmates but don't know how his upper story is." Of another he wrote, "I know C. slightly; have heard him highly spoken of—his blood is good—see if he is available." [98]

Maury's pleasure over serving with Dornin was shattered on September 24 when Commodore Jones spent a brief time with Maury in Fredericksburg and told him that the Secretary of the Navy had decided to assign three lieutenants to Dornin's ship, the *Relief.* As Maury had been a lieutenant only three months, he knew that this change meant he would not be the executive officer or "first" of the ship, as he termed it, but the third ranking lieutenant.[99] This was a bitter disappointment to Maury.

Commander Jones's squadron was scheduled to rendezvous at Norfolk in the fall of 1836, so Maury made plans to "break up housekeeping" and have his wife and child board with relatives while he was off on the long trip. Then he heard that the expedition might not go out, and he wrote begging for definite information. He had to know at once if he was to continue the lease on the Ellis house.[100]

After each mail stage clattered in from Washington, Maury visited the post office. But the battle royal over the expedition continued in Washington, and Maury fretted through another fall and winter, although he used his time for study.[101]

By the spring of 1837 Secretary Dickerson had forgotten his promise to Maury and ordered him to duty in the frigate *Macedonian*. Maury was so furious that he used the expression "that imbecile Secretary and his minions" when discussing the matter with an intimate.[102] He promptly declined the post and demanded a furlough [103] even though he badly needed the pay of active duty, for Ann was approaching her second confinement.

Husband and wife were just getting used to having a second baby, a little girl born on June 25 whom they named for his mother Diana, when a letter arrived from Dornin urging Maury to reconsider and go on the expedition. Dornin reported that, once at sea, Maury was to receive appointment from Commodore Jones as astronomer of the expedition.[104] Maury could not resist the appeal of a scientific appointment. He decided that Dornin was right—he'd better calm down and serve with the expedition.

Early in September he was made acting astronomer to the expedition and went to Philadelphia to increase his limited knowledge of that science.[105]

He stayed in a boardinghouse and studied astronomy, as he described it, "in a planked observatory in Rittenhouse Square where our telescopes, transit instruments, chronometers, theodolites, ——— [word illegible] clocks, sextants etc. and all sorts of magnetic apparatus" were located. Of his instructor he wrote: "Professor [Walter R.] Johnson is a plain man and holds the rank and title of Philosopher in the Corps. He has had the instruments [for celestial navigation] here for some time and appears to be indefatigable." [106]

On October 17 Maury called on the Secretary of the Navy in Washington. Dickerson told him that his appointment as astronomer of the expedition was just about to be signed. Then Maury left for Fredericksburg and there received his official appointment as astronomer, dated October 21 but retroactive to September 5.[107] For the first time he was able to make decent provision for his wife and their babies, for his compensation—to begin as of September 5—was to be $2,500 a year, including pay and one ration per day, very different from the $1,200 a year he had been getting since June, 1836, when he became a lieutenant "on waiting orders." [108]

At this point Maury was so encouraged that he wrote Secretary Dickerson to request specific instructions concerning his duties as astronomer. He also suggested that he would like further responsibilities "which, I believe, have not been assigned to any member of the scientific corps of the expedition; such, for instance, as observations on ebb, flow, and other tidal phenomena; on the set, rate, breadth, depth, and the like of currents at sea; on the prevailing winds of whatever sea; on the variation of the needle; on the latitude and longitude of places already known, or which may be discovered; and on any other subjects of general interest to the navigator, and which may serve to guide mariners in the navigation of whatever seas the expedition shall visit." [109]

Thus Maury, as early as 1837, pleaded with the Navy for a chance to work in the field of science in which he knew there was such need for systematic observation. But his hopes were to be dashed by a development over which he had no control; he was suddenly thrust right into the middle of the conflict between Commodore Jones and Lieutenant Charles Wilkes.

Wilkes, an officer of marked scientific ability, had been sent to Europe to buy chronometers and other scientific instruments for the expedition.[110] Commodore Jones instructed Maury to secure these instruments from Lieutenant Wilkes. The authorization was vague, and the instruments were not forthcoming.[111] And so, on November 4, the much-harassed expedition commander wrote to Secretary Dickerson:

> I again send Lieutenant Matthew F. Maury to Washington, for the purpose of receiving the chronometers and other instruments said to be in depot at that place for the South Sea Surveying and Exploring Expedition. By the enclosed letter I am informed that it is your intention that Lieutenant Wilkes shall select the instruments for the expedition. I hope it is not intended thereby to permit Lieutenant Wilkes or any other person to *withhold* or *make any other appropriation* of any instrument or instruments which have been imported for this expedition; especially do I request that the very *identical books, instruments and charts, etc.,* and everything thereunto pertaining be all sent to the expedition, for which they were purchased. . . .
>
> There is no occasion for detaining the chronometers twenty days longer at Washington to obtain Lieutenant Wilkes' rates of those

delicate instruments, for they must all be tested by new ratings after they are returned to this place and put on board the respective vessels, and as this indispensable preliminary may require several weeks, at this season, before we can arrive at conclusions sufficiently satisfactory to justify our departure on so important a voyage, the fear of hard winter setting in before we can get away may be justly apprehended.[112]

Jones was even more specific when he issued orders to Maury eight days later and stated, "His (Lt. Wilkes's) conduct in reference to the expedition, since his return to the United States, has been such that I should not be willing to trust him to make any *selections* or calculations whatsoever for the expedition." [113]

Finally on November 29 Maury was able to report to Commodore Jones that he had secured *some* of the instruments and had compared them with the list of those purchased by Lieutenant Wilkes for the expedition, as published in House Document No. 138, 24th Congress, 2nd session. He listed a number of valuable instruments that were missing.[114]

Commodore Jones passed on Maury's report to Dickerson. The Secretary promptly issued orders instructing Lieutenant Wilkes not to take the U.S. brig *Porpoise,* to which he had been assigned, to sea until the matter of the instruments was cleared up. Wilkes, of course, had not taken the missing instruments but apparently had showed his animosity for Jones and the expedition by simply depositing the bulk of the instruments in the naval store in New York. Wilkes could not account for all the instruments but stated that he believed the macromicrometer had probably been used by the scientific corps of the expedition in Philadelphia.[115]

The wrangle over the instruments was just one evidence of the personal animosity and rivalry for control that had bogged down the whole expedition. The final blow to Jones came when Secretary Dickerson sent him a set of sailing orders and instructions that the commodore declared "required of me to summon two or more of my subordinates to certify, and before my face seal up, and then deliver into my hands for safe-keeping, all journals, reports, records and collections, etc., made by those under my command." [116]

Owing to Dickerson's personal dislike of him and questioning of his professional ability, Jones had twice before offered to withdraw from command of the expedition. Now he felt that Dickerson had impugned both his honesty and his honor. Jones wrote the Secretary that the imputation in these orders precluded his continuing in command of the expedition, and on November 30 he officially asked to be relieved from

117

the command. Jones set forth various important reasons plus a severe cough and chest cold as the basis for his request. Secretary Dickerson chose to accept the temporary illness as "abundantly sufficient" reason and on December 6 wrote to relieve Jones of the command of the expedition.[117]

It had been one of the unhappiest chapters in the history of the Navy, and the end was not yet. Maury and fellow officers of the expedition were uncertain what their future would be. Jones's ships were placed under the custody of Commodores Hull, Biddle, and Aulick until a new commanding officer could be appointed. Secretary Dickerson now offered the post to one officer after another, including such men as Captains William Shubrick, Lawrence Kearny, Matthew C. Perry, and Francis H. Gregory.[118] None wanted to go through what Commodore Jones had experienced for nineteen months. They declined the appointment. There were rumors and counterrumors as to who would get the command. The situation had become virtually a public scandal.

President Van Buren decided the Secretary of the Navy was unable to secure a suitable commander and turned authority in the matter over to Secretary of War Joel Poinsett.[119] In the search for a leader Poinsett interviewed many officers. He sent for Matthew Maury and requested him to name point-blank, as Maury later told a friend, the officer without regard to rank that he thought best qualified for the command. Maury afterwards believed that Poinsett had expected him to name himself and planned to give him the command. Maury was undoubtedly tempted but could not bring himself to do this and instead merely gave Poinsett a list of the officers belonging to the expedition and put his own name, as the most junior of the lieutenants, at the bottom of the list. "He froze up in disgust . . . and gave Wilkes the command, and so I was the gainer, for I preserved my integrity." [120] The end of the remark had reference to Maury's conviction that Wilkes had maneuvered to obtain the command.

Wilkes's appointment caused a furor in the Navy because many officers his senior had been passed over and because, instead of having one ship under him, as befitted his rank, Wilkes now had a whole squadron. A senior lieutenant ordered to serve under him flatly refused the appointment. Daniel Carl Haskell, in his introduction to the history of the expedition, describes Lieutenant Wilkes: "Impetuous and dominating, he was a resolute, determined man of great driving power. He was often in conflict with both his superiors and subordinates, and was known as the 'stormy petrel' of the Navy." [121]

After reflecting on the situation in which he found himself, Maury told the Secretary of War that he would give his fullest assistance to any officer in the Navy except Wilkes, whose behavior about the instruments made such service impossible. Poinsett's reply was that Lieutenant Maury could be detached, if he still desired it, when Lieutenant Wilkes joined the expedition.[122] Maury accepted this offer and on June 9, 1838, after receiving Navy orders relieving him from the Exploring Expedition to the South Sea, applied for active service, stating that he would prefer duty with a hydrographical survey but, if such were not available, he wished to be ordered to sea.[123]

In the summer of 1838 Maury was once again back in Fredericksburg "on waiting orders." He was desperately anxious for the Navy to give him something to do soon. He tried to fill in the hours by playing with small Betty and soon gave to baby Diana a nickname that was to stick, Nannie Curly.

It was excruciating to him to be kept idly "hanging by his eyelids," as he put it, while the best years of his life slipped by.[124] Anger mounted within him when he thought of the waste of trained officer personnel. The whole wretched dispute about the expedition had damaged the Navy in the eyes of the public and discouraged its own officers.

Maury tried to put his feelings and his convictions on paper. They turned into five articles criticizing the blundering of former Secretary of the Navy Mahlon Dickerson and calling on the new Secretary, James K. Paulding, to restore the prestige of the Navy. These articles appeared in the Richmond *Whig and Public Advertiser,* over the pen name "Harry Bluff," and excited much attention both in and out of the Navy.[125] They were thought to have been written by a high-ranking captain, and Maury did not disabuse anyone of the idea.

In the autumn, still having received no orders, Maury prepared seven more articles pointing out things that needed to be corrected in the Navy. These were written under the pseudonym "Will Watch" and were published as letters from "Will" to his old messmate "Harry Bluff." They appeared in the same Richmond newspaper during December.[126]

In early December, 1838, Maury received orders to report to Washington. There he learned that he had been assigned to serve under Lieutenant James Glynn on a survey of the harbor of Beaufort, South Carolina, and other harbors on the North Carolina and Georgia coast, to search out the best location for a Navy yard.[127] Glynn had received this assignment following his resignation as hydrographer of the exploring expedition. Maury promptly went home to pack and soon reported to Glynn in Portsmouth, Virginia. On January 4, 1839, still smarting from thwarted dreams of scientific exploration, Maury wrote to his New York cousin, Matthew Maury: "I came down here about three weeks ago under orders to prepare a little nut shell of a steamer for surveying harbours in North Carolina and the coast between the Mississippi and the Sabine." [128]

Meanwhile his friend Thomas Dornin was working on a plan to get the Navy to send the two of them to the northwest coast of the United States to survey the mouth of the Columbia River. Maury asked his New York relatives to get statistics on the Columbia River area from fur merchant John Jacob Astor.[129] As the weeks passed, Maury grew increasingly unhappy in his "nut shell," the steamer *Engineer;* and on February 11 he wrote to F. R. Hassler, superintendent of the Coast Survey, offering his services as head of a surveying party.[130] Neither Dornin's plan nor Maury's application to Hassler produced any results.

When the harbor surveys had been completed, Maury returned to Fredericksburg to spend a leave with his two little girls and his wife, whom he found looking "like a whip-poor-Will." [131] To Ann he confided the concern he had felt about his aging parents ever since his brother Dick's death, which had occurred the preceding November. Richard Maury had tried to resume management of the 200-acre Tennessee farm but had found it too much for him. Maury's mother and father were temporarily being cared for in the old home by Dick's widow, Peggy Bond Maury, but some permanent arrangement had to be made for them. Matthew and Ann decided that he should make the trip to Franklin to persuade his parents to come back with him to Fredericksburg to live with Ann and the children.[132] He was, however, unable to start on the journey until he heard from Lieutenant Glynn that the little steamer *Engineer* was to be replaced by the brig *Consort,* which would not be ready for their use before October. Maury's leave was therefore automatically extended until the *Consort* was ready.

On August 25 Maury wrote his cousin Ann Maury in New York that he would leave "next Friday or Saturday for the Tennessee trip. I expect soon to be called into service again, first to assist in constructing proper charts of the harbors we have surveyed and then to prosecute the survey of other places. I expect to be ordered on this work from Tennessee but hope, by going now, to gain time for all my purposes." [133] This hope was not fulfilled. A month later he informed her from Franklin: "The Navy Department will not allow me time to wait here for the rising of the waters for river boat travel and I am afraid to venture with the old people on the very rough road between this and Louisville, Kentucky." [134]

Maury had not seen his parents in nine years. He quickly arranged for his mother and ailing father to spend that winter with his sister Betsy, Mrs. Kemp Holland, at her home in Mississippi, 35 miles downriver from Memphis. He believed that the greater comfort and nursing care Betsy could provide would put his father in condition to make the trip to Virginia the following spring. He prepared to leave Tennessee by stage as soon as his Navy orders reached him. He advised his New York cousin that he would see her at the end of October.[135]

On his way to report to the *Consort* in New York, on October 17, 1839, Maury was continuing his trip by a night stagecoach trip through Ohio. At Lancaster, in spite of the fact that all nine seats inside the coach were occupied, the agent accepted three additional passengers. One of these was a woman. Maury gave his place inside the coach to her and climbed up to sit on the right-hand side of the driver. Some of the passengers complained that the stagecoach was overloaded, that a driver, twelve passengers, and luggage made it topheavy. The protest was ignored by the agent, the driver plied his whip, and made a fast run over the turnpike to Somerset, where the horses were changed. It was after midnight when the stagecoach reached an obstruction and had to take a detour because the bed of the turnpike was being rebuilt. The temporary dirt road had been in use only a few days. Clouds obscured the light from the moon, and the coach was not equipped with lamps. In spite of the poor visibility the driver was busily engaged in conversation with the other two men besides Maury who were riding the top of the coach. The driver commented that the stagecoach was overloaded for this stretch because the newly made road was very soft. He had hardly made the remark when they reached a section along the side of a slope and the right wheels of the vehicle left the track, pulling to the right into the loose, soft shoulder of the narrow road. The driver urged his horses ahead as they were beginning an ascent. Vainly he tried to bring the coach back into the center of the road. The horses whinnied in terror as the stagecoach listed to the right, careened violently, and turned over.[136]

Maury was hurled through the air. As he hit the ground he felt a severe stabbing sensation in his right leg. The pain was so immediate and so intense that he knew serious injury had been done. He felt certain that a fracture was involved and ordered the driver not to attempt to move him until medical help came. One of the stagecoach passengers volunteered to ride one of the horses into Somerset for help.[137]

As he waited, Maury's thoughts were grim, for he fully realized the seriousness of a leg injury to a naval officer. He also dreaded the kind of local medical treatment he would receive. After a wait that seemed interminable to the suffering man, the passenger returned to the scene of the accident with another coach and a doctor, and Matthew was lifted into the replacement coach and driven into Somerset.[138]

There was no hospital in Somerset, located midway between Zanesville and Lancaster, Ohio, so Maury was taken to a small local inn called the Hotel Phoenix. Here the doctor made a thorough examination. His diagnosis was: a bad longitudinal fracture of the femur (thigh bone) and a transverse dislocation of the knee joint, tearing of the patella ligament, depression below the patella (kneepan or kneecap), and longitudinal fracture of the external condyle (large end) of the femur.[139] The small-town practitioner correctly diagnosed the trouble and was able to get the knee joint back in place, but he botched the job of setting the fractured thigh bone, a procedure that had to be endured without an anesthetic.[140] It soon became obvious that the bone was improperly set, so Maury had a competent physician come from a larger Ohio town. The bone had to be broken and reset. This treatment, again without anesthetic, was agony and, Maury admitted, "gave me 20 to 30 hours of a most excruciating pain." [141]

The injured man could hardly have been confined under worse circumstances. The Phoenix, a tavern where the stages stopped, was run by Jake Breakhill, a rough former waggoner, and his fiery-tempered wife described by Maury as a cross between a "snapping turtle and a steamboat." [142] His room was heated solely by a small open fire; and as no fender was supplied, the floor in front of the fireplace caught fire three times before Maury could browbeat his host into providing some protection. The bedroom was supplied with a cracked "looking-glass" and "a striped rag called here a carpet, the office of which is to secrete dust," Maury wrote. He said an indifferent maid came briefly each day and "shook the rag" but refused to dust or scrub the floor. "She catches the bed in the middle, gives it a shake, pitches it a punch in the side as she lets go to push up the covering and with one toss of it 'the bed is made.' " [143]

The food furnished by the tavernkeepers was wretched. Matthew longed to have his wife with him to nurse him and was cheered when a letter came by stage saying that Ann was coming. But shortly thereafter another letter arrived with word that Ann had started on the journey but had been taken ill in Maryland.[144]

On the 6th of November Maury was relieved to hear that Ann had got home safely and also to learn "the fact that John Minor (son of General Minor) is a volunteer on his way to nurse me. It is an inexpressibly great favor for I stand much in the need of the services of some friend. I employ a little boy 13 years old to wait on me, the only nurse I could get. He is an excellent little fellow but, not being able to get proper food, I have for the last 5 or 6 days been living on roasted apples and milk, cooked by Jim in my room." [145]

Maury called in Dr. G. W. Boerstler, who was Senator Thomas Ewing's family physician in Lancaster. He advised the injuries were so extensive that recovery would take three or four months.[146] At last the young officer knew the severity of the situation. He fumed as he recalled how "as arrant a quack as ever helped a sinner to his grave manipulated at the dislocation" and promised to have him on crutches "in three or four days." [147] The ill man found it hard enough to eat the greasy soup and mush that the tavern provided, but his appetite was further discouraged by having to use spoons locally called "Brackbills," which Maury described as "dirty pewter things as greasy as a slushed monkey's tail." [148] Dr. Boerstler brought him a silver spoon to use, and this infuriated the host and landlady of the Phoenix so much that they stopped speaking to the doctor.[149] Maury reported to his family the tavernkeepers' dislike of their patient: " 'He's an aristocrat,' said the knowing ones, and for ought I know, I may have been reported at Washington as an enemy to the administration. You can have no idea of the unique set about me." [150]

By mid-November Maury's first cousin was in attendance; the patient's gratitude was touching. He wrote: "John Minor has come. . . . I had no idea that the presence of any friend would have been so medicinal, his coming was like the breaking up of a fever. . . . His mother, you know, is blind, he is her mainstay in affording her society and in ministering to her comfort. Therefore, as soon as I can get out of bed, I shall insist on his return. . . . Should I venture out too soon and bring on secondary inflammation, the loss of a leg would be the consequence. . . ." But he was already planning how he could get to New York—by traveling canal and river boat to New Orleans and thence by ship to the east coast port. "For I am still under orders to the *Consort* and have made it a principle to obey orders." [151]

Meanwhile, Maury relieved his boredom by having John Minor teach him French. John made a trip to Lancaster, 18 miles away, to buy a French grammar.[152]

"I was up today," Maury reported on December 7, "for the second time but not without the appendage of a fracture box bound about the leg . . . leaning on shoulders of two, I walked a few steps today; I am so wasted that I could tread much more firmly . . . on the *pet* [injured leg] than I could on the spindle shank." During the one and a half hours he sat up he got his bed made—only the second time this had occurred since his arrival. His schedule was to walk a little daily until December 15, when Dr. Boerstler would come and replace the "fracture box by a strengthener made of binders board saturated in mucilage and put on while wet, so that when dry, it may have adapted itself to all the inequalities of the joint. In this shield I expect to travel and weather out the winter." [153]

Maury was so enfeebled that the change from bed to convalescence brought on a severe cold and sore throat, but he continued to get up and, with his injured leg wrapped in red flannel and propped on a chair, wrote letters. A cigar box served as his desk and an unsnuffed candle furnished the illumination. "Before the fire is a tin-pot containing a decoction of red pepper which I use as a gargle . . ." he wrote. "This pot I have just learned answers the double purpose of a teapot to make the 'passengers' tea in and shaving can to Abram, a Canadian patriot who boasts in the dignity of ostler and boots to the Phoenix." [154]

Christmas Day found Maury still in Somerset, far from home, but jubilant over his progress:

> As Davy Crockett would say, "I may now begin to holler as I am in the opening." John sent to Gainesville for a hack in which—*Deo Juvante*—I shall leave the woods on Saturday next. . . . I hop out on the porch every day to take airing and to inure myself to the weather. We have a fine snow for sleighing, I hope it will hold, traveling will be much more easy and much less fatiguing.
>
> I hope to be in Wheeling on 1st—seven days to Frederick, Maryland, and three or four thence to New York. [155]

The snow did hold, and the first lap of the journey, across the Alleghenies, was made by sleigh. From Frederick he went by railroad or by "the cars," as they then expressed it. When Maury reached New York to report to his ship, he found to his dismay that the *Consort* had sailed. However, he was welcomed and made much over by his 93-year-old uncle, James Maury, and his favorite cousins, Mat, Rutson, and Ann Maury. The two brothers were successful New York import-export merchants and had advanced money to him to pay the expenses of his illness. The crippled man now spent some days resting in his uncle's comfortable house at 349 Fourth Street, about a half block east of Broadway. [156]

Maury reached Fredericksburg late in January. His first act was to send a request to the Navy Department for pay owed him that he might repay his cousins' loan. But his effort to put on a brave front fooled no one, for he was unable to dress or undress himself or to get out of bed without assistance. [157]

Neither Maury nor his family could avoid thinking about one insistent question: Was this injury to keep him from naval service only temporarily or had it ended his career in the Navy?

CHAPTER VII

Campaign for Naval Reform

Maury set himself to the job of getting his leg back in shape as fast as possible. After a few weeks of short, uncertain walks around his room he was able to say he was "beginning to regain the use of the muscles except the lifting one that is the rectus muscle." This was a serious difficulty that no amount of determination could overcome. "I have no power to operate through it on the tendon which was torn from the lower part of the knee-pan so that I cannot prevent the knee from sinking under me. This then, you see, is the seat of the great injury; though more ungainly, I sometimes think a stiff knee would have been more serviceable than a weak one." [1]

He had been through a terrible ordeal, and it was far from over. No one knew better than he that it would take much time for his injuries to heal, but it was tiresome to hear the fact stated repeatedly. He managed to control his impatience but not a fear that gnawed in spite of every effort to banish it—the dread that even time might not restore the damaged leg to strength sufficient for sea duty.

Maury turned to the Source that had never failed him; he sought God in prayer on a level commensurate with his anguish of spirit. In the still hours of the night, when pain precluded sleep, he lay in the darkness and let the words of the Psalms, learned in childhood, flow through his mind and gird his faith. Seeking to vanquish his fear, he composed a prayer he was to use every night for the remaining years of his life.

Lord Jesus, thou Son of God and Redeemer of the world, have mercy upon me!

Pardon my offences, and teach me the error of my ways; give me a new heart and a right mind.

Teach me and all mine to do thy will, and in all things to keep thy law.

Teach me also to ask those things necessary for eternal life.

Lord, pardon me for all my sins, for Thine is The kingdom and the power and the glory, for ever and ever,

Amen. [2]

It was not Maury's nature to cry out for miraculous intervention, but his prayer reveals his awareness of need for a new heart and a right mind that he might accept whatever was to be.

By February 15 he had faced the fact that he might have to find an alternative to duty on shipboard. He shared his ponderings with his cousin Ann Maury, who had been so understanding during his stay in New York.

> Sometimes I think—when I become desperate—that I'll write, some-times I have a notion to take to books and be learned but then such vast fields and pastures and wastes and seas of unexplored knowl-edge appear on the horizon, my ignorance sickens at the prospect. I am reminded of how little, how very little I do know, just enough to be sensible of this fact.
>
> Then I'll content myself with cultivating a few little patches of knowledge. What shall they be? Shall they be light or heat?—storms or currents?—ship building or ship-sailing?—steam or trajectiles?—hollow shot or gravitation?—gases or fluids?—winds or tides?— _____?
>
> And in the wilderness of subjects the mind is confused and knows not which to choose so I play with the children and bend the knee, which though now more readily bent, does not admit of but very little more flexing than before.[3]

He could write of such matters to his cousin, for Ann had received an excellent education in England. She had also benefited from associa-tion with her mother's cultivated English relatives and with the people her father had entertained in their home while he had been consul at Liverpool. Since their return to the United States Ann had accompanied her father for a visit to former President James Madison.[4] She was in-terested in affairs of state as well as the maximum development of the gifts of each individual, and it was not surprising that Maury frequently wrote her of his thinking on serious subjects. He had complete trust in her capacity to understand his yearnings and his thought processes, and he never indulged in any talking down to her because she was a woman.[5] She was, in a sense, his safety valve in this period of his life. When his feelings became too pent up, he wrote to her. That she was far away made confidences easier, but the fact was that he could discuss problems of the mind with her in a way that he could not with his wife.

His own much-loved Ann Herndon Maury had genuine intelligence, as is revealed in her few extant letters, but she was not given to theo-retical ponderings.[6] She was content for her husband to probe and weigh debatable issues; to her that which was familiar, settled, and accepted seemed more desirable. Having been without either parent since she was thirteen, she wanted security in love and in a home. Extremely sensitive of spirit, she was gentle in her approach to others and never anxious to meet new people or face new situations.[7] Her diffidence and her lack of robust health turned Maury into a protective husband. That she needed his protection as much as he thought she did is open to question, but she did nothing to dispel his belief.[8] Few women came closer to the Victorian ideal than did Ann Herndon Maury in her deep personal piety and willingness to submerge her own individuality in the development of her husband and children. To Maury she represented an ideal to such an extent that his references to her provide only a faint picture of her as a flesh-and-blood woman.

Maury had just begun to rejoice in the advent of an unusually early spring when word reached him that his uncle James Maury had died in New York. Knowing that the old consul's daughter had devoted herself to the care of her father and would now feel grievously bereaved, he wrote immediately urging Ann to adopt the sentiments of her father "concerning what is becoming from the living to the dead." These he pointed out to her "were particularly Christian-like and I think very wise. There is a sanctity of grief which we would not invade but . . . there is a luxury too which should not be indulged. Acquaintance with grief may be good but companionship is dangerous; first wasting the body to poison the mind, therefore we would persuade you to recreation and absence for a time from scenes around you. . . . Face to the south where you will meet the spring time of the year and catch from it something to soften if not to soothe your grief." [9]

In further persuasion he added a postscript: "We have had and have yet a spell of very charming weather. The honeysuckle is in leaf—the buds on the fruit trees are beginning to peep thro' their winter foldings and everything is putting on its spring dress." [10] He himself was making use of nature's curative power and hobbled daily into the yard. He wrote: "When the children run off with the crutches, I feel that with but a little more strength I should jump up and chase them over the yard." [11]

Self-pity was to be avoided at any cost and Maury usually managed to maintain an objective attitude toward his predicament.

By March his therapy to body and spirit had brought general improvement and greater confidence in his leg. Maury wrote to James K. Paulding, appointed Secretary of the Navy by President Van Buren, asking to be assigned to some duty that could be performed on crutches.[12] Doubtless there was desk work in the Navy Department in Washington that could have been given him. But perhaps the department reasoned that a young lieutenant who had won national praise for a book on the theory as well as the practice of navigation might not be too comfortable to have around an office.

When some time had passed and no orders had arrived, Maury rallied his courage and decided to turn into an advantage this enforced absence from the sea. His leg might keep him from a pitching deck, but nothing could keep him completely idle. His mind refused to admit the possibility of continued uselessness.

In the March days of 1840 the dry-docked naval officer, like any other convalescent, sat thinking through his life and assessing what was good and what was bad about it. He had spent fifteen years in the United States Navy. He loved it with the passion that a man feels for his work when it is right for him. Because of his devotion to the service he was violently angered by the things that were wrong, many of which he felt could so easily be remedied. Ever since his days as a midshipman in the *Brandywine,* Maury had heard officers complain among themselves over Navy policies and methods that needed to be changed, but naval officers felt hamstrung about getting the government to make the changes.[13] They occasionally wrote letters to a newspaper under noms de plume, but these were desultory efforts.

Maury and his close friend, William Lynch, had long discussed methods of improving the service and together had planned "overhauling the records on file at the Department of the proceedings of court martial with the view of preparing a Digest." [14] Earlier when they had proposed it to Mahlon Dickerson, the Secretary had encouraged them to do this by offering them a room to work in. Maury felt this was a job he could do during his convalescence, but the new Secretary refused him the opportunity. Maury's fellow "reformer" tried even more drastic action, which Matthew described in this way: "Lynch . . . went to Washington to urge, in the name of the officers—the expediency of increasing the effective force afloat &c. The Secretary of the Navy directed Lynch to leave Washington for that he—the Secretary—wished to bring up a bill and have the credit of originating it." [15]

Maury had seen nine years of duty at sea and had observed all the major phases of work done by the Navy. His surveying work had given him a chance to study harbors and coastal installations, and during the frustrating months while he had waited for the exploring expedition to put to sea he had gathered much detailed information on the naval service. Over the years he had also done considerable reading on the naval history of the world's great maritime nations. Now, with long hours available for contemplative study and evaluation, he began to fear the bungling and inefficiency in the Navy might jeopardize the future of the United States. He had tackled the subject in fragmentary fashion in his newspaper articles published in 1838. Now he conceived the idea of writing a series of bold, blunt articles that might stir up the civilian populace about the alarming situation in the nation's first line of defense.

He would both inform and place blame where blame was due in articles that would be crusading weapons. The time for gentlemanly protest was over. The facts must be told, told in words that would thunder as loud as the long guns in a ship of the line. The Navy was full of dry rot. It had to change. If he could not serve on shipboard, he would see what he could do to improve the situation of fellow officers who were on such duty. He would fight for the education that midshipmen desperately needed. He pondered which publication would carry his words to the eyes of the most people and to the attention of those in Washington who had the power to alter the situation.

A magazine edited and published in Richmond, the *Southern Literary Messenger,* had an excellent circulation and commanded attention. In January of the preceding year Maury had had an article, "Direct Trade with the South," published in this journal and had been pleased with the response to his urging the use of the great circle route for ships plying between American and English ports.[16] The *Messenger* had treated him well; now he resolved to offer his articles on the Navy to this publication.

Maury decided to call this series "Scraps from the Lucky Bag." The lucky bag was the receptacle on a ship that received all the oddments that were lost and found, from "shoe of middy" to "purser's slops." [17] Thus Maury gave himself freedom to range and not to have to hew to just one line of thought throughout the series. As he intended remaining an officer in the United States Navy, he deemed it wise to keep his identity unknown by writing under the pen name "Harry Bluff," which he had used in the earlier articles. Only the editor of the *Messenger,* Thomas W. White, Maury's wife, and a few other members of his family, knew Harry Bluff's identity.[18] They kept the secret well.

In April the first article appeared. It dealt with the deteriorating condition of the United States Navy. Harry Bluff detailed the problems for the average reader, unfamiliar with the Navy and its needs.

> The great interests which this arm of national defense was designed to guard and protect, demand that it should be placed upon a better footing; for it has not kept pace with the improvements of the age. . . . Nearly a half century gone by, Congress passed an act for the building of six small frigates; and without any settled policy or fixed principles as to a Navy, the government upon the

most simple and economical plan, organized a mere handful of officers for those ships. To correspond with a Navy upon so small a scale the ladder of promotion in it had but a few steps—Lieutenant, Commander, Captain—and this officer stood on the topmost round. . . .

Times have changed since then. The maintenance of a Navy is no longer a matter of doubtful expediency. . . . The very interests which point to the necessity of a Navy, and which brought it into existence, require for it a vigorous and healthy system. But many of its laws are wrong—many of the principles engrafted upon it, have, by the changes of time, become defective. Experience points out many amendments and improvements which should be made: and necessity *calls loudly* for reorganization.[19]

He launched into a subject he had heard discussed from Port Mahon to Guayaquil and wherever American naval officers served, the want of sufficient grades in the scale of promotion:

We have a Navy respectable in force—sending its squadrons to different seas—boasting of the largest ships and the finest specimens of naval architecture in the world. True policy and self respect require that the Navy and those squadrons should be commanded by officers similar in rank and equal in grade to the officers of other Navies. . . . Their want of rank often places American officers in embarassing situations.[20]

He pointed out the need to increase the Navy if it was to give adequate protection to the growing commerce of the nation, safeguard American citizens abroad, and uphold the country's prestige. This article was reprinted, almost in its entirety, first in the New York *Express* and later in the *Army and Navy Chronicle*.[21] The young man for whom the Navy had no billet was soon reaching a national audience.

In May a second article came out in the *Southern Literary Messenger*. Maury supplied information on the lack of seaboard fortification and the country's unpreparedness in case of war. However, he reserved most of his fire for the wholly inadequate education provided for naval officers. He reminded the public that, if Army officers needed to be taught, so did those of the Navy, and he urged, as a minimum substitute for the Army's West Point, that there should be a school ship for the instruction of midshipmen. In connection with the proposed program he asked:

And why may not Midshipmen learn in their school-ship the principles of Naval architecture? Why should not the Navy officer be taught to plan the model of your ship; and, submitting his plan and drawings, have the privilege also of superintending the construction of his castle—the fort in which he is to sink or swim?

Naval gunnery and pyrotechny, hollow shot, tactics and discipline, should all have their allotted time in the course of instruction and receive each its due quota of attention in the school-ship. Languages too, though last, yet not least . . . should be included in the system. . . . For the Navy officer, whose calling takes him to all countries and among all people, no plan of education can be complete unless it contains at least one of three languages, either French, Spanish or German.[22]

He produced facts and statistics to prove the exorbitant cost of the inadequate system of officer education then in use. "In a national point of view, the *building* of officers, or, which is the same thing, the fitting them for the duties of their profession, is quite of as much importance as the building of ships." [23] This statement, made in 1840, was far ahead of its time.

The editor of the *Messenger* came to Fredericksburg on May 3 to see Maury, to ask for more articles, and to request a *Navy Register* in order to send copies of the "Scraps from the Lucky Bag" articles to every officer. The author refused the last request, fearing that an ambitious promotional scheme was involved. To White he gave only the names of eight or ten officers. Maury was not completely won by Thomas W. White, whom he described as a "rara avis." [24] At this time Maury had not had much experience with editors, and he evidently felt White was pushing him too fast.

This feeling played some part in his holding his third article, which was completed in June [25] but not submitted until months later.

Maury was also extremely discouraged because his leg had worsened. Low in vital energy, he felt no inclination for study but sat for hours in meditative thought. The recurrence of severe pain in his leg had brought back dread that his Navy career might be over before it had barely started.[26]

Thinking of the loneliness bachelor Rutson Maury might now be feeling in the family home on Fourth Street in New York, he wrote, likening a house stripped of its usual inhabitants to something he had experienced: "I think the most lonely place in the world is a man-of-war when her crew is paid off, the sentinels taken down from their posts, the officers relieved from their watch and all hands, except one's self, gone ashore." A house, he continued, was much the same with its usual occupants gone.

"My panacea for ennui is the pen. There is no time, hardly, when I enjoy more refined pleasures than when, deprived of companions, I dip into the inkstand for friends that are far away. Therefore I seldom or never feel lonesome." [27]

In the months ahead there was plenty of ennui for Maury. Fredericksburg was a town of great charm but there was no library to supply him with the type of reading matter he desired. Friends lent him their books, but few of these were on scientific subjects. There were, however, four semiweekly newspapers published in town, and these kept the convalescent informed as to national, state, and local affairs.[28] More specific information came to him from Rutson and Mat Maury, who secured for him all kinds of facts on shipping and exports.[29] Fellow officers in the Navy were always willing to dig up information he might want and pass it on by letters. This enabled him to finish certain articles he had commenced.

Had Maury been able to continue the harbor survey duty to which he had been assigned, his pay would have been $1,500 a year. The pay for a lieutenant not on active duty but on what was termed "waiting orders" was $1,200.[30] Maury was fortunate that the rent for his two-story, clapboard house averaged only $130 a year.[31] However, since the accident, he had been hard pressed financially. Because his injury had been incurred when he was traveling under orders to report to his ship, Maury had asked the Secretary of the Navy if the department would "pay broken leg expenses, $1,008." This request had been refused in February, 1840.[32] Maury had, therefore, sought a settlement for damage from the stagecoach company. Senator Thomas Ewing of Lancaster, Ohio, had arranged for Maury to make a deposition concerning the accident and had then handled the case for him.

In midsummer, 1840, Maury received the good news that the jury in the U.S. Circuit Court at Columbus, Ohio, had returned a verdict in his favor. Damages had been assessed at $2,325, to be paid by the stagecoach proprietor, held responsible because his agent had overloaded the coach and his driver had failed to stop when the coach had left the center of the road.[33] When Maury received this money he decided to invest it as a measure of protection for Ann and his children, should his leg continue to retrogress.

Late in August he received orders to report in Washington for a complete examination of his leg by Navy surgeons. On September 2, 1840, he was examined by Surgeons John A. Kearney and Bailey Washington, who reported to the department that Maury should "be rated at three-fourths a degree of a total permanent disability." [34] One consolation in this medical decision was that it showed an improvement from the preceding February, when Surgeon John C. Mercer had certified his injury "under the head of total disability as regards duty."[35] Another small consolation was that he was granted a pension of $12.50 a month, retroactive to the date of his accident.[36]

While in Washington Maury extracted from Secretary of the Navy Paulding a promise that orders would be issued him to return to hydrographic work in the harbor of Beaufort, South Carolina.[37] He went home happy in this expectation.

Once more Maury found himself in Fredericksburg for the birth of a child. On October 9, 1840, Ann Herndon Maury's third pregnancy resulted in the birth of a long-hoped-for son.[38] The baby was named Richard Launcelot Maury for his father's favorite brother, who had died in Tennessee in 1838.[39] Like his uncle, the little boy was called Dick.

That fall Maury watched the stormy national political scene and, for once, took sides. He was opposed to Van Buren and believed General William Henry Harrison the better choice for the Presidency. He referred to his political interest as "hobby riding" and commented, "Not having had anything better to do of late, I have been riding hobbies at a furious rate. I have now dismounted to let them blow." [40]

After a two months' wait for the orders, Maury reluctantly concluded that the surgeons' report had made it impossible for Secretary Paulding to keep his promise. As a result he decided in November to resume his writing activity.

His first action was to submit for publication No. 3 of the "Scraps from the Lucky Bag." In this article, which appeared in the December, 1840, issue of the *Southern Literary Messenger,* Maury described in detail his plan for educating midshipmen. He again attacked the use of "pickup" civilian instructors and recommended that the midshipmen be taught by naval officers. He pushed further the subject of curriculum, which he had outlined in May, recommending a rounded course of study to include languages, chemistry, natural history, astronomy, naval architecture, drawing, some international and maritime law as well as gunnery, tactics, and mathematics. These subjects would be taught in a four-year course with the midshipmen sent on a two months' cruise each summer, including some trips to foreign waters. He thought each young man should serve two years at sea after the course, then stand examination and receive his commission.

These early articles suggested a school ship as the place for this training but, after the public received his opinions with favor, Maury admitted that the school ship idea was a compromise on his part, that what he really wished to see established was an academy for the Navy fully equal to the Army's West Point. He suggested Memphis, Tennessee, on the Mississippi River, as a central location, but he wanted the academy "even if it has to be built on top of the Rocky Mountains." [41] His major plea for the academy came later in another series of articles that appeared in 1841 in the *Messenger*.

Maury, of course, was not the first to advocate such a school; thoughtful naval officers had long discussed the need of such an establishment. But he marshalled the facts well and gave a firsthand account of the ineffectiveness of schoolmasters and schoolrooms on the ships to which he had been assigned. He wrote with the emotion of one who had yearned for a suitable naval education and been denied it. His fervor and his gift of clothing the facts in language that got across to the general public and to the politicians raised a tidal wave of interest in the need for a naval academy. Officers of the *Delaware,* 74, out of their own funds, had one "Scrap" printed in pamphlet form and laid on the desk of every congressman.[42] Civilians who had given no thought to the issue were now aroused. They notified their representatives in Washington of their interest. The discussion continued and helped pave the way for the United States Academy at Annapolis.[43]

Today the Navy is not unaware of Matthew Fontaine Maury's services to naval education, as well as to navigation, and the handsome west wing of the main academic hall at Annapolis bears his name.[44] That histories of the U.S. Naval Academy do not always mention the part Maury played in its founding is doubtless due to their very natural emphasis on George Bancroft, who was Secretary of the Navy in 1845 when the academy actually got under way, and on Franklin Buchanan, who served as first superintendent of the institution.[45]

Thomas W. White, editor of the *Messenger*, was enormously impressed by the extent of public reaction to Maury's articles. He was even more excited in December, 1840, by a new "dollars and cents" article that the lieutenant had just delivered to him and which Maury himself felt might bring about the reorganization of the Navy that he and most fellow officers believed imperative. On December 13 White wrote him: "I am hard at work for I intend to be the instrument of placing you at the head of the Navy Department." [46] This and an "indiscreet puff" in another publication disturbed Maury so much that he quoted the old proverb, "God save me from my friends." [47] Like an eighteenth-century pamphleteer, he was writing to bring about specific reforms, and he wanted his words to burn into the minds of his readers. The furthest thing from his mind was political office. He had been proud of his cousin Abram P. Maury's being elected to Congress from his home district in Tennessee,[48] but he himself had no desire to be embroiled in politics. Possessed of a passionate love for the Navy and belief in what it could be, he had "no fear of being victimized" by the service for his criticisms, he said, even if it became generally known that he was Harry Bluff. "Though Commodore Morris and a few others array themselves against me, I think the body of the Navy is for me," [49] he stated after a fellow officer had written him, "It is the opinion of all hands here that you are a proscribed man." [50]

Disregarding his friends' warning, Maury brought out, in the January, 1841, issue of the *Southern Literary Messenger,* his most fearless article to date. In it he lashed into the graft involved in building ships and the resulting high cost to the public. He chiefly blamed the Board of Navy Commissioners. His revelations created a sensation in Washington and infuriated the powerful trio of commissioners to such an extent that they issued a defense of their policies. Maury rebutted in subsequent articles. The essence of Maury's charges was that vessels were built at twice the sum they ought to cost, the labor to repair cost over twice as much as to construct ($600,000 to repair for the first time a ship which it only cost $294,000 to build), the same articles for one ship cost four or five times as much as their duplicates for another, and that it cost twice as much to repair ordnance and stores for a ship as it took to buy them.[51] To support such allegations Maury furnished further impressive figures and facts.

He called for the system of three Navy commissioners to be replaced by a bureau system offering the checks and balances of divided responsibility, and he outlined how these bureaus would function. He recommended that the Secretary of the Navy should have an assistant undersecretary who should be a captain in the Navy and would supervise the bureaus.

Not suprisingly, the three commissioners were enraged over the proposed change.[52] But many thinking men felt that these proposals offered an efficient new setup that would streamline the Navy. Naval officers circulated Maury's January and February articles widely. The officers of the *Ohio,* 74, wrote him in praise.[53] As might have been expected, the secret of his authorship had leaked out, and soon it became generally known that Lieutenant Matthew F. Maury had written the controversial articles.

As usual when they have been adequately informed of deplorable situations, the American people prodded the Congress that had been so reluctant to spend money on a peacetime Navy, and the articles by Maury were quoted as proof that change had to come. His name was suddenly on the tongues of men interested in the state of the nation. The *National Intelligencer,* published in Washington, proposed that this officer who so clearly saw the defects of the service and had a well-formulated program for its overhaul should be the man to direct its reorganization. The paper urged that newly installed President John Tyler make Maury the Secretary of the Navy.[54] Other newspapers took up the suggestion, and for a while there was much talk of it. The proposal was that Maury would resign his Navy commission, become a civilian, and then be made secretary. An article in the *Southern Literary Messenger* revealed that, at this time, "Many of his brother officers came forward and encouraged him in his great undertaking and many both in and out of the Navy urged the appointing power to promote him to the head of the Navy Department."[55] This writer likened Maury to Lord Vincent, who had brought about a system of reform in the economic administration of the British Navy.

Maury's own reaction to the cabinet position proposal is given in a letter he wrote on January 10, 1841: "I was much annoyed at finding myself put in nomination for the secretaryship, for I thought it was a sure way of defeating the object of the 'Scraps.' Though I think now the effect will be to call public attention to them and consequently to the condition of the Navy and thus lead to reform on the one hand, while, on the other, it will whet up the animosity of the old officers, a portion of them at least, so as to gain for me the *honor* of a sly cuff from them now and then."[56] A fortnight later he informed his parents, still in Tennessee: "I do not think there is much danger of my having a cabinet appointment inflicted upon me. The newspapers continue to discuss the subject though, with much earnestness. That I should be thus brought forward and commended is, of course, exceedingly gratifying to me as I am sure it must be to you also. In these times of party rancour and bitter political strife, high places in the state edifice are far from being desirable to those who value peace of mind."[57]

And Maury placed a high value on peace of mind. This came to him largely through being occupied in work that he felt needed to be done and to which he could give his full interest, and through feeling that he was caring properly for his family. "Family" for Maury was never narrowed to his own wife and children. When his cousin Richard B. Maury had died in 1838 without leaving any estate,[58] Maury had welcomed to his home his early benefactor's widow and two children. Maury had become the legal guardian of these two young people, Sally Fontaine Maury and John Minor Maury.[59] Because of his highly developed sense of family loyalty and responsibility, Maury's home was continuously crowded.[60]

To anyone with a lesser power of concentration, study and writing in such a crowded household would have proved impossible. The women and children liked to hover close to the stove and this enabled Maury to get a few feet away, but not far, for he stated: "I am now writing in the parlour and though there is no fire in the room, the warmth from the stove in the dining room makes the air in here as . . . balmy as a spring morning." [61] His years of having to study in the crowded steerage of a man-of-war had taught him how to work in the midst of noise.

The 35-year-old lieutenant felt rewarded that his articles had aroused people about the "lamentable condition" of the Navy. There was criticism, chiefly from those whose efficiency and methods had been challenged. A rebuttal of some length that reached the editor of the *Southern Literary Messenger* was signed only with the initials "C.S." and gave no address for its author. Editor White published the criticism in the March, 1841, issue but stated editorially that he did not think "C.S." had proved anything contrary to facts stated in the "Lucky Bag" articles.[62] In the April *Messenger,* and again in the combined May-June number, there appeared letters praising the crusading series and urging that the nation insist on Navy reorganization. In the latter issue was also published another "Lucky Bag" article in which Maury replied to criticisms and supplied further proof of his charges.

In July, 1841, the *Messenger* acknowledged that Maury was the author of the series and carried a biographical sketch of him written by "Brother Officer," who admitted, "It was not to be expected that Lieutenant Maury would not meet with opposition in his fixed determination to wage a relentless war against the internal foes of his country, by his vigor as a reformer, his irreconcilability to all abuses and his resistless energy in trying to put them down." In conclusion, the anonymous naval officer stated that the "Scraps from the Lucky Bag" had engendered "an enthusiasm which has not subsided and will not subside until the whole navy is reorganized." [63]

Since September, 1840, Maury had longed to go back to active duty. On June 10, 1841, while he was in Richmond attending to some legal business and conferring with the editor of the *Messenger,* who wanted more articles, Maury received a letter from Washington. It brought him a request from his former commanding officer, Thomas ap Catesby Jones, newly appointed commodore of the Pacific Squadron.[64] Jones's flagship was to be the frigate *United States,* and he wanted Maury to go with him as his flag lieutenant. The commodore saw no reason why "the game leg" should prevent satisfactory performance of a duty that did not call for strenuous physical exertion. Maury was delighted at the prospect and wrote the same day to the Secretary of the Navy George E. Badger.

Sir:

Notwithstanding my crippled condition, I think I shall be able to perform any of the lighter duties at sea which do not call for much bodily exercise, as of Flag-Lieutenant for instance, to which office in the Pacific Squadron Commodore T. ap C. Jones has signified a desire that I should be appointed. That duty, or any other elsewhere to which I am able, and with which the Department should see fit to entrust me, shall be undertaken with pleasure.

> I am, very respectfully
> Your obed. servant
> M. F. Maury
> Lt., U.S.N.[65]

Maury returned to Fredericksburg happy over the prospect of serving as flag officer for Jones. Nor did he allow Ann's dislike of the idea to discourage his enthusiasm in the weeks that followed.

In August Maury developed circulatory trouble and a touch of malaria, a common summer complaint in those days of undrained marshes and unscreened houses. However, he took the medication prescribed for these ailments and went ahead with his plans to go to sea.

Late in September Commodore Jones visited Maury in Fredericksburg and said there would be some further delay before sailing as he had "a paper war" with the Navy Board of Commissioners to wind up in Washington. He advised Maury to remain at home, even after his orders came, since the flag lieutenant was not required in Norfolk to prepare the ship for sea.[66] A few days later Maury received official orders to proceed to Norfolk and report on October 4, 1841, to Commodore Thomas ap Catesby Jones for duty on board the frigate *United States.*[67] Maury followed his commanding officer's instructions and stayed on in Fredericksburg.

During this period, Maury endeavored to put all his own financial affairs in order, and he wrote a simple holographic will. In this he instructed that, in case of his death, his debts were to be paid promptly, stipulating that the first to be paid was the $200 his schoolmate William C. S. Ventress had lent him when he entered the Navy in 1825. This he noted had not been paid "because after I became able to pay it, I had lost all traces of my friend." [68]

His holdings, "of which by the way there is a beggarly amount," were to go to his wife "in whom I have every confidence" and at her death to meet the necessities of their children. The final paragraph of this simple testament, signed on November 2, 1841, read: "In preference to any fortune that can be named, I desire our son to have a good education. After that, if he have health, he can without a cent of patrimony work his way through the world as his father did before him." [69]

For his articles in the *Southern Literary Messenger*, Maury's account book showed a total of $660 paid. This had been invested. On November 11, 1841, Maury listed his assets at $5,309, his debts, including loans he had secured, at $2,215.42. After seventeen years in the Navy he had accumulated $3,093.58 as his net estate. [70]

Friends and relatives in Fredericksburg were fearful that Maury might lose the power to walk, or even his life, if he went to sea at this point in his recovery. They attempted to dissuade him. When that failed, Judge John Tayloe Lomax went to the community's leading physicians, Drs. William Browne, George F. Carmichael, and B. R. Wellford, who were personally familiar with the extent of Maury's leg injury and its degree of recovery. From these respected men Lomax secured a written statement that Lieutenant Maury was in no physical condition for sea duty in a man-of-war. [71] Without informing Maury, the judge sent this information with an explanatory letter to recently appointed Secretary of the Navy Abel P. Upshur. [72]

On November 15 Secretary Upshur wrote Maury: "The accompanying letter from Judge Lomax and certificate of Drs. Browne, Carmichael and Wellford are enclosed to you with the request that you will make known to the Department your own wishes upon the subject." [73] Maury was stunned by the judge's action. At the same time he knew it had been taken with good intention. After much distressing reflection and family advice, he concluded that he should not go against medical judgment that he had to admit was sound, unpalatable as it was. On November 18 he wrote the Secretary, in embarrassment and frustration, that "this was done without my knowledge or consent" but that the opinion of the three physicians left him no alternative but to violate his career-long rule "by asking to be relieved from orders to sea." [74] Four days later Upshur replied, officially relieving Matthew from his orders to report to the frigate *United States*. [75]

His chance at sea duty officially ended, Maury, in quiet dejection, mulled over the question: What was the likelihood that he would ever get back to sea if nearly two years of care had not healed his injured leg? In contrast to his unhappiness was the relief felt by Ann, his family, and his friends.

Fortunately, at this time, the thwarted officer received recognition of his scientific writings and his work to increase naval interest in science; he was elected a corresponding member of the National Institution for the Promotion of Science, later renamed the National Institute.[76] This organization, established in Washington in May, 1840, was heir to the mantle of the earlier Columbian Institute for the Promotion of Arts and Sciences. Among those elected as corresponding members were such distinguished men as Professor Joseph Henry, of the College of New Jersey, at Princeton; Alexander Dallas Bache, president of Girard College of Orphans, Philadelphia; Denison Olmstead, professor of natural history at Yale College; Jacob Whitman Bailey, professor of chemistry and mineralogy at the U.S. Military Academy at West Point; and such foreign scientists as Professor Charles Wheatstone of King's College, London; Adolphe Quetelet, the astronomer royal of Belgium; and Professor F. G. W. von Struve, director of the Russian Imperial Central Observatory near St. Petersburg.[77]

Undoubtedly it was a source of satisfaction to Maury that the first bulletin of the National Institution carried an article by him urging a scientific exploration of the bottom of the sea. In it he pointed out that there was almost no authentic information on this subject, and a vast need for it. He suggested that this was an investigation that the Institution could encourage simply by persuading the government to issue certain instructions to the officers of the West Indies Squadron and those of the revenue service: "The fifteen or twenty revenue cutters along the seaboard, if furnished with 'drags' to 'troll' [sic] the bottom in light winds, would greatly promote the objects of the institution. If those vessels which use the *troll* could be induced to keep a record of their labor, such records would, in the course of time, enable the institution to construct a chart of the coast, showing the unproductive from the fruitful and habitable parts of the bottom of the ocean—a work which would have the merit of being both useful and new." [78]

Maury would have given much to have been able personally to carry out this study of the bottom of the sea, but his lameness prevented and in the succeeding months he had to content himself with renewing his "battle of the pen" for improvement of the Navy. As he had concluded his "Scraps from the Lucky Bag" series when it was officially admitted that he was Harry Bluff, he started a new series entitled "Letters to Mr. Clay"—Henry Clay then U.S. senator from Kentucky. For these articles he adopted the nom de plume "Union Jack."

In the first "Letter," published in the *Southern Literary Messenger* in October, 1841, Maury enlarged on his earlier pleas for an academy for naval officers. He also recommended establishment of a school to train engineers for Navy and merchant marine steam vessels. He pointed out that France and England were gaining great commercial advantage by granting subsidies for the building of ocean steamers and by forming steamship lines to girdle the globe. "Give but a decent encouragement to the well-known industry and enterprise of American citizens, and fleets of ocean-steamers will speedily go forth under the 'stars and stripes' to out-do the 'lion and the cross' with commerce in peace, and to match them, with their guns in war." [79]

The government should pay at least one fifth of the prime cost of these large steamers, Maury declared. In return, the owners should agree to have the steamers commanded and navigated by government officers, keep guns on board in time of peace, and turn the vessels over to the government at a par valuation in time of war. Maury pointed out that private yards could build such steamers at half the cost of the Navy yards and that merchants would use and maintain these ships until needed in case of war, while the Navy would leave them in ordinary to deteriorate. [80]

In the "Letters to Mr. Clay" series, Maury also fought for the development of the West. He recommended establishment of a full-scale Navy yard at Memphis for development and protection of the Mississippi River, and he urged that a steam packet canal be built to link the upper Mississippi to the Great Lakes. He also campaigned for Pensacola or some point on the Georgia or eastern Florida coast to be made a strong naval fortification such as Gibraltar was to the Mediterranean. [81]

In mid-February, 1842, one of Maury's Navy friends came from Washington to try to persuade him to pull wires to obtain orders to the Navy's Depot of Charts and Instruments, an office that performed certain scientific functions for the service. To this suggestion Maury replied: "I do not know that there would be anything in this procedure on my part inconsistent with the *public* code of morals, rectitude, etc. for there are many and high examples of pulling wires for one's own advancement. But the mere circumstance of going *secretly* to work about it has something in it repugnant to the 'mens conscia.' " [82]

However, Maury felt differently after he received word from an officer in Washington that a Navy bill had just been drawn up proposing a hydrographical bureau, authorizing the Secretary of the Navy to put either a *civilian or officer* at the head of it, and that "Citizen Blunt [a publisher of commercial charts] is thought to be after the place." [83] This was too much for Maury. When so many trained officers had no Navy work to do, he could not tolerate the idea of this job going to a civilian. He wrote Rutson Maury: "I am urged to put in my claims for it. . . . I should rather not apply for the place but rather than that it should go out of the Navy for an occupant, I will do all I can to prevent it." [84] But all he could bring himself to do was to write to the Secretary that *if* a hydrographical bureau was to be established he would like to be considered for it.[85] A separate bureau of hydrography was not created at that time, however; nor was any offer of a Washington position made to Maury that winter or early spring.

Maury continued to work on articles for the *Southern Literary Messenger* partly because he hoped they might have some effect on national policy and partly because of his continuing need to supplement his Navy leave of absence pay.

In the April, 1842, issue of the *Messenger*, Maury turned his attention to a problem involving the United States and England. A patrol was being maintained at that time by naval vessels of various powers determined to prevent any further exportation of Africans for slavery. In efforts in this connection, Maury stated, England had repeatedly boarded and searched American vessels on the pretext of looking for slaves. He expressed grave fear that Britain was reverting to the abuse of the freedom of the seas that had brought on the War of 1812 and was using her participation in "The Christian League" as an excuse for searching American ships. He questioned England's altruism if, as was reported, her nationals were pushing the opium trade and permitting millions of Chinese to be enslaved by the drug habit. He stated his personal opposition to the slave trade and his belief that the United States would join with Great Britain and furnish warships to put down the trade once the mother country proved her sincerity in the matter.[86]

Moreover, in mentioning the strong feeling that then existed in the United States toward Great Britain because of the position she had taken on the boundary between Maine and Canada, Maury made it clear that, unlike some, he wanted no war with England. "On the contrary, I should view a war between the United States and Great Britain as one of the greatest calamities, except a scourge direct from the hand of God, that could befall my country." And then he stated: "In the Navy, there is but one sentiment and one feeling on this subject; it is, avert war, honorably if you can; if not, let it come: right or wrong, the stars and stripes shall not be disgraced on the ocean." [87]

This was blunt writing, but it carried the ring of sincerity. The boy who had studied in the old field school and in the country academy in Tennessee had come a long way in his thinking. He was concerned with and informed on issues of import to all mankind. He was willing to risk his naval commission to say and write things that he felt needed to be articulated. Although there was no immediate reaction, this kind of initiative and daring appealed to Americans everywhere. In the nation's capital the obvious capabilities of his mind had not gone unnoticed.

June, 1842, finally brought orders from Secretary of the Navy Upshur. The separate bureau of hydrography had not been created, but Matthew Maury was to report to Washington to serve as superintendent of the Depot of Charts and Instruments.[88] Washington meant professional and scientific opportunity—at last the waiting was over.

Maury promptly made family arrangements. His wife was expecting a child, and it was decided that she and the children would remain in Fredericksburg until the birth of the baby. With her would stay Mr. and Mrs. Richard Maury, who had arrived from Tennessee about the middle of May under escort of young Dabney, whom Maury had sent for them. Seventy-six-year-old Richard was not in condition for another immediate move.[89]

With family details taken care of, Maury left Fredericksburg for the 50-mile trip to the nation's capital.[90] The journey was short, but it took him from three years of "waiting for orders" back to active Navy duty and to the responsibility of command. The prologue was over, rich and varied as had been its preparation. The curtain was about to go up on the main drama of Matthew Maury's life.

CHAPTER VIII

Scientific Opportunity at Last

It was July 4, 1842, when Maury reached Washington to report for duty as superintendent of the Navy's Depot of Charts and Instruments.[1] The 36-year-old lieutenant was celebrating not only his nation's independence day but his own as well, for he was heartily glad to be through with the long injury-enforced exile from active duty. The city to which he came was not greatly different physically from the Washington he had first seen seventeen years earlier. A difference existed, however—to be felt rather than seen.

Washington, in 1842, was the capital of a nation far more sure of itself than had been the young republic in 1825. The push to the West, and the opening of new territory had not been halted by economic difficulties. The country had survived not only Andrew Jackson's long fight against the Bank of the United States but also the panic of 1837 and a financial depression that was still continuing.[2] Citizens spoke with pride of the fact that the first wagon train of settlers had left Independence, Missouri, for California, and that Colonel John C. Frémont was off to explore and map the far West.[3] Another source of pride to Americans in the summer of 1842 was the return of the U.S. Exploring Expedition after successfully exploring a vast area of the Pacific and the coastal waters of Antarctica.[4] In naval circles there was regret that Lieutenant Charles Wilkes had marked the return of the expedition he had commanded by preferring charges against a number of his officers. Their courts-martial were held in New York in the weeks following Maury's commencement of duty in Washington.[5]

The age of oceangoing passenger steamships had begun four years earlier when the *Great Western* had crossed the Atlantic in fifteen days.[6]

The United States Navy in 1842 was making some experimental moves towards steam for seagoing vessels but owned only four small steamers for river, bay, and coastal use.[7] The majority of the Navy's officers and men were strongly in favor of sail. Some believed steam never would be perfected. Most held that steam was not suited as power for ships that had to go to the far places of the world and stay out for several years at a time. The pride of the service was its fleet of 60 ships of sail, of which 37 were engaged in active sea service.[8]

The Navy's Depot of Charts and Instruments, which Maury was to head, had been founded late in 1830 and had been commanded successively by Lieutenants Louis M. Goldsborough, Charles Wilkes, and James M. Gilliss, all officers of scientific ability. During his superintendency, Lieutenant Wilkes had purchased a house on Capitol Hill and moved the Depot to his dwelling, where it had remained during Lieutenant Gilliss's superintendency. On taking command in July, 1842, Maury decided the Depot should be moved. It was known that, at the conclusion of the court-martial proceedings against his officers, Wilkes would return to Washington to take up residence in the building occupied by the Depot. Maury, therefore, found a suitable building at 2422-2424 Pennsylvania Avenue NW, and moved the Depot's equipment and large collection of records there.[9] Just after the transfer had been completed, he wrote: "The house, in which the office now is, is a double one and though the four rooms below are now occupied, two of them will accommodate the offices and the instruments very well. I shall, with the Board's consent . . . occupy the two others as dining room and parlor." [10] He did not mention that the bedrooms upstairs had already been assigned him for himself and family; the instruments to which he referred were the astronomical, meterological, hydrographic, and navigational instruments used or serviced at the Depot of Charts and Instruments.

A prime function of the Depot was the determination of time. With a telescope mounted at right angles to a horizontal axis, a clock and a chronograph, observations were made of the time of transit of the sun and fixed stars over the meridian of Washington to determine solar and sidereal time. Against time thus secured through celestial observation, the officers on duty at the Depot checked their standard clock and by that checked the Navy's chronometers for the least variation from absolute accuracy. These portable timekeepers, used at sea to determine the longitude of a ship's position, could throw a navigator's calculations off by miles unless he possessed information as to their rate of error. Highly accurate, the marine chronometer was also highly sensitive and, once set and started, was never reset; rather, each instrument was rated every time it was returned to the Depot at the conclusion of a voyage. The record of its rate of variation was sent with the chronometer when again it was issued to a ship putting to sea. Maury also examined and purchased new chronometers when they were needed.[11]

Matthew Fontaine Maury

Sextants, quadrants, barometers, and thermometers were some of the other instruments for which Maury had responsibility. Meteorological studies were a part of the routine work of the office, with particular emphasis laid on study of the direction and force of the winds.[12]

Charts by which the ships of the Navy navigated and all needed nautical books were also under care of Maury at the Depot. Like the instruments, they were issued to a departing vessel and returned to the Depot at the end of a cruise. The hydrographic work of the Navy was assigned to this office but was not in a progressive stage when Maury took command.[13]

In addition to his duties at the Depot, Maury kept an eye on Capitol Hill, where Congress had under consideration two Navy bills. His main concern was for passage of the bill to reorganize the Navy. Embodied in this bill were many of the reforms for which he had crusaded in his magazine and newspaper articles. Abolition of the old three-officer Board of Commissioners and establishment of a bureau system were the most hotly debated features of the bill. The opposition had been well organized by the commissioners, who stood to lose their jobs and had naturally stirred up their friends on Capitol Hill.

The other Navy bill called for an appropriation with which to build a structure to house the Depot of Charts and Instruments and a much-needed observatory. This was first introduced as a Senate bill and went to the House under the sponsorship of Representative Francis Mallory (Whig) of Virginia. Maury's predecessor at the Depot, Lieutenant James M. Gilliss, had persuaded the Navy commissioners to seek this appropriation, and Secretary of the Navy Abel P. Upshur also was squarely behind the bill.[14]

The need for an observatory in the nation's capital had been recognized since the presidency of Thomas Jefferson and had been ably proclaimed by the Columbian Institute for the Promotion of Arts and Sciences, the forerunner of the National Institute, to which Maury belonged.[15] In 1821 a joint resolution of Congress had authorized William Lambert, an amateur astronomer and mathematician who was a clerk in the Pension Office, to determine "the longitude of the Capitol from Greenwich, or some other known meridian in Europe." Lambert engaged William Elliott, who was a teacher of mathematics, a clerk in the Patent Office, and publisher of Washington guidebooks, to make the computation with the aid of a well-regulated clock, a transit instrument and a meridional line. Following this rough determination of longitude, a statement was issued: "Nothing now remains to confirm the result of these observations but building an observatory here, and having corresponding observations made in Europe. Nothing, perhaps, would so

146

effectually accomplish the object of fixing the first meridian at Washington, as the erection of an observatory, supplied with suitable instruments, from which corresponding observations with other places could be made; and Washington would; of course, be considered the first meridian for America." [16] This was highly desirable because the first or prime meridian (from which longitude is reckoned) was then, in most nations, the meridian that passed through the capital of a country.[17]

President John Quincy Adams had urged a "lighthouse of the skies" and since his return to Washington as a member of the House of Representatives had recommended that a national observatory should be built with the funds left to the United States government by the Englishman James Smithson.[18] But the question of how the Smithson bequest should be used by the government continued to be debated.

In the hot, humid summer of 1842 Congress at last was actively considering the matter of voting direct government funds to build an observatory to serve the nation—an observatory to be run by the Navy. Maury longed to see the bill passed.

Because his salary was only the standard $1,500 for a lieutenant on duty other than commanding a ship at sea,[19] Maury had to live as frugally as possible. He kept "bachelor hall" until the time when Ann, the children, and his parents could come to join him in Washington. Ann's confinement was not due until late October and so her husband had to content himself until after that event with "Miles, the porter acting in the manifold capacity of chamber maid, cook and dining room servant." [20] Faced with the expense of temporarily maintaining two establishments on his limited pay, Maury reported with glee that in one week he and Miles had spent only 48 cents for groceries. He mentioned that he had also frequently had "a midshipman to tea." [21] Tea was, of course, a light evening supper, not an afternoon party, but that week it must have been very, very light indeed. For his heavier midday meal Maury was obviously doing without meat and making the most of vegetables that country people then brought to town and sold at extremely low prices.

During this period when he was organizing his work at the Depot Maury found "The additional exercise which I have been obliged to take here has proved of the utmost service to the leg. On one or two occasions, I have been on my feet from eight or nine in the morning till eleven at night. The leg strengthens under it all the time. I am on my feet standing or walking most of the day; but, unless I go to the city [the area around the President's house], I never touch my cane." [22]

Meanwhile, the members of Congress continued to debate the Navy bills until August 31, when, in a great rush to wind up their work and go home to their families and political fence-mending, the House and

Senate voted both bills on the same day.[23] Secretary of the Navy Upshur was authorized to contract for a building to cost not over $25,000 to house both the Navy's Depot of Charts and Instruments and the long-desired observatory.[24] The Secretary immediately dispatched Lieutenant James M. Gilliss to Europe to observe the best astronomical instruments in use there and to have similar ones made for the Washington Observatory.[25]

To the delight of Maury and other forward-looking naval officers, the reorganization bill that had been passed included the section abolishing the Board of Commissioners and replacing it with five bureaus: Yards and Docks; Construction, Equipment and Repair; Medicine and Surgery; Provisions and Clothing; Ordnance and Hydrography.[26] Maury must have felt extremely gratified for the part his Harry Bluff articles had played in bringing about this badly needed reform. He expected that he would receive some "cuffs" from the ousted commissioners, but Commodore Charles Morris was to be the only one who gave outward evidence of resentment.[27]

The new superintendent had by now familiarized himself with the functions of the Depot of Charts and Instruments and had had time to study some of the charts of rivers, bays, and the oceans of the world that were issued by his office. Lewis J. Darter, Jr., in the *American Neptune,* stated: "When Maury assumed office in 1842 he became convinced that his chief duty should be the preparation of ocean charts. Less than two months after he took up his post he had to admit that the files of the office could furnish no hydrographic information as to certain portions of the Gulf of Mexico. Charts on naval vessels were found to be over 100 years old and quite useless." [28]

Maury bluntly advised the Secretary of the Navy: "Up until this time our public ships depend upon other nations for their charts of distant seas but also of our own waters . . . [we are] dependent upon foreigners for the information by which we determine latitude and longitude at sea. The charts used by an American man of war when she enters the Chesapeake Bay, on her way to this city [Washington] are English and we are dependent upon the English Admiralty for them." [29] This to Maury meant only one thing. It was time the United States made some real contributions to hydrography, over and above what the Coast Survey had been able to achieve. Information for navigators had been a passion with Maury ever since he had served as acting sailing master of the *Falmouth.*

Part of the material stored in the Depot consisted of a mass of dusty logbooks. These books contained the handwritten daily record of nearly every voyage made by a ship of the United States Navy since its founding. At the conclusion of a cruise, the ship's log was sent to the Depot to be kept as an official Navy record. Maury started burrowing into the logbooks and became excited when he realized the information that could be culled from them.

Some logs contained little of value. Others had been kept in great detail. Carefully analyzed and correlated information from all these volumes, Maury decided, would produce the kind of information for a navigator that he had fruitlessly sought before he sailed from New York in the *Falmouth*. He explained to the midshipmen serving under him what he believed could be achieved and had them sort the logbooks, dividing them by areas. He decided to begin by studying the logs of voyages from New York to Rio de Janeiro because there were many logs for this frequently made voyage.[30] Maury and his junior officers, working on this project when other duties permitted, slowly began to extract from these logs every scrap of information as to force of winds encountered, fog, rain, unusual ocean currents, and other natural phenomena observed, as well as length of runs made under each day's conditions. The research was tedious. But Maury persuaded his coworkers that the mass of facts they were cataloguing would enable him to determine and state for use by ships making that voyage the average conditions prevailing for each season of the year along that route.

In midsummer the announcement of the cessation of hostilities between the United States and the Seminole Indians of Florida had caused Maury to hope that he might secure for the Depot the services of his brother-in-law, William Lewis Herndon.[31] Maury had been unhappy the year before when Herndon had been put in command of "the little diedapper schooner *Wave* that is employed along the coast of Florida chasing Indians." Maury had commented at that time, "I wish it were somewhere else for I should hate to shame my sword in their blood—inasmuch as they have all the right on their side and are fighting for their homesteads and everything that is dear to the heart of man."[32] At the end of the summer Herndon came up for shore duty after his unpleasant tour of patrolling the coast of Florida in the war against the Seminoles. It took no great effort for Maury to persuade the Secretary to assign Lewis Herndon to the Depot. Twenty-eight-year-old Lieutenant Herndon had been in the Navy since he was fifteen.[33] On October 15 Maury wrote happily: "He [Lewis] and his wife [Mit] are messing with me now . . . which takes away the bachelor character of the establishment."[34] Herndon and Maury were both quiet-spoken men, short of stature, devoted to family, possessed of a high sense of duty and dedicated to the service whose uniform they wore. Because of mutual respect and affection, they worked well together. With Herndon on his staff, Maury felt set for a winter of strenuous work.

During his busy organizational months at the Depot Maury had kept in constant touch with his wife by frequent letters. In mid-October Maury was hurriedly summoned to Fredericksburg because Ann had become quite ill. The flare-up was soon over, and on October 21 she gave normal birth to a second son, who was named John Herndon Maury.[35]

Three days after John's birth, Maury was back in Washington writing out a very prosaic requisition to secure basic equipment for the Depot from Major W. B. Scott, Navy agent in the capital city.[36]

Following the establishment of the five bureaus to direct the work of the Navy, the Depot of Charts and Instruments was placed under the Bureau of Ordnance and Hydrography.[37] Maury was now directly under the newly appointed chief of this bureau, Commodore William Montgomery Crane, who had become a midshipman in the Navy in 1799. Crane had taken part in the bombardment of Tripoli and been a lieutenant in the *Chesapeake* on her ill-fated cruise when the British frigate *Leopard* forced her surrender. He had fought throughout the War of 1812 and had later commanded both the Portsmouth (N.H.) Navy Yard and the U.S. Mediterranean Squadron before becoming a Navy commissioner.[38]

Although Commodore Crane had been a member of the abolished Board of Commissioners he evinced no ill will toward Maury for his revelations about the board and urging of the bureau system in his "Scraps from the Lucky Bag" series. Crane had always been popular with his men and was known as an upright and honorable officer, and Maury soon concurred with this opinion.[39]

On November 9 Maury submitted to Commodore Crane his estimate of the budget for the Depot for the first half of the coming year. He recommended that there be four lieutenants who would receive $3,000, eight passed midshipmen $3,000, one clerk $500, and one draftsman $500.[40]

The months of systematic study of the logbooks had by this time convinced Maury that, if additional facts were to be supplied him by ships at sea he could produce a completely new type of chart for mariners. He would be able to advise a navigator, in advance, of the average winds and currents his ship would encounter in a certain season in any charted ocean area, as well as the safest course to sail. Analysis of the many logs of voyages from New York to Rio de Janeiro had shown him that navigators were fighting nature rather than using it on that run. Adequate information on the winds and currents would reveal the natural path or sea lane and would show how it varied in different seasons.[41]

ABSTRACT LOG.

(1). ―――

(2). ―――

(3). ―――

(4). ―――

(5). LOCAL DEVIATION:―

Before sailing.					*When arrived.*			
SHIP'S HEAD.	DEGREES OF DEVIATION.	SHIP'S HEAD.	DEGREES OF DEVIATION.		SHIP'S HEAD.	DEGREES OF DEVIATION.	SHIP'S HEAD.	DEGREES OF DEVIATION.
NORTH. .		SOUTH. .			NORTH. .		SOUTH. .	
N.N.E. . .		S.S.W. . .			N.N.E. . .		S.S.W. . .	
N.E. . . .		S.W. . . .			N.E. . . .		S.W. . . .	
E.N.E. . .		W.S.W.. .			E.N.E. . .		W.S.W.. .	
EAST. . .		WEST. . .			EAST. . .		WEST. . .	
E.S.E. . .		W.N.W. .			E.S.E. . .		W.N.W. .	
S.E. . . .		N.W. . . .			S.E. . . .		N.W. . . .	
S.S.E. . .		N.N.W. . .			S.S.E. . .		N.N.W. .	

(1). Enter the class of the vessel, her name, country, and the name of the captain.

(2). If the vessel is of iron or wood, and mention the quantity of iron, if any, in the cargo.

(3). Enter the names of the places at which the vessel has called during her voyage.

(4). Name the meridian from which the longitude is calculated.

(5). Give the table of local deviation at the commencement and at the end of the voyage; and state in the log the manner in which it was determined, and if the vessel was loaded with any iron when the observation was made, or whether any iron as cargo was taken on board after the observation was made.

If practicable, the operation should be repeated during the voyage.

The first page of one of the Abstract Logs conceived and prepared by Maury for distribution to mariners. At the completion of each voyage these logs, filled in with the information requested by the form, were forwarded to Maury, who, with his staff at the U.S. Naval Observatory and Hydrographical Office, tabulated and evaluated the data. Charts were then made describing the average sailing conditions prevailing along any route for each season of the year.

DATE.	HOUR.	LATITUDE BY		LONGITUDE BY		CURRENTS.		MAGNETIC VARIATION OBSERVED.	WINDS.		BAROMETER.	
		Observation.	D. R.	Observation.	D. R.	Direction.	Rate.		Direction.	Rate.	Height.	Ther. attach'd.
I. 31.	2											
	4											
	6											
	8											
	9											
	10											
Noon.	12											
	2											
	3											
	4											
	6											
	8											
	10											
	12											
II. 1.	2											
(1)	(2)	(3)	(4)	(5)	(6)	(7)	(8)	(9)	(10)	(11)	(12)	(13)
[a]	[b]	[a]	[c]	[a]	[c]	[a]	[a]	[a]	[a]	[a]	[a]	[a]

ABSTRACT LOG FOR THE

DATE.	HOUR.	LATITUDE.	LONGITUDE.	CURRENTS.		BAROMETER.		THERMOM.		FORMS AND DIRECTION OF CLOUDS.	PROP. OF SKY CLEAR.	HOURS OF FOG A. RAIN B. SNOW C HAIL D.	MAGNETIC VARIATION OBSERVED.
				Direction.	Rate.	Height.	Ther. attach'd.	Air.	Water.				
I. 31.	4												
	9												
Noon.	12												
	3												
II. 1.	8												
	4												
	9												
Noon.	12												
	3												
	8												
2	4												
	9												
Noon.	12												
	3												
	8												
3	4												

Second page of the Abstract Log. Recognizing the difference in instruments and routine on board American ships, Maury provided a special form at the top of pages 2 and 3 for men-of-war, while merchant ships were to use the lower form. Maury found it extremely difficult to convince Navy captains that the requested hydrographical and meteorological information had sufficient practical value to justify the time and effort required to make the many observations.

THERMOMETER.		FORMS AND DIRECTION OF CLOUDS.	PROPOR. OF SKY CLEAR.	HOURS OF FOG A. RAIN B. SNOW C. HAIL D.	STATE OF THE SEA.	WATER.			STATE OF THE WEATHER.	REMARKS.
Dry bulb.	Wet bulb.					Temp. at surface.	Specific gravity.	Temp. at depth.		
										This form is intended more especially for men-of-war.
(14) [a]	(15) [b]	(16) [a]	(17) [a]	(18) [a]	(19) [c]	(20) [a]	(21) [b]	(22) [b]	(23) [c]	(24) [a]

MERCHANT SERVICE.

WINDS.	RATE.	REMARKS.
(Latter part.)		This form contains the minimum of what must be furnished by American merchantmen, in order to entitle them to a copy of Charts and Sailing Directions. It is hoped, however, that many of them at least will be willing to do more, and to fill up the man-of-war log. Forms of this will be given to all who will ask for them.
(First part.)		
(Middle part.)		
(Latter part.)		

Third page of the Abstract Log. Skepticism as to the practical value of the logs began to disappear early in 1848 when the *W. H. D. C. Wright,* sailing according to the information provided by the charts and *Sailing Directions,* reduced the sailing time between Baltimore and Rio de Janeiro by 17 days.

Describe on a blank page, in the beginning of your Abstract, the instruments you have on board, the manner of using them, and of making the observations.

BAROMETER (corrections to) . . .
$\begin{cases} \text{Index error.} \\ \text{Capacity.} \\ \text{Capillarity.} \\ \text{Mean height above the sea.} \end{cases}$

Compared by Mr.

with the standard at   185

THERMOMETERS (correction to). [Number your thermometers, and state the corrections that are to be applied to the various readings of each, to make them correct.]

FORCE OF THE WIND indicated by numbers (sailing by the wind).

0. Calm.	5. With royals.	9. Close-reefed topsails and
1. Ship has steerage.	6. Top gallants over single	courses.
2. Clean full 1 to 2 knots.	reefs.	10. Close-reefed main topsail
3. Clean full 3 to 4 knots.	7. Double-reefed topsails.	and reefed foresail.
4. Clean full 5 to 6 knots.	8. Triple-reefed topsails.	11. Stay sails.

FORMS OF CLOUDS ARE: cirrus (*Ci.*); cumulus (*Cu.*); stratus (*St.*); nimbus (*Ni.*), etc. [See Plate XVI.]

Last page of the Abstract Log as it appeared in the 6th edition (1854) of Maury's *Explanations and Sailing Directions*. The information requested was that which had been agreed upon by delegates of the ten maritime nations at the Brussels Marine Meteorological Conference in 1853.

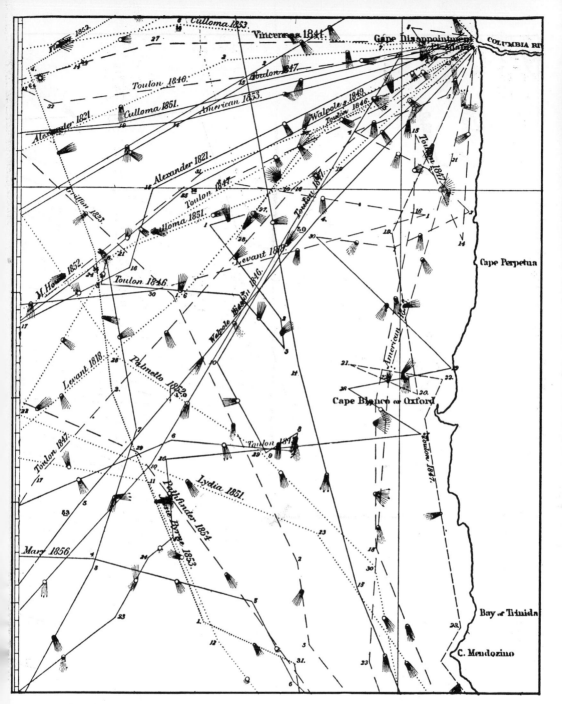

Section of Wind and Current Chart of the North Pacific, No. 5, Series A—one of the first charts prepared by Maury and his staff at the U.S. Naval Observatory and Hydrographical Office. The brushes indicate the winds, the head of the brush pointing toward the direction from which the wind blows, the width of the brush indicating the degree of variation of the direction of the wind during the day. The strength of the current is expressed in knots by numerals and an arrow (see track of the Palmetto in 1852). Published in 1849, this chart quickly proved popular with mariners by making it possible to reduce the sailing time necessary to get from Atlantic coast ports to the gold fields of California.

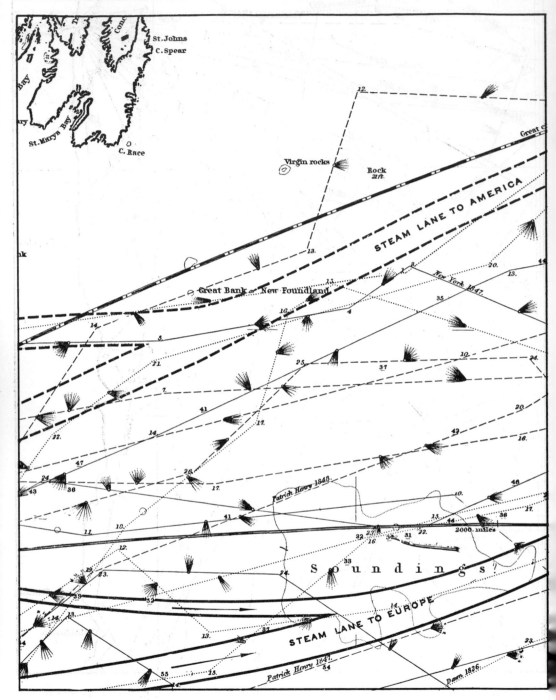

Section of Wind and Current Chart, No. 6, Series A, showing the North Atlantic near Newfoundland. This third edition of the chart (first issued in 1849) shows the steamer lanes to and from Europe developed by Maury and charted by him in 1855 to increase navigational safety and reduce the cost to shipping resulting from collisions at sea.

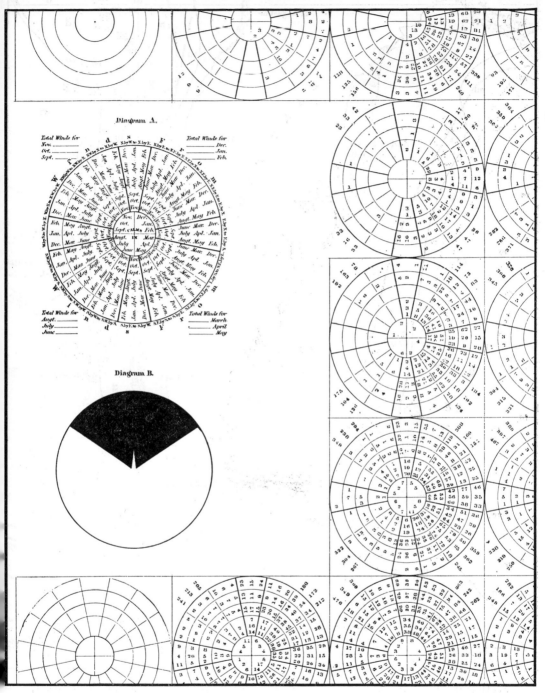

Section of Pilot Chart of the South Atlantic, No. 1, Series C, 1853. This chart shows the relative number of times in every 5° square of the South Atlantic that the wind had been reported by mariners as blowing from each direction during a particular month. By cutting out the black part of Diagram B and placing the diagram over one of the squares, the mariner was able to estimate the frequency and kinds of winds he might encounter in that portion of the ocean during the month of his voyage.

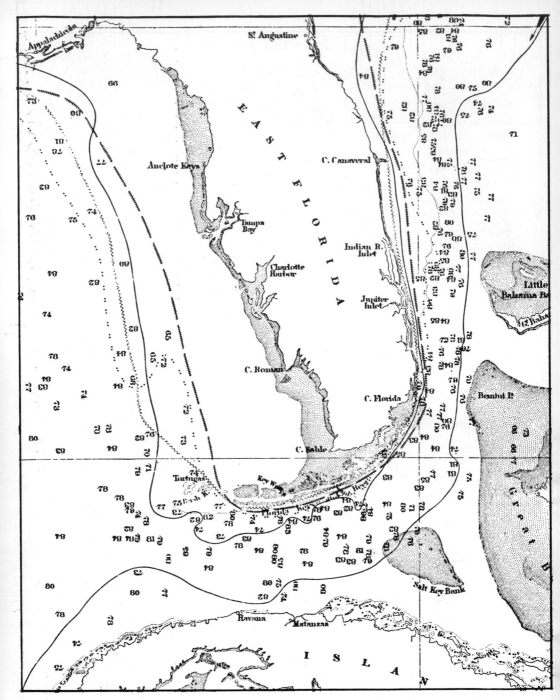

Section of Wind and Current Chart of the North Atlantic, Thermal Sheet No. 1, Series D, 1852. The figures indicate the temperature (Fahrenheit) of the water at the surface at the place of observation. They are placed to provide information for particular seasons; thus numbers standing upright show the temperature at that location in the winter, numbers upside down the temperature in the summer, spring and autumn being indicated by numbers standing on their right and left sides. To determine the depth of submarine currents, Maury later perfected non-conducting cylinders to bring up water from the desired depth in order to take its temperature on board.

Maury was fully aware that his proposed type of chart and sailing directions represented a radical departure from the type then in use by mariners. In his years at sea he had found true the verses of the 107th Psalm: "They that go down to the sea in ships, that do business in great waters; these see the works of the Lord, and his wonders in the deep." [42] As he weighed the proposal he would make, Maury later told his family, that verse came often to his mind but even more frequently the words of the 8th Psalm: "Thou madest him to have dominion over the works of thy hands . . . and whatsoever passeth through the paths of the seas." Those words convinced Maury that he was right in his belief that there were natural paths through the sea, even as there were natural paths through mountain passes, if man would but persist until he discovered them.[43] The need was great. The lack of adequate charts was causing unnecessary loss of life at sea.

With persuasive, quiet enthusiasm Maury laid his chart plan before Commodore Crane, who saw the value of the proposal and understood Maury's need for all possible additional information. He promptly authorized action, and a circular was sent out by the Bureau of Ordnance and Hydrography ordering that captains of Navy send in navigational, hydrographic, and meteorological data to Maury at the Depot of Charts and Instruments.[44]

Following issuance of this circular in late 1842 there began a period of waiting for Maury—to receive response from that appeal for information—but it was also a time of personal grief. His father, whom he had brought with the rest of the family to the Depot in November, was failing rapidly. Richard Maury's refusal to complain in spite of suffering evoked high admiration in his son, who declared of his father, "Never have I seen a more beautiful character than that worn by him in latter years." [45] On January 30, 1843, Richard Maury died.[46]

The study of the logbooks continued and while it was both absorbing and time consuming, Maury still carried on the routine duties of Depot superintendent in connection with the navigational instruments and charts and daily reports on the weather. By January, 1843, a weekly weather journal was being sent by the Depot to the *Army and Navy Chronicle and Scientific Repository*.[47] The *Chronicle*, published in Washington, made a weekly feature of these early meteorological reports.

The amount of systematic meteorological work being carried on at the Depot was sufficient for Commodore Crane to offer Maury the assistance of James P. Espy, who after lecturing in England on the nature of storms, had returned to the United States and the preceding May been appointed professor of mathematics in the Navy.[48] On March 9, 1843, Maury wrote back to his superior officer: "In reply to your letter of yesterday, I have the honor to say that Professor Espy may be advantageously employed here in assisting and comparing meteorological observations." [49]

Pennsylvania-born Espy, a pioneer in this field, was often called "the storm king," though John Quincy Adams termed him "the storm breeder." [50] He created no storms at the Depot, but neither did he render any service, for he soon departed to make independent studies elsewhere.

It could have been helpful to Maury had meteorologist Espy remained, because the many scientific programs under way at the Depot were causing the superintendent to overextend his energies. In a letter to his cousin Ann Maury in New York he reported: "I think I am more scared than hurt. The doctor has said I was destroying myself with over much headwork and in consequence I have had to hold up somewhat. But it is a hard case that one's brains will not stand the work of one's will.

"Certainly it was that, after working all the time from 9 or 10 in the morning till 1 or 2 at night, I began to look and feel badly, and that since I have knocked that off, I am looking much better." [51]

An interest that gave Maury relaxation during this period was keeping posted on the progress of a bill that had been reported in the United States Senate on January 25 proposing creation of the additional naval ranks for which he had earlier campaigned. The bill called for one admiral, two vice-admirals, 70 captains, 100 commanders, 350 lieutenants, 500 midshipmen to be authorized as "the naval peace establishment of the United States." [52] Maury was hopeful that the rank of admiral might be added to the service even if the expansion was not approved, but Congress did not pass the bill.

Although he had for the time being eliminated night work, Maury continued daily to extract information from the old ships' logs. It was a laborious task, even with the assistance of his young officers, who worked harder when he was by their side. But he was heartened that ship captains were responding to the circular issued by the Bureau and were sending in data. In March he reported: "The charts sent by Commodore Kennedy have been examined. A portion of them are out of date, several being more than 120 years old. Others are valuable." [53]

In another report he stated: "The extracts from the Journal and Logs of Captain Patterson contain much valuable and interesting information—some of it will prove useful to the ships of war now fitting for the East Indies. It is hoped that Captain Patterson will find leisure to complete what he has so well begun." [54]

On March 30, 1843, the *Army and Navy Chronicle* announced that "Directions for approaching the West Coast of Sumatra," just prepared by Maury, were "among the first fruits of the circular of the Bureau of

Ordnance and Hydrography requesting reports on all things noticed by ships." [55]

During the spring of 1843 Maury conceived a plan to make possible his obtaining the information needed for the new charts he wished to make. He knew that the interest of a great many people would have to be aroused if the effort was to succeed. The National Institute for the Advancement of Science, of which Maury had been elected a director in January, had grown in size and power. Among its leaders were the Secretary of War and the Secretary of the Navy, the Chief of Engineers of the Army and other prominent officials, as well as the former President of the United States, John Quincy Adams, now serving in the House of Representatives.[56] The meetings of the Institute were well attended, and Maury saw the "stated" meeting in 1843 as a logical place to secure backing for his scientific project. At this gathering in July he laid before the members his plan for the government to issue carefully prepared blank charts to all public cruisers, to require that these charts be filled in with notations of all hydrographic and meteorological observations made on each voyage and be returned to the Depot of Charts and Instruments for study and use. The members of the Institute promptly appointed a committee to meet with the Secretary of the Navy and to urge that he authorize blank charts to be supplied all naval vessels.[57] The Secretary received the committee, heard their recommendations, and acceded to their request.[58]

To interpret to the public the need he had laid before the scientific society in Washington, Maury prepared an article, "Blank Charts on Board Public Cruisers," which was published by the *Southern Literary Messenger,* in its August, 1843, issue.[59] The same publication had carried an article the preceding January entitled "The Navy and the West," in which Maury had urged the establishment of a Navy yard at Memphis, on the Mississippi River.[60]

Maury found it extremely difficult to persuade Navy captains to have the required observations made on their ships and the charts filled in and sent to the Depot.[61] However, one prominent officer whom he interested was a man under whom he had served, Captain Francis H. Gregory, now commanding the ship of the line *North Carolina.* On August 29 Maury wrote Captain Gregory a memorandum of the subjects on which he needed information sent to the Depot for the chart program.

> The tracks of as many vessels as can be obtained, with dates.
> The prevailing direction and force of wind for each day of passage.
> Temperature of air and water with heights of barometer.

Storms, their duration and direction.

Limits of Gulf Stream force and set of currents.

Icebergs, their place and date when seen.

Accounts of phenomena of all sorts with remarks and observations illustrating.

The advantages of any particular route from one port to another.

Fields of sea weeds, their position.

Limits of the Sargasso sea [part of the Atlantic Ocean northeast of the West Indies noted for much gulfweed on its surface].

Errors of (existing) charts.

What points along our own coast most require additional lighthouses.

Maury continued: "Though it is advisable to have as many tracks as possible, yet those of vessels crossing the ocean at the same time are most wanted especially tracks of Havre, London and Liverpool packets." He concluded: "But few captains will be able, I suppose, to give information under all of the above named heads. But as much as can be given will be thankfully received though it be simply the track of a vessel." [62]

In September, satisfied that he had sufficient data in hand for one chart, Maury wrote Commodore Crane: "I respectfully request that I may be authorized to construct a general chart of the Atlantic from the best sources of information within my reach and that the map be kept here so that corrections of every ascertainable error may be made as soon as needed." He pointed out that the cost of engraving would be small and that the Depot would not have many printed at one time as changes would be made as more information was obtained and then new editions would be issued. Maury had the temerity to remind his chief of America's hydrographic inadequacies and declared that the time had come for action, "when it is considered how little we have as a nation done for navigation that we, at this moment, are dependent on a foreign government even for the charts of our own lakes and inland seas." [63]

In the fall of 1843 the second edition of Maury's *Navigation* was published. As there was under way a movement to make this a required textbook for midshipmen, the author started, in late November, to further enlarge and improve the contents. Maury, who had never lost his early love for mathematics, wished to add more spherical trigonometry and illustrative diagrams. To use as models for diagrams for the third edition, he had a wooden sphere cut into blocks and found these helpful in his efforts to simplify the lessons on "the doctrine of the sphere." [64]

When 1843 drew to a close Maury could look back on a year of con-

siderable progress in his work at the Depot. It had also been a period
when he had assumed the settling of his parents' estate following the
death of his mother, Diana Minor Maury, on May 19, 1843.[65] That task
kept him in touch with his brothers and sisters, and this gave him pleasure. Like most American families, the Maurys had scattered widely.[66]

In 1844 Maury intensified his studies on an ocean phenomenon that
had long fascinated him—the current known as the Gulf Stream. Benjamin Franklin had earlier sought to find the answer to the riddle of
this powerful current, but in 1844 it was still a mystery.[67] Maury developed his theories on the source and nature of the Gulf Stream and began composition of a paper on the subject.

As one of the six directors of the National Institute, Maury was also
absorbed in preparation for America's "first National Congress of Scientific men," [68] which the Institute was arranging to be held in Washington in April. The first meeting took place the morning of April 1,
1844. In addition to the host members and patrons of the Institute, the
members of the American Philosophical Society and of the Association
of American Geologists and Naturalists were included.[69] President John
Tyler made the opening address, and also presided. The second meeting
was held on April 2, when Maury gave the main speech of the day on
"The Gulf Stream and Currents of the Sea." [70]

Only members of the Institute and their distinguished guests were
permitted to attend. After the event, a Virginia cousin who was visiting the Maurys at the Depot wrote to Matthew's first cousin Lucian
Minor: "I suppose you have heard of M's admired speech on the Gulf
Stream before the members of the Institute. He had quite an august
auditory—the Corps Diplomatique—Heads of the Departments etc. etc.
They say he was as pale as ashes for the first few minutes but soon recovered and elicited great applause." [71]

The paper that Maury delivered before this assembly was published
in the July issue of the *Southern Literary Messenger* and was also reprinted in pamphlet form.[72]

Maury was already being spoken of as an authority in marine research.
On May 14 he gave a paper "On the Currents of the Sea as Connected
with Meteorology" before the annual meeting of the Association of American Geologists and Naturalists in Washington. Following delivery of this
lecture, the Association appointed a committee of seven scientists to
present to the "Secretary of the Navy the importance of the information which our public cruisers might collect with regard to the Gulf
Stream and other subjects of general interest." The committee presented
Maury's paper to the Secretary "in evidence of the meagerness of our
information with regard to the Gulf Stream." [73]

As a scientist Maury gained great satisfaction from Samuel F. B. Morse's successful demonstration of telegraphy when, on May 24, Morse flashed a message from the U.S. Supreme Court room in the Capitol to Baltimore.[74]

At the Depot Maury's work continued to go well. He commented to a friend, "My duties here with old Commodore Crane are quite agreeable—he is a most excellent officer and it is pleasant to do duty under him." [75] Maury considered that Secretary of the Navy Upshur and he were "pretty good friends" [76] and found pleasure in seeing fellow officers as they came and went from various duties. He was delighted when his old friend Thomas A. Dornin arrived in Washington, wearing the insignia of a commander.[77] About another fellow officer he remarked, "Dick Rudd grows fatter and fatter and looks younger and younger under the honors of promotion." [78] The comment sounds wistful. Maury had been in the Navy nearly nineteen years and, despite his achievements, was still a lieutenant, with no promotion in sight.

Maury's reputation as a fighter for naval power was enhanced during that summer by Congress's acting favorably on the establishment and expansion of Navy installations on the Mississippi and in Florida as urged by him. On July 14 he wrote a relative: "The Maritime Interests ["Maritime Interests of the South and West," which had been published in the *Southern Quarterly Review* in 1843] took well with Congress. It was republished by the House. The Committee on Military and Naval Affairs based their reports upon it and carried all their measures through, the Memphis Navy Yard included. I mean the measures of defense, and the suggestions about the Peninsula Navy Yard." [79]

Nearly two years had passed since Congress had appropriated money for building an observatory and permanent home for the Depot of Charts and Instruments. The first step in the project had been President Tyler's selection of its location—a 17-acre property George Washington had hoped would be used for a national university, platted as "Government Reservation No. 4" and even called "University Square." [80] Construction had then started with the Observatory and Depot building being placed on an elevation that had formerly been called Peter's or Braddock's Hill but in 1844 was known as Camp Hill. The site was 95 feet above ordinary high water, but between it and the Potomac lay marshy flats. The new structure was located between D and E streets at 23rd Street, about 1 mile west of the White House and 2.2 miles west of the Capitol.[81] The original building is still used by the Navy, though not for astronomical observations.

During the early summer Maury and his wife twice walked from the Depot to see how the new building was progressing. Ann, though again "in the family way," was not unduly fatigued and enjoyed the view of

156

the city, the surrounding country, and of Georgetown College, about one and a half miles to the northwest.[82] Maury was thinking of considerably more than the view.

In late August, with the Observatory nearing completion, there was great speculation in Washington as to the man who would be made superintendent of the government's first observatory, first major scientific establishment. Maury hoped for the assignment, desired it wholeheartedly.[83] Various candidates had been proposed. There were many who felt that Lieutenant James M. Gilliss should be given the position. He had emphasized astronomical work when he had earlier been superintendent of the Depot, had gone abroad to order the astronomical instruments for the Observatory, had supervised construction of the building and installation of instruments. Others, believing a civilian should be engaged for this high scientific responsibility, zealously urged that William C. Bond or some other out-of-uniform scientist should be appointed. To this latter proposal the Navy was unitedly opposed—a naval officer should be the superintendent.

On September 4, by a General Order signed by Secretary of the Navy John Y. Mason, Maury's *Navigation* was made the chief textbook on the subject to be studied henceforth by midshipmen in their courses on shipboard or in the schools at Navy yards.[84] The politically minded saw in this a favorable omen for Maury. Mason had been given the Navy portfolio by President Tyler the preceding March. He was a Virginian, had been a strong advocate of naval preparedness during his years in Congress and was expected to choose a Navy man.[85] But which—Gilliss or Maury?

In considering which man to appoint Mason had to remember that the new establishment was to combine many phases of scientific work for the Navy. Maury proponents pointed out that hydrography was one of them and that in that field their candidate had given the Depot a scientific reputation it had not previously enjoyed. His record proved him a hard worker, able to get others to work, and an efficient administrator. His advocates recalled that Maury had been the astronomer appointed to go with the Exploring Expedition under Commodore Thomas ap Catesby Jones and had at that time studied astronomy in Philadelphia. He had also carried on some astronomical work at the Depot of Charts and Instruments. Maury's great ability in mathematics, evidenced in his textbook *Navigation,* was a major recommendation, since so much of astronomy depends on the mathematical reductions or computations made after the observations.

At last Secretary Mason reached a decision. On October 1 the announcement was made. The superintendent of the new Naval Observatory would be Matthew Fontaine Maury.[86]

CHAPTER IX

Superintendent of the United States Naval Observatory

Keen with anticipation of the opportunity ahead, Maury began his duties as the first superintendent of the United States Naval Observatory on the morning of October 8, 1844.[1]

The building itself was pleasing. The central portion, on which was mounted the Observatory dome, gave a sense of foursquare solidity while wings extending on both east and west sides added symmetry to the front elevation of the structure. The entrance was on this front, or north, side and admitted one to a central hall that gave easy access to four rooms, each about 17 feet square, that were duplicated on the floor above. Directly under the observation dome the central hall opened into a circular area from which corridors led to the wings. A wing extending to the south provided further work space, and a subterranean passage connected the main building with an underground magnetic observatory, where studies of the earth's magnetism would be made.[2]

Maury wasted no time in allotting areas of the building to the different programs of work to be carried out there—astronomy, hydrography, and meteorology. An initial task was placement of the instruments, records, and general equipment, which were moved from the former Depot of Charts and Instruments to the new Observatory. Maury set his staff of junior naval officers, Navy professors of mathematics, and several civilian employees to creating working order while he himself made a study of the astronomical instruments that had been installed some weeks earlier under the supervision of Lieutenant James M. Gilliss.[3]

Maury's examination of the instruments led to the distressing discovery that they had been damaged by being mounted before the condition of the building warranted. Avoiding any reference to Lieutenant James M. Gilliss's responsibility in the matter, Maury reported the damage to his superior, Commodore Crane, only four days after taking over the Observatory. He advised that, as a result of this finding, he planned to wait to mount the Meridian Circle "until the columns for its support have had ample time to settle, walls to dry." [4]

An even more serious matter he reported, however, was that he "found it necessary to dismount entirely every instrument on account of a cement of sulphur which had been used about them." [5] Elemental sulphur had been melted and utilized to fasten the metal stanchions of the instruments into holes in the stone bases. The sulphur, exposed to the moist air rising from the Potomac and its flats, had slowly formed an acid gas and sulphurous acid that had begun corrosion of the metal of the instruments. [6] This damage necessitated a careful cleaning of the valuable instruments, which had been made by skilled experts in Munich, Berlin, and London. [7] The work had to be done slowly, as did the removal of the "sulphur cement" from the bases.

Another source of frustration was the delay in arrival of the mercurial pendulum clocks ordered for use with the astronomical instruments. [8]

In December, 1844, Maury received a letter from F. A. P. Barnard stating that the new University of Alabama Observatory was ready for observations and asking the Naval Observatory superintendent "to make observations in concert for the purpose of establishing the difference of longitude." [9] Since one of the major functions of observatories was to determine longitude, the distance east or west of a prime meridian expressed in degrees, with 15 degrees representing a difference of one hour in time, it was a great disappointment to Maury that the Naval Observatory was not yet ready to carry out this joint study. He explained the delays and offered to make the observations as soon as possible. [10] To his chagrin, however, he had to write much the same reply in March, 1845, to Benjamin Peirce, professor of mathematics at Harvard College, which had recently completed its observatory. [11] In exasperation, Maury in mid-April informed the chief of the Bureau of Ordnance and Hydrography that it was imperative to finish the excavation and to sod around the Observatory as the dust was injuring the instruments. He also stated that because of the layout of the building, gaseous fumes rose from the furnace in the basement and were having a chemical effect upon the instruments. Maury recommended that the second problem be overcome by constructing an outbuilding for a hot-water heating plant from which heat could be piped into the Observatory. This was eventually done. [12]

Maury also found the location near the Potomac, while visually attractive, to be a drawback, for the miasmas or mists that hung over the nearby marshes or flats that extended to the river were damaging the astronomical instruments in the Observatory. [13] In summers to come workers at the Observatory were to be plagued by mosquitoes from the flats and by malaria, a malady that was common in Washington until the flats were drained and filled.

Meanwhile the repair of the damage done prior to Maury's superintendency was finally concluded and the instruments remounted. In the hemispherical, revolving dome was the Observatory's most powerful refracting telescope, the Equatorial, resting on a massive block of granite supported by a conical pier of brickwork, which rose from the foundation of the building. Below, in the south wing, was mounted the Prime Vertical Transit Instrument, the West Transit Instrument in the west wing, and the Mural Circle and the Meridian Circle in the east wing.[14]

On April 1 Maury had the honor of receiving at the Observatory former President John Quincy Adams, who, as a congressman, had not long before sought to have the funds bequeathed to the United States by Smithson used to build a national observatory to be under the direct control of the President and Congress rather than under the direction of one of the services.[15] By some strange circumstance Adams had failed to realize during construction of the new "Depot" that it was to be an observatory with extra space in which the Depot work was carried on. He was annoyed that the Navy had "beat him to the draw." [16] Whatever annoyance he had felt was now outweighed by his curiosity to see this "lighthouse of the sky." Adams disapproved the lack of a house and garden for the superintendent and the unfinished state of building and grounds. He stated that valuable observations could be made at the Observatory and concluded his visit by saying he would return to try out the astronomical instruments.[17] Accordingly, Maury got in touch with science-loving Adams on the first clear evening, and the former President decided "to go and look through the large refractor at the nebula in the sword of Orion." Maury was also able to give Adams a good look at "a cluster of spangles in Auriga, the blazing light of Sirius and the double stars, orange and blue, in Andromeda." [18]

Ten days after John Quincy Adams had enjoyed his evening of "astronomizing" with Maury at the Observatory, George Bancroft, the new Secretary of the Navy, paid a call on Adams. The latter, in his seventy-eighth year, thought Bancroft too profuse with words. However, when the Navy Secretary asked his advice as to whether magnetic observations should be carried on at the Observatory, Adams counseled that they should be and urged also that the Navy promptly build the superintendent's residence.[19] Though it was not an observatory established exactly as Adams had planned, the Naval Observatory was for the next nine years usually referred to as the National Observatory and so considered.[20] Adams was genuinely interested in it, and Maury sent him detailed information on the progress made there.[21]

Following the remounting of the astronomical instruments, Maury had set himself to mastering knowledge of the functions and "space-pene-trating powers" of each instrument. He had begun the training of junior naval officers on his staff to serve as observers with the instruments, working in conjunction with the professors of mathematics assigned to the Observatory.[22] His aim, he stated, was "to have at least two observers for each instrument; so that when the night is clear there may always be an eye for every Telescope in the Observatory." [23]

Maury himself began a systematic and continuing program of study of the works of the European astronomers who had recently made major strides in the study of space. He studied the writings of Friedrich Georg Wilhelm von Struve, director of the new Pulkovo Observatory near St. Petersburg, Russia, of England's great astronomer, John F. Herschel, and those of the earlier Sir William Herschel, whose discovery of the planet Uranus in 1781 had been only one of his important contributions to astronomy. Maury's mathematical mind took delight in learning the new method (trigonometric parallax) to determine the distance of Cygni 61 from the earth. Madler's theory on the "Central Sun" was studied by Maury together with other "great works," which he said, "mark the progress of, and stamp the spirit of the age upon, Astronomical pursuits." [24]

In spite of his intensive efforts to launch the astronomical work of the Observatory while simultaneously carrying forward the hydrographic and meteorological work of his office, Maury still managed time with his family. When the Depot was moved to the new Observatory the Maurys remained in the rented Pennsylvania Avenue building. It was planned that they would move to a smaller dwelling, but the time was not then suitable, as Ann was soon to have her fifth child. On November 13, 1844, she gave birth to a daughter, christened Mary Herndon but soon nicknamed Tots.[25]

During Ann's recovery Maury took the older children with him every Sunday morning to St. John's Episcopal Church, in Lafayette Square near the White House. This was the church the Maurys attended throughout their stay in Washington.[26]

Maury was one of the fortunate mortals who wake up with a happy outlook on the day, and he never objected to his children crowding around him as soon as he had opened his eyes. He would then get up, fling open the shutters of his bedroom, and exclaim, "Let us let in the blessed light of day." This was the signal for the children to get a small shaving can, fill it with water and set it on the fire to heat. Then their father crouched in front of the fire and stirred the water as he muttered dramatically, "Double, double, toil and trouble, fire burn and cauldron bubble" and more of the witches' incantation from *Macbeth*. The children enjoyed Maury's make-believe and joined in the chant to the best of their ability.[27]

Late in the afternoon, when Maury knocked off work for a period, he would walk the young ones around the hilltop on which the Observatory was situated, explain the seasonal changes in foliage, and start them on an observation of nature. At home, after tea, he regaled them with tales of his boyhood.[28]

In late April of 1845 Maury received authorization from the Secretary of the Navy, through the chief of the Bureau of Ordnance and Hydrography, to seek bids from Washington builders for construction of a superintendent's house to be connected with the east wing of the Observatory, the cost not to exceed $5,000.[29] Soon thereafter Maury received similar authorization to rent a house for $350 a year, and on July 1 he moved his family to this small downtown dwelling until the completion of the superintendent's house at the Observatory.[30]

By May, 1845, the three naval lieutenants and six passed midshipmen assigned to duty at the Observatory had made progress in their training as astronomical observers. On May 7 the staff was strengthened by the addition of U.S.N. Professor of Mathematics Joseph S. Hubbard,[31] and further augmented the following autumn by U.S.N. Professor of Mathematics Ruel Keith.[32]

Maury himself was the principal observer with the Equatorial in these months and throughout the first two years of observations at the Naval Observatory and also occasionally observed at the other instruments.[33] In September, 1845, he wrote to a relative who had visited the Observatory: "Those superb clusters in Perseus which you used to see in the west are now in the east. Sirius, with his 'Dawn of Day' in the telescope, has disappeared and the glorious nebula of Orion culminates by day; but then there is that exquisite double star in Andromeda—orange and emerald, that, too, is in the east." [34]

To the members of the Virginia Historical Society he declared:

> To me the simple passage through the Transit instrument of a star across the meridian is the height of astronomical sublimity.
>
> At the dead hour of the night, when the world is hushed in sleep and all is still; when there is not a sound to be heard save the dead beat escapement of the clock, counting with hollow voice the footsteps of time in his ceaseless round, I turn to the Ephemeris and find there, by calculation made years ago, that when that clock tells a

certain hour, a star which I never saw will be in the field of the telescope for a moment, flit through and then disappear. The instrument is set;—the moment approaches and is intently awaited;—I look;
—the star mute with eloquence that gathers sublimity from the
silence of the night, comes smiling and dancing into the field, and
at the instant predicted even to the fraction of a second, it makes its
transit and is gone! With emotions too deep for the organs of speech,
the heart swells out with unutterable anthems; we then see that
there *is* harmony in the heavens above; and though we cannot hear,
we feel the "music of the spheres." [35]

With the preparatory period behind him at the end of his first year
at the Observatory, Maury reached a conclusion as to the major objective toward which the astronomical work should be directed. In December, 1845, he began discussions of his plan with his superiors in the Navy
Department. He proposed that the observers at the Naval Observatory
be assigned

> regularly and systematically to penetrate, with our excellent Tele-
> scope, every point of space in the visible heavens, with the view of
> assigning position and magnitude [degree of brightness], and of cata-
> loguing every star, cluster, nebula or object that should pass through
> the field of view.[36]
>
> The plan [he emphasized] seeks to avoid doing over again what
> has already been well done. . . .
>
> The intention is to make a contribution to Astronomy worthy of
> the nation and the age, and so to execute the undertaking, that
> future Astronomers in all time may say of it, such a star was not
> visible in the heavens at the date of the Washington Catalogue, be-
> cause it is not there [in the catalogue], and such a star that is now
> missing, was in the heavens because it is in that work. Such, at least,
> is the point aimed at. How far we shall fall short of it remains for
> results to show.[37]

Secretary Bancroft approved Maury's ambitious plan and in his subsequent official authorization for the project recapitulated some of the
reasons Maury had advanced for it:

> The most celebrated European catalogues of the Stars, "Bessel's
> Zone Observations" and "Struve's Dorpat Catalogue" of double
> stars, having extended to only fifteen degrees South of the Equator,
> and the Washington Observatory, by its geographical position, com-
> manding a zone of fifteen degrees further South, and being provided

with all instruments requisite for extending these catalogues, you are hereby authorized and directed to enter upon the observations of the heavens commencing at the lowest parallel of South Declination, which you may find practicable. You will embrace in your Catalogue all stars even of the smallest magnitude which your instruments can accurately observe.[38]

In mid-December word reached the Naval Observatory from Europe that Biela's Comet had been identified in the heavens over Rome on November 28 and had been seen two nights later by observers in Berlin.[39] This was welcome news as astronomers were eagerly awaiting another look at this comet that had first been seen in 1826 and had reappeared periodically since.[40] News of Biela's visibility in European skies caused Maury to issue orders for all his observers to be on the alert for the comet. Each night he and his associates searched the skies with the Observatory's telescopes. No one has described Maury's experience better than Bernard de Voto:

> The new year began, the year of decision, and on January 13 at Washington our foremost scientist, Matthew Maury, found matter for a new report.
> Maury was a universal genius but his deepest passion was the movement of tides [actually secondary to his interest in winds and currents]. In that January of '46 he was continuing his labor to perfect the basis for the scientific study of winds and currents. Out of that labor came the science of oceanography, and methods of reporting the tides, not only of the sea, but of the air also, that have been permanent, and a revolution in the art of navigation. But he had further duties as superintendent of the Naval Observatory, and so by night he turned his telescope on Biela's comet. That night of January 13, 1846, he beheld the ominous and inconceivable. On its way toward perihelion, Biela's comet had split in two.[41]

This was a remarkable experience and significant observation, and Maury reported it in a brief article "Duplicity of Biela's Comet," which was published in England in the *Royal Astronomical Society Monthly.*[42] A continuing flow of reports on observations, including those made by him, went from Maury to the Secretary of the Navy, such as, "I enclose the parabolic elements of the new comet, computed by Professor Hubbard from my observations of last night and the two preceding nights. A more extensive series of observations may afford arguments for more perfect elements." [43]

Start of the major program to catalogue the stars was made on March

6, 1846, when the official order came through from the Secretary to Maury, but systematic observations had been carried on throughout the preceding year.[44] Not long after the new work was launched, the results of earlier efforts were published in Washington, as *The Astronomical Observations Made During the Year 1845 at the National Observatory under the Direction of M. F. Maury, Lieutenant, United States Navy, Superintendent*. (In another printing, this book bore the title *The Astronomical Observations Made During the Year 1845 at the U.S. Naval Observatory*. These different names for the Observatory and the term "Hydrographic Office" were used interchangeably until December, 1854, when the Secretary of the Navy officially ruled that the proper designation was "The United States Naval Observatory and Hydrographical Office.")[45]

Official circles were much pleased with this book, finding in its 554 pages proof of the quality and quantity of astronomical work being done at the new Observatory. Among those who had participated in the observations were Joseph S. Hubbard, Ruel Keith, and John C. Coffin, all Navy professors of mathematics whose work under Maury was fully acknowledged by him in the preface of the book. This was the first volume of astronomical observations issued by an American observatory and, as such, caused a stir in European circles.[46] Maury was particularly pleased to hear that the book had established the Naval Observatory as the equal of those in the Old World. An insight into his feeling about the reception of the observations can be gained from a letter to a close friend, William M. Blackford, editor of a newspaper in Lynchburg, Virginia:

> The colleges . . . are warm in their commendation of the volume. . . . They all think more of it than I do; but what amuses me, that almost every one expresses surprise that *Navy* officers should be able to do such things. We have beat Greenwich all hollow, there is no doubt; yet we shall do better next time. . . . I have solved a problem that has often blistered my heart and proved that Navy officers are fit for something else besides scrubbing decks at sea and tacking ship.[47]

Maury had not gotten over the fact that civilians had earlier declared no one in the Navy was fit to be superintendent of the Naval Observatory, a statement he had branded to the Secretary as "the repetition of a practical libel." [48]

A matter of far deeper concern to Maury, however, that April and early May of 1846 was the imminence of war between the United States and Mexico. Since March 12, when John Slidell had been informed that the Mexican government would not receive him as minister pleni-potentiary from the United States, events had moved rapidly. General Zachary Taylor, who had earlier been sent with United States Army troops to defend the borders of Texas, had proceeded to the east bank of the Rio Grande River and started construction of a fort. The Mexicans had immediately ordered him to withdraw beyond the Nueces River. On April 25 Mexican troops had crossed the Rio Grande and captured or killed all members of a U.S. Army reconnoitering party. This news was not to reach Washington for some time, but on that same date President Polk began preparations of a war message to be delivered to Congress.[49]

On May 11, 1846, two days before Congress officially declared war against Mexico, Maury tendered his services and those of every officer at the Observatory to Secretary of the Navy George Bancroft, for duty in the waters off Mexico or "wherever our services are most required." [50] This offer was repeated more than once as the war with Mexico progressed. Maury's nephew Dabney H. Maury, who was like a son to him, was badly wounded in the war, and Maury's brother-in-law, Kemp S. Holland, died just off the mouth of the Rio Grande while returning from Monterrey.[51] The Navy Department continued to consider Maury's services essential at the Observatory but did detach many of his junior officers and the frequency with which these assistants were removed soon became a major problem.[52]

One of the many visitors whom Maury received at the Observatory in the summer of 1846 was an English author, Sarah Mytton Maury, who had come to Washington to interview leading men for a book in preparation. As a widow she had shortly before married Maury's half-English cousin, William Maury, who lived in Liverpool. Sarah Mytton Maury made a great point of the fact that she was not Maury's blood relative but a writer who wished to describe him as a significant American of the time. Her sketch of Maury, published in her book *The Statesmen of America in 1846,* was of the highly laudatory type then fashionable in belles-lettres. In spite of its excess the account provides an example of the kind of partisanship that Maury inspired in many with whom he came in contact.

> He is a man of science, equally well versed in the secrets of the sea and of the sky; an accomplished mariner, an admirable astronomer and mathematician and a superior author on many subjects; he writes excellent English.
>
> He is a great favourite with his brother officers, both for his ability and his kindly nature . . . and he is held in great estimation at

Washington for his admirable regulations at the Observatory, his eminent, professional knowledge and industry, his good judgment in political affairs, and his exceeding moral worth.

"Pray ask him to come and see me often," said Mr. Calhoun [Senator John C. Calhoun], "he is a man of most excellent thought."

Maury is lame; but to this accident is owing the development of the most touching traits of his character and perhaps of his choicest talents. . . . I have never seen his temper ruffled, nor that serene and intelligent countenance overcast; his philosophy is that of the Christian, enduring . . . and manly. . . .

He cordially approved of the Mexican War, and was zealous that the Navy should share the glory of the strife. He himself, forgetful of the . . . suffering limb, and of a constitution injured by its effects, would instantly seize the boarding pike and cutlass and leap to the oar.[53]

The Naval Observatory staff had been strengthened in February, 1846, by the addition of a civilian astronomer, Sears Cook Walker, who had for some years been the director of the small High School Observatory in Philadelphia.[54] At that institution Walker had begun the training of Professor Hubbard, with whom he was now again associated at the Naval Observatory.

In the autumn of 1846 Maury ordered Sears Walker to concentrate his studies on the planet Neptune, which had recently been discovered almost simultaneously by Urbain Jean Joseph Le Verrier of Paris and John Couch Adams of Cambridge University. Maury's instructions were that Walker should trace backward the path of Neptune to try to discover whether some astronomer had earlier observed it and recorded it as a fixed star. After months of painstaking research Walker discovered, on February 2, 1847, that the planet Neptune had been identified as a fixed star on May 8 and 10, 1795, by Joseph Jérôme Lefrançais de Lalande, the director of the Paris Observatory and had been so recorded in his 1802 catalogue of 47,000 stars, *Historie Céleste Française*. This discovery opened up a whole new study. Working from observations made between 1795 and 1847, astronomers went to work to determine the orbit of the new planet. A report on this Observatory finding went forth promptly to Secretary John Y. Mason,[55] who had returned to head the Navy Department on September 10, 1846,[56] when George Bancroft was appointed minister to the Court of St. James's.

Because he had received advanced training as an astronomer and had concentrated his studies on that one field of science, Sears Walker had, from the beginning of his employment at the Naval Observatory, been critical of Maury's astronomical knowledge and reluctant to follow his orders. Friction was the inevitable result. Early in 1847, Sears Walker's service with the Naval Observatory was terminated.[57] Maury considered it a dismissal "under fire" but wrote this interpretation of the event to his friend Elias Loomis, professor at Union College, Schenectady, New York: "Mr. Walker was unwilling to comply with the rules of the office, as the officers do, and it was better therefore that he should quit. He wanted to be excused from attending the office entirely and occupy himself upon such subjects only as he should fancy. Mr. W., moreover, was a much better computer than observer; he could compute day in and day out but our night observations would knock him up." [58]

Sears Walker was promptly hired by his old Philadelphia friend, Alexander Dallas Bache, superintendent of the Coast Survey, who had originally recommended him to Maury.[59] Possibly Bache suggested to Walker that he discuss his previous astronomical work at the Naval Observatory with Joseph Henry, the distinguished physicist and former professor at the College of New Jersey (which became Princeton). For the past nine months Henry had been secretary of the new Smithsonian Institution.[60]

Sears Walker called on Joseph Henry in the original, turreted Smithsonian building. Without authorization, Walker deposited with Henry an abstract of his observations made for the Naval Observatory and expressed the hope that this abstract might be published in Europe.[61]

Maury knew nothing of this conference at the time and was barely able to believe the developments that followed. One of the leading scientific publications of the time was Professor Heinrich C. Schumacher's *Astronomische Nachrichten*, published in Altona, Germany. Volume XXVI of this journal reached the Washington Observatory late in the summer of 1847. To Maury's amazement he found published therein a letter from Professor Henry and the abstract on the planet Neptune made by Sears Walker while a regular working member of the staff of the United States Naval Observatory. The letter from the secretary of the Smithsonian, dated May 29, 1847, and addressed to Schumacher, read:

> I beg leave to present to you the accompanying abstract of the researches of Sears C. Walker, Esq. with regard to the orbit of Neptune. A memoir containing a full account of the investigation will be published in the course of the year in the *Transactions of the Smithsonian Institution* but as everything connected with the new planet is of special interest at the present time, this abstract may not be thought unacceptable to the readers of your valuable Journal." [62]

(signed)   Joseph Henry

In a footnote to the article in the *Astronomische Nachrichten* was printed a letter to Joseph Henry, signed by Sears C. Walker:

> In compliance with your invitation I send you an abstract of my researches on the orbit of Neptune which led to the detection on the 2d of February last of its identity with the missing star of Lalande's Manuscript of the Historie Celeste of May 8 and 10, 1795.[63]

After his initial astonishment had passed Maury came to the conclusion that Henry's signature to the letter must have been forged, that the letter was certainly unauthorized.[64] He had profound respect for Henry who, while teaching at Albany Academy, in Albany, New York, had discovered electromagnetic self-induction and had even preceded Michael Faraday in his discoveries in electromagnetism, though Henry had unfortunately not recorded his findings until after the Englishman had proclaimed his.[65] Recalling "the mutual pledges of good will and promises of kind offices which each made the other in behalf of the two noble Institutions," [66] Maury simply could not believe that Henry had taken this action. It was unthinkable to him that the head of the Smithsonian would have transmitted an account of official work done at the Naval Observatory for publication in Europe. Even more incredible was the idea that Joseph Henry would be planning to publish an account of important astronomical work belonging to the Observatory in the *Transactions of the Smithsonian Institution*. Being a straightforward man himself, Maury reasoned that, as Henry's name had doubtless been used without his knowledge, the distinguished man of science would be happy to clear up the episode by a disavowal of participation in it.

However, the prestige of the United States Navy was involved and Maury drafted a letter which he showed to his commanding officer, the chief of the Bureau of Ordnance and Hydrography. Commodore Crane considered the matter sufficiently serious to require the approval of the Secretary of the Navy. These two officials concurred that Maury's letter should be sent,[67] and on the 20th of September the following communication was dispatched:

> Professor Joseph Henry, Sec'y of Smithsonian Institution.
>
> I beg leave to call your attention to a communication date Washington 1847, May 29th purporting to be from the Sec'y of the Smithsonian Institution and addressed to the Editor of the *Astronomische Nachrichten*. It is published under your name August 2, 1847 in no. 605 of that popular journal. Said communication relates to a discovery made at this Obs'y. with regard to the planet

Neptune, in which also both myself and office are concerned. Wherefore I request of you the favor to state whether that communication be genuine, and if it be genuine, whether the *abstract of the researcher,* transmitted by you, was furnished by Mr. Walker of his own free will and accord or at *your invitation* as therein stated.

Be pleased to reply at your earliest convenience and oblige.

(signed) M. F. Maury, Lt. USN
Superintendent [68]

Henry's reply, written October 11, did little to straighten out the matter. Professor Henry stated that Walker had several months before deposited with him a memoir the Smithsonian agreed to include in their publications "and as Mr. Walker was desirous that his researches should be known abroad as early as possible, I agreed to transmit to Professor Schumacher an abstract of the results obtained up to that time provided, as is usual in such cases, the abstract were prepared by Mr. Walker himself." Henry, from the secure position of his earlier achievements, informed the Navy lieutenant that he regarded the "categorical form" as "unpleasant" and unusual in "Scientific Correspondence" and requested that Maury state "explicitly" the grounds of his complaint.[69]

As the grounds were to Maury self-evident, it was hard for him to understand Joseph Henry's position in the matter. Surely the ethical problem did not need to be spelled out to this brilliant man. But once again, on October 20, Maury wrote back assuring Henry "that our previous intercourse calls for nothing on my part but respect, good will and kind feelings. Permit me further to assure you that so far from courting, I desire to avoid all controversy." [70]

Having stated his personal position, Maury then proceeded to comply with Professor Henry's request and pointed out in detail that the Naval Observatory had been injured by Henry's transmitting for publication abroad

> articles which represent you as taking sides in the name of the Smithsonian Institution against the Observatory in a controversy in defence of its own rights. Articles which represent you, the head of one Government Institution, as seeking out a person who had just been compelled to leave in official disgrace, another Institution under the same government, and inviting from him, for publication, a statement of labor performed at the Observatory, which statement wrongs both it and myself, articles which represent you as laying hold, in the name of the Smithsonian Institution, on the labors of the Observatory, with intent to appropriate the same without due

acknowledgment and by the publication thereof in the transactions of the Smithsonian Institution to forestall the Observatory before the public with an account of its own labors; and that account not a correct one. . . .

The discovery that Lalande made observations upon the planet Neptune more than 50 years ago is among those labors and the account of this discovery belongs to the Annals of the Observatory and will appear, when it is convenient to the government that it shall appear, in the regularly printed volume of observations which gives a full account of the labors performed at the Observatory from epoch to epoch and I complain that you, without regarding the rules and usages of official intercourse or the comity, which obtains among men of science, but in derogation of all, should attempt to array the Smithsonian Institution against the Observatory—one public institution against another—to forestall it with an account of its own work and use its labors in the name and for the purposes of the Smithsonian Institution without leave or due acknowledgment, receiving your materials at the hands of an acknowledged subordinate, who, acting under my authority had obtained them for the purposes of the Observatory.[71]

To this blunt and specific set of charges Henry replied in a brief note that he felt he had "done no intentional or unintentional harm to the Observatory."[72] Henry's complete disavowal of wrong in the matter baffled Maury and is still puzzling. Perhaps Henry had been made angry by the tone of Maury's letter and was simply unwilling to admit that he had made a careless mistake in his willingness to give assistance to Sears Walker. Possibly Henry believed the Observatory would not give full credit to Walker for his work and this belief may have caused him to feel justified in the steps he had taken. Whatever the causes for Henry's actions, or the reasoning behind them, he obviously did not intend to explain them.

Smarting under the injury he felt had been done the Observatory and himself, Maury, on November 15, wrote once more to try to persuade Henry to set the matter right. As Henry had denied that wrong had been done, Maury again pointed out that Walker's work had been done for the Naval Observatory, on its time, on its pay, and in its service, and belonged to that institution. Maury was still too angry to be either diplomatic or persuasive. He was again bluntly factual. He concluded by asking Henry to send Schumacher a statement to be published in the *Astronomische Nachrichten* advising "the rights of property which the Observatory has in those researches." He told Henry: "I have thus, my dear Sir, endeavored to impress you with a sense of the wrong which without intending it you have caused to be done to the Observatory and I have asked you to afford such redress only as I under like circumstances would be willing to afford. Hoping that you will feel in the foregoing nothing personally offensive or unpleasant for I assure you that I have intended nothing of the kind." [73] The letter did not alter Henry's attitude nor cause him to issue the requested statement. Henry simply ignored the issue, but neither he nor Maury forgot it.

In view of Professor Henry's unchanging attitude, the logical deduction seems to be that the physicist was acting out of loyalty to his own group of scientific friends whom he considered the men who should control science—including Sears Walker who was a protégé of Alexander Dallas Bache, superintendent of the Coast Survey. These *savants* and *scientifics,* who were or had been college professors, felt that men who had not been similarly trained were not scientists but charlatans and should be denied recognition. [74]

To persuade his closest professional friend to take the executive direction of the Smithsonian Institution, Alexander Dallas Bache had on December 4, 1846, written Professor Joseph Henry: "Science triumphs in you, my dear friend, and come you must. Redeem Washington. Save this great National Institution from the hands of charlatans." [75]

Bache had long ago conceived a messianic role in American science for himself and his "elite corps" of friends—an idea shared by Henry. [76] Since this ambition was to affect Maury's entire scientific career and influence the oceanographer's posthumous fame, it seems pertinent to examine the reasons behind it.

In the first place, Alexander Dallas Bache was the great-grandson of Benjamin Franklin and grandson of Alexander J. Dallas, who had been Secretary of the Treasury under Madison. His own generation of relatives—Baches and Dallases—possessed an established social position and the ability and ambition to make the most of this advantage. [77] In addition to having been born and reared among people who moved in fashionable urban society, Bache had been blessed with a first-class mind. He had obtained a scientific education at the public institution which Maury, as a youth, had longed to attend—the United States Military Academy at West Point. There Bache had excelled in his studies and in his final year had become the admiration of a "plebe" who was, years later, to do much for him in Washington—Jefferson Davis of Mississippi. [78] But, after getting a West Point education, then considered the best scientific one available in the United States, Bache had not found a life under military orders to his liking. He had served for only three years in the Army and resigned his commission to enter the field of education in Philadelphia.[79] There he had served twice as a professor at the University of Pennsylvania and between those periods of teaching had been chosen president of the embryonic Girard College for Orphans.[80] Because of a long delay in its opening, Bache had become principal of Central High School and subsequently city schools' superintendent.[81] The Philadelphia City Council had been highly critical of Bache for the amount of money he had spent in Europe (making a survey of education there while planning the organization of Girard) and later for his opposition to too much emphasis on Latin and Greek in the curriculum of the schools, as well as for what the Council held to be "softness" in his disciplinary policies.[82]

Tired of "acrimonious controversy" about his work and desirous of earning a higher salary than teaching offered,[83] Bache had turned his eyes toward Washington when a position became available there through the death in 1843 of Ferdinand Rudolph Hassler, the founder and long-time superintendent of the United States Coast Survey (now the Coast and Geodetic Survey).[84] Since the head of the Survey also supervised weights and measures, the position carried a good salary, and Bache had decided he would like to have the appointment. During his years in Philadelphia as a professor and organizer of education, he had taken an active part in the newly founded Franklin Institute and in the American Philosophical Society, which his great-grandfather, Dr. Franklin, had founded. Members of both bodies had become his close friends and none more so than Joseph Henry, then professor of physics at the nearby College of New Jersey.[85] In his biography of Alexander Dallas Bache, Merle M. Odgers reveals that it was Henry who had organized a campaign among these intellectuals to assist Bache in getting the Coast Survey post he desired. In one of these letters Henry had written of his friend, "No other living man is so well qualified as himself to fill this office." [86]

A large number of commendatory letters had been sent to high officials and friends, and the campaign had been successful. Biographer Odgers comments: "The President, Mr. Tyler, issued the commission [to Bache] in spite of the avowed and vigorous opposition of Secretary of the Treasury, Mr. John C. Spencer. . . ." [87] Spencer was the department head under whose jurisdiction the Coast Survey carried on its work and so, on reaching Washington, Bache had applied himself successfully to winning Spencer's approval.[88] But Bache had soon learned that many people were unhappy over the Coast Survey's being under the Treasury and considered that the agency's work of charting the coast and harbors should be a natural function of the hydrographic office of the Navy. The Navy itself was, of course, the chief proponent of this view and repeatedly tried to secure control of the Coast Survey.[89] The Survey used naval officers to do most of the surveying of coastal waters, and the Navy resented the fact that it received no credit for this work. Maury himself believed that American hydrography would move forward more efficiently if consolidated under one office and that the Navy, which supplied the officers for the surveys, should have control of them. He did no published writing in behalf of this change, but, when requested to do so, did present a memorandum of his views to the Secretary of the Navy.[90]

Dallas Bache had earlier written high praise about Maury's scientific abilities and his textbook *Navigation*.[91] When Bache had reached Washington in 1843, Maury had extended every professional courtesy, and the two men were seemingly friendly.[92] However, Bache had wanted Lieutenant James M. Gilliss to be made superintendent of the Naval Observatory, and Bache and his friends had never changed their opinion that Maury should not have been given the appointment. Bache was also annoyed that Maury was studying, speaking, and writing about the Gulf Stream. The great-grandson of Franklin regarded this as a subject that belonged to his family almost by hereditary right because of "Honest Ben's" original investigation of the current.[93] Bache soon arranged for his brother, Lieutenant George Meade Bache, on detached duty from the Navy, to make investigations of the Gulf Stream for the Coast Survey, only to have that venture end in tragedy when George Bache was washed overboard.[94]

A dominating characteristic of Dallas Bache was his desire to win men to a personal allegiance to himself.[95] When the professor came from Philadelphia to become superintendent of the Coast Survey, Maury had already been hard at work at the Depot for a year and was constructing his first chart of the Atlantic. Bache must have soon realized that here was a man who would not be subject to his personal magnetism nor have time for gathering weekly with other men to wine, dine, and talk.

When Bache had urged Henry to save the Smithsonian from being run by someone not of their group, and therefore a "charlatan," he articulated one of his deepest beliefs. For Joseph Henry and their mutual friends, Bache had limitless admiration; for scientists outside their circle, contempt. This scorn Bache revealed in his actions and in allegorical allusions but not in forthright speech.[96] In the years ahead, whenever Bache was in Washington, he kept in touch with Henry by note, in addition to seeing him regularly. In these communications Bache often used veiled phrases to hint at some unseen enemy who was threatening his or Henry's work.[97] Bache was also fond of employing an initial or code name for a person about whom he was writing. Suspense, mystery, intrigue—all captivated the dramatic but able Bache.[98] He sometimes made Joseph Henry nervous, but their close friendship was to endure.[99]

Bache's ambitions, jealousies, and especially his fear that Maury's rising fame as a hydrographer might yet cause the Coast Survey to be placed under the Navy are understandable grounds for his enmity to the superintendent of the Naval Observatory and Hydrographical office. It is, however, difficult to see how a man of Bache's intellectual capacity could have justified the inconsistency of his thinking in insisting that the only worthy scientists were those dedicated in utter purity to "Principia" and "Theoria," [100] when virtually his whole work from 1843 until his death was in applied or practical science—charting the coasts, supervising weights and measures, and serving on the Lighthouse Board. Similarly, Joseph Henry, once he took the secretaryship of the Smithsonian Institution, did much to encourage others to pure research but himself no longer had the time for it. Instead, he too worked at practical research on such projects as developing more efficient fuels for lighthouse lamps and the improvement of acoustics in public auditoriums.[101]

There was also great irony in Bache's looking down on those who had not received the mental disciplines and training of a higher education. He reverenced the scientific contributions of his great-grandfather Franklin, who had certainly gone to no college,[102] and of Joseph Henry, who had been educated only at Albany Academy, a boy's preparatory school of a high caliber offering excellent courses in science and mathematics but not differing greatly from Harpeth Academy,[103] where Maury had been educated. Of course, Bache was right that a scientist needed all the theoretical education he could possibly get. But wise old Dr. Franklin would surely have grieved over an exclusivist attitude that denigrated the discoveries and resultant achievement of a scientist because he had not graduated from a university in a day when relatively few Americans had that opportunity.

Fortunately for Maury, there were great numbers of men of intellect in the mid-nineteenth century who were heirs to Franklin's spirit if not to his blood. These approved Maury's unceasing endeavor to discover new facts about the physical world and gave him all possible help. A scholar in Washington who was typical of these believers in Maury was a Jesuit father, the Reverend James Curley, a professor and head of the observatory at Georgetown College. Between Curley and Maury there was a constant exchange of scientific ideas, and Curley, through his connection with Rome, early put Maury in touch with the brilliant minds at work there.[104] Admiration was mutual between these two men whose observatories were separated by little more than a mile. Father Curley had Maury address the Philodemic Society at Georgetown in 1846.[105] This friendship and ones later with other Roman Catholic scholars reveal a total lack of religious prejudice on the part of Huguenot-descended Matthew Fontaine Maury. He was proud of the courage of his forebears; but he was a man of science dedicated to the search for the facts and the meanings of the physical world, and there was no place in his thinking for Protestant-Catholic strife.

An educational institution that acknowledged Maury's contribution to knowledge at this point in his career was the University of North Carolina. In late May, 1847, with President Polk and Secretary of the Navy Mason, Maury traveled from Washington to Chapel Hill, North Carolina, to receive an honorary master of arts degree.[106] He enjoyed the sociability of the trip and the somewhat unusual circumstance of receiving a degree in the presence of the President of the United States. Maury, who had longed for higher education for himself, worked for it for others, and had rejoiced when the United States Naval Academy had been established at Annapolis in 1845,[107] was gratified by this academic recognition.

To superintend all the work going on at the Observatory and to "pull his weight on the oar," Maury had, throughout this period, continued to work fifteen hours a day and had seldom permitted anything to alter his schedule. However, on December 5, 1846, he had been called home, as requested by him, when his wife went into labor and he had an anxious time until Ann was safely through a difficult delivery.[108] The baby was their sixth, a little girl whom they had named Eliza Hull but who, because of a solemn face, was soon to be nicknamed Glum.[109]

Ann's health continued poor throughout the following winter months, and Maury was relieved when, in the spring of 1847, he finally received the orders to start construction on a superintendent's house at the Observatory. This would provide the reassurance of proximity as well as more space and comfort for his wife and children.[110]

Maury was still on his lieutenant's pay of $1,500 a year, but when his children suffered malarial chills in June and early July, 1847, and Ann continued unwell, he decided they needed a respite from Washington. He moved them into the Virginia countryside to the modest but popular Swink's Summer Boarding House, 12 miles from the capital.[111] Away from the mosquito-breeding flats of Washington, Ann's health improved, and the children loved the freedom of farm life. Maury drove out every Saturday afternoon, returning in time for work on Monday morning. On Sundays he usually took the children for a picnic at the Great Falls of the Potomac, some three miles from Swink's establishment. At the Observatory Maury found the days from Monday to Saturday dragged badly with his family away, but he took satisfaction in having his "many yawls" in a safe and healthy summer "harbor." The cost was $22 a week, which he regarded as excessive but unavoidable.[112] In the fall they would be able to move into the new house.

At the Observatory Maury's astronomical program moved ahead in spite of his having to admit to his friend Professor Elias Loomis, mathematician and astronomer: "The Mexican War has taken away some of my most efficient observers. The catalogue I find to be an undertaking indeed."[113] The chief difficulty Maury was suffering from his shortage of staff was the inability to keep on schedule the complicated, time-consuming mathematical computations, or reductions, that had to follow the astronomical observations.[114] In spite of this he was able in 1847 to report: "A catalogue of about 1,200 stars, most of them unknown to existing catalogues, is the result of the first year's work in this field."[115]

His earlier conviction was stronger than ever that "Great undertakings, such as this Catalogue, whose value and importance are confined to no country and limited to no age, are beyond the power of Astronomers working single-handed. They require a large force and abundant facilities, such as individuals cannot afford, and therefore fall peculiarly within the province and duties of government."[116]

To United States Minister George Bancroft, in London, Maury wrote that his dream was of a time when there could be a "concert of action and division of labor among the Astronomers and Observatories of all nations," but he resignedly admitted that "since this is impracticable it becomes the more important that each should work steadily and faithfully in the particular field which he may select."[117]

CHAPTER X

Charting the Winds
and Currents of the Sea

The hydrographic work of the Naval Observatory forged steadily forward. Maury transmitted to his staff his own enthusiasm for devising new charts that would show both the winds and the currents encountered at sea. By the latter part of 1846 Maury had reached a point in his investigations that made him hopeful of soon having something worthwhile to show for the tedious study of the old logbooks.

During the autumn of 1847 Maury sent his promised report to John Quincy Adams on the astronomical work of the Observatory. He took the opportunity to add to it an account of the other programs in progress, especially that of developing new charts.

> There is, also, much hydrographical duty to be performed: Charts are to be corrected or compiled; and the undertaking has been commenced here of preparing "wind and current" charts of the three grand oceans, viz.: the Atlantic, the Pacific and Indian.

> These charts are intended to generalize the experience of navigators in such a manner that each may have before him, at a glance, the experience of all. The track of each showing the time of the year, the prevailing winds and currents encountered, with all other information obtained, is projected on the charts.

> The first sheet, of which there are 8, of the Atlantic, drawn by William B. Whiting, Lieut. U.S. Navy, has already been published, the other seven are in the hands of the engraver.

> I send, herewith, a copy of sheet 1, and ask the favor of you to accept it. It relates to the Gulf of Mexico, and you will observe that it exhibits the prevailing currents and winds of that region at a glance, and with a perspicuity, certainty and generalization that written accounts cannot give. Books, if I may say so, impart information through the ear—these charts through the eye, and, therefore, in a manner and form much more condensed and available.

You will observe, by this chart, that the general currents in the Gulf of Mexico are almost as regular in their courses and as sharp in their outlines as is the Mississippi river itself. So that, with this sheet as a guide, a vessel, by turning a little to the right, or a little to the left, according to its indications, may convert an unfavorable into a favorable current, and the reverse.

Another important result to flow from these charts is the removing of all doubt as to those "Vigias," including rocks, reefs and shoals, which, by reason of the uncertainty as to their existence and position, disfigure the best general charts, harass navigators, and stand in the way of commerce.[1]

Thus, five years after he had arrived at the Depot of Charts and Instruments and first discovered the pile of old logbooks, Maury's study of them had produced the wholly new kind of charts that his genius had envisioned. And how fitting that the first of these charts that were to revolutionize navigation was drawn by Lieutenant William B. Whiting, who, when a midshipman in the *Falmouth,* had been ridiculed because he had predicted that Maury would achieve great things.[2]

The studies that produced this first chart had persuaded Maury that mariners had been sailing what were, in effect, long detours on their voyages from New York to Rio de Janeiro. A tradition among sea captains had been the belief that a ship would encounter hazardous currents if she followed a straight course south to Rio. Navigators had always, therefore, zigzagged their way on this much-traveled run. Maury computed that by the old route to Rio some ships had actually sailed the equivalent of three crossings of the Atlantic. Captains argued that if a ship fell to the leeward of Brazil's Cape St. Roque she would not be able to beat round it. In the area of this cape the prevailing trade winds blow from the southeast. Thus, to get around this bulge on the Atlantic coast of South America, navigators tacked to the east whenever there seemed a remote chance of experiencing trouble. Some captains had taken to crossing the equator much farther to the east than was necessary, only to find themselves in a region of calms or bedeviled by contrary winds from the southwest.[3]

In his years of comparing log entries made in this area Maury had discovered that the inshore current of St. Roque was far from dangerous and that, to the contrary, winds were favorable to the ships that kept fairly close to land. Hence, concerning Cape St. Roque, Maury proclaimed to navigators, "Stand boldly on, and if need be, tack, and work by under the land."[4] This was a revolutionary instruction, but Maury was so sure that his new route was safer as well as shorter that he called it "Fair Way to Rio." He gave explicit directions as to the longitude in which navigators should cross the equator in each month of the year.

It was, however, one thing to propose and another thing to persuade stubborn old salts to abandon their long-established habits.[5] But one courageous merchant captain decided to test Maury's route. He was Captain Jackson, commanding the bark *W. H. D. C. Wright* of Baltimore. Jackson was an old hand on the Rio run as he twice yearly took a cargo of flour to Brazil and returned with the hold of his ship filled with coffee. He followed Maury's sailing directions for the new route and took his ship into the harbor at Rio in February, 1848, just 38 days from the Virginia Capes. This was a saving of 17 days over the usual passage of 55 days. Then following Maury's directions for the return passage, Jackson made the trip in 37 days—proving that the initial timesaving was not merely a matter of luck. As a result, Captain Jackson was back in Baltimore 35 days before he was expected.[6] The news flashed from ship to dock, from dock to shipowner, and up and down the waterfront. This new route was no impractical idea of a theoretical naval officer. Maury knew what he was talking about; Jackson had proved it.

Public attention was directed to the achievement in an editorial in the Baltimore *American* for May 18.[7] Thereupon word spread to Philadelphia, New York, and Boston, where the coffeehouses rang with talk of what the new route meant. Every day saved at sea lessened the danger to seafarers, reduced by that much the risk of shipwreck or storm damage to cargo, and thus—and not the least important—cut the cost of shipping. From lowliest cabin boy to owners of packets or clippers—all considered Maury's new route to be news of tremendous importance, an accomplishment of the first magnitude.

At once his *Wind and Current Charts* were in great demand. Five thousand of them were soon distributed.[8] But they could not be bought except at the price of co-operation. Maury had worked out and printed a 10-page "Abstract Log for the Use of American Navigators." This pamphlet interpreted the meaning of the *Wind and Current Charts* and supplied twelve different blank forms, which were to be filled in by navigators using the charts. Careful instructions were given as to how to make the needed observations at sea and how to record them. The completed Abstract Logs were, at the end of the voyage, to be returned to Maury at the Naval Observatory, where the information would be tabulated for use in future *Wind and Current Charts*.[9] After years of "quarrying" old logbooks that varied greatly in form and content and had not been kept with an eye to scientific usage, Maury knew just how much the chart work would be expedited if the needed information were gathered systematically and reported identically. His superiors gave him full backing, and the United States Navy offered free of charge to any navigator who promised to make the observations, record them and return, a *Wind and Current Chart* of the North Atlantic.[10]

Since symbols were used, the charts, as Maury had written John Quincy Adams, were almost pictorial: "The winds are denoted by small brushes, the head of the brush pointing to the direction from whence the winds blow, the length of the brush showing the comparative force." Also delineated were

> a gale of wind, a fresh breeze, a moderate breeze, a light breeze, a very light wind, light variable airs, a moderate breeze with fresh squalls, a light breeze with fresh squalls.
>
> Currents are denoted by arrows, the length of the arrow being proportionate to the strength of the current: the figures beside the arrows show the number of knots.
>
> The Roman numerals denote the degree of Magnetic Variation as recorded by the vessel near whose track they are placed.
>
> The figures with a line drawn under them thus 80 show the temperature of the water.
>
> The name of the ship which has supplied the route and the year of the voyage is recorded.[11]

Sheets 2 and 3, it is interesting to note, showed the course Maury had sailed in the *Falmouth* in 1831, as well as that of the *Macedonian,* which he had seen in Rio in 1826, plus those of numerous other famous Navy ships.

Maury's *Wind and Current Charts* were valuable to all mariners but were of even greater significance to the captains of a new type of American ship—the clipper. In 1832 a Baltimore shipbuilder had incorporated some of the speed features of the earlier small Baltimore clippers to produce the *Ann McKim,* the first true clipper.[12] Other shipbuilders had adopted her design but altered the measurements to increase cargo space, and with the launching in 1845 of the *Rainbow,* built by John W. Griffiths in a New York shipyard, the clipper era had begun. Long, narrow, with a fine bow, and with the greatest beam aft of the center, the clipper was built for speed.[13] Soon after Jackson's fast round trip, the clipper captains began using the *Wind and Current Charts* and following the routes Maury recommended to achieve still faster voyages.

By mid-July, 1848, Maury had received the track charts of four vessels that had sailed his new route to the equator. The average time of southward passage for each of these ships had been 10 days less than by the old route.[14] But it was no surprise to Maury when he examined the logs and track charts as they came in and observed that many sea captains stuck doggedly to the old way, scorning the *Wind and Current Charts*. Maury was patient, for he knew men of the sea were slow to accept anything new; he understood their inclination to continue the old traditions. He was amused when it occurred to him that the character of a ship's captain could be read from his track at sea. He wrote, "A crazy fellow always makes a crooked track." [15]

Maury soon came to believe that his *Wind and Current Charts* could also be used to shorten the passage of the packets running from New York to Liverpool and Le Havre, a day for the first named and a week off the voyage to the French port.[16] His studies had convinced him that "They all keep too far to the South on both voyages." He wrote an English friend: "I want tracks of results in all parts of the Atlantic and Pacific. I want those of English vessels especially in the Canada, New Orleans and North of Europe trade. Pray ask him [no name] to lend me a hand with English ship owners." [17]

As England was at that time the greatest maritime power in the world, it is fitting to let a leader of British science, Lord Wrottesley, tell us the method Maury used to discover new routes. These are the words with which Wrottesley explained the process to his fellow members in the House of Lords:

It is time that I should now explain how these charts are constructed, and routes discovered. The whole ocean is divided into squares, the sides of which represent 5° of longitude, and 5° of latitude; in the midst of these squares the figure of a compass is drawn; with lines representing sixteen of the compass points, the intermediate points being omitted; the logbooks are then searched for observations of the directions of the winds and of the proportion of calms in each of these squares; in the centre of each compass so drawn are placed two numbers, one representing the total number of observations obtained in the square, the other the percentage of calm days.

By the side of each of the lines representing the sixteen points of the compass, are written numbers, which denote the percentage of the winds that have been found to blow from that quarter, and at the extremity of each line are numbers, which show the percentage of miles a ship will lose if she attempt to sail 100 miles through that particular square in the particular direction indicated by the line in question. Now that number is obtained as follows.

By the resolution of simple problems in sailing, it is known that if the wind will not allow a ship to lie within six points of her course, that is, if it be a head wind, she will lose sixty-two miles (omitting fractions) in every 100 that she sails, or in other words after sailing 100, she will only have made thirty-eight good in the wished-for direction; in like manner if she can sail within four points she loses twenty-nine miles, and if within two points, only eight; having therefore the percentage of winds that will make such deviation from the desired course necessary, it is easy by a common proportion to calculate the total amount of space lost, or detour (as Maury calls it), for every given direction, for every 100 miles sailed within the square.

When a course has to be traced, therefore, all the squares are carefully examined and by a very laborious system of trial and error, the combination of squares is found, which gives the route most likely to succeed by ascertaining those through which the loss is a minimum. I say most likely, for of course this is only a problem of chances, and the event may be adverse, as in the case of insurances, but is less likely to be so, as observations are multiplied.

I should explain that in performing this process, currents and calms are taken into account, and that there are separate compasses drawn, and separate routes traced for each of the twelve months of the year; for though the winds are assumed to be so far constant for individual months as to give an average on which some reliance may be placed, when the number of observations is sufficiently large, this is by no means the case throughout the whole year. When the twelve compasses have been delineated and filled up, they are combined by a peculiar and neat arrangement of the numbers within concentric circles, into one, and a chart of the ocean, containing these combinations, is termed a pilot chart.[18]

Lord Wrottesley was but one leader across the Atlantic who early joined mariners in recognizing that Maury had put an end to navigation "b' guess and b' God" for all who were willing to use the findings of systematic, scientific investigation of the sea.

In Washington Maury found his long hours of work less trying after the superintendent's house on the Observatory grounds was completed. He could go quickly from his desk to his home for dinner and back to work.[19] It was also easier to offer hospitality to distinguished guests who called at the Observatory. But the cost of entertaining proved burdensome, for Maury was still struggling along on the inadequate pay of a lieutenant. Congress had voted a salary of $3,000 a year for the superintendent of the Observatory, but the congressman who had drafted the bill, no doubt thinking to honor Maury for his work with the charts, had called him "the Superintendent of the Marine." As a result, inasmuch as neither Maury nor anyone else held such a title, the auditors of the Treasury had not been willing to pay him the authorized salary.[20] The long wait for Congress to clarify its meaning was, to say the least, difficult for Maury. In mid-April, 1848, he commented to a friend, "No pay yet and I am very tired of living on such slender means. Better times I hope are coming. This poverty is a terrible weight upon one's will and wants." Two months later he wrote hopefully to a cousin: "The pay has almost passed the House, and I begin to think of increasing expenses in the way of education etc. for the children, church and social facilities for Nannie." [21] But instead the matter dragged on that summer while all the Maurys had their annual bout with malarial chills and fever. Finally, on August 25, 1848, Maury reported to the same interested relative, "Congress declared the 'Superintendent of the Marine' to mean me . . . the pay was made to commence March 3rd, 1847." [22] The lawmakers had at last made concrete expression of their appreciation by making the pay increase retroactive to the period over a year earlier when Maury's scientific work had first earned international acclaim for the hydrographic work of the United States Navy.

After twenty-three years of naval service, Maury at last had sufficient income to relieve his mind of continued worry about proper support of his family. However, he knew that more official funds would have to be made available to the Observatory if he were to increase the scope of his investigation of the winds and currents to chart additional new "paths through the sea."

Among the first to grasp the extent of the potential savings that Maury's oceanographic research could effect were Robert Bennett Forbes [23] and other merchants and shipowners of Boston. In June, 1848, they had offered to raise $50,000 to buy a vessel to put at Maury's disposal to try new routes that his investigations suggested. Maury had expressed his appreciation but pointed out that this was a government program and should be carried out by Navy ships.[24] The merchants had "then petitioned Uncle Sam to detail a man of war for the purpose, to which the old gentleman readily gave a pie-crust promise," Maury had told a friend.[25] This sounds cynical, but Maury had been burned before by political promises and the long wrangling involved in bringing them to fruition.[26]

There were, however, political figures with whom Maury enjoyed occasional visits. Among these was South Carolina's John C. Calhoun, now back in the Senate after service as Secretary of State, having previously twice been Vice-President as well as Secretary of War.[27] Although disagreeing with the elder statesman on some of his proposals, Maury admired Calhoun's mind and his powers of expression. But their chief mutual interest was westward expansion of the railroads. Another man in high office whom Maury saw occasionally was James Buchanan of Pennsylvania, who had been minister to Russia and U.S. senator prior to appointment by President Polk as Secretary of State.[28] While Calhoun and Buchanan were both Democrats, neither Maury's friendships nor his professional relationships were confined to men of any one party or way of thought. In these years he was still hopeful that the national leaders would act as statesmen rather than politicians, and he was critical when they didn't.

As always Maury found time to give a helping hand to young people. He secured a berth in the Navy's Engineer Corps for a cousin, John Minor (Jack) Maury, but was equally solicitous for youths he did not know.[29] Concerning one of the latter he wrote: "He is from Richmond, came here on foot and on his own hook after his Midshipman's appointment. I am not, I think, wanting in reverence for the commandment [Honor thy father and thy mother] but whenever I come across one of these run-away boys my heart always warms up towards him. I mean these brave fellows that have dared the world and are consistent in their energies." [30] Whether Maury was able to get this boy an appointment was not stated; but later he did procure a naval appointment for his nephew Dick Van Buren Holland, whose father had given his life in the Mexican War.[31]

By the end of the summer of 1848 the number of track charts and properly filled out Abstract Logs reaching the Observatory had greatly increased.[32] Not all captains who received copies of the *Wind and Current Charts* kept their agreement to fill in the logs and return them, but many did; and Maury and his associates were busy working on new charts.

In the meantime a major development among scientists had taken place—the formation of the American Association for the Advancement of Science. The progenitors were the American Association of Geologists and Naturalists and the National Institute for the Promotion of Science. The latter society had entertained the former in Washington in 1844, and Maury had spoken before the convention and later, separately, to the geologists. The name for the new association was a rough approximation of half the name of each organization.[33] It was expected that the new society would be to the United States what the very active British Association for the Advancement of Science was to England.

As a member of the new scientific body, Maury went to Philadelphia to attend the first meeting, held on September 20, 1848. Because he had proposed the most comprehensive plans for the organization, William C.

Redfield was elected president. Typical of the self-taught scientist of the early nineteenth century, Redfield, after starting life as a saddler, had gone on to make contributions in the study of American fossil fish and as a pioneer meteorologist. His business acumen had led him to promote the first barge line on the Hudson River.[34]

At a meeting held on Friday afternoon, September 22, Redfield presided, and Maury gave a full scientific report on the *Wind and Current Charts*. He stated that hundreds of ship navigators were now sending to the Observatory abstract logs of their voyages. With pride he added, "Never before was such a corps of observers known." But, he pointed out to his fellow scientists, his critical need was for more "simultaneous observations."

"The work," he stated, "is not exclusively for the benefit of any nation or age." [35] The minutes of the A.A.A.S. meeting reveal that because of the universality of this "view on the subject, it was suggested whether the states of Christendom might not be induced to co-operate with their Navies in the undertaking; at least so far as to cause abstracts of their log-books and sea journals to be furnished to Lieutenant Maury at the National Observatory at Washington."[36]

William Barton Rogers, professor at the University of Virginia and later founder of the Massachusetts Institute of Technology, offered a resolution: "Resolved that a Committee of five be appointed to address a memorial to the Secretary of the Navy, requesting his further aid in procuring for Lieutenant Maury the use of the observations of European and other foreign navigators, for the extension and perfecting of his charts of winds and currents." [37] The resolution was adopted and, in addition to Rogers, the following members of the Association were appointed to the committee, Professor Joseph Henry of Washington, Professor Benjamin Peirce of Cambridge, Massachusetts, Professor James H. Coffin of Easton, Pennsylvania, Professor Stephen Alexander of Princeton, New Jersey.[38]

This was scientific co-operation, and Maury went back to Washington with great hopes for the future. He was also much pleased by the scientific success of an exploration just completed by a fellow naval officer and friend, Lieutenant William Francis Lynch. With a paucity of sea billets available once victory in the Mexican War had been assured the United States by the capture of Mexico City in September of 1847, Lynch had conceived the idea of a Navy expedition to explore the Dead Sea and the River Jordan, and he had secured authorization from Secretary of the Navy Mason for the project. The exploration had been carried out in two sectional boats especially made for Lynch before he left the United States in the store ship *Supply*. Lynch and his party of four officers and nine seamen had suffered great hardships but had brought back invaluable scientific data on the area that Maury reported in an article published in the *Southern Literary Messenger* that September of 1848.[39]

In the subsequent autumn months more charts were completed at the Naval Observatory and were sent to the engraver. By 1849 eight of the 35.3 by 24.1 inch sheets had come off the presses in Washington. These covered the Atlantic Ocean, North. Then followed the charts of the Atlantic Ocean, South. The Indian Ocean was next charted; the Pacific Ocean, North followed, and, subsequently, the Pacific Ocean, South. These were all in Series A, Track Charts.

Series B was more specialized and included a Trade Wind Chart for the Atlantic and a Monsoon and Trade Wind Chart for the Indian Ocean.

Series C, in 1849, began what were to become the famous Pilot Charts of the United States Navy. One of these was an improved and enlarged version of *Atlantic Ocean, North, Wind and Current Chart,* while special areas were now covered, such as the coast of Brazil and Cape Horn, as well as the Pacific and Indian oceans.[40] Some of the knowledge of currents was gained by enlisting seamen of all co-operating vessels to mark position and date on paper, seal in a bottle and throw overboard. Finders were asked to record and send to Maury the date as well as the latitude and longitude where the bottle had been picked up or had come ashore.[41] This simple practice brought results then; and today, even with the techniques devised by modern science, it is still used by oceanographers.

Series D consisted of Thermal Sheets, which recorded the temperature of the surface of the ocean at the place and time the observation had been made. Maury made these charts pictorial by using colors and symbols to distinguish the different temperatures.

Storm and Rain Charts formed Series E and supplied in every square of five degrees the number of observations that had been made for each month, the number of days there had been rain, a calm, fog, lightning and thunder, or a storm, as well as the quarter from which the storm had blown.[42] These and all the other charts were the result of the most detailed work, but Maury's interest did not flag because, as he said, "Some new discovery, some new fact or law of nature is continually starting up before us as we proceed with our investigations." [43]

The sheets of the Whale Chart of the world made up Series F and provided information on breeding habits, migrations, and the places where the most whales were to be located in different seasons of the year. Because they proved of immediate practical value to the whaling fleet, then an important segment of America's merchant marine, they brought down on Maury's head the ridicule of certain critical savants.[44] However, these studies, in which Maury was assisted by his brother-in-law, Lieutenant William Lewis Herndon, revealed a fact that gave promise of a scientific break-through. The possibility stirred Maury into writing to the scientist whom he admired more than any other of his era, the German naturalist and explorer, Baron Alexander von Humboldt.[45] Through his friend, Professor Rumker of Hamburg, Maury, in 1849, sent a set of *Wind and Current Charts* to Baron von Humboldt with mention of various findings that had been made but with details of new deductions he had just made from the Whale Chart. He reported that whales bearing the harpoons of whalers in one arctic sea had been taken by whalers working in a different ocean. These findings, Maury commented, "tend to show that there is occasionally a water communication from strait to strait—in other words a northwest passage?" [46] The question mark, hallmark of the inquiring brain, was necessary until there was further proof. Maury's theory was to be proved correct in a few years when British naval officer and arctic explorer, Sir Robert John LeM. McClure discovered the connecting strait (later named for him) and became the first to establish the existence of a northwest passage.[47]

In all his preoccupation with his own work Maury retained a lively interest in developments on the national and international scene. The preceding year, when France had deposed Louis Philippe and set up the Second Republic, Maury had commented, "That is a glorious move in France if the people will only continue it like men and not like beasts." He had predicted that in fifty years, "If we will only continue true to ourselves that ball which the United States has put in motion will roll around the world" and that then "you would see the people of Europe, sovereigns all. Subjects will be as scarce there as princes are here." [48]

The Maurys themselves had gained a new "sovereign" of the household on January 9, 1849 when Matthew Fontaine Maury, Jr. had been born.[49] The little boy was to grow into a real companion to his father and to earn his nickname, Brave.

The *Wind and Current Charts* and *Sailing Directions* assumed prime importance when the wild rush to get to California began in 1849. The discovery of gold near Sutter's Mill in the Sacramento Valley the preceding year had set off the stampede, and speed in reaching California became the first consideration of the fortune hunters [50] and of shipowners who would transport and supply the gold seekers. This general demand for speed in reaching California, as well as the national government's interest in protection of its people making the long voyage, undoubtedly precipitated action on a piece of legislation desired by Maury. This was the fulfillment of the "pie-crust promise" that "Uncle Sam" had given Boston merchants months before.

On March 3, 1849, Congress passed an act the second section of which authorized that three small Navy vessels be made available to assist Maury in further studies of the winds and currents of the sea and in his search for shorter and safer sea routes.[51] Maury could have used the three, but since Congress had not appropriated operating funds for the research vessels, Maury felt himself fortunate to get one ship assigned for this work.[52] October 1 found him drafting detailed instructions as to observations and investigations to be carried out by the U.S.S. *Taney,* which sailed shortly thereafter. The ship was commanded by Lieutenant J. C. Walsh.[53]

In the spring of 1849, Maury had urged that a railroad be built across the Isthmus of Panama. Some of the most daring of the gold seekers were taking ship from New York to Aspinwall (Colón) on the Atlantic side of the Isthmus and hacking their way through the jungle to the Pacific side, where they could board a ship and sail north to California, but the mortality among such adventurers was dreadful. Maury was convinced that a railroad could and should be built across the narrow Isthmus of Panama instead of constructing a railroad across Mexico's Tehuantepec Isthmus, where the greater distance would require more rail. A letter from him on this subject had been read to Congress during its deliberations on the matter and published in the July, 1849, issue of *De Bow's Review,* while a fuller article entitled "Panama Railway and the Gulf of Mexico" appeared in August in the *Southern Literary Messenger.*[54] That fall Maury traveled to Tennessee to preside over the Memphis Convention, where the delegates from fourteen states discussed, among other subjects, a ship canal across the Isthmus of Panama and a national railroad from the Mississippi River to the Pacific. Maury's views expressed at this gathering were reported in Washington's *National Intelligencer* on November 29 and December 1. He was appalled when he received a check from a business that stood to gain from his views and promptly returned that $500 and refused the offer of more to come.[55]

The third meeting of the American Association for the Advancement of Science was held in Charleston, South Carolina, beginning March 12, 1850. New members on the Association's committee on Maury's *Wind and Current Charts* included William C. Redfield and Professor Arnold Guyot of Cambridge, Massachusetts, formerly of Switzerland, a meterologist of great ability. Maury was a member of the committees on the Prime Meridian, on Weights and Measures, and on Publication of an Astronomical Journal. On successive days Maury presented papers on "The Influence Arising from the Discovery of the Gulf Stream upon the

Commerce of Charleston," "The Application of the Electro-Chronograph in determining the Figure and Density of the Earth," "The Currents of the Atlantic Ocean," and "The General Circulation of the Atmosphere." [56] He returned to Washington refreshed by association with his fellow scientists.

As a result of his studies, Maury had, by 1851, shortened the passage from New York to San Francisco by 40 to 44 days. The average time of ships *not* using the *Wind and Current Charts* was 187½ days to California—only 144½ days for those that did.[57]

The value of Maury's charts and *Sailing Directions* was dramatically demonstrated by their use in the great races of clipper ships from New York to San Francisco. These spectacular events captured the imagination of the public, and landlubbers who would never have heard of them from Navy use alone came to know about Maury's routes. In 1851 Captain Josiah P. Creesy in the *Flying Cloud,* using Maury's charts and following his route, established a record by making the New York to San Francisco voyage in 89 days and 21 hours. In one day this sleek clipper, length 235 feet, beam 41, depth of hold 21½ feet, tonnage 1,782, built by Donald McKay, sailed 374 nautical miles, which to the landsman means a shade over 18 statute miles per hour.[58] San Francisco went wild when the *Flying Cloud* arrived and clipper men swore that steam could never beat such an achievement. Feeling was intense between those who advocated sail for long cruises, steamers for short, and those who were exclusively for steam.

To no one's surprise, clipper ships could not resist turning the 15,000 miles between New York and San Francisco into a race course. Many a clipper found the winds so favorable along the route Maury had delineated for this voyage that the topsails had to be reefed not more than twice. A great race took place in 1851 between the *Raven,* the *Typhoon,* and the *Sea Witch*—all three ships being supplied with Maury's charts. The *Raven* was the victor, making the run in 105 days, though she had in 1850 made the passage in 97 days while using Maury's charts and directions.[59]

No wonder Maury wrote of the New York to San Francisco race cruise: "Some of the most glorious trials of speed and prowess that the world ever witnessed, among ships that 'walk the waters,' have taken place over it. Here the modern clipper ship—the noblest work that has ever come from the hands of man—has been sent, guided by the lights of science, to contend with the elements, to outstrip steam, and astonish the world." [60]

Probably the most celebrated of these New York to California races was one made in the autumn of 1852 by the *Wild Pigeon,* Captain Putnam, the *John Gilpin,* Captain Doane, the *Flying Fish,* Captain Nickels, and the *Trade Wind*, Captain Webber. The departures were spaced as the clippers were racing against time. The *Wild Pigeon* sailed October 12, the *John Gilpin* October 29, the *Flying Fish* November 1 and the *Trade Wind* November 14. The *Wild Pigeon* had bad luck on winds as she sailed south, so the *John Gilpin* and the *Flying Fish* gained on her, but the *Flying Fish* did not obey the Maury instructions as to course. Describing this part of the race Maury wrote:

> The *Sailing Directions* had cautioned the navigator, again and again, not to attempt to fan along to the eastward in the equatorial doldrums; for, by so doing, he would himself engage in a fruitless strife with baffling airs, sometimes re-enforced in their weakness by westerly currents. But the winds had failed, and so too, the smart captain of the *Flying Fish* evidently thought, had the *Sailing Directions*. They advise the navigator, in all such cases, to dash right across this calm streak, stand boldly on, take advantage of slants in the wind, and by this device, make easting enough to clear the land. So, forgetting that the charts are founded on the experience of great numbers who had gone before him, Nickels, being tempted, turned a deaf ear to the caution, and flung away three whole days and more of most precious time, dallying in the doldrums.[61]

The master of the *Flying Fish* recorded in his log his regret over this mistake; but afterwards he fully made up for the error, and when the *Flying Fish* and the *Wild Pigeon* rounded the Horn they were both one day ahead of the *John Gilpin*. Small wonder that the captain of the *Wild Pigeon*, when he sighted a clipper ship on December 30, was unable to believe it could be the *Flying Fish*, which had left New York three weeks after him!

Sailing north up the west coast of South America, the two had a nip-and-tuck race. The *John Gilpin* added to the excitement by crossing the equator two days after the *Flying Fish* and the *Wild Pigeon* "and made the glorious run of 15 days thence to the pilot grounds of San Francisco." "The *Flying Fish* beat: she made the passage in 92 days and 4 hours from port to anchor; the [*John*] *Gilpin* in 93 days and 20 hours from port to pilot; the *Wild Pigeon* in 118. The *Trade Wind* followed with 102 days, having taken fire, and burned for eight hours on the way.[62]

In referring to this race, Maury asked, "Am I far wrong, therefore, when I say that the present state of our knowledge with regard to the physical geography of the sea has enabled the navigator to blaze his way among the winds and currents of the sea, and so mark his path that others, using his signs as fingerboards, may follow in the exact track?" [63]

Among the other remarkable runs made by clipper ships using Maury's charts and directions was one he reported to the Secretary of the Navy in the spring of 1853. This was a passage by the *Sovereign of the Seas* from the Sandwich (Hawaiian) Islands to New York in 82 days. On one of these days she sailed 374 knots or 433¼ statute miles.[64]

It was Maury's perception and leadership in determining the best routes or "paths through the seas," and marking them on charts that any navigator could follow that gave him his well-known title, "Pathfinder of the Seas."

From this time on Maury had little trouble in getting captains to use the charts and sailing directions or in persuading them to fill in the Abstract Logs furnished by the Observatory in Washington. On these the navigator was required to enter the latitude and longitude daily at noon, the hourly rate of current, variations of the compass and barometer, the reading of the thermometer in both air and water at 9 A.M. daily, plus the direction and force of the wind every 8 hours. Rain, fog, sudden changes in wind and the time of change also were to be recorded, as was the sighting of flocks of birds or whales.[65]

By the end of 1851 Maury could report a thousand American ships on the high seas were faithfully recording this information and at the end of each voyage sending it in to him.[66] The letters that accompanied these logs kept the naval scientist enthusiastically at work. One such came from Captain Phinney of the clipper *Gertrude,* who sent "abstracts of my two passages over your southern routes," declaring, "Such as it is, I am happy to contribute my mite towards furnishing you with material to work out still farther towards perfection your great and glorious task, not only of pointing out the most speedy route for ships to follow over the ocean, but also teaching us sailors to look about us and recognize the wonderful manifestations of the wisdom and goodness of the great God. . . . For myself I am free to confess that for [the] many years I commanded a ship . . . I yet feel that until I took up your work I had been traversing the ocean blindfold." [67]

An example of the exact determinations that were made possible by Maury's study of wind and currents occurred when the *San Francisco* was disabled in a hurricane on Christmas Eve, 1853. The ship, bound for California, had sailed from New York with a regiment of soldiers on board. She had proceeded only 300 miles from Sandy Hook and was crossing the Gulf Stream when violent hurricane winds ripped her sails, dismasted her, and placed her at the mercy of wind and wave. On December 26 a small brig, the *Napoleon,* sighted the helpless ship in Latitude 38° 20′ N, Longitude 69° W, but due to heavy seas was unable to assist her. Instead, the *Napoleon* sailed as fast as possible to New York to report the situation. Other ships also sighted the powerless *San*

Francisco but found it impossible to get up close enough or to send boats to help her. When word of the disaster reached Washington, the Secretary of the Navy determined to send two fast revenue cutters to the rescue but first requested that Maury calculate the position at which the drifting *San Francisco* would be found.[68]

Here was one of Maury's most dramatic challenges and opportunities. After fifteen years' study of the Gulf Stream, he knew her powerful current, but he systematically studied the squares on his *Wind and Current Chart* and *Thermal Chart* for that section of the Atlantic, carefully made computations in his usual tiny, imperfectly formed numerals, and rechecked his figures for the effect on the drifting wreck of both winds and currents. Picking up his large blue pencil he placed an X at that spot on the chart to which the *San Francisco* would have drifted by the time the cutters could reach her. Then he wrote out detailed instructions for the rescue ships to follow in locating the ship and gave them to his superior, the chief of the Bureau of Ordnance and Hydrography.[69]

The cutters sailed immediately and followed Maury's instructions. Before they reached the *San Francisco,* three other ships, the *Kilby,* the *Three Bells,* and the *Antarctic,* had fallen in with her and rescued those passengers left on board after 179 had been swept into the sea. The officers of the cutters learned that the *San Francisco* had drifted to almost the exact spot at which Maury had said she would be found, that it was there that the rescue had just shortly before been effected.[70] This event proved to many who had remained skeptical that Maury's charts were indeed worthwhile.

Hazards of seafaring had been greatly reduced, and the new sea routes achieved large savings for the navies, merchants, and shipowners of the world. The shortening of one route alone gives an indication of the scope of the saving. The long-accepted British Admiralty route from England to Australia and New Zealand passed near the Cape of Good Hope but Maury's new route called for navigators to sail 600 to 800 miles farther westward and then bear southward until they reached the belt of prevailing strong westerly winds. Those "brave west winds," Maury pointed out, would drive their ships forward at incredible speed and would do the same for them on the return voyage, which he recommended be made by Cape Horn.[71] Maury's new globe-circling route cut the passage by one third for American sailing vessels and by one fifth for British. This meant a £1,300 saving per 1,000-ton ship on each voyage made by a British vessel.[72]

Even before Maury developed *Wind and Current Charts* and *Sailing Directions* for the Indian Ocean it was estimated in Bombay that those works would save the British from $1,000,000 to $2,000,000 annually in the commerce with India. The total saving effected each year for British commerce was computed at $10,000,000.[73] By 1855 the average voyage from New York to San Francisco was cut to 136 days while scores of vessels sailed it in less than 110 days.[74] It was estimated that the United States saved $2,250,000 annually on the outward voyage of freight shipped to South America, China, and the East Indies, with similar large savings on the other routes. The marine insurers benefited greatly, and the merchants and underwriters of New York were so appreciative that in 1853 they presented Maury with a handsome silver service and also a purse of $5,000.[75]

Throughout the rest of Maury's tenure of office as superintendent of the Naval Observatory the *Wind and Current Charts* were under constant revision as new information came in. Maury frankly admitted errors and quickly corrected them.[76] The rule by which he worked he announced repeatedly in his *Sailing Directions:* "To keep the mind unbiased by theories and speculations; never to have any wish that an investigation would result in favor of this view in preference to that, and never to attempt by premature speculation to anticipate the results of investigation, but always to trust to the observations." [77]

Some of the theories that Maury deduced from his studies were criticized by contemporary scientists. Sir John Herschel of England, who believed all ocean currents were caused by the winds, made long and persistent denial of Maury's "theory of marine currents as due to different specific gravities of polar and equatorial waters." [78] Sir Charles Lyell, British geologist who long thought that the continents and oceans had repeatedly changed places during their developmental history, stoutly opposed Maury's views of submarine circulation. Some of Maury's most debated theories were later verified by the extensive deep-sea and surface current observations by British oceanographer William B. Carpenter.[79]

The practical men of the sea, however, were not interested in scientific argument about conclusions that Maury had reached from his studies—only in the value to them of his work. The contemporary viewpoint of the British Admiralty on the effectiveness of Maury's *Wind and Current Charts* and *Sailing Directions* was expressed by Admiral Robert Fitzroy, Royal Navy, when he declared: "No criticism can destroy the intrinsic value of such systems of average as those by which the results were drawn [by Maury] from accumulations of facts. Opinions of their value have not varied since the first consignment reached the Board of Trade [London] in 1854-55." [80]

The British admiral and meteorologist was paying tribute to Maury's discovery that sailing ship routes depended on the distribution of atmospheric pressure and to his method of making use of the climatological average of pressure distribution to determine new routes.[81]

Each year, as more and more observers sent in information, Maury enlarged the *Explanations and Sailing Directions,* which accompanied the charts, until the eighth edition, published in 1858-1859, ran to 1,300 packed pages that had to be divided into two volumes. With Maury's departure from the Observatory in 1861 and the complete involvements of the country in Civil War, publication of the charts was suspended. Fortunately the United States Navy Hydrographic Office left behind the animosities engendered by war and again began publishing the pilot charts in 1883. The May, 1884, chart not only indicated the winds but once more carried Maury's old sailing ship routes across the Atlantic and to the equator. Other charts were gradually published until the series was complete in 1915.[82] On each chart was printed this statement: "Founded upon the researches made in the early part of the nineteenth century by Matthew Fontaine Maury while serving as a lieutenant in the U.S. Navy." Today's Pilot Charts, while offering all the knowledge that modern oceanography has gained, still acknowledge their debt to the pioneer who first conceived them. This is perhaps the memorial that Maury himself would have liked best.

CHAPTER XI

For Scientific Co-operation Between Nations

Maury's scientific investigations caused him to think increasingly in terms of the world. As a boy he had been anxious to get out into broader fields of experience than the family farm in a narrow valley could offer. In his mature years Maury's sights were extremely broad in scope. He enjoyed the fact that his superintendency of the Observatory permitted him to work in three fields of scientific endeavor—hydrography, meteorology, and astronomy. He believed that his varied studies were all related by one theme—discovering information that would be useful to the human race. He had an ardent love for his country and was eager for the United States to make contributions commensurate with the capabilities of her people. But Maury was more internationalist than nationalist. His interest in the nations and people of the world had begun in 1825 on his European and Mediterranean cruise in the *Brandywine,* had been nurtured in South America and on his voyage around the world. His study of astronomy, of the currents of the sea, and of the winds that stopped at no national border had by 1850 further widened Maury's horizon. He had become convinced that international co-operation was a necessity in the physical sciences.

After the Observatory staff had been increased, Maury had ceased to serve as a regular observer at the astronomical instruments and had evening hours free. Occasional evenings were devoted to attending dinners given by the British or French minister, the Secretary of War or of the Navy, or by a member of Congress.[1] Because of his interest in naval protection for the Mississippi and reclamation of the "drowned lands" of that river, Maury was in close touch with the Tennessee delegation in Congress.[2] He saw a good deal of congressmen who were working for a railroad to the Pacific coast and development of the Northwest.[3] He was also on friendly terms with the Virginians in Congress and in high positions in the government. His closest personal friend in Washington was his second cousin, John Walker Maury, who was president of the Bank of the Metropolis. Having served as an alderman since 1845, Walker Maury, as he was called, was active in the life of the city, and was soon to become Washington's mayor for two years.[4] He worked closely with William Wilson Corcoran on efforts to beautify the city and to secure needed hospitals.[5] Through Walker, Maury came to know Corcoran and work with him to strengthen the capital's scientific society, the National Institute, of which Maury was a director and later president.[6]

Most evenings, however, found Maury on the Observatory hill. He usually tried to conclude his official duties at six o'clock so that he could join his family for tea (supper). Ann was a capable housekeeper and served good food, though simple. Her husband believed in the pleasures of the table and in quiet service—so that conversation could be enjoyed.[7] Because he felt no subject was too complicated to be made clear to intelligent boys and girls, he brought his newest thoughts straight to the family for discussion.[8] He would elaborate some new thought or plan and ask for reactions and opinions from his young people. He was good at simplifying complex topics, and the children could seldom resist his enthusiasm.

After tea Maury prepared for an evening of work on his personal project of the moment, such as an article he was writing for some magazine. He worked up to it by a "constitutional" that consisted of walking back and forth across the parlor, smoking vigorously as he walked, he said, "to refresh myself after the labors of the day and prepare for those of the night." [9] He dictated personal letters, first one to Betty, then one to Diana. Many of Maury's letters were written to distant acquaintances who could supply him with information needed for the advancement of his projects. He was given to stating his own views freely but also to asking for the views of his correspondent. An exchange of ideas was as necessary to Maury as it had been to Jefferson, Madison, and Monroe. To his close friends he wrote as if he were talking to them in person, and this process relaxed and renewed him for the evening's more serious writing.

At a round marble-topped table in the center of the parlor "with his papers spread out, the bright light falling on his bald head [top of head prematurely bald] and shining on his brown curls, while he sat unconscious of what was going on around him; whether it was music, or dancing, or reading aloud or romping, he would write away, or read what he had written, or talk to himself and shake his head." [10]

It was in this evening period that Maury carried on his extended writing efforts in behalf of freedom of navigation of the Amazon River. Over the years Maury had corresponded with United States naval and diplomatic officers stationed in South America and thus added to the knowledge he had gained of that continent while serving in her waters as a young officer. He had also read widely on the subject. In 1849 he took time to put together his material and soon afterwards began to urge that the Amazon Valley be explored so that the world could gain more information concerning its potential. Proud of the recent Navy-sponsored exploration of the Dead Sea which his friend Lieutenant William F. Lynch had commanded, Maury believed that the Navy could do an equally fine job on the Amazon. When Whig Zachary Taylor succeeded Democrat James K. Polk as President in 1849, William Ballard Preston of Virginia succeeded John Y. Mason as Secretary of the Navy. Maury brought to Preston's attention some of his exploration ideas, and the Secretary received them favorably but took no action because of his short tenure of office resulting from the death of President Taylor on July 9, 1850.[11] When Millard Fillmore was elevated from the Vice-Presidency to the Presidency, he chose William Alexander Graham of North Carolina for Secretary of the Navy.

Secretary Graham, whom Maury had met several years before in Chapel Hill, North Carolina, listened with interest when Maury laid before him proposals for an exploration of the Amazon.[12] The United States had earlier been refused permission to send a steamer up the Amazon for scientific exploration. In September, 1850, Dom Pedro II, Emperor of Brazil, approved a law authorizing Brazilian steam navigation of the river.[13] Thus it seemed that Brazil intended to continue her policy of keeping the door tightly closed on the mightiest of rivers. Since large-scale exploration was not to be permitted, Maury proposed a substitute plan to Secretary Graham. Maury's brother-in-law, Lieutenant William Lewis Herndon, who had recently served at the Observatory, was at that time on duty on the west coast of South America. He and a fellow officer, Passed Midshipman Lardner Gibbon, "were ordered to cross over the Andes from Lima, and descend the Amazon as they might," stated Maury.[14] The two officers left Lima on May 21, 1851.[15]

During the long months of silence that followed the start of the expedition, Maury wrote a series of seven articles in the form of letters that were published in the *National Intelligencer* between November 17 and December 3, 1852. The articles bore the title, "The Amazon and Atlantic Slopes of South America," and were signed "Inca," but it was common knowledge that Maury was the author.[16] He described the commercial, mineral, and agricultural potentialities of this rich but undeveloped area and pleaded for the Amazon to be opened to the ships of all nations.

After Maury's "Inca Letters" were published as a pamphlet in 1853,[17] they were translated and published in those nations through which the Amazon flowed. The first general reaction of Brazilians was that the United States was trying to dictate domestic policy to their nation. There were, however, some Brazilians who discussed the desirability of opening the river.[18]

Early in 1853 William Lewis Herndon returned to the United States and came to the Observatory to stay with the Maurys. He reported that, in order to gain more information, he and Lardner Gibbon had decided to part in the high Andes and proceed downstream by separate tributaries, each making his own way down the Amazon to its mouth.[19] Herndon, who was slight of stature, was physically exhausted by the ordeal he had been through. Maury's wrath was stirred and he declared that "in consequence of this Japanese [closed-door] spirit that still lingers in Brazil, our officers, in pursuit of science and of knowledge for the human family, were, by this dog-in-the-manger policy, compelled to undergo all sorts of exposure, and, living on monkeys and sea-cows, to descend that mighty river, from its sources to its mouth, on rafts, in dugouts, and upon such floating things as they could find. The reports of these officers will no doubt open the eyes of the country to the importance of this region." [20]

Maury was understandably fascinated by Herndon's journal. It opened with an account of the officers' ascent of the western slopes of the Andes. Then came this description of Herndon's emotions when he reached a headwater of the Amazon:

> Though not yet sixty miles from the sea, we had crossed the great "divide" which separates the waters of the Pacific from the waters of the Atlantic. The last steps of our mules had made a striking change in our geographical relations—so suddenly and so quickly had we been cut off from all connexion with the Pacific, and placed upon waters that . . . danced by our feet on their way to join . . . the dark blue ocean that washes the shores of our own dear land. They whispered to me of home, and my heart went along with them. I thought of Maury, with his researches concerning the currents of the sea; and, recollecting the close physical connexion pointed out by him as existing between these the waters of the Amazon and those of our own majestic Mississippi, I musingly dropped a bit of green moss, plucked from the hillside, upon the bosom of the placid Morococha, and as it floated along I followed it, in imagination, down through the luxurious climes, the beautiful skies, and enchanting scenery of the tropics, to the mouth of the great river that this little lake was feeding; thence across the Caribbean sea, through

the Yucatan pass into the Gulf of Mexico; thence along the Gulf Stream, and so out upon the ocean off the shores of our own "land of flowers." [21]

Herndon was joined at the Observatory by Gibbon, and they prepared their official report, which was published by congressional authorization. Herndon's account of his journey was published in 1853.[22] Gibbon's account, published in 1854, became the second volume of their joint story, *Exploration of the Valley of the Amazon*.[23] During their stay at the Observatory, Maury talked nightly with the explorers and gained much fresh information on the Amazon.

Interest in the adventurous exploration was widespread, and editors asked Maury to prepare articles on the subject. These appeared in *De Bow's Review* in February, May, June, and July and in the *Southern Quarterly Review* in October, 1853. On fire with enthusiasm for this subject, Maury revealed Brazil had ordered the arrest, if he ever came there, of the great European scientist Alexander von Humboldt, who had traveled elsewhere in South America. This alone, Maury said, showed the stupidity of the "closed door" policy. He presented his estimate of the wealth that opening the Amazon would bring both to Brazil and to other countries and even outlined a plan by which free navigation could be brought about.[24]

According to a pamphlet published at that time in Charleston, South Carolina, entitled *Maury on South America and Amazonia*, "The credit of reviving in the United States the question of the agricultural and commercial benefits to be derived from developing the natural advantages of the slopes of that country [Amazonia] is eminently due to Lieutenant Maury of the Navy." [25]

Aside from his writing Maury used his personal suasion to influence men in Washington in behalf of free navigation of the Amazon. That his efforts reached beyond congressional and cabinet ranks is revealed in a letter he wrote in September, 1852, to his newspaper-editor friend, William Matthews Blackford, who had earlier served as U.S. chargé d'affaires at Bogotá (Colombia): "Do you see the recalled Brazilian minister is sent home in the *Saranac*? Since Mr. Webster [Secretary of State Daniel Webster] would not be moved to action with regard to the great Amazonian question, this expedient was resorted to by Mr. Graham [Secretary of Navy William A. Graham] of sending S_____ [illegible] and S_____ is pledged to agitate the question at home, both with the government and in the public prints. It is his request. I have drawn up for him the papers which he is to present and the arguments he is to use—a curious piece of private history." [26] Maury was apparently referring to Luis Pereira Sodre, who ceased to represent Brazil as chargé d'affaires in Washington in September, 1852.[27]

Maury's chief influence on Congress in the matter was effected through his memorial for the free navigation of the Amazon, which had the backing of the 14-state economic congress, the Memphis Convention, and was presented to the House early in 1854 and favorably reported by Representative Ingersoll to the House of Representatives on February 23, 1855. The memorial stated the reasons why it would be to the advantage of the nations of the world for the United States to make formal request of Brazil to open the Amazon to the ships of all countries.[28]

In South America, the republics of Bolivia and Peru took the lead in the attempt to persuade Brazil to open the river. Both nations were anxious to be able to have their ships proceed from their countries' tributary rivers into the main stream of the Amazon and so to the Atlantic. This privilege had been denied them by Brazil. Angered by the necessity for transporting all her exports across the Andes to her sole port, Cobija, on the Acre River, to the Pacific and thence around Cape Horn, Bolivia passed a decree on January 27, 1853, declaring that no power shall "arrogate sovereignty over the Amazon and La Plata." The decree stated that both great streams into which her rivers flowed, were "free to all the nations of the globe." It further established nineteen free ports on Bolivia's own rivers and guaranteed $10,000 to the first steamer to reach any of these free ports via either the La Plata or the Amazon.[29]

On April 5 Peru passed a similar decree, declaring her portion of the waters of the Amazon system thrown open to all nations and establishing two free ports. As a further inducement Peru offered free transportation across the Andes to immigrants who would settle in her valleys along the upper reaches of the Amazon. Ecuador, New Granada (Colombia), and Venezuela joined in the movement to have the Amazon opened to general commerce.[30]

In Brazil popular opinion changed gradually from opposition to acceptance of the proposal. Brazilian writer Nabuco de Aranjo stated: "After the publication in the *Correio Mercantil* in 1853 of his [Maury's] memorial and his description of the Amazonian region, locked up from the world by a policy more exclusive than Japan's or Dr. Francia's, the cause of the freedom of navigation was triumphant. Tavares Bastos himself received from the book by Maury the patriotic impulse which converted him into a champion of this great cause." [31] The opposition of Dom Pedro II greatly slowed the opening of the river. But in 1867 the ships of other nations were finally granted official permission to sail the waters of the Amazon.[32]

In addition to his having proposed the naval exploration that played such an important role in study of the Amazon region, Maury also strongly favored the Navy's sending Lieutenant Thomas Jefferson Page, who had been on duty at the Observatory, to explore the Río de la Plata. Page's report of his exploration in the *Water Witch* of that other mighty South American river was published in the Secretary of the Navy's *Annual Report, 1856.*[33] Maury also gave assistance to other naval explorers. He worked on charts with naval explorer Lieutenant Edwin De Haven, who commanded the First Grinnell Expedition to the arctic, both before the expedition left and on its return.[34] But Maury made a greater scientific contribution to the Second Grinnell Expedition, commanded by the Navy doctor, Elisha Kent Kane.

Through his long studies of currents, winds, and other oceanographic data, Maury had come to the conclusion that there was an open polar sea. His theory was denounced by some scientists, but Dr. Kane concurred in the belief. Before sailing from New York, in May, 1853, Kane spent much time at the Observatory to learn Maury's thinking about the arctic, especially his deductions and theory on open water.[35] In the summer of 1854 Kane sent a sledge party headed by William Morton from their arctic base to explore farther northward. The party reached a 3,000-foot peak and after ascending it some 400 feet, they later reported to Kane, they saw "a boundless waste of waters stretching away toward the Pole. Not a particle of ice encumbered its surface . . . rolling surf like that of more genial climes . . . a fluid sea in the midst of whole continents of ice . . . eye surveyed at least 40 miles of uninterrupted water in a northern direction. The point thus reached . . . was about 500 miles distant from the Pole." [36]

The sledge party could not push on, as they had no boat, but Kane, believing that the water stretched at least a great way toward the North Pole, named it the Polar Basin. On his return to the United States Kane proposed that the open polar sea be named after Maury, but Maury declined and urged Kane to let "his name go upon the waters." [37] Today those icy waters very properly bear the name Kane Basin.

Maury's oceanographic studies had led to his *Wind and Current Charts* and to the help he was able to give naval explorers, but they did not endear him to astronomers, who criticized him for giving priority to the hydrographic and meteorological work of his office. The publishing of the charts and the explanations and sailing directions had eaten heavily into the Observatory's funds for publishing, and Maury had not been able to overcome the retardation of the astronomical program caused by the loss of naval observers and computers to sea duty during the Mexican War. In 1851 there was published a 673-page volume, *Astronomi-*

*cal Observations made during the year 1846 at the National Observatory,
Washington,* this being the second volume of the Observatory's astronomical publications.[38] Maury was not pleased over the delay in publication but was satisfied in his own mind that he was making the best
possible use of the Observatory work force.[39] Astronomical observations
were carried on continuously under the original plan, and the cataloguing of stars proceeded on a systematic basis.[40] In 1851 Maury wrote two
astronomical articles—"On the Variable Light of Clio," published in the
Astronomical Journal, Cambridge, Massachusetts, and "Observations of
Petersen's Comet of 1850" for the *Astronomische Nachrichten* of Kiel,
Germany.[41]

Some of the significant meteorological studies made by Maury in this
same year of his career were described by him in articles that were widely
published. They were "Circulation of the Atmosphere," "On the Probable Relation Between Magnetism and the Circulation of the Atmosphere," "Red Fogs and Sea Dust," [42] "On the Geological Agency of the
Winds," and "Of Clouds and the Equatorial Cloud Ring." [43] The last
two papers were read by Maury to the sixth meeting of the American
Association for the Advancement of Science held at Albany in late
August, 1851.

At this meeting Alexander Dallas Bache retired as third president of
the A.A.A.S., and Swiss-born Louis Agassiz, professor of natural history
at Harvard, was installed as the new president. In his farewell address
Bache enunciated much of his philosophy of science. The speech is note-
worthy for its revelation of the difference in his approach to science
from that of Maury—a difference that was to lead to altercations between
them. After giving a description of a "master charlatan," or quack doctor, whom he had seen dressed in court costume with buckled shoes,
putting on a show in a small country town of France, Bache described
his fears for science in the United States:

> Our real danger lies now from a modified charlatanism, which
> makes merit in one subject an excuse for asking authority in others,
> or in all, and because it has made real progress in one branch of
> science, claims to be an arbiter in others. Sometimes this authority
> is thrust on men who, not having the force to enlighten those who
> press them as to their real claims, injure the cause they would fain
> promote, by being too impressible. Merit thus moulded assumes the
> form of the impressing body. Whether the authority be seized or
> accepted, it is unlawful; the usurpers wear the shoes and buckles,
> if not the whole costume. This form of pretension leads men to
> appeal to tribunals for the decision of scientific questions, which

are in no way competent to consider them; or to appeal to the general public voice from the decisions of scientific men or scientific tribunals, in matters which, as they only are in possession of the knowledge necessary to make a right decision, so they can only give one which is valid. In a country where every thing is free, and every one may obtain a hearing, notoriety is often dearly purchased by the sacrifice of some portion of real reputation. Let us firmly discountenance the wearing even of buckles. . . .

I remember well the chilling effect produced upon me, when young, by the remark of one of our leading literary men, applied to a distinguished scientific writer, that he was not a "mere *dry* man of science." . . . It was not then, and is not now, the prevailing fault of our science to be dry; nor is dryness one of the tendencies of our Association. I have sometimes thought there was danger of the opposite.[44]

Speaking of the formation of the A.A.A.S. Bache declared:

Some of us had studied the workings of the British Association [for the Advancement of Science], and had been convinced of the absolute necessity for the attendance there, from year to year of the men of the universities, to give a tone to the proceedings; and were alarmed, perhaps, at the forays into the domain of science, which had there been witnessed in some of the less powerful sections, and even into the park [sic] of Section A itself.[45]

Bache was thus propounding one of his favorite themes—a fear that science would be ruined in America by pretenders to knowledge. He could allude to their "forays," but discretion prevented his naming the men he had in mind. He was expressing his belief in "men of the universities" as those who would give "tone" and act as a high tribunal for science. He was praising the laboratory men of science and deploring the practical or applied scientists who believed that science both could and should be explained to the people in terms they could understand. The outgoing president was thus almost certainly making allusion to his mistrust of military or naval control of any branch of scientific endeavor—a disapproval that had undoubtedly been intensified by a struggle he had recently been through to avert the Navy's wresting the Coast Survey from his direction and the jurisdiction of the Treasury Department.[46]

Having expressed his personal attitudes, Bache proceeded to the official acknowledgments necessary for him to make as outgoing A.A.A.S. president. He stated: "The recommendations already made by the Association have met with signal success. Among these I may note . . . the expeditions under charge of Lieut. Maury for examining special questions connected with winds and currents." [47] The statement was, of course, not praise for Maury's work but, more important, information for the members that their recommendation had been followed and "expeditions" had been sent out by the act of Congress of March 3, 1849, granting Maury three small ships for furtherance of wind and current studies.

Maury was placed on two A.A.A.S. committees—one on astronomy and one on uniform standard of weights and measures—but ironically not on the committee on meteorology, the field in which he was then making his greatest contribution. [48] Months later in Washington, Joseph Henry, secretary of the Smithsonian Institution, asked Maury whether he was on the Association's meteorological committee. Maury replied rather tartly, "If I be on the meteorological committee, I have not been informed of it, you asked me the question you know in Albany. Of course you know whether I be off or on, my services in helping to carry out are at your command." [49]

At the A.A.A.S. meeting in Albany meteorologist Arnold Guyot, an associate of Secretary Henry's, reported that the Smithsonian had volunteers at 50 points in the United States who were making meteorological observations and sending in reports to Henry as a result of the program "with reference particularly to the nature of American storms" that Henry had launched in 1847. [50] In 1851 Maury reported that observers on 1,000 ships at sea were making meteorological observations and sending them in to him at the Observatory—a part of the program he had started at the Depot of Charts and Instruments in 1842. [51] It was almost inevitable, therefore, that competition should develop between Henry and Maury in this field of study to which both had committed themselves and the government institutions they headed.

That autumn of 1851, in Washington, a development on the Cabinet level was to ignite a very long fuse that would in time burn its way to powder and cause an explosion. Secretary of State Daniel Webster received a communication from the British government suggesting the possibility of American co-operation with Britain's Royal Engineers in the making of uniform meteorological land observations at foreign stations. On November 14, 1851, the Secretary of State wrote Secretary of the Navy William A. Graham to ask the extent to which the Navy of the United States would be prepared to unite with the British on the proposal. [52]

Secretary Graham promptly sent a copy of the inquiry, plus the printed pamphlet detailing the method of observations used by the Royal Engi-

neers, down the chain of command to Maury via Commodore Charles
Morris, newly appointed chief of the Bureau of Ordnance and Hydrography, superior officer to the Observatory superintendent.[53] Maury at
once saw the possibilities inherent in Great Britain's tentative proposal.
He drafted a reply to his bureau chief in which he pointed out that some
land observations similar to those of the Royal Engineers were already
being made in the United States. He did not describe those made by
the Army Signal Corps, for he understood that the Army was expected
to make its own reply to the Secretary of State. He did refer to the observations made in the states of New York and Massachusetts and by
the Smithsonian Institution—"Most of which differ more or less from
those recommended by Major General Sir John Burgoyne for the 19
'foreign stations of the Royal Engineers.' " [54]

And then began Maury's historic proposal:

> I do not mean to draw comparisons, or to imply that of the Ameri-
> can and English systems, one is better than the other; far from it—
> *each* is good; and if either be adopted and made common to the
> two countries the science of meteorology would be vastly benefitted
> and advanced thereby.
>
> If the government of the United States . . . without proposing
> amendments to the English system, were to direct its officers, who
> are engaged with meteorological observations, to adopt the plans,
> modes and methods of that system, it would create confusion among
> our observatories, and be as likely to retard as to advance the prog-
> ress of meteorological research in the United States.
>
> For this reason, I beg leave to suggest a meteorological conference.
>
> By authority of the government I have been permitted to invite
> this co-operation of American ship masters in making daily, in all
> parts of the ocean, as they pursue their voyages to and from, a series
> of meteorological observations.
>
> By an Act of Congress, authority has been given for all the vessels
> of the Navy to do the same.

He then described this work and its results and stated that, as the
better part of the globe is covered by ocean,

> we must look to the sea for the rule, to the land for the exceptions.
> Therefore, no general system of meteorological observations can be
> considered complete unless it embrace the sea as well as the land.
> The value of the researches conducted at this office with regard to
> the meteorology of the sea would be greatly enhanced by co-opera-
> tion from the observatories on the land. . . .

The atmosphere envelopes the earth, and all nations are equally interested in the investigations of those laws by which it is governed. There is Russia, upon whose territories the sun, except in the long night of the Polar winter, never sets, perhaps she, of all nations has gone to the greatest expense in establishing meteorological observations on land, in collecting and publishing results, etc. From what has already passed between [A. T.] Kupffer, the Russian meteorologist (also in charge of mines), and myself upon the subject, I am induced to believe that he is already authorized, by the proper authorities in that country, to confer with the proper authorities in this, as to the establishment of a uniform system of meteorological observations on the land, for the two countries.[55]

Maury pointed out that observers were already at work at certain stations.

For these reasons, therefore, I respectfully suggest that as an amendment to the British proposition, a more general system be proposed: that England, France, Russia and other nations be invited to cooperate with their ships by causing them to keep an abstract log according to a form to be agreed upon and that authority be given to confer with the most distinguished navigators and meteorologists both at home and abroad, for the purpose of devising, adopting and establishing a universal system of meteorological observations for the sea as well as for the land.

Maury packed most of his dream into that last long sentence: the many nations to work together—a universal system—both sea and land. Thus the idea of this international conference was entirely his, but he was careful, both in his original communication and thereafter, to speak of it as "an amendment to the British proposition." [56]

Maury's recommendation was dispatched through Commodore Morris to Secretary of the Navy Graham, who promptly urged it on Secretary of State Daniel Webster. Deciding to back the plan, Webster enclosed Maury's report with his official reply to the British chargé d'affaires in Washington.[57] The United States government thus, in 1851, proposed to England that a conference be held to plan a united meteorology of land and sea. Secretary Graham, on December 6, advised the Secretary of State "that for the purpose of giving practical effect to these views the Superintendent of the Naval Observatory is authorized to confer as to such an uniform plan with her Britannic Majesty's officers and others of proper jurisdiction at home and abroad and in concert with them to agree upon a system of observations both for the sea and land, and which by being common, effective and of easy execution may be followed by meteorologists and navigators generally." [58]

Four days later, after Maury had received this official authorization, he started his organizational work. The first persons of "proper jurisdiction" to whom he wrote were Abbott Lawrence and William Cabell Rives, U.S. ministers to England and France. Both men were his personal friends. From Lawrence he wanted names and addresses of all with whom he should confer in England.[59] To Rives he stated: "It would greatly facilitate the move if the French Government would express a wish that the Meteorological Convention in which details are to be arranged, which you see is a part of the plan, should be held in Paris. The desire that it should be so held in August next has already been expressed on the part of Russia." [60]

Another friend whom Maury quickly interested was the French minister to the United States, the Count de Sartiges. Other ministers in Washington who were informed in succeeding December days were those representing Russia, Spain, Prussia, Belgium, Portugal, Argentina, and Chile. Letters also went to the chargés d'affaires of Denmark, Austria, the Netherlands, Sweden and Norway, Sardinia, Guatemala, the Two Sicilies and Parma, Mexico, Nicaragua, Venezuela, and Peru.[61]

Encouraged by Sartiges's "lively interest" and immediate response, Maury wrote Lewis Cass, Jr., the United States chargé to the Pontifical States, to ask him to lay the proposal before "the proper authorities at Rome and solicit the co-operation of the Holy See whose worldwide missionaries . . . would be a superb corps of observers." [62] A letter also went from Maury to the Honorable George P. Marsh to ask him to interest Turkey, to Luther Severance, the U.S. commissioner to the Sandwich Islands (Hawaii), Peter Parker, U.S. commissioner to China, and to United States chargés in various other countries.[63]

Maury's next step was to enlist the support of distinguished foreign scientists. Alexander von Humboldt was approached through Baron von Gerolt, the Prussian minister in Washington, who had the preceding March delivered to Maury a letter of praise from Humboldt.[64] At that time Maury had written back to the renowned European scientist: "Your approval of such an undertaking [Maury's oceanographic investigations] strengthens mightily my hands for good and facilitates more than I can express the task before me; it removes difficulties, breaks down obstacles, makes friends for the work and enlists many laborers for the field, who were before looking on in idleness." [65]

Another letter went to Robert Walsh, U.S. consul in Paris, Maury's friend since midshipman days. He asked Walsh to bring the subject informally to the notice of "Arago, Jons and a few other such noble spirits and get such endorsations from them of the Congress of Meteorologists as will assist in commending it to the public mind." Dominique François Arago, the French astronomer and physicist, must, of course, be at the conference, Maury continued, and he asked if, in view of Arago's feeble health, it should not therefore be held in Paris. Maury's keen understanding of the American mind is revealed in this sentence to Walsh, "You know how a voice from across the water moves us here." [66]

Communications went forth directly to Professor Johann von Lamont, astronomer royal of Bavaria, Professor Christian Gottfried Ehrenberg in Berlin, hydrographer-astronomer Captain William H. Smyth, R.N. of England, James Glaisher, Secretary of the British Meteorological Society, the Reverend Michael A. Banclavi, professor of physics at the University of Genoa, Lieutenant Marin H. Jansen, of the Royal Dutch Navy, Dr. George Buist, Bombay, H. Piddington, Calcutta, to the secretaries of the Royal Society of Science in Denmark and a special letter to Professor P. Angelo Secchi, director of the Observatory in Rome.[67] When Secchi had been honored by the Vatican for his scientific work, Maury had written Father Curley at Georgetown College, "Let's join a hurra for Secchi and the Pope." [68]

The next phase of the campaign that Maury had mapped out was to secure total co-operation at home. Maury's first move was toward the Smithsonian Institution, which had an established, functioning program of land meteorology that especially emphasized the study of severe storms. On January 14, 1852, Maury sent Secretary Joseph Henry pamphlets and other information about the plan of co-ordinated international meteorological effort and wrote him about the American proposal for "a system of observations both for the sea and the land." Maury concluded: "The Secretary of the Navy having authorized me to confer with others upon the subject and in concert with them to establish such a system— therefore, by virtue of the authority thus conferred, I have the pleasure to solicit the assistance of the Smithsonian Institution in devising and to invite its co-operation in giving effect to such a general system." [69]

Three days later Maury wrote similarly to seek the aid of Professor Alexander Dallas Bache, superintendent of the U.S. Coast Survey, Surgeon General T. Lawson, U.S. Army, who had charge of the Army meteorological work, Colonel J. J. Abent, chief of the Bureau of Topographical Engineers, Professors William C. Redfield, J. P. Espy, Arnold Guyot, Denison Olmstead, Benjamin Silliman of New Haven, and Dr. Robert Hare. Members of the Cabinet also were informed of the effort toward international co-operation.[70]

On January 22 Maury again wrote Joseph Henry and suggested that the conference proposal made the time propitious for the enlistment of more states of the Union in making meteorological observations. Maury proposed that a special letter be sent to each governor citing the example of New York and Massachusetts in making such observations. The communication should call for the purchase of instruments "to be used in concert with you," Maury explained to Henry. In conclusion Maury told Henry that he would write

> if in your opinion it is desirable. Or perhaps you might be willing to relieve me in the matter and write them yourself or to take any other course which may have the effect of enlisting more of the states in your corps.
>
> At any rate I should be glad to confer with you . . . for I wish it to be distinctly understood, that, excepting the new invitation to others to co-operate, I do not and cannot think for a moment of having anything to do with the observations on shore. I mean as I have done to confine myself exclusively to the sea, and I have supposed that should the proposed conference result in anything, that you and your associates would undertake the general charge of the observations on the land in the United States.[71]

Nothing came of Maury's proposal for a letter to states. Maury did meet with Henry on March 2 and again reaffirmed his willingness to co-operate with Henry in the Smithsonian's program for observations on land.[72]

Joseph Henry wanted to enlarge the Smithsonian's study of American storms and was at this time working to secure further co-operation with the British in Canada.[73] This may have caused him to fear that his plans would receive a setback from the international meteorological conference proposed by Maury. Henry did not inform Maury of his opposition to having land meteorology included in the agenda of the proposed conference.[74] However, Joseph Henry on May 6, 1852, wrote his views on the matter to Colonel Edward Sabine in England, the person with the most influence in deciding whether England voted for meteorology of both land and sea to be considered at the gathering.[75] Henry's opposition was concurred in by Alexander Dallas Bache, who expressed the crux of the professors' opposition to the type of intergovernmental co-operation proposed by Maury. Bache wrote Henry: "For my part I think the British and American Associations [for the Advancement of Science] are the proper *mediums* of communication and not the government of the two countries, bringing the politicians in between the savans [sic]." [76] At the time when Secretary of State Webster had asked the Navy to reply to the British proposal for meteorological co-operation, he had made the same request to the Army and through Secretary of Navy Graham to

Joseph Henry as the executive head of the Smithsonian Institution.[77] Perhaps the fact that Maury had produced a proposal that had been accepted as United States policy had caused Henry's opposition. But, whatever the cause, Henry's continued unwillingness to co-operate on this international effort was eventually to lead Maury to a re-evaluation of the Smithsonian secretary and a shift from the attitude Maury had expressed in his letter of January 22, 1852.

Meanwhile, in England, the government, upon receipt of the American reply to their inquiry, had asked the Royal Society to advise concerning the proposed meteorological conference. Colonel Sabine, of the Royal Engineers, who was secretary of the Society, opposed inclusion of the land in the proposed plan. Others agreed with Sabine, and it was eventually recommended to the British government that land meteorology be left out of consideration at the proposed conference. The major factor in the decision of the Royal Society was probably the belief that countries that already had observers at work would not readily yield their own type of forms to those adopted by a "congress of nations." [78]

However, the report to the British government by the president and council of the Royal Society strongly recommended consideration of meteorology of the sea stating that "the proposition of Lieutenant Maury to give a greater extension and a more systematic direction to the meteorological observations at sea appears to be deserving of the most serious attention of the Board of the Admiralty." [79] The report then detailed the work already accomplished by Maury in marine meteorology. It concluded with a recommendation that the government agree to confer on marine meteorology and co-operate in observations at sea.[80]

Necessarily it had taken time for the president and council of the Royal Society to render its opinion to the government, and more serious delay was then occasioned by a change in governments, which brought a new set of political leaders into power.[81]

By November 6, 1852, Maury had received information on the Royal Society's recommendation that the British government back a conference on co-operative effort on marine meteorology. He sent a review of the situation to John Pendleton Kennedy, of Baltimore, who had become Secretary of the Navy the previous June. Maury reported that, unlike the Royal Society, the British Meteorological Society, the Academy of Sciences of France, and the Royal Danish Society had favored inclusion of both land and sea meteorology at the conference. But, because of Britain's decision, Maury continued, "I would recommend that the United States . . . abandon for the present at least that part of the 'universal system' which relates to the *land* and direct our efforts mainly to the *sea* where there is such a rich harvest to be gathered." Maury requested that the British Board of Admiralty and the ministers of marine of the leading powers be invited to appoint officers to a conference on marine meteorology "at such time and place as shall be agreed upon." [82]

After due consideration the Secretary of the Navy and other high officials reached the decision that the United States would issue an invitation to a conference limited to adopting a universal system for observations at sea.[83]

On April 19, 1853, Maury wrote Captain Henry James, of the Royal Engineers in Edinburgh, telling him of the American decision and the reason for it. He stated, "I am a lover of harmony and admit that a half loaf is better than no bread therefore I think it was well for me under the circumstances to abandon the land for the sea." [84]

In England when the third week of April, 1853, had begun and the British government had still given no answer to the United States whether it would back the conference by sending delegates, Lord Wrottesley decided to take action. A distinguished astronomer who had served the Royal Astronomical Society as president, Lord Wrottesley was also a Fellow of the Royal Society and chairman of the Parliamentary Committee of the British Association for the Advancement of Science.[85] Wrottesley had become keenly interested in Maury's *Wind and Current Charts*. As a scientist Wrottesley could visualize what it would mean to have a universal system of observations that would expand Maury's system until accurate knowledge for all seas was obtained. On April 26, 1853, Lord Wrottesley rose in the House of Lords to urge that England send delegates to the conference and agree to participate in the universal system of observations. He was aware that his associates were more interested in profits than in science. He centered his opening remarks on the "important benefits to be conferred on the trade and commerce of the country" by joining in "the scheme." [86] Continuing, he said:

> It will also add to our stock of scientific data in the departments of hydrography and meteorology, to an extent which it is hardly possible to over-estimate.
>
> The United States Government having sanctioned the adoption of the plan in their own country, and being fully sensible of its value, and that in order to its effecting all the good that it was capable of producing, it required to be extended, invited the co-operation of the principal maritime nations for that purpose, and particularly that of this country.[87]

Explaining the history of the handling of the proposal since its reception by the British government, Wrottesley pointed out that both the Royal Society and the British Association for the Advancement of Science had recommended that Great Britain participate in the proposed marine meteorological conference and program. Deploring the delay that had occurred, he remarked that it seemed strange since the project was one "the importance of which it is not very difficult for any one possessed of ordinary acuteness to recognize at a glance." [88] After a detailed presentation of the project and of the history of Maury's investigations and his resulting *Wind and Current Charts* and *Explanations and Sailing Directions*, Wrottesley ended this section of his speech by reading from the report of the Royal Society:

Short as is the time that this system has been in operation, the results to which it has led have proved of very great importance to the interests of navigation and commerce. The routes to many of the most frequented ports in different parts of the globe have been materially shortened—that to St. Francisco in California by nearly one-third; a system of southwardly monsoons in the equatorial regions of the Atlantic and on the west coast of America has been discovered; a vibratory motion of the trade-wind zones, and with their belts of calms and their limits for every month of the year, has been determined: the course, bifurcations, limits, and other phenomena of the great gulf stream have been more accurately defined; and the existence of almost equally remarkable systems of currents in the Indian Ocean, on the coast of China, and on the Northwestern coast of America and elsewhere, has been ascertained. There are, in fact, very few departments of the science of meteorology and hydrography which have not received very valuable additions; whilst the more accurate determination of the parts of the Pacific Ocean, where the sperm whale is found (which are very limited in extent), as well as the limits of the range of those of other species, has contributed very materially to the success of the American whale fishery, one of the most extensive and productive of all their fields of enterprise and industry.

Lieutenant Maury is enthusiastic in the cause; he sees the benefits that must arise from the extension of this system of observations, and he invites the co-operation of all maritime nations; but to which does he look with the most longing eyes and the best hopes of success? . . . it is to the Government of this country that the demand for co-operation, and for the interchange of observations, is most earnestly addressed by the Government of the United States. [89]

Lord Wrottesley pointed out that the proposed program would not be costly. He concluded with an earnest plea that the British government vote to co-operate with the United States in its proposal. The House of Lords cheered, but, in the time-honored manner of parliamentary bodies, the lords avoided making a decision and continued the matter for further consideration.[90]

On hearing that no decision had been reached after Lord Wrottesley's speech, Maury felt it unwise to wait longer for England, since Russia, Denmark, the Netherlands, Sweden, and Norway had agreed to the conference. On June 18, 1853, he wrote the Navy's new Secretary, James C. Dobbin, to ask the department's sanction for the conference to be held in Brussels beginning Tuesday, August 23.[91] The request was approved and, on June 25, Maury sent out notifications to the representatives of favoring nations that the conference would be held in Brussels in late August "by invitation of this government." [92] Even though the British government had still not indicated whether or not it favored the conference, an invitation was extended to Her Britannic Majesty "in the hope that the most powerful maritime nation in the world would participate." [93]

Maury now began his personal preparations for his first trip out of the United States in nearly two decades. He wanted Ann to accompany him, but she felt she could not leave their baby, Lucy Minor Maury, who had just passed her second birthday on May 8, nor their other five young children. It was a relief to Ann, who didn't care for travel or public appearances, when her husband suggested that he might take their two older girls with him. Appreciative of how much he had learned from his early travels, Maury decided that the trip would be of great educational value to Betty and Diana. As a result of this decision, Maury was asked by his brother-in-law, Lieutenant William Lewis Herndon, U.S.N., and his cousin John Walker Maury, mayor of Washington, to include their daughters, Ellen Herndon and Ellen Maury, in his party. Knowing that he would have no time to spend with his daughters during the conference, Maury decided it would be well for his girls to have their cousins as companions and agreed to the proposal.[94]

Aware of the responsibility that would be his in Brussels as the proposer of the conference and sole representative of the inviting power, Maury thought of the one man he would like to have beside him on this journey—the former principal at Harpeth Academy, James Hervey Otey, Episcopal bishop of Tennessee. He wrote asking his "preceptor" to make the trip and, in some embarrassment, expressed his regret that he could not offer to cover the expense involved.[95] It was a disappointment to Maury when Bishop Otey, whose wisdom he had so long respected, replied that his heavy schedule of church duties would prevent his going.[96]

In early July a New York mariner, Captain Morgan, arrived at the Observatory to see Maury. He represented "the Merchants, Underwriters, Shipmasters and others engaged in foreign trade at New York" and brought from them a purse of $5,000 as a gift to Maury. In his presentation Morgan stated that he and his associates desired to express in this way their appreciation of Maury's researches that had done so much to make navigation safer and voyages swifter.[97] Maury must have earlier heard rumors that such a gift was coming and predicated his plan for taking his daughters with him on having this sum. His letter of thanks to the donors reveals that he was greatly moved by their generosity and the remarks that they had sent with the purse.[98] Upon receipt of this sum, the largest he had ever had in his possession, Maury decided that the better part of it should be reserved for furthering the education of his sons.

On July 15 Maury was awarded a recognition from the academic world that gave him a further sense of support—an honorary LL.D. from Columbian College (now George Washington University) in Washington, D.C.[99] This, coupled with the LL.D. he had received twelve months earlier from the University of North Carolina,[100] "strengthened his hands," in his opinion, as he prepared for a journey on which he would meet men of academic achievement as well as those schooled by practice.

Maury and his four young companions left Washington on the morning of July 20, 1853, and three days later sailed from New York on the Liverpool steamer.[101] His preparation for the coming conference having long been completed, Maury was able to relax on board ship and enjoy the crossing. The gay conversation of his daughters and cousins kept him amused, and he thought it a capital joke when the other passengers named the four "The Magpie Club." [102] If any of his fellow voyagers considered the girls, all in their late teens, to be an unusual entourage for a delegate on his way to an international conference, Maury did not. It seemed a very logical arrangement to him because he never allowed devotion to family to precede his dedication to work, but neither did he consider the two in conflict.

When Maury landed at Liverpool he was invited to meet the merchants of that port on the subject of the uniform plan of observations at sea. At a large gathering at the Town Hall, Maury addressed these men. Subsequently, these private shipowners and underwriters of Liverpool and Leith petitioned the British government that England co-operate fully in the plan proposed by Maury.[103]

From Liverpool Maury went for an important conference with Lord Wrottesley at Wrottesley Hall near Wolverhampton. Wrottesley brought

Maury up to date on efforts to swing England into line on the Brussels Conference. He reported that Sir Robert Inglis had spoken in favor of the conference in the House of Commons on July 13 as a follow-up to his own earlier speech in the House of Lords. Wrottesley went on to inform Maury that outstanding leaders had presented the whole matter to the first Lord of the Admiralty five days later and had urged that the British Navy send delegates to the conference. The Admiralty still had the matter under consideration, Lord Wrottesley reported to Maury. In spite of this Maury enjoyed his stay at historic Wrottesley Hall, as did the girls.[104]

On August 18 a large audience of shipowners and underwriters packed into Lloyd's, in London, to hear Maury explain his work and the proposed program. Maury was pleased by the response and considered the meeting at Lloyd's a triumphant success.[105] No doubt one reason for this was Maury's stated belief that new charts he had under preparation would soon permit ships to go from England to Australia in 60 or 65 days! [106] Maury's Liverpool and London speeches were published widely in leading papers of the United States, so his own nation was able to keep up with the progress of the international undertaking.[107]

Just before sailing from Dover for Calais, Maury received the news he had so long hoped for. He was overjoyed to learn that Great Britain had decided to send delegates to the conference.[108] The Admiralty more than made up for its country's delay, to Maury's way of thinking, by sending as the Navy delegate the arctic explorer, Captain Frederick William Beechey, R.N., who also had made notable contributions to hydrography through his surveys of the North African and Irish coasts.[109] The other British delegate was to be Captain Henry James, of the Royal Engineers.[110] Both men were Fellows of the Royal Society and well known for their scientific work.

On Tuesday, August 23, 1853, the first International Maritime Meteorological Conference was called to order in the official residence of Belgium's Minister of the Interior in Brussels.[111] The delegates to this history-making conference were:

FOR BELGIUM

Lambert Adolphe Jacques Quetelet, Director of the Royal Observatory, and Perpetual Secretary of the Royal Academy of Sciences, Letters and Fine Arts.

Victor Lahure, Captain, Director General of the Royal Navy.

FOR DENMARK

P. Rothe, Captain-Lieutenant, Royal Navy, Director of the Depot of Marine Charts.

FOR FRANCE

A. de la Marche, Hydrographic Engineer of the Imperial Navy.

FOR GREAT BRITAIN

Frederick William Beechey, Captain, Royal Navy, F.R.S., Member of the Naval Department (Admiralty) of the Board of Trade.
Henry James, Captain, Royal Engineers, F.R.S., M.R.I.A., F.G.S.

FOR THE NETHERLANDS

Marin H. Jansen, Lieutenant, the Royal Navy.

FOR NORWAY

Nils Ihlen, Lieutenant, Royal Navy.

FOR PORTUGAL

J. de Mattos Corrêa, Captain-Lieutenant, Royal Navy.

FOR RUSSIA

Alexis Gorkovenko, Captain-Lieutenant, Imperial Navy.

FOR SWEDEN

Carl Anton Petersson, First Lieutenant, Royal Navy.

FOR THE UNITED STATES

Matthew Fontaine Maury, LL.D., Lieutenant, United States Navy.[112]

Because the conference was to be limited to marine meteorology, the delegates were all naval officers with the exception of the host scientist, M. Quetelet, and Britain's second delegate, Captain James, who was an expert on land meteorology.

Maury was asked to serve as president, but he declined and nominated Quetelet.[113] The Belgian scientist, who was noted not only as an astronomer but as a statistician who worked out the first rules for census taking, was elected presiding officer. Maury was asked to make the opening address and outline the aims of the conference, which he did in simple French remembered from his study when invalided by his stagecoach accident.[114]

The conference met daily. The first order of business was for the delegates to gain a clear understanding of the system that had been developed by Maury and the knowledge that had been gained by observations made by naval and merchant vessels of the United States. In proposing that the same system could become worldwide through all nations joining in making the observations, Maury stressed that the system should be voluntary for merchant ships, with masters free to decide whether or not to accept the *Wind and Current Charts* and keep the abstract logs, but that it would doubtless be advisable for navies to order their ships to use them.[115]

Maury had a few months earlier been authorized to offer his charts to the navies and merchant vessels of certain interested maritime nations on the same gratuitous basis as practiced in the United States.[116] He explained at the conference that the American government would extend this offer to mariners of all nations who would keep an abstract log and send it in for use in further charting the seas, their winds and currents. Once this generous attitude on the part of the United States was fully understood by the delegates the possibility of agreement on main proposals appeared likely.

That Maury had some misgivings about which way the key delegate, Captain Beechey of the Royal Navy, would vote is evidenced by a remark written to Maury from Washington by Lieutenant George D. Minor, acting superintendent of the Observatory. Reporting on the "warm and natural interest" with which his "co-labourers" were following Maury's progress, Minor commented:

> I prophesy that Beechy [*sic*] will become a convert to your system: he possesses brains and they are *all* that are necessary for him to ascertain that truth and utility are the basis of all your works . . . that you have been working upon what was believed to be unprofitable fields—that you have made them productive, that your exertions are not paralyzed by other men's *impossibilities*. . . .
>
> I have no doubt you will impress him in your own peculiar and gifted way with the high value that a "pilgrim of the wave" ought to place upon your works.[117]

Minor knew the importance Maury placed on Britain's vote.

A supporter of the plan from the beginning of the conference was the Dutch delegate, Marin Jansen, whose government had already begun meteorological co-operation with Maury.[118]

Agreement first had to be reached on the specific observations that should be required, how they were to be made, at what hours, and with what scientific instruments. It took lengthy discussion to reach unanimity on adoption of instruments because it would be necessary for identical instruments to be used by observers of all participating nations. The delegates worked their way through their disagreements on these points until accord was reached.

They next developed the form of an abstract log to be kept on all armed naval vessels of the participating countries and evolved a some-what simpler abstract log for merchantmen to use in making observations. Notes to explain the system of co-operation were carefully worked out.

At the end of the second week the delegates had come to agreement on the mechanics of the system to be followed. They were ready for the final decision.

The vote was unanimous. The delegates recommended that the universal system of marine meteorological observations be launched and that the abstract logs they had just adopted be used by the seamen of their own nations and by those of countries that would join in the plan.[119]

The delegates closed the conference on September 8 with a formal expression of their hope that, in the event of war, belligerents would respect the meteorological program and that the abstract logs would be given immunity as instruments of scientific research for the benefit of mankind.[120]

Before leaving Brussels the delegates were guests of honor at a dinner given by Leopold I, King of the Belgians. A Belgian newspaper reported that "H.M. the King entertained himself a long time with Lieutenant Maury." [121]

The success of the conference was hailed by the press of Europe and of America.[122] In describing the conference later, Maury wrote with understandable relish:

> Rarely before has there been such a sublime spectacle presented to the scientific world. All nations agreeing to unite and co-operate in carrying out one system of philosophical research with regard to the sea. Though they may be enemies in all else, here they are to be friends. Every ship that navigates the high seas, with these charts and blank abstract logs on board, may henceforth be regarded as a floating observatory, a temple of science.[123]

Having been authorized to travel "under orders" to confer with scientists, Maury left Brussels for a short tour of Holland, Germany, and France. He had expected to go on to Russia to visit Professor von Struve, director of the Central Observatory, at Pulkovo, near St. Petersburg but apparently found that the $1,000 the Navy had authorized him to draw from Baring Brothers in London for his expenses while abroad would not permit the Russian trip.[124]

In Berlin Maury visited Baron Alexander von Humboldt, author of the scholarly, many-volumed description of the physical universe, *Kosmos*.[125] Both Maury and Humboldt had traveled widely in South America and were interested in the exploration of the interior. Humboldt had written on the Orinoco, Maury on the Amazon River. The Prussian was a student of the geographical distribution of plants, the American of the possibility of transplanting alpaca and vicunas to portions of the United States where they might thrive. The two men discussed climatology and meteorology, and Maury found his host eager to hear about the findings of the Navy ships that had been assigned to assist him in his oceanic researches. In giving Humboldt a full report on the Brussels Conference, Maury mentioned that his original proposal had been for a universal system of observations for both land and sea. Baron von Humboldt encouraged him to work for just such an over-all consideration of meteorology and later repeated this in a letter.[126]

Other visits of particular value to Maury were those with Christian G. Ehrenberg, the German naturalist, and with France's great astronomer, Urbain J. J. Le Verrier.[127] He conferred with naval scientists in England before sailing from Liverpool on October 5.

Sixteen days later Maury and the four girls reached the Observatory in Washington and were given a joyous reception.[128] Maury was happy to be back with his Ann and his younger children. Though tired, he was eager to implement the conference decisions.

Secretary of the Navy Dobbin received Maury's report of the conference with approbation and without delay committed the United States to full participation in the universal system. On November 3 a general order was issued by the Navy Department that began with these words: "The form of the 'Abstract Log' recommended by the late Maritime Conference at Brussels is hereby affirmed and adopted for use in the Navy of the United States. It is recommended to navigators generally and will be faithfully kept on board of all vessels in the naval service." The order continued with instruction to commanding officers to "transmit copies of the abstract logs kept on board to the Chief of the Bureau of Ordnance and Hydrography [Maury's superior officer] at the end of a cruise and at such other times as he may direct." [129] Copies of this official order were dispatched to the naval authorities of the other nations that had participated in the conference.[130] A similar process of official authorization was followed by the other participants to validate the actions of their delegates at the conference.

In early November Baron von Grabow called on Maury to explain why Prussia had not been represented at the conference and to advise officially that his country would co-operate in the plan adopted.[131]

Maury was also advised that it was "only through inadvertence" that the Spanish government had failed to have a representative at the Brussels Conference, that Queen Isabella II wished to be informed on the results of the meeting. The journal of the proceedings, a document printed in both French and English, was sent to the Spanish envoy in Washington to be conveyed to Her Majesty. A copy of the Secretary's order to United States Navy ships and an offer to supply *Wind and Current Charts* and *Sailing Directions* to any merchantmen under the Spanish flag that agreed to keep logs also were sent.[132]

Within four months Portugal, the city of Hamburg, the republics of Bremen and Chile, and the Empire of Brazil were either already participating in the plan or about to do so.[133] By 1854 Maury could declare, "Nations owning more than nine-tenths of all the shipping in the world have come into this plan."[134]

The next year England further enlarged the scope of her participation by creating the Meteorological Bureau of the Board of Trade and placing in charge Post Captain Robert Fitzroy, R.N., an able meteorologist and hydrographer who had surveyed the coast of South America before going on inactive naval duty to serve as governor of New Zealand.[135] The Dutch intensified the work at their newly founded Meteorological Institute, assigning their Brussels Conference delegate, Lieutenant Marin Jansen, to duty there.[136] Pope Pius IX placed the influence of the Vatican behind the international effort by authorizing special flags to be flown at the mast of any vessel co-operating in the plan and by establishing a decoration for seamen of the Papal States, to be awarded only to those who kept the abstract logs prescribed by the conference.[137]

As these nations, and those which subsequently joined in the undertaking, sent to Maury and his co-workers at Washington the systematized information from the seas of the world, he was able to revise charts already issued, correct errors, fill in gaps, and prepare new charts for the Indian Ocean and charts on specialized subjects such as monsoons, trade winds, storms, and rain. The quality and volume of the observations reaffirmed for Maury his belief that ordinary seamen were fully capable of adding to scientific knowledge.[138]

In the fifty years subsequent to the Brussels Conference, Dutch seamen turned in three and a half million of the prescribed abstract logs accurately filled out, American seamen five and a half million, British seamen seven million, and German seamen more than ten and a half million.[139] The brittle pages of old logbooks studied by Maury in 1842 had multiplied into "loaves and fishes" for the mariners of the world.

However, despite the successful launching of international marine meteorological studies following the Brussels Conference, neither Maury nor the other delegates to that conference were satisfied with the observations' being confined to the sea. Upon their return home the conference delegates began a concerted effort to bring about a second conference which would include observations on land. They were convinced that the two could not be separated. Quetelet felt the conference imperative and wanted it held at the first possible date. Captain Henry James, of the British Royal Engineers, favored the idea.[140] On January 17, 1854, Maury wrote Marin Jansen in Holland: "Sabine was for it then he was against it, now he is for it again. Airy [who had been made astronomer royal in 1835, in charge of Greenwich] is in favor of it, so are all the land meteorologists of the continent not excepting Lamont [Johann von Lamont, professor of astronomy, University of Munich]. Ballot [Buys Ballot, leading Dutch meteorologist] I know is for it." [141]

Maury advised Quetelet: "Heaven seems to smile on the glorious scheme. . . . Dr. Witherspoon, U.S. Army, . . . having charge of the Meteorological Observations that have been carried on since 1819 by the Medical Staff of the Army, has been up to say that we may rely upon the co-operation of that staff in any system which the congress may propose." [142]

That offer left Joseph Henry of the Smithsonian Institution as the only head of a major American meteorological program opposed to the proposal.

Maury strongly believed that the congress to cover land and sea meteorology should be called by a *government,* not by a scientific *society,* for "when governments are invited to take counsel together, governments have the means of giving effect to those counsels." [143] The government that he thought should call the conference was the British, and the leader to make the proposal was, in his opinion, "Sir John Burgoyne, who proposed the land co-operation, in the first place." Maury also suggested that the conference should be held in some other city rather than to ask Brussels to play host again.[144]

Firm on the point that he was not the person either to propose the conference or to play a leading role in it, Maury, nevertheless, was filled with enthusiasm for the subject and in February, 1854, he wrote Quetelet: "I am on the housetops with the hopes of co-operation and representation both from Brazil and Chile at our next Congress." [145] In Europe, scientists Quetelet, James, H. W. Dove, A. T. Kupffer, and others worked hard to get the British government to invite meteorologists to such a congress.[146] But there were still those in England who did not like the idea of yielding their sovereignty of decision to a universal form laid down by such a congress for all nations. Others in America disagreed with Maury that the government was the agency to handle such matters, believing that they would be better handled by the scientific societies.[147]

The efforts of Maury and of European scientists for a second conference were undoubtedly hampered by a development that might have been expected to prove helpful. This was the receipt by Maury, subsequent to the Brussels Conference, of a large number of honors, medals, and orders. He was made a member of the Imperial Academy of Sciences of Russia, the Royal Academy of Sciences, Letters and Fine Arts of Belgium, an Associate of England's Royal Astronomical Society, and a member of some forty other learned societies in the United States, Europe, and the Orient. He was made a Knight of the Dannebrog by the King of Denmark, Knight of the Order of Tower and Sword by the King of Portugal, Knight of the Order of St. Leopold by the King of the Belgians, Knight of the Order of St. Anne by the Czar of Russia, and Commander of the Legion of Honor by the Emperor of France. He received the Great Gold Medal for Science and the Kosmos Medal (the latter at the request of Alexander von Humboldt) from the King of Prussia, the Gold Medal of the Paris Universal Exposition and another Great Gold Medal from the Emperor of France, the Gold Medal of the King of the Netherlands, the Great Gold Medal of Arts and Sciences from the Emperor of Austria, the Gold Medal of Sardinia, the Gold Medal struck especially by order of the King of Sweden and Norway, a collection of all 13 medals struck during the pontificate of Pius IX, as well as handsome jeweled pins sent by the Czar of Russia and Archduke Ferdinand Maximilian of Austria to Maury's wife.[148] Maury was unquestionably proud of these honors. In his references to them in letters to relatives or close friends, however, he took care to make light of them.[149]

According to law, Maury had to seek the consent of Congress to be permitted to keep the foreign decorations.[150] This gave publicity to them, as did Washington newspaper stories, and further annoyed his critics, Joseph Henry and Alexander Dallas Bache. In his biography of Bache, Merle Odgers said, "When his friend Henry learned that Bache was to receive the Royal Geographical Society [of Great Britain] medal he gleefully expressed the hope that Bache would have to petition Congress to be allowed to accept the honor and 'thus be obliged to take the shine off the man on the hill.' " [151]

Henry's resentment is understandable when one reads Thomas Coulson's biography of him. Joseph Henry had in 1841 written Hans Christian Oersted, Danish physicist, to explain his successful investigations and ended with the explanation: "I mention these results of my earlier labors because I think I have not received from them the credit in Europe which is my due." [152] That he had not, at the time, was true because Europe continued to honor Michael Faraday for discovering electromagnetic self-induction without similarly honoring Henry, who had earlier made the identical observation but had failed to publish an account of it before Faraday's announcement. In America, however, Henry had been accorded full recognition for his major achievement in physical research.[153]

If he wanted to avoid the antagonism of Joseph Henry, Maury made a grievous mistake in continuing his drive for land meteorology to be considered together with marine meteorology. But, with his conviction that weather does not stop at the water's edge, and his unquenchable determination, it is difficult to see what other course Maury could have pursued. Even had he wanted to leave the field for Henry, which he did not, Maury could not, without negating all his oceanic work, abdicate the position of international leadership to which the Brussels Conference had raised him.

The rivalry extracted a high price. On June 22, 1857, Maury reported to Lieutenant Marin H. Jansen, on duty with the Dutch Navy in Batavia, "Jealousies among the so-called scientifics have prevented me from carrying out my plans as to another meteorological conference," [154] and nearly a year later he was writing Belgium's astronomer royal, Quetelet:

> "The green eyed monster" is at work here in certain quarters and thus I am somewhat interfered with. I see at present no prospect of another conference of land co-operation, unless you on your side will inaugurate a system for Europe and so shove us into it.
>
> Daily, however, the Brussels Conference stands out in bolder and bolder relief. It is destined to be regarded as an era, and the most memorable era that has yet occurred in meteorology and sooner or later that plan of meteorological co-operation and research . . . is bound to be extended to the land also.[155]

He was to hold that view and to work ceaselessly for the longed-for conference until the end of 1860,[156] when the shades of impending national tragedy fell across the United States and blotted out hope of any further undertaking involving co-operation at that time. But the seed thought had not been planted in vain.

CHAPTER XII

Maury and the Atlantic Cable

In the year 1842, when Maury began his oceanic research in Washington, the inventor Samuel F. B. Morse made an experiment in underwater telegraphy in New York harbor. That October Morse "stretched a submarine conductive cable from Castle Garden to Governors Island in the harbor and was able to demonstrate to a committee of the American Institute the possibility of effecting electric communication through the sea, although the transmitting cable was destroyed by the anchor of a vessel almost as soon as telegraphic operations had commenced." [1] The destruction of the cable was a major disappointment, but Morse predicted that someday such communication could be established across the Atlantic. Most men denounced or ridiculed the idea. Not, however, Maury, who believed that patient study and effort would provide the key to victory over nearly every problem posed by the forces of nature. In 1851 a submarine cable connection was established between England and France. Not long afterwards other cables were laid under relatively narrow bodies of water. One of these cables was between Liverpool and Dublin, and it cut nine hours from the time required to send messages by fast steamer. [2]

In November, 1852, an English engineer, Frederick N. Gisborne, stretched the first submarine cable of any length in America, from Canada's Prince Edward Island across Northumberland Strait to the shore of New Brunswick province. [3] Gisborne was proceeding with a further extension of his work and plans to connect Newfoundland with Cape Breton Island, Nova Scotia, when his financial backers dishonored his bills. This halted his operations in the fall of 1853. [4] Early in 1854 Gisborne went to New York to seek further capital for his cable project. He approached Cyrus West Field, a successful American paper manufacturer who had inherited from his clergyman father a sense of obligation to serve mankind. [5] Field was very much interested that Gisborne had established in the new world an underwater telegraph on a limited scale and had a franchise from the legislature of Newfoundland. However, the vision that gripped Field was not of short-range cable communication but of the possibility that a cable might be laid to provide fast communication between Europe and America and put an end to the two weeks' wait then necessary for mail brought by the fastest of the trans-Atlantic ships. Field immediately perceived that two major problems would be involved in spanning the Atlantic with an insulated telegraph line. Could a cable be laid on the bed of the Atlantic Ocean—and if this was possible, would it then be practicable to transmit messages over such a cable? [6]

Cyrus Field, we are told by his brother in *The Story of the Atlantic Telegraph,* "determined to apply to the highest authorities in his own country. . . . To get some light in his perplexity, Mr. Field, the very next morning after his interview with Gisborne, wrote two letters, one to Lieutenant Maury, then at the head of the National Observatory at Washington, on the nautical difficulties of the undertaking, asking if the sea were itself a barrier too great to overcome; and the other to Professor [Samuel F. B.] Morse, inquiring if it would be possible to telegraph over a distance so great as that from Europe to America?" [7]

It was natural for Cyrus Field to turn to Maury. The preceding November he had invited Maury to meet him in New York, but Maury had been unable to leave the Observatory.[8] Field was, however, well informed on Maury's achievements.

In addition to being recognized as the foremost authority in the world on the winds and currents of the sea, Maury was also known to have been conducting deep-sea soundings to study the floor of the ocean.[9] Since 1840, when he had first recommended that government vessels be ordered to investigate the bottom of the sea, Maury had been working toward this objective. His authorization to proceed with this work had been included in the congressional act of March 3, 1849, which began: "And be it further enacted that the Secretary of the Navy be directed to detail three suitable vessels of the Navy in testing new routes and perfecting the discoveries made by Lieutenant Maury in the course of his investigations of the winds and currents of the ocean; and to cause the vessels of the Navy to co-operate in procuring materials for such investigations, in so far as said co-operation may not be incompatible with the public interest." [10] Maury had felt that a knowledge of the depths of the ocean was vitally necessary to a better understanding of the tides, their law of motion, and tidal waves.[11]

The first problem to be worked out had been the invention of an instrument capable of accurate measurements at great depths. Naval officers of England, France, and Holland had sounded successfully in depths not in excess of 10,000 feet but had not achieved accurate measurements beyond that depth.[12] In attempting to devise a system that would overcome this problem, Maury had tried many methods. Concerning those earlier struggles he said:

> First, there was the shot and line. It was thought that common wrapping twine previously marked and placed to the length of several miles on a reel, would, if attached to a 32 lb. shot, give us a good measure of the depths of the ocean. . . . When we came to make the trial out upon blue water, it was found . . . that the undercurrents would sweep the line out of the perpendicular, deflecting it with curves of many convolutions, never permitting it to cease to run out even after the shot had touched the bottom and we discovered that instead of a mere bit of wrapping twine we required twine of the strongest threads that could be spun to withstand what sailors call the *swig* of these sub-marine forces. . . .
>
> It was proposed to attach a screw-propeller-like [*sic*] to the plummet, so arranged that by the aid of machinery the number of revolutions made by this screw during the descent of the plummet would be recorded. The instrument was made and worked beautifully. But then there was the difficulty of hauling it up: and to haul up six or eight miles of line from the depths of the sea was no slight undertaking. So that clock work would not do.
>
> Next came an old sea captain who had been in the whaling business where they now sometimes blow up whales with torpedoes. So he thought a torpedo was the thing after all; and he sent me a beautiful contrivance. He dispensed with a line altogether and had his torpedo so arranged that it would explode as soon as it touched the bottom. Then by first ascertaining its law of descent, and the rate, with which the explosive force, when set free, or the sound would travel through water, and then observing the time elapsed between the first plunge of the torpedo into the sea, and the sound of the explosion or the appearance of the bubble on the water, the arguments, it was held, would be obtained, for the exact perpendicular depth of the ocean, then and there. But, in deep water, the ship would drift out of the way before the report of the torpedo could reach surface. So it would not do.[13]

Various other suggestions had been made, and most of them had been tested. Gradually Maury and his associates had concluded that soundings should be made from a boat and not from the transporting ship, since the smaller craft would permit the sounder to hold the line perpendicular. To establish the law of descent, the officers had found that they must always use a line of the same size and make, as well as a sinker of the same shape and weight. Knotting the line every 100 fathoms and timing it, as it descended, they learned that the average time of descent from 400 to 500 fathoms was 2 minutes 21 seconds, from 1,000 to 1,100 it was 3 minutes 26 seconds, while from 1,800 to 1,900 fathoms took 4 minutes 29 seconds.[14] Referring to these experiments Maury said, "We could tell very nearly when the ball ceased to carry the line out, and when, of course, it began to go out in obedience to the current and drift alone; for currents would sweep the line out at a uniform rate while the cannon ball would drag it out at a decreasing rate."[15]

With this much knowledge in hand, the schooner *Taney,* Lieutenant J. C. Walsh commanding, had been sent out under Maury's directions, in October, 1849, to make soundings every 200 miles across the Atlantic. The voyage had not been completely successful because, in a severe storm, the *Taney* had proved herself unseaworthy, and Walsh had had the bad luck to lose a good deal of his sounding equipment. In spite of these difficulties, enough soundings had been made on this cruise "to invest the subject with renewed interest."[16] In 1851-1852, the U.S. brig *Dolphin,* with 56 men on board, had cruised for Maury under the command of Lieutenant Samuel Phillips Lee, made soundings, charted the Rocas Reef (lying to the northeast of Brazil's Cape St. Roque), which had never before been marked, and had reported that 20 reputed dangers could be removed from existing charts.[17]

Other naval officers, by order of circulars from Commodore Lewis Warrington and Commodore Charles Morris, had also co-operated with Maury in making deep-sea soundings while on duty in warships of the Navy.[18]

Maury, in 1852, had set to work to depict his knowledge on an orographic map. He had been assisted in this undertaking by William Flye, one of the Navy's professors of mathematics then stationed at the Observatory. The map had presented a profile, or vertical section, of the bottom of the ocean between America and Europe near the parallel of 39° north latitude. It had been published as Plate XV of Maury's 1853 *Sailing Directions,* while Plate XIV had been a preliminary depth map of the basin of the North Atlantic.[19]

"These were the first maps of the kind ever attempted for 'blue water,'" Maury had told the Secretary of the Navy.[20] Blue water was the nautical term for the deep water of the ocean as opposed to the shallower waters close to shore.

In 1852-1853, the brig *Dolphin,* under the command of Lieutenant

Otway H. Berryman, U.S.N., had made deep-sea soundings across the Atlantic for Maury, returning to Norfolk, Virginia, on March 7, 1853.[21] A week later Maury wrote Berryman: "I welcome you back and have been feasting all day over your abstract logs—rejoicing in its 'deep sea soundings'. . . . You have done so well I shall certainly want you to go again and so, I think, does the Commodore. . . . [I] had conversation with him today and he thought weather not suitable for you to go again until May, in which I concur." [22]

But delighted as he was, Maury had said, "What is the use of knowing how deep it is unless we know what is at the bottom of it and where was the mechanical skill that would contrive for us the means of bringing up from miles below the surface feathers from old ocean's bed [Neptune's feather bed], be it ooze or mud, or rock, or sand; for we did not expect to find it a graveyard." [23]

Maury had designed an instrument to bring up specimens of the bottom and had it made up by a skilled New York mechanic named Baur, but it had worked well only in the offings and not in the great depths.[24] Others had worked on devices, but none had overcome the chief problem —they could get no line of sufficient strength to haul up a plummet heavy enough to carry the line down to the bottom. A young Virginian, Passed Midshipman John Mercer Brooke, in charge of chronometers and other instruments at the Observatory, had reached the conclusion that the only solution "was to have the plummet so arranged that on touching the bottom it would cut the line and send up a specimen." He had drawn a careful sketch of the instrument that he thought would do the job and had presented the idea to Maury, who had hailed the concept and had promptly instructed a machinist named Greble to work with Brooke on making a model in the Observatory workshop.[25]

In Brooke's sounding apparatus the cannon ball had detached from the line on touching the bottom, and a light iron rod had been left attached to be drawn up with the specimen of the bottom adhering to it in a cavity. This cavity had at first been smeared with tallow as an adhesive for the ooze that lay on the floor of the sea, but it had been found that the "barrel of a quill" inserted in the rod worked even better.[26] The new device had been put on board the *Dolphin*, as Lieutenant Berryman prepared to take the brig out of Norfolk in the late spring of 1853 to resume deep-sea soundings and other investigations for Maury. "Brooke's deep-sea apparatus was first used at 1.20 P.M., July 7, 1853, by Midshipman J. G. Mitchell—made from a boat—took 6 hours," Maury wrote in a report to the Secretary of the Navy. The depth had been 2,000 fathoms (12,000 feet) and Maury declared simply but joyfully of the new apparatus, "It worked." [27]

Referring to Midshipman Mitchell, Maury later said, "This promising young officer made every deep sea sounding that was made in the *Dolphin* during that cruise—save one only—and to him belongs the honor of bringing up the first specimen that was ever obtained from the bottom of the sea." [28]

Lieutenant Berryman and his officers had thought that the substance they had brought up was simply clay; but they had preserved it in jars, as instructed by Maury, and had safely delivered it to him on their return in November, 1853. Maury had sent half the specimens to Professor Jacob Whitman Bailey, professor of chemistry, mineralogy and geology at the United States Military Academy, and half to Professor Christian G. Ehrenberg, noted microscopist whom Maury had recently visited in Berlin. [29] After Maury had received from Bailey a complete analysis of these 1853 soundings, he had drawn a bathymetrical map of the North Atlantic with contour lines drawn in at 1,000, 2,000, 3,000, and 4,000 fathoms. [30]

Berryman's soundings, made at intervals of 200 miles, going across the North Atlantic and returning, had convinced Maury of the existence of a relatively shallow plateau across the bottom of the ocean although the raised area was found to be slightly farther north than first believed. [31] Maury had been profoundly interested in the analysis of the samples taken from this plateau. They consisted, Professor Bailey had advised, of microscopic calcareous shells (Foraminifera) and a small number of silicious shells (Diatomaceae) that showed no signs of abrasion and among which was not one particle of sand or gravel. [32]

This was the moment that called for the deductive power that is often called genius. Long tedious planning and preparation had gone into the securing of these specimens, but it was Maury who perceived their meaning.

On February 22, 1854, Maury reported his deductions to Secretary of the Navy James C. Dobbin:

> The result is highly interesting, insofar as the bottom of the sea is concerned, upon the question of a submarine telegraph across the Atlantic; and I therefore beg leave to make it the subject of a special report. . . .
>
> From Newfoundland to Ireland, the distance between the nearest points is about 1600 miles and the bottom of the sea between the two places is a plateau which seems to have been placed there especially for the purpose of holding the wires of a submarine telegraph, and of keeping them out of harm's way. It is neither too deep nor too shallow, yet it is so deep that the wires being once

landed will remain forever beyond the reach of vessels' anchors, icebergs, and drifts of any kind, and so shallow that the wires may be readily lodged upon the bottom.

The depth of this plateau is quite regular, gradually increasing from the shores of Newfoundland to the depth of from 1500 to 2000 fathoms as you approach the other side.[33]

After giving further facts, Maury continued:

Lieutenant Berryman brought up with Brooke's deep sea sounding apparatus specimens of the bottom from this plateau. I sent them to Professor Bailey of West Point for examination under the microscope. This he kindly gave, and that eminent microscopist was quite as much surprised to find, as I was to learn, that all the specimens of deep sea soundings are filled with microscopic shells, to use his own words "not a particle of sand or gravel exists among them."

These little shells, therefore, suggest the fact that there are no currents at the bottom of the sea whence they came, that Brooke's lead found them where they were deposited in their burial-place after having lived and died on the surface and by gradually sinking were lodged on the bottom.

Had there been currents at the bottom these would have swept and abraded and mingled up with these microscopic remains the débris of the bottom of the sea, such as ooze, sand, gravel and other matter. But not a particle of sand or gravel was found among them. Hence the inference that those depths of the sea are not disturbed by either waves or currents.

Consequently a telegraphic wire once lodged there, there it would remain as completely beyond the reach of accident as it would if buried in airtight cases.

Therefore, so far as the bottom of the deep sea between Newfoundland or the North Cape, at the mouth of the St. Lawrence, and Ireland is concerned, the practicability of a submarine telegraph across the Atlantic is proved.[34]

Quod erat demonstrandum—what happier words could a scientist write?

On the morning of February 24, as Maury was finishing his report to the Secretary and assembling material to be sent with it, he received Cyrus Field's letter asking whether a cable could be laid at the bottom of the ocean. Maury wrote Field that day and said he believed his report to the Secretary would supply the answer to the question. He mentioned to Field that he considered the trans-Atlantic telegraph so important that he had recommended that "the government should offer as a prize for the first message across, a slice out of the public lands." [35] At this same time Maury wrote to Samuel F. B. Morse a full report of his findings. Morse had called at the Observatory in mid-February to ask Maury's opinion, but Maury had been absent from Washington on Navy business.[36]

Once he had received Maury's assurance that there was a section of the bottom of the Atlantic along which a cable could safely lie and Morse's advice that messages could be sent over such a long telegraphic wire, Cyrus Field decided to proceed with the Atlantic cable undertaking. He consulted his brother, David Dudley Field, already a distinguished lawyer in New York, and enlisted the support of his New York neighbor Peter Cooper, a business giant who had made a great fortune from the manufacture of iron and glue and the operation of iron and coal mines. Cooper was just the industrialist Cyrus Field needed in the cable undertaking, for when others had laughed at railroads Cooper had in 1830 designed and manufactured America's first railway locomotive, the "Tom Thumb." This locomotive had been credited with "putting the pioneer Baltimore and Ohio railroad on its feet." Not only did Cooper have the imagination to see and believe in the practicability of the transoceanic cable, he had the means to back it. When the banks refused to finance the undertaking, Cooper invested large sums, as he said, "in what then appeared to most men a wild and visionary scheme; a scheme that many people thought fitted those who engaged in it for an asylum." [37]

Other men who risked large sums were Moses Taylor, Marshal Owen Roberts, Chandler White, and Cyrus Field. They were the original group who formed the New York, Newfoundland, and London Telegraph Company, with Dudley Field as counsel. The company was incorporated in April, 1854, in Newfoundland.[38] The charter for the company that Cyrus Field obtained from the provincial government of Newfoundland gave him "exclusive rights for 50 years of landing ocean telegraphs on the coast of Newfoundland." [39]

At the formal beginning of the new company, Cyrus Field wrote Maury on April 15, 1854, offering him a financial connection with the enterprise. Lieutenant Maury promptly declined, pointing out ". . . for of course it would be improper, if I were a party concerned, to use any official influence which I might possess with the government, in order to further a scheme in which I am privately interested. . . . I have the success of the enterprise much at heart and would be glad to do what I rightfully may to forward it . . . and hope you will succeed in crossing the Atlantic with it at an early day." [40]

Field consulted Maury about the possibility of the United States government's supplying the company with ships, but the naval officer replied, "I don't think that you can get the government to furnish two large steamers to lay the wires for it has them not. I have asked the Secretary to fit out the *Dolphin* again but the war in Europe absorbs attention here and I don't think it at all likely she will be fitted out for the present, at any rate." [41]

Maury, unfortunately, was all too correct in his estimate of the delay that the Crimean War would cause. His great desire to send the *Dolphin* out to recheck the Newfoundland to Ireland soundings was not to be fulfilled until a peace treaty in 1856 ended the war, in which France, England, and Sardinia fought as allies of Turkey against Russia.[42] On April 24, 1854, Maury offered to present the plan for the cable at the annual meeting of the American Association for the Advancement of Science about to be held in Washington. He asked Field for all the facts in order that he might give the scientific assembly a full account of the undertaking. An amusing sidelight on this offer was that Maury concluded his note by asking Field, "Will you take over a parcel to England?" [43] This probably was a package of his recently published 772-page 6th edition of his *Sailing Directions*. The postage charges on sending these long scientific books was enormous, one package having cost over $300.[44] Maury always got any of his friends going abroad to carry books, pamphlets, and reports. In this instance, Field was going to England to order a cable to span the Gulf of St. Lawrence. He also was to confer with John W. Brett, the father of submarine telegraphy in Europe.[45]

As chief promoter of the cable, Field was naturally in frequent communication with Maury and made numerous trips to the Observatory to confer with him. Field continued to offer to reward the naval officer for his assistance to the cable undertaking, and finally Maury said there was only one recompense he would accept. This was a pledge that the United States Naval Observatory might have the first privilege of the trans-Atlantic line for the determination of the longitude of Washington—in comparison with Greenwich—and to have this as soon as the cable was made operable.[46] The minutes of the proceedings of the board of the company show that a motion to this effect was passed on June 21, 1855. It declared "that Lieutenant M. F. Maury shall have the use of the wires of the New York, Newfoundland and London Telegraph Company as requested. . . . The right to them free of charge for purpose of determining longitude and to use them first." It was signed "Peter Cooper, President." [47]

When Field received word that the manufacturer had shipped the cable by bark from England, he chartered a steamer to go to Cape Ray, Newfoundland, to be present for the laying of the cable to Cape Breton

Island, Nova Scotia.[48] The company thought that this would be easily accomplished, and Field invited a group including a few prominent journalists to accompany him. One of the first invitations went to Maury and his family.[49] Most of Maury's family were already visiting relatives in the Virginia foothills. He was trying to get away from Washington to join them and thus escape the malarial bouts he suffered in the summer. Maury at first declined Field's invitation, partly because neither his wife nor the girls wished to go. Then, though he had promised to go to visit his good friend Franklin Minor at his thousand-acre farm "Ridgeway" in Albemarle County, Virginia, Maury decided he should make the cable expedition.[50] With his two oldest sons and Betty, who came from Virginia to join him, he boarded the train for New York; but on reaching that city Maury was upset to learn how long the cruise to Newfoundland would take. It was more time than he felt he should be out of the country, and so they reluctantly headed south again without boarding ship.[51]

In early 1856 Cyrus Field asked Maury's advice on the kind of cable the company should now try to lay, since the construction of the first one had not been satisfactory. It had been insulated "by first surrounding the core with tarred hemp, which in its turn was enveloped spirally by 18 strands of iron wire, each strand consisting of seven No. 22½ gauge wires. The total weight of insulating material . . . amounted to 400 pounds to a nautical mile of cable." [52]

In May Maury outlined to Field his ideas on how the new cable should be made. He insisted that the wire needed only a light gutta-percha covering, that size and heaviness were to be avoided. He believed that when laying "the cord," as he preferred to call it, weight would cause it to run out too fast and that the effort to hold it back might break it. Once again he reminded Field, "There is no running water at the bottom of the deep sea along the telegraph's plateau and nothing to try the strength of any electric cord, however slender when once lodged there." [53]

Maury acknowledged that, of course, the wire or cord would have to be more heavily protected on its two ends where the floor of the sea rose toward the shore. Field was interested in Maury's view and asked him to state what changes in the company's present plan would have to be made. Maury, ever hopeful of converting the cable authorities to his belief, wrote Field on June 13 urging the lighter cord for "as long as you are in deep water. The alterations would be in the conducting wire, and upon your idea of having the conducting wire to consist of several." [54]

At the time when he thought they might change over to his idea of the lighter cord, Maury told Field that if this was done,

234

Soundings though still important and very desirable are not essential. If the alternative could be presented of laying the cable without first making any more soundings, or laying it without first making experiments at sea with 20 or 30 miles of the new fashioned cable, I should say by all means let the soundings alone and give us the experiment. . . . I am willing to communicate to you confidentially all my plans and notions and to let you go ahead without any _____ [word illegible] about it or I'll give them all to you and let you take out letters patent as you like.

The Secretary has sent for me, I suppose in relation to the soundings. [And also relative to this Maury wrote] I saw Major Ripley yesterday. He hopes to get a vessel for deep sea soundings. It would be unfortunate if the Coast Survey were to be mixed up in it for that's my thunder.[55]

This Major Ripley (to whom Maury gave no further identification)[56] was apparently pulling political wires to get a ship for the Coast Survey to use for soundings, and Maury was annoyed since he had asked Secretary of the Navy James C. Dobbin on May 5, 1856, for three vessels with which further to explore "the bottom of the ocean with Brooke's sounding apparatus."[57]

The act of Congress that had authorized the use of small government ships for oceanic investigations had specified that they were to be used to carry out Maury's program. Deep-sea soundings were Maury's prerogative as head of the Navy's hydrographic work. How could the Coast Survey be mixed up in it? The answer lay in the ambition of the superintendent of the Coast Survey, Alexander Dallas Bache. Ever since he had come to the Coast Survey in 1843, Bache had harried Maury spasmodically, and the naval scientist had fought back.[58]

Both were able men; both were authorized to carry out programs of hydrography, determination of longitude, and allied studies for the government offices they headed. A certain amount of professional rivalry was inevitable, especially in view of competition for appropriations from Congress. However, as a result of Maury's success, more than professional rivalry seemed to develop in Bache. It was a compound of many things, but undoubtedly Bache feared the work and control of the Coast Survey would be transferred to Maury and the Navy Department.

Even without their professional competition the two men would not have been personal friends. Their personalities and their attitudes were too disparate.

Alexander Dallas Bache counted as his intimate friends the various professors whom he had known in the North before he came to Wash-

235

ington, and these supplied a satisfying type of wholehearted personal approval that his temperament seemed to require.

With these men Bache had formed a club, the Scientific Lazzaroni, a title bestowed as an amusing irony since the *lazzaroni* were Neapolitan beggars and these professors, or former professors, considered themselves the high priests of science in America, destined to give authoritative leadership thereto. The Scientific Lazzaroni gathered periodically for meetings that were carefully planned to include intellectual discussion, lavish dining and wining. In the interim between gatherings, which were held in Philadelphia or some other convenient location, the Lazzaroni wrote frequently to each other and especially to Bache, whom they addressed as "My dear Chief," "Dearest Chief," "Most Potent Chief," with Benjamin Peirce of Harvard preferring "Most Darling Chief," while John F. Fraser, of Philadelphia, enjoyed calling Bache "Dear Grandpa and Chief." Peirce was referred to as "the functionary." [59]

Friendships were necessary to Maury but not this type of fervent cliquishness. His major struggle was to find time for his official work and his writing, but he was active, as has been seen, in several major scientific organizations. Unlike Bache, however, he had no desire to organize a group that would control science in the United States. But he did fight to keep under his control the investigations that he had begun and developed at the Observatory and that had been officially designated as his specific work and responsibility.

In addition to the Scientific Lazzaroni, Bache headed up an intimate group in Washington called "The Club," which included some political figures in addition to himself and Joseph Henry. The club met regularly on Saturday nights, usually at Bache's residence but sometimes at Henry's. Among the frequent visitors was Jefferson Davis of Mississippi, who as a plebe had so greatly admired First Classman Bache at West Point.[60] Jefferson Davis had first come to Washington in 1845 to serve in the House of Representatives but had resigned in June, 1846, to command a regiment of Mississippi Rifles in the Mexican War. Having distinguished himself in the war, he was in 1847 appointed U.S. senator from Mississippi to fill an unexpired term and was then re-elected. He resigned from the Senate in November, 1851, to make an unsuccessful race for the governorship of his state but in 1853 was appointed Secretary of War by Franklin Pierce.[61] Davis had been appointed a Regent of the Smithsonian Institution, on behalf of the Senate, in 1847 and re-appointed early in 1851. From 1853 to 1857 he was automatically a part of the Smithsonian directorship as Secretary of War. In 1857 he re-entered the Senate.[62] The great ability of Jefferson Davis was admired by Smithsonian Secretary Joseph Henry as well as by Bache.[63]

As a result of Bache's determination to replace Maury as the man supplying Field with oceanic information, there now developed a secretly maneuvered episode that created open wrangling and damaged the prestige of American science both at home and abroad.

In the early forties it had been planned that a Naval Almanac and Ephemeris was to be one of the labors carried out at the Naval Observatory.[64] However, when money was finally voted for its establishment in 1849, the Almanac office had been set up at Cambridge, Massachusetts, under the command of Lieutenant Charles Henry Davis, U.S. Navy.[65] Davis had studied at Harvard and wanted the Almanac to have the benefit of the mathematical brilliance of Professor Benjamin Peirce.[66]

Prior to being made superintendent of the Nautical Almanac, Davis had been one of the naval officers attached to the Coast Survey and had worked directly under Bache. In addition to having studied under Benjamin Peirce and having secured his services for the Nautical Almanac, Davis had married Mrs. Peirce's sister.[67] Davis was thus closely aligned with two of the most prominent members of the Scientific Lazzaroni. Moreover, his son, in his biography of Charles Henry Davis, says of his father: "In his frequent visits to Washington he generally stayed with Bache at the Coast Survey Office, or with Henry at the Smithsonian Institution, with whom his scientific work had also brought him into close intimacy." [68] Speaking further of his father's connection with Bache, C. H. Davis added: ". . . he was almost constantly in consultation with the superintendent on matters relating not only to the internal policy of the work [Coast Survey], but in defending and supporting the institution in its relations with Congress. . . . On one of these occasions Davis was brought into close relations with Jefferson Davis, who had undertaken the defense of the Coast Survey in the Senate." [69]

In earlier years Charles Henry Davis and Maury had been good friends [70] and Maury, as well as Bache and Henry, had seconded Davis for the superintendency of the American Ephemeris and Nautical Almanac.[71] In 1852 Davis, Maury, and Bache had successfully collaborated on a survey and report on the harbor of Charleston, South Carolina.[72]

However, Maury had become increasingly irritated by Davis's habit of delay in returning the mathematically trained men whom Maury lent from the Observatory to the Almanac.[73] Davis had resented Maury's criticism and had written Henry of his change of attitude toward Maury.[74] This resentment had undoubtedly increased in February, 1853, when Maury had addressed to Davis probably the most sarcastic letter he was ever to write. "Pray don't go to the expense of doing up in gilt those *Nautical Almanacs* for the Observatory. Nor need you take the trouble of having illuminated and done up in vellum that copy of the

'Theoria Motus' that you are going to present to our library. We are not proud and will take them in the sheets. But in plain English, when shall we have copies of the *Nautical Almanac* for distribution?" Maury signed it "In very great haste," [75] but the tone had been caustic no matter how badly he had needed almanacs to distribute to ships going to sea. Ten days later Maury had written Davis "to correct the possibility of any misunderstanding" [76] and after receiving the almanacs wrote: "They are elegant . . . the Secretary of the Navy seized all. Please send more." [77]

Early in 1855 an action within the Navy Department had caused a move on Maury's part that had built up further conflict with Bache. On January 8 Secretary of the Navy James C. Dobbin had written Commodore Charles Morris, chief of the Bureau of Ordnance and Hydrography, deploring the great number of wrecks that had been occurring among vessels approaching Sandy Hook and officially asking that Maury's suggestions and views on the subject be sought as to how to reduce their number.[78] Indeed, the shipwreck situation in that area had become so serious that President Franklin Pierce, in his message to Congress, had called attention of the lawmakers to the number of ships that had piled up on the Long Island and New Jersey shores.[79] On January 9 Commodore Morris had written Maury:

"From the conversations and examinations which we have already had on this subject, I feel well satisfied that directions may be framed and information be furnished, by which the dangers of approaching the entrance to New York in thick weather or at night may be materially diminished if proper attention be given and due precaution taken by masters of vessels." [80] And then the bureau chief ordered Maury to formulate such directions.

It is not clear why the Coast Survey had not revised their earlier chart and sailing directions for this section of the coast, but Maury, under orders that undoubtedly pleased him, set to work to produce an accurate chart of these waters and sailing directions to accompany the chart. He was convinced that any master who used these aids, sounded with his lead, and also took the temperature of the water to determine the depth, could safely navigate these offings even in fog. Maury's directions were published as a pamphlet in May, 1855, and for at least the next six months there were no more shipwrecks.[81]

This Navy action was unquestionably viewed by Bache as an infringement on the work assigned to the Coast Survey, while the Navy took the view that the shipwrecks had to be ended without delay and that the Coast Survey had shown no signs of bringing this to pass. In any event, the success of Maury's chart and instructions did not endear him to

Bache, and it was subsequent to this that Bache and Commander Charles Henry Davis conceived an ingenious plan designed to take from Maury and give to Bache the controlling voice on future soundings.

Commander Davis had an extremely able brain and the gift of putting plans into words, and it was apparently he who thought up what Bache, with his fondness for veiled terminology,[82] called "The Steamer Plan." In all their plannings and references, Bache, Henry, Davis, and their intimate associates used a code by which they referred to Maury as "M." or "Emmy," "the Commander," or "the man on the hill." [83]

In early November of 1855 Commander Davis wrote Bache a letter that was listed in the original index of the Bache collection of letters in the Library of Congress.[84] The letter has since been removed, but Bache's reply shows very clearly that Davis, in the missing letter, had outlined his Steamer Plan.[85]

On November 9, 1855, Bache wrote from New York to Commander Davis in Cambridge, Massachusetts: "We leave tomorrow for Washington and as soon as I have seen the General, I will write to you in relation to the time of meeting here. The Congressioners are coming together slowly as election time is just over." [86] In conclusion Bache stated succinctly: "The steamer plan is *first rate* if Mr. D. can see it." [87]

The first part made reference to the fact that the initial step in putting their plan into action was to see "the General," the name used by Bache and his associates for Jefferson Davis, who was at that time the Secretary of War in President Pierce's Cabinet. Davis's military rank in the Mexican War had been that of colonel. President Polk had offered Colonel Davis a commission as brigadier general of volunteers, but Jefferson Davis had declined the commission because he believed that the right to confer this rank belonged to the state where the volunteers had been raised.[88] However, as far as legislative matters in Congress were concerned, Secretary Jefferson Davis was a general indeed for Bache and the Coast Survey.[89] Bache's veiled concluding remark "if Mr. D. can see it" referred to Mr. Dobbin, the Secretary of the Navy.

In reply to Bache, Commander Davis, in Cambridge, Massachusetts, wrote: "I await with impatience and even anxiety to hear what Mr. Dobbin says to you." [90] It is not hard to understand why Charles H. Davis felt anxiety over the plan he and Bache were promoting, nor any wonder that it would take one Cabinet member to persuade another Cabinet member to implement it, for the plan called for the Secretary of the Navy to order a small Navy ship and naval officers to make deep-sea soundings from Newfoundland to Ireland without the knowledge of or direction of the Navy's hydrographer, Maury, who was in charge of just such investigations in blue water. Commander Charles Davis also advised Bache, "I will attend to the 'Sailing Directions' and keep myself ready to move at your summons." [91] For Bache, superintendent of the Coast Survey, to be thus asking that a vessel sound under his directions and employ the technique used by his office was directly contrary to the basic law of the Coast Survey as set forth by Congress. The law stated that the Coast Survey was to work "within twenty leagues [sixty miles] of any part of the shores of the United States" with the only extension being that it was "lawful for the President of the United States to cause such examination and observation to be made with respect to St. George's Bank [100 miles east of Cape Cod] and any other bank or shoal and the soundings and currents beyond the distance aforesaid to the Gulf Stream." [92]

The Steamer Plan called for soundings along the line of the telegraphic plateau earlier discovered by naval officers sounding for Maury. However, Bache and Commander Davis were counting on secrecy and their power to persuade their friend Secretary of War Davis to convince Secretary of the Navy Dobbin to set the plan in motion. They were well aware that Secretary Davis had great influence with Secretary Dobbin, for whom he sometimes substituted at meetings.[93]

Dobbin was, of course, being asked to take from Maury a hydrographic specialty that had been officially placed in his hands and which he had brought to a high degree of success. Dobbin, who had been in the Cabinet since March, 1853, was informed on Maury's achievements, and had acknowledged them with praise in his annual reports.[94] The Secretary of the Navy was also fully aware that the March 3, 1849, act of Congress under which steamers could be sent out by the Navy for deep-sea soundings specified that they were for the purpose of furthering Maury's investigations.

On May 5, 1856, Maury wrote Secretary Dobbin to request assignment of three vessels to be used for deep-sea soundings that "would answer many interesting questions in physics but also encourage the Atlantic cable laying." [95] Two days later Dobbin replied; he acknowledged having had the authorization of the act called to his attention and stated, "I very highly appreciate your suggestions and feel a deep interest in the subject. But I am constrained to say that the limited number of men allowed by law, and the demands on the services of the Navy for the protection of our Commerce &C will not permit me to foster and encourage the laudable enterprize you allude to as my inclination would prompt me. The matter shall not escape my attention and will be prosecuted if possible." [96]

Toward the end of that month Cyrus Field sent Maury copies of letters that had passed between Peter Cooper and Secretary Dobbin. Cooper also had requested a ship for soundings to assist the Atlantic cable project and had received from the Secretary of the Navy the same reply as that sent to Maury—there were neither ships nor men available.[97]

On June 14, still having received no word from Dobbin that one ship, if not the three he had requested, would be available for soundings, nor any inkling that there was a Steamer Plan being promoted by Alexander Dallas Bache and Commander Davis, Maury left Washington for a trip to St. Paul, Minnesota, where he was to speak at the laying of the cornerstone of the hall of the Minnesota Historical Society.[98] His son Dick accompanied him.

Evidence suggests that Dobbin knew of the Steamer Plan before this date but, once Maury had left Washington, certainly the proponents of the plan must have immediately pressed the Navy Secretary to put the plan into execution. Nine days after Maury had left, Secretary Dobbin wrote to Secretary of the Treasury James Guthrie, under whose jurisdiction the Coast Survey operated:

> in consequence of the services of Lieutenant O. H. Berryman and Midshipman John S. Barnes being immediately required on special duty under the Act of Congress dated 3 March, 1849, the Department has this day, detached these officers from Coast Survey duty and without the formality of transmitting their orders through the Treasury Department.
>
> The place of these officers will be at once supplied upon a requisition from the Suptdt. of the Coast Survey.[99]

If Secretary Guthrie ever read the letter he may have puzzled over the strange wording, but he could hardly have suspected the plan that it represented. The two officers were men whom Maury had trained in deep-sea soundings but who were serving a tour of duty on survey work for the Coast Survey. That Dobbin did not go through channels in handling their orders suggests that he was either in a great hurry or did not wish to reveal the plan to Secretary Guthrie. The cleverest part of the scheme was that Berryman and Barnes were thus assigned to the steamer *Arctic* to make a soundings cruise across the Atlantic under Dobbin's own direct orders without the name of the chief mover, Bache, being involved. Even though Dobbin had quoted the 1849 act of Congress as authorization for the cruise, he still did not advise Maury, or his co-workers in the program, that a steamer was being sent out to make deep-sea soundings.

It was not until Maury reached New York on his way home, apparently, that he finally heard the news. When he learned that the *Arctic* was being ordered out, but not under his directions, he was furious. It was incomprehensible to him that the Secretary of the Navy would lend himself to such a deliberately surreptitious maneuver. He was outraged that the legitimate work of the Hydrographic Office of the Navy was being given to others to perform.

As the Atlantic cable officials also had been denied a sounding vessel, Maury got Cyrus Field to visit the *Arctic,* then fitting out in New York for the cruise, to ask Lieutenant Berryman, in command of the vessel, to permit him to see his orders. Field promptly showed Maury a copy of Berryman's orders which proved that the *Arctic* was being sent out under the second section of the act of March 3, 1849.[100] That was all that the superintendent of the Naval Observatory and Hydrographic Office needed to know. He determined to fight the issue to a finish. Boarding the train for Washington, he must have gone straight from the station to call on Secretary Dobbin.[101] All that Maury requested of Dobbin is not known, but it is obvious that he demanded that since the ship was being ordered out under the law designed to give him assistance, all information from the cruise should be sent to his office, officially designated to handle such matters. Dobbin that day, July 10, wrote to Lieutenant O. H. Berryman, U.S.N., commanding U.S. steamer *Arctic,* New York, the following order:

> It is desirable as early as practicable after your arrival on the West Coast of Ireland that duplicates of your abstract Log and specimens of soundings be sent to the U.S. Naval Observatory.
>
> It may perhaps be unnecessary to add that I desire you not to give any publicity to your observations, or their results before they have been communicated officially to the Department, nor in fact until you have received its permission so to do.[102]

Perhaps Dobbin had disliked the proposal from the start and had been overpersuaded. In any event, he was certainly now fearful that Berryman might take it upon himself to release information on his soundings as a part of the Steamer Plan.

But the Secretary made no effort to alter the Coast Survey technique to be used on the sounding cruise. The *Arctic* had been equipped in New York with a steam reel belonging to the Coast Survey. This reel held 10,000 fathoms of line and necessitated that soundings be made from the bow of the ship, a technique frowned on by Maury. The vessel was supplied with Massey Indicators on which the Coast Survey placed great reliance for deep-sea soundings. These self-indicating machines were used to measure vertical depth instead of Maury's simpler method of noting the time intervals of descent of the line.[103] An ardent believer in Massey's machine was William Petit Trowbridge, Bache's Coast Survey assistant.[104] Trowbridge had himself made a similar machine, which had worked well in coastal soundings but had not proved satisfactory for blue water. The Coast Survey authorities had a mechanical expert, Joseph Saxton, work on the dials of the *Arctic*'s Massey Indicators and adjust them so that they were expected to register 21,000 fathoms without readjustment.

The simple but highly effective Brooke's Deep Sea Sounding Apparatus, with which Berryman had achieved so much when working under Maury's direction, had been altered for this expedition. In place of the round shot used by Brooke, Berryman had substituted a conical lead sinker weighing between 100 and 150 pounds.[105] In other words, the machines and instruments as well as techniques of soundings were those favored by the Coast Survey and not those which had proved successful for Maury and his Navy associates in their pioneering program of deep-sea soundings.

The *Arctic* sailed from New York on July 18, 1856, leaving St. John's, Newfoundland, on July 31 for soundings along the line of the telegraphic plateau. The next day the steam reel broke down.[106] After making soundings at regular intervals on the way across, the *Arctic* reached Queenstown (Cobh), Ireland, on August 23. Berryman, returning in the same latitudes, made soundings especially in areas not sounded on the way out.[107] The *Arctic* reached the United States on October 14, and Berryman and his crew were then ordered back to work with the Coast Survey, with which he had been serving before the soundings cruise.[108] The borrowed "steam reel" and other Coast Survey instruments were also "put in complete order" and placed on board the Coast Survey steamer *Vixen* at New York.[109]

Berryman's official soundings journal, abstract log, chart, notes, and specimens were sent to the Naval Observatory, in accordance with the orders Secretary Dobbin had issued after Maury had called upon him in July.[110] On receiving the information, Maury started a study of the material but immediately perceived that the soundings Berryman had recorded on a chart he had made in Ireland were not identical with those the lieutenant had recorded in his Abstract Log, or sounding journal. Also, there were substantial variations between those made going out and ones made in the same area on the return voyage. And the new soundings Berryman had made did not agree with those he had reported three years before that had been recorded by Maury on his bathymetrical map made in 1854.[111]

Maury inquired about some of the differences, and Lieutenant Berryman made a new chart. Not only did this chart vary from one Berryman had released, in spite of Dobbin's orders, to British associates of the New York, Newfoundland, and London Telegraph Company, but his several reports differed from each other.[112] Finally, in reporting on this cruise of Berryman's, Maury told Field that "his official records are utterly at variance and irreconcilable with each other. In short, his work in the *Arctic* does not add one iota to the information we already possessed concerning the depth of the Atlantic." [113] This was in sharp contrast to Maury's praise of Berryman's earlier work.[114] Maury believed the Massey Indicator, which the Coast Survey had persuaded Berryman to use, had caused the errors and that Berryman had "made no attempt either to test its accuracy or to ascertain its errors." [115]

Late in December, 1856, the Washington *Union* published a letter signed "B," which criticized Maury for his stand on the soundings made by Berryman the preceding summer in the *Arctic*. The same newspaper on January 1, 1857, carried Maury's reply. Of the soundings made in the *Arctic*, he said, "I found them wanting and said so and for this I am charged with unjustly assailing Berryman. . . . In conducting physical researches may we not treat according to their merits the material brought before us?" [116]

Just five days earlier Maury had written Cyrus Field, urging him to come to Washington concerning a resolution that was about to be presented to the government. This letter reveals Maury's efforts to secure the full assistance of the United States government in laying the cable. It was a jolly, Christmasy letter, and Maury advised Field he would expect him to stay with them and had a room ready for him at the Observatory. He then continued: ". . . we may be able to get the *Niagara* to lay the wire—so that it will be the best service ever yet rendered by a man of war steamer. Bring Morse, Mr. Cooper and a few others. I think that by waiting on the President in a body we might render all the world . . . some service." [117] Maury was to be proved right in this assumption. The government did, in time, grant use of the *Niagara* to lay the cable.[118]

Cyrus Field was in Washington, in the early part of 1857 to secure support for the cable and called on every member of the lame-duck Congress in session at the end of the Pierce administration. Alexander Dallas Bache was helpful to the cable promoter in introducing him to congressmen, as few were more expert in soliciting appropriations than Bache,[119] but Field did not find lobbying a pleasant experience.[120] The British Parliament had earlier voted the cable an annual subsidy after distinguished scientists Michael Faraday and William Thomson had stated their belief that the cable could be laid and would work.[121] Now the United States Senate passed, by a single vote, a bill guaranteeing an annual subsidy of $70,000 to the cable company. This was passed on March 3, 1857, and was on that same day declared legal by Attorney General Caleb Cushing.[122] The next day President Pierce concluded his duties as the nation's chief executive, and one of his last acts was to sign the bill granting the cable subsidy.

On March 7 Cyrus Field wrote Maury, asking him to advise the company as to the best route to be followed by the steamer that would attempt to lay the cable the following summer. Field enclosed with his letter recommendations that had been made to the company by Colonel George Everest, who urged "the great circle route." [123] Field also asked Maury to advise them of the best time for the attempt to be made. Maury, who had already been working on both these questions, now intensified his studies, with the assistance of Lieutenants Reed Werden and Richmond Aulick and on March 28 he wrote Field a full report, which was published in London as a 10-page pamphlet of very small print. Much of it deals with detailed scientific information for Field's use, but excerpts will give the gist of Maury's recommendations. Addressing himself to the issue raised by Colonel Everest, Maury stated:

> The great circle route is really impracticable for no navigator can steer his vessel for any length of time along the arc of the circle. Practically, the vessels employed to lay the cable must be actually steered along the sides of a polygon and not along the arc of a circle. The shorter the sides are, the less the ship will have to change its course in passing from one side to another of this polygon, the less will she deviate from the great circle. . . . I therefore recommend the paying out steamers should, after meeting and joining wires in mid ocean, attempt the polygonal rather than the great circle route.[124]

Continuing to Field, Maury wrote: "You asked me also to state the best time for laying the cable. . . . For many years the whole subject of gales, fogs, rains and lightning for the entire North and South Atlantic has been under discussion and I am just preparing to announce some of the results derived from upwards of 260,000 days of observations." He advised Field that special investigations "based on 46,000 days of observations made along the route to Europe" had been described in the 7th edition of his *Sailing Directions*. These were pertinent to the question of the best time for laying the cable:

> The records of 29 vessels give us Diagram B which shows a steady barometer at sea for the 20th of July annually but an unsteady one for the two preceding and following days. . . . The enterprise upon

which you engage is an important one—good weather for it is very desirable, nay almost indispensable. . . . Perhaps it would be wise for the steamers not to join cables until after the 20th of July. I think that between that time and the 10th of August, the state of both sea and air is usually in the most favorable condition possible and that is the time which my investigations indicate is the most favorable for laying down the wire. . . . I wish you good luck.[125]

This action in supplying Field with this special oceanographic information for the cable laying provides an interesting insight into the man Maury. Only one month earlier Maury had written Field that he felt the Atlantic Telegraph Company had not acted right in continuing to circulate the chart of Berryman's recent deep-sea soundings after being told they were not to be relied on. "So the Observatory has been attacked. All the documents etc. are at the Observatory, come and see. They are worthless." [126] The attack on Maury's evaluation of the soundings was continuing, but Maury was a scientist and so, without question, made the studies necessary to advise Field when to lay the cable. However, once more in early May he tried to get Field to realize the seriousness of the errors in the 1856 Berryman soundings, concluding: "I shall be happy to see you here and to submit his official reports and documents to your inspection and examination." [127]

Cyrus Field's unwillingness to condemn errors made by Berryman is certainly understandable. He had one great objective—to lay the Atlantic cable. He sought and accepted help in that cause from all who could further the work. Field was obviously not willing to criticize Berryman, who had made the pioneer soundings that had led to Maury's discovery. And Field was not going to alienate Alexander Dallas Bache by taking sides in the controversy.

Those who were backing Berryman's soundings continued to complain of injustice in Maury's having declared them inaccurate. On May 11, 1857, Maury asked the new Secretary of the Navy, Isaac Toucey, recently appointed by President James Buchanan, to "have all logs, charts &C examined by competent officers not connected with the Observatory, examine and report to the Department the degree of reliability to be placed upon the soundings stating whether they were properly made, faithfully recorded, and how far they are entitled to credit." [128]

Had Secretary Toucey followed Maury's request, the debate might have been ended. Instead, after a delay of two months, the Secretary issued an order to Lieutenant Reed Werden, Lieutenant Richmond Aulick and U.S.N. Professor of Mathematics Joseph S. Hubbard to make a complete review of the soundings made by the *Arctic* the previous year between Newfoundland and Ireland and report concerning their accuracy.[129] Perhaps these were the best qualified naval experts on deep-sea work available to make the review, but the choice did not make Maury happy because they were men he had trained and they were at that time working with him at the Observatory. Each of the three men had a distinguished record and undoubtedly gave an unbiased report, but when their findings agreed with Maury's, it was inevitable that Berryman's friends in the Coast Survey would not accept the official Navy report and would continue the controversy.[130]

The discrepancies between Berryman's last soundings and those made earlier by him and by others for Maury had, of course, raised serious doubts about the depth and position of the telegraphic plateau. These had to be resolved before the difficult task of laying the cable could be attempted.

The British government agreed to assist the cable effort by sending out Lieutenant Joseph Dayman, R.N., in H.M.S. *Cyclops* to sound from Ireland to Newfoundland.[131] Dayman, using a modification of Brooke's deep-sea sounding apparatus and timing the line at its 100-fathom marks as recommended by Maury, started sounding early in the summer of 1857 along a line just to the north of that sounded by Berryman in the *Arctic*. His work was done with great care and confirmed the existence of the telegraphic plateau as proclaimed by Maury following the earlier soundings.[132] Dayman, like Maury, believed that the errors made by Berryman in his 1856 soundings derived from failure to ascertain the error of the Massey's Indicator he had used.[133]

In the beginning of this summer of 1857 the Atlantic Telegraph Company, Ltd., the company that had been formed to handle cable matters in Britain, released an up-to-the-minute account of the progress of the cable effort. It quoted Lieutenant Maury as having officially stated to the U.S. Congress, "The only practicable route for submarine telegraph between the U.S. and England appears to be along the plateau of the Atlantic, whereon it is proposed to lay the wire that is now in the process of construction." The account continued: "In accordance with this conviction and in anticipation of the success which is to be realized, the Lieutenant prophetically christened the transverse cable-land ledge of the North Atlantic the 'Telegraph Plateau' even before the completion of the prophecy had become the especial charge of commercial enterprise." [134]

The cable history then described the developments of late June and early July, 1857:

"At the present time the cable is being stored away in the vessels which have been provided to float it out in the Atlantic. . . . The British Government has placed at the service of the company the fine 91 gun line battleship *Agamemnon.* . . . The American Government magnificently sent over to bear its share in this national work its splendid new frigate *Niagara.*" [135]

Of this coming undertaking *Harper's New York Weekly Journal of Civilization* editorialized, "What satire this work will be upon these war-like armaments! . . . What would Nelson and Collingwood have said of meeting a foreign frigate in mid ocean to lay a cable at the bottom of the sea." [136]

The need for telegraphic communication between the Old World and the New was so great that the project had aroused enthusiasm on both sides of the Atlantic, the success of the cable becoming a matter of prayer for many religious-minded persons. There was real fervor about this ef-fort as many considered it a step toward international peace. The emo-tion about it, as revealed in the journals of the day, would be hard for a modern, who enjoys almost instant communication, to understand. The Atlantic cable was top news in newspapers in both America and Eng-land.[137]

On July 29, 1857, the United States steam frigate *Niagara,* with her half of the cable on board, accompanied by the U.S. *Susquehanna,* a powerful paddle-wheel steamer, arrived at Queenstown, Ireland, to join the British paying out ship-of-the-line *Agamemnon* and her accompany-ing ships, H.M.S. *Leopard* and H.M.S. *Cyclops,* commanded by Captain Dayman.

The shore-end of the cable was secured in a little cove at Valentia (Valencia), Ireland, on August 5, and two days later the squadron sailed. The *Niagara* started paying out the cable, and for a time all went well. But then trouble developed with the machinery and the cable broke. It was spliced. They tried again, but there was more trouble. On August 11 all signals ceased.[138] After 330 nautical miles, the cable had broken—in 2,000 fathoms of water.

A consultation of officers and engineers was held and it was decided that the remaining 1,847 miles of cable left on board the ships was in-sufficient to continue. Cyrus Field started at once for England in H.M.S. *Cyclops* to urge immediate renewal of the undertaking, but the direc-tors of the Atlantic Telegraph Company voted to postpone the effort un-til 1858 and ordered that all possible improvements be made meanwhile in the paying-out machinery.[139]

As was inevitable, many who had earlier doubted that telegraphic com-munication across the Atlantic would ever be established again, con-demned the project as impossible of accomplishment. But not Maury, who still believed completely that the Atlantic telegraph could and would be laid, though he had predicted failure for this particular effort as early as July 9, 1857, when he wrote of the cable to his friend Quetelet, "It is entirely too heavy." The bottom was calm, he reminded the Belgian astronomer royal, "my researches concerning the physics of the sea have already clearly indicated. It [the cable] only wants strength sufficient to overcome resistance in reaching the bottom and by paying it out slack it will sink quietly through currents without resistance. I endeavored to press this simple fact upon them but failed, I suppose to make my facts and reasons clear to them. But, as I said, let us hope for the best." [140]

The failure to lay the cable inevitably kept alive the argument about the soundings. Friends of Maury were disturbed over the effect of the episode, believing that the whole plan had been designed to cast doubt on Maury's authority as an oceanographer. The European scientists who admired Maury's work were anxious to hear his account of the problem, which was published in 1857 in Petermann's *Mittheilungen* under the title "Das Telegraphen-Plateau des Nord-Amerikan Atlantischen Ozeans." [141]

In spite of the unfortunate wrangle about the soundings, preparations were made for another attempt to lay the cable. A new technique was to be tried. Instead of landing a shore-end at Valentia and then moving toward the middle of the Atlantic to make a junction of the cable, "It was decided that the ships should proceed to a point midway between Trinity Bay [Newfoundland] and Valentia, there splice the cable, and then turn their bows east and west and proceed to their destinations." [142] On June 10, 1858, H.M.S. *Agamemnon,* and U.S.S. *Niagara,* similarly stowed with cable, sailed from Plymouth, England, in company with H.M.S. *Valorous* and H.M.S. *Gorgon.* The weather was perfect on the day of departure, but by midnight winds had risen to storm intensity. For sixteen days the *Agamemnon,* stowed with 2,840 tons of dead-weight of cable, battled the seas. The *Niagara* rode out the storm with less difficulty. Finally on July 25, four days after the appointed time, *Agamemnon* and *Niagara* effected their rendezvous in mid-ocean, and the next day first spliced the cable. But there were more breaks, and within a few days 300 miles of cable were lost. [143] The ships were forced to return to Queenstown. The board of directors of the Atlantic Telegraph Company, Ltd., met to decide whether to abandon the cable effort. Some despairing directors voted against another trial; but Cyrus Field and Professor William Thomson won the day, and it was decided that one more attempt would be made. [144]

On July 17, 1858, the four ships sailed again. On the morning of July 29 the *Agamemnon* and the *Niagara* met once more in mid-ocean and shortly after noon of that day spliced the cable. At 1:45 A.M., August 5, the *Niagara* dropped anchor in Trinity Bay, Newfoundland, and by 6 A.M. the end of the cable was carried into the telegraph house on shore "and received very strong electricity through the whole cable from the other side of the Atlantic." [145] The *Agamemnon* had reached Dowlas Bay, Valentia, Ireland, with her half of the cable at almost the same hour as the *Niagara* had completed her voyage.[146] In the next few days brief messages went back and forth across the cable, though one day only voltaic currents were received.

The first official message sent over the Atlantic cable was from Queen Victoria to the President of the United States, on August 16, 1858. President James Buchanan answered by cable the same day. The President in his reply stressed, "It is a triumph more glorious, because far more useful to mankind, than was ever won by conqueror on the field of battle." Buchanan called for the cable "to be a bond of perpetual peace and friendship between the kindred nations" and for it to be "forever neutral even should hostilities arise." [147] The response of the directors of the Atlantic Telegraph Company in England was this triumphant message: "Europe and America are united by telegraphic communication. 'Glory to God in the highest, on earth peace, goodwill towards men.' " [148]

In the United States cannons were fired, church bells rang, speeches were made, and the more serious attended services of thanksgiving held in churches.[149] The cable was hailed with even more rejoicing on August 21 when, within fourteen hours after the collision of two trans-Atlantic steamers, the *Europa* and the *Arabia,* a ship took word to the cablehead, which flashed to the world the news that no lives had been lost and that all on both ships were well.[150]

There was constant fear that the cable might cease to function, but the public was reassured on August 25, by an announcement: "The cable works splendidly." [151] As a result, preparations were made in New York for the greatest victory celebration that city had ever held. The event was planned for September 1 and 2. Among other invitations that were sent were three to Washington: to Matthew Fontaine Maury, Alexander Dallas Bache, and Joseph Henry. Maury decided to attend the gala affair. Bache also accepted the invitation, but Henry told Bache that he felt it unwise for him "to take a part in the celebration. I might be called out and in the heat of the moment say something which would not be in good taste or in proper keeping with the occasion." [152] This probably had reference to the battle then raging between Henry and Samuel F. B. Morse over credit for telegraphy, Henry having discovered the principle that made it possible and Morse having developed the practical telegraph.[153] Morse, of course, was to be present and honored in the Atlantic cable celebration.

In the early hours of Wednesday, September 1, every approach to New York was crowded. People were streaming in by carriage, horseback, the railroad, and ferryboats. Every ship in the harbor was dressed with flags. Broadway, with Chinese lanterns strung aloft, was, according to the New York *Times,* "fantastically decorated." [154]

In the parade up Broadway the man who had refused to be discouraged, the chief promoter of the cable, Cyrus Field, rode with New York's Mayor Tibman in a carriage pulled by six horses. Throughout the length of the parade, the crowd wildly cheered Field.[155]

Following the parade, a mass meeting got under way in the Crystal Palace, New York's large hall for special occasions. The concluding speech, the "History of the Ocean Telegraph," was given by Cyrus Field's brother, Dudley Field, who had served throughout the undertaking as legal counsel for the company. He told how Frederick N. Gisborne had applied to Matthew D. Field to help him raise funds for his telegraph to Newfoundland and that this member of the Field family "thus applied to, came to Mr. Cyrus W. Field and myself. We had several conversations on the subject. Then it was that the thought of extending the line across the Atlantic suggested itself. Mr. Cyrus W. Field wrote to Lieutenant Maury, to inquire about the practicability of submerging a cable, and consulted Professor Morse about the possibility of telegraphing through it. Their answers were favorable." [156] Throughout his talk Dudley Field stressed that co-operation between the United States and Great Britain had made possible the victory.

At eight o'clock the following night, September 2, six hundred people sat down to dinner at the Metropolitan Hotel. The hosts were the members of the Common Council of the City of New York and the guests of honor were Cyrus Field and the officers of H.B.M. steamship *Gorgon* and the U.S. steam frigate *Niagara.* In his speech at the dinner, Field paid special tribute to those who had done most for the cable, including his partners and engineers of the company. He then toasted

> Lord Clarendon and Sir John Pakington, the present First Lord of the Admiralty, and Sir Charles Wood, the late First Lord of the Admiralty, the Secretary of the English Treasury, Captain Washington, Hydrographer of Her Majesty's Navy, the United States government, the President and Secretary of the Navy, the Governments of Newfoundland, Prince Edward Island, Nova Scotia, Canada and Maine.
>
> Those never-to-be-forgotten philosophers, Lieutenant Maury,

Professor Morse, Professor Faraday, Professor Bache and Professor W. Thomson who have rendered most efficient aid without receiving any compensation.[157]

A toast was proposed to the United States Coast Survey and Lieutenant Berryman, to which Professor Bache replied, being often interrupted by loud cheers. This was followed by a toast to the health of Samuel F. B. Morse, and it was answered with loud applause. Next came a toast to "Lieutenant Maury—The indefatigable investigator of the courses of winds and currents, and of the ocean depths," to which the diners responded with cheers.[158] At this victory celebration the good work that men had done for the cable was remembered, and any errors that had been made were momentarily forgotten.

However, the past was not to be left to bury itself, for the Coast Survey had sent its version of the whole unhappy story of Berryman's 1856 soundings to Professor Benjamin Silliman's *American Journal of Science and Arts,* which published it in the September issue that came out just after the New York celebration of the cable triumph. By September 9, 1858, the New York *Times* wanted a statement from Maury in reply to the article. He replied that as yet he had "not seen the article itself nor any account of it except a short newspaper account received this A.M. which says that according to that article, 'Lieutenant Berryman's observations are considered more reliable than Lieutenant Dayman's.' "[159] Maury then gave his reasons for believing Berryman's soundings faulty and Dayman's accurate.

When Maury did secure the *Journal* article he found it to consist chiefly of a report to Bache by the assistant superintendent of the Coast Survey, Professor W. P. Trowbridge, dated May 31, 1858, with a statement that the substance of the report had been given by Bache's permission at the April meeting of the American Association for the Advancement of Science.[160] Maury immediately asked Dr. Silliman to print an article by him explaining his position. He added that "the Coast Survey could not by any fair means have been in possession of Berryman's journal when that paper was prepared."[161] Maury also pointed out that the Coast Survey had questioned the existence of a submarine "plateau" and explained exactly what he meant by that word, "a bench—a shelf— a rise in the bottom."[162] Silliman refused the request and Maury tried once more, reminding the editor that "you have unwittingly given the authority . . . of the most influential scientific journal in the country to assist in the perpetuation of an outrage and wrong. I therefore submit it is not fair to deny me a hearing."[163]

Inasmuch as the *Journal* had also, in the September issue, carried a second unsigned editorial-type article condemning Maury's position, Silliman's second refusal seemed a clear indication of alignment with Bache. Ordinarily the *Journal* would have been considered the logical place for both sides of the question to have been presented.

Because of the timing of the article, Maury realized that Bache would attempt to prevent his long-planned use of the cable to determine the difference of longitude between the Naval Observatory in Washington and the Royal Observatory in Greenwich, England, whose longitude is the zero, or prime meridian, from which longitude is reckoned. It was obvious to Maury also that Bache intended to continue his efforts to have a controlling hand in deep-sea soundings. Maury determined to fight back with every weapon at his command. On September 24, 1858, he wrote Secretary of the Navy Toucey an official report on Bache:

> I beg leave to call your attention to Article XVII in the September number (No. 77–1858) of the *American Journal of Science and Arts*. That article is an official one from the office of the Coast Survey. In it the labors of the Observatory are not only appropriated without acknowledgment, but the attempt is made to come between this office and its specialties.
>
> This is the second time that complaint has been made against the Superintendent of the Coast Survey for an improper interference with the affairs of this office and to admit that one Bureau of the Government may step from its own sphere of duties to grasp at and pass upon the labors of another would be dangerous.
>
> Therefore, that the Superintendent of the Coast Survey may be admonished and restrained within the limits which the law assigns for that work, I have to request that you will bring the subject matter of this communication to the notice of the Honorable the Secretary of the Treasury and oblige.[164]

Having already advised the Secretary of the Treasury, under whose jurisdiction the Coast Survey functioned, that the New York, Newfoundland, and London Telegraph Company had in 1855 given the Naval Observatory the first right to establish the longitude of Washington and having offered the results to "such bureaus of the Treasury Department as may have need of them," [165] Maury now secured authorization to proceed with the longitude determination. Knowing that Bache had created a difficult situation for Cyrus Field by requesting permission to allow the Coast Survey to make this determination, Maury, on September 28, 1858, reported to Field:

> I have by the authority of the Secretary of the Navy written both to the English Admiralty and the Astronomer Royal requesting

their co-operation in determining, when it shall be convenient to the company, the difference of Longitude between the Observatories of Greenwich and Washington and with this invitation I sent each a copy of the resolution of the company in 1855 giving the right to this Observatory so to determine.

The Secretary of the Treasury was also officially informed of the steps thus taken under authority of the Navy Department. So that I suppose you will have no more trouble with Dr. Bache in the premises.[166]

Maury apparently expected the Secretary of the Navy to persuade the Secretary of the Treasury to enjoin Bache from further efforts to deprive the Naval Observatory of carrying out this determination of longitude, one of the essential scientific functions for which the Observatory had been established.[167] If Maury thought Bache would be stopped this easily, he was certainly unduly optimistic.

Bache was busy swinging his heavy artillery into place for battle. His first move was to ask Joseph Henry, secretary of the Smithsonian Institution, to bring his influence to bear on Secretary of the Treasury Cobb. In reply Henry, on September 28, 1858, wrote Bache that, in response to

your request that I would call on the Secretary of the Treasury relative to the outrageous proposition of Maury. I called early in the evening and remained at his house until 10 o'clock but I did not see him. I called this morning at the Department and found [Philip] Clayton [Assistant Secretary of the Treasury] with whom I had a long and earnest conversation on the subject. He thought it was a fortunate circumstance that the Department could have the Longitude from Greenwich determined without cost since the government was endeavoring to economise as much as possible. I, however, informed him that it would be far from a matter of economy, that it would cost the government much more if done by Maury than by yourself and when it was done there would be no certainty as to its correctness.

While we were engaged in this conversation the Secretary himself [Howell Cobb, Secretary of the Treasury] came in and appeared to take a more sensible view of the case than Clayton did. He said he wished the Survey [Coast Survey] was in charge of the Navy Department and that he had endeavored to place it there.

He, however, agreed with me in the opinion that while it was under his charge you should be defended. He stated that he had sent the letter to you and when he received your exposition he would confer with the Secretary of the Navy on the subject. I spoke to him with freedom as to my opinion of the course taken by Maury on this and other cases.[168]

Henry added, "We have much at stake in this matter . . . if we make a false step we may even be deprived of the power to render any service to Dr. Gould." [169]

The closing remark had reference to the battle royal in which Henry, Bache, and all their intimate scientific group were then engaged to try to keep their friend Dr. Benjamin Apthorp Gould, Jr., on as director of the Dudley Observatory in Albany, New York. Bache headed the Scientific Council which included Gould, Benjamin Peirce, and Joseph Henry. The Council believed it should control the handling of the Dudley Observatory while the Trustees, who were the leading citizens of Albany and represented those who had given the money to build and equip the observatory, had requested Gould to leave and Bache to remove magnetic equipment, belonging to the Coast Survey, which he had placed on the Dudley grounds.[170]

Aside from the issue of saving the reputation and job of his protégé, Dr. Gould, Bache was fighting to keep his Coast Survey instruments and men on the grounds of the Dudley Observatory.[171] Bache's view, however, had disturbed the Cabinet officer to whom he was answerable, Secretary of the Treasury Howell Cobb. Cobb had twice had the Solicitor of the Treasury request Bache to supply full information on the dispute. Unsatisfied by two replies that Bache had written in late September, Cobb demanded on October 5 that Bache supply the requested facts in order that a legal decision could be reached on whether the Coast Survey was or was not invading the rights of the private corporation that owned the Dudley Observatory.[172]

Equally concerned over this quarrel was Chief Justice of the United States, Roger Brooke Taney, who was a Regent ex officio of the Smithsonian. On October 4 Joseph Henry reported to Bache that the Chief Justice had sent for him to urge that he and Bache withdraw from the violent Dudley Observatory controversy. Henry said of Taney, "I found him much troubled on account of our quarrel and the fact that the affair would be represented to our disadvantage as officers of the government interfering in matters of this kind." [173]

Henry also reiterated what he had reported earlier: that the Secretary of the Treasury "had been trying to transfer the Coast Survey to the Navy Department and that it was his present opinion that was the place for it. He . . . [Cobb] laughingly quoted a passage from one of Dr. Gould's letters as to the method of puffing adopted by scientific men." And, two weeks later, Henry wrote to Bache: "I do not like the expression in your letter relative to the separation which the enemy may make in our ranks." [174]

Earlier, in mid-March, Joseph Henry had called on "the General" to get Jefferson Davis to back them in the Dudley Observatory situation, and in the intervening months the statesman from Mississippi had been very active on behalf of his friend Bache.[175] Now, in late October, Bache asked Jefferson Davis to visit the Secretary of the Treasury in the hope that the Senator from Mississippi, who had so recently been Secretary of War, could convince his fellow Southerner, Howell Cobb, where Henry had failed with him.

Jefferson Davis accepted the mission and on October 27, 1858, reported to Bache, "I called to see the Secretary of the Treasury and had a full, not wholly unsatisfactory conversation with him. I also had a conversation with him in relation to deep sea soundings and the charge of intervention. He appeared gratified to learn how defensible the position of his bureau was, and hoped you would give the commander sharp pickle. [Maury had by this date been promoted to the rank of commander.] So far as the temper manifested is concerned, the interview was gratifying," Davis concluded.[176] Jefferson Davis's alignment with his friend Bache against Maury is further indicated in a note written a few days before the visit to Cobb in which Davis advised Bache:

"As to noninterference with Com. M. your past course sufficiently expresses your rule of conduct, it might do to notice the proposition as introductory to his assumption in relation to Longitude. But you could not, of course, treat him as one whose orbit could interfere with yours." [177]

These letters reveal the highly organized opposition that Maury faced in his scientific work, especially in relation to the Atlantic cable. That he did not always handle his defense of his work as diplomatically as he might have is also revealed. Wounded pride is evident. But the fact remains that the whole controversy between these men of stature was one of those tragic, time-wasting, energy-frittering, science-damaging conflicts that achieve nothing but harm.

Bache's campaign to prevent Maury from making the first measurement of longitude for Washington over the Atlantic cable proved a wasted effort. In October the cable ceased to transmit. Try as they could to find the damaged section, the engineers were unsuccessful. The silence that reigned across the Atlantic was particularly discouraging after the brief triumph of intercontinental communications.

Cyrus Field was not daunted, but there were Jeremiahs who wailed about the amount of money that had been poured into the undertaking and questioned whether telegraph communications across the Atlantic would ever be established.[178] In a lecture given that November, Maury promptly stated his unequivocal belief that the cable would ultimately operate successfully.[179] His unflagging support meant much to Field who, in mid-May, 1859, wrote Maury and, as usual, offered to serve him in any way that he could on a coming trip to England.

"I know of nothing that you can do for me except to 'hurry up' the Atlantic Telegraph," Maury replied and added, "I should be glad if you would report progress now and then. Success depends mainly upon the kind of cable to be used and as soon as that is decided, I would like to know it. Wishing you a pleasant trip and *complete* success." [180]

In August, 1859, when Field asked Maury to serve on the Atlantic Telegraph Company's "Advisory Committee in America," Maury wrote back suggesting a new route "in view of recent findings concerning the electric need of booster stations," and mapped out such a route. He suggested that Field study the new 1859 edition of his Orographic Map of the Atlantic. The route would be 510 miles from the north of Scotland to Iceland, 720 miles from Iceland to Cape Farewell, and 640 miles from Cape Farewell to Newfoundland. Maury concluded: "You ask my opinion about the route via Iceland & Greenland . . . if you find suitable landing places &c it is *the* route. No satisfactory opinion can be given until we are enlightened upon that . . . point. I see it announced in the papers that your company has decided upon a light cable with iron service only for the shore ends. You recollect that in 1856, I urged this subject upon you by letter and by conversation most earnestly. I am glad to see that the company has come 'round." [181]

Maury's last correspondence with Field concerning the Atlantic cable took place in 1860. By that time the clouds of coming division and strife within the United States were too ominous to encourage further immediate action on the cable. Believers in the cable, however, were sure that when the clouds lifted the cable would be laid. Maury's oceanographic researches had played a major role in making the effort possible. They were a matter of record—and the great objective of permanently linking the continents was to be realized.

CHAPTER XIII

The Physical Geography of the Sea

Dissemination of scientific knowledge for the use of others was considered by Maury to be as essential a function of the scientist as the investigations and evaluation that had produced the information. Because of this belief, he worked "under forced draft" in the autumn of 1853 to produce the manuscript of the 6th edition of *Explanations and Sailing Directions to accompany the Wind and Current Charts.*[1] He wanted especially to report on the results of the Brussels Conference, from which he had just returned, and to present a full account of the oceanographic information gained through the Observatory's investigations in the preceding year. To the chapter on the investigations of the depths of the sea—90 pages long—he gave the title suggested by Alexander von Humboldt when the Prussian scientist had praised Maury's oceanic investigations and declared them to be a new department of science—"The Physical Geography of the Sea." [2]

For the publishing of this edition of the *Sailing Directions* Maury had gone back to the Philadelphia firm of E. C. and J. Biddle, which had, in 1836, brought out his first book, *Navigation*. As each chapter was finished at the Observatory it was sent off to the publishers. In December the Biddles, who were nearing the end of printing the 772-page volume of *Sailing Directions,* asked Maury to come north to confer with them. Maury regretfully replied that the press of official business would not permit his coming. However, his nephew, Lieutenant Dabney Herndon Maury, U.S. Army, was in Philadelphia, and Maury asked him to see the publishers. While Dabney was in their office, one of the Biddles took him aside and asked him to give his uncle a message—they believed that Maury's knowledge of the sea would be of interest to many others besides the mariners who read the *Sailing Directions.* Biddle recommended that Maury prepare a book on the subject especially for the general reader and warned that he should do so as rapidly as possible and secure a copyright or he would soon see "some Yankee bookmaker steal his thunder and reap a fortune from it." [3] The Biddles had watched Maury's career of arduous labor too long to want to see someone else capitalize on it, and they knew that some professional writer could glean sufficient information from the six editions of the *Sailing Directions* to do just that.

The Biddles further advised that Maury should give the book the title *The Physical Geography of the Sea.* Feeling confident that the book would have wide appeal, the Philadelphia publishers generously suggested that it should be published by a firm capable of larger distribution than they could manage. They mentioned the suitability of the New York house of Harper and Brothers. [4] Maury concurred in all their opinions. He asked Harpers if they would be interested in publishing his book and received a prompt reply that they would.

Maury began work on this manuscript in the spring of 1854, settling to the task each evening as soon as he had concluded his official duties and had his light supper. [5] Some evening at this meal, before he started his nightly writing, humor-loving Maury must have reminded his family of a story about his book writing that had long been going the rounds among their Virginia kith and kin. Years before, when he was writing his first *Explanations and Sailing Directions to accompany the Wind and Current Charts,* one of Ann's relatives had come to visit them in Washington and had returned to Virginia to report to the family that "Mat" was writing a book. "A book?" had queried one of the old ladies present. "What is it about?" "Winds and currents," she had been told. At this she had thrown up her hands in despair, exclaiming, "Well! Ann will come to want!" [6]

And so Ann would have had she and the children been dependent on funds from those books, for they were, of course, official government publications from which Maury derived no financial return. His name was used on the charts and *Sailing Directions* to give the weight of his scientific authority to them as well as due credit to him, who had conceived them. *The Physical Geography of the Sea,* however, was to be a personal undertaking, written in his off-duty hours, and he was indeed hopeful that it would yield profits that would keep Ann from the want the elderly relative had forecast for her!

The Biddles' warning of possible appropriation of his material made Maury drive ahead at an even faster pace than usual. By this period of his life Maury's handwriting had become very hard to read, especially when he was writing rapidly. In a manuscript he scratched out words and phrases and replaced them with interlineations in which the words were so small, cramped and run together that only his trained copyists could decipher them. Betty and Diana, his two older daughters, having long been his amanuenses, seldom had to ask questions as they copied their father's rough draft of *The Physical Geography of the Sea*. Occasionally, when he was not sure he had simplified a scientific fact sufficiently for the general reader, Maury would stop writing and read the passage aloud to the family. Then, Diana recalled, they were "invited and encouraged to criticize." [7]

This "magnum opus," as Maury hoped *The Physical Geography of the Sea* would prove to be, was finished on June 20, 1854.[8] On the following December 1 Maury joyfully reported that it was "two-thirds through the press" and ten days later he read the last proof.[9] He took special pleasure in dedicating *The Physical Geography of the Sea* to George Manning, of New York, who had been so faithful as the agent in charge of all distribution of the *Wind and Current Charts*.[10]

Early in 1855 Harper and Brothers brought out the first edition of *The Physical Geography of the Sea*. The text revealed that Maury had achieved his objective of presenting his scientific findings in a style that the general reader could both understand and enjoy. In the introduction Maury explained: "I shall treat of the economy of the sea and its adaptations—of its salts, its waters, its climates, and its inhabitants, and of whatever there may be of general interest in its commercial uses or industrial pursuits, for all such things pertain to its Physical Geography." [11]

He devoted the first chapter to the great current that had for years been the object of intense study on his part—the Gulf Stream. His love of his subject matter is revealed in some of the most felicitous phrases ever used by a scientist:

> There is a river in the ocean. In the severest droughts it never fails, and in the mightiest floods it never overflows. Its banks and its bottom are of cold water, while its current is of warm. The Gulf of Mexico is its fountain, and its mouth is in the Arctic Seas. It is the Gulf Stream. There is in the world no other such majestic flow of waters. Its current is more rapid than the Mississippi or the Amazon. Its waters, as far out from the Gulf as the Carolina coasts, are of an indigo blue. They are so distinctly marked that their line of junction with the common sea-water may be traced by the eye.[12]

Some of Maury's theories concerning the Gulf Stream, especially that concerning its cause or origin, were disputed by other contemporary scientists, including such distinguished men as Sir John Herschel and C. Wyville Thomson.[13] But Maury was a pioneer investigator of this phenomenon of the sea; and although research in later years proved some of his concepts wrong, he was a bold workman who believed that beginnings had to be made. Like British oceanographer William B.

Carpenter, Maury worked on the basis that "truth emerges out of error rather than out of chaos." [14]

Maury stated that, "Every physical fact, by whomsoever observed, is, when placed in its true connections, a discovery and invention; all such facts are like the sheaf of magic wheat—the more it is threshed the more it yields." [15]

The chapter on the "Influence of the Gulf Stream upon Climates" revealed Maury's religious concept of the physical world. He was often criticized, he admitted, for mixing religion and science, but he profoundly believed in the divine order of nature. He felt that the Bible and science were in agreement and that any seeming irreconcilability between them would be solved when man saw more clearly.

> The inhabitants of the ocean are as much the creatures of climate as are those of the dry land; for the same Almighty hand which decked the lily and cares for the sparrow, fashioned also the pearl and feeds the great whale. Whether of the land or the sea, the inhabitants are all His creatures, subjects of His laws and agents in His economy. The sea, therefore, we infer, has its offices and duties to perform; so may we infer, have its currents, and so, too, its inhabitants; consequently, he who undertakes to study its phenomena, must cease to regard it as a waste of waters. He must look upon it as a part of the exquisite machinery by which the harmonies of nature are preserved, and then he will begin to perceive the developments of order and the evidences of design which make it a most beautiful and interesting subject for contemplation. [16]

Seeking to interest the layman in the atmosphere, Maury wrote:

> Hence, to the right-minded mariner, and to him who studies the physical relations of earth, sea and air, the atmosphere is something more than a shoreless ocean, at the bottom of which his bark is wafted or driven along. It is an envelope or covering for the dispersion of light and heat over the surface of the earth. . . . It is a laboratory for purification. . . .[17]
>
> . . . To evaporate water enough annually from the ocean to cover the earth, on the average, five feet deep with rain; to transport it from one zone to another; and to precipitate it in the right places, at suitable times, and in the proportions due, is one of the offices of the grand atmospherical machine. . . . What a powerful engine is the atmosphere! and how nicely adjusted must be all the cogs, and wheels, and springs, and pinions of this exquisite piece of machinery, that it never wears out nor breaks down, nor fails to do its work at the right time, and in the right way! [18]

261

A chapter entitled "Currents of the Sea" described the Red Sea Current, the great Equatorial Current, the Mediterranean Current, the Humboldt Current, the China Current, the Cold Asiatic Current, and the Brazil Current. The proof that there were undercurrents that coursed far below the surface of the sea, Maury said, had been supplied by investigations carried out by Lieutenant J. C. Walsh and Lieutenant S. P. Lee on their deep-sea soundings expeditions.[19]

A colorful account of how whales had provided a scientific clue made good reading. Maury explained that whalers marked their harpoons with the date and the name of their ship. To the surprise of whalemen, "whales that have been taken near the Bering's Strait side with harpoons in them bearing the stamp of ships that were known to cruise on the Baffin Bay side of the American continent" and the dates were too close together for them to have gone from the Atlantic side to the Pacific "around either Cape Horn or Good Hope." It was known that the right whale could not go through the tropical regions of the ocean and also that the right whale of the northern hemisphere was a different animal from that of the southern. Maury declared:

> Thus the fact was established that the harpooned whales did not pass around Cape Horn or the Cape of Good Hope, for they were of the class that could not cross the equator.
>
> In this way we were furnished with circumstantial evidence affording the most irrefragable proof that there is, at times at least, open water communication through the Arctic Sea from one side of the continent to the other, for it is known that the whales can not travel under the ice for such a great distance as . . . that. . . .
>
> But this did not prove the existence of an open sea there; it only established the existence—the occasional existence, if you please— of a channel through which whales had passed. Therefore we felt bound to introduce other evidence before we could expect the reader to admit our proof, and to believe with us in the existence of an open sea in the Arctic Ocean.[20]

The account continued with a report of the efforts that had been made and were being continued to prove the existence of the long-sought Northwest Passage.

A field of investigation with which Maury had long been preoccupied was "The Salts of the Sea," and he devoted a chapter to this seldom-considered subject.

> Take for example, the coral islands, reefs, beds and atolls, with which the Pacific Ocean is studded and garnished. They were built

up of materials which a certain kind of insect quarried from the sea water. The currents of the sea ministered to this little insect—they were its *hod carriers;* when fresh supplies of solid matter were wanted for the coral rock upon which the foundations of the Polynesian Islands were laid, they brought them; the obedient currents stood ready with fresh supplies in unfailing streams of sea water from which the solid ingredients had not been secreted. . . . Hence we say *we know* that the sea has its system of circulation, for it transports materials for the coral rock from one part of the world to another; its currents receive them from the rivers, and hand them over to the little mason for the structure of the most stupendous works of solid masonry that man has ever seen—the coral islands of the sea.[21]

Maury had very carefully chosen plates to illustrate certain subjects that might prove difficult for the public to understand. The first plate in the book was a diagram of the winds. This chart was the result of 1,159,353 separate observations on the force and direction of the wind and some 100,000 observations on barometric readings at sea.[22] It served to explain the chapter entitled "The Winds" and also, to some extent, the chapter on "The Climates of the Ocean." There was also an isothermal chart of the Atlantic Ocean giving average water temperatures for March and September. To clarify a subject discussed in his chapter on "Storms," Maury included a chart of the actual path of a hurricane spawned in the West Indies. A chapter on "The Drift of the Sea" was illustrated by a chart showing the information then available.

For the more scientifically oriented reader there were chapters on "The Probable Relation between Magnetism and the Circulation of the Atmosphere," "Red Fogs and Sea Dust," and "The Equatorial Cloud Ring."

Two chapters on subjects in which Maury was the world's pioneer investigator were destined to be popular with all readers—"The Depths of the Ocean" and "The Basin of the Atlantic." The story of the development of deep-sea soundings was recounted with all the zest that Maury felt for this field of investigation.[23] A sketch of John Mercer Brooke's deep-sea sounding apparatus was included, as well as an account of how this instrument was used to bring up the first samples from the great depths of the floor of the sea. Two plates showed what had been learned with regard to the elevations and depressions in the bed of the sea.[24] Another chapter, in which Maury told how he had discovered new routes for ships to sail and how these were affecting the cruises of men-of-war as well as of merchantmen, presented information of special interest to men of commerce.[25] Maury managed to convey his own enthusiasm on each subject discussed, and the book which could have been dry was not.

The Physical Geography of the Sea received high praise from critics reviewing it in leading American journals, and the public response was such that the book had five printings in America within the first year of publication.[26]

The foreign distribution of the book was of particular importance to Maury. He and his colleagues saw a foreign edition of the book as an instrument to further their campaign to interest more nations in participation in their system of meteorological observations. So that the relationship could not possibly be missed, Maury had the book published in England under the title of *The Physical Geography of the Sea and Its Meteorology;* and he dedicated it to Lord Wrottesley, who had played the leading role in persuading the British government to join in the cooperative marine meteorological system. Sampson Low, Son and Co. were Maury's British publishers.[27]

The first to translate the book into a foreign tongue was a naval officer who had been a delegate to the Brussels Conference—Lieutenant Marin H. Jansen, on duty at the Netherlands Meteorological Institute. This translation was published in Holland in 1855.[28] It was followed by editions in German, French, and Italian.[29]

Of all the remarks made about *The Physical Geography of the Sea* most gratifying to Maury was the praise he received from such European scientists as Baron von Humboldt, Quetelet, and Edme François Jomard.[30] One of the founders of the Geographical Society of Paris, the noted Egyptologist Jomard wrote Maury, "[concerning] your important work, *The Physical Geography of the Sea*—I have taken a first reading and, I regard it as a true present made to physicists, geographers and navigators, as well as to the commerce of all nations. I congratulate you, Sir, upon the accomplishment of a work so difficult, so useful, so laborious." [31]

Maury knew the influence that the leading British publications then had on the educated men of America as well as those of England. Engaged as he was in trying to bring about a second international conference on meteorology, he considered it enormously helpful when *Blackwood's Magazine, Westminster Review, British Quarterly Review, North British Review,* and the *Edinburgh Review* hailed his book as a leading contribution to scientific literature. The last-named publication said of *The Physical Geography of the Sea:* "The extent of scientific information which this work conveys, or its easy unaffected style, cannot be at all gathered from the mere enumeration of the subjects of which it treats. The book must be read to be appreciated." [32]

In the Royal Astronomical Society *Monthly Notices,* Maury's work was termed "one of the most fascinating books in the English language." [33] The *Revue des Deux Mondes,* in Gallic style, stated: "Often indeed his powerful imagination makes of Maury a veritable poet and his descriptions recall involuntarily those stories of the Thousand and One Nights! . . . where Gulnore pictures . . . marvellously the mysterious realms of the profundities under the sea." [34]

As Maury gained further knowledge about the sea he revised the text of his book for the new editions that came from the press—nineteen in all in England and eight in America, where the eighth edition was dedicated by Maury to his early teacher and continuing friend, William C. Hasbrouck.[35]

Dr. C. Alphonso Smith, when head of the English Department of the U.S. Naval Academy, said of *The Physical Geography of the Sea:* "It was the first book to embrace the entire sea as its theme and thus to bring three-fourths of the world into the domain of recognized and intelligent principle." [36] Three quarters of a century after Maury had written his text, a modern handbook of oceanography, edited for Britain's famed Challenger Society by G. Herbert Fowler, declared of *The Physical Geography of the Sea:* "It is a book which is thoroughly imbued with the spirit of scientific research and marked by the boundless enthusiasm of its author, and though some of its facts are out of date, and the theoretical treatment appears fantastic in the light of the knowledge acquired since its appearance, it remains a model for writers of popular science."[37]

In the same year that *The Physical Geography of the Sea* was first published, 1855, another much smaller but significant publication by Maury came off the presses. This booklet was very different in style, tone and intent. It was a practical scientific work to overcome a problem that had long existed but had recently become acute.

A few months earlier the people of the United States had been shocked by a sea disaster that had cost three hundred lives when in October, 1854, the U.S. mail steamer *Arctic* and the French steamer *Vesta* had rammed each other in a thick fog in the North Atlantic. Numerous other collisions had occurred earlier in the same iceberg-infested, fog-laden reaches of the North Atlantic most frequently traveled by passenger ships plying between the United States and Europe. The public had joined shipping men in declaring that the loss of life at sea must be stopped.[38]

In Boston, Maury's friend, Robert Bennett Forbes, a prominent shipowner, had thought of an idea that might alleviate the problem. He had immediately sounded out Maury as to the practicability of his idea that lanes might be laid down in which steamers would be required to travel between the Old World and the New.[39] After a careful preliminary study, Maury had declared in December, 1854, that he could work out a system of lanes.[40]

Early in January of 1855 Maury had received a formal request from a group of prominent underwriters, shipowners, and merchants of Boston to perfect his tentative steamer-lane plan and prepare a chart "exhibiting the routes suggested, so laid out as may in your judgment, best answer the purpose in view of lessening the liability of collision without materially lengthening the passage." [41] In five weeks Maury had completed the work and sent the committee charts showing the lanes that steamers should take, explanations of the lanes, and tables of distance. He later supplied more facts and stated, "The following summary of wrecks and collisions ought to plead, trumpet-tongued, in favor of our lanes." [42]

Maury's proposal was published in New York in 1855 by the Board of Underwriters and was entitled *Lanes for the Steamers Crossing the Atlantic*. The booklet explained that the lanes were laid out to keep ships away from icebergs and fogs, in so far as possible, as well as to avoid collisions. Maury had determined the position of the lanes by studying logs of 46,000 days of observation of winds, currents, and weather in the part of the North Atlantic through which the ships would travel.[43] Two lanes were laid down, each 20 to 25 miles wide. Maury proposed that ships bound from Europe to the United States should use the northernmost lane and eastbound steamers should travel a lane from one to ten degrees to the south. Because of meteorological and other factors, the lanes were different for summer and winter.[44] The lanes were also clearly depicted on a chart that was published, in addition to the booklet.[45]

The idea offered hope for greatly reducing, if not eliminating, collisions at sea, and Maury received many inquiries for further details. To one friend he explained:

> These lanes are narrow, sailing vessels are requested not to run along in them; but to shear off alongside of them by night. So that they are like a double track railway—everything on the same track and in the same lane, going one way.
> The lane to Europe lies along the Gulf Stream and takes a route where the weather is fine and delightful.[46]

The United States Navy soon required that their vessels use the lanes, and many commercial steamers traveled in them exclusively. When the Navy found that resistance to the new idea continued among some of

266

the merchant sea captains, men noted for their rugged independence, action was taken to try to increase merchant marine use of the lanes. The Hydrographic Office combined all the material on the subject that Maury had published in the 7th and 8th editions of the *Sailing Directions* and in 1872 published them as a booklet—*Steam Lanes Across the Atlantic.*[47]

After the *Ville de Havre* sank in the Atlantic in 1874, the London *Times* editorialized, "If she had followed Maury's steam lanes, this terrible loss of life and ship would have been avoided." [48] At least one steamship line, however, advertised that travelers could trust the safety of its ships because they followed "Maury's Steam Lanes." [49]

In 1889 a Marine Conference was called in Washington "to decide the momentous question of fixed routes for steamers crossing the North Atlantic." [50] The plan, much as originally outlined by Maury, was finally generally accepted in 1898.[51]

In recent decades, whenever there has been a collision in the Atlantic, the blame has usually been placed on the ocean giants' having veered from the authorized lanes in an effort to make speed. But this is the exception rather than the rule today, and the present safety of Atlantic travel owes a very real debt to Maury's early charting of the lanes.

Even as *The Physical Geography of the Sea* and *Lanes for the Steamers Crossing the Atlantic* differed from each other in subject matter and style, so did a third Maury publication of the year 1855—*Rules of Conduct.* This was the text of an address that Maury gave to the literary societies of the University of Virginia on June 28, 1855. In this address, printed as a pamphlet by popular demand, Maury tried, as always, to create interest in the study of the physical world. He also revealed his philosophy of work and his love of his fellow man.

> There are some here who though not seamen are nevertheless about to become masters of their own acts, and who are about to try the voyage of life upon a troubled sea. I have been some little time on that voyage; and it is so that, whenever I see a young man relying upon his own resources and setting out alone upon this long voyage, my heart warms towards him. I always desire to range up along side of him, to speak to him kindly, and whisper words of encouragement in his ear.
>
> . . . .
>
> In entering upon your duties as a citizen, recollect your excellent training here: it has given you many advantages; therefore, do not

neglect to lay down rules of conduct by which they may be most improved.

Whatever may be the degree of success that I have met with in life, I attribute it, in a great measure, to the adoption of such rules. One was, never to let the mind be idle for the want of useful occupation, but always to have in reserve subjects of thought for the leisure moments and the quiet hours of the night. When you read a book, let it be with the view to special information. . . .

It is surprising how difficult one who attempts to follow this rule finds it at first to provide himself with subjects for thought—to think of something that he does not know. . . .

But as we study the laws of nature . . . It is like climbing a mountain: every fact or fresh discovery is a step upward with an enlargement of the view, until the unknown and the mysterious become boundless—self infinitely small; and then the conviction comes upon us with a mighty force, that we know nothing—that human knowledge is only a longing desire.[52]

Maury continued with details of subjects that had interested him and the suggestion of others that might be pursued, urging that the works of nature not be studied as the result of chance or accident but as a "machinery which was planned and arranged in the perfection of wisdom!"

Movement, progress, is a law of the physical world; there rest and decay are correlative terms. The stars cannot stand still and keep their places; a planet by going back would be hurled into destruction, and even the plant of the earth that ceases to grow straightway withers and dies. And so it is in the moral world: the progress of man must be upward and onward, or downward and backward. His mind cannot stand still. There is no such thing as a stationary condition for the human understanding. To stand still is death; to go backwards is worse.[53]

When he wrote and spoke those words in the summer of 1855, having learned "that human knowledge is only a longing desire," Maury was still as filled with that desire and as passionate for future opportunity as he had been when he had entered the Navy.

CHAPTER XIV

The Plucking Board

Whenever a man accomplishes work so obviously meritorious that he is acclaimed by both the general public and his professional colleagues, there are always some associates who, for their own reasons, are critical. In Maury's case, they were the old sea dogs who disapproved of having scientific methods introduced into the Navy, the officers who resented Maury's being kept on duty at the Naval Observatory and Hydrographical Office while they had to go to sea and leave their families for long stretches of time, and a handful of officers who disliked him personally and begrudged his fame.

The fact that a small minority of naval officers held one or more of these oppositional attitudes had undoubtedly contributed to Maury's still being a lieutenant in 1855 after thirty years in the Navy. He had received his midshipman's warrant early in 1825, when James Monroe was President of the United States, and had since served under nine other Commanders in Chief: John Quincy Adams, Andrew Jackson, Martin Van Buren, William Henry Harrison, John Tyler, James Knox Polk, Zachary Taylor, Millard Fillmore, and Franklin Pierce.

He had developed the United States Naval Observatory and Hydrographical Office from a small Depot of Charts and Instruments into an institution of world standing. As its superintendent, Maury directed three programs of vital importance to the Navy—astronomy, hydrography, and marine meteorology, as well as the purchasing, safekeeping and distribution of the Navy's nautical instruments; for this he received a salary of $3,000. It was twice the $1,500 that he would have been paid as a lieutenant doing any of the Navy's routine shore jobs that demanded no major responsibility. He also had use of the superintendent's house, though he paid for fuel and light.[1] However, Maury was a man in uniform, subject to orders, and to any such, in any nation, rank is important. Rank is esteemed not only as a recognition of service satisfactorily performed and the source of increased pay but as of psychological value when dealing with others, such as representatives of other nations, as Maury so often did.

There can be no doubt that any man of Maury's intelligence would have resented being kept a lieutenant for nearly thirty years. It was one subject, however, on which Maury kept silent.[2] Apparently he did not openly complain about his rank because he suspected that that was the price he paid for being allowed to remain at the Observatory to carry on his many-faceted program of oceanic investigation. He may also have accepted the fact that, in his years of campaigning for reform within the Navy and for the advancement of the scientific programs of the Naval Observatory and Hydrographical Office, he had stepped on too many toes. His associates, however, were outspokenly bitter about Maury's low rank. This sentiment had been summed up by Maury's second-in-command just after the Brussels Conference. Lieutenant George Minor had written George Manning that he blushed for the United States for letting Maury remain a lieutenant:

> If he had been a native of the British Isles (and I thank God he is not) he would long ago have been made an admiral with his breast glittering with all the orders of Europe. It is true our own people have honored him but it has been done in their private capacity, New York especially has marked her appreciation of his useful labors with a characteristic liberality . . . but the general government ought to do something. . . . It reaps the rich harvest without rewarding the skilful and faithful laborer.
>
> There is every prospect of Maury's growing old as a simple Lieutenant. . . . But his posthumous fame will not be dependent upon them. . . . He will live in History, long after each and every one of them is forgotten.[3]

In Congress also there were men who felt that the nation had not properly rewarded the naval scientist. On January 29, 1855, Senator Stephen R. Mallory of Florida brought in a report of the Senate Naval Affairs Committee, of which he was chairman, recommending a special appropriation for Maury in recognition of service rendered the country by his *Wind and Current Charts* and *Sailing Directions*. Senator Mallory made an eloquent and detailed speech urging that the Senate vote for the committee's recommendations. He pointed out that many nations had long had hydrographic officers on duty but that Maury was the first one to conceive and make the type of charts now proving so useful. As proof, he pointed to the fact that England, after adopting Maury's plan of collecting data for a series of wind and current charts, had created a special department for this work and assigned "one of the

most distinguished and accomplished officers of the British Navy," [4] Rear
Admiral Robert Fitzroy, to head it. Mallory stated that Maury handled
duties that, in other nations, were carried out by three different super-
intendents. His specific reference was to Great Britain, where the Greenwich Observatory, controlled by the British Admiralty, was headed by
Sir George Biddell Airy, astronomer royal; where Captain John Washington, R.N., was in charge of hydrography for the Admiralty; and Admiral Fitzroy was the director of the Admiralty's new meteorological
program.

"It would appear, therefore," continued Senator Mallory, "that the
American Officer has carried out his idea, not at the expense of his duties proper, but in *addition thereto*. It may be supposed that he was
stimulated to their performance by the energy that originality gives, and
the excitement which is always attendant upon discovery and conscious
progress towards the development of useful results." [5]

Mallory told the senators that Maury had had a right to secure a copyright for his charts and directions and should be recompensed all the
more by the nation because he had not sought this for himself.

"The policy of the country in some cases, as in that of prize-money,
dictates extraordinary rewards to its public servants. Men-of-War are provided, and officers are paid to cruise against the enemy; yet the law provides not only pensions, but prize-money for their efforts in the strict
line of their duty." Mallory concluded his speech with these words:
". . . your Committee think that a sum of money, insignificant indeed
in comparison to his services, yet sufficient to remove his anxieties and
cheer his hopes for the future of those dependent upon him, might be
justly bestowed. Your Committee recommend that a sum of 25,000 dollars be thus appropriated, and report a Bill accordingly." [6]

The proposal of the committee may seem remarkable now, but about
the same time the British Parliament voted £10,000 to Captain Robert
J. LeM. McClure, R.N., his officers and crew for their discovery of a
northwest passage while on duty in arctic explorations. McClure, who
was also knighted for this discovery, received as his share of the government appropriation approximately the sum that Mallory proposed for
Maury. [7] The senators in Washington, however, sat on the purse strings
of the United States, and Maury did not receive the award.

The year 1855 was one of intense activity for Maury. He was advancing all the programs to which he was committed. The publication of *The
Physical Geography of the Sea* brought a steady flow of letters from men
whose position was such as to necessitate a reply from Maury. He was
directing the work of a portion of his staff in the production of a book
on astronomical observations scheduled for publication the following

year.[8] Maury kept a close eye on the preparation of the new *Abstract Log for Men-of-War,* which was being rushed to press for use in making the systematic observations at sea agreed on at the Brussels Conference. This book was published by E. C. and J. Biddle in Philadelphia. Eight pages supplied instructions on the observations to be made and 202 pages of blank forms were included for use in recording the required observations.[9] It was at this time, also, that Maury was engrossed in plotting the lanes for steamers crossing the Atlantic and in writing the text for the booklet published on that subject.[10] And in this same year he was doing all that he could to assure a favorable reception in Congress of his memorial urging that the United States officially request Brazil to open the Amazon to free navigation.[11]

Maury devoted time in 1855 to counseling Cyrus Field on the Atlantic cable. That year the *Annual of Scientific Discovery* carried Maury's views "On the Construction of a Submarine Trans-Atlantic Telegraph." [12]

In that busy period Maury prepared an article on "Barometric Anomalies about the Andes" for the *American Journal of Science and Arts* [13] and an address he had been asked to deliver to a meeting of Maryland leaders.[14] By request, Maury wrote his personal convictions on "The Bible and Science" for a religious publication, the *Southern Churchman.*[15]

Maury's important pioneer plea for "Meteorology for the Farmers" was published that year in the *American Farmer.* In this article Maury recommended that the systems of meteorological observation that had done so much for the improvement of navigation and commerce be extended to the land.[16] His plan was approved by the Virginia State Agricultural Society, and their resolution was published in the *Southern Planter.*[17]

Since 1850 major effort had been expended in Washington on an effort to draft a bill that would improve the efficiency of the Navy. Maury and his Navy friends who were in those years on shore duty in the United States or at home awaiting orders had conferred and corresponded on the subject.[18] They had also met with congressmen to promote their belief that changes were needed in the Navy structure. As early as November 1, 1850, Maury had been in correspondence with Captain Samuel F. Du Pont (who was waiting orders) concerning their mutual efforts to eliminate problems within the naval service by passage of an effective Congressional bill.[19] On July 20, 1851, Maury had written his long-time friend, Commander Thomas A. Dornin: "I send you, [David G.] Farragut, [Robert B.] Cunningham, [Samuel] Barron, and [Arthur] Sinclair each two copies of [Chairman of House Committee on Naval Affairs Frederick Perry] Stanton's report. Work's the word and quick's the motion now, so drive ahead. It is not all we want, yet we want all it proposes, therefore give us a helping hand through the press and hammer away while Congress is in blast." [20] Maury's advice was sought by Senator Stephen R. Mallory on the naval reform bill he was going to introduce in the Senate.[21]

On February 28, 1855, Congress passed Mallory's bill, "An Act to Promote the Efficiency of the Navy." The chief object of the act was to increase efficiency through eliminating deadwood and thus make promotions of good men possible. Toward this end a board of officers was appointed to implement the law by sitting to "make a careful examination" of all officers of the Navy from the rank of passed midshipman upward to decide which ones were "incapable of performing promptly and efficiently all their duty both ashore and afloat." [22] This board was to report its findings to the Secretary of the Navy, who was to review the list, add his recommendations, and forward them to the President for executive action.

The Navy Retiring Board commenced deliberations on June 20, 1855, and, with some days missed because of sickness of members and time out for the July Fourth holiday, sat on weekdays from 10 A.M. to 3 P.M. until deliberations were concluded on July 26. The findings of the Board concerning the 700 officers whose careers had been considered were not then released but were sent to the Secretary of the Navy.[23]

In August Maury was able to leave Washington for his annual vacation. Fatigued from his heavy labors of the preceding months and desirous of avoiding his usual seasonal bout with malaria, Maury went to the mountains of Virginia for a quiet rest.[24] By mid-September Maury was at Ridgeway, near Charlottesville, visiting his friend and kinsman Franklin Minor. Maury had looked forward to this visit as he wished to discuss his program of meteorology for farmers with Minor, who farmed his 1,000-acre property along scientific lines.[25]

At Ridgeway on September 19, 1855, Maury received an official communication—a letter from Secretary of the Navy James C. Dobbin which had been written in Washington two days earlier:

> The Board of Naval Officers assembled under the Act to promote the efficiency of the Navy, approved February 28th, 1855, having reported you as one of the officers who in their judgment should be placed on the Reserved List on leave-of-absence pay, and the findings of the Board having been approved by the President, it becomes my duty to inform you that from this date you are removed from

the Active Service List and placed on the Reserved List on leave-of-absence pay.

> You are, however, not detached from the Naval Observatory. I avail myself of the authority of the law to direct that you continue on your present duty.[26]

If the development had not been so serious, Maury could have appreciated the irony. The reorganization for which he had worked had inexplicably eliminated him, one of its mentors. He could hardly believe it.

The next day Maury wrote Secretary Dobbin. After the usual beginning of a formal service letter, he got to the heart of his reply with these words:

> This announcement has taken me by surprise.
>
> I have been in the Navy upwards of thirty years. During this time I have aimed, in every station to which I have been called, to serve my country truly. Well—with what success the Department and the public can judge better than I, suffice it to say, that I am not aware that any charge or accusations or even any complaint of duty neglected or badly performed during this long period has ever reached the Department against me. Nevertheless in the judgment of the Board I should be and have been placed under official disgrace.
>
> This is a severe blow, and I feel it as a grievous wrong. May I not therefore be permitted to know what is the accusation against me, and who my accusers were before the Board?
>
> As soon as health and the miasma of the Observatory will permit, or sooner should you desire it, I propose to return to the Observatory and to enter upon the discharge of duty there in the new relations to which your communication has consigned me.[27]

Secretary Dobbin replied that the late Navy Board had reported no reasons and therefore the department could not grant Maury's request to be informed as to what accusations were made or who made them.[28] On learning this, Maury's sense of injustice was so outraged that he determined he would fight to the death a finding by a "star chamber" court.[29]

He wrote to Robert Hatton in Nashville, Tennessee: "When the bill creating the Board was proposed I attached very little importance to it, but I thought that its tending would be in a wholesome direction for I supposed that everything would be fair and above board. The first day the Board met, and I understood that its sittings were to be secret, I denounced it." [30]

When Maury reached Washington he was further angered to learn that the Navy Retiring Board had kept no record of their deliberations. This, he wrote William Blackford, had only one significance: "These men had the grudges that had been accumulating between 25 and 50 years against their brother officers. They were determined to feed them fat and in their eagerness to gratify them they forgot the suggestion of common prudence and deliberately resolved to suppress all marks that might lead to detection. If they had been determined to do right they would have kept a record to show the public such was the fact." [31]

In a letter of October 1, 1855, written from the U.S. Naval Observatory and Hydrographical Office, Maury stated his feelings frankly to the Secretary:

> A grievous wrong has been done and in appealing to you to interpose with the authority of the Department to help me to right it, it is proper that I should state the grounds of my complaint and indicate the extent of the redress which I crave at your hands.
>
> My complaint is that I have been tried and condemned by my peers without a hearing; and that not withstanding that the law did not require of them secret judgment in the premises, yet they proceeded so secretly in my case, that they not only reported no reasons for their finding but I am given to understand that they preserved no minutes of the accusation against me, made no memorandum of the evidence, kept no record of their votes, nor returned a list of accusers or witnesses.
>
> Nor is this all. I complain of the cruelty of the sentence that they have pronounced against me; and I think you will agree with me that the punishment is excessive.
>
> Their sentence deprives me of valuable professional privileges; it casts a stigma upon my name, and it inflicts Naval death;—for being tried without a hearing I am found incompetent to do the duties of my profession, and pronounced to be now and forever unworthy of any naval preferment whatever.
>
> Is there anything I beg to know, either among the files of the Department, or anywhere else within your knowledge, to sustain such an imputation? If there be, I challenge its production and ask a lawful trial.
>
> The law requires specific charges but these are vague and the finding of the Board is cruelly so. What is the ground of this "incompetency" for which it has adjudged me to be overslaughed, or rather what is it not? It is drunkenness; it is disaffection; it is moral turpitude; it is every thing that can be brought within the category

of military crimes and misdemeanors; it is anything that envy, hatred and malice may invent.

May I not know the nature of this secret accusation, and be confronted with the witnesses against me?

The right not to be condemned unheard is very dear to every American heart; and charges without specification are most abhorrent to it. I am persuaded that all the rightful authority of the Department will be most readily exercised by you in homage of these great first principles of justice, and that you will be most happy to assist me by all lawful means in your power to secure this right.

Seeing therefore that the Board which did this wrong did it privily and kept no record, I consider it a most fortunate circumstance that all its members are Navy Officers subject to your immediate orders; that the accusations and witnesses are fresh in their minds and at your bidding, I may know from them my offenses and accusers. I therefore earnestly request that you will cause the precept of the Department to issue orders commanding the officers who composed that Board to make known the accusations against me with the names of accuser and witnesses, that charges with proper specifications may thereupon be framed and I be brought to fair and open trial according to law.[32]

The Board had consisted of fifteen naval officers. The five captains were William B. Shubrick, Matthew C. Perry, Charles S. McCauley, C. K. Stribling, and Abraham Bigelow. The commanders were G. J. Pendergrast, Franklin Buchanan, Samuel F. Du Pont, Samuel Barron, and Andrew H. Foote. Lieutenants John S. Missroon, Richard L. Page, Sylvanus W. Godon, William L. Maury, and James S. Biddle completed the "plucking board," as it came to be known.[33]

Commanders Du Pont and Barron, two protagonists for the reorganization bill, had served as members of the Board; Lieutenant Maury, another protagonist, had been disgraced by it. Concerning Board member Sylvanus W. Godon, Maury wrote Franklin Minor: "Sylvanus is an old shipmate and friend of mine. . . . He is the one I told you who said he had had his eyes upon me ever since I entered the service and whose ambition it was to get above me! He has succeeded. Bueno!" [34]

Maury was extremely upset that one of his blood had served on the Navy Retiring Board. Lieutenant William Lewis Maury was a great-grandson of the Reverend James Maury even as Matthew Maury was a grandson of the Virginia clergyman. While they were not close cousins, Maury was devoted to the younger officer, whom he called Lewis. When Maury returned to Washington he was not able to see Lewis, who was in

New York. He learned, however, from his second-in-command, Lieutenant Samuel Phillips Lee, that Lee had received a letter in mid-September from Lewis asking about the response in Washington to the actions of the late Navy Retiring Board. Lieutenant Lee gave Maury a copy of the reply he had sent Lewis on September 18. The letter had been written by Lee before he had heard of the actions against any man but Maury.

> You rightly infer that there is great excitement here about the action of the late retiring board. Lists, confessedly and mischievously erroneous, are in circulation here and from them no considered opinion can be formed. But I know officially the action in regard to M. F. Maury. It fills me with astonishment and indignation. I have all along been under the decided impression that the Board had not taken any such untoward course. . . . It will be a great public wrong to have his eminent achievements and public works ignored in this way. The act is suicidal! . . .
>
> I am bound to believe that the Board acted under honest but mistaken convictions of duty and Naval policy. There can be no doubt, in my humble judgment of Maury's pre-eminent capacity for command, ashore or afloat. Nor can the opinion be sensibly sustained that hydrographical should be inactive duty in the Navy and that our organization should imitate the Army policy of little side-corps.[35]

Maury had heard in mid-August that Lewis was ill in the North. At that time Maury had written Ann Maury in New York that "The odious business of that Board helped to make him sick. A nice fellow is Lewis." [36] When he heard nothing from Lewis even after his return to Washington, Maury wrote again to Ann trying to find out how to communicate with Lewis. He thought she would know because Lewis, a widower, was courting Ann's orphaned niece, who lived with her.[37] Maury wrote:

> Never have I, in the whole course of my life, regretted anything, short of the death of a friend, more than I do Lewis Maury's connection with that Board. No man can love right and hate wrong more than he does.
>
> He was inveigled in some way, I cannot tell how, to do what I know was abhorrent to his notions. I weep over it, and regret it with an intensity of feeling I cannot describe. To think that Lewis, who is himself so pure and noble, should be mixed up with that Board so that neither he nor his friends can separate him from the rest—I cannot express what I have felt and still feel about it. I have

heard every other member of the Board pulled to pieces except him. . . .

Is Lewis in New York or where will a letter reach him? I imagine he will have no difficulty in answering my questions unless he is under some pledge about secrecy to the other members of the Board.

While no correspondence at this time between Lewis and Maury has been found, nor any evidence that they met, Maury's attitude indicates that Lewis either wrote or sent word to him that he was under a pledge of secrecy and therefore could reveal nothing about the vote of the Navy Retiring Board. Maury knew, of course, that Lewis had been ordered to serve on the Board and had liked it no better than had Matthew Perry.[38] It had probably never entered Lewis's mind that he would be called on to vote to overslaugh his kinsman, the superintendent of the Naval Observatory and Hydrographical Office. That the issue had arisen had been a total surprise to Maury; it had certainly been a similar surprise to his kinsman. And once the Board had begun discussion of his relative, Lewis could hardly have resigned from the Board without resigning his commission.[39] While his cousin's involvement added greatly to Maury's distress, he was to hold no enmity toward Lewis for his service on the Board.[40] Maury must, therefore, later have learned from Lewis that he had fought against the vote and tried to dissuade the Board from its action. In the autumn of 1855, however, Lewis could supply Maury with no information about the transactions of the Navy Retiring Board. He had given his oath to remain silent.

In October Maury tried in vain to get the Secretary of the Navy to require the officers of the Board to state the basis on which they had judged him inefficient. Secretary Dobbin advised that the members of the Board were now dispersed but that he would call them together if ordered to do so by the President.[41] He urged Maury not to consider his change of Navy status as a blemish on his record and praised his "spotless character and eminent service." [42] The superintendent of the Naval Observatory, who frankly admitted that he was "grieved as well as mortified," probably snorted with indignation when he read Dobbin's conflicting statements.[43]

Maury wrote his lifelong spiritual adviser, the Right Reverend James H. Otey, (Episcopal) Bishop of Tennessee, who had been his principal at Harpeth Academy:

I have been in the service, as you know, upwards of 30 years. During all that time no complaint of duty neglected or accusation for any cause has ever reached the Navy Department against me.

278

In short, whatever my shortcomings may have been as a sinful man, as an officer, accountable only to his government, my conduct has been without reproach; and yet I have been brought into official disgrace—for what?

This monstrous inquisition. . . . The excuse which they will offer for the slur they have cast upon me will be, I suppose, that I am lame. Mere bodily activity, in an officer of my rank, is comparatively of little value, when taken in connection with the mental activity.

Officers are expected—at least, it is generally so in the upper grades —to work rather with the head than the hand, and, moreover, I am bodily as active as a majority of the Board, and if broken legs disqualify, at least one member of the Board should have borne me company, for his leg was broken twice over. . . . Besides, this Board has left untouched other crippled officers, both above and below me.[44]

As Secretary Dobbin would not require the Board to make known their official reasons, Maury wrote all of the fifteen officers and asked them to tell him their reasons as individuals for voting him out of the active Navy and line of promotion. Maury was naturally depressed and restless while he awaited their answers. Always frank, he did not now attempt to hide the hurt he felt over being placed in "official disgrace," as he termed it.[45]

When the replies finally began arriving there was little satisfaction in them. The most distinguished officer of the Board, Commodore Perry, who had commanded the expedition to Japan, replied that he had served on the Board with great reluctance and expressed the wish that, "In justice to those who have been affected by the action of the Board, I cannot but hope that steps may soon be taken by the proper authorities to develop the causes and explain the circumstances which have brought about this painful change in our common service." [46]

The frankest reply came from the junior member of the Board, Lieutenant James S. Biddle: "However rare be the attainments of an officer or unrivalled his qualifications for some most important professional duty on shore, he must be broken out for sea in turn, because he owes it to his brother officers to perform his share of the 'most unpleasant service.' " [47] Maury was particularly interested in Biddle's comment because the law that had empowered the Board had not authorized the members to make any "distinction between duty ashore and duty afloat." [48]

In a petition to the Senate and House of Representatives, which Maury drafted shortly afterwards, he pointed out that he was an officer of inferior rank subject to orders of the Navy Department and that he had been retained on shore duty by command of his superiors who could, at any moment, have ordered him to sea had they not deemed his services to be of more value to the country ashore than afloat. He added, "It is submitted that there be comparatively but few officers in the Navy capable of performing promptly and efficiently all their duty both ashore and afloat." [49]

In October Secretary Dobbin had informed Maury that he was "mistaken in supposing that there was any feeling in the public mind on the subject; that the pieces which had appeared in the public prints did not express the popular sentiment." [50] When the newspapers continued to attack the work of the Navy Retiring Board the Secretary must have had to revise his opinion.

The newspapers especially denounced the Board for having placed on the Reserved List both Maury and Commodore Charles Stewart, who was beloved as "Old Ironsides" for his role in capturing the British ships *Cyane* and *Levant* while commanding the *Constitution* during the War of 1812. Stewart and Maury shared intense resentment for having a stigma cast upon their reputations through unstated charges, but there the similarity of their positions ended. Stewart was seventy-seven years of age, Maury was forty-nine. Maury was a lieutenant desirous of promotion, while Stewart was No. 1 on the Navy's list, and there was no higher rank to which he could be promoted.[51]

The *National Intelligencer,* Washington newspaper seen daily by the officers of the government and congressmen, stated: "In the case of Lieutenant Maury, all right-minded men, without respect to party, have spoken and unanimously said, 'Let his sword be restored to him with all the honor and reparation due to injured merit. Let this be done, and done quickly!' " [52]

The November issue of the *Scientific American* took the same position and added facts to support its criticism of the Board:

> There seems to have been, on the part of the Board, a feeling which induced its members to take advantage of their irresponsible power to strike down almost every officer who had in any way distinguished himself by his scientific attainments; and in doing this they all took very good care to look out for No. 1, as will be evident from the following statement, which any one may verify for himself by examining the Naval Register. Of the officers whom the Board were called upon to scrutinize, there were 362 on the Naval List ranking above the youngest lieutenant on the Board, while below were 322. Every one of the 362 of the higher rank who was removed or retired, promoted or advanced one or more members of

the Board, and we accordingly find that they blackballed 138. But on the lower list, the retirement of any member of which could not affect the Board, we find they only retired 46 out of 322.[53]

These figures may have been misleading, since there almost certainly would have been more men with problems of health in the senior ranks. But the American public was made aware of how greatly the removals of certain officers had advanced the members of the Board.

An editorial in the New York *Herald* stated: "I understand there is now in press, and will shortly appear, a history of the lives and eminent services of the late Retiring Board, entitled 'Lights and Shadows of the Fifteen.' It will embrace all the shade in the lives of those fifteen Spartans, from their entrance into the service up to their 'Thermopylae defeat' of 201 brothers in arms, by which gallant action they 'promoted themselves.' " [54]

Of all the battles through which Maury had struggled in Washington, this was the first that hurt him so grievously that he could not shake off his concern and pitch wholeheartedly into his work. When invited to give a major speech to the Maryland State Agricultural Society he asked to be excused, stating that, "The proceedings of the late Navy Board have unfitted me just now for close reflection and study." [55]

Maury must have had mixed emotions when the word of new honors and recognition from abroad reached him at the Observatory, where, as a result of the Board's action, he now served at a salary of $1,200 a year —an amount that would not pay his family's grocery, clothing, and school bills—and where he served with the dubious authority of an officer no longer on active duty.[56] The honors continued to come because each year Maury added to the stock of oceanographic and navigational information of the world through new *Wind and Current Charts,* new editions of the *Explanations and Sailing Directions,* and other publications such as *The Physical Geography of the Sea.* The honors were also a recognition of Maury's part in launching the universal system of meteorological observations at sea. Each year more nations joined in the international program, the results multiplied.[57]

One occasion when Maury received a foreign tribute occurred in October, 1855. Edward de Stoeckl, Russian chargé d'affaires who represented the Czar's government in Washington, came to the Observatory for an official call on Maury. Diplomat Stoeckl brought Maury an autographed letter sent by His Imperial Highness, the Grand Duke Constantine, Lord High Admiral of the Russian Navy. This brother of the Czar had long been an admirer of Maury's work and wrote to state how much he would like to present a "testimonial of my esteem" but, as the laws of the United States prevented this, had instead to confine himself, he said, to an expression of his own sentiments:

"They are as exalted as your own merits; and in my official capacity, I may say to you that you do honour to the profession to which you belong, as well as to the great nation which you have the honor to serve." [58]

When the Russian representative had left the Observatory, Maury must have thought of the old proverb, "The prophet is not without honor save in his own country." Other nations thought he honored the United States Navy, but his own brother officers had cut him down. And these fellow wearers of the Navy blue would not even give him a chance to know what allegations had been brought against him or permit him to stand trial that he might disprove them.

The day after the Russian chargé had been at the Observatory the *National Intelligencer* published a report of Stoeckl's visit and Grand Duke Constantine's letter.[59] The New York *Herald* later carried the news and stated editorially: "This is a high but deserved compliment to Lieutenant Maury, who has just been retired by the action of the late Retiring Board of the Navy. Maury has many powerful friends in the United States and abroad. The people of France, England, and Germany know more of such men as Maury, than they do of our most prominent politicians, and through such as Maury our country gains credit; his being retired has occasioned surprise and displeasure throughout the country. There will be a great deal said about it." [60]

Bearing out the *Herald's* remark was the presentation made soon thereafter of a gold medal from the republic of Bremen, on which occasion Rudolph Schleiden, Bremen's minister resident in Washington, said:

It affords me great pleasure to hand you in the name of my government the accompanying gold medal. Its German inscription may be thus rendered in English:

"To the promoter of science, to the guide of navigators, Lt. M. F. Maury, an honorary acknowledgement of the Senate of the Republic of Bremen."

This inscription, better than could any expressions of mine, shows the sense of high appreciation in which your eminent merits in regard to all maritime interests are held in my country the citizens of which are perhaps more generally engaged in navigation and therefore more benefited by your valuable discoveries and directions than those of any other country. Your name which has so long been an ornament of the U.S. Navy is and will ever be gratefully remembered in Bremen.[61]

The view generally accepted by the public was that the Navy Retiring Board had used Maury's lameness as excuse for their action. Referring to Maury's injury, which caused him to limp but had not prevented his modernizing navigation, the New York *Journal of Commerce* said:

> Lord Nelson lost both an eye and an arm, yet his name was mighty in battle. Our officers have lost neither arms nor eyes, it is true; but they stand on the records of their country disgraced. Although Messrs. Mallory and Clayton [Senator John M. Clayton, of Delaware] deny that any action of the Senate can wipe this disgrace off, we must beg to differ. Let these officers be restored to their former positions, and then if any charges rest against them on the records of the Navy Department, let them be tried, and, if found guilty, condemned. The papers have already spoken in loud tones against the proceedings of the Board, and will continue to issue their anathema maranathas until justice is done to these much injured officers. We ask by what rule was this Board selected? Did they pass the ordeal of a secret inquisition? Or have they since their appointment passed another "careful examination" by a Board? [62]

The newspapers kept up their campaign to have Maury restored to his place on the active list as rapidly as possible. Their opinions may have had some effect on Secretary Dobbin and caused him to make a tentative gesture, which Maury reported to Franklin Minor on November 15, 1855:

> He [Dobbin] admitted that there were some officers, by supposition twelve or fifteen, that ought not to be ruled out and ought to be put back, and asked me to advise with him as to the mode of getting them back—speaking by way of hypothesis, he put this case: suppose he and the President, consulting with the Senate, should satisfy Senators as to these twelve or fifteen cases; that Senators should agree to confirm the nominations and that the President, then revoking twelve or fifteen commissions, should send in his blackballed nominations.
>
> My reply was, it was unlawful to promote blackballs, and that the President and Senate could not repeal a law. He admitted the difficulty and said he only threw it out as a suggestion. I told him that mere promotion would not satisfy me, that the Board has cast a professional stain and that that must be wiped out. [63]

Throughout these weeks of effort to have his reputation cleared Maury consistently stated that his complaint was "not against the Secretary or President, but against the Board." [64] On December 11 Maury reported privately to Robert Hatton of Nashville on the attitude of President Pierce: "I do not understand that the President desires to be 'mixed up' with the Board. Leading Democrats in Congress do not intend to stand by the Board, and the President, I am assured—'entre-nous'—is most anxious to have me restored." [65]

On January 21, 1856, Senator John Bell presented a petition to Congress for full restoration of Maury's previous status in the Navy.[66] The House of Representatives, being very much occupied with the internal political activities attendant on electing a new Speaker, did not immediately take up the matter of Maury's petition or those presented by other officers. The Senate, however, soon launched debate on the action of the late Navy Retiring Board. It was to prove one of the longest and most heated controversies the halls of Congress had ever heard.

As was to be expected, the chairman of the Senate Naval Affairs Committee, Senator Stephen R. Mallory, led the defense of the Board that had been created by the bill he had introduced. Many men in and out of Congress, however, were startled by the type of comments Mallory made about Maury in the Senate. They could not help but wonder who or what had caused the Florida senator so completely to reverse his position on Maury. Only twelve months had passed since Mallory had lavished the naval scientist with praise and urged the Senate to vote him a gift of $25,000.[67]

The leaders of the attack against the action of the Navy Retiring Board in the first Senate debates in 1856 were Senator John Bell of Tennessee, Senator Robert Toombs of Georgia, Senator John Jordan Crittenden of Kentucky, Senator Robert Hale of New Hampshire, and Senator Sam Houston of Texas. In defense of the Board Senator Mallory's chief allies were Senator Judah P. Benjamin of Louisiana and Senator John M. Clayton of Delaware. They were strongly backed by Senator Albert G. Brown of Mississippi.

The debate in the Senate got into full swing on January 10, 1856. Senator Benjamin was an early speaker in defense of the Board. With his usual suavity he pointed out that although the fifteen officers of the Board had not been able to attain perfection and strike from the list of officers "exactly such men as ought to be stricken out," that fact had not lessened their responsibility to carry out their assigned task.[68] Senator Benjamin continued with a rebuttal of the charge that the Board had not spent adequate time in deciding the professional fate of so many officers.

Senator Toombs leaped into the fray. He was at his best in this kind of debate, and he shot right back at Benjamin:

"The Senator from Louisiana has admitted that the Secretary of the

Navy had made a mistake in conferring upon the Board, by means of his instructions, an authority which the law itself did not confer.

"Moreover, the Secretary, while conceding that the findings of the Board were in some cases wrong, had nonetheless confirmed their proceedings as a whole. That action was fatal to the whole procedure of the Board." [69]

Senator Brown of Mississippi strongly defended the President's decision to back the Board's findings.[70]

Since the Board had been a "court of special and limited jurisdiction," [71] Toombs denounced it for having kept no record of its proceedings. Records would have shown whether members had exceeded their power by striking from the roll any officer for any reason other than actual inability to perform his duties on shore and at sea. Since the Board could produce no such evidence, its proceedings became void, Toombs averred.

Senator Crittenden suggested canceling the action of the Navy Board by repealing the law that had empowered it to act and thus allowing all proscribed officers to revert to their status before the Board met.[72]

Concerning the issue of the Board's having kept no record of their vote and reasons therefor, Senator Mallory admitted this to be the case, but said that each member of the Board had his private notes.[73] These, however, were not produced.[74]

In a long reply to Mallory, Senator Toombs pounded the point that "Even the Inquisition brought its victims face to face with their accusers," and concluded, "All these despotic proceedings Senator Mallory sought to excuse by proposing what he deemed excellent reasons for retiring old captains. . . . So what did Senator Mallory suggest? Since there was nothing for so many old captains to do, he deemed it expedient to help the situation by adding thirty-odd young and vigorous commanders to the list. . . . The real cause for these subterfuges was impatience for command." [75] This point had nothing to do with Maury but was an indirect way of reminding the senators that the commanders on the Board had all become captains.[76]

On February 13, after listening to praise of the Board's action by Senator Benjamin of Louisiana, Senator Hale of New Hampshire rose to speak:

> Let me take the case of Lieutenant Maury, for it has been quoted. The terms of the act required the dismissal or retirement of officers who were not competent to perform all the duties of their respective grades, ashore or afloat. I take it that one of the duties of a naval officer is to do exactly what Lieutenant Maury has been doing

at the National Observatory, because his position there was assigned to him by the Government as part of his duties as a naval officer, and he has been obliged by law to perform these duties. Well, sir, this board has undertaken to place Lieutenant Maury on the reserved list, because he is not competent, in their judgment, to do all the duties of a naval officer ashore and afloat. I should like to ask if the fifteen men who composed that board felt themselves competent to do the duties which Lieutenant Maury has been doing? If not, and those duties are naval duties, as the law required that every naval officer retained should be competent to perform all the duties of a naval officer ashore and afloat these men ought to be turned out. . . .[77]

Certainly, the honorable Senator from Louisiana will not say that Lieutenant Maury has disgraced himself, that he has been engaged in pursuits derogatory to the character of an officer or a gentleman, or that he has been doing anything else than the duties required of a naval officer ashore.[78]

To this Senator Mallory, to prove his contention that Maury had for years avoided sea duty, replied by listing the shore duty that Maury had received and stated:

"Mr. Maury's reputation as a civilian—call it what you please—would never awaken a throb in the heart of an American seaman. . . . I acknowledge that Stewart's [Commodore Charles Stewart] dead body put on the *Pennsylvania* tomorrow would probably render her impregnable and unconquerable; but you might fill her with Maurys from keel to deck and they would not awaken a response in the seaman's heart."[79]

Mallory continued: "The Honorable Senator from New Hampshire classifies the duties of the commander of the Observatory with those of a naval officer. I do not." His statement rang out through the Senate chamber: "I draw a broad line of demarcation between them. I say that, according to the universal acceptation of a naval officer, he is a mariner upon the great deep. There is the legitimate theatre and the only theatre for his ambitions."[80]

Emotion engendered by the rough and tumble of parliamentary debate had perhaps driven Mallory to a more sweeping declaration of position than he had intended to make.

Senator Hale, knowing a vulnerable statement when he heard one, rose to his feet and, in his clear New England voice, took issue:

"Allow me to ask the Senator, how does he classify the preparation of the Nautical Almanac? Is that a naval duty? The officer at Cambridge who has charge of the preparation of the Nautical Almanac was promoted while the officer in charge of the Observatory here was degraded." [81]

Hale was speaking of naval officer Charles Henry Davis, who had worked frequently on shore since 1842, when he had first accepted duty with the Coast Survey, and who had been on shore duty continuously since he had become director of the Nautical Almanac and Ephemeris in 1849.[82]

Mallory admitted that "There has been a larger number of officers in the Navy than can find legitimate employment at sea." Because of this, he said, the department has "assigned them to duties which are not legitimate and strictly proper for sea officers—Observatory, Nautical Almanac, exploring expeditions, and to the Lighthouse Board." [83] But still he gave no answer to the question why, of two men occupying positions which he judged "not strictly proper for sea officers," [84] one had been promoted and the other demoted. It was soon clear that Mallory had no idea of shifting from his statement that, "If the Board has erred in any case whatever, there was no error in the case of Lieutenant Maury." [85]

On February 14 Senator Butler of South Carolina, in rebuttal to remarks by Senator Mallory concerning Maury's lack of recent sea duty, pointed out that an officer who had remained on shore could at any moment have been ordered to sea by the Secretary of the Navy. He added:

> Sir, every man who can fight is not necessarily the only person who can perform high functions in the military or naval service. If Lieutenant Maury were to demonstrate to the world, by his *Wind and Current Charts,* the best manner of navigating ships, and if he were to discover laws of the universe under which life would be better protected, will you tell me that because he did not learn it on a quarter deck it should be of no use?
>
> That which would induce other governments to raise monuments to him for his discoveries is to be the source of detraction because he happens to have a little more science than suits the taste of many gentlemen.

Senator Toombs took the floor to say he had been told that the overslaughed officers had the sympathy of the Secretary of the Navy. Then he thundered, "They do not want sympathy. They want justice!" [86]

The opposition was so heavy and gave so little evidence of giving way that Mallory, as a good political leader, felt it wise in late February to make a concession. He proposed a bill under which a number of the officers who had been retired or placed on the Reserved List would have an opportunity to have their cases reviewed.[87] Maury hailed this as a weakening on the part of Mallory and the Secretary of the Navy and, in a letter to Franklin Minor, said of the bill, "It was drawn in concert with Dobbin and is . . . a regular 'give-in.' I saw him [Dobbin] today for a little while, and told him I thought it would do, with some alterations in details, in which he concurred, and he had me submit them as amendments. I also saw [Senator] Bell today. He told me the [Naval Affairs] committee were very desirous to know if the bill were satisfactory to me." [88] Maury also informed Minor: "Bell tells me that my honors have excited the jealousies of the Scientifics [Bache and Henry] and others so you may expect all sorts of accusations and insinuations." [89]

At this time the Senate Naval Affairs Committee requested that Captain William B. Shubrick, who had been the senior officer of the Retiring Board, supply the committee with a report on the method by which they had selected their list. This request, however, resulted in a report that was essentially a eulogy of the Board.[90] The officers of the Board had been under heavy fire and were now fighting for their own professional lives, even as were Maury and the other officers who had been retired or placed on the inactive list.

The Senate resumed debate on the action of the late Navy Retiring Board on March 11. Senator Iverson of Georgia attacked the Board with the charge that they had followed star chamber procedure and proposed that the members of the Board be called before a Senate committee to tell under oath why they had voted as they did. He urged that this information should then be passed on to the officers who had been removed from active duty. Iverson said he was not at all satisfied with Mallory's proposal of a board of review, as the members would still be interested officers. Then he charged the Board with a marked desire for promotion, stating that "I know that the inferior officers had nothing to do apparently with the decision of the cases above them but . . . there was a community of interest of feeling and of object which pervaded the whole board." [91]

The senator pointed out that of the five lieutenants on the Board three were made commanders as a result of the action of the Board, while the lowest ranking man, Lieutenant James Biddle, had risen from No. 189 on the Navy list to No. 50. Senator Iverson stated that all five commanders on the Board had advanced to the Navy's highest fixed rank at that time—captain—and that, while there was no higher title the five captains could receive, they had all advanced in rank, with the senior officer of the Board, Captain Shubrick, going "from number 7 to number 2 with only an infirm man as number 1 who has since died so Shubrick is now number 1." [92]

The members of the Navy Retiring Board had not answered to the satisfaction of the senators why they had been in such a rush. It was brought out that the Board had sat for 140 hours to decide the professional fate of 700 officers. That broke down to 13 minutes for consideration of each man's career.[93] The fact then emerged that there had been unanimous agreement in the Board on only 150 officers, which proved that more than 50 officers had been overslaughed against the better judgment of some of the Board.[94] The surmise among Maury protagonists was that the vote against him had not been unanimous. It doubtless seemed likely to them that William Lewis Maury, Richard L. Page, and probably Samuel Barron had voted against placing Maury on the Reserved List.[95]

Senator Sam Houston, who had appointed Maury a midshipman thirty-one years earlier and followed his career with pride, on March 18 challenged the right of the Board to judge Maury "inefficient" because of a broken leg when a member of the Board—Lieutenant Missroon—had been not only retained on active service but been promoted in spite of a twice-broken leg.[96] Mallory rushed to the defense of Lieutenant Missroon, stating that there was no similarity in the cases since Missroon had first broken his leg while on duty at sea, had served two years at sea, had it broken for a more perfect set, and had since served again at sea.[97] Mallory made no reference to the fact that Maury's leg had been broken when he was traveling under orders to join his ship, that Maury had volunteered for sea duty, and that he could have been ordered to sea any time the Navy Department had so desired.

Following this extended debate there was an interim during which the senators busied themselves about other business, members of the beleaguered Board worked to defend the action they had taken, and Mallory drafted a new proposal that would give the listed officers a chance to be heard.[98] In the latter part of March Maury recommended to his friends that they accept Mallory's new bill, as he had come to believe the chairman of the Naval Affairs Committee sincere in a desire to rectify some of the wrong that had been done.[99] However, at this same time Maury took action to disprove Mallory's claim that he had resisted sea duty and sought to remain on shore.[100]

March 31 saw the senators in battle temper. Houston of Texas and Slidell of Louisiana went at each other relentlessly. Mallory would yield nothing; neither would his opponents. So the debate continued.[101] On April 28 and again the next day Senator Bell of Tennessee gave a most careful and detailed defense of Maury. He took up one after another the points made by Mallory and by Senator Clayton.

Referring to Clayton, Bell stated:

"The Honorable Senator from Delaware neither admitted nor denied that Lieutenant Maury was a man of science, but he seemed to think that his pretensions in that respect are entitled to no great consideration. . . .

"Sir, I think it is manifest, from the tenor of the remarks of the honorable Senator from Delaware and others, that they have no just appreciation or even knowledge of the extent and value of Lieutenant Maury's public services." [102]

Senator Bell sketched the value of Maury's scientific achievements and challenged Mallory on many of his statements. "I do not charge the honorable Senator with seeking to do any intentional injustice to Lieutenant Maury. He was very zealous in vindicating the Board," but Bell added, "he undertook to prove that Lieutenant Maury had avoided sea service, and sought his present employment." [103]

Bell admitted that one of Maury's efforts to get sea service had been foiled by the action of Judge John Tayloe Lomax in 1841 in sending a certificate from three Fredericksburg doctors stating that Maury's leg was not strong enough for such duty. Bell read the senators the letters from these physicians and pointed out:

"Neither my friend from Florida, nor my friend from Delaware, in all that they have said, ever did Lieutenant Maury the justice to admit, or notice the fact, that he had applied for orders to sea during the Mexican War, although I had previously brought that fact to the notice of the Senate." [104]

Senator Toombs criticized Mallory for many proposals in his new bill and ended by emphasizing that, though he considered Maury and Stewart particularly wronged, he demanded justice for all the listed officers. [105]

Debate was heavy on May 15 and again on May 16, when Senator Mallory once more spoke in full defense of the Board, declaring that the system of promotion by seniority was the chief reason for the alarming weakness of the Navy. He pointed out that the British Navy promoted for merit rather than on a basis of seniority, but he did not urge that the rule of seniority be abandoned. Instead he favored use of the Naval Retiring Act as a means of purging the service of its incompetent officers, thus making seniority a safe rule for advancement. [106] This exposition had obvious merit, as there was no question that there were many elderly men kept on Navy rolls. But it had little to do with Maury, who had just celebrated his fiftieth birthday.

Senator Butler of South Carolina took offense at Mallory's insistence on physical perfection as the prime requisite for an officer and demanded, "Is this the way in which you will use intellect? Do you regard merely, legs and arms, and thews and sinews?" [107]

Matthew Fontaine Maury as photographed by Bendann about the time Maury left for Brussels and the launching of international marine meteorology in 1853

Official U.S. Navy Photo

The 44-gun frigate *Brandywine,* to which Maury reported in 1825 to begin duty as a midshipman in the U.S. Navy. The *Brandy* had just been selected to transport Lafayette back to France after his triumphal tour of the United States.

The sloop-of-war *Vincennes,* the first American naval vessel to circumnavigate the globe. Maury was on that cruise, which ended at New York on June 8, 1830.

Library of Congress

The frigate *Potomac* in which Maury returned to the United States from the Pacific in 1834 after serving as sailing master of the sloop-of-war *Falmouth*. This view was taken from a painting by J. Searle made while the *Potomac* rode at anchor in Valparaiso harbor.

The C.S.N. cruiser *Georgia,* purchased and fitted for the Confederate Navy by Maury in Great Britain in 1863. Maury also bought and fitted the cruiser *Rappahannock* while on secret service duty for the Confederacy in England.

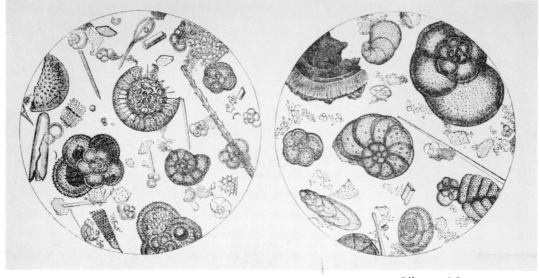

Magnified specimens of diatomaceae and foraminifera found in eight jars of "ooze" from the bottom of the Atlantic sent to Maury by Lieut. Otway H. Berryman after the brig *Dolphin* ran a line of deep-sea soundings across the North Atlantic under Maury's instructions in 1853

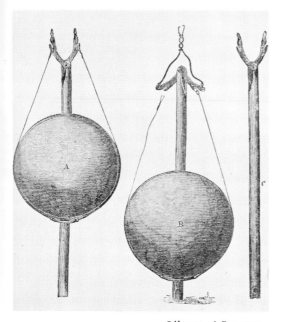

Brooke's deep-sea sounding apparatus, the first instrument to bring up samples of the bottom of the ocean at depths as great as 12,000 feet, invented by Passed Midshipman John Mercer Brooke while serving at the U.S. Naval Observatory under Superintendent Maury

One of the European advocates of Maury's work, Baron Alexander von Humboldt, whose *Kosmos* is one of the world's greatest scientific writings. His discovery and tracing of the cold current off the west coast of South America led to its being named the Humboldt Current.

The U.S. Naval Observatory and Hydrographical Office as it appeared during Maury's superintendency, 1844-1861. The sketch, published in Bohn's *Hand-Book of Washington* in 1854, somewhat exaggerates the height of the dome. The superintendent's house (on the left) was added in 1847.

Principal of Harpeth Academy, from which Maury graduated, and later Bishop of the Diocese of Tennessee (Episcopal), James Hervey Otey was a great friend and advisor to Maury

Maury with his close friend, the Reverend Doctor Francis W. Tremlett of London, on May 28, 1868, when Cambridge University conferred the honorary LL.D. on Maury

Maury in London in 1868 with members of his family and his good friend
Marin H. Jansen of The Netherlands Royal Navy. Back row, left to right:
Eliza Hull Maury, Captain (later Admiral) Jansen, Lucy Minor Maury,
Mary Herndon Maury, Matthew Fontaine Maury, Jr., Diana Fontaine
Maury Corbin. Beside Maury in front are his granddaughter Nannie Maury
Corbin (Diana's child), and his wife Ann Hull Herndon Maury.

The house occupied by Maury as professor of physics at Virginia Military
Institute, Lexington, Virginia, from 1869 until his death in 1873

Maury's eldest son, Col. Richard Launcelot Maury, 24th Virginia Regiment, Pickett's Division, C.S.A.

Mrs. Matthew Fontaine Maury about five years after the death of her husband

The man audiences saw as Maury lectured in 1859-1860

The unveiling of a plaque to Maury on October 26, 1910, at the house in Richmond where Maury devised the first electrically detonated torpedoes used in warfare

Monument to Maury, Pathfinder of the Seas, unveiled in Richmond, Virginia, in 1929. Sculptor, F. William Sievers.

The memorial to Maury in Goshen Pass, Virginia. This spot seemed so peaceful and beautiful to Maury after the distressing events of the war years that, at his request, his body was carried through this mountain pass en route to permanent burial in Richmond.

Maury Hall, U.S. Naval Academy, Annapolis, Maryland, named for Matthew Fontaine Maury in 1915 in recognition of his contributions to the sciences of navigation and oceanography. A bust of Maury stands in the Hall of Fame for Great Americans at New York University.

A senior statesman, Senator John J. Crittenden of Kentucky, was angered by Mallory's defense of the Board's having judged an officer's morals as an indispensable element of his efficiency. Crittenden charged that the Board was a "star chamber on morals" and demanded of Senator Mallory what the late Board would have done with the Duke of Marlborough, who had been a highly efficient officer yet base of character.[108] Mallory sought to avoid an answer by restating his views on the value of morals.[109] Crittenden would not be denied. Mallory replied with a literary allusion and concluded the subject of Marlborough by remarking, "It must be said, however, that he was a very bad man, though one of the best soldiers in the world. . . . The question of his over-all efficiency was never submitted to a board of examiners!" [110]

Senator Toombs interjected, "How would Lord Nelson have been treated by the board?"

Crittenden replied, "He certainly would have been dismissed. The honourable Senator would have dismissed Lord Nelson."

"On account of Lady Hamilton?" asked Toombs with relish.

"Yes, sir, he was of too amorous a temper." [111]

Mallory did not mind this type of parliamentary thrust and readily admitted that any board would have kept Nelson on active duty.[112]

This debate on the subject of morals as a cause for retirement or furloughing only added to Maury's unhappiness. He had pointed out repeatedly that the very fact that no specific charge was made against him or the other overslaughed officers laid them all open to the suspicion of immorality in the eyes of the public, who could never know them personally.[113]

After long hours of debate on May 16 and May 21, there were other such pressing matters needing the attention of the Senate that further discussion on the Navy Retiring Board action was postponed.

Matters had progressed somewhat in Maury's favor as, in the new bill that Senator Mallory had drafted to amend the act of the preceding Congress to promote the efficiency of the Navy, there were included provisions to create a scientific corps as well as to create the rank of admiral, which rank the bill proposed should be given to "Old Ironsides," Commodore Stewart. The scientific corps would take charge of the Naval Observatory, the hydrographic work, the Nautical Almanac, and any other scientific matters designated by the Secretary of the Navy. In discussing this proposal in the Senate, Mallory had told his colleagues, in a shift apparently designed to placate Maury's defenders, "The Committee had an earnest desire that that distinguished officer [Maury] should be at the head of the corps." [114] The bill included a proposal that Maury be made a captain.

At first Maury thought this corps idea might work out well, but he soon came to realize that it would be impossible to persuade the ablest of the young officers to serve in a cut-off, specialized group, where promotion would be even slower than in the line.[115] Therefore, he was pleased when one of his defenders, Senator John Hale of Maine, made a motion that Section 7, establishing the Scientific Corps of the Navy, be stricken from the bill. On July 10, 1856, the Senate concurred with the motion and voted to strike that section from Senate Bill 113.[116]

Maury regretted that unavoidably the vote eliminated the proposal that he be made a captain and Commodore Stewart an admiral. Maury had not only long stressed the need in the U.S. Navy for a statutory grade higher than that of captain but had also emphasized the importance of promotion to a naval officer. Only recently he had written his friend, Neill S. Brown, former Governor of Tennessee, "Lucre, to the right-minded officer, becomes iron when weighed against professional advancement and promotion." [117] However, the whole bitter battle had drained so much out of Maury that he admitted at this time that he only wished he had been left in peace in his "lowly position on the Naval Register" so that he could get on with his work.[118]

On July 15, 1856, the Senate passed the long-debated "Act to Amend 'An Act to Promote the Efficiency of the Navy'"—Senate Bill 113. The chief provision of this bill was to grant to all officers who had been overslaughed as a result of the actions of the Navy Retiring Board of 1855 the right to request a naval court of inquiry where they could show cause why their naval status should not have been changed.[119] The Senate had voted, but the decision would not be law until concurred in by the House of Representatives.

When, shortly afterwards, the Senate was called on to confirm the nomination of the officers up for promotion Senator Toombs and other senators were still vehemently opposed. Toombs, in reproachful tones, reminded his fellow lawmakers that "the Naval Board were judges in matters in which they were personally interested and had benefitted by being promoted" and condemned this as "inconsistent with the foundations of civil liberty." [120] But the Senate, doubtless exhausted with the whole question, voted to confirm the promotions of most of the officers on the list.

In all the months of Senate debate the House of Representatives had taken no action on a House bill to amend the 1855 Navy Act, introduced in February by Representative Thomas L. Clingman of North Carolina. The bill had, without debate, been referred to the Committee on Naval Affairs and had stayed there ever since.[121] On July 28, 1856, however, Senate Bill 113 was taken from the Speaker's table in the House and, after a suspension of the rules, was referred to the Committee on

Naval Affairs.[122] The consensus was that no action on the bill was imminent in the House and the overslaughed officers would have a long wait before the representatives decided whether to grant them the right to naval courts of inquiry as voted by the Senate.

In that same July the steamer *Arctic* put to sea for deep-sea soundings under the Steamer Plan devised by Commander Charles Henry Davis, U.S.N., for Coast Survey Superintendent Alexander Dallas Bache.[123] Having observed the acuteness of mind that Charles Henry Davis had shown in formulating the Steamer Plan—which had given the opportunity to issue directions for the soundings by the Navy ship to Bache rather than to Maury, who had pioneered the blue-water soundings—Secretary Dobbin decided to make use of that planning ability in the Board crisis. On November 7 he sent a telegram to Charles Henry Davis, superintendent of the Nautical Almanac, Cambridge, Massachusetts: "Proceed to Washington immediately." [124] Eight days later the Secretary ordered Davis back to Cambridge "having completed business for which ordered to Washington." [125] The business had been to draft a plan of defense against the future attacks that were expected to be made in Congress on the decisions of the Board. Charles Henry Davis had worked with board member Captain S. F. Du Pont in preparing this further defense of the Board.[126]

It was not until the Thirty-fourth Congress was well into its third session, in January, 1857, that the House of Representatives finally got around to a vote on "An Act to amend 'An Act to promote the Efficiency of the Navy.'" Representative Samuel P. Benson of Maine was the only member to speak strongly in favor of the bill. Apparently the representatives had already made up their minds as to the merits of the bill, for debate was short and centered almost entirely on the procedures to be followed in implementing the act. On January 12, 1857, the House voted 159 to 50 to pass the Senate bill that gave to any officer whose naval status had been changed by action of the Navy Retiring Board of 1855 the right to make written application for a hearing of his case before a naval court of inquiry.[127] No confrontation with the original Board was provided, but an overslaughed officer could receive an investigation into his "physical, mental, professional and moral fitness" for service in the United States Navy. The bill called for the findings of each court to be passed on to the President, who would make the final decision on the officer. In case of a favorable finding, the action of the 1855 Board would be reversed and the officer restored to his former rank on the active list.[128] The bill was signed by President Franklin Pierce, and in early February, 1857, Secretary of the Navy Dobbin set in motion the machinery to assemble officers to be members of the first court of inquiry.[129]

CHAPTER XV

Court of Inquiry

Because of the Navy Department's unyielding support of the actions of the Retiring Board, many men were concerned that full justice might not be granted the petitioning officer by the courts of inquiry to be set up by the department.

From the University of Virginia, Professor of Law John B. Minor wrote his first cousin expressing concern that the trials might be the same as courts-martial. On February 25 Maury replied, allaying Minor's fears on that point by explaining the difference between a court-martial, before which an officer is ordered to appear, and a court of inquiry, before which an officer is "generally brought at his own request." [1] On April 6, 1857, Maury sent his request for a court of inquiry in a letter to the new Secretary of the Navy, Isaac Toucey of Connecticut, who had just taken office the preceding month upon the inauguration of James Buchanan as President. [2] Maury was No. 95 in the order of application of the 118 officers who asked for hearings. [3]

On February 20, 1857, a naval court of inquiry had convened in Washington to carry out the provisions specified in the act Congress had passed on January 16. [4] The court had got off to a lumbering start, largely because of the many witnesses called to testify for or against the officer being investigated. The process had seemed so interminable that shortly after Secretary Toucey had taken office he had ordered two additional courts of inquiry organized to sit in Washington. [5] Three captains were assigned as the members of each court to hear the evidence and one judge advocate to prosecute the case. [6]

On May 4 Secretary Toucey issued a circular stating that "due to the great number of witnesses summoned before the Naval Courts of Inquiry . . . the Judge Advocate and the applicant before the court shall enter a stipulation to receive the depositions of witnesses on either side, the same being by any authority competent to administer an oath sent to James M. Carlisle, Judge Advocate, Washington City." [7] Even depositions did not greatly speed the procedure, however, for in early June Maury reported to Franklin Minor: "The Courts are proceeding slowly —Jack Nicholas is up now. I never go in there and therefore cannot say how he is getting along. None of the findings yet have been made known —nothing to go by." [8]

The hearings dragged on through the hot Washington summer. Maury was summoned to testify in the cases of some fellow officers and was appalled to learn that the courts were taking up minor indiscretions committed by officers as very young midshipmen.[9] He had no concern for himself on that score as he had earlier scrutinized his record and remarked that he was glad he had not slipped as a youth.[10] However, he thought this digging into the past put a dreadful strain on the officers so questioned.

When it became clear that his case would not be called for a long time, Maury in August took Ann to the Virginia mountains for a stay in the hope that they could both avoid the malaria attack to which they were subject.[11] Maury was also anxious to get away from Washington and the speculation about cases before the naval courts. He felt the need of the refreshment he derived from nature as a preparation for the ordeal that lay ahead. While enjoying the cooler altitudes of the Allegheny Mountains, Maury received word from Secretary of State Lewis Cass that the imperial government of France "impressed with his [Maury's] great services daily rendered to navigation of every country" wished to bestow on him the "Order of the Legion of Honor." [12] Secretary Cass sent Maury a copy of the reply of the American minister to France, John Y. Mason, advising the Foreign Minister of France, Count Walewski, "that the tender of so high a mark of appreciation . . . is very gratifying to me his friend and will be to the government and people of the United States. The Executive Department cannot give authority to accept—only the Congress." [13] The copies of this exploratory correspondence about the proffer of France's high honor must have been gratifying for Maury to receive at that particular time.[14]

On his return to Washington in September Maury settled down to work on preparation of an 8th edition of the *Explanations and Sailing Directions to Accompany the Wind and Current Charts.* There was new information he wished to make available as a result of publication of two charts of the Pacific Ocean, South, five sheets of charts for the Indian Ocean, a greatly improved chart of the Atlantic Ocean, North, and one of the Atlantic Ocean, South, all of which had been prepared and published in the preceding two years. Much new data had reached Maury and his associates at the Observatory in the abstract logs that had come in steady flow from the ships of the nations participating in the universal system of meteorological observations agreed on at the Brussels Conference. Maury wished to make available to mariners the sum of his oceanographic knowledge to date.[15]

Maury was barely launched on preparation of the new book, however, when news reached him that Ann's naval officer brother, William Lewis Herndon, had on September 12 lost his life at sea. The reports told of Herndon's heroism in effecting the rescue of a large number of the men and passengers on the storm-foundered U.S. mail steamer *Central America* under his command.[16] Herndon had chosen to go down with the ship rather than permit his boatswain's boat to attempt to rescue him and thus risk being engulfed by the sinking steamer. The death of Lewis Herndon was a deep personal blow to Maury, as well as to Ann. Between the two brothers-in-law had existed a tie of close friendship as well as the bond of mutual professional respect. Maury had thought up the plan to explore the Amazon River; Lewis had carried it out. Lewis had worked for two tours of duty with Maury at the Observatory. Lewis had lived and died by the code that Maury felt befitted an officer and a gentleman. Heavy of heart with his own sense of loss, Maury invited Lewis's widow and daughter to become members of his household.[17]

By October 10 Maury felt that surely his case must soon come before one of the courts of inquiry. On that day he wrote Secretary Toucey to ask if he could be advised as to the points to which he was to answer before the Court of Inquiry.[18] Toucey replied with an evasive letter that indicated Maury would hear the issues in court.[19] Previous practice in the Navy had been to inform an officer of the grounds on which his conduct was being inquired into, and Maury was greatly disturbed that Toucey would not supply him with this information in order that he might properly prepare his defense.[20]

At last the court summons came. On a bleak Wednesday morning, November 25, 1857, Maury set forth from the Observatory to go downtown to present himself at the Court of Inquiry he had requested the preceding spring. At "10½ o'clock A.M.," the Judge Advocate of the Court, Charles H. Winder, opened the proceedings. He read the Precept of the Navy Department, by which Commodore E. A. F. Lavalette, U.S.N., had been appointed president of Naval Court of Inquiry No. 1, and the orders by which Commodore Samuel Mercer, U.S.N., and Captain Henry A. Adams, U.S.N., had been appointed members of the Court. Judge Advocate Winder asked Maury if he wished to take exception to any member of the Court or to himself as Judge Advocate, to which Maury replied that he had no cause to challenge the Court as constituted.

The Judge Advocate swore in the members of the Court, and the President administered the oath to the Judge Advocate: "You do swear truly to record the proceedings of this Court, and the evidence to be given in the case in hearing." [21] It would have been permissible for the Judge Advocate to have a clerk or stenographer record the proceedings but in Maury's case the transcript indicates that Winder kept the record himself. The Judge Advocate had previously fulfilled one of his functions by issuing summonses to all the witnesses required for the investigation. When the hearing started Winder would not only record the proceedings but conduct the examination of witnesses. His essential role was that of prosecutor and on him fell the responsibility of bringing out all the facts in the case. [22]

With the opening formalities concluded, Maury must have expected an immediate start of his long-awaited hearing. Instead the President announced that the Court was organized but that, because there were no witnesses present, and the next day was Thanksgiving, it would adjourn until "Friday at 10½ o'clock A.M." [23] Maury knew how to mask his feelings, but he undoubtedly seethed with frustration. This kind of contempt for the value of a man's time, this unnecessary postponement represented a type of wastefulness that he had fought all his life.

Thursday, November 26—Thanksgiving Day—found Maury and his family chiefly thankful that on the next day he would be able to learn the grounds on which the Navy Retiring Board had placed him on the inactive list.

The Court was called to order promptly at 10:30 Friday morning, November 27, and the record of Wednesday's proceedings was read. Maury was permitted to read a statement that he wanted on the record of the hearing of his case to show that he had not been given information that would have permitted him to prepare for the hearing. After preliminary remarks about the laws governing naval courts, Maury read the letter he had written Secretary Toucey on October 10 asking to be advised on the points to which he was to answer before the Court of Inquiry. He also read the Secretary's refusal to give him the information. [24] Maury next produced the text of the reply he had written to Secretary Toucey on October 15:

> I have had the honor to receive your reply of the 13th to my request of the 10th inst.
>
> I perceive that I have not made myself understood, and therefore crave your further indulgence.
>
> I wished to know wherein my fitness for the Naval service is to be challenged, and am answered that the "Department prefers no

charges against the persons appearing before the Courts of Inquiry, now in session here."

I was aware of this, it is, I believe customary for Officers, who come before Courts of Inquiry, whether at their own request or not, to come without charges; but they nevertheless come, I respectfully submit, with a knowledge of the allegation on account of which their conduct is to be inquired into. This is the practice and the law, and the Act of January last, provides that the Courts of Inquiry *now in session here shall be governed* [Maury's italics] by the laws and regulations which govern other Courts of Inquiry. . . .

Is it my fitness now? Is it my fitness as it appeared to the Navy Board of '55 or is it my fitness at all times since I first entered the Navy? And in what respect morally, mentally, physically, or professionally is it to be challenged? The Department has certified that I am without reproach, and its files show nothing against me. . . .

The most cherished sentiments of my nature revolt at the idea of placing myself in the category of one who appeals to the law, and then quietly submits without protest to that as law, which is contrary to law.[25]

Maury continued to read the balance of the letter in which his protest was reiterated and his request for information renewed. He informed the Court that Secretary Toucey had not replied.[26]

The preliminaries were over; the questioning of witnesses was about to begin. This was not a jury trial, but a naval hearing conducted in a very formal manner. But not even the ordered routine of naval court procedure [27] could dispel tension from the room—an officer's future hung in the balance.

The first witness was called. Commodore Joseph Smith, U.S.N., stepped forward and was sworn by the President of the Court. Smith was to be "a witness on the part of Lieutenant Maury." [28]

The Judge Advocate called on Maury to begin questioning his witness. Maury, in accord with his right, had elected to conduct his own defense. He had seen no reason to employ an attorney or to select another officer to represent him at the Court of Inquiry. Maury was sworn by the President of the Court and began the examination of Commodore Smith. His first questions established that Commodore (captain by rank) Smith was chief of the Bureau of Docks and Yards, had been in the Navy 49 years and had known Maury 25 years, having first met him when Maury had come in from sea in the *Potomac* in 1834. The commodore stated, "From what I saw of him on board his ship, and from conversations I had with him, I considered him a first rate officer in all respects. His general reputation in the Navy is that of an efficient and capable officer." [29]

Maury: Have you ever known broken leg sailors to be in the service as able bodied seamen?
Smith: I have.
Maury: Did they perform their duties efficiently?
Smith: They did perform efficiently all the duties that were assigned to them. Men with fractured limbs are not made topmen of usually. I have known them to be topmen [stationed aloft].
Maury: As to lameness, how did theirs compare with Lieutenant Maury's?
Smith: I have known one or two men in the service as lame as Mr. Maury. . . .
Maury: Did you ever know a sailor who was not more lame than Lieutenant Maury to be discharged, on account of lameness?
Smith: I do not remember any such, from fractured limb. . . .
Maury: Is Lieutenant Maury's lameness such as to prevent an efficient discharge of duty at sea?
Smith: From all appearances, I should think it was not.
Maury: Do you consider Lieutenant Maury fit for the Navy in all respects?
Smith: I do, eminently so.[30]

Having questioned his witness on points that he knew were in the minds of the members of the Court, Maury sat down.

The Judge Advocate cross-examined the witness. He asked, "From your experience as a Naval Officer, are there not occasions, occurring in service afloat, in which lameness such as Mr. Maury's, in the commander of a vessel, would prevent him from performing his duty efficiently?"

Commodore Smith replied, "I don't know of any." [31]

Having no further questions for Commodore Smith, Judge Advocate Winder read the testimony of the witness. It being found correct, Commodore Smith was discharged by the Court.

The same procedure was followed with the second "witness on the part of Lieutenant Maury," Commodore John H. Aulick, a veteran of 48 years of naval service and a captain by rank. In reply to questions from Maury, Aulick testified that he had served nearly three years in the *Brandywine* with Maury. "I was 1st Lieutenant and he a midshipman. For a young officer he was very efficient. . . . His deportment was very correct and he was very studious." [32]

That having been a long time ago, Maury began more specific questioning.

Maury: Do you know Lieutenant Maury well enough to form a correct estimate of his professional qualifications, and fitness now?

Aulick: I think I do. From frequent conversations with Lieutenant Maury on professional subjects, I think he is an efficient officer in any position. From my knowledge of Lieutenant Maury's mind, I think it quite impossible that he could forget the knowledge of his profession acquired in 9 or 10 years active sea service. For my own part I know I could not forget it, though with less mental ability. . . .

Maury: Have you ever known broken leg sailors to be in the service as able bodied seamen?

Aulick: I have known men evidently lame, but whether from broken limbs or not, I cannot say—they performed their duties efficiently. I have known officers in our service, and in other services with wooden legs, who performed their duties efficiently. I know of one instance (then Midshipman, now Captain Graham) who served with me on board the Frigate *United States,* who had a wooden leg, and . . . he performed his duties satisfactorily.

Maury: As to lameness, how did theirs compare with his [Maury's]?

Aulick: I should say greatly to their disadvantage.

Maury: Did you ever know a sailor or an officer of good standing, who was not more lame than Lieutenant Maury, to be discharged the service or refused duty on account of that lameness?

Aulick: I never did.

Maury: Is Lieutenant Maury's lameness such as to prevent an efficient discharge of duty at sea?

Aulick: In my opinion it is not. I have known some, more lame than Lieutenant Maury to perform their duty efficiently. . . . In our service I remember, then, Midshipman, now Captain Graham. In the British service, Sir James Gordon, and Sir George Collier, the last infinitely more lame than Lieutenant Maury. He commanded a 50 gun ship, and although he used a stick and crutch he appeared to be very efficient.

Maury: Do you consider Lieutenant Maury fit for the Navy in all respects?

Aulick: Entirely so.[33]

Commodore Aulick's testimony had been so clear that the Judge Advocate decided to forego cross-questioning him. The testimony was read over and the witness discharged.[34]

At this point Judge Advocate Winder called a third witness for Maury—Captain Robert B. Cunningham. When Cunningham had been sworn in, the Judge Advocate indicated Maury should begin questioning. Maury's first two questions established the fact that Cunningham had seen 43 years of naval service, had served with Maury in the *Brandywine* in 1826 and 1827, and again with him in the *Vincennes* from 1827 to 1829. After supplying that preliminary information, Captain Cunningham concluded with the statement: "I never met an officer, who in so short a period of service, developed such satisfactory proficiency, I speak now of professionally [*sic*]. His conduct during his whole term of service with me, I considered unexceptionable in all respects, both as an officer and a gentleman." [35]

Maury then put to Cunningham the same questions he had asked the preceding witnesses and received much the same answers. As his final statement in replying to the question about Maury's "fitness now," Captain Cunningham said bluntly, "I believe him qualified to command a ship or a squadron." [36]

Those words must have been exceedingly gratifying to Maury, but he continued immediately with his interrogation.

> *Maury:* Is Lieutenant Maury's lameness such as to prevent an efficient discharge of duty at sea?
> *Cunningham:* It is not. I have seen a man more lame than he perform the active duties of a seaman satisfactorily. He had a compound fracture of the thigh, yet he was one of the very best men on board. He could lay out and furl a sail as quick as any man in the ship. He stood his two hours at the wheel.

Maury having concluded his questioning of Cunningham, the Judge Advocate cross-examined: "Do you believe that Lieutenant Maury is physically able to perform all the duties that may devolve upon the commander of a public ship in war, as well as in peace?"

Captain Cunningham replied, "I do, under any circumstances." [37]

The Judge Advocate questioned Captain Cunningham no more. The testimony of the witness was read and, being found correct, Cunningham was discharged. That concluded questioning of witnesses for the day. [38]

At this point Maury asked the Judge Advocate to clarify some points by making a statement about his position at the Observatory. He probably wished this statement made because the record of his naval service that Winder had lying before him included no reference to the years he had served at the Observatory. [39] Maury undoubtedly felt that the failure to mention his period of duty there might cause the members of the Court to think that those years had not been spent on official duty.

After acceding to Maury's request, Winder recorded in the transcript: "The Judge Advocate here, at the request of Lieutenant Maury admits the fact that the Observatory is a branch of the Bureau of Ordnance and Hydrography of the Navy Department, and that Lieutenant Maury was ordered to the superintendence of the Observatory at its establishment, and that he has continued in that position ever since." [40] The Judge Advocate read a section of the August 31, 1842, act of Congress that had established Maury's post, concluding with the words, "but the appointment of any officer in the Navy, to any offices or clerkships in this Act, shall in no manner whatever interfere with his grade in the service." [41]

After this reading the Judge Advocate "proceeded to offer evidence on the part of the Government." He called I. G. Smith, a clerk in the Pension Office of the United States, which had charge of issuing Navy pensions.

The Judge Advocate asked, "Are these the papers filed in that office by Lieutenant Maury, with his application for a pension, and upon which a pension was granted?"

Clerk Smith answered, "They are." [42]

The Judge Advocate thereupon turned over the government's witness to Maury for questioning.

> *Maury:* Does Lieutenant Maury receive a pension now?
> *Clerk Smith:* I believe not. I am not aware that he does.
> *Maury:* When was it stopped?
> *Clerk Smith:* The records of the Treasury will show that fact. I do not know.[43]

The Judge Advocate remarked that the Pension Office had no cognizance of the payment of pensions but only issued the certificates. Winder admitted that Maury was not receiving a pension.[44]

Letters from surgeons who had examined Maury's leg just after the stagecoach accident in 1839 were next introduced by the Judge Advocate. Maury's pension request, made four months after the crippling accident, was read, as were statements by naval surgeons who in 1840 had declared him eligible to a pension that brought him $12.50 a month. The sixth page of such evidence read to the Court was a letter from Maury written in June, 1841, to the Secretary of the Navy. In it Maury had pointed out that since naval surgeons had determined his degree of disability was "three-fourths" (75 per cent), he believed he was entitled to receive more than $12.50 in pension.[45]

With this the Court of Inquiry adjourned for the day.

Maury had suspected that the Navy Retiring Board of 1855 had based their decision on the ruling of surgeons in 1840 and 1841. Now he knew it. The introduction of that petty, temporary $12.50 monthly pension must have seemed such an absurdity as to make Maury wonder again how some of the members of that Board had ever voted a man onto the inactive list on such out-of-date evidence. But Maury had to face the fact that what one group of fellow officers could do another could do. He had tried to evaluate the impact of the testimony of the officers who had appeared in court that day but had been unable to form an opinion. The members of the Court had disciplined themselves over too many years of command to reveal their reactions in a matter of high professional import.

On Saturday, November 28, the first witness called before the court was Navy Surgeon W. S. W. Ruschenberger, "a witness on the part of Lieutenant Maury." The Judge Advocate instructed Maury to start his questioning.

> *Maury:* How long have you been in the Navy—and what is your rank?
>
> *Ruschenberger:* I have been in the Navy since August, 1826, and am a surgeon.
>
> *Maury:* Did you ever serve with Lieutenant Maury, if so, when and how long?
>
> *Ruschenberger:* I served with him on board the *Brandywine* from September, 1826, to the close of 1828. He was a midshipman and I a Surgeon's mate. Again on board the *Falmouth,* from June 1831 to the beginning of 1834 [actually late 1833]. Part of the time Mr. Maury was Master and part of the time Lieutenant. I was surgeon on board.
>
> *Maury:* What was Lieutenant Maury's standing as an officer?
>
> *Ruschenberger:* Lieutenant Maury ranked in the first class as to efficiency. He was always very zealous in the discharge of his duties.

Maury then requested that Surgeon Ruschenberger give a history of his examinations of Maury's broken leg. The Navy surgeon did so and stated that he had originally in January, 1840, shortly after the accident, considered that the injury was "irreparable."

Maury: To what extent does it interfere with his locomotion?

Ruschenberger: At the present time his locomotion is abated very slightly indeed, I think."

Maury: Do you know of any cases of fractured limbs on the part of officers on the active list, whose physical fitness for the Navy is unquestioned?

Ruschenberger: I remember the case of Lieutenant Missroon [John S. Missroon, who had been a member of the Navy Retiring Board and had been promoted] who had a fractured leg which was unsuccessfully treated. He submitted to an operation in October 1842. . . . The result of that operation was the shortening [of] the limb half an inch, certainly more than a quarter. I am not aware that his ability to perform his duty has even been questioned. Mr. Missroon's case was less disabling than Mr. Maury's as they originally presented itself [*sic*].

Maury: Is the leg of Lieutenant Maury as serviceable as his [Missroon's]?

Ruschenberger: I think in reference to the serviceableness of the limbs of the two men [they] are equal. Lieutenant Maury's injury is more apparent to the eye, but I think the power and spirit in each is equal.

Maury: Do you now consider the injury which Lieutenant Maury received in the leg such as physically unfits him for the naval service?

Ruschenberger: I think not. I think Lieutenant Maury is in every respect eminently qualified for the Navy.

Maury: Upon what duty was Lieutenant Maury engaged when you first saw him after the injury of 1839?

Ruschenberger: I believe he was on his way to join his ship.[46]

The Judge Advocate then cross-questioned Ruschenberger. He elicited the fact that the witness had not recently given Maury a physical examination but had formed his opinion by observing his locomotion. The Judge Advocate questioned the surgeon closely on the reliability of an opinion formed in that way.[47]

Dr. Ruschenberger answered: "All opinion is conjectural. The opinion formed in 1840, based upon an examination made at the time, has been proved by lapse of time to have been partially incorrect. The fact that his condition has gone on improving to an extent not contemplated at that time—that he is enabled now to move about without crutches, or other artificial supports, justifies me in the opinion that his limb has recovered its tone and vigor to such an extent as to enable him to perform efficiently his duty as a naval officer, without any reasonable danger of relapsing." [48]

The next witness was another physician and surgeon—Dr. James M. Minor, attached to the Brooklyn City Hospital, who had earlier been a Navy surgeon for over nine years. Dr. Minor, Maury's first cousin, testified that he had examined Maury's leg shortly after the accident and that he "was undoubtedly disqualified for the time being for the active duties of a Lieutenant on ship board, but I had formed no opinion as to the permanency of the injury. I have seen Lieutenant Maury constantly since that time, and there has been a continuous improvement up to the present time. . . . I examined his leg last evening and I am satisfied that the parts have consolidated . . . and that it is in a great deal better condition than its outward appearance would indicate. . . . I believe his locomotion is sufficiently vigorous and active to perform his duty at sea." [49]

As Maury's final question to Minor he asked, "What is your opinion of Lieutenant Maury's fitness for the naval service?" Dr. Minor answered, "I regard him as eminently fit in all respects." The Judge Advocate did not cross-examine Dr. Minor.[50]

Captain Thomas A. Dornin followed Minor on the witness stand. He testified as to his many years of sea service with Maury, making statements similar to those of previous witnesses, and concluded by stating that he considered Maury "eminently qualified under all heads" for Navy duty and not incapacitated for sea duty by his leg.[51]

Commander S. C. Rowan was the next witness to describe the years he had served at sea with Maury as well as their duty together under Commodore Thomas ap Catesby Jones in the 1837-1838 preparations for the South Sea Exploring Expedition. Rowan stated, "His standing as an officer was of the very highest order and the greatest promise. . . . I consider Mr. Maury eminently qualified under all heads for any duties that may be assigned him."

When questioned by Maury whether Maury's lameness was such as to interfere with efficient discharge of duty at sea, Rowan said crisply, "It is not." [52]

Again the Judge Advocate elected not to cross-examine but read the testimony of Commander Rowan. When this record was found correct, the witness was discharged.[53]

Maury announced that he had no further evidence to offer and wished to rest his case.[54]

In support of the Navy Retiring Board's position, the Judge Advocate then read an abstract from the files of the department listing Maury's orders and his leaves. The last two items on the list were:

1842 June 29—To charge of Depôt of Charts
1855 Sep. 17—*Reserved List*—leave—but to remain on duty at the
Naval Observatory [55]

This was an ironical description of the service Maury had rendered the United States and the Navy between the years 1842 and 1857.

At this point in the hearing the Court ordered the Judge Advocate to issue a precept to Surgeon W. S. W. Ruschenberger and Dr. James M. Minor to make a personal examination of Maury's physical condition and to give special attention to a study of his leg.[56]

The surgeons and Maury withdrew from the room and the examination was made. When the three returned to the Court, the surgeons were asked to present their findings.[57] Dr. Ruschenberger gave a precise medical description of the injury originally suffered by Maury and its degree of recovery. He concluded: "I see no reason to change the opinion I have given in my testimony—on the contrary it has been confirmed by my examination—I found the leg in a much better condition than I had supposed." [58]

Dr. Minor testified: "I have seen no reason to change or modify the opinion I have already expressed. The views I now entertain are precisely the same in all respects, as those I expressed before." [59]

The testimony was read for accuracy, and the witnesses discharged.

The Judge Advocate announced that "There being no further evidence to be offered on either side, the case is here closed." [60]

Maury was asked if he wished to make any remarks, but he replied that he did not—that "relying with confidence upon the justice of the Court," he left the case in its hands. He then walked from the room. The doors were closed, and the members of the Court of Inquiry proceeded to a consideration of the evidence in order that they might send their recommendation to the Secretary of the Navy, as ordered by him.[61]

Questions must have occupied Maury's mind as he made his way back to the Observatory. Would the members of the Court ask themselves what but malice could have prevented the 1855 Navy Retiring Board from having required that an up-to-date medical examination be given his leg? Would they acknowledge the absurdity of the Navy's keeping officers equally lame in the active ranks while declaring him incapable of such duty? Would they consider justice had been served by the promotion of Lieutenant Missroon at the very time Maury had been placed on inactive status. If the Court of Inquiry did recommend his restoration to the active list, would Secretary Toucey approve the finding? And if so, what would be the decision of the President—and would the Senate confirm? All those questions would require answers in the affirmative if he was to have a chance at an unrestricted Navy career in the future.

On December 17 Maury wrote William M. Blackford:

> The finding of the court is not known. I take it in my case that it is restoration but nevertheless the proceedings are shameful.
>
> Am in the midst of the 8th edition of *Sailing Directions.* . . . The force at Observatory much crippled—petty hostility.
>
> You see the Secretary [of the Navy] makes no allusion to the Observatory and ignores poor Lewis altogether—work of petty jealousy or something else as mean.[62]

Maury was obviously grieved that Secretary Toucey in his annual report on the Navy had paid no tribute to William Lewis Herndon for carrying out the highest traditions of the sea when the *Central America* had sunk in September.[63]

From Maury's lack of comment on the subject in any of his letters in late December, 1857, and early January, 1858, it seems that he remained throughout those weeks in suspenseful ignorance as to his fate. It is possible that no word leaked to him because the action concerning him was an executive proceeding of the Senate. On December 22, 1857, the Senate received a communication from President Buchanan: "I nominate . . . Matthew F. Maury, now a lieutenant on the reserved list, to be a commander in the Navy, from the 14th of September, 1855, on the active list, to take rank as such, next after Commander James F. Schenck." [64] The Senate proceeded to refer it that day to the Committee on Naval Affairs.[65] If Maury heard that, it certainly gave him no assurance that the Senate would endorse his reinstatement to active duty and promotion. The chairman of the committee, Senator Stephen R. Mallory, might well use his power to defeat this move since he could hardly be expected to look on it with favor after his violent earlier opposition.

On January 11, 1858, the Naval Affairs Committee reported to the Senate a resolution recommending favorable action in the case of the President's nomination for promotion of Maury and a number of other naval officers.[66] One week later the Senate, by unanimous consent, proceeded to consider the committee's resolution and voted to "advise and consent" to the appointment of Maury and his fellow officers nominated by the President. Much of Maury's battle had been fought in the Senate. His victory was won there on January 18, 1858.[67]

Some of the senators who had been so angered by the action of the 1855 board against Maury must have rushed the news of the favorable senatorial vote to him as soon as it was cast. However, the public announcement did not appear in the Washington newspapers for another five days.[68]

The end of the month was at hand before Maury at last received official notification—a letter from the Secretary of the Navy, dated January 29, 1858.

> Sir: The President of the United States, by and with the advice and consent of the Senate, has appointed you a Commander in the Navy from the 14th of September, 1855, on the Active List. I have the pleasure to enclose herewith your commission, dated the 27th instant, the receipt of which you will acknowledge to the Department. I am respectfully, I. Toucey.[69]

The vindication was complete.

However, the battle, which had lasted two and a third years, had taken a heavy toll out of Maury's spirit and creative energy. It had been a shock to him to learn the lengths to which personal dislike or personal ambition could drive fellow officers. Nor did his victory lull Maury into thinking all would be fair sailing for him in the future. Men who had gone to such lengths to limit his opportunities might well try again.[70] The courts of inquiry had reversed the findings of the Board in 62 cases out of the 118 applications for restoration. The trials had dragged on so long, however, that one officer had died before he was heard, eight had withdrawn their applications and one applicant had failed to appear. The decisions in 46 cases had not been changed.[71]

The action of the 1855 Navy Retiring Board and resistance thereto had converted Senator Stephen R. Mallory from a staunch advocate of Maury to an enemy, and this change was to make a difference in Maury's future career. Senator Judah P. Benjamin and Captain Franklin Buchanan, who had sat on the Board, also were men not apt to change their attitudes or to like having lost a battle.

It must, however, be pointed out that, aside from the wrong done to certain officers such as Maury, there did exist drastic need of reorganization of the Navy and there were many do-nothing officers who should have been retired or put on the Reserved List. Numerous reform features, for which Senator Mallory and his colleagues worked, were incorporated into the reorganization of the U.S. Navy in 1861 and in ensuing years.[72] The basic aim had been right and was eventually achieved, but the methods of the 1855 Naval Board had deserved the condemnation they received.

CHAPTER XVI

Crusade for a United States Weather Bureau

When Maury had first taken charge of the Depot of Charts and Instruments in 1842, he had started his meteorological work on a small scale and by early 1843 had begun sending short bulletins on the weather to be published by a Washington newspaper.[1] New and finer meteorological instruments had been made available when the Depot had been merged with the newly built Naval Observatory in 1844, and an enlarged meteorological program had been carried on there.[2] In 1851, Maury had begun his campaign for a worldwide system of co-ordinated observations. He had stated repeatedly, as he did in a letter to the Earl of Rosse, English astronomer and president of the Royal Society, that neither the laws of the great atmospherical ocean nor the movement and phenomena of the atmosphere could be properly studied or thoroughly investigated until observations, both by land and sea, enabled meteorologists to treat the atmosphere as a whole.[3]

When consulted, late in 1851, by the Secretary of the Navy concerning Britain's proposal for joint action on land meteorology, Maury had recommended that an international conference should be held to consider a universal system of observations for both land and sea. Among the scientists whom Maury had written to solicit co-operation were the men in charge of the meteorological program that had been carried on by the Medical Corps of the Army since 1819, those responsible for the meteorological observations sponsored by a few states, and Joseph Henry, secretary of the Smithsonian Institution.[4]

As far back as December, 1847, the Board of Regents of the Smithsonian Institution had appropriated "for instruments and other expenses connected with meteorological observations, one thousand dollars." [5]

James P. Espy had been appointed a meteorologist in the Navy Department in August, 1848, and in that same year an appropriation had been voted by Congress for meteorology under the direction of the Secretary of the Navy; but Professor Henry had feared interference from this. So, according to the Smithsonian Report for 1848, "in order that the observations thus established may not interfere with those undertaken by the Smithsonian Institution, that officer (the Secretary of the Navy) has directed Professor Espy to co-operate with the Secretary of the Institution." [6] Joseph Henry had in that way sought to have the Navy limit the rugged independence that Espy had shown when as a U.S.N. professor of mathematics he had been assigned to work with Maury from 1843 to 1845 on the meteorological program of the Depot of Charts and Instruments.

In the winter of 1848-1849 a circular, signed by Henry and Espy, requesting weather observers for the Smithsonian, had been distributed by members of Congress to their constituents.[7] These circulars also had been sent to individuals who had previously been making observations for the office of the Surgeon General of the Army in the program sometimes referred to as Sanitary Meteorology.[8] Others receiving the circular were citizens who had been making observations under the state programs of New York and Pennsylvania. Perhaps the most significant bloc of individuals to receive this circular was a group of 143 persons who had previously sent in reports on severe storms to James P. Espy. In February, 1849, blank forms had been prepared and sent out, and it was hoped that about 400 observers would use them.[9] On February 9 Professor Henry had jotted in his notebook that "I have in mind a fine scheme with the telegraph. Instantaneous observations, on the Aurora, on the Thunderstorm, the beginning of storms . . ." could be reported.[10]

Henry had consulted and gained approval of his plan by William C. Redfield, the founding president of the American Association for the Advancement of Science, an able and self-taught meteorologist. On March 12, 1849, Joseph Henry had recorded this in his notebook and had added: "The following places should be made stations: Portland, Boston, New York, Philadelphia, Baltimore, Washington, Norfolk, Charleston, Savannah, Mobile, Pensacola, Augusta, Nashville, New Orleans, Galena, St. Louis, Chicago, Buffalo, Albany, Boston." [11] While this ambitious program had not been promptly realized, the Smithsonian Institution had developed a sizable corps of observers who reported observations from different points in the United States.[12]

In addition to Espy, who had proved difficult for Henry to manage, other meteorologists who contributed to the early meteorological work of the Smithsonian were Arnold Guyot, who had come over from Switzerland at the suggestion of his friend Louis Agassiz, and James H. Coffin, professor of mathematics and astronomy at Lafayette College, Easton, Pennsylvania.[13]

When Maury had informed Joseph Henry in the early days of January, 1852, that the United States was proposing an international conference on meteorology of the land and sea and that he had been authorized by the Secretary of the Navy to enlist the support of scientists in the United States, as well as abroad, Henry had become alarmed.

On January 3, 1852, Professor Henry had noted in his journal: "The institution is liable to danger from internal disunion, from combinations from without of interested persons and from a tendency to go into a state of repose spending its income in the accumulation of materials rather than in the production of new results." [14]

From the first Henry had had this problem of keeping the Smithsonian moving along lines of philosophic and scientific investigation as opposed to becoming strictly a museum and library.[15] On January 24 he had jotted in his journal: "Saw Maury at the supper of the Secretary of War [Charles M. Conrad], promised to meet him some day this week on the subject of meteorology." [16] But three days later Henry had first met with his friend and ally, Alexander Dallas Bache, to draw their plan for the development of North American meteorology. Henry had recorded in his journal January 27, 1852:

> Consultation with Prof. Bache on the subject of meteorology, agrees to the Proposition that:
> 1. The Army takes the west, 2. The Smithsonian the east,
> 3. The British Government the north, 4. The Observatory the sea,
> 5. The returns of all given to the S.I. [Smithsonian Institution] [17]

Henry's plan was essentially continental, although including the sea widened the scope.

On March 2 Henry had noted, "Lieutenant Maury called, will co-operate in meteorology," and on April 16, "Wrote to Lieut. Maury asking aid for the Astronomical Journal." (Presumably this was a request that Maury write articles for the journal edited by Dr. Benjamin Apthrop Gould, Jr.) Professor Henry had then recorded on April 17: "Long interview with Senator Dawson, will go for all that may be asked by the Smithsonian Institution. Danger of the Institution from without. Hint from Gould as to the jealousy of scientific men—those who would enjoy the honor without the labour of science." [18]

On May 1 Henry's entry had been: "Mr. Seaton . . . urges the importance of being at all times prepared for an attack." Five days later Professor Henry had noted: "Wrote to Col. Sabine relative to action of Royal Society." On May 31 he had recorded: "Letter from Col. Sabine relative to meteorology. Royal Society will recommend the co-operation of the English government in meteorological sea observations. Wrote to Lieut. Maury recalling his proposition of co-operating with the Smithsonian Institution." [19] These notations had been written at the time when the Royal Society had under consideration the proposal of the United States government to Great Britain for joint effort in comprehensive meteorological observations with a conference to be held to set up the program.

Henry had been much relieved that the Royal Society had recommended that the British government participate only in a joint program for meteorological observations for the sea. Even so, Henry had not seemed pleased that Maury had won half his program for international meteorological co-operation, for Henry had hastened to remind the superintendent of the Naval Observatory of his agreement with the Smithsonian. After the success of the Brussels Conference, when European scientists were working with Maury to bring about a second international conference, Henry still had not been interested, and Maury then decided to proceed independently.

On November 7, 1854, Maury wrote the Secretary of the Navy urging extension of meteorological observations to the land. He concluded with these words: ". . . should it at any time be adjudged expedient so to enlarge the field of my researches as to include *agricultural* as well as *commercial* meteorology, I am ready at the bidding of the department to submit a plan with the details thereof for your consideration." [20]

Maury described his proposal for a national weather service and appealed for co-operation from farmers in an article published in the August, 1855, issue of the *American Farmer*. On September 18, 1855, Washington's influential *National Intelligencer* reported Maury's proposed plan and declared: "There can be no doubt that the Government will lend its aid to the furtherance of this great work. Lieutenant Maury states that such an office as will be required in Washington to carry out the details of this plan is already in existence. It was established by Mr. Calhoun when he was Secretary of War and it is under the control of the Surgeon General of the Army. The meteorological observations that are made at our military posts are discussed and published at this office. The plan, it will be perceived is similar to the one which has been so successfully adapted on sea." The *Intelligencer* concluded with the information that Maury was endeavoring to get the people to persuade their representatives in Congress to do as much for farmers as the United States government had "permitted to be done at sea for commerce and navigation." [21]

Maury called the program that he proposed "Meteorology for the

Farmers" or "Agricultural Meteorology." Having grown up on a farm in an area devoted solely to agricultural pursuits, Maury was aware of the seriousness of the loss that farmers sustained from unexpected weather. Having proved that ordinary sailors at sea were fully capable of making weather observations, Maury urged that farmers could do the same on land, as could also railroad agents, teachers—in fact, anyone who was willing.

It seemed that many people were willing. On November 20, 1855, Maury received from a man in Missouri a letter that included two newspaper clippings giving the information that the legislature of Missouri had authorized the establishment of five meteorological observation stations and voted the money for them. Maury's correspondent was in charge of them and said that he stood ready to co-operate by making observations and using the forms Maury proposed. This was but one of many offers and at this time Maury said of his plan, "It goes on swimmingly! I have almost volunteers enough now with offers of service and friendly aid, and signs of encouragement are pouring in." [22]

A few weeks later Maury sent a message in a letter his daughter Diana was writing Franklin Minor: "Lord Wrottesley says that they in England are ready to follow our lead about the meteorology for the farmers. He is President of the Royal Society." [23]

That December an article in the New York *Tribune* greatly disturbed Maury. He wrote a friend that the newspaper article stated that his plan was intended to act as a rival to that of the Smithsonian. Maury declared:

> I knew the notion would be injurious to the working of the meteorological plan if it got out, so I wrote a letter to the *Tribune* in my own name to show what Henry of the Smithsonian was after, and what I was after, and that the two plans were no more rivals of each other than the astronomical observatories which are springing up in various parts of the country are to this one. So far from being rivals, they are quite the contrary, &C. Nevertheless, you can see how my plans for the public good may be embarrassed. It is time for scribe and scriber to dress for the party, and for scribee to undress for bed.
>
> Good-night.
>
> M. F. Maury, Per Nannie (Curly) [Diana] [24]

At this time Maury did not realize that there was really serious opposition to his plan on the part of Joseph Henry. In the communication he sent to the *Tribune* Maury stated:

My friend Professor Henry will no doubt feel as much surprise as I do, to learn that we are setting up rival schemes. The Smithsonian Institution has from the beginning been engaged in a system of Meteorological Observation—this we all know.

When Professor Henry entered the field meteorological in the name of the Smithsonian, the U.S. Army with its Medical Corps had already been at work in it for 25 or 30 years; their observations extend all over the country. But no one threw obstacles in the way of the laudable efforts of the Smithsonian by reminding amateur meteorologists—those whose voluntary aid was invoked—that this was a rival scheme to Mr. Calhoun's of the Army which had so many stations occupied. There was *no* rivalry in the case; the Army observations were for one purpose, the Smithsonian for another. Professor Henry may, I suppose, be presumed to know what is the particular object which, in organizing the Smithsonian System of Meteorological Observations, he had in view. He says—"*The great object of the Smithsonian collections of meteorological observations is to settle definitely* [italics are Maury's] the question as to the origin, progress and character of the winter storms of our country."

The great object that I have in view, is to extend to the land for the benefit of agriculture and other great interests the system of observations that have done so much for commerce and navigation. . . . The object that I have in view is to co-operate with, not to work in opposition to the Smithsonian Institution, the Meteorological Department of the Surgeon General of the Army, or any establishment whatever.

The *field* is an immense one, and there is room without rivalry or opposition in it for all the laborers and all the talents that a dozen other systems could absorb. These systems would only act in co-operation, not in rivalry, and . . . each, I have no doubt, would derive valuable aid and information from the other.[25]

Maury evidently thought that the field was so immense that there was room for all, but this was either profound optimism or the utmost naïveté. He felt so strongly about dealing with "the grand atmospherical machine" [26] as a whole that he let his enthusiasm blind him to the possible reactions of the secretary of the Smithsonian. He was soon to learn what Henry actually felt.

In January, 1856, the United States Agricultural Society met in Washington. At the meeting on January 10, held in the auditorium or hall of the Smithsonian Institution, a former president of the New York State Agricultural Society, Dr. Beekman, submitted a resolution urging that the Society recommend to Congress that "the system of meteorological co-operation and research which has done and is doing so much for commerce and navigation at sea" be extended to the land; he submitted a second resolution specifying that a committee of three be appointed from the Society "to communicate the above resolution to each member of Congress and to solicit his co-operation. The result of these applications in behalf of the great agricultural interests of the country to be reported at the next meeting of the Society." [27]

The United States Agricultural Society's President Meder had asked Maury to speak at this meeting.[28] Excerpts from the official report of the meeting tell what occurred:

"In the progress of discussing the observations thus obtained from the sea, we have arrived at that point at which observations on the land are found to be essential to a successful prosecution of our investigation into the laws which govern the movement of the grand atmospherical machine. At sea we have the rule, on the land we look for the exceptions," declared Maury. "We want to see the land, therefore, spotted with co-laborers observing also according to some uniform plan, and such as may be agreed upon in concert with the most distinguished meteorologists at home and abroad; and I have addressed myself to the agricultural interests, and the sanitary interests of the country because they have the deepest stake in the hedge. For the same investigations precisely that will subserve these interests, will also subserve the interests which science and all the industrial pursuits of man have in the investigation. . . .

"Baron Humboldt [Alexander von Humboldt], among others, has expressed the most earnest desire to see such a concerted plan of observations inaugurated among meteorologists. He would, I am assured, be most happy to assist in maturing it, and stands ready with his counsel and advice to that end. Jomard and Le Verrier, of France, as Arago was, are in favor of the plan. So too, are Quetelet, and Dove, and Kreil, and Kupffer, and Lamont, and Littrow, and Secchi, of Rome, Pegado, of Portugal, and Jansen and Ballot, of Holland, and Ihlen and Petersson, of Norway, and Sweden, and Rothe, of Denmark, and many eminent men and renowned meteorologists of England. These, with Wrottesley, Sabine and a host of others, stand ready to co-operate with us and to observe each for his own government, according to any plan that shall be agreed upon.

"How was this system of maritime co-operation brought about? By means the most simple."

Here Mr. Maury narrated the history of the Brussels Conference.

"I have seen it stated in one of the public prints of the day, that this plan is a rival scheme to that which the Smithsonian Institution has already in hand; that the two plans are hostile. I have no doubt that the idea of rivalry in such a subject astonished my friend—if he will allow me so to call him—the distinguished Secretary of this Institution, quite as much as it did myself. Are the offices which the States of Europe have created to assist in the investigation of the winds and currents of the ocean, rival establishments of the one in Washington? Are the agricultural societies which are scattered over this broad land, and each of which is doing so much good in its own way, rivals of each other? Or are the astronomical observations which are starting up in the various parts of the country, rivals of the National Observatory here? . . .

"Whatever facts or observations shall be elicited by this system of investigation, will be as heartily at the service of Professor Henry and the Smithsonian Institution, as I am sure the abundant materials that are contained in his office are at the service of any establishment, institution or individual in the country who may desire to use them for any special investigation or particular research. . . .

"In conclusion, permit me to say that, in carrying out *any* system of observations for the benefit of agriculture, we should not lose sight of the importance of publishing *daily* reports, in such manner as to be *widely* circulated." [29]

Prof. Joseph Henry, Secretary of the Smithsonian Institution, objected to the resolution as offered, and hoped it would be modified. He thought that if an appropriation was asked from Congress, it should be for meteorology in general, and not for any particular system, or to be under the direction of any individual. The rivalry alluded to by Lieut. Maury could not exist. He (Prof. H.) was merely the representative of the Smithsonian Institution, and as such he would explain its connection with meteorology. . . .

To carry out this idea the Regents had given attention to a number of objects. Among others, they had established a system of meteorological observations, on which they had already expended about $15,000. They had collected a large amount of valuable meteorological information, which they had not the means of publishing to the world. The primary object of the system was to solve the problem of American storms, and for this purpose they had adopted the plan first suggested by Prof. Mitchell, of the University of North Carolina, and successfully carried out in particular cases by Prof. Loomis. . . .

The original plan has been extended and ordinary meteorological results arrived at. . . . Several of the States of the Union had joined the Smithsonian Institution and placed their meteorological results at its disposal.

In order to increase the means of usefulness, the Institution had lately entered, as it were, into a copartnership with the Patent Office, and a grant had been obtained for the purchase of a number of instruments; one hundred rain-gauges had been procured for distribution to the most important points of the Union, and the returns would hereafter be regularly published in connection with the Patent Office Report.

Prof. Henry stated that he had a high estimation of the talents of Lieut. Maury, and, he believed, a just appreciation of the results of his labors. He had mapped down on the chart of the globe numerous tracks taken by navigators, and noted the different winds they encountered, and thus helped the mariner to choose the path which would offer the prospect of the most favorable passage. This, however, said Mr. H., though of great importance, was in itself a simple matter, and involved no great scientific attainment, and certainly implied no particular ability to apply a meteorological system for the seas to the *land* for *agricultural* purposes. The methods and objects are entirely different. The latter problem is one of much complexity, and, in order to devise a proper system, the subject should be submitted to a commission of the scientific men of the country who had paid particular attention to meteorology and to the problems connected with agriculture. Prof. H. again declared that he would admit no rivalry between himself and Lieut. Maury, because *he* was merely the representative of the Smithsonian Institution, and whatever was done by it would be accorded to the name of Smithson [Englishman whose legacy had made possible the Smithsonian] and not to that of Prof. Henry. He looked for no personal advantage from his connection with this system; but, on the contrary, whatever Lieut. Maury has done is in his own name, although at the expense of the government, he thought Lieut. Maury had not treated the Institution with due courtesy on this occasion; that in his communications to the public he had ignored what the Institution had done, and the first information it had received that Lieut. Maury contemplated a system of meteorology for the *land,* was obtained from the newspapers. . . .[30]

C. B. Calvert, President of the Maryland Agricultural Society, with all due deference to science, thought that the good sense and observation of plain men had been of immense importance to scientific research. The matter of meteorological discoveries at sea had been carried out by common sailors, under the direction of Lieut. Maury, and if it were a matter so easy of discovery why had not all the science of former ages demonstrated it? It remained for the patient and long-continued observation of plain sailors, under the direction of that practical man of science whom kings delight to honor, to find out the laws controlling the ocean storms. He did not wish the resolution to be amended so that the matter would be placed in the hands of merely scientific men. Let the observations on land be made by plain farmers, at little or no expense, under the direction of Lieut. Maury, and then such observations would be made as would be of practical importance. He wished to see scientific and practical men unite in this great work; there was enough for all to do. But with due respect to Prof. Henry and the Smithsonian Institute [sic], he would not have the matter pass from the hands of the eminent and distinguished man who had not only proved himself a scientific man, but a man of practical science.[31]

Lieut. Maury was very sorry that Professor H. had taken such a view of his efforts in meteorology. The field was wide, and it was well known that Professor Henry had not sufficient funds at his command to carry out the plan in all its details. Instead of creating a rivalry, he wished this plan to be regarded as co-operating with the Smithsonian Institute. He well knew that Prof. H. led a life of labor, and that his high attainments entitled him to the greatest deference and highest consideration in maturing this plan, and all this he was always ready to accord. With these feelings he had deferred the meteorological conference for a year, at Prof. H.'s request. But now observations upon the land was [sic] a necessity; he could not wait longer to make a commencement. If this proceeding should prevent the co-operation of the Smithsonian Institute, it was a matter greatly to be deplored; but still the work must go on. He knew that the Professor could have no personal feeling in the matter, but that the idea that damage to the Institution's reputation caused his opposition to this measure. The idea Lieut. Maury considered as erroneous, and hoped that further consideration would convince the learned gentleman of the fact.[32]

S. H. Huntington, President of the Connecticut State Agricultural Society, regretted that the matter had assumed the phase of rivalry between these eminent gentlemen. . . . Dr. Beekman read the resolutions again, and stated that they seemed sufficiently explicit. He was glad that it had created a spirit of rivalry between the men of science. When emulation commenced, a greater advancement would be made in any subject.[33]

After some informal conversation upon the motion, the Chair put the previous question, and the resolutions were adopted by a large majority. The President thereupon appointed Messrs. Poore, Huntington, and Calvert as members of the committee.[34]

Whatever hopes or illusions Maury may have harbored until that day concerning Joseph Henry's attitude toward him were at an end. The secretary of the Smithsonian had publicly announced that he considered Maury neither a scientist nor capable of devising a meteorological plan for the land. Henry had also reiterated his position that the only arbiters of such a matter would be a commission of *scientific men*. By intimation it was clear that Henry felt he should decide who was a scientist and who was not. Maury was fully familiar with this view held by Henry and Bache, for he had five years earlier heard Bache, in a speech before the annual meeting of the American Association for the Advancement of Science, call for a "high tribunal" of men dedicated to pure science to sit in judgment on their fellow scientists, or "pretenders" to knowledge as Bache considered most of the American scientists outside the coterie of which he and Henry were leaders.[35]

Henry's opposition to having Maury move into a position of active leadership in land meteorology in the United States is certainly understandable. Maury would have been far wiser to have stuck to the earlier proposals he had made of having a separate bureau established or that the Army's pioneering meteorological service be modernized and used as the central office for a national weather service. The fact that Maury envisioned a service as wide in scope as the one he had already implemented at sea had led him into the trap of offering to direct the proposed land service. However, from the derogatory remarks Henry made about Maury it would seem that even had Maury not proposed to direct the program, Henry would have opposed any meteorological plan conceived by the naval scientist.

Maury's personal reaction to Henry's remarks at the meeting was described by him in a letter to Franklin Minor:

> I attended the U.S. Agricultural Society yesterday, by invitation, and spoke to the resolution about the plan meteorological. I had a regular scientific fight, and though the result was all I could have desired, yet it was utterly disgusting to encounter such miserable signs of jealousy and small feeling. You know that I have been after this Meteorology for the Farmers persistently since 1851, and that the Brussels Conference urged it; and you may recollect my telling you that I had had an interview last year, before leaving the city

for the summer, with the Secretary of the Interior and the Commissioner of Patents in favour of their taking it up.[36]

In mid-January officers of the Agricultural Bureau came to see Maury at the Observatory and proposed "to cut loose from the Smithsonian" and work with him in his proposed system.[37] Maury again stated: "I do not see how the Smithsonian plan and ours at all interfere. I am for a quiet life. But unless the Agricultural Bureau wakes up and takes views very different from those expressed to me, not much will be done there. He speaks of wanting two or three clerks!" [38] That kind of limited approach was the very thing Maury was trying to get away from. He wanted a national weather organization that would be adequate to the need. He believed the whole country had to be aroused to the need and the government authorities stirred to action, and he obviously thought that neither the Agricultural Bureau nor Professor Henry was going to fight for meteorology on the grand scale that was necessary.

In the early months of 1856 Maury's plan for "Meteorology for the Farmers" was taken up by the Agricultural Committee of the Senate. In April a bill was drawn to appropriate $20,000 to establish a system of daily observations and reports to the country.[39] In June Maury was greatly encouraged and believed Congress would go ahead with the idea and even establish a special bureau to handle it. But by August he was discouraged as to the fate of the bill, for Congress seemed no longer interested in meteorology or any other scientific endeavor.

The meteorological bill did not come to a vote in 1856, but Senator James Harlan of Iowa and his Agricultural Committee did in December of that year draw up a 10-page report urging the extension to the land of the System of Observations carried on at "The National Observatory," as the Naval Observatory was still generally called. This report was presented to the Senate on December 18 to accompany Senate Bill 481—the bill sponsored by Senator Harlan to create the general weather service proposed by Maury.[40]

Feeling as he did about Maury, Joseph Henry, of course, rallied his forces to fight the Harlan bill. One method used to attack Maury's proposals for a program of land meteorology was the writing of letters to newspapers. As was often done in that era, the letters were not signed by the writer but submitted under a pseudonym.[41] An example of this type of pro-Smithsonian, anti-Maury effort was a letter written by X on February 18, 1857, and published a few days later in the Boston *Atlas:* "The Physical Geography of the Sea being a failure, it necessarily follows that the physical hydrography of the land must be a success." In referring to a previous letter he had sent, X stated:

I wrote in sober earnest, keenly feeling the reproach which is brought upon our land by such emanations from a government office [Naval Observatory and Hydrographical Office] . . . and it is time that even half-educated people should protest against our being held nationally responsible for the character of the essays which are ceaselessly issuing from the "Hydrographical Office." Our scientific repute abroad may not be very high, but it is not quite so low as though entrusted to the "Chief Hydrographer." Let those be held responsible who keep him in office,—but not the seminaries of learning in the United States, nor those who give their attention to study. . . .

Why did the chief hydrographer give lectures on snow storms to the estimable and unoffending Secretary of the Navy? The cat has slipped out of the bag. Only let Congress add $25,000 to the $80,000 now annually appropriated for the Naval Observatory, and the storms shall do no damage in future either to ships or crops. . . . It [a program handled by Maury] is fearful to contemplate.[42]

X commented that he had supposed that the 247 regular observers who sent in meteorological reports to the Smithsonian Institution were the best qualified to handle such matters. He concluded with a criticism similar to that made by Henry at the U.S. Agricultural Society meeting the preceding year: "I had always supposed that educated men were more likely than ignorant ones to deduce correct results even from data of equal value." [43] This allusion to Maury's lack of a college education was a favorite and recurring point of attack. The Maury-Henry rivalry was one more proof that, though "lighthouses do not compete," men do.

Whether right or wrong, Maury's position in the matter was that he had directed meteorological observations for the government longer than had Henry, had developed the largest corps of meteorological observers that had ever gathered information on a systematic basis, had proved that he could get the co-operation of the government on such an ambitious, over-all plan and was dedicated to making this not just a national or continental plan of action but one in which many nations would join the United States. He had his nucleus organization established and ready to bring about this international participation in a universal system of land and sea meteorological observations. The scientists in Europe who had worked with Maury on this since 1853 only waited for the United States to take the lead so that a conference could be called and their nations agree to a common effort.[44]

Never having been in the confidence of Joseph Henry, Maury naturally was unaware of how early Henry also had envisioned the use of the telegraph in meteorology. He mistakenly believed that Henry had

got the telegraph idea from him.[45] But by 1857 Maury knew that Henry
was receiving weather information by telegraph and posting this data
on a large map of the United States located in the turreted, castle-like
building of the Smithsonian—the first such weather map in the country.[46] In Maury's view, however, this did not go far enough and did not
provide telegraphic warning. The heart of the need, Maury declared,
was instantaneous evaluation and prompt dissemination of the findings
by telegraph.[47]

The bill that would have made Maury's proposal the law was defeated
in the Senate in 1857.[48] It is possible that those who persuaded the lawmakers to vote it down found useful to them Maury's involvement at
that time in his effort to be restored to full Navy status. He was certainly not in a position to lobby for his meteorological bill, for the Navy
Retiring Board issue had yet to be settled. The halls of Congress had
rung with his name for two years, and that may have been a handicap
to the weather bill. Maury considered that "dogs in the manger" had
worked behind the scenes and achieved the bill's defeat.[49] These were
the men who said Maury was not a true scientist because he sought to
interest the people as a whole in science and to enlist their co-operation in his projects. Maury's reaction was expressed to Lieutenant Felix
Julien, of the Imperial French Navy, whom Maury wrote to praise his
meteorological research:

> It would be difficult for me to overestimate to you the high ap-
> preciation I have of the services you have rendered and are render-
> ing. . . . That's right!
> Popularize our field of labors; it abounds in rich harvests, and
> none are so feeble but that they may glean something.
> It is a mistake—and I have no sympathy with those philosophers,
> who mounted on their scientific stilts stalk about the physical do-
> mains of the earth saying, "Those who would follow us must mount
> stilts as high." Therefore, as I said, you are doing a good service in
> popularizing the field in which we labor.[50]

Henry's known opposition apparently caused Maury to fight even
harder for eventual acceptance of the idea of a central government
weather bureau. He resolved to arouse public interest to such a pitch
that Congress would have to act. In November, 1858, Maury secured
leave and set out on a tour to give 25 lectures in twelve cities, including Rochester, Buffalo, Cleveland, Kalamazoo, Indianapolis, Chicago,
and St. Louis.[51] Maury accepted a fee of $125 for each of these lec-
tures [52] because he was in financial straits after trying to support his

large family on $1,200 a year for the preceding two and a half years.[53] The acceptance of these fees distressed Maury just as it had when he had been forced to do the same thing in 1856. At that time he had written Franklin Minor that he thought it would be more fitting if he were working tobacco behind Minor's house.[54] The fee taking gave Joseph Henry and Dallas Bache another epithet for Maury—"the pecuniary." [55] However, fee or no fee, Maury used the lecture tour to campaign for a weather service that included forecasts and two of his lecture topics were on "Extending to the Lakes [Great Lakes] a System of Meteorological Observations" and "A Careful Meteorological Survey of the Lakes." [56]

Maury had early that year urged Secretary of the Navy Dobbin to supply meteorological instruments and require keepers of lighthouses on the lake shores to spend ten minutes a day making observations. Maury recommended immediate action because of the mounting toll of life and loss of property caused by storms over the lakes, where 866 persons had lost their lives and nearly $10,000,000 worth of property had been destroyed by storms.[57]

In urging lake meteorology Maury called attention to the fact that Army Captain George Gordon Meade and his corps of assistants were already at work on the "Northern Lake Survey" and therefore "that all the observers, instruments and appliances needed to make the observations required were at hand willing and ready for the work." [58] The one additional step needed was for the observers to report their observations daily by telegraph to Captain Meade's office and for that office to send the information out that same day to the cities of the Great Lakes section. Maury reminded the people that the Army meteorological system was not telegraphic but reported weather in retrospect to provide information on the climatology of the country.[59]

During Maury's stay in Buffalo he came to know Captain E. P. Dorr, president of the Lake Board of Underwriters, who had subject to his orders marine inspectors or surveyors "at all the principal cities around the lakes." Maury unfolded his entire plan to Dorr. After Maury's departure from Buffalo, Captain Dorr drew up "a memorial to Congress, asking them to enact a law and appropriate funds to carry out Maury's plan. This was sent to him (Maury) at Washington by me, approved and returned," Dorr stated. "I then sent to each important city upon the lakes . . . procured the signatures of all prominent men, and then forwarded to each member of Congress representing the districts. . . ." [60]

Because the proposal was not voted by Congress, Maury went on tour in 1859 to stir more citizens to action. He addressed the North Alabama Mechanical and Agricultural Society on "A System of Agricultural Meteorology for Farmers and Daily Weather Reports by telegraph from all parts of the Country, for the Benefit of Mankind." [61] He also spoke in Tennessee, and memorials were sent by Southern men asking Congress to establish a weather bureau according to Maury's plan.[62]

However, in 1859 men in Congress grew less sanguine that the slavery issue could be resolved to the satisfaction of both North and South. Already there were signs that the Union might break apart. Men increasingly voted according to sectional thinking, though there were some statesmen who did not. It was hardly a promising time to expect Congress to vote to establish a strong national weather bureau in Washington. And those of the scientists who believed Maury's program might rival or even eliminate their own continued to work against his plan. Maury believed that in spite of sectional bitterness the plan for a national weather bureau might have gone through but for the opposition of the scientific bloc led by Joseph Henry and Alexander Dallas Bache. Maury received frequent inquiries from European scientists as to the reasons for the animosity of the "professors."

On December 7, 1860, Maury gave his friend Adolphe Quetelet, the astronomer royal of Belgium, a résumé of the opposition's complaints against him. As they had long ago dubbed him "a practical scientist," Maury called the professors "the closet men of science" because of their insistence that devotion to theoretical investigation was the true test of the scientist. To Quetelet he wrote:

> To return to the animosities or the jealousies or whatever they be, to which I have alluded. It is only now and then that I see anything of them; it may be that I am blind, but I feel them in the air —I take them in by suction. Let me see how nearly I can state the grounds on which they are said to rest.
>
> "He does not," say the closet men of science, "treat the question before him always *secundum artem*. He pushes his speculations oftentimes beyond the limits which the facts before him would authorize a prudent and cautious investigator to go; therefore we cannot recognize him as a true disciple."
>
> Is not that the way they talk?
>
> Now for the other side: "The *main* object of his labors is to benefit navigation and to obtain practical results. Upon no other plea would his government permit him to labor in this field. He is therefore compelled to work by stealth, as it were, and to treat questions of science merely as questions that are incidental to the main object for which his office was established. Not only so—he has to work for and with a class of men—'old salts'—most of whom hate what is called science and feel a sort of contempt for your so-called man of

science. His success depended upon interesting these men in his labours, and in inducing them to become, almost without their knowing it, themselves active and efficient laborers in the cause of science;—and, but for his having won the confidence of these men and gained their sympathies—but for the great body of seamen being made to feel that he was rendering good service to their calling— he and his plan of research would have fallen into disrepute without trial. Moreover, in treating the questions of science as they arose, he had to treat in a way that would most interest his fellow labourers at sea." [63]

Maury then gave his side of the picture:

Has he not therefore by his tact and by his deep sympathies with the sailor at sea, rendered better service to the cause of science than he could have done by following the rigid reserve and cold formulae of calculating analysis?

As an illustration of my mode of treating questions of physical research at sea, please see Chapter XXII, *Physical Geography of the Sea and its Meteorology*, London, Sampson Low, Son & Co., November, 1860. . . . The facts upon which the chapter is based were stated in the naked, dry, and *scientific* way, to navigators as you see by the note, eight years ago. They excited no interest, attracted no attention, and consequently caused no progress. But before I left London, and, after this chapter [written in popular style] had appeared, a Russian officer came to me and said he was bound to the Cape of Good Hope—this subject of actinometry [measuring the direct heating power of the sun's rays] was most interesting and he pledged himself to make the observations therein called for.

So much for knowing how to make the most of the material one has to deal with. The true problem with which I have had to deal was so to use my opportunities as to produce the greatest good to the greatest numbers. By the fruits of my labor let me be judged.[64]

Maury refused to yield to discouragement. In a letter praising recent scientific accomplishments on the part of Professor H. W. Dove, of Berlin, Maury declared: "It is the comprehensive mind, the patient disposition, and the brave heart that do most in a field like meteorology." [65] He felt the system he proposed must come and kept plugging away for it. He wrote an article on the subject for the *Southern Planter* in August, 1860, and his correspondence in 1861 still showed him at work on the project.[66] His hope that year was that the new administration might put his bill through.[67]

But 1861 was not the year for optimism in the United States. The Union crumbled and artillery became the voice of the land. From 1861 to 1865 war prevented any possibility of a weather bureau's being established. It did not, however, put out Maury's fire on this subject, and he was to live to carry on the crusade. His future work was to prove that he was not just fighting to direct the program, he was battling to see that the United States had a comprehensive weather service.

CHAPTER XVII

Maury the Man

Achievement was a necessity for Maury, but so was human affection. His dedication to realizing the full potential of his mind made him a scientist, but his ability to give and to receive affection made him a balanced human being. He was sustained in the difficulties through which he passed by his conviction that he was doing useful work, by his reliance on God, and by the warmth of affection given him by his wife, his children, his relatives, and his friends.

His heart had played no trick on him when he had fallen in love with petite, auburn-haired Ann Herndon. Her femininity exactly suited his strongly masculine nature. He was the active as well as the titular head of their household, and Ann would have had it no other way. When she disagreed with him, she did not argue—she was too sensitive a woman to enjoy dispute and too wise to think she would ever win a battle of words with her husband.[1] But she was no spineless creature— Ann had her own way of influencing Matthew Maury without making a direct issue of it. He had a great admiration for her character and for her ability to develop character in their children.[2] He loved her for the way she stuck to principle and backed him in his determination to do the same. When he was under attack and hard pressed in spirit, he found in her gentleness and genuine sweetness a comfort and a quiet strength that enabled him to regain perspective.[3] Ann's sustaining love undoubtedly played an important role in keeping Maury from becoming a bitter, vindictive man.[4]

Maury was a thoughtful husband. Because of Ann's small appetite, her frequent headaches, and lack of physical stamina, Maury sought to protect her from unnecessary strain. That his own vital energy and emotional drive could at times exhaust one of lesser fiber probably never entered his head. He did learn, however, that he could not transfer his energy to Ann, and so he took on some duties of the home normally carried out by the wife. When the house that they occupied adjoining the Observatory had to be papered and painted one summer, Maury arranged for Ann to go to Fredericksburg until the work had been completed. He picked out the wallpaper for each room and chose the color of paints.[5]

Ann was proud of her husband's national position and international reputation, but she did not enjoy the social responsibilities that they brought her. She much preferred the company of their own family and of their numerous Virginia relatives to that of official Washington society.[6] Her natural modesty made her diffident among strangers, and the formal social affairs to which she occasionally had to accompany her husband were a trial to her. In fact, it was only because of Maury's encouragement and insistence that she would hire a carriage and set out on the round of calls that were *de rigueur* for the wife of a man in his position in Washington.[7] Maury may have fretted some over her social disinterest, but he preferred that to the ambitious worldliness of some of the women he met at functions in Washington.[8] It was no secret that Ann would have preferred to continue living in Fredericksburg had a suitable career been possible for her husband there. Realizing this, Maury arranged for Ann to go there as often as possible to visit her kith and kin and also to have her relatives come to Washington to stay with them.[9]

Romantic love had carried them through the usual adjustments required in the first years of marriage, but it was the coming of children that brought maturity and depth to Ann and Matthew Maury's devotion to each other. In that day of large families, neither regarded the number of their children as a problem—the children were their great mutual interest. The harmony between Maury and his wife might have decreased had he been a man bored or irritated by children. Instead he found his children interesting and highly enjoyable as companions. Relaxation with them was the balance wheel to his long hours of mental concentration at the Observatory.

Because of his disapproval of the type of embroidery and belles-lettres education then offered in schools for girls,[10] Maury elected to teach his daughters himself. He was convinced that girls as well as boys could learn about science, and he set out to prove his theory. When his oldest child, Betty, was twelve he launched her and his next younger daughter, Diana, on a course of elementary chemistry. The breakfast hour was devoted to teaching. He had a chemical chart hung in the dining room and he taught with gusto—without neglecting his buckwheat cakes and preserves, his favorite morning meal. Maury assigned lessons and required the girls to work at them diligently. He was strict but had an understanding of the limits of youthful absorption.[11] The third daughter, Mary, recounted an anecdote that shows one tactic he used in teaching his younger girls:

"Sometimes he would make mistakes on purpose to see if we would catch him and, if we failed to correct him, he would say 'You little rascal, your head is wool gathering.' And when we failed to catch the meaning of the text and he asked us what the lesson was about, we halted and stumbled and would say, 'We know what the lesson is about but we can't tell you.' He would smile and say, 'Then your head is just like an old gourd stuffed full of newspapers—a great deal of information in it which you can't get out or make use of.' " [12]

In addition to being able to joke his children out of laziness, Maury also practiced his belief that the carrot was more productive than the thistle. When someone sent him the gift of a small telescope and Diana showed an interest in it, he offered it to his young daughter as a prize if she would take lessons from him at the big telescope in the dome of the Observatory. He agreed to give the small instrument to her as soon as she learned to make a properly completed astronomical observation. To his pleasure, Diana won the prize in a month. [13]

Maury was an evocative teacher. His delight was in stirring curiosity in the minds of his children and in engendering the kind of enthusiasm about learning that makes a child willing to endure the disciplines of study. [14]

In training his children he had only two absolute rules—they were never to lie; and they were to obey, without question, if he or Ann gave them a direct order. However, a request was usually adequate, and he resorted to a command only if childish misbehavior necessitated it. Even as he believed in the order of nature he believed in order in family life. The children knew the rules and knew where they stood. If they chose to disobey either of the two cardinal rules they were punished. [15]

As his sons reached the suitable age, Maury sent them to day school in Georgetown (then still a separate town but now a much-favored residential section of the city of Washington). [16] Maury was relying on the fact that the boys' schools of the time gave an infinitely superior education to that offered by the female institutes. However, he became dissatisfied with the schooling the boys were getting in 1852. Evidently he considered they were required to study too much Latin and too little science [17] for he worked out a plan with Secretary of State Edward Everett, John Walker Maury, president of the Metropolitan Bank and mayor of Washington, and several naval officers stationed in Washington to engage a British teacher for their sons. [18] When Maury went to England in the summer of 1853, en route to the Brussels Conference, he asked C. Piazzi Smyth, astronomer royal of Scotland, to engage for him a young man who was especially competent as a teacher of mathematics and science.[19] As a result a Scotsman, J. M. D. Meiklejohn, came to Washington and gave intensive schooling to Maury's two older sons, Richard and John, as well as to the sons of the other fathers who had joined in the project. Meiklejohn not only taught the boys but held planned exercise periods each afternoon and took the youths for long weekend hikes.[20]

On evenings when he had no visitors Maury sometimes read aloud to his family from Shakespeare.[21] In the hope of overcoming a stutter that his son John had developed, Maury persuaded the boy to memorize some of Marc Antony's speeches and deliver them from memory. He encouraged his children to read the classics.[22] Declaring that the reading of novels was to students what mint juleps were to the tippler—"a serpent in disguise"[23]—Maury forbade his children to read light novels. This met with some rebellion on the part of the girls, who thought romance fully as important as serious education.[24] Maury urged his sons and the young men who sought his advice to read the biographies of great men and books about the field of work they hoped to enter.[25]

While demanding faithful study from his sons, Maury stressed that no mental development would have any value unless their moral development was equivalent. A sample of the philosophy that he instilled into Dick, John, and his much younger son, Matthew Jr., was included in a letter Maury wrote Hamilton Lieber when that young man was entering the United States Naval Academy:

> Make it a rule to ask yourself at night what you have learned during the day, and do not be content until you get a reply, and always learn something if it be only the meaning of a word from the dictionary. . . .
>
> Make it a rule never to offend, nor to seek cause of offence [sic] in the conduct of others. Be polite to all, familiar with but few. Do not be quick to take offence; you will never find a gentleman who will willfully and without any cause, real or imaginary, offend another. Therefore, whenever you imagine yourself aggrieved either by an equal or a superior officer—when you are in doubt as to whether the offence were intended or not, go straight up to him, state the case, and ask the meaning of the intention. Never let imaginary offences, slights or cuts find a place in your breast—they sour the disposition. . . .
>
> He only is truly brave who has the courage to do right. . . . The doing right, the acting up to principle, may sometimes seem to you to be inexpedient, or it may have the appearance of making you

unpopular—but this principle of conduct will build up a character founded on the rock which nothing can shake; and let me assure you that it is unwise and always wrong for a man to have enmity in his breast between himself and his conscience. When principle is involved, be deaf to expediency. It is a dangerous word to all classes of men. I would, if I could, teach you almost to hate it.[26]

One of the ambitions of Maury's life was to give his sons the college education that had been his family's tradition but that circumstances had denied him. In the fall of 1858 he was proud that Dick was enrolled as a student at the University of Virginia, but Maury found his son's college expenses so hard to manage within his pay that he secured leave for a month, traveled 5,000 miles, and gave twenty-five lectures.[27] He did not like speaking for money, but he did like having enough money for Dick's college fees.[28]

Maury's children had the greatest love for their father and thought he had no equal. They were, however, perfectly capable of growing weary of copying his long papers and grumbled about it occasionally to close relatives. The girls also joked about their father's hard-to-read handwriting, his misplacing pages of a manuscript, and the necessity for hunting for them.[29]

Maury's children had no difficulty in "leaving the nest" at the normal time. Betty, the oldest child, was the first to marry. Maury regretted only that Betty carried on the family habit of marrying a cousin [30]—William Arden Maury, the son of Maury's friend and second cousin, the late John Walker Maury.[31] As a father, Maury doubtless would have preferred for Will to have had a more substantial income, but he praised Betty for having chosen a young man of character and proudly gave her away at the wedding in 1857.[32] A year later Diana married Spotswood Wellford Corbin of Farley Vale plantation on the Rappahannock River, less than 15 miles from Fredericksburg.[33] Diana had been gone barely a week from the Maury home at the Observatory when her father wrote her on May 9, 1858. "I have been thinking so much of you, and missing you so sorely, and loving you so tenderly," but he did not hesitate to warn her, "The one great point which, after duty to God, you are to keep constantly in view is, to identify yourself with your husband. . . . The husband's affairs are, in the married life, the affairs of the State." [34]

Ann's niece, Ellen Herndon, who had become like a daughter of Maury's household after her father's death at sea, married on October 25, 1859. Maury gave her in marriage to Chester Alan Arthur, destined to come to Washington as President.[35] Following these marriages of the older girls, teen-age Mary and Eliza became Maury's scribes.

While Maury had a well-developed domestic nature and managed to crowd into a busy life a rather remarkable amount of time with his children, it was not always time spent solely with them. They were allowed to remain in the parlor or, when of sufficient age, to come to the table when he and Ann were entertaining the interesting guests who called at their home.[36] Because of this inclusion, they were trained not to initiate conversation but to reply when addressed by their father's famous visitors. Doubtless some of the guests were disconcerted by the presence of the young people, but a Victorian savant was more accustomed to carrying on learned conversation in the midst of a family than would be an intellectual of today. French astronomer Urbain J. J. Le Verrier had no difficulty in telling Maury, in the presence of the children, of the steps that had led to his discovery of the planet Neptune. He went on to entertain the Maury youngsters by describing how he had buried his telescope to avoid having it seized by political insurrectionists in France and showed them the telescope, which he had brought with him.[37] The noted German chemist, Justus von Liebig, delighted Maury with his accounts of agricultural chemistry and the children with numerous jokes.[38]

In the 1850's many of the distinguished visitors who came from abroad to Washington visited the Naval Observatory and Maury. Some came for a call, some were invited to dinner or tea, and some stayed in the Maury home. They were from all over the world—a highly educated Parsee from India, a papal astronomer from Rome, a French hydrographer, a British duke and his wife, a Norwegian naval officer who had been his country's delegate to the Brussels Conference, an explorer returned from the arctic, the Amazon jungles, or from the antarctic, or a planter from Virginia or Tennessee.[39] Men who hoped to achieve came as well as those who had achieved. Foreign diplomats stationed in Washington came often.[40]

To make his salary cover the food for his large family and the number of guests he either wanted to entertain or felt professionally obligated to entertain, Maury maintained both a vegetable garden and a strawberry patch at the Observatory, and he also had fruit trees grown from slips sent him by country friends.[41] Even so, the Maurys' entertaining was on a very restricted scale compared to the elegant soirées of the Count and Countess de Sartiges, the stag parties of British Minister John F. Crampton, the Congressional dinners of William Wilson Corcoran, or the famous matinée dances of Senator John Slidell of Louisiana and his beautiful French wife.[42] But people liked to come to the Maury home— the food was in the old Southern tradition, a suitable wine was served, and the conversation was excellent.

A chief feature of the Maurys' entertaining was a visit to the Observatory itself to view the heavens through the great telescope. One such visit was made by the wives of a great number of Southern senators and representatives who formed the Congressional "mess" at Brown's Hotel. The party was apparently arranged at one of the sumptuous parties given by Maury's friends, Mr. Justice Campbell and his wife. Mrs. Clement Claiborne Clay, wife of Senator Clay of Alabama, declared, "At the home of the Campbells one met not only the legal lights of Washington but scientists and travelers. . . . A frequent visitor at this home was also Professor Maury, the grand road-master of the ocean, who by the distribution of his buoys, made a track in the billows of the Atlantic for the safe passing of ships." [43]

And then Mrs. Clay, who was a little confused about the use of buoys, continued: "I remember an amusing visit paid by a party from our mess to the observatory of Professor Maury. It was an occasion of special interest. Jupiter was displaying his brilliancy in a marvelous way. For no particular reason, in so far as I could see, the Professor's great telescope seemed to require adjusting for the benefit of each of the bevy present. I noticed Professor Maury's eyes twinkling as he went on with this necessary (?) preliminary, asking betimes, 'What do you see?' 'Nothing clearly.' 'Well, permit me.' And after several experiments he would secure at last, the right focus. When all of his guests had been treated to a satisfactory view of the wonders of the sky, Professor Maury delivered himself somewhat as follows:

" 'Now, ladies, whilst you have been studying the heavenly bodies, I have been studying you' and the quizzical expression deepened in his eye.

" 'Go on,' we assented.

" 'Well,' said the Professor, 'I have a bill before Congress (mentioning its nature) [evidently the Harlan bill] and if you ladies don't influence your husbands to vote for it, I intend to publish the ages of each and every one of you to the whole of Washington.' " [44]

The man whom Mrs. Clay and her lighthearted friends visited that day in 1857 commanded attention by a quality of inner authority rather than of physical appearance. Maury stood a mere five feet six in height. His most noticeable feature was a bold head with a broad deep forehead. His brown hair, which earlier had been luxuriant and curly, was thinning badly on top of his head. He continued to have a high color in his cheeks. When not in conversation his eyes often wore a faraway look as he lost himself in thought. But, when talking to someone, Maury looked directly at the person, and his eyes showed his reactions, especially when enthusiasm made them light up. His mouth was wide, with a full lower lip. His hands were small and well shaped, and he used them effectively to emphasize a point in speaking. His voice retained the soft intonation of a Southerner. He still had a noticeable limp when walking but did not use a cane as he had for years immediately following his stagecoach accident.[45]

In dress, Maury was meticulous in his mature years although he told his children that he had been careless as a youth before he had learned the importance of appearance.[46] When not in Navy blue uniform, Maury wore the black broadcloth suit, white shirt, and black silk cravat that was then standard city attire for gentlemen in Washington.[47]

Maury never was able to amass financial holdings of any size, but he had one asset that was enviable. Since boyhood he had been able to make friends and keep them. Soon after Maury had left Harpeth Academy, William C. Hasbrouck had quit his youthful post-college teaching career and become a lawyer in Newburgh, New York. Despite their difference in vocations and long periods of not seeing each other, the old tie held. When the children of the two men were old enough to travel, Maury and Hasbrouck exchanged family visits whenever finances and vacation plans permitted.[48] Hasbrouck became Uncle Hazzy to the Maury children, and Maury's son John, when he thought he might like to become a lawyer, asked if he could spend a year as an office boy in Hasbrouck's law firm to discover if he had an aptitude for law. Hasbrouck was delighted to have the boy not only work for him but share his home.[49] Having prospered in his legal practice, Hasbrouck worried about Maury's lack of financial security. In 1859 Maury, who had no flair for profitable investment, liquidated some poor-paying stocks, added some remains of the money made on his recent lecture tour, and turned over $5,000 to Hasbrouck to handle as he saw fit.[50]

Of Maury's Navy friends, those who were closest to him were men with whom he had sailed in his years at sea. He and William Francis Lynch had been devoted to each other since they had cruised together as midshipmen in the *Brandywine* in 1825. Maury admired Lynch's competence as an officer and his cultivated mind and imagination.[51] Following publication of his account of the naval expedition he had led to explore the Dead Sea and River Jordan area, Lynch wrote another book, *Naval Life,* and dedicated this to Maury for his consistent "support of the best interests of the Navy." [52] When Lynch had marital difficulties and was separated from his wife, Maury kept in touch with him and helped him to make new friends and resist the depression he was experiencing in his loneliness.[53]

The sensitivity of feeling that made Maury worry about Lynch's personal unhappiness was not a sporadic outburst. Maury thought a good officer was a gentleman and a gentleman should live up to the full meaning of the designation. When his brother-in-law and valued friend Lewis Herndon went down with his ship, Maury gathered reports from survivors of the sea tragedy and compiled them for the Secretary of the Navy. He chose these words to end his account of Herndon's rescue efforts—efforts that had resulted in 152 of his crew and passengers being saved:

> Everything that could be done by the best sea-captain to save his ship was done to save this one. . . . There was no lack of skill or courage. Order and discipline were preserved to the last; and she went down under conduct that fills the heart with unutterable admiration.
>
> Affectionate in disposition, soft and gentle in his manners, he won the love and esteem of his associates, and became a favorite throughout the service. None knew him better or loved him more than, Respectfully, M. F. Maury, Lieutenant, U.S.N.[54]

The qualities Maury admired in Herndon were ones he possessed himself, with the exception of universal popularity. Perhaps Maury's closing this report with the reference to Herndon's popularity reflected a touch of envy.

Wit, good nature, and professional ability drew Maury to Irish-born Thomas Aloysius Dornin, whom he had first come to know in 1826 when they had sailed together in the *Brandywine* for the west coast of South America. Maury's other close friend from those years was steady, intelligent Stephen C. (Darby) Rowan, who had been his messmate on the world cruise of the *Vincennes*. From the spring of 1851 to the following spring, Dornin and Rowan were in Washington on duty as assistants to Captain David Farragut in drawing up a book of ordnance regulations for the Navy. Maury, Dornin, and Rowan made the most of that year, getting together for evenings of discussion that often turned into debate —lengthy, passionate, and extremely invigorating to the participants.[55]

At one time Maury had considered devoting his energies to naval ordnance, a technological field in which he kept abreast of developments.[56] By 1853 Maury had developed a strong belief in big guns and little ships.[57] With Maury, conviction required expression, and so off went many letters on the subject to fellow naval officers. One such, written in 1859, was to Marin H. Jansen, who had returned from duty in the Dutch East Indies and was serving as chief of the Bureau of Matériel for the Dutch Navy. Maury wrote:

335

Henceforward . . . in my judgment . . . in sea fights . . . this new and improved ordnance being brought to bear, victory is to depend first upon markmanship—second upon markmanship—thirdly and lastly, upon markmanship.

When Uncle Sam makes me Secretary of the Navy—which will be, Jansen, when thou art King—the Prince of Good Fellows you already are—I will have for the Navy a corps of trained and skillful marksmen. . . . One or more ships shall be always at sea, before some rock or another, firing away and practicing always for their training in all conditions of sea and weather, and until the pupils become expert.[58]

Jansen was almost as ardent a champion of international co-operation in meteorology as Maury and like him had suffered naval criticism for his scientific interests. After some years of service at the Dutch Meteorological Institute, Jansen had faced a naval review board that had ordered him to sea duty in the Orient. The difference had been, however, that in Holland the board had sat in open session, and the secrecy that Maury had so deplored on the part of the 1855 U.S. Navy Retiring Board had been totally absent.[59]

While in the Orient Jansen had sent Maury a kimono. Maury, who was no slavish follower of custom, saw nothing unusual in his wearing the comfortable robe at home in the evenings. The figure he cut was described by his daughter Diana. "Sometimes he would walk up and down the two parlours wrapped in a light blue Japanese dressing-gown, quilted with eider-down which was a present from Captain Jansen, the long ribbons, which should have been fastened around his waist, trailing behind him, or gathered up like reins in the hands of the little ones, who trotted after him, backwards and forwards, calling out 'gee, woa!' or 'Back, sir!' —he paying not the slightest attention but dictating gravely." [60] The scene has its comical aspect but illustrates Maury's lack of self-consciousness and his ability to concentrate even when surrounded by his younger children.

His gift of concentration was of particular interest to one of his friends, William Leigh, a naval officer who served under Maury on board ship and at the Observatory. Leigh said of him: "He had in a very unusual degree control over his mind and could at will drop one subject and take up another—he could do everything with it, it seemed to me, but keep it from acting—he could direct the machine but could not stop it. . . . Equally remarkable was his powerful imagination. It was this that lifted him above the man of mere mental power, that often lent the charm of

336

eloquence to his conversation and had much to do, no doubt, with his popularity as a lecturer." [61]

Leigh considered that Maury was "by nature of a genial and social temperament with a quick appreciation of humour and fun, his pursuits made him not a grave but a very thoughtful man." William Leigh added that after working long hours by day with Maury he also spent as many evenings as possible with him. "I took more interest in his society than in any other." [62]

Perhaps the most graphic account of the qualities that caused men to like Maury was written not by a personal friend but by the New York journalist, Nathaniel Parker Willis, editor of the *Home Journal*. After making a five-day trip with former Secretary of the Navy John P. Kennedy and Maury, Willis described his reaction to Maury:

> He made me subject to his personal magnetism, and while with him I had secretly vowed myself and my pen to the service of his interest and reputation thenceforward. . . . During the time that we were together on that trip, he was, unconsciously to himself, to me an exquisitely interesting study of character. I had long heard of him, and knew what the public generally knew of his pursuits; but my conviction was strengthened every day that he was greatly under-valued by common repute, and that he was of a far deeper intellect, and much more of a natural philosopher, than the world, with all his repute, gave him credit for. . . . Under his exceeding modesty and reserve, there seemed to be a vein of the heroic and romantic so hidden, that he was seemingly unconscious of it, and I was quite sure before I parted with him that he was one of the *sans peur et sans reproche* class of men; yet willing to pass for only the industrious man of science which the world takes him for. Under the strong magnetism of his sincere and simple manner, I formed an irresistible attachment to him, and longed to set the world right as to his qualities.[63]

More matter-of-fact is this remark made by Colonel (later General) Francis H. Smith of the Virginia Military Institute: "His [Maury's] conversation was interesting to the thoughtful in the richness of the lessons he drew from common things. He would couple facts, regarded by others as unconnected, and thereby disclose unsuspected relations. . . . This detection of a hidden meaning in the simplest matters shows the inexhaustible nature of truth, and is the mark of a superior mind." [64]

In connection with Colonel Smith's statement it is interesting to note that in a letter condemning ivory-tower intellectuals and proclaiming his interest in the quality and professional dedication of a man, Maury commented to a mutual friend: "What you say about Colonel Smith illustrates my doctrine about great men, for all useful men are great; it's the talent of industry that makes a man. I don't think that so much depends upon intellect as is generally supposed; but industry and steadiness of purpose—they are the things." [65]

The dedicated enthusiasm and pertinacity of Cyrus Field endeared him to Maury. In the years in which Field was coming so often to the Observatory to show Maury samples of cable under consideration for the Atlantic telegraph, the two men debated endlessly the question of the proper weight of cable. One day when Field was particularly obdurate about wanting to use a very heavy cable, Maury resorted to his oft-used type of quip, "What do you want with anything so stout as that? Do you expect young whales to amuse themselves by swinging on it?" [66] It was typical of his way of making a point.

Maury had the uncommon good fortune of having relatives whom he also counted as valued friends. He was devoted to his hardheaded, dryly factual first cousin Rutson Maury, stayed with him when in New York, and corresponded with him regularly. Their letters were, as often as not, marked by spirited remarks expressing total agreement on some points and equally as often total disagreement on others. For Maury's use in his work, Rutson gathered all kinds of data on commercial shipping and export commodities. But Rutson did not hesitate to tell Maury, "Your forte is Science and not Trade or Political economy." [67]

Another first cousin who admired Maury chiefly for his "masculine common sense" [68] but also spoke his mind freely when he thought Maury was off on a tangent, was law professor John B. Minor.[69] The Navy Board action and the continuing harassment of Maury by Bache and Henry made Professor Minor extremely anxious to have Maury leave Washington and use his intellectual gifts in the field of education. Minor was instrumental in the University of Virginia's offering Maury, in 1859, the soon-to-be-established chair of Physical Geography and Agricultural Science.[70] However, Maury turned down the professorship [71] as he also declined a tentative offer of the presidency of the College of William and Mary.[72]

Agricultural science was one of Maury's hobbies. Like many boys born and bred on a farm, he retained sufficient fondness for country life to consider it ideal for his vacations. These he liked to spend with his kinsman and friend, Franklin Minor, on his 1,000-acre farm in Albemarle County, Virginia. Maury, who had recommended the use of marl to farmers in the 1830's,[73] enjoyed keeping abreast of the scientific ideas Franklin Minor was trying to introduce in his farming. It was on Minor that Maury tested his proposals for government crop forecasts and other features of his proposed agricultural meteorology.[74] And it was in letters to Franklin Minor that Maury most frequently confided his personal feelings. Minor made at least one visit a year to Maury at the Observatory, and his arrival was the occasion for Maury to chill a bottle of champagne when, as he put it, "there were enough shots in the locker" to permit it.[75]

Maury's friendship with the man who had been his boyhood principal at Harpeth Academy in Franklin, Tennessee, the Right Reverend James Hervey Otey, continued to be most meaningful to him where matters of an ethical or spiritual nature were involved. In a crisis Maury always consulted his early mentor, and Otey had the deepest admiration for Maury. In 1859 Bishop Otey was extremely busy in a campaign to build the University of the South at Sewanee, Tennessee, on a mountain plateau above the altitudes at which malaria flourished.[76] He consulted his former student as to plans for the new institution. Among the suggestions that Maury offered was a recommendation to Otey that he use a dispersed cottage system—or at least not make the dormitories too large—and that he place only two men in a room. Maury believed this would cut down the tendency of youths to gather for mass pranks and would reduce noise for the student who found concentration difficult.[77]

Nothing would satisfy Otey but that Maury make an address at the laying of the cornerstone of the University of the South. And so, in the autumn of 1860, Maury deferred a business trip to England to go to southern Tennessee to make this speech on October 10.[78] There were some 8 bishops, 200 clergy, and 4,000 laymen in the audience that heard Maury that day.[79] In his role as a scientist, he spoke of his personal belief in religion as the basis for any comprehensive understanding of the natural world.

> Physical geography makes the whole world kin. Of all the departments in the domains of physical science, it is the most Christianising. Astronomy is grand and sublime; but astronomy overpowers with its infinities, overwhelms with its immensities. Physical geography charms with its wonders, and delights with the benignity of its economy. Astronomy ignores the existence of man; physical geography confesses that existence, and is based on the Biblical doctrine that the earth was made for man. Upon no other theory can it be studied, upon no other theory can its phenomena be reconciled. . . .
>
> Here, in the schools which are soon to be opened . . . the masters of this newly ordained science will teach our sons to regard some of

the commonest things as the most important agents in the physical economy of our planet. They are also mighty ministers of the Creator. . . .

I have been blamed by men of science, both in this country and in England, for quoting the Bible in confirmation of the doctrines of physical geography. The Bible, they say, was not written for scientific purposes, and is therefore of no authority in matters of science. I beg pardon: the Bible *is* authority for everything it touches. What would you think of the historian who should refuse to consult the historical records of the Bible because the Bible was not written for the purposes of history? The Bible is true; and science is true . . . they are both true; . . . and when your man of science with vain and hasty conceit announces the discovery of disagreement between them, rely upon it the fault is not with the Witness or His records, but with the "worm" who essays to interpret evidence which he does not understand.

When I, a pioneer in one department of this beautiful science, discover the truths of revelation and the truths of science reflecting light one upon the other and each sustaining the others, how can I, as a truth-loving, knowledge-seeking man, fail to point out the beauty, and to rejoice in its discovery? . . .

As a student of physical geography, I regard earth, sea, air, and water as parts of a machine, pieces of mechanism, not made with hands, but to which, nevertheless, certain offices have been assigned in the terrestrial economy. It is good and profitable to seek to find out these offices . . . and when, after patient research, I am led to the discovery of any one of them, I feel with the astronomer of old, as though I had "thought one of God's thoughts,"—and tremble. Thus as we progress with our science we are permitted now and then to point out here and there in the physical machinery of the earth a design of the Great Architect when He planned it all.

Take the little nautili. Where do the fragile creatures go? What directing hand guides them from sea to sea? What breeze fills the violet sails of their frail, little craft, and by whose skill is it enabled to brave the sea and defy the fury of the gale? What mysterious compass directs the flotilla of these delicate and graceful argonauts? Coming down from the Indian Ocean, and arriving off the stormy cape they separate—the one part steering for the Pacific, the other steering for the Atlantic Ocean. Soon the ephemeral life that animates these tiny navigators will be extinct; but the same power which cared for them in life now guides them in death, for though dead their task in the physical economy of our planet is not finished, nor have they ceased to afford instruction in philosophy.

The frail shell is now to be drawn to distant seas by the lower currents . . . the lifeless remains descend from depth to depth by an insensible fall even to the appointed burial place on the bottom of the deep. . . . Some day science will sound the depth to which this dead shell has fallen, and the little creature will perhaps afford solution for a problem a long time unsolved; for it may be the means of revealing the existence of the submarine currents that have carried it off, and of enabling the physical geographer to trace out the secret paths of the sea.

Had I time I might show how mountains, deserts, winds, and water, when treated by this beautiful science, all join in one universal harmony,—for each one has its part to perform in the great concert of nature.

The Church, ere physical geography had yet attained to the dignity of a science in our schools, and even before man had endowed it with a name, saw and appreciated its dignity,—the virtue of its chief agents. What have we heard chanted here in this grove by a thousand voices this morning?—A song of praise, such as these hills have not heard since the morning stars sang together:—the BENEDICITE of our mother Church, invoking the very agents whose workings and offices it is the business of the physical geographer to point out! In her services she teaches her children in their songs of praise to call upon certain physical agents, *principals* in this newly-established department of human knowledge,—upon the waters above the firmament; upon showers and dew; wind, fire and heat; winter and summer; frost and cold; ice and snow; night and day; light and darkness; lightning and clouds; mountains and hills; green things; trees and plants; whales, and all things that move in the waters; fowls of the air; with beasts and cattle,—to bless, praise, and magnify the Lord! [80]

The speech was in keeping with Maury's central religious belief—that God had created the universe in harmony and expected man to discover the laws of that harmony and live by them.[81] God was both cosmic and personal to Maury, and he considered the Bible to be the divinely inspired handbook of life.[82] He had a lively conscience, examined his behavior by the yardstick of Christ's teaching, and was not ashamed to tell his children that he often had to ask God for forgiveness.[83] He wove his religious beliefs into his writings and speeches but was not given to personal conversation about them. He disliked pious mouthings and gloomy

341

religious talk.[84] He believed that God would sustain a man through any difficulty.[85] As early as 1840, when he formulated the prayer he used nightly thereafter, Maury had declared his acceptance of Jesus Christ as his Savior and the Redeemer of the world.[86] He adhered to the teachings of the Episcopal Church and regularly attended service on Sunday at St. John's, Lafayette Square, Washington.[87] But still he did not yield to Ann's pleading that he be confirmed in the church so that he might receive the sacrament of Holy Communion.[88] According to a statement he made later, his reluctance was based on a belief of personal unworthiness, not on doctrinal doubts.[89]

Maury's religious concept was a part of his sense of wonder about nature and about life. Some of his reactions to the beauties of nature were so filled with this sense that they possessed a rhapsodic quality.

His religion also determined his basic approach to his fellow man. He was incurably optimistic in his expectancy of good in men and experienced the greatest difficulty in believing that any man wished him evil.[90] It took him a long time and every kind of proof before he could believe that a man he had once admired was less admirable than he thought. He was slow to reach that conclusion, but when he did he was through with any but the most punctiliously correct professional relationship— and only if his work made that a continuing necessity.

No man achieves as Maury did without ambition. His ambition had been fired in boyhood by his determination to use the mind he had been given and by a revolt, whether conscious or unconscious, against his father's lack of success. By the time he was nineteen Maury had developed a philosophy of action that refused to acknowledge the possibility of failure. He was going out into the world, he was going to learn all he possibly could, he was going to do something useful on a scale big enough to command his full devotion, and he was going to be recognized for it. He wanted recognition and believed that any man who did good work should receive it. He believed in praise as a great incentive; he gave it to others and wanted it for himself.

Philosophically, Maury did not consider a great deal of money the ultimate desideratum and refused to leave naval service in order to make the larger sum that his ability could have commanded in the commercial world. This meant merely that he preferred to do that which he conceived he was intended to do rather than spend his time in the pursuit of wealth. No man could for years struggle to feed and clothe his family and relatives on too little salary without hungering for the money to do it properly, to educate his children, to take the kind of vacation trips he would like to give his family, to entertain without severe restrictions.

Both Maury and his wife were born of families that—with exceptions like his father—had lived well for many generations. Maury would have enjoyed being able to indulge his children more than he did. He was determined that his low salary should not deprive them of the social life of the class into which they had been born and in which they moved. Diana and Betty made their debut in Washington society but their "coming out" party was an extremely simple affair. Maury earned the money for this by his writing done in his free time. The same was true of the wedding reception that he gave Betty at the Observatory residence.[91] Maury undoubtedly felt that in his youth he had been cheated of some of the good things of life, and, like most such fathers, he worked hard to see that the experience was not repeated with his children.

One luxury in which Maury indulged himself and Ann was an occasional short summer stay at the White Sulphur Springs in Greenbrier County, Virginia (later West Virginia).[92] This was probably the most fashionable of all the mountain watering resorts to which Southerners, Washingtonians, and Baltimoreans flocked to avoid the chills and fevers of the malaria season.[93] Some of the accommodations at "The White" were available at a very modest rate, and Maury never attempted the extended stay that many of his wealthy friends made each summer. Fortunately, a week or two at the resort refreshed him enormously, he wrote a former Navy colleague.[94] Maury might have added that it was advantageous to his various projects for him to keep in contact with the leaders in many fields who vacationed at the White Sulphur Springs.

Maury was knowledgeable about his family background and proud of his forebears.[95] Unlike many wellborn Virginians, he spent little time in discussing his ancestors or their achievements. His greater interest was in living people.[96] While fully appreciating the value of good breeding, Maury gave no hidebound allegiance to belief in an aristocracy of birth. His writings indicate that he held the true aristocracy to be one composed of men of virtue and talent. In Maury's opinion, the talent would be made use of by the virtue of hard work.

People who indulged in social snobbishness were laughable to Maury. This was illustrated by a remark he made when he heard that a former messmate of his who had borne him a grudge since duty together in South America had started a rumor about his birth. The gossipmonger had put out a story that Maury and William F. Lynch had been taken in youth from a poorhouse and placed in the Navy by a commodore who wanted to prove the unimportance of heredity. Maury recounted the fable to one of his relatives and commented that it was not his idea of a story that could do a man harm. "Now, I am so constituted that had I come from a poorhouse—so far from being ashamed of it, I should have been disposed to consider it a matter of pride." [97]

Neither Maury's virtues nor his faults of character can be considered apart from the great motivating force of his life. One uncontrollable drive—the pursuit and dissemination of knowledge—resulted in his greatest accomplishments and his most distressing professional and personal experiences. This drive led Maury to become one of the last of the universal scientists, rather than one of the relatively new breed of scientists who confined themselves to a single field of investigation. With Maury's versatility of mind, curiosity, and unflagging enthusiasm, it is not surprising that he refused to confine his efforts. He stated succinctly, "I am strongly anti-pigeonhole." [98] Conflict with rival scientists was an inescapable result.

The intensity of Maury's drive for knowledge as a young midshipman had undoubtedly irritated his shipmate Sylvanus W. Godon and led to that officer's jealousy of him and determination to get ahead of him.[99] Maury's drive to disseminate knowledge, coupled with ambition for recognition, had in 1836 produced his first book *Navigation*. That scientific textbook had stirred up the wrath of old-line officers, who opposed Maury's insistence that midshipmen should know the theory as well as the practice of navigation. First at the Depot of Charts and Instruments and then at the Naval Observatory, Maury's demand for steady application to work as well as his preoccupation with excellence and efficiency must have caused some junior officers to dislike him.[100] Thus a virtue was carried by Maury to a point where it constituted a problem in his relationships with others. This facet of his character undoubtedly created some of the animosity that led to the Navy Retiring Board's action against him in 1855.

His inability to tolerate inefficiency or avoidable delay in work caused Maury to criticize Charles Henry Davis's slow production of the *Nautical Almanac and Ephemeris*. That criticism, ably aided and abetted by the unfriendly efforts of Alexander Dallas Bache, cost Maury the friendship of Davis.[101] The resulting action against Maury was Davis's formulation of the Steamer Plan for Bache and the subsequent long, bitter dispute about the inaccuracies of the deep-sea soundings made by Berryman on that expedition.

Maury's universality of interest was a source of recurring difficulty with scientists who thought he invaded their fields of study. Had Maury been able to deny himself his interest in promoting adequate meteorology for the land he would have betrayed his own conviction about national and international needs, but he would have saved himself from much of the derogation heaped upon him by Joseph Henry.[102]

One of Henry and Bache's criticisms could have been avoided by Maury had he not pursued a policy that was a part of his plan for the dissemination of knowledge—the announcement by him of a scientific finding in his oceanographic work when he believed he had established reasonable proof. Maury's theory was that the finding should be made known promptly so that other men could investigate or debate it into certainty or denial.[103] His critics condemned him for this, claiming that he was seeking further glory.

Occasionally Maury's versatility of interests caused him to enter non-scientific fields in which he was not an expert. When he sought to promote merchant shipping direct from southern ports to Europe, this naturally irritated New York businessmen.

Even Maury's admiring children must at times have wearied of his constant effort to disseminate knowledge. A born teacher, as had been his grandfather, the Reverend James Maury, Matthew Maury was certain that everyone was or could be as fascinated by learning as he. The fact that his drive to learn had, without benefit of college training, made him an American scientist of worldwide reputation infuriated some academicians. In spite of gaps in Maury's formal intellectual training, this criticism seems rather vindictive for an age when a considerable number of able scientists were self-taught men like William C. Redfield, first president of the American Association for the Advancement of Science.

If a man is known by his enemies, then Maury should be very well known, for those who pitted themselves against him were both able and articulate. Maury hotly resented their efforts to keep him from achieving work that he considered he should do for the welfare of mankind. At such times a sense of injustice boiled up in him, and he grew very angry. When he thought a scientific rival had appropriated a proposal he had made, he commented bitterly, "They would steal a man's brains—that's my thunder." [104]

Maury wanted to have his time free to work and fight for the purposes to which he devoted himself and was infuriated when he had to stop to defend himself.[105] But when he became convinced it was necessary, he marshalled his full energies for battle. A man who believed in forthrightness and direct confrontation, Maury fought best in open conflict. Proud and defensive under attack, he was as doggedly determined to win a struggle with adversaries as he was in his physical research. He could be stubborn, dogmatic, opinionated, disputatious, or overbold. When he felt his work was being undercut, Maury could write a slashingly sarcastic letter.[105] He was a man who said what he thought at times when silence might have been wiser. He increased his own vulnerability

345

by refusing to swerve from what he considered a course of altruistic virtue.

While resisting to the hilt any criticism based on a determination to undermine his authority as a scientist, Maury took criticism in his stride when he felt it was made with sincerity. He examined the criticism until he was positive as to its merit and not infrequently ended by agreeing with his critic. To Professor Elias Loomis of New York University Maury wrote in 1859: "I am very much obliged to you for taking even so much thought about our labors here as to make a suggestion. . . . You are not singular. There is a great diversity of opinion among navigators as to the best manner of presenting the information contained in the Pilot Charts—All agree as to its value." [106] Maury explained that he worked constantly on recasting the material to try to present it more clearly. A few months later he remarked to Lieutenant Edouard Vaneechout, of the Imperial French Navy, on duty in Washington, "I have never yet been satisfied with the Pilot Charts. . . . Still seeking to improve them." [107]

The intensity of criticism that Maury faced undoubtedly enlarged the understandable satisfaction and pride he took in his accomplishments. He surely indulged in moments of smugness when he thought how international recognition of his achievements must gall Bache and Henry. His ego swelled a bit with his spreading fame. He was properly modest in public, but in the privacy of his home Maury must have enjoyed it when occasionally his small children demanded that he pin to his jacket the numerous orders and medals he had received. [108] Pride he had —there is no evidence of vanity.

Maury was a person about whom men had no halfway feelings. The people who admired him—and they were more numerous but less articulate than his critics—held views about him diametrically opposed to those proclaimed by his adversaries. In addition to speaking of his religious faith and superior intellectual power, they referred often to his genial nature, patience, enthusiasm, unfailing courtesy, humor, kindness, lack of pretense, and above all, to his driving determination to render service to his fellow man.

But on one point there could be no disagreement between friend or foe—Maury was a man of courage. It had taken the courage of youthful conviction for him to go against his father's will and enter the Navy, to make the journey to Washington virtually without funds. It had required courage and persistence for him to study intently on board ship when fellow midshipmen wanted him to skylark with them, to stay in the Navy when he longed to earn the higher pay of a civilian so that he could marry Ann, to write a scientific book when Navy superiors frowned on science. Throughout his ordeal of suffering that resulted from his stagecoach accident, Maury was a man of courage. While punctilious about obedience to Navy orders and in observance of protocol, he had always had the courage to speak out against wrongdoing in Navy matters. It had taken courage even to begin the monumental labor that led to his *Wind and Current Charts* and *Sailing Directions*. With the arrival of success and the criticism of competitors, Maury's courage had not faltered. He had faced the action of the Navy Retiring Board in 1855 with courage and had fought the issue through to victory.

In 1859 Maury was distressed over the rising tensions between the Northern and Southern sections of the United States. He realized that a maximum of clear thinking and a minimum of emotional acts were vital to re-establish unity between the states of the Union. Little did he realize, however, how the future was going to test his mettle. He would have need of every ounce of his persistence and courage—great courage.

CHAPTER XVIII

Efforts to Save the Union

Ever since he had been nineteen Maury had expended his energies for the United States Navy—he was dedicated heart and soul to the Navy, even though a clique would have had him out. Who had worked longer hours for the Navy? Who had more strenuously fought the encroachments of rival services? Who had struggled harder for education within the Navy, for adequate rank for its officers? The Navy blue uniform and the gold epaulets, which he kept in a tin case on the chest of drawers in his bedroom, were to him more than a symbol of his rank. They stood for the service itself. Maury never let anyone forget or slight the United States Navy.

Towering above all was the Union of the states. Maury held that states not only should but could work together in harmony, no matter how disparate their interests might be. He believed that nations could find agreement; surely states within a nation could achieve as much. There marched with Maury the memory of the Brussels Conference, where ten nations had overcome differences, achieved agreement, and then had gone on to create a worldwide and continuing co-operation in marine meteorology. There was a way, he contended passionately, that the very real differences between the Southern and Northern states could be resolved.[1]

Maury believed in the rights of the states as reserved to them by the Constitution of the United States.[2] He did not like slavery, but he accepted it as deeply rooted in the economic and social system of the South and thought it could not be suddenly ended.[3] He loved Virginia, the place that had welcomed his oppressed forebears long before the Union had been dreamed of, the state that had given him birth.[4] He also had strong emotional ties with Tennessee, where he had spent his youth and whose people had always backed him.[5]

An advocate of free trade and direct taxation, Maury agreed entirely with the Southern position that the protective tariff, which had been made the law of the land by the Northern majority in Congress, worked a hardship on the agrarian South.[6] He considered it an inequity that the protective tariff enriched manufacturers and industrialists of the North some $80,000,000 yearly with none of this going into the Treasury of the United States. The tariff had been a burning issue between North and South for decades.[7] The North, believing that the nation's economic future lay in industrialization rather than agriculture, regarded the tariff as necessary to permit the development of American industry.[8]

On the furiously debated question of rights to the public lands, the territories of the West, Maury also believed that the Federal legislation enacted in the middle and late 1850's denied the people of the South their fair share in these lands. He did not consider that the North had the right to forbid the South to extend its way of life, including slavery, to the commonly owned territories.[9] The North, convinced that slavery was both a great moral and economic wrong, was determined to prevent its extension. No one put this issue more succinctly than Abraham Lincoln, when he declared that the South thought slavery was right and the North thought it was wrong.[10]

Maury, however, was of the opinion that there had been a good deal of hypocrisy in the North concerning slavery; he could not forget that when the institution was abolished in Northern states, many slaves from that section had been sold to men in the South.[11] He considered the institution of slavery a curse and that the ideal was to remove the shackles of bondage, but he did not regard slavery as the ultimate moral sin that it was considered by his first cousins in New York or by some of his Minor cousins who had freed their slaves and repatriated them to Africa.[12] Having always tried to set his moral principles by the Bible, Maury had searched the Scriptures and reported, "The Bible does not condemn slavery and neither shall I." [13]

These major differences, and multitudinous lesser ones, between the people of the North and those of the South demanded settlement, in Maury's opinion, within the Union.[14]

He believed that the greatest single strength of the Union was that it had been formed by sovereign states joining together in a voluntary confederation.[15] This was the view on which he had been reared, was the concept generally held in the Southern states, and one that had been shared by a good many men in the North, especially in the earlier years of the republic.[16] Implicit in this concept was the right of a state to withdraw from the Union. The idea of secession was not wholly Southern—there had been threats of secession in New England during the War of 1812 and later.[17] But the threat of secession had by 1859 become the chief weapon used by the leaders of the cotton states of the deep South. They

349

declared vehemently that if the Southern states could not secure redress of their wrongs within the Union, then they would withdraw and again assume their position as sovereign and independent states.[18]

As the talk of the hell-for-secession cotton planters of the deep South and the thunderings of the abolitionists in the North grew louder in the autumn of 1859, Maury became alarmed that these extremists were creating an atmosphere in which peaceful agreement could not be reached. He grew vastly impatient with the endless talk of the politicians and decided that they were reveling in propounding their views rather than dedicating themselves to finding a workable solution.[19] The John Brown raid fanned emotions to even greater heat.[20] On December 30, 1859, Maury wrote Franklin Minor, "It will never do to suffer this Union to drift into dissolution." [21] On the same day he wrote the Right Reverend James H. Otey an 11-page letter that revealed his agony of spirit about the threat to the Union. Speaking of his native state, Maury declared that Virginia had an obligation to exert herself to preserve the Union, her "most precious legacy." [22]

By mid-March of 1860 Maury was again writing Bishop Otey: "As for the Union . . . the dissolution of it will, I fear, come before you or I would be willing to see it. With statesmanship among our rulers, patriotism among our politicians, and virtue among the people, it need never come." [23]

Having long known that worry achieves nothing,[24] Maury sought to cast it off and proceed with his duties at the Naval Observatory and Hydrographical Office. For him the old Latin proverb *"Laborare est orare"* had proved valid. He still found that to work is to worship, to labor is to pray. The doing of useful work, he believed, gave man a measure of happiness that he could find in no other way.[25] Perhaps this dedicated enthusiasm was what led his British counterpart in marine meteorology, Admiral Robert Fitzroy, to declare that Maury's outstanding trait was "personal disinterestedness." [26]

During the early months of 1860 Maury earnestly sought to arouse interest in an expedition to the antarctic. He reported to the Secretary of the Navy that "Our investigations of the winds at sea . . . show a great diminution of barometric pressure about the South Pole. . . . There is reason to believe that the climate of those unknown regions render them inhabitable. The improved appliances, with the information which present skill and research afford, would seem to promise a degree of success now that was beyond the reach of previous explorations in that quarter." [27] That June Maury mapped a route that an exploring party should follow, starting from Melbourne, Australia, and proceeding through Emerald Isle to a place of rendezvous. From this point, he proposed that "land and boat and ice parties" should fan out to explore the antarctic continent. He marked on this map an unexplored region around the South Pole of "eight million square miles." [28]

In October of 1860, in conjunction with his trip to speak at the laying of the cornerstone of the University of the South at Sewanee, Tennessee, Maury spoke in Nashville on the state of the nation.[29] His address was in marked contrast to that of Robert Lowndes Yancey, who, before the same audience, made an impassioned plea for secession and war.[30] Maury, in his quietly forceful, nonoratorical type of delivery, urged the people to face the issues threatening to divide the country but to try to work out a solution based on moderation.

Late in October Maury sailed from New York for England, where he had been summoned by his English publishers to secure the copyright for a new edition of *The Physical Geography of the Sea and Its Meteorology* [31] and had also been invited to address the Royal Geographical Society. Maury was on the high seas during the time that the momentous question of the American presidential election was decided. As the Atlantic cable was not in operation,[32] he did not learn the results of the election until some days after his arrival in England on November 14, 1860.[33] Almost simultaneously he heard that Abraham Lincoln had been elected on November 6 and that, in the following days, the legislature of South Carolina had set in motion the machinery for a convention to discuss secession from the Union.[34] Maury pondered the implications of these developments. He saw a portent in the fact that only the border states Tennessee, Kentucky, and Virginia had given their electoral votes to presidential candidate John Bell, leader of the conservative element in the South who, though they supported slavery, placed the Union first. Bell, who had been Maury's leading champion in the Senate after the action of the Navy Retiring Board, had not received a majority in any of the cotton states, where the cry for secession was loudest.[35]

Maury made a favorable impression with his speech to the Royal Geographical Society, "On the Physical Geography of the Sea in connection with the Antarctic Region." He also addressed the British Association for the Advancement of Science "On the Climates of the Antarctic Regions as indicated by observations upon the Height of the Barometer and Direction of the Winds at Sea." These had been the major scientific subjects Maury had had under investigation for months.[36] In addition to presenting this scientific information, Maury also made a plea for Great Britain to unite with other leading powers to send an expedition to explore the antarctic and make meteorological and astronomical observations. Lord Ashburton, president of the Royal Geographical Society, was greatly interested in Maury's proposal and Captain John Washington, the chief of England's Hydrographic Office, promised his support.[37]

Maury saw nearly all of his scientific friends in England as well as Marin H. Jansen, of the Royal Dutch Navy, who came across the Channel to join him.[38] An event that gave Maury an evening's distraction from his worry about developments in the United States was a dinner at Lord Ashburton's, where he and Jansen enjoyed the conversation of England's author and critic John Ruskin and historian Thomas Carlyle.[39]

Once on the steamer *New York* bound for home, Maury could devote his full time to considering the fact that the Union was about to suffer dismemberment unless some immediate action could bring a truce between the sections. Congress had proved unable to settle the raging controversy. Maury decided a people-to-people type of mediation might work. He drafted an appeal urging the Governor of New Jersey to have his state appoint commissioners to act as mediators between North and South.[40] At the same time, he wrote his friend, Commodore Robert Field Stockton, who after a colorful Navy career had entered New Jersey politics and served in the U.S. Senate, "urging him to use his influence with his State upon this subject and have himself sent as her commissioner to the Southern States." [41] Maury next busied himself with letters to Southern leaders urging that they co-operate with the plan. The substance of all his urgings was similar to that expressed in a letter Maury wrote a short while later to General William Giles Harding, of "Belle Meade," Nashville, Tennessee.[42]

> The plan of which I speak, and which is on foot, is for New Jersey to undertake the office of mediator between sections—to send her commissioners to the people of Alabama and Mississippi, as assembled with their sovereignties in convention, and there to ask for a statement of the terms and conditions on which they will be content to remain in the Union.
>
> In reply to this request, the Southern people are too generous and have too much self-respect to ask anything of the North which they, in like circumstances, would not be willing to give.
>
> As soon, therefore, as this mediator can get a statement from the aggrieved party as to what would be satisfactory to them, she will lay the ultimatum of the South before the sister states of the North, asking a respectful and attentive consideration of the same and suggesting that those states that are willing to accede to the terms proposed instruct their representatives in Congress to go for such a bill,

incorporating the terms of such ultimatum as amendments to the Constitution to be thence referred back to the States according to its provisions for adoption.

Thus New Jersey will have the honor of soliciting from the people in their sovereign capacity the terms on which a new lease on time is to be acquired for the Union. She will have the honor of presenting to the quiet men of the country, North and South, something tangible for them to go upon—something around which they can rally, and by which the federal machinery may be readjusted and brought again into beautiful working order.

New Jersey is the only one of the old thirteen [states] north of Mason and Dixon's line whose statute book has never been blurred with any act of unfriendly legislation towards the South—and she occupies the proud position of having been always faithful to the constitution, true to herself, and mindful of the rights of her sister states.

P.S.—want to bring force on Governor of New Jersey to act fast as it may be too late for Alabama and Mississippi as it is too late for South Carolina [already seceded]—get up meeting in Nashville to assure New Jersey her commissioners would be received at the South with most friendly consideration and utmost respect—get the papers to take the same ground—things have gone beyond the reach of the politicians [I feel the help of] quiet men like yourself [is] needed [or] the ship is going to continue the drift which for so many years has been constantly and steadily setting it towards the breakers.[43]

As his steamer plowed through the heavy seas of a wintry North Atlantic, Maury's thoughts were filled with foreboding. He had disliked having to be out of the United States at a time of national crisis and was frustrated by his lack of up-to-date information on domestic developments. From the steamer he wrote his friend William Hasbrouck to tell him that he had dedicated a new American edition of *The Physical Geography of the Sea* to him and to ask pitifully, "Do we belong to the same country yet, Hasbrouck?" [44] And well he might ask, for almost as soon as Maury reached the United States, the South Carolina Convention, meeting in Charleston, on December 20, 1860, unanimously repealed that state's 1788 ratification of the U.S. Constitution and adopted an ordinance of secession from the Union.[45] On the day after Christmas Major Robert Anderson, U.S. Army, evacuated the undefendable Fort Moultrie on Sullivan's Island in Charleston harbor and moved his small Federal garrison to the larger Fort Sumter, at the entrance to the harbor. The next day South Carolina troops seized Fort Moultrie, a small fort called Castle Pinckney not far from Charleston's Battery, the United States customhouse and post office.[46] In Washington people debated whether President Buchanan would yield to the demand of the commissioners South Carolina had sent and evacuate the United States troops from Fort Sumter.[47] Maury and every other thinking man in the country watched to see if other Southern states would follow South Carolina out of the Union.

Maury's proposal for mediation had met with some response but early in January, 1861, he was forced to report to Franklin Minor: "The New Jersey plan did not take—has missed fire—I reckon. But because it fails, we should not be disheartened." [48]

In the nation's perilous situation Maury grew desperate over the lack of effort toward conciliation and once more tried to halt onrushing events. On January 3, 1861, Maury wrote Governor William F. Packer of Pennsylvania to plead for the Keystone state to mediate between North and South.[49] He explained that he would not apologize for venturing to write because the alarming crisis of the nation justified the "quiet people" in "stepping a little out of their usual way." Reminding Governor Packer that Virginia had acted as mediator "in the nullification times of South Carolina . . . with happiest results," Maury launched into his proposal:

> We have the people, in no less than seven of those States, assembling, or preparing to assemble, in their sovereign capacity to decide, in the most solemn manner known to them, whether they will remain in the Union or no. The most remarkable feature in the whole case is, it appears to me, this—that here we have a national family of States that have lived together in unity for nearly threescore years and ten, and that a portion of them are preparing to dissolve these family ties and break up the Union, because—because of what, sir? Ask legislators, ask governors, ask whom you will, and there are as many opinions as to the causes of discontent and the measures of redress, as there are leaves in the forest. . . .
>
> We have heard a great deal of this from politicians, partisans and others, but if the people of any one of the Southern States, acting in their sovereign capacity, have ever remonstrated with the people of the Northern States as to the causes of dissatisfaction and complaint, and thus laid the matter formally before you of the North, I cannot call it to mind. Neither has any Northern State so much as inquired of the people of any Southern State, either as to the

cause of their offence, or as to terms and conditions upon which they would be willing to remain in the Union.

It does appear to me that in and out of Congress we are all at sea with the troubles that are upon us; that the people, and the people alone, are capable of extricating us.

You, my dear sir, and your State—not Congress—have it in your power to bring the people into "the fair way" of doing this. This brings me to the point of my letter—then why will not the great State of Pennsylvania step forth as mediator between the sections? Authorize your commissioner to pledge the faith of the keystone State, assembled likewise in their sovereign capacity, but that she will recommend it to her sister States of the North, for like action on their part, and so let the people, and not the politicians, decide whether this Union is to be broken up.

I am sanguine enough to believe that the great body of the Southern people entertain opinions, sentiments and feelings in conformity with my own in this matter.[50]

At the same time Maury wrote Judge J. S. Black of Pennsylvania, urging him to work with Governor Packer and bestir their state to offer her good services and mediate the differences.

Maury was hopeful that such a move might still prove effective. He wrote Lord Wrottesley, whom he had recently seen in England: "We are in the process of national disintegration. There is a substratum of good hard sense in the country which would yet bring all right if we could get at it." [51]

But time was running out. On January 9, 1861, South Carolinians fired on the steamer *Star of the West* as she sought to enter the harbor at Charleston to bring troop reinforcements to Fort Sumter. Mississippi seceded that day, Florida the next day, and Alabama on the 11th. As the report of each secession reached Washington, the pall of gloom deepened.[52]

Maury was profoundly shaken when, on January 12, a special session of Virginia's General Assembly voted that delegates should be elected to a convention to decide on secession. If Virginia seceded, hope of reunification was over.[53] However, Maury felt more hopeful a week later when the Virginia legislature issued a call for all the states to send delegates to a peace conference to convene a fortnight later in Washington.[54] He was also heartened by the efforts of Governor John Letcher to keep Virginia to her Union "moorings." [55]

When news reached Washington of Georgia's secession from the Union on January 19, the tension in the capital grew almost unbearable.[56] For

355

days rumors had swept Washington that the senators from the seceded states of the deep South were about to make their announcement of withdrawal from their seats in the United States Senate. A private agreement had been reached among those senators that Monday, January 21, was to be the day of their public declaration, and the word spread through the city in time for crowds to gather outside the Capitol and within the building. The wife of the senator from Alabama, Mrs. Clement C. Clay, described her impressions on that morning of what she declared "all knew would be a day of dreadful import." [57]

> I accompanied my husband to the Senate, and everywhere the greeting or gaze of absorbed, unrecognizing men and women was full of trouble. The galleries of the Senate, which hold, it is estimated, one thousand people, were packed densely, principally with women, who trembling with excitement, awaited the denouement of the day. As, one by one, Senators David Yulee, Stephen R. Mallory, Clement C. Clay, Benjamin Fitzpatrick, and Jefferson Davis rose, the emotion of their brother Senators and of us in the galleries increased. . . .

> As each Senator, speaking for his State, concluded his solemn renunciation of allegiance to the United States, women grew hysterical and waved their handkerchiefs, encouraging them with cries of sympathy and admiration. Men wept and embraced each other mournfully. At times the murmurs among the onlookers grew so deep that the Sergeant-at-Arms was ordered to clear the galleries; and, as each speaker took up his portfolio and gravely left the Senate Chamber, sympathetic shouts rang from the assemblage above. Scarcely a member of that Senatorial body but was pale with the terrible significance of the hour. There was everywhere a feeling of suspense, as if, visibly, the pillars of the temple were being withdrawn and the great Government structure was tottering; nor was there a patriot on either side who did not deplore and whiten before the evil that brooded so low over the nation.[58]

So wrote the wife of Senator Clay of Alabama.

To many in Washington the nation seemed doomed. Maury refused to yield to this gloomy view and that same day wrote to some of his powerful friends in Tennessee, the state in which he had spent most of his youth, offering to serve her as a delegate to the Peace Conference soon to begin sessions at Willard's Hotel.[59]

Maury knew, however, that the stampede to secession would continue unless some drastic concession was made to the South. He decided to test out such an idea on his pro-Lincoln, pro-Union, antislavery first

356

cousin in New York, Rutson Maury, with whom he argued such matters by mail. In late January he wrote Rutson that "a proposition from the *people* of the South" must be laid "before the *people* of the North. . . . The sine qua non with it should be, in my judgment, the right of veto over any unfriendly legislation in Congress that the North may hereafter attempt. . . .

"I have been trying to move Virginia to call for a truce and, in concert with other Southern States, to propose to the people of the North the ultimatum of the people of the South, insisting upon this . . . veto." He declared: "The South is blocked to expansion and that in itself is death. . . . The disease—the root of the thing is not in cotton or slavery, nor in the election of Lincoln. But it is deep in the human heart. The real question is a question of Empire." [60]

Rutson replied that "an ultimatum from the border states would never do and should never be submitted to by the free states." He said the veto power was impracticable because "South Carolina wants everything their way. I wish that the South had more men of the *self-made* class, like yourself." [61]

An astute import-export merchant, Rutson Maury kept in daily touch with Northern sentiment by personal contact in Wall Street and through wide reading of newspapers. He knew that the North would never grant any such veto, because of the issue of extension of slavery to the Western territories. Rutson's reply failed to convince Maury, who, whether knowingly or unknowingly, was being guided more by wishful thinking than by the carefully reasoned thought he exhibited in scientific matters.

Disregarding Rutson's condemnation of his plan for a veto in the Senate to give the South a balance of power with the North's greater voting strength, Maury wrote out his proposal for former President John Tyler and then called on the elderly statesman. His visit produced no definite result, Maury reporting to Franklin Minor that "I had a long talk with Mr. Tyler—found him full of Virginia abstractions. I think I satisfied him that no parchment provision would stand." [62] Maury was afraid that the Peace Conference would only draw up statements of position rather than press for specific action.

Haunted by this fear, Maury at this point wrote Lord Wrottesley, pleading for England to use her good offices to ward off catastrophe in America. Plaintively he asked, "Now, why can't you help us to settle this difficulty? Get Parliament to offer resolutions that would lead to a solution." [63]

On February 4, 1861, the Peace Conference convened with 131 delegates from twenty-one states—none from the seceded states and none from Michigan, Wisconsin, Minnesota, Oregon, or California. The sessions were held in secrecy, and the press was excluded.[64] Maury, who had earlier hoped that something might be worked out by this body, soon was convinced it would achieve nothing.[65]

He turned his eyes longingly toward the Virginia Convention, assembled in Richmond. On February 7 Maury wrote this body:

> There is no hope for Virginia getting the seceded states back into the Union right now, they will be missing for awhile, but they have not gone out, they have been shut off from the "Blue of the Union" to twinkle, let us hope, only for awhile in another constellation. Therefore, let Virginia stay in and see that their places are kept vacant for them. Let her renew her vow to cease not until she sees them back there each one in its own place, shining as brightly and as beautifully as ever.[66]

But Maury was fully aware that the hotheads in the seceded states might precipitate military action. On February 11 he wrote Jabez Lamar Curry, who had left his seat in Congress to return to the republic of Alabama, "I hope you will not commence war—wait." [67]

Having despised the defeatist attitude all his life, Maury despised it in this time of travail for the nation. He refused to stop trying to ameliorate the situation, which had worsened with Louisiana's secession on January 26 and that of Texas on February 1. One week later the congress of delegates from the seceded states, meeting in Montgomery, Alabama, adopted a provisional constitution of the Confederate States of America and on February 9, 1861, elected Jefferson Davis provisional President and Alexander H. Stephens provisional Vice-President. On the 18th Davis was inducted into office at Montgomery.[68]

Saddened by the fact that "seven states have left the Union, seven remain highly inflamed," Maury "talked" the whole situation over in one of his long letters to Bishop Otey. Knowing Otey's strong convictions about the preservation of the Union, Maury ended with the one positive proposal that he felt could still be made:

> The four barrier states should remain in the Union the better to mediate between the two Confederacies [like many Virginians, Maury often used that term for the Union] . . . to get such new guards as the seceded states may with honor accept and with safety return to us . . . for the purpose of so shaping events, the arranging of political parties, as to insure at the next presidential election, if not before, the success of the re-annexation party, for, that such a party, in case there be no civil war, will and ought to be formed with the help of these barrier States in the Union, there can be no probable room for doubt.[69]

Maury was relieved that the Confederate Congress, in session at Montgomery, Alabama, pledged the free navigation of the Mississippi River, that business was still being transacted between North and South and that the mails were moving freely.[70] The extremists pressing for war were being held in check, and in the first days of March Maury hoped desperately that the situation could yet be redeemed. He was disgusted at the suspicions, rumors, and fears that were going the rounds in Washington and took it as a matter of course that President-elect Lincoln was not molested on his way from his home in Illinois to Washington.[71]

On March 4, 1861, Abraham Lincoln was inaugurated President of the United States. Maury's feelings were very mixed as, four days later, he donned full-dress uniform to go to a presidential reception for officers of the armed services. He buckled on his handsome sword, which was decorated with a sea serpent and a spread eagle surrounded by an oval of thirteen stars, and proceeded to the White House.[72] He was anxious to see President Lincoln face to face and to hear any remarks that the new Commander in Chief might address to his guests.[73] However, Maury's opportunity was apparently too limited for him to form any personal opinion of Lincoln sufficiently definite to record.

Maury very naturally had more opportunity for conversation with Secretary of the Navy Gideon Welles, and a few days after this reception he said to a friend, "The new Secretary promises finely as compared to Toucey, the most corrupt and mean official I have ever known." [74]

Throughout these difficult weeks Maury endeavored to keep the routine work of the Observatory moving and to complete the scientific papers he had on his desk. Earlier his spirits had flagged to such a low level that he had exclaimed to a relative, "I cannot work. Am I not making myself miserable . . . ?" [75] He had managed to rally his spirits, however, and in mid-February had completed and sent to the printer his second nautical monograph, *The Barometer at Sea,* to follow his first in the series, *The Winds at Sea.* He had then doggedly set to work to write a third monograph, *The Southeast Trade Winds of the Atlantic.*[76]

However, Maury interrupted his writing in early March long enough to study the ship's journals a captain had kept in Far Eastern waters over a five-year period. Maury thanked the man in Swatow, China, not only for the journals he had sent but for "the promise of logs from Siamese ships." [77]

On April 1 Maury received at the Observatory the Belgian minister to the United States, E. Blondeel van Cuelebrouk. The envoy delivered to Maury a tribute from the King of the Belgians and the Belgian government for his "invaluable services" dating back to the Brussels Conference, stressing that his government would have made a more tangible

359

award "but for the laws of the United States." [78] The honor, coming at that time, must have seemed to Maury like something from another life.

To rest his mind, Maury alternated work on his study of the antarctic and writing he was doing on that subject, with his efforts on the third nautical monograph. He sought to enlist Russian interest in his proposal for an international exploration expedition to Antarctica. Replying to a letter from Russia's delegate to the Brussels Conference in 1853, Captain A. Gorkovenko, Russian Imperial Navy, Maury wrote: "Russian navigators, as I have before had occasion to remark, have added renown to their flag and always acquitted themselves with honor. I am glad to know that you are about to take up your unpublished explorations in the Arctic regions. Of course it will give me pleasure to do all that I can in helping you to give them circulation." [79]

Then Maury launched into what was on his heart:

> I wish you would turn your attention to the Antarctic regions and help me plead the cause of exploration there. I am sure the Antarctic winter, for reasons fully stated in the last London edition of *The Physical Geography of the Sea,* is very much less severe than the Arctic and that with steam, the improvements and the experience of the last twenty years in polar explorations, it would be easy to lay open that unknown part of the world.
>
> I did myself the honor last year to address your go-ahead Grand Duke [Constantine] upon this subject. . . . I should very much like to see a joint expedition sent there . . . and an Expedition, properly equipped and sent there, will do the world a service. [80]

After sending that letter, Maury finished a formal 44-page proposal for an international expedition to Antarctica. In it he advanced his deductions about the climate in the area of the South Pole and stated the scientific objectives that should be the aim of the expedition. He also prepared a brief history of previous antarctic explorations. On April 10, 1861, Maury sent his completed antarctic dossier with a copy of his recently published monograph *The Barometer at Sea* to each major diplomatic representative in Washington. [81]

The new French minister to the United States, Henri Mercier, was enthusiastic about Maury's scientific ideas and sent the material on to France for publication. [82] Lord Lyons, the British minister, sent his copy to London but attached a note advising the Foreign Office not to thank Maury for the copy of his monograph in view of the tense political situation in the United States. [83]

During the first few days of April, 1861, many people in both North and South had continued to believe that the Federal troops would be evacuated from Fort Sumter, in the harbor of Charleston, and armed conflict with the South Carolinians thus be avoided.[84] Maury had clung to that hope. His longing for Virginia to remain in the Union had received encouragement when the Virginia Convention, meeting as a committee of the whole, had taken a test vote on April 4 and the delegates had voted 2 to 1 against secession. However, the Virginia Convention had continued its sessions in secret thereafter, and no one knew what might ultimately be decided.[85] Ringing in Maury's ears since March 26 had been ominous words that he had reported that day to a fellow Virginian, "I had a few minutes' conversation with [General William T.] Sherman. He says if Virginia secedes, there will be war." [86] War—that hideous final resort—Maury dreaded it for his country, for his family, for himself.

By April 10 a clash of arms at Fort Sumter seemed almost inevitable. Washington had closely watched to see if any significant results would come from the efforts of peace commissioners sent by Jefferson Davis, President of the Confederate States of America. Their aim had been to persuade the Federal government to accept on an amicable basis the separation that had occurred, to cede Federal forts to the Confederate government and grant recognition to the fledgling nation.[87] President Lincoln's Secretary of State, William Henry Seward, who had announced that "there is a higher law than the Constitution" and had regarded the differences between the sections as an "irrepressible conflict," had refused to receive the Confederate commissioners.[88] He had considered such an act on his part might be construed as recognition of the Confederate States. Justice John A. Campbell and Justice Samuel Nelson of the Supreme Court had subsequently acted as intermediaries between the commissioners and Seward in the hope of an eleventh-hour compromise. Campbell had received assurance from Seward that Fort Sumter, in the harbor of Charleston, South Carolina, would be evacuated by Federal troops. The justice had reported this to the Confederate commissioners, who officially sent this assurance by mail to President Davis.[89] Much later it was said that Secretary of State Seward's promises were unauthorized, that he had acted without the President's approval, but when the United States authorities attempted to provision Fort Sumter, the South regarded the act as a breach of faith on the part of Lincoln's government.[90]

On April 12, when it was known that Fort Sumter was to receive large stores of provisions and was not going to be evacuated, the South Carolina forces began the bombardment of the fort to prevent revictualing of the troops stationed there. Sumter surrendered on April 13, 1861. In the exchange of cannonading, no lives had been lost, but the die was now cast.[91] The Federal troops evacuated Fort Sumter on the 14th. The next day President Lincoln called on state governors to raise 75,000 soldiers to bring back into the Union those states that had seceded.[92]

Washington was a national capital preparing for war. Maury was nearly at the end of the hopes by which he had sustained himself and declared, "Civil war is like a conflagration! There is no telling when or where it will stop, as long as there is fuel to feed it." [93] He was understandably relieved that his wife and the younger children were in Fredericksburg on one of their frequent visits to relatives. Dick and Davy (John Herndon) were at the University of Virginia, Diana and her husband at Farley Vale plantation not far from Fredericksburg, and his oldest daughter, Betty, was the only one left in Washington.[94] Maury was without family at the Observatory, as Betty and her husband lived on the other side of the city.

Alone and heavy of heart, Maury knew that at any hour the long-dreaded choice of allegiance might have to be made. So far he had followed the only course that had seemed honorable to him. He had continued to serve the United States, he had worked to preserve the Union, he had urged his native state, Virginia, to stay in the Union and strive to bring the seceded states back. He hoped Virginia still might follow that course, but the action at Fort Sumter and President Lincoln's call for troops made this far from likely. Through his mind surely passed in review his years of service to the Stars and Stripes as well as personal arguments for his staying with the United States Navy. The promotion to captain that had so long evaded him would almost inevitably come in time. He would be given the full staff to do the scientific work that an enlarged Federal Navy would need. Money would be appropriated for practical research. But the picture did not tempt him. Too long had he believed that if Virginia, the state that had given him to the Union, left the Union, she had the absolute right to his services.[95] He had never hidden that conviction—many people knew that he held this belief.[96] Re-examining it, Maury was once more convinced that this was the only choice he could make. He had heard that some officers planned to remain with the United States but to ask for posts where they would not have to wage actual war against the South, but to him that was a subterfuge.[97] He held that no man could serve in uniform with mental reservations.[98]

The next day all kinds of rumors circulated through Washington, but on April 17 there was still no definite word whether the Virginia Convention had voted on the secession issue.[99] Maury was both relieved and touched that day to receive a letter from his kinswoman Mrs. Franklin Minor of Ridgeway offering refuge to Maury's family if Virginia seceded and they had to leave Washington. Maury had hoped against hope; now

he had to bow to stern reality. He replied, "Things are rapidly developing and we may soon be seeking shelter indeed . . . for as soon as Virginia declares she's out, I'll follow." [100]

Maury set himself the task of finishing his last nautical monograph
for the U.S. government. On April 18 the Washington *Star* reported that
there was an unverified report that the Virginia Convention had passed
an ordinance of secession. But there was no definite word until the next
day, when the same Washington paper assured its readers that Virginia
was out of the Union. By the afternoon of April 19 Maury and everyone else in Washington knew positively that Virginia had taken the de-
finitive step. Actually, the secession ordinance had been voted by the Virginia Convention in secret session on the afternoon of April 17, but it
was not announced until nearly noon on the 18th to give Virginia troops
time to seize the arsenal at Harpers Ferry and the Federal Navy Yard
at (Gosport) Norfolk. It then took another day for the report to reach
Washington and be published. [101]

The night of April 19, 1861, was a black one for Maury. He would
resign on the morrow, and this would be his last night in the beloved
Observatory, which he had supervised since it was turned over to him
an empty shell of a building. This scientific institution was his creation.
Here he had labored and uncovered great truths. Here he had received
the plaudits of many, the condemnation of others. Here he had poured
his enthusiasm into young officers until they, too, had caught fire and
made significant contributions. He thought especially of Lewis Herndon,
who had gone down with his ship, of John Mercer Brooke and George
Minor, who now had the same choice to make as he. He knew that the
breaking of the old loyalty was agony to them as well as to himself, to
his friend William Francis Lynch, [102] and to all Southerners who had
served so faithfully under the flag of the United States. But neither
thought nor grief could change the situation. He had not wanted this
break to come, but it had, and he now would go with his state. He could
not fight his own.

He must pack a few personal belongings and get ready for the morrow. He hung up his uniform, remembering that he had worn the Navy
blue for thirty-six of his fifty-five years.

On April 20, 1861, Matthew Fontaine Maury put in his last day as
an officer in the United States Navy. Some navigational instruments had
to be dispatched to the New York Navy Yard, letters dictated, his records brought up to date, and his desk cleared. [103] Two days earlier he had
sent to press the monograph *The Southeast Trade Winds of the Atlantic,* described by him as "one of the most valuable contributions that I

have ever made to navigation"—his farewell to the Navy he had served with the full intensity of his nature.[104]

At three o'clock on that Saturday afternoon Maury concluded his work, transferred all the public property in his care to Lieutenant William Whiting, "the proper officer in charge," [105] and turned over his sword as an officer of the United States Navy.[106] He instructed his secretary, Thomas Harrison, who had worked with him for nearly twenty years, to write his resignation from the Navy that he might sign it. Harrison tried to fulfill the order but could not. Diana Maury Corbin tells us: "[The secretary] presenting the unfinished paper with one hand . . . covered his eyes with the other and exclaimed, with a choking voice and gathering tears, 'I cannot write it, sir!' He knew it was the death warrant to his [Maury's] scientific life—the cup of hemlock that would paralyze and kill him in his pursuit after the knowledge of nature and nature's laws." [107]

And so Maury wrote his own resignation and dispatched it to President Lincoln.[108] He had no illusions of going on to a more glorious career. He would answer the call that Virginia had made for her sons to return and enter her service.

Maury was aware that the Old Dominion could not long stand alone. She would almost surely join the Confederacy. But for Maury nothing was sure except the agonizing step he was taking at that moment. From the Observatory he gazed somberly across the Potomac River to the soil of the state that had given him birth and to which he would now go.

Dressed in a black broadcloth civilian suit,[109] Maury walked out of the United States Naval Observatory and Hydrographical Office. His heart was bursting with emotion, and he made no effort to hide the tears that flowed down his cheeks.[110] A hack carried him that afternoon of April 20, 1861, for the last time down the hill on which the Observatory was situated, and along the route he had so often taken to downtown Washington. On the banks of the Potomac, not far from where he had gone on board the *Brandywine* in 1825, Maury turned for one long last look at Washington. It had been for him more than a city, it had been the capital, the mind and heart of the nation he had loved and served to his fullest capacity. What was past was no prologue for him—it had been life itself—work attempted, work achieved—the power and the glory—the hate and the spleen—hurt and disappointments—but always the opportunity to press on to further knowledge. Now there was only duty, the duty he saw for himself. Maury went to purchase a ticket and begin his journey to Richmond [111] and whatever the future might require of him.

CHAPTER XIX

War Comes to Virginia

Couriers came and went from the Governor's office. Men of military bearing and others with the manner of the politician about them moved in an almost steady stream through Virginia's Capitol Square on Sunday morning, April 21, 1861. A burning look of exaltation was in the eyes of some, but for the most part the faces of these men bore an expression of grave determination. They came by hack, by horse, and by foot as they converged on the office of John Letcher, Governor of Virginia. Among them was a rather short man, in his middle fifties, who walked with a perceptible limp. There were few who did not recognize Matthew Fontaine Maury, for they had either heard him speak or seen his picture repeatedly in newspapers or magazines. The domelike head, the eyes that alternately revealed the brooding look of the thinker and the direct gaze of the man of action, the firm, strongly masculine mouth, were unmistakably the features of Virginia's only officer-son whose name was then known throughout America and across the civilized world.[1]

In his quiet, easy voice Maury presented himself to the Governor's secretary and was quickly received by Letcher himself. There was no time to waste, and Maury immediately liked the Governor for indulging in no formalities other than a cordial greeting and then going straight to the fact that the Virginia Convention had on the preceding day authorized an Advisory Council of Three to assist him in mobilizing the state for the invasion that was almost certain to come. Letcher added that he had appointed Judge John L. Allen, president of the Virginia Court of Appeals, and Colonel Francis H. Smith, superintendent of the Virginia Military Institute, to the council and wished Maury to serve as its third member.[2] The post was immediately accepted, subject to confirmation, and Maury asked for some preliminary facts on the conditions of Virginia's defenses. He was relieved to find that Letcher was a realist and was aware of the invitation to invasion that the long tidal rivers of Virginia presented to the Federal Navy.[3]

As if in verification of this danger, the tocsin that very morning sounded in the guardhouse in Capitol Square to warn that the U.S.S. *Pawnee* was reported steaming up the James to shell Richmond. Across 9th Street, in St. Paul's Church, the din of the great bell fell on the ears of the worshipers just as the rector was preparing to dismiss them. There was none of the usual pleasant peacetime gossip after that service either at St. Paul's or in the many other churches throughout the city of 37,000 inhabitants. Men seized whatever arms they possessed and rushed to the banks of the James River, as did the volunteer companies and the Governor. The *Pawnee* failed to appear. It had been a false alarm, but it reminded Virginians that they had chosen the way of danger and that their position could scarcely be more vulnerable.[4]

Meanwhile that morning Maury's appointment was unanimously confirmed by the Virginia Convention,[5] and the Governor's Advisory Council met, elected Judge Allen president, and secured a secretary. The first official act of the council was to send a unanimous recommendation to Letcher that Colonel Robert Edward Lee be appointed "Commander of the Military and Naval Forces of Virginia," a post which the Virginia Convention had authorized on April 19.[6] Maury and his two colleagues respectfully urged the Governor "that a special messenger be commissioned to communicate with Colonel Lee in the event of his appointment." [7] Although preoccupied with that Sunday's alarm about the *Pawnee,* the Governor immediately dispatched a courier to Lee at his home, "Arlington," on the Virginia side of the Potomac just across from Washington, to tender the high command to Lee and to inform him that his rank would be that of major general.[8]

In the council Maury's capacity for quick and almost total assimilation of facts and figures soon gave him the picture of Virginia's dire lack of defense equipment. Of the 60,000 small arms, which the state had in storage in Richmond and Lexington, only 6,000 were percussion muskets. The rest were flintlocks that would have pleased Daniel Boone but were not what infantry needed for rapid fire. There were, Maury discovered, 3,200 barrels of powder on hand,[9] but about the general situation he was to moan to a close relative, "Not percussion caps enough for a half dozen rounds and no munitions to work with. No tents. No camp equipment. It was impossible for our forces to take the field—no commissariat—'no nothing.' " [10]

However, from Norfolk on April 22 came news that the Virginia flag now flew over the Norfolk Navy Yard, the only first-class yard the United States government had established in the South, the yard in Pensacola possessing only secondary equipment. The Governor and his Advisory Council learned that the Federal officer in charge of the Norfolk Navy

Yard had the night of April 19 given orders to his 800 officers and men
to burn all ships at the docks and in the shiphouses; to spike guns in
the parks; break up machinery, destroy everything; and evacuate the
yard. Commodore Hiram Paulding, sent from Washington in the U.S.S.
Pawnee to bring off the vessels at the yard, had been two hours too late
in arriving to stop the destruction. Paulding and his fellow officers of
the relief expedition agreed that the work of destroying the yard should
be completed the night of April 20 and the troops then evacuated.
When all Federals had evacuated the yard and boarded the relief ships,
the *Pawnee* and the sloop-of-war *Cumberland* crossed Hampton Roads
and anchored under the protection of the guns of Fortress Monroe.[11]
Powder was still exploding and firebrands flying through the air when
the citizens of Norfolk and the two local military companies had broken
into the yard and had started salvaging what they could from the holo-
caust. They had saved the granite dry dock—though this was mined and
about to go up—and 1,198 practically undamaged guns, including many
new Dahlgrens. Small arms, ordnance, and all types of equipment had
been hauled out of the burning yard, and the Virginians finally had
managed to put out the fire on the 44-gun frigate *Merrimac*, but not
until she had burned to the waterline. The *Merrimac*'s water-soaked
hull soon sank to the bottom in the shallow water where she had been
berthed.[12]

Virginia now had a Navy Yard, but nearly $10,000,000 worth of dam-
age had been done to the equipment and the ships awaiting repairs.
Moreover, the yard was almost directly across Hampton Roads from
Fortress Monroe,[13] which the Federals still held and which was considered by many an impregnable military bastion. Major effort would have
to be expended to defend Norfolk.

Maury had spent the past thirty-six years of his life learning about
the United States Navy, and possibly no man had a better over-all concept of the resources at the command of that service. He was completely
informed on the achievements in ordnance of his friend John A. Dahlgren, knew the guns and stores available at the Washington Navy Yard
and at other yards, knew the ships, equipment, and navigational instruments. In addition, he was personally acquainted with most of the exceedingly able men who would command those ships. Maury was able
to go down the *Navy Register* of the United States and tick off the capaci-
ties of his former fellow officers who hailed from the North or West and
had stayed with the Union. He added up the assets of the North and
came to the conclusion that the South would have to use desperate
remedies to meet such overwhelming odds.

At once his mind turned to the possibility of using torpedoes, the term then employed for fixed mines that were detonated either mechanically or electrically. Experiments had been made on torpedoes for decades, but in 1861 their effectiveness had not been actually proved in warfare.[14] Maury, however, believed that electrically detonated torpedoes could be effectively used in bays, harbors, and rivers and secured permission to send an agent north to obtain insulated wire, of which none was to be had in the South, nor even any factories that could make it. On April 22 he dispatched a Richmond merchant to New York to purchase this wire, which was essential to his scheme.[15]

That afternoon Robert E. Lee, who had missed the Governor's courier, arrived in Richmond and was tendered the command of Virginia's military and naval forces. He accepted the responsibility at once.[16] The next day, April 23, Lee was escorted before the Virginia Convention by a delegation of four of its members. In the crowded hall normally used by the Virginia House of Delegates every man rose as Lee entered. On the speaker's platform sat Maury with the two other members of the Governor's Advisory Council, Judge Allen and Colonel Smith, all three having earlier been officially introduced to the assemblage. They were on the left of the president of the Convention, John Janney, while to the presiding officer's right sat Alexander H. Stephens, Vice-President of the Confederate States, who had just arrived as an emissary from his government to that of Virginia. Stephens was flanked by Governor Letcher.[17]

It was a moving sight as Lee became a major general of Virginia and received the over-all command of her forces. The strikingly handsome man replied with fine simplicity to the praise heaped on him in the speech by President Janney. Maury, like everyone who knew Lee, felt a new surge of hope. In view of the chaotic state of military affairs when Lee took command, probably no higher praise could have been given him at the time than Maury's terse statement to a friend, "General Lee is clearheaded and cool." [18]

The granting of the command to Lee and his acceptance of it were joyfully hailed by the press of the state. The Lynchburg *Virginian* editorialized: "We rejoice that this distinguished officer and worthy son of Virginia has withdrawn from Lincoln's army and thrown himself upon the bosom of his native State. It was what we expected of the man. Captain Maury has done likewise; and thus, these two noble men, the very flower of the Army and Navy of the late United States, respond to the call of their glorious old Mother." [19]

Maury was thus often called *captain* because that title was the customary courtesy address to commanders in the Navy of the period [20] and because he had so long held a major command as superintendent of the

Naval Observatory, a position that many people felt should have automatically carried the rank of captain. However, Maury's fixed rank in the Navy of the United States at the time of his resignation was commander; and, in accordance with a provision established by the Virginia Convention for all officers who left the Federal services,[21] this was the rank in the Virginia Navy tendered him on April 23, 1861. After four more days of legislation, the Convention passed an ordinance creating the Navy of Virginia, and Maury shortly thereafter received his engraved commission as a commander in that service of 2,000 men.[22]

Maury had been astonished to receive a communication from U.S. Secretary of the Navy Gideon Welles, requesting to know the reasons for his resignation from Federal service. On April 26 Maury replied:

> I am not aware of any law or rule that requires an officer tendering resignation to give reasons therefor. In this case, however, I have no objections to state them. They are these: our once glorious Union is gone; the state through which and for which I confessed allegiance to the Federal government has no longer any lot or part in it. Neither have I. I desire to go with my own people and with them to share the fortunes of our own state together. Such are the reasons for tendering my resignation, and I hope the President will consider them satisfactory.[23]

Maury's hope was certainly wishful thinking, for the preceding day, April 25, the Virginia Convention had ratified an agreement of temporary union with the provisional government of the Confederate States, subject to the ordinance of secession being approved by the state's voters on May 23.[24] In addition, the Confederate Congress soon voted to move the capital from Montgomery to Richmond. These developments could only mean that the Federal government would regard Virginia as a military combatant and prepare to invade her territory as soon as preparation and strategy dictated.

A Virginia Navy had been voted into being, but the state possessed not a single ship of war, and there were only two merchantmen considered suitable to be converted for naval use.[25] In view of this lack of ships, the decision was made that the experienced naval officers who had left Federal service could best be used to command the batteries that were being constructed at strategic points on Virginia's bays and tidal waters.[26]

The battery designed to protect the terminus of the Richmond, Fredericksburg and Potomac Railway at the point where Aquia Creek entered the Potomac was commanded by Maury's friend Captain William Francis Lynch; [27] and, a little later, Maury's friend Commander William Leigh was assigned to defend West Point (Virginia) and Commander

T. J. Page to defend Gloucester Point.[28] The protection of vital Sewell's Point near Norfolk was entrusted to Lieutenant William Lewis Maury,[29] Maury's cousin who had served on the Navy Retiring Board.

However, on May 1 Commodore G. J. Pendergrast, commanding the U.S.N. Home Squadron, had reported to Washington that he now had sufficient naval force off Fortress Monroe to blockade Virginia ports.[29] This blockade by the Federal Navy marked the end of coastal steamer or sailing vessel transportation between Virginia and the Northern states. Train travel to the North already having ceased, Maury could not send another agent north for insulated wire as he had hoped to do ever since the first man had failed in his mission.[30] Adjusting quickly to the fact that his plan for electric torpedoes would have to wait for the needed wire, Maury set himself to perfecting mechanical torpedoes.

Meanwhile, the Advisory Council had recommended that its membership be increased to five; and on April 30 General Thomas S. Haymond and Robert L. Montague, Lieutenant Governor of Virginia, were appointed to the council.[31] On May 11 the council of five men unanimously advised Letcher to proceed with a proposal to raise the hull of the much-damaged *Merrimac*. They recommended acceptance of the bid of B. and I. Baker of Norfolk to deliver her in the dry dock at (Gosport) Norfolk Navy Yard for $5,000.[32] As a result, Maury later stated, "Quick to perceive and prompt to act, as in the emergencies of the war he ever was, his Excellency caused it to be done." [33]

On returning to his room that night Maury saw, for the first time, a copy of the Boston *Evening Traveller* in which he was accused of a wide range of treacheries. It was a shock to read this notice in the May 4 issue of the Boston paper:

> $5,000 reward for the Head of Jeff Davis
> $3,000 for the Head of Gen. Beauregard
> $3,000 for the Head of the Traitor, Lieut. Maury [34]

It was no easier for Maury to accept being called traitor than it would be for any other decent man. It took a considerable period of time before he could philosophize that his ancestors had been called that by the British when they had fought for America's independence. He felt he was in a similar position, fighting for Southern independence from a no longer acceptable government.[35]

The Boston newspaper blamed Maury for the removal of the lights from the lighthouses of Cape Henry and Cape Charles and the major points on the Virginia rivers. The accusation was not precise, but the implication was that Maury had arranged for these acts before leaving the U.S. Naval Observatory. The paper further declared that "The meanest of the yet discovered [evidences of treachery] is that he removed buoys from Kettle Bottom Shoals leaving the administration to find it out as best they could." [36] Maury was also accused of having taken maps of three Southern states from the Observatory when he left his former post. He categorically denied all the charges,[37] but in the heat of war his denial was not published nor would it have been believed in the North. These accusations were widely circulated and, throughout the war, Northern newspapers singled Maury out for venomous attacks. It was perhaps inevitable that he should be so condemned, since he had previously been so lavishly praised by the press of the great cities of the coast and lakes whose commerce his work had aided.

The immediate result of the various accusations against Maury was, as he wrote William C. Hasbrouck: "The President refuses to accept my resignation. The object of this will be to you plain enough. But in such a case the halter has no more terror than the musket. Death is death—our cause is just and we enter the contest in bright armor." [38]

On May 23, 1861, Virginians flocked to the polls to ratify Virginia's secession ordinance, and this vote gave the approval necessary for the Confederate capital to be moved to Richmond. Little time was wasted. President Jefferson Davis reached Richmond on May 29, and the members of his Cabinet arrived by June 2. Among these was the former United States senator from Florida, Stephen R. Mallory, now Confederate Secretary of the Navy.[39]

The next afternoon Maury, with Judge Allen and Colonel Smith, had an important conference with President Davis. The mission of the committee was to discover the terms on which the President would accept the Virginia officers into the Army and Navy of the Confederacy. The committee was not pleased when Davis stated that he would not follow the Virginia Convention's ordinance prescribing rank but might reverse the grade of some officers "by appointing an officer now of inferior rank to a higher grade than another who may have ranked him in the United States service." [40] However, after three days of discussion, the Advisory Council recommended that Governor Letcher issue a proclamation transferring the Virginia forces to the Confederate government.[41] All officers of the Virginia Navy were thus transferred to the Confederate Navy by June 10, with no individual action being necessary on the part of the men involved.[42] The Governor and his Advisory Council had made the arrangement but, within a period of four days, the council was unanimously advising the Governor "to protest to President Davis his plan to appoint Virginia Navy officers to lower grades in the Confederate service and to ignore certain Virginia Navy Commissions." [43]

Maury was, on June 11, 1861, appointed a commander in the Confederates States Navy, the rank he had held in the short-lived Virginia Navy.[44] On the same day he unburdened himself to Franklin Minor:

> I begin to feel very useless. I am afraid that there is too much "red tape" yet left in this world. I hope it may not tie us down.
>
> I am afraid the President is not surrounded by men for the times, things do not go on as well as I think they might but perhaps my notions are overwrought . . . we have some small men and little sets in our Confederate States government.
>
> Davis, it appears to me, is grasping after patronage. Don't think he likes Lee. Lee told me yesterday he did not know where he was —nor do I. I can see, though, how that [transfer from Virginia to Confederate authority] may have provided ground for an honest misunderstanding. But it's bad in times like this so to jar your general that he does not know whether he is in or out of power.
>
> As I say, things do not look right to me. Where the wrong is, I am not so clear, but, the biggest promotion seems to be on the other side. You may rely upon it, the Confederate States Government has come here feeling that there is between it and us something of antagonism.[45]

This friction between the kings of cotton from the deep South and the men of Virginia was a very real problem in that early summer of 1861 and was never entirely resolved.

In addition to concern over whether cotton was a weapon that would bring England and France in on the side of the Confederacy, as believed by leaders of the Confederate States, Maury was worried about his own professional situation. From the date that he was transferred from the Virginia Navy to the Confederate States Navy, his letters to relatives revealed his fear that his services would not be used to effective purpose. His new supreme commander, President Jefferson Davis, had worked against him in Washington. Davis had undoubtedly aided Alexander Dallas Bache in his Steamer Plan attempt to wrest deep-sea soundings from Maury's control.[46] Davis had later used his influence with a Cabinet member to help Bache prevent Maury's making comparisons of longitude with Greenwich.[47] Maury also had reason to believe that Jefferson Davis had not favored his being restored to the active list of the Navy.[48] In addition, Confederate Secretary of the Navy Stephen R. Mallory had led the fight in the United States Senate against Maury's reinstatement to active duty after the action of the Navy Retiring Board in 1855.[49] And a member of that Navy Retiring Board, Captain Samuel Barron, was in charge of the Office of Naval Detail and Equipment in Richmond in June, 1861.[50] Soon Captain Franklin Buchanan, another and less friendly member of the Navy Retiring Board, was to be placed in charge of the Confederate Navy Department's Office of Orders and Detail.[51]

Maury was staying in the home of his banker-stockbroker cousin, Robert Henry Maury, at 1105 East Clay Street,[52] less than a block from the large Brockenbrough house, which was being renovated for occupancy by President Davis and his family. It was a great comfort to Maury to be with kinspeople, as he needed to discuss where he should try to establish his wife and younger children. He had accepted for them the temporary hospitality of his cousin John Minor in Fredericksburg[53] but hoped to be able to rent a house in Charlottesville. Space was at such a premium in Richmond and house rentals had soared to such an extent that Maury could not consider bringing his large family there. His plan to move them to Charlottesville had to be delayed because the gentle and sensitive nature of his wife had suffered a severe shock from the outbreak of war, and she was ill in bed in Fredericksburg. Her brother, Dr. Brodie Strachan Herndon, advised Maury that, until she was better, Ann should remain where she was, close to her own nearest of kin.[54]

After Maury learned of the bitter Northern feeling toward him, he worried about the safety of his daughter Betty who, with her husband and her small child, was still in Washington. He feared she would be imprisoned, for in addition to her relationship to him, her husband, William Arden Maury, was known to favor the cause of the South. On May 24, when 5,000 Federal troops crossed the Potomac onto Virginia soil, took possession of Alexandria, and cut the telegraph wires to Fredericksburg and Richmond, Maury sent Betty a letter "by private hand," [55] as individuals could still get through to Washington though the public mails no longer passed between North and South. In this letter, he commanded Betty, Will, and their child to leave Washington at once.

On Saturday, June 8, inasmuch as no meetings of the Advisory Council were scheduled for that weekend, Maury boarded the cars for Fredericksburg and was overjoyed to find Betty, Will, and their little girl safely established with his wife, younger daughters, and Matthew Jr., at the John Minor home at 214 Caroline Street. Betty had important news to tell her father. The night before she had left Washington, William C. Hasbrouck had come to see them on his way to Richmond to try to persuade Maury to change his mind and return to the United States Navy. They had told Hasbrouck of the frightful danger he was running in crossing the lines and had dissuaded him from continuing the journey.[56]

When Maury learned of the courage and devotion of this man, he was profoundly moved but not surprised, for he had received letters from Hasbrouck declaring that, though they were on opposite sides of the great struggle, yet their personal friendship would always endure.[57] Maury had written in similar vein and had signed over to Hasbrouck a few lots he owned in West St. Paul, Minnesota.[58] Maury pressed his daughter for further details on the conversation with Hasbrouck, and Betty's eyes flashed. She turned to the family and reported, "I told him that I was proud of my father before, but I was a hundred times prouder of him now, that, if he had considered his own personal welfare, he would have remained with the North." [59]

Maury wanted to hear how Betty and Will had managed to get out of Washington. His daughter told of three vain efforts to secure a pass through the lines and of finally achieving it through General of the Union Armies Winfield Scott. Betty continued, "General Scott asked whether Will was any relation to Captain Maury of the Observatory, now in Richmond. The clerk, who had carried the note making the second application, did not know and said he was not. The old General little knew that I was his daughter." [60] Betty could hardly tell her story for laughing at one of the problems of their hazardous two-day trip to Fredericksburg. As she and Will drove from Alexandria to Manassas in a small carriage, which they had managed to rent for $25, they had been stopped frequently by sentinels. "Every time," Betty related, "the baby sang Dixie and I had to bribe her with a sugar cookie. We missed the train at Manassas and had to stay in the carriage." [61]

On Sunday Maury was delighted when his daughter Diana and her husband Wellford Corbin came up from their plantation, which was located much too close to the Potomac for safety. Corbin, who had volunteered and was now a lieutenant in Virginia's Provisional Army, was dressed in a gray uniform that Diana had made out of an old suit. He wore a sword taken from a French officer at Waterloo. On the blue flannel shirt worn by his son-in-law Maury noticed some buttons from one of his own discarded Federal uniforms. When he questioned the suitability of the letters on the buttons, Diana tossed her head and replied, "The U.S. stands for United South." [62]

Maury rose very early Monday morning, caught the Richmond, Fredericksburg and Potomac train, and was back at work in Richmond at nine o'clock, for the two communities were little more than 50 miles apart.[63] Whenever weekend duties permitted, Maury made this trip to see his wife and children. Having found it impossible to rent a house in Charlottesville, he had asked his bachelor kinsman, John Minor, to let him start paying rent for the Fredericksburg house.[64] Minor, whose red beard was streaked with white, moved into his little outside office but took his meals with the Maurys and enjoyed their attentions to him.

374

Having left college to volunteer, Maury's son Dick was already Lieu-tenant Richard Launcelot Maury, Virginia Provisional Army.[65] John Herndon Maury, whom his father still called Davy or Dave, was drill-ing a company of students at the University of Virginia, where he was a student. He was threatening to leave his studies at any moment and seek active duty in uniform.

Just after the middle of June Maury was in the office of the Confed-erate States Navy Bureau of Orders and Details in Richmond, conferring with Captain Samuel Barron and some other officers, when George N. Hollins came in to greet them all. Hollins had made his way from Bal-timore on the steamer *St. Nicholas,* had got off at a plantation on the Patuxent River, crossed to the Potomac and thence to Richmond to re-port to Secretary of the Navy Mallory. He had been promptly given a commission as captain in the Confederate Navy, this being the rank he had just resigned in the U.S. Navy. Hollins wasted no time in describ-ing to the cluster of officers a plan that he had conceived en route to Richmond. His scheme was to capture the steamer *St. Nicholas* and with her take the U.S.S. *Pawnee,* which the *St. Nicholas* was then regularly supplying in the Potomac.

The officers told Hollins that Secretary Mallory would probably not approve the plan but that Governor Letcher would. Captain Hollins immediately walked into Mallory's office and asked for permission to ap-ply to the Governor about the plan. Having obtained permission, Hol-lins went to Governor Letcher, who agreed to the proposal and issued a draft for $1,000 with which to secure arms in the North. Letcher next introduced the captain to Richard Thomas of Maryland, later called Colonel Richard Thomas Zarnova, saying that Thomas could be trusted to go north and purchase arms for the secret expedition.[66] The Gover-nor suggested that Maury help work out the details of the plan with Hollins so that they could secure official approval.[67] In declaring his be-lief that the undercover expedition could succeed, Maury stated, "But delays in such matters are always dangerous."[68] They had to wait for President Davis's permission to execute the plan.

Maury told a close friend, "I could not take an active part in this secret expedition. But for my lameness, I would have volunteered and gone as a 'foremast' hand. The next best thing I could do was to send Dick. Bless his heart."[69] In addition to his son Dick, Maury also arranged for the inclusion of Jack Maury, a protégé who was a captain in the Virginia Provisional Army, and Naval Lieutenant Bob Minor, who had worked with him at the Observatory.

The imaginative plot involved young Richard Thomas's traveling to Baltimore on the *St. Nicholas,* securing arms, and then returning on the steamer—posing as a woman traveler with a marked French accent. The arms were to be hidden in the stylish traveler's trunks.

All went according to the carefully worked out plan. Early in July, 1861, Captain Hollins and a number of young officers went on board as passengers when the steamer stopped at various landings. At midnight the signal was given and Thomas removed his female disguise. Hollins and his twenty-four fellow "passengers" threw off their civilian clothes to reveal uniforms beneath. No resistance was offered to their taking possession of the vessel. The Confederates changed the course of the steamer and headed for the Virginia shore, where they had to wait for Army reinforcements, which were late in arriving. The capture of the *Pawnee* had been predicated on the fact that the *St. Nicholas* had been regularly allowed to come alongside the Federal ship to transfer supplies, but surprise and perfect timing were imperative for success. The *Pawnee* was commanded by Maury's close friend of happier days, Commander Stephen C. (Darby) Rowan, senior Federal officer on the Potomac River. Because of the delay, news that the *St. Nicholas* had been captured reached the *Pawnee* before the attacking craft got to her. On learning of the plot, Rowan retreated to Washington and thus cheated the *St. Nicholas* of her main target. But the determined Confederates steamed the *St. Nicholas* down to Chesapeake Bay, where they captured a brig and two schooners, all with valuable cargoes aboard.[70] The four vessels were welcome additions at the beginning of July, 1861, to the ship-hungry Confederate Navy.

As the defense of Virginia had now been integrated into the over-all defensive plan of the Confederate government, the Governor's Advisory Council had held its last meeting on June 19 and been dissolved.[71] This gave Maury more time for the experiments he was making on torpedoes. In late May he and his associates on the council had unanimously advised that the Board of Visitors of the University of Virginia be requested to establish at the university "a laboratory in connection with the Ordnance Department of this State, for the purpose of assisting in the preparations of munitions of war and that the duty of superintendence and management be assigned to suitable professors to whom no additional compensation be given." [72] The action had been taken, and in late June the laboratory had been put under Confederate authority. Maury co-operated closely with Professors Socrates Maupin and Dr. James Lawrence Cabell in their work at this laboratory. On May 31 he advised them that nitric acid was available in Richmond but stated, "Our minds are at a loss with regard to sulphur. I understand that there is a large quantity of quick silver in St. Louis, brought there from the Pike's Peak miners. I have sent for a *ton* for we shall want *many* millions of caps, besides electrical batteries for blowing up vessels etc." [73]

Maury carried on his experiments in the bedroom he occupied in his cousin's house and tried every possible method of exploding minute charges of powder, which he submerged in a portable metal bathtub used by the children of the household.[74]

Tanks for submerging powder, equipped with triggers for explosion and other mechanical appliances were quickly made by Talbott Brothers and the Tredegar Iron Works in Richmond.[75] On July 3 Maury had sufficient makeshift equipment to make the first trial against enemy ships. With the utmost secrecy he took his equipment to Norfolk and out to Sewell's Point. There were five ships of the Federal fleet riding at anchor in Hampton Roads off Union-held Fortress Monroe. Maury decided to try to blow up the two flagships, the *Minnesota* and the *Roanoke,* as well as the sailing sloop-of-war *Cumberland.*[76]

Friday and Saturday nights Maury sent an officer in a rowboat to reconnoiter the ships, but his reconnaissance was hampered by a little steamer keeping watch by circling the vessels. On Sunday Maury, through his glass, watched every move made on the target vessels. When he saw the Stars and Stripes lowered a little and the church flag raised above it, he knew the men on board were worshiping God and he began to find his mission increasingly difficult to perform. He shortly afterward told his children that when he considered that the men on those ships believed their cause as righteous as he did his, he found it very painful to proceed with the effort to blow them all into eternity.[77] But, as he declared, "War is a scourge," [78] and so he completed his preparations.

Five small boats were loaded with the torpedoes and gear, and at ten o'clock that night, July 7, 1861, Maury gave the order to shove off from Sewell's Point. He was in the lead boat with the pilot, four oarsmen, and an entire torpedo rig. Each of the other boats was manned by one officer and four men and carried its own torpedo equipment.

Describing the moment, Maury said, "The night was still, clear, calm and lovely. Thatcher's comet was flaming in the sky. We steered by it, pulling along in the plane of its splendid train. All the noise and turmoil of the enemy's camp and fleet were hushed. They had no guard boats of any sort. As with muffled oars we began to near them, we heard 'seven bells' strike." [79]

Maury and two boats approached one vessel and gave the order to drop torpedoes. Maury declared:

> They were in pairs [the torpedoes] connected together by a span 500 feet long. The span was floated on the surface by corks, and

the torpedo barrels, containing 200 pounds of powder, also floated at the depth of twenty feet, empty barregas, painted lead color, so as not readily to be seen, serving for the purpose.

The span was connected with a trigger in the head of each barrel, so set and arranged that when the torpedo, being let go in a tide way under the bows and athwart the hawse had fouled, they [the torpedo barrels] would be drifted alongside, and in so drifting tauten the span, and so set off the fuse, which was driven precisely as a ten second shot fuse, only it was calculated to burn fifty-four seconds, because it could not be known exactly in which part of the sweep alongside the strain would be sufficient to set off the trigger.[80]

Having planted their torpedoes, the first two boats were ordered to drop back, and Maury went with the other two to place their charges. He gave his orders in whispers. All during the operation the men could hear the little sentinel ship, her steam up, though she did not circle as she had the two preceding nights. As they rowed away they strained to hear sounds of pursuit. When they reached the first boats, Maury ordered all to shore except the boat in which he and his crew waited for the explosion. For them it was a grim time, for they knew well that, at the very first detonation, the calcium light at Fortress Monroe would be lit, and the little steamer was capable of catching them in a few minutes, with hanging for Maury, if not for his crew. After what seemed an interminable wait, Maury had to accept the fact that there was no longer any chance for the fuse to ignite. The effort had failed.

They rowed back to Sewell's Point, which took a long hour to reach.[81] Maury was already pondering the cause of the failure. He was to discover that the type of fuse he had used would burn at 15 feet under water but not in a pressure of 20 feet of water, which was the depth to which the torpedoes had been dropped that night.[82]

Maury made a quick trip to Fredericksburg to see his family. As usual, he gave them a full report of this experience. When he remarked that, had the vessels been blown up, he would have picked up the survivors in the water, his daughter Diana thought of the flag officer on the *Roanoke*, G. J. Pendergrast, and his attitude toward her father when a member of the 1855 Navy Retiring Board. "Papa, would you have picked up 'Pender'?" she asked. Maury replied grimly, "I should like to have seen him and asked him if he thought I was fit for active service *now*." [83]

Returning to Richmond, Maury worked to perfect his torpedoes. As soon as he had overcome the problem presented by the fuse, he asked Secretary of the Navy Mallory to grant funds for large-scale use of torpedoes. In July he showed the Secretary two torpedoes he had made, but

Mallory's reaction was unfavorable. "Your man Mallory pronounced them humbugs," [84] Maury told a friend. Like many others at this time, Mallory doubted the potential of this system of defense. Even Ann opposed her husband's introduction of torpedoes, on moral grounds, and this latter issue weighed heavily on him. [85] However, his scruples were abandoned when the North declared all medicines and surgical instruments to be contraband of war. [86]

"It is a business, this thing of blowing up men while asleep that I don't glory in," Maury wrote a relative, "and nothing but the implacability of the enemy would induce me to undertake it. But has not Lincoln sent forth against our women and children the pestilence that walketh in the darkness? Against all rules and usage he has made medicine contraband of war. I strike at their fighting men in their strongholds, he at us all in our sick chambers." [87]

Maury had an ally in Governor Letcher, who believed in the torpedoes and agreed to assign Maury two barrels of blasting powder to use in demonstrations that might win over Mallory. By early August Maury had persuaded Secretary Mallory and Charles Magill Conrad, chairman of the House Committee on Naval Affairs of the Confederate Congress, to witness an underwater explosion in the James River at Rocketts, just below Richmond. Governor Letcher also was present. [88]

For the experiment Maury borrowed the gig of the C.S.S. *Patrick Henry*, formerly the steamer *Yorktown*, which had carried passengers from Virginia to New York. Maury and his son Dick were rowed out in the gig to the middle of the channel just opposite the wharf. The torpedo, an oak beer keg filled with powder and weighted to sink, was carefully lowered to the bottom, the men taking great care not to put any strain upon the trigger, which was at full cock. The boat pulled clear, and Maury gave the signal for the explosion. Dick pulled the lanyard, which was attached to the trigger. He described the result:

"The explosion was instantaneous; up went a column of water fifteen or twenty feet; many stunned or dead fish floated around; the officials on the wharf applauded and were convinced and shortly after a naval bureau of 'coast harbor and river defense' was created and Captain Maury placed at its head with the very best of intelligent, able and zealous younger naval officers for assistants." [89]

The explosion he had seen convinced Secretary Mallory that torpedoes could be effective, and he immediately asked the Confederate Congress to appropriate $50,000 for Maury's development of torpedoes with which to mine the bays and channel ways of Southern rivers. [90] But the Congress moved slowly, and Maury complained of having to "lay on his oars" while he awaited an appropriation. [91]

Maury, however, continued busy in trying to meet other desperate needs of the Confederacy. Of this time he later told an English gathering:

> On our side we had everything to improvise. . . . A short time before the battle of Manassas was fought, I had a note from General Lee to say that, unless I could furnish him with percussion caps, he should have to withdraw our army from the field. We had 40,000 percussion caps, and the machines with which the caps were made that fought that battle were manufactured between the 18th of April and the day of the battle July 21, 1861—the machines and the caps both.[92]

In late July and early August Maury carried on a campaign to persuade the Confederate authorities to follow up their great victory at Manassas (Bull Run) by a peace offer to the United States government. This, he proposed, should be sent to Washington under a flag of truce. He took the matter up with Governor Letcher, William B. Preston, and the venerable John Tyler, former President of the United States. Preston particularly responded to the proposal and asked Maury to draft a tentative peace offer to lay before the Vice-President of the Confederacy. Maury admitted to an intimate, "My notion is not that this offer will bring peace but it will be the seed of peace. It will strengthen the hands of the peace party at the North." [93] The proposal was never sent and would not have been accepted as Maury proposed that the North avoid further bloodshed on both sides by accepting the political separation of the South from the Union. Maury continued to urge the Confederate authorities to make a peace offer after each battle won by the Southern forces.

In July and August, 1861, Maury was also in correspondence with officers responsible for the defense of the Mississippi and proposed that torpedoes be used to mine the river. Major General Leonidas Polk, commanding Department No. 2 at Memphis, became deeply interested in using this method of defense and asked that Maury be assigned to him.

Meanwhile, in the weeks during which he waited for the torpedo appropriation, Maury wrote a 30-page article designed to interpret the Southern position to the peoples of England, France, and Holland. James Murray Mason, whom Maury had known in Washington as a member of the U.S. Senate, promised to take these papers abroad when he sailed soon for England to serve as Confederate commissioner.[94]

Maury also worked furiously on articles presenting proposals for the improvement of the Confederate Navy. His main points were these:

Prompt action in giving ships to the paper navy was imperative. The administration had waited too long; the Federal blockade of the coast was now effective, and so the Confederacy was prevented from building oceangoing vessels at her seaports. Because of a serious scarcity of iron, skilled mechanics, shipyards, and shops, the South could not hope to build as many ships of war as the North possessed. But the Confederacy could and should build a fleet of highly mobile small steam launches, armed with big guns. Cruising on smooth water in groups and firing from a distance, these "mosquitoes" would be hard to hit but could sting large Federal ships to death. Such a fleet of gunboats could defend the bays and rivers of the South and even clear them of Federal warcraft, Maury stated. At the end of September he sent off the first of these articles to the editor of the Richmond *Enquirer,* and it was published on September 27. Maury had signed the letter "Ben Bow," but this did not deceive anyone as to the identity of the writer.[95]

As soon as the Confederate Congress appropriated funds for the torpedo work, Maury had torpedoes manufactured and shipped to the Mississippi, sending detailed instructions for their use because he was unable to go there himself.[96] All of the torpedo work was carried out *sub rosa* as it was a part of the Secret Service of the Confederacy.

Maury now laid plans for another sortie at Hampton Roads to attempt to blow up Union ships anchored off Fortress Monroe. He decided on Wednesday night, October 9, when there would be no moonlight to increase the dangers of the expedition. He and Bob Minor were to go for the *Savannah* and Jack Maury for the *Minnesota,* both men having been carefully schooled by him in the handling of the torpedoes.[97]

Two days after the article in the *Enquirer* appeared Maury received an order from the Navy Department detaching him from the torpedo work and placing him on "special duty." He was stunned by being taken away from perfecting the use of torpedoes and also by the nature of the mission on which he was ordered. He confided to Franklin Minor:

> The government has made a contract with certain individuals in New Orleans to purchase arms etc. in Cuba and is furnishing the money. So that you see I am sent simply to hold the purse strings and see that the arms are good, a duty for which any officer of the Army or Navy is as well qualified as I.
>
> I am ordered by Mallory to report to New Orleans for this duty, the Secretary of War, not having an Army officer to send, asks for a Navy officer. I am sent, thus showing that in Mallory's judgment I can be better spared than any officer of the Army or Navy. I go

as a matter of course and am as likely to turn up in Fort Lafayette [Federal prison at entrance to New York harbor] as in Richmond.[98]

Maury was ordered to leave for Cuba as soon as possible but was instructed to put his personal affairs in order first. He was to proceed to New Orleans, leave by a small sailing craft and run the blockade, though a fast Confederate steam man-of-war had been unable to achieve this for two months.[99] On October 5 Captain Franklin Buchanan, in charge of the C.S.N. Office of Orders and Detail, ordered Maury's young assistant, Lieutenant Robert D. Minor, to take over the torpedo work and to receive from Commander M. F. Maury "such instructions as will enable you to carry out his views relating to it." [100]

Hastening to Fredericksburg, Maury worked out arrangements for his family for the winter. He had to enter his daughters Mary and Eliza in what he considered an unpromising school and had little Lucy set to lessons with her aunt Mary Herndon. He talked over plans for the coming marriage of his son Dick to pretty Susan Crutchfield and expressed the hope that Dick could get leave for this from his post in northern Virginia, where he was stationed as major of the 24th Virginia Infantry.[101]

Either Jefferson Davis, Stephen Mallory, and Franklin Buchanan were repeating their Washington pattern of opposition to Maury or the clue to Mallory's sudden order lay in this remark Maury made to a friend: "The Governor and Hunter [Confederate Secretary of State] are quite taken with my dogma 'Big Guns and Little Ships.' " [102] The Navy Secretary may have interpreted Maury's proposal as being competitive to the work then going on to convert the raised hull of the *Merrimac* into an armor-plated vessel, or ironclad, as they were called. John Mercer Brooke, inventor of the deep-sea sounding apparatus, had, early the preceding June, presented to Mallory a design by which the hulk of the former steam frigate would be built up with 45-degree inclines to be covered with iron plate. The revolutionary feature of Brooke's proposal was the extension of the ends of the vessel and "in order to protect them from the enemy they were to be submerged two feet under the water so that nothing was to be seen afloat but the shield itself." [103] Mallory, who wholly believed in the future of ironclads, approved, and arrangements were quickly completed with Joseph R. Anderson, president of the Tredegar Iron Works, for an intensive drive to roll the plates with which to ironclad the *Merrimac* and to cast the special rifled guns Brooke had designed for her.[104] John L. Porter, a naval constructor, had designed a similar craft, but his plan called for a beak. To the *Merrimac* Porter now added a cast-iron beak designed to act as a ram.[105] The work on the conversion of the *Merrimac* was in progress at the time of Maury's proposal, but the whole project was carried out under the utmost secrecy and it is not clear how well informed he was on the subject. Brooke later testified that he "believed" Maury was opposed to ironclads.[106]

Maury knew that it was one thing to attach iron plates to an existing frigate hull and build up a superstructure, and use the engines found in her. But it would be a different matter to build a fleet of completely new ironclads in the South. For once he was fighting for a traditional method rather than promoting the revolutionary one. He held that armed craft were needed fast and that the gunboats he proposed could be built in 120 days if construction could be started while the weather was good.[107] They would be used to drive Federal ships from Chesapeake Bay, the Potomac, and other Virginia rivers, and thus make possible repossession of Fortress Monroe.

On October 8 Maury outlined his whole proposal to Governor Letcher. The craft were to be only 21 feet in beam, 112 feet in length, draw 6 feet of water, and mount two rifled pivot guns of the largest caliber. "The floating gun carriages, propelled by steam" were to ride only two feet above the surface of the water and thus present the smallest possible target to the enemy. The craft were to "have neither cabin, nor steerage, nor any accommodation on board." [108] The men would take precooked food and stay out two days at a time. Maury estimated that each vessel could be constructed for $10,000 and could be built in river yards without too great a number of skilled mechanics. Maury proposed that simultaneously with building of the gunboat fleet a battery of heavy rifled cannon should be placed at Willoughby's Point to assist the ships in taking Fortress Monroe.[109]

Still waiting for the expected telegram that would start him on his way to Cuba, Maury was greatly distressed when he received a report from Bob Minor that he had carried out a part of the plans Maury had drafted in September, had on October 10 made the proposed attack on the *Savannah*, anchored off Fortress Monroe, and failed.[110] Lieutenant Minor had let go his torpedoes at a distance of 800 yards from the Federal ship and fouled his rope. Maury concluded that the failure was due to the fact that the torpedoes had been dropped at too great a distance from the target.[111] He now pinned his hopes on what his other torpedo trainee, Jack Maury, would achieve in a second try to blow up the *Minnesota* also riding at anchor in Hampton Roads. Maury was profoundly disappointed when he received a letter on October 16 reporting that Jack Maury had engaged a pilot to take him out to torpedo the *Minnesota*, but the pilot had been befuddled with drink and failed to find the flagship in the night darkness. The only encouragement was that Jack had retained his torpedoes and equipment and planned to try again.[112]

In official circles in Richmond there was serious criticism of Navy Secretary Mallory's seemingly capricious order to send Maury out of the country on a secondary mission. One of the chief critics of the order was Naval Affairs Chairman Conrad, who regarded Mallory's action as a virtual cancellation of the Confederate Congress's recent appropriation for the development of torpedo warfare.[113] This opposition was effective, and on the morning of October 24 Maury, who was still in Fredericksburg, received an official letter stating that his orders to proceed to Cuba had been recalled.[114] No reason for the action was given.

Very much in contrast to this episode was the next development in Maury's life. On October 28 he received two letters from the Russian minister to the United States, Baron de Stoeckl, whom he had long known in Washington. The envoy had sent the letters through the British consul at Charleston, South Carolina, and advised Maury that he should reply through the same channel. The purpose of the communication was an invitation from H.I.H. the Grand Duke Constantine of Russia, brother to the Czar.

> St. Petersburg,
> July 27th, 1861

My Dear Captain Maury,

The news of your having left a service which is so much indebted to your great and successful labours, has made a very painful impression on me and my companions-in-arms. Your indefatigable researches have unveiled the great laws which rule the winds and currents of the ocean, and have placed your name amongst those which will ever be mentioned with feelings of gratitude and respect, not only by professional men, but by all those who pride themselves in the great and noble attainments of the human race.

That your name is well-known in Russia I need scarcely add, and though "barbarians," as we are still sometimes called, we have been taught to honour in your person disinterested and eminent services to science and mankind. Sincerely deploring the inactivity into which the present political whirlpool in your country has plunged you, I deem myself called upon to invite you to take up your residence in this country, where you may in peace continue your favourite and useful occupations.

Your position here will be a perfectly independent one; you will be bound by no conditions or engagements, and you will always be at liberty to steer home across the ocean in the event of your not preferring to cast anchor in our remote corner of the Baltic.

As regards your material welfare, I beg to assure you that everything will be done by me to make your new home comfortable and agreeable; whilst at the same time, the necessary means will be offered you to enable you to continue your scientific pursuits in the way you have been accustomed to.

I shall now be awaiting your reply, hoping to have the pleasure of seeing here so distinguished an officer, whose personal acquaintance it has always been my desire to make, and whom Russia will be proud to welcome on her soil.

Believe me, my dear Captain Maury.

Your sincere well-wisher,

CONSTANTINE,

Grand Admiral of Russia [115]

Stoeckl's own letter advised Maury by what route he was to go to Russia as well as where he was to go for passport, money, and all needed information.[116]

Maury, who had received orders to report back to Richmond on October 27, laid the Russian invitation before his family. Gathered in the parlor on the evening of the 26th, they discussed the pros and cons of the matter and took a vote. Since they felt he was not appreciated in the Confederacy, Maury's wife and eldest daughter declared that he should accept. His daughter Diana and his two sons-in-law voted "No," declaring that "he ought not to forsake his country in her hour of need. He ought to stay and do the best he could." [117]

The vision held out to Maury of resuming a scientific life, of living in peace with his family around him, was tempting after the buffeting he had just been through. Referring to Constantine's offer, he commented to a friend, "It was a noble act, and an elegant sprig of what to me feels something like laurel. Though Mallory is trifling with me and desires to blight, still I have that within me which tells me I am capable in some way or other of rendering the state good service. Therefore, I have said to my Russian friends, *pardon*." [118] Once again Maury had faced the challenge of deciding between his own personal welfare and success and loyalty to his people. Once again he had made his decision on the basis of that loyalty.

On November 2 the Confederate administration officially withdrew objection to Maury's continuing his torpedo work, and he started again to organize a new expedition.[119] He trained the officers of the C.S.S. *Patrick Henry* in his technique. When every officer on board volunteered for the dangerous duty, Maury entrusted his precious torpedoes to them that they might use them against the enemy when time and circumstance were propitious.[120]

On resumption of the torpedo work Maury received from Franklin Minor a plea to abandon that effort. Maury took the time to explain he fully understood the danger and the nature of the work he was doing, as well as the view some took of it. He regarded it as a means to the end of driving enemy ships from Southern rivers, bays, and harbors.

> I have had, Frank, the inward struggle—a sore one it was—but thanks be to God, I feel that the way is clear, the path of duty is plain, and as may be my straits so will my strength be. My answer is this—and in this you will see my philosophy and my reasoning too—I have acquired an influence for good in a certain way—but in this our great trial—I find myself as powerless for good as tho' my name were unsung by sea and land. There needs, therefore, some fresh proof to convince the people, that if they will but afford me the opportunity, I can in war serve as well as some are pleased to say I have done in peace.
>
> If I am to lie here and rust because Davis conspired with Bache against me, then had I not better accept the Grand Duke's invitation and go to Russia?

Maury stated that he rejected such an idea and would continue with the torpedoes because "It becomes me to give the proof before I put them into other hands." [121]

In November he was often in attendance on a committee of the Virginia Convention that had under discussion his gunboat proposal.[122] Finally, action on this matter was turned over by the Virginians to the Confederate Congress,[123] of which both houses, on December 23, 1861, passed "An Act to authorize the President to be constructed a certain number of gunboats." The following day President Davis approved the bill that authorized construction of not more than 100 of the small gunboats as proposed by Maury. The Congress also approved a board of naval officers therefor and appropriated $2,000,000 for the construction of the "mosquito fleet." [124] Maury was placed in charge of the building of the gunboats and was designated as the officer to have over-all command of them when completed.[125]

From the time of this appointment onward, Maury was usually addressed as commodore, the customary title for a naval officer who commanded or had commanded a squadron of ships. Some persons, however, continued to call him captain or used the title of his fixed rank, commander.[126]

386

Maury journeyed to Fredericksburg that Christmas Eve to spend the holiday with his family. The weather was extremely cold, and he was seized with a bout of what he believed to be rheumatism. The pain was severe, and the attack confined him to bed until early January.[127] He was desperately anxious to get back to Richmond and start the building of the gunboat fleet authorized on December 24. He was greatly upset that so much fine building weather had been lost since October 8, when he had made his first official proposal for the construction of craft to rid the rivers and bays of Federal ships.

By mid-January, 1862, Maury was in the Confederate capital driving hard to secure materials, line up workmen, and start construction of the gunboats. Ten days later he was still pleading with Mallory for ship's carpenters and artisans.[128] To help him in the paper work necessary to the undertaking, Maury brought his second son, John, to Richmond to act as his clerk. John had been drilling fellow students at the University of Virginia but could no longer curb his impatience to enter the service of the Confederacy.[129]

Maury, on January 19, wrote a report on the progress on the gunboats to William Francis Lynch, who had added his support to the project. Lynch was at this time a commodore in command of a Confederate flotilla of small vessels off the coast of North Carolina. Maury explained that, when operative, the 100 gunboats would be divided into divisions of five to ten boats that would move as a squadron under an experienced Navy officer. He stated that each boat would need a crew of forty, one second lieutenant to be rated as such, or as master or mate, and one lieutenant to be in command. Maury asked his friend to think how to get these junior officers and advise him. Maury also wrote that if his son John Maury liked the idea he wanted him to try for a master's place in one of the boats and asked Lynch if he could find any way to use the youth in the meantime in operations off the Carolina coast. "Be candid, my friend, and don't let your desire to serve me embarrass you in any way." [130]

Lynch was delighted at the thought of having John serve with him, and Maury's 19-year-old son went to join Lynch, barely escaping capture on February 10, when ships of the North Atlantic Blockading Squadron fought an engagement with Lynch's gunboats off Elizabeth City, North Carolina, and captured the commodore's flagship.[131] After that John went with the crews trying to supply timber by cutting trees in the Virginia woods with which to build the 100 gunboats.[132] Maury's theory was that green timber would serve for these little craft just as it had for Perry's fleet on the Great Lakes in the War of 1812.

A part of Maury's original proposal that was not carried out by the government was the recommendation that the men who had formerly served as ship's carpenters at the Norfolk Navy Yard and were now in the Virginia military forces should be given their discharge upon pledge to work on the gunboats at half their former pay.[133] Skilled artisans were nearly as rare as trained officers in the agricultural South. Maury appealed to his friend General William Giles Harding, who at his 5,000-acre plantation Belle Meade near Nashville had created the finest thoroughbred stable in America. He asked General Harding to round up all the boiler plate that could be found in Tennessee, to try to drive the best bargain possible but not to stand on price as, "We must have it." [134] It was so difficult to secure engines for the gunboats that Maury sent out an agent to look for old locomotive engines.[135]

Maury's project had become a race with time and a struggle with scarcity. Some gunboats were laid down at a yard on the Rappahannock, some at a yard on the Pamunkey River, some at a yard on the York, and six in the Norfolk Navy Yard. By mid-March information about work at two of these yards had reached Washington.[136] But meanwhile spies had also reported to the United States Secretary of the Navy the facts concerning the rebuilding of the steam frigate *Merrimac* as an ironclad. In the North a frantic attempt was being made at Greenpoint, Long Island, to build a competitor ironclad according to an even more radical Monitor-type design by John Ericsson.[137]

In Richmond Maury's early associate at the Observatory, John Mercer Brooke, was supervising special work that went on night and day at the Tredegar Iron Works. There furnaces roared and the noise of the rolling mills was deafening as they turned out the two-inch-thick iron plates for the *Merrimac*. Even more carefully Brooke watched the casting of four rifled guns of the new design he had conceived. Two were six-inch and two were "seven-inch rifles, heavily reinforced around breech with three-inch steel bands, shrunk on." These new grooved-bore Brooke guns were far more accurate than the other six old-fashioned nine-inch smoothbore guns that were to complete the armament of the *Merrimac*.[138] Daily a shipment of the heavy plates for the *Merrimac* moved down the James River to the Norfolk Navy Yard to be bolted on the remodeled vessel. Maury had no part in this work on the *Virginia*, as the *Merrimac* was rechristened, but, like all other naval officers, he had an enormous interest in the result. When, on March 8, 1862, the *Virginia* sank the U.S.S. *Cumberland*, destroyed the U.S.S. *Congress*, and caused three other Federal ships, including the *Minnesota*, to run aground in Hampton Roads, no one was more elated than Maury.[139]

Almost simultaneously with the report of the *Merrimac*'s first success news reached Richmond of the arrival in Hampton Roads of the incredibly strange-looking turreted Union ironclad, the *Monitor,* captained by another of Maury's former Observatory associates, Lieutenant John Lorimer Worden.[140]

Lest the French hear only the Federal version of the historic duel fought by these clumsily powerful craft in Hampton Roads on March 9, 1862, Maury promptly wrote a report to Captain A. de la Marche, director of meteorology in the Ministry of the Marine of France.[141] All too well did Maury know that Europe saw almost exclusively the Northern newspapers and seldom got a report that gave news of any Southern achievement.

The battle of the ironclads, which was to revolutionize naval fleets and sea warfare, had an immediate effect on Maury's program for the 100 small gunboats.

In the days subsequent to the battle between the *Monitor* and the *Merrimac,* the House Committee on Naval Affairs of the Confederate Congress decided, as its chairman C. M. Magill reported,

> that this experiment fully established the efficacy of iron-plated rams
> and the inability of wooden vessels, however formidable, to contend
> with them; consequently that it was the policy of this Government,
> in the scarcity of workmen and materials, to confine themselves to
> the construction of this description of vessels, at least within the
> limits of the Confederacy. We all expected for some time a commu-
> nication from the Secretary of the Navy [Mallory] on this subject,
> with the suggestion that he might be authorized to discontinue the
> construction of the wooden gunboats. But after waiting for some
> time, and no suggestion being made by the Secretary to that effect,
> the committee unanimously determined to bring in a bill directing
> the President to discontinue the construction of the small gunboats
> above mentioned.[142]

This bill, passed by the House of Representatives on March 17, authorized President Davis to suspend the building of gunboats and to use the balance of the appropriation originally voted for the small wooden gunboats to build ironclad vessels equipped with rams.[143] On March 29 Secretary of the Navy Mallory wrote President Davis in reference to the House of Representatives' bill, ending his discussion of the matter with this recommendation: "I suggest for your consideration the expediency of completing those vessels already commenced according to the original design, but of making ironclad gunboats of the others as far as the appropriation will allow. Fifteen of these boats have been commenced; these vessels can not advantageously be plated, but will be serviceable as originally designed." [144] Shortly after this the Confederate Senate concurred in the bill that had been passed by the House. This was a severe blow to Maury, but he bowed to the inevitable—his gunboat fleet would never be completed.[145]

By April, 1862, the South's critical shortage of pig iron had increased rather than lessened. If the ironclads were to be built, fabricated iron of every sort would have to be collected throughout the Confederacy. This was a task in which the women of the South could participate. Maury gave encouragement to the Ladies' Defence Association of Richmond to start a drive to outfit a second Confederate ironclad to be built and placed on duty in the James River. On April 4 Maury drafted for the Association an appeal for all iron railings from yard fences, iron balconies of houses, iron pots, old stoves, broken plows "however small the quantity to be delivered to the Tredegar Iron Works, put in the furnace, reduced and then wrought into shape or turned into shot and shell." [146] The women of Virginia were urged to donate their silver and jewels, to send money, building materials, or grain from their farms; and instructions were given how and where to deliver each contribution.

On April 18, 1862, Henri Mercier, the French minister to the United States, who had come through the lines to Richmond, presented an invitation from Emperor Napoleon III to Maury to come to France to continue his scientific work under full assurance that he would receive every courtesy and assistance. Maury expressed his deep appreciation but stated that he could not accept the invitation as he must continue to serve his native state.[147] Perhaps the ironical thought crossed his mind that once France had driven out his forebears and Virginia had received them. In any event, he and Mercier, whom he had known in Washington, settled down to a long serious conversation. They discussed the naval significance of the recent battle of the ironclads about which Maury had written Alexander de la Marche. Mercier and Maury exchanged views on the *Trent* affair, in which Captain Charles Wilkes of the U.S.S. *San Jacinto* had the preceding fall removed the Confederate commissioners to France and Great Britain from a British ship. Though the entire talk was on the basis of an interchange of private opinion, the two explored the possibility of French recognition of the Confederacy.[148] Maury was informed on the subject; he had recently prepared a "memorandum of proposals to be made to France" for Colonel James Lawrence Orr, chairman of the Committee on Foreign Relations of the Confederate States Senate.[149]

With work on his gunboat fleet stopped, Maury intensified his efforts to develop a satisfactory electric torpedo. The Richmond Medical College tendered him the use of its laboratory and supplied him with batteries. However, Maury carried out most of these investigations at the Clay Street home of Robert H. Maury, which still stands. On the building is a plaque: "In this house, Matthew Fontaine Maury, LL.D., U.S.N., C.S.N., invented the submarine Electrical Torpedo, 1861-62." [150]

A more accurate statement is that of Bernard Jaffe in his *Men of Science in America:* "Both Robert Fulton and Samuel Colt had previously experimented with electrical mines, but Maury was the first American to devise improved submarine torpedoes set off electrically and actually to employ this new weapon in warfare." [151]

This first use came about in the spring of 1862 after Maury received word from Dr. Morris, president of the Telegraph Company in Norfolk, that ten miles of insulated wire had been washed ashore by the waters of Chesapeake Bay. This was wire that had been left in the water by the Federals after an unsuccessful effort to lay a submarine telegraph from Fortress Monroe to the Eastern Shore of Virginia. [152] Once Maury had this insulated wire he could plant electric torpedoes in the James River to prevent Federal ships from reaching Richmond and capturing the capital of the Confederacy.

The personal danger involved in his work of mining the James River was not ignored by Maury, and on May 4, 1862, he wrote a will with full instructions for the care of his family. He stated that, if he fell in battle, he wished merely a sailor's grave. [153] At this time, he was particularly concerned about the future of his family. Earlier, when he had seen that Fredericksburg must inevitably fall to the Federals, he had requested that his wife and children remain quietly in that town, but it had worried him to hear of their house being searched and his papers ransacked at the home of British Vice-Consul Goolrick, where he had placed them for safekeeping. [154]

To add to his distress, John left at this time for Mississippi, where he was to be an Army lieutenant assigned as an aide to Brigadier General Dabney Herndon Maury, Maury's nephew who had resigned his U.S. Army commission to enter the Confederate service. [155]

The fighting below Richmond was now intense and, in the battle at Williamsburg on May 5, Maury's eldest son Dick was in the thick of the charge made by part of General Jubal Early's brigade. Dick's superior officers were killed or wounded, and he was left in command of the 24th Virginia Infantry. In the charge made by 1,100 men, nearly 500 were left on the field. Dick was not hurt. His father took natural pride in the declaration made by the opposing Union general (Hancock), who declared that the word "immortality" ought to be inscribed on the banners of the 24th. [156]

Maury was working long hours daily to mine the James River, while other officers labored with equal intensity to place obstructions across the channels to keep Federal gunboats from ascending the river to Richmond. By June 19 Maury had completed his mission and reported to Secretary Mallory:

> The James River is mined with fifteen tanks below the iron battery at Chapin's (Chaffin's) Bluff. They are to be exploded by means of electricity. Four of the tanks contain 160 pounds of powder; the eleven others hold 70 pounds each. All are made of boiler plate. They are arranged in rows as per diagram, those of each row being 30 feet apart. Each tank is contained in a water-tight wooden cask, capable of floating it but anchored and held below the surface from three to eight feet, according to the state of the tide. The anchors of each are an 18-inch shell and a piece of kentledge, so placed as to prevent the barrels from fouling the buoy ropes at the change of the tide. Each shell of a row is connected with the one next to it by a stout rope thirty feet long and capable of lifting it in case the cask be carried away. The casks are water-tight, as are also the tanks, the electric cord entering through the same head.
>
> The wire for the return current from the battery is passed from shell to shell and along the connecting rope, which lies at the bottom. The wire that passes from cask to cask is stopped slack to the buoy rope from the shell up to the cask, to which it is securely seized to prevent any strain upon that part which enters the cask. The return wire is stopped in like manner down along the span to the next shell, as per the rough sketch. At 4 (in the sketch) the two cords are frapped together, loaded with trace chains a fathom apart, and carried ashore to the galvanic battery.
>
> For batteries we have 21 Wollastons, each trough containing eighteen pairs of plates, zinc and iron, ten by twelve inches. The first range is called 1, the second 2 and the third 3, and the wires are so labeled. Thus all of each range are exploded at once.
>
> Besides these, there are two ranges of two tanks each, planted opposite the battery at Chapin's (Chaffin's) Bluff. When they were planted, it was not known that a battery was to be erected below. These four tanks contain about 6,000 pounds of powder. The great freshet of last month carried away the wires that were to operate the first pair, 'A' [in a diagram enclosed that showed the location of each mine].
>
> Lieutenant Davidson, who with the *Teaser* and her crew has assisted me with a most hearty good will, has dragged for the tanks

without success. They rest on the bottom. Could they be found, it was my intention to raise the four, examine them, and if found in good order, place them below the range, 'I.'

Lieutenant William L. Maury, assisted by Acting Master W. F. Carter and R. Rollins, was charged with the duty of proving the tanks and packing them in casks. There were eleven others, each containing 70 pounds of powder. When tested in the barrels and found ready for use, they will be held in reserve in case of accident to those already down. A larger number was not prepared, for the want of powder. There are a quantity of admirable insulated wire, a number of shells for anchors or torpedoes, and a sufficient quantity of chains for the wires remaining. They will be put in the navy store for safe-keeping. The galvanic batteries: viz., 21 Wollastons and 1 Cruikshank, the latter loaned by Dr. Maupin of the University of Virginia, with spare acids, sulphuric and nitric, are at Chapin's (Chaffin's) Bluff in charge of Acting Master Cheeney. He has also in jugs a sufficient quantity mixed to work the batteries and ready to be poured in for use.

It is proper that I should mention to the Department in terms of commendation the ready and valuable assistance afforded by Dr. Morris, president of the telegraph company, and his assistant, especially by Dr. Goldwell. My duties in connection with these batteries being thus closed, I have the honor to await your further orders.[157]

This completed the pioneering phase of Maury's work on the electric torpedoes, and the work was ready to be turned over to a junior officer. This was done the next day when Lieutenant Hunter Davidson, whom Maury had been training since the end of April, was ordered to "relieve Commander Maury in the charge of devising, placing and superintending submarine batteries in the James River." [158] Davidson took over immediately but had the misfortune, on July 4, of failing to estimate a tide and grounded the *Teaser*. The grounded ship with Maury's descriptions, instructions, and diagrams that showed the position of the mines fell into the hands of the enemy.

Maury wrote: "With this [the complete description] before them, the Federals constructed by way of experiment an electrical torpedo, planted it in the water near Baltimore, sent a vessel over it and as she entered its field of destruction, exploded the machine and, to use their own expression, 'blew her to toothpicks.' " [159]

He also declared: "The chief improvement in the James River torpedoes over preceding ones consisted of an arrangement which enabled the operator to use the self-same wire for testing his torpedoes daily after they were planted and then of exploding them at will." [160]

"The narrowest and shallowest parts of the river were selected, the torpedo placed in mid-channel and a range established for the purpose of knowing when a vessel was passing over it. There was no necessity for cross bearings, though a plan of triangular connections, with two observers, cross bearings and telegraphic communications . . . was submitted to the government in the winter of '61-'62." [161]

Later, when the James River torpedoes had long prevented a Federal fleet from ascending that water highway to Richmond and had blown one ship to bits, Maury was asked about his connection with the work. He stated: "All the electrical torpedoes in that river were prepared and laid either by myself or by Lieutenant Davidson, who relieved me after having been instructed by me as to the details of the system. These were the first electrical torpedoes that were successfully used against an enemy in war." [162]

It was perhaps inevitable that Jefferson Davis, who had disliked Maury since the mid-fifties when Alexander Dallas Bache had turned the Mississippi senator against the Naval Observatory superintendent, should make no mention of Maury's name in connection with electric torpedoes in his *Rise and Fall of the Confederate Government*. However, the facts in the records of the Confederate Navy Department [163] invalidate Davis's claim of pioneer honors for General Gabriel J. Rains, who did not take over the Torpedo Bureau of the Army until October, 1862. J. Thomas Scharf, who wrote a *History of the Confederate States Navy*, also ignored Maury's work and divided the honors between Rains, Hunter Davidson, and Beverley Kennon, all of whom made definite contributions to torpedo technology but subsequent to Maury's initial mining of the James. The official records leave no doubt that Maury's work preceded and paved the way for that of the other men. Also, throughout the rest of the war Maury did further important research on electric torpedoes which he reported to the Confederate Navy and which was made available to these very officers. Later the U.S. Secretary of the Navy was to report to Congress that "the [Federal] Navy had lost more vessels from Confederate torpedoes than from all other causes combined." [164]

On May 30 and 31, 1862, the muffled sound of cannonading could be heard in lower Richmond. Fighting was heavy at Seven Pines, only a few miles below the capital of the Confederacy. Maury knew that the 24th Virginia Infantry was committed and, like any devoted father, prayed for the safety of his eldest son. Late on the second day his suspense of waiting was ended. He described the moment: "Yesterday, about 6, a horseman rode in to say Dick was hit and wanted to be sent for. I got

394

a carriage and the road was lined with wounded men and officers. I found Dick a-smiling and whistling on the roadside about 5 miles from town. He was hit by a musket ball on the right arm about half way below the elbow. . . . His horse had been shot from under him." [165]

In that day's battle the commanding Confederate general, Joseph E. Johnston, received a wound that was to change history in the sense that it incapacitated Johnston and necessitated a change of command. About the time that Maury was taking his wounded son back to Richmond, President Davis, who had ridden out to observe the fighting, was informing Robert E. Lee that he would be given Johnston's command.[166]

As for Dick Maury, the surgeons set his badly fractured arm and advised him that he would be unsuited for active duty for an extended period.

This was a period of low spirits for Maury. Early in June, in the ironic wording he used when referring to Mallory, he confided to Franklin Minor: "I had a talk with your friend 'Mal' today. I told him my occupation [gunboat fleet] was gone, that I did not want to be a drone, and asked what use he could make of me. He thought I would be of use doing nothing—so there you are." [167]

In another letter, a few days later, Maury described the plight of Richmond with the enemy only about eight miles from the city and the Confederate Army having to fight on half rations. He stated that, with all tidal water in Virginia in the hands of the enemy, Secretary Mallory had proposed that he should undertake to build a Navy that would go down and capture Fortress Monroe. Maury commented, "That, I should say, is a considerable stirring up. Less than a year ago, I was to be banished for advocating a Navy. Now, time all our naval waters have been taken away, and we have nowhere to float a Navy, we are to have a Navy to take the strongest fortress in America. Hurra for 'Mal.' " [168]

At the end of June Maury received orders to serve on a general court-martial to convene at Richmond on July 5 for the trial of Flag Officer Josiah Tattnall, C.S.N. Tattnall was charged with culpable destruction of the *Virginia* (*Merrimac*) on May 11, 1862, in Hampton Roads instead of taking her up the James to a place of usefulness.[169] Officers detached and ordered on the court were: Captains Lawrence Rousseau, Franklin Buchanan, and Sidney Smith Lee (who was replaced by Captain George N. Hollins), Commanders Matthew Fontaine Maury, Robert G. Robb, Murray Mason, Eben Farrand, A. B. Fairfax, and George Minor; Lieutenants William Lewis Maury and Robert B. Pegram. This trial was a very unpleasant duty for all these officers, for Tattnall had enjoyed a long and distinguished naval career. They well remembered that it had been Tattnall who had taken his U.S. squadron to the relief of the British in China declaring, "Blood is thicker than water." [170] These men also knew some of the difficulties that had confronted their fellow officer when he had taken over after Buchanan's incapacitating injury suffered in the *Virginia*'s duel with the *Monitor*. In the court testimony they learned just how unreliable had been the engines of the *Virginia*.

Finally the trial was over. The court voted an honorable acquittal for Tattnall, finding that he had offered the enemy battle since early in April and been refused, as the Federals preferred waiting to capture the *Virginia* when her provisions ran out. The court also found that when Norfolk had to be yielded to the Federals Tattnall had no choice but to abandon and burn his ship and that, with the advice given him by men familiar with the James, he had followed the right course in not attempting to take her up the river.[171] Thus Maury participated in the final action concerning the converted *Merrimac*, even as he had taken part in the original vote to raise her.

In the hot summer weeks of 1862 Maury drafted a 16-page letter to his old friend, Octave de Chabannes, Admiral of the French Navy, and a 22-page document to Rear Admiral Robert Fitzroy in London.[172] Through these communications Maury sought to interpret the position of the South and to urge that France and England recognize the Confederate government. Since the beginning of the war there had been periodic proposals to send Maury abroad to carry on work of this nature, but his own great desire was to command a fighting ship. The only approach to such an offer that he ever received occurred on August 23, 1862. " 'Mal' very kindly sent for me Saturday," Maury wrote to Franklin Minor, "to say that there was a gun boat in Charleston I might have. But, as she can't go to sea and is only for harbor defense, I thought it best to decline her tho' I told him if ordered, I'd go. He was very proper, considerate and kind." [173]

Only four days after this conference widespread criticism against Secretary Mallory's handling of the Navy Department came to a head in the passage of a "joint resolution by the Congress of the Confederate States that a joint select committee on the part of the Senate and five on the part of the House be appointed to investigate the administration of the Navy Department under its present head." [174] The Senate concurred the next day.

Some twenty-four hours later Maury received orders that he was to run the blockade and proceed to Europe on Secret Service. He, of course, accepted the duty but asked permission to try to get his daughters, sister-in-law, and young son out of Fredericksburg so that he might know they were beyond the reach of Major General John Pope, who was treating the populace of Fredericksburg with extreme severity.[175] But the South's great victory at Manassas (Second Bull Run), on August 30, 1862, changed everything. The next night the Federals burned their pontoon bridges at Fredericksburg and began the evacuation of the town. Military use of the Richmond, Fredericksburg, and Potomac Railroad prevented Maury's going by train so he hired a carriage. With his wife, who had been in Albemarle for Dick's wedding to Sue Crutchfield, Maury proceeded to Fredericksburg. They stopped off at "Old Mansion," near Bowling Green, to see their daughter Betty who, with her child, had been boarding there. Maury was able to spend a week in Fredericksburg and all his family reached there for a farewell with the exception of John, who was on duty in Mississippi.[176]

It was decided that Maury's 13-year-old son, Matthew, should accompany him to England. Small for his age, the boy was called Matsy by the family and Brave by his father. Maury and his young "aide" left Fredericksburg early on Monday, September 15. In Richmond Maury arranged for passage on the *Hero,* scheduled to sail on the 24th from Charleston, South Carolina.[177] Mallory and other officials held final conferences with Maury and gave him secret verbal instructions for his mission abroad.[178]

Maury himself was not impressed by the mission on which he was being sent, for he felt the Southern authorities were dispatching too many men to purchase ships and munitions for which the Confederate government simply could not supply the cash. He believed that he could have been more useful to "the cause" at home and that he was really being sent into "banishment" by President Davis and Secretary Mallory.[179]

Many other people also considered that the outspoken Maury was being got out of the way. It was certainly understandable, if this was the objective, for Davis was particularly susceptible to criticism of his policies and appointments, and Mallory knew that Maury had considered the Navy Department dilatory in launching certain needed efforts. Though personal animosities may well have entered into the appointment, Maury was pre-eminently fitted for foreign service on behalf of the Confederate government. His scientific achievements had earned him an enviable reputation in England and on the Continent, one which assured him entrée to the highest circles of government, science, and marine commerce. With the scarcity of ships, the loss of the Norfolk Navy Yard, and river shipyards in Virginia and elsewhere in the South, the lack of all kinds of material, and Maury's own personal lameness, it is hard to conceive what better use Davis and Mallory could have made of his services. A possible alternative would have been to have thrown the administration's full backing behind Maury in his torpedo warfare.

The two Matthew Maurys left Richmond at 4 A.M., September 22. After innumerable railroad changes, a steamboat ride across the river at Wilmington, North Carolina, a missed train and other troubles, they reached Charleston on the 24th.[180] Maury wrote his wife that they expected to sail that night and declared, "The Yankees, I hope, will all be asleep and let us go. If we get caught, I expect soon to be exchanged. The Brave and I will have a 'bully' time in prison."[181]

But when the *Hero* put out through the harbor that night enemy craft were hovering off the bar, and she had to turn back. And now began a period of wearing suspense and frustration. Each day the *Hero* was scheduled to leave, and each day the way was barred by vessels of the blockading fleet. General P. G. T. Beauregard, commanding the Department of South Carolina and Georgia, took advantage of the delay to confer with Maury, as did other Confederate leaders.[182] This, however, did little to lift Maury's spirits, and he wrote often to Ann reminding her that, for safety's sake, he would henceforth address her as "My dear friend."[183] He instructed her to address him care of Fraser, Trenholm and Company in Liverpool and urged her to see that the children not risk use of their names but employ the numeral he had assigned to each. He admitted to worry about his son John, and his nephew Dabney, and wondered how they had fared in the fighting at Corinth, Mississippi. But he tried to be cheerful and ended his last letter from Charleston: "I shall leave a note behind to be sent you in case the carrier pigeon brings back word 'all's well.' I am thinking and dreaming about you all the time."[184]

CHAPTER XX

To England on Secret Service

Heavy clouds obscured the light of moon and stars above Charleston on the night of October 9, 1862, and Maury thought that at last he could sail for England. He and Brave were rowed from a dock to a small light-draft steamer, the *Herald,* which had been substituted for the heavier steamer *Hero* and made ready for an attempt to run the Federal blockade. With the father and son was Midshipman James Morris Morgan, C.S.N., who had assisted Maury in placing torpedoes in the James River the preceding June. Young Morgan had been ordered to act as Maury's aide on the voyage and to report for assignment to a Confederate cruiser that Maury was to purchase and equip in England.[1]

The *Herald* weighed anchor and steamed slowly out from Charleston's inner harbor through the channel, guarded by Fort Moultrie on the north and Fort Sumter on the south, into the open sea. With all lights covered, the small steamer was on the point of attempting to cross the Charleston bar when the clouds parted. The sudden light from the moon revealed a Federal sloop-of-war dead ahead. "There was no use trying to hide," young Morgan related. "She also had seen us, and the order, 'Hard-a-starboard!' which rang out on our boat was nearly drowned by the roar of the warship's great guns." [2]

The aim of the Federal gunners was not accurate, however, and the *Herald* was able to steam back into Charleston harbor. Three nights later a drizzling rain gave promise of protection, and the *Herald* headed out for another try. The little steamer almost grounded on the bar but bumped her way across, evaded the blockaders and, making less than seven knots, chugged out to sea, where she soon ran into winds of gale proportion and high waves. With siderails only a few feet above the level of the sea, the *Herald* shipped so much water that her engine went out of commission. Repairs were made, and on the fifth day out the *Herald*'s captain approached a schooner and asked for the latitude and longitude. Midshipman Morgan reported:

We limped away and went on groping for Bermuda. Capt. Coxetter had spent his life in the coasting trade between Charleston and the Florida ports, and even when he commanded for a few months the privateer *Jeff Davis,* he had never been far away from the land. Such was the jealousy, however, of merchant sailors toward officers of the Navy that, with one of the most celebrated navigators in the world on board his ship, he [the captain] had not as yet confided to anybody the fact that he was lost.

On the sixth day, however, he told Commodore Maury that something terrible must have happened, as he had sailed his ship directly over the spot where the Bermuda Islands ought to be! Commodore Maury told him that he could do nothing for him before ten o'clock that night and advised him to slow down. At ten o'clock, the great scientist and geographer went on deck and took observations, at times lying flat on his back, sextant in hand, as he made measurements of the stars. When he had finished his calculations, he gave the captain a course and told him that by steering it at a certain speed he would sight the light at Port Hamilton by two o'clock in the morning.

No one turned into his bunk that night except the commodore and his little son; the rest of us were too anxious. Four bells struck and no light was in sight. Five minutes more passed and still not a sign of it; then grumbling commenced, and the passengers generally agreed with the man who expressed the opinion that there was too much d——d science on board and that we should all be on our way to Fort Lafayette in New York Harbor as soon as day broke. At ten minutes past two the masthead lookout sang out, "Light ho!"—and the learned old commodore's reputation as a navigator was saved.[3]

Maury, Brave, and the midshipman secured accommodations at a modest, whitewashed hotel facing St. George's harbor. During their first days in Bermuda young Morgan learned something about Maury which he described in this way:

> Not knowing of his world-wide celebrity, I was surprised to see the deference paid him by foreigners. We had no sooner settled ourselves at the hotel than the governor sent an aide to tell Lieutenant Maury that he would be pleased to receive him in his private capacity at the Government House. In Europe the commodore was only known as "the great Lieutenant Maury"; they entirely ignored any promotions which might have come to him.
>
> The commandant of Fort St. George also called on him, but took pains to explain that it was the great scientist to whom he was paying

homage, and not the Confederate naval officer. As the commodore's aide I came in for a little of the reflected glory and had the pleasure of accompanying him to a dinner given in his honor on board the H.M.S. *Immortality* at Port Hamilton.[4]

Maury had to wait two weeks in Bermuda to catch the British Royal Mail steamer from St. Thomas on which he planned to proceed to Halifax, Nova Scotia. While on the peaceful British island, he and Brave made use of the opportunity to shop for items needed by the womenfolk of his family in Virginia. Maury was pleased to find the people so friendly to the Southern cause. He was not surprised to learn of their active dislike for Acting Rear Admiral Charles Wilkes, who commanded the United States' blockading fleet cruising off Bermuda.[5] The British could not forget that Wilkes had stopped the British Royal Mail steamer *Trent* on November 8, 1861, and, over the protest of the ship's captain, had removed the Confederate commissioners, Mason and Slidell, and carried them off as prisoners. British fury had forced the commissioners' release, but the *Trent* affair had nearly caused war between Great Britain and the United States.[6] Wilkes's highhanded action had not surprised Maury at the time—he had given up his post as astronomer to the South Seas Exploring Expedition in 1838 rather than serve under Wilkes because of imperious behavior on the part of Wilkes at that early stage of his career.[7]

The moment the Royal Mail steamer *Delta*, in which Maury was to take passage, reached Bermuda waters, the United States sloops-of-war *San Jacinto* and *Mohican* appeared offshore but remained just outside the three-mile limit. Rumor spread that Acting Admiral Wilkes, commanding the *San Jacinto*, was going to remove Maury from the *Delta* in a repetition of his Mason and Slidell removal from the *Trent*. Wilkes had boasted to Bermudans that he had been made an acting rear admiral for that affair.[8] It was feared that Wilkes thought he could win further acclaim at home by capturing Maury. The likelihood of trouble seemed very real when the two United States warships fell in behind the small British vessel as she left the harbor. However, when the *Delta* rounded the headland she met the British man-of-war *Immortality* and sloop-of-war *Desperate* coming from Port Hamilton to prevent a possible incident. The British warships fell in behind the *Delta* and gave continuing protection. Whatever had been the intention of the United States blockade commander, the *Trent* affair was not repeated.[9]

After a five-and-a-half-day passage, which Maury described as "boisterous and tedious," he, Brave, and Morgan were landed at Halifax on the night of November 9. The Confederate flag was run up over the hotel

where Maury stayed, and he was heartened to find pro-Southern sentiment strong among the people of Halifax.[10]

Midshipman Morgan recounted that, "The governor of the colony of
Nova Scotia, the general commanding the troops, and the admiral of the
fleet, all treated 'Lieutenant' Maury, as they insisted on calling him, with
the most distinguished consideration, inviting him to dinners and recep-
tions, etc., to which, as his aide, I had to accompany the great man." [11]

Maury did not have many days to wait for the big Cunard paddle-
wheel, full-rigged steamer *Arabia*, which plied between Boston and Liverpool. Once on board, the three Southerners, of course, faced a hostile
attitude on the part of the Northerners who had embarked at Boston.
Maury was, therefore, grateful to find interesting company in Captain
Richard Cooper, of the Royal Scots Fusiliers, and in the Earl of Dun-
more, who had obtained a leave of absence from his post as a lieutenant
in Her Majesty's Life Guards and gone, incognito, to the South to observe some of the early battles of the war.[12]

Unfortunately for Brave and his father, the *Arabia* hit rough weather
as she steamed eastward in the latitudes called the "roaring forties," and
Maury's aide recorded an episode of his chief's discomfort:

> Commodore Maury was a deeply religious man. He had been lame
> for many years of his life, but no one ever heard him complain. He
> had been many years in the Navy, but had scarcely ever put his foot
> on board of a ship without being seasick, and through it all he
> never allowed it to interfere with his duty. He was the only man I
> ever saw who could be seasick and amiable at the same time; while
> suffering from nausea he could actually joke! I remember once enter-
> ing his stateroom where he was seated with a Bible on his lap and
> a basin alongside of him. I told him that there was a ship in sight,
> and between paroxysms he said, "Sometimes we see a ship, and
> sometimes ship a sea!" [13]

On arriving in Liverpool on November 23, 1862,[14] Maury proceeded
immediately to the office of Fraser, Trenholm and Company,[15] at 10
Rumford Place, to report his arrival to Captain James D. Bulloch, the
Confederacy's Secret Service chief in England, who had already fitted
out the *Alabama* and was in charge of securing and fitting out three
other cruisers.

Maury carried authorization from Secretary Mallory for Bulloch to
be responsible for Maury's travel expenses and pay. Mallory, however,
in the official order, made it very clear to Bulloch that Maury had special authorization to carry out certain projects. Maury also had general
authority to purchase ships to serve as cruisers.[16]

After several days of acquiring information in Liverpool, where he stayed at the Adelphi Hotel, Maury moved on to London to quarters that had been engaged for him in Sackville Street. These proved too expensive so, shortly after his arrival, he moved up to the third floor of the same building. Even in the cheaper rooms Maury found living in London almost prohibitive on Confederate pay. He invited young Morgan to be his guest. Doubtless the youth proved useful as a companion to Brave, for the midshipman described Maury as being very busy. "All day long there would be in front of the house a string of carriages with coronets on their doors, while their owners were paying their respects to the great 'Lieutenant' Maury." [17]

Lord Wrottesley, Rear Admiral and Mrs. Robert Fitzroy, Sir Henry Holland, and other old friends were busy welcoming and entertaining him, as were the British officers whom he had come to know on the *Arabia*.[18] Marin H. Jansen came across the Channel to be with him.[19] Jansen took Brave sightseeing in London while Maury conferred with Confederate Commissioner James M. Mason on the status of the negotiations for recognition of the Confederate government carried on in England by Mason and in France by Commissioner John Slidell.[20] Mason, who had long been a senator in Washington and had known Maury there, wanted Maury's full report on developments at home. The financing of Confederate purchases in England and on the Continent was discussed.

Between appointments Maury did some hurried shopping for clothing, which Ann and the girls had listed as their most pressing needs. He spent $375 on these purchases and shipped the box in the *Princess Royal*, estimating it would be worth $1,000 if it could get through the blockade to the Confederacy.[21]

By December 20, 1862, Maury had formed definite ideas as to the type of vessel he would first seek to purchase and outfit as a Confederate cruiser. On that day he wrote Jansen, who was visiting the British shipyards for his own edification, and asked his Dutch friend to keep an eye out for a vessel that he described. "She should be not over 15 feet draft —good under canvas—fast under steam, with ability to keep the sea for a year—using steam only when necessary in the chase." [22]

Two days later Maury was glad to see in the London *Times* a lengthy letter he had drafted to impress on the English people the hopefulness of the Confederate cause. It was his first attempt in Great Britain to influence public thinking in favor of the South.[23]

Friends in Liverpool invited Maury to bring Brave there for Christmas. While on this visit he wrote his wife, rejoicing over news of the Confederate victory at Fredericksburg but asking, "Where are you and where are your children? You may be in Richmond but we cannot feel sure that any of our conjectures as to your whereabouts are true." [24] It was the first of many expressions of concern about his family's lack of a safe refuge, a worry that was to haunt him throughout the war.

New Year's Day, 1863, found Maury and his son back in their London lodgings and cheered by a visit from J. M. D. Meiklejohn, the school-teacher who had gone to Washington in 1853 to teach the Maury sons. Meiklejohn told his former employer about his small Rose Hill School for boys, located in Bowdon, a pleasant village nine miles from Manchester. It would have been a fine place for Brave to continue his schooling, but Maury decided to keep the boy with him and continue the instruction he had been giving.

On his fifty-seventh birthday, January 14, 1863, Maury scratched a hasty note to his wife and among other things mentioned that "I have been in conversation for the last two hours with an M.P. about recognition. He came to talk about it." [25]

Though Captain Bulloch was never officially so informed, he later expressed the belief that Maury had been sent to England with confidential instructions for action of a political nature.[26] Certainly Maury's activities bore out Bulloch's conclusion. His work for political recognition of the Confederate States was carried on quietly and on a person-to-person basis, but his effort was systematic and constant.

At the same time Maury worked to interpret to the people back home in the Confederacy the attitude of the British. He wrote: "Many of our friends here have mistaken British admiration of Southern 'pluck' and newspaper spite at Yankee insolence as Southern sympathy. No such thing. There is no love for the South here. In its American policy the British government fairly represents the British people." [27]

He pointed out three major factors that worked against the South: the Yankees had intimidated the British government with threats of dire disaster if it recognized the South; since 1850 one and a half million Britishers had gone to the United States, mostly to the North; the war speculators were opposed to peace. Maury frankly admitted that "The sympathy here for us is mostly confined to the upper classes and this sympathy is in the main more apparent than real. . . . We are gaining ground here, it is true, but, before we can expect any aid or comfort, we must show our ability to get along without it." [28]

On January 23 Maury wrote his wife that he had heard from none of them for two months and revealed an anguish he had never before expressed: "My dreams are nightly of death and mutilation of children and friends." [29] The prophetic quality of these dreams he was to learn much later.

However unhappy his sleep, Maury's waking hours were spent in intense activity that had to be carried on in such secrecy that it amounted to stealth. Always there were agents who reported to United States Minister Charles Francis Adams the activities in England of the officers engaged in the Secret Service of the Confederate States. A typical example of this surveillance was a letter sent on January 9 by an assistant secretary of the legation in London to the United States consul in Liverpool, advising that "an armed steamer is to leave Liverpool tomorrow with important messages from Commodore Maury (who is still in England), Mason and Slidell. A man by the name of Hope is the bearer of these dispatches and will go on the steamer." [30]

Maury was much relieved when word came that the important dispatches he had sent by Captain J. Lawson of the *Princess Royal* two months before had reached Secretary Mallory in Richmond.[31] When blockaders captured his ship, the captain had escaped with the dispatches but had been unable to save the box of clothing Maury had sent his family.

Father and son set themselves to save to repurchase the needed clothes but found it difficult, as their living was costing about $50 a week in the bedroom and sitting room they occupied at 10 Sackville Street. Brave wrote his mother describing the maid who serviced their rooms, "Pa calls her the donkey engine because she is so small and darts about so quick and like a little engine." [32] Brave himself was darting about London a good deal in these days as he carried confidential messages from his father to Commissioner Mason.

In early February, 1863, Maury received orders from Richmond that the time had come to purchase and equip, as rapidly as possible, a ship for Confederate naval officers to command as a cruiser operating against United States shipping. Secretary Mallory sent $1,500,000 in cotton certificates to Maury by Lieutenant William Lewis Maury, who reached England about February 1.[33] These cotton obligations certified that cotton would be delivered thirty days after the holder of the paper had so requested. Commissioner Mason believed it wiser to finance ship purchases by using these certificates than by selling Confederate bonds.[34] However, Mason and Maury were in complete agreement that great care had to be exercised in disposing of the certificates to prevent lowering the value of cotton, their government's one cash commodity. Maury, therefore, held back on the sale of the certificates and also waited in the hope that money might be available from the £5,000,000 loan that Commissioner John Slidell had been negotiating with the Paris banking house of Emile Erlanger and Company. However, when Maury found he could purchase a ship then being built at Dumbarton-on-the-Clyde, he borrowed against the certificates he held [35] and turned over the money to his agent, Thomas Bold of Liverpool. Bold went to Glasgow to purchase and equip the uncompleted 550-ton iron screw steamer,[36] which was tersely described by a Yankee sea captain as "clipper-built, fiddle head, full poop, brig rigged, short, thick funnel." [37]

During the purchase negotiations Lewis Maury, who was to command the vessel when completed, stayed with Maury in London. Maury was devoted to this cousin and found his company a cheering experience. However, when the outfitting of his ship began, Lewis went to Scotland, where he lived, incognito, in a small village not far from the Clyde.[38] There he could receive an occasional visitor without attracting undue attention. Through these visitors Lewis kept informed about the progress on the ship he was to command and sent suggestions as to what he wanted done. However, the main supervision of the altering and fitting of the ship was, amazingly enough, carried out by Marin Jansen, who ran an enormous risk to his own career in the Dutch Navy by thus helping Maury and the Confederate cause.[39]

On March 6 Maury wrote Lewis Maury, "Say what small arms and big guns you want and you shall have them." [40] The next day the new ship was launched under the name *Japan,* and two weeks later Lewis came down from Scotland to confer with Maury on final plans for arming the ship.[41] It was all dangerous business to be transacting in a neutral country.

A crew of about fifty men was shipped at the Sailors' Home in Liverpool, the seamen signing articles for a voyage to Singapore and any intermediate ports for a time period of two years. With a care intensified by the American war, British customs authorities inspected the *Japan* minutely before she was cleared from Greenock, in ballast, on April 1, 1863. They found absolutely nothing on board that indicated she was intended for war purposes,[42] though Charles Francis Adams and his men had different ideas.

Just before the *Japan* sailed, under British registry, Lieutenant William Lewis Maury and his small staff, which included Midshipman Morgan, left a secluded English Channel seaport, New Haven, in a small steamer, the *Alar*.[43] On board were the guns and ordnance stores for the *Japan*. The Confederates had learned that Adams's agents expected the *Alar* to rendezvous with the *Japan* at the island of Alderney.[44] The vessels carrying out Maury's plan, therefore, shifted their course, and the two steamers met off the small French port of Ushant. In a stretch of smooth water between that island and Brest, Lieutenant Maury was able to complete the transfer of a 32-pounder Blakely rifle, two 24-pounders and two 10-pounder Whitworth guns, as well as munitions and supplies.

The Confederate naval officer and his staff then boarded and took command of the *Japan,* changing her name to *Georgia* and duly commissioning her as a Confederate man-of-war.[45] Some of the seamen who had been signed for the voyage refused to enter the Confederate service and were returned to England in the *Alar.* From these men United States Minister Adams secured information and made representations to Her Majesty's government that the Foreign Enlistment Act had been flouted. Two Britishers named Jones and Highatt, who had shipped the seamen, were tried at the Liverpool Assizes before Lord Chief Justice Cockburn. But British law apparently did not consider the offense too serious, for each man was only fined £50.[46]

Meanwhile, the *Georgia* was cruising across the South Atlantic, which had been assigned her as an area likely to produce prizes. The first United States merchantman she captured was a vessel of between 3,000 and 4,000 tons, the *Dictator,* bound from New York to Hong Kong with coal and a cargo valued at $86,000. On June 8, off the entrance to Rio de Janeiro harbor, the *Georgia* captured a big clipper ship, the *George Griswold,* and had to bond her as neutral cargo. Five days later the *Georgia* captured a fast clipper bark, the *Good Hope* of Boston, took all her supplies, removed the crew, and burned the ship. Also captured were the full-rigged mechantman *Constitution,* bound from Philadelphia to Shanghai, and the *John Watt.*[47]

This cruise was carried out under great difficulties as Lewis Maury found the *Georgia* incapable of pursuit under sail. Consequently, her fuel consumption was enormous, and this necessitated frequent coalings, which meant delay and risk of capture.[48] The *Georgia* was, of course, regarded as a privateer by the United States but as a warship by the Confederate States. She came under the category best described by James Russell Soley, Assistant Secretary of the Navy under Harrison, when he said of the Confederate cruisers, "Most of them answered all the legal requirements of ships of war; they were owned by the Government and they were commanded by naval officers acting under a genuine commission." [49] Soley pointed out that "there is no rule of law which prescribes the place where a government shall commission its ships" and added that the cruisers were not guilty of any practices "contrary to the laws of war." [50]

These commerce destroyers were loathed by United States authorities not only because of losses inflicted but also because of the reduction of shipping caused by their threat. Maury's role in purchasing and fitting these cruisers increased Northern animosity to him as did the strongly worded public letters he wrote to British and European leaders in behalf of the Southern cause.

Just after the *Georgia* sailed from Scotland, tragic news had reached Maury and Brave. Young Moncure Robinson, of Virginia, who had run the blockade, had brought a letter from Robert H. Maury, with whom Maury had stayed in Richmond, extending sympathy to Maury over the loss of his son John, missing for over a month. The letter had been written in Richmond on February 28, so it placed John's disappearance as having taken place late in January.[51] In his grief Maury abandoned the anonymity of his code salutation and began a note, "My dear, dear wife —My heart is gone from me—my poor dear Davy [John]—no purer nor better spirit has been given up in this war. If he had to die, I hope he died as nobly as he lived." [52]

A week later Maury wrote to Ann from Bowdon, near Manchester, "I came up here last Saturday to put your little son to school with your old teacher." [53] Explaining that he thought Brave would be better off at Meiklejohn's Rose Hill School, since he feared his sadness of spirit might depress the boy, he also mentioned that he might at any time have to go to France on official business. Temporarily, Maury took a parlor and bedroom in Bowdon and stayed there until his official plans were clear. Brave came home to him after school was over each day. The landlady supplied them with very plain meals, and their total expenses did not exceed $15 a week—one piece of comforting news Maury could write home during this period of dreadful anxiety.[54]

For several weeks Maury received no further word concerning John's death or capture. He wrote home: "Talk! I can talk of him all day and then think of him the live long night. His old overcoat that was razeed down for Brave—I used to think sometimes, when Brave went visiting in it with me in London—it looked a little shabby—now it's comely. It has its memories. Brave has orders to protect it. It is the only tangible thing, save a letter, that I have of the lad—very precious to me was that child." [55]

Months were to drag by before Maury learned many details of John's disappearance. Conflicting evidence kept coming in. But the basic facts were eventually put together. Four days after Maury, in England, had dreamed of death and mutilation of his children, his son John, had borrowed the field glasses of Brigadier General Dabney H. Maury, C.S.A., on whose staff he was an aide, and ridden off on a reconnaissance along the east bank of the Mississippi River. None of the officers noticed John's absence until his saddled but riderless mare was found near a break in the levee, four miles south of Vicksburg. A Texan, Major Burnett, who was devoted to the missing young officer and was an experienced tracker, examined the whole area and found that John had apparently swum his mare across the break in the levee and then ridden south along its top. At a certain point the tracks of the mare showed she was halted and then, apparently in an effort to return to camp, the mount had retraced her steps to where she had been found. At the farthest point to which the mare had been ridden, the major found a cartridge box marked with large initials I.V., plus some cartridges, scraps of paper, and small piece of rubber cloth. The initials on the cartridge container were presumed to stand either for the Illinois, Indiana, or Iowa Volunteers. The evidence indicated that an enemy scouting party had seized John. Some 300 paces from the spot, the Texan found footprints and other signs that five or six men had boarded a boat and shoved off into the Mississippi.

After this much was known at General Dabney Maury's headquarters, Colonel Jacob Thompson, who had served as United States Secretary of the Interior under Buchanan, was sent, under a flag of truce, to General U. S. Grant to ask if John was among the Federal prisoners. The Confederate officer was received with courtesy by General Grant and Commodore David Dixon Porter, who said he had known John well at the Observatory in Washington. General Grant stated that he would have inquiry made and that word would be sent to General Maury if his young aide was among the prisoners. No word was ever received from Grant, and so it was believed that John was not a prisoner.[56]

Later, however, there was a disturbing report from a Union officer who produced the field glasses that John had been using when he disappeared. This man stated that John Maury was a prisoner not far from Grant's headquarters at the very time the inquiry was made under a flag of truce. The story that was finally believed by most of the Maury family was that of a man who said he had been in the raiding party and had seen John captured, carried across the Mississippi to the Federal side, and there shot by one of the men in the party. The whole action had doubtless been carried out far from the eyes of a Federal officer, and every effort of the family in the years to come failed to clarify the picture. Rumors continued to spring up of someone who had seen John alive, and Maury was tortured by hope each time this occurred. Each rumor, however, was thoroughly traced, Union prison records were examined, and always the search proved fruitless. The complete story was never to be known.

In the month after Maury first learned of the loss of his son his sorrow so affected his vitality as to cause concern among his English friends.[57] He was, however, too disciplined an officer to allow his personal grief to interfere long with the performance of duties entrusted to him.

In April he met members of the Board of Admiralty in Sheffield, to witness the rolling of armor plate 4½ inches thick, 4½ feet wide, and 45 feet long. Knowing that this presaged the building of ironclads, and ironclads only, Maury commented, "and thus perished the wooden walls of Old England." [58] The day of the sailing ship was nearly over.

On April 21 Maury wrote to Jansen in Holland that he had "plenty of orders and no money," adding, "However, I hope soon to be in funds and, when I am, I want to go to France and contract for a cupola ram which I have asked to have the command of." [59] He longed for clean-cut action at sea, away from the watchful eyes of Mr. Adams's agents. He stated at this time, "If I had had money and officers I could, since I have been here, [have] fitted out half dozen just as good to prey upon Yankee commerce as the *Alabama*." [60]

On May 25, 1863, Maury went to France to negotiate with shipbuilder L. Arman of Bordeaux for a twin-turreted ironclad. Arman, addressing himself, out of Gallic courtesy or ignorance, to "Admiral" Maury, declared, "I pledge myself in one month after the signing of the agreement to furnish you the proof of the authorization to export the armament that you will have to place on the vessel and will build with a very short delay, six ships of the same kind." [61] Diplomatic maneuvering had been going on, and it looked at this time as if the French Emperor would allow these warships to be built and to slip out to sea to waiting Confederate officers. Maury conferred in Paris with Commissioner Slidell on this point, knowing that Napoleon III was interested in having ironclads built in France so that his naval constructors could study them.[62]

Returning to London, Maury received orders from Secretary Mallory to confine his attention "to anti-mercantile cruisers." However, Maury first reported the arrangements he had made in France: "I had a contract already drawn in which for 1,500,000 francs, say $300,000, builders agreed to furnish a double steamer—twin screws—armored ram of 1358 tons displacement . . . maximum speed not less than 11 knots—to be delivered at sea armed and equipped in seven months. But you observe the 'agent for the loan' [Erlanger loan] announced conditions which made it impossible for the work to proceed." [63]

Maury now started scouting for a small vessel that could be equipped and armed as a Confederate cruiser.[64] In September he found that the *Victor*, a 500-ton screw steamer that had served as a dispatch boat of the Royal Navy, might be obtained. As a Confederate officer, Maury could not buy the vessel direct from the neutral British government, so on October 6 he gave his English agent, Thomas Bold, 100 cotton certificates as a first installment of pay for the *Victor*. Bold turned this over to a responsible British mercantile firm, which then purchased the ship, final payment being made on November 14.[65] The *Victor* had neither masts nor rigging on board, so the British government followed its usual policy of allowing the purchasers to equip her at the Sheerness Dockyard with sufficient fittings to take her to sea. Mr. Rumble, who was inspector of machinery there, closely supervised the whole process and made certain that no warlike equipment was put aboard.

The work necessary on the *Victor* for her to put to sea on a trial run had not been finished when Maury discovered that word of the purchase had leaked to Adams. For this reason, on the night of November 24, 1863, he had the *Victor* hurried out from Sheerness and headed across the Channel. Midway to Calais she was boarded by a small party of Confederate naval officers. Orders were read, the Confederate flag was run up, and the *Victor* was commissioned a Confederate ship of war under the name *Rappahannock*.

The uncompleted *Rappahannock* suffered a slight accident to her machinery that night and put into Calais the next day. The United States minister to France promptly remonstrated with the Emperor's government, but the latter refused to order the Confederate vessel out as she had sought asylum under an apparent necessity. However, the authorities at Calais were ordered to prevent any armament or warlike stores being put on the *Rappahannock*. At the time that this vessel put into Calais, Maury turned over his authority for her to Samuel Barron, flag officer of Confederate naval activities in France.[66] Though the *Rappahannock* never cruised against United States merchantmen, she did serve by tying up two American vessels that had to patrol off Calais to prevent her putting to sea.[67] The *Rappahannock* was later used by the Confederates as a depot and as a rendezvous for officers who were to go out in the ironclad ram *Stonewall,* which was completed too late to achieve anything for the Southern cause.[68]

It has often been stated that Maury was sent abroad primarily to further his investigations concerning torpedo warfare. From his activities, however, it seems probable that his secret verbal instructions from Secretary Mallory must have placed equal emphasis on ship purchasing. During the first months of Maury's time in England he gathered information from every possible source on torpedoes and also on guns and sent it to Richmond, but his diary and letters reveal that it was not until August 21, 1863, that he believed his findings were so important that he should begin laboratory experiments on torpedoes. He then wrote his old friend Piazzi Smyth, the astronomer royal for Scotland, to ask if the magnetic exploder developed by Charles Wheatstone and the phosphide fuse perfected by the chemist Abel could be bought and, if so, where and for how much.[69] Late in September Maury ordered two of these magnetic exploders at £21 each and 500 of Abel's fuses from a London firm and had them shipped to him at Bowdon. When information as to the composition of this fuse was refused him, he analyzed it himself to see if the Confederates could manufacture it and immediately sent exploders and fuses to Richmond.[70] All he could do was hope that the ordnance works in Richmond would be able to secure the materials needed to duplicate the fuses.

Meanwhile Maury missed no chance to carry on the propaganda phase of his mission. On August 17, 1863, he wrote an 11-page communication to the London *Times* on "Prospects of the Confederates," [71] and at the end of the month he attended the annual meeting of the British Association for the Advancement of Science at Newcastle-on-Tyne. He was shown marked attentions there and had an opportunity to discuss scientific matters with many of his British colleagues.[72]

Maury worked closely with the Southern Independence Association, of Manchester, and even more closely with the London Society for Promoting the Cessation of Hostilities in America, in which the Reverend Francis W. Tremlett, rector of St. Peter's Church, Belsize Park, was a leader. Tremlett had been one of the first Englishmen to call on Maury when he arrived in London, and they had become close friends. The Anglican clergyman was heartily in sympathy with the Confederate cause. On November 1, 1863, he preached a sermon at St. Peter's that Maury considered such an admirable call to a Christian end of the war in America that a plan was evolved to send a copy of this sermon to the clergyman in charge of every parish in England.[73] Each rector, vicar, or curate was urged to solicit the signatures of his parishioners to an enclosed petition to end the war.

In the area of personal affairs Maury was pleased that Brave had not permitted his sorrow over John's loss to keep him from doing good work in school. By December, 1863, Brave had worked his way to top scholastic honors at Rose Hill. To celebrate this and because he also knew that it was unwise for them to remain alone spending the holidays talking about John, Maury accepted Christmas invitations that would give his son a rest and a glimpse into another world than that of the schoolroom. The father and son went first to Liverpool to visit the Bolds and to have Christmas dinner with the Lairds, the shipbuilding family for whom Maury had a particular fondness and respect.[74]

Wrottesley Hall, near Wolverhampton, was the scene of their next visit. Maury enjoyed hours of talk with his host Lord Wrottesley. It was a valuable opportunity for Maury to discuss recent scientific and technological advances in England. The two men also talked of their continuing hope for an international meteorological conference that would deal with the weather of the land as well as of the sea. Wrottesley liked particularly to reminisce about the events leading up to the Brussels Conference in 1853 and Maury's visit to Wrottesley Hall at that time. He told Brave about the visit and took him out to the summerhouse so that the boy could see where his father had carved his initials.[75] Lord Wrottesley also showed Brave the oak tree on his grounds where tradition said Charles II had hidden while fleeing from Cromwell.

From Wrottesley Hall Maury and his son journeyed to Stowe to be the guests of the Duke and Duchess of Buckingham. The Duke had long urged Maury to make this visit and had been most gracious in recalling the hospitality extended him long ago at the Observatory in Washington. Maury wrote his wife to report how charming the Duchess had been to Brave and to him, adding, "Her Grace—whose hair and eyes and complexion are all of the colour of 'somebody' whom I love and admire above all women on the face of this earth. Stowe is the grandest and most magnificent country residence I have yet seen. The House presents a larger front than the Capitol in Washington and the grounds are superb." [76] But Maury found it hard to enjoy the sumptuous meals at Stowe when he thought of his family in Virginia reduced by war conditions to a diet so meager as to be inadequate for the maintenance of vitality.[77]

Conditions had grown increasingly difficult for the Confederate naval officers who were attempting to secure vessels in Europe or keep them at sea. Commander John Newland Maffitt had had his health severely damaged by his long cruise in the *Florida*, as had Commander William Lewis Maury in the *Georgia*.[78] The latter ship was no longer operative, but in January, 1864, Flag Officer Samuel Barron issued an order for a desperate effort to break the *Rappahannock* out of Calais, to effect a rendezvous off Morocco with the *Georgia* and receive her armament.[79] The latter ship waited in vain, since the *Rappahannock* could not make good an escape from the French port.

Even so, William L. Dayton United States minister to France, on January 26, 1864, wrote back to United States Secretary of State William H. Seward, "It is a matter of great surprise in Europe that, with our apparent naval force, we permit such miserable craft to chase our commerce from the ocean; it affects seriously our prestige." [80]

The cruisers had wrought heavy damage, but the United States was from this time onward to have less and less to fear at sea from the Confederates. The Southerners' dream of having ironclads built in France had collapsed in 1863, when Napoleon III withdrew his tacit approval after remonstrances from England and the United States.[81]

In the winter of 1864 there arose a further complication with the French because of Napoleon III's decision that Mexico, which he had conquered, should receive as its emperor the Archduke Maximilian of Austria. As Emperor Maximilian would, of course, be supported in Mexico by French troops, the Confederate government was anxious to win the friendship of Maximilian and his government-to-be. Great effort was made toward this end and for a while it appeared that Maximilian would recognize the Confederacy and enter into a close tie with the government in Richmond. As his part in this international intrigue Maury carried on a considerable correspondence with Maximilian, who had previously honored him for his scientific achievements. Maximilian again extended praise and appreciation to Maury and particularly thanked him for calling his attention to "the possibilities of California," [82] a diplomatic way of referring to proposals for separating California from the Union and restoring the area to Mexico.

With the prowess of Southern arms on the wane, however, Maximilian abandoned his idea of receiving Confederate Commissioner Slidell in Paris. On April 10, 1864, a delegation that had come from Mexico proclaimed Maximilian emperor, and five days later he sailed for Vera Cruz.

Early in May Maury became ill of an intestinal disorder. When he did not respond to the treatment of the local physician in Bowdon, Confederate Navy Surgeon B. W. Green came from Paris to advise and care for him.[83] After the severe phase of the illness had passed, Maury was very weak but able to resume work at his desk.

At this time he was greatly occupied with correspondence concerning the drive of the Society for Obtaining the Cessation of Hostilities.[84] The committee in London consisted of such men as Lord R. Cecil, Lord P. Cecil, the Marquis of Lothian, Lord Wharncliffe, Mr. Justice Halliburton, the Marquis of Bath, the Hon. C. W. Fitzwilliam, A. J. B. Beresford-Hope, and W. S. Lindsay, a member of Parliament as well as the largest shipowner in England.[85] Maury went to London on June 9 to assist the committee in their effort to submit to Lord Palmerston, the Prime Minister, proof, through signed petitions, that there was a strong feeling in the British Isles that Her Majesty's government, either with other powers or alone, should tender friendly offices to endeavor to bring about a cessation of hostilities in America, without endeavoring to force a reunification of South and North.[86]

Maury was upset over a delay in the committee's visit, but they finally made the official call to Lord Palmerston on July 15, 1864. However, the British government still refused diplomatic recognition of the Confederate States and would not take action on the peace move. After the deputation's return from the conference with the Prime Minister, Maury wrote his wife, "Palmerston said Her Majesty's government is in entire

sympathy with the South but the time is now not auspicious to interfere." [87] This careful political utterance on the part of Palmerston dashed
the hopes of the leaders of the committee, but they resolved to make one
more try through the House of Commons. Maury set about drafting the
appeal for the committee.[88]

During his stay in London Maury, who was still suffering acute pain,
sought the professional advice of his friend, Sir Henry Holland, physician in ordinary to Queen Victoria. Afterwards Maury wrote his wife,
"He prescribed, among other things, a plentiful supply out of his own
barrel of hominy, sent from Baltimore, but made, I think, by the taste
and the looks, in good old Fredericksburg." [89]

Not helpful to Maury's recovery was receipt at this time of word that
his eldest son, Dick, had been dangerously wounded on June 16 in a
charge on General B. F. Butler's position below Richmond. Dick's regiment was reduced to 150 men in this assault. He had been shot through
the hips, and the surgeons believed the wound would probably prove
fatal. Eight days after the event, however, a report was sent to Maury
that his son would live but would undoubtedly be crippled.[90] In addition to this distressing news came word that Maury's son-in-law Wellford Corbin had been captured in the fighting around Petersburg.[91]

On June 19, 1864, the most famous of all the Confederate cruisers, the
C.S.S. *Alabama,* was defeated off Cherbourg in an old-fashioned sea duel
to which she had challenged the U.S.S. *Kearsarge.* When the *Alabama*
sank, Captain Raphael Semmes escaped in a small craft and reached
England. There he joined Maury as a guest of the Reverend Francis W.
Tremlett at his home at Belsize Park, London.[92] Semmes gave Maury a
firsthand account of the 23-months' cruise of the *Alabama,* in which she
had captured or destroyed shipping that the United States government
later valued at $19,021,428.[93]

During the preceding months Maury had been quietly pursuing further investigations concerning improvements that could be made in the
use of torpedoes and had sent valuable new findings to the Confederate Navy Department in midwinter, when Commander William Lewis
Maury returned to Richmond. He had also shipped a supply of newly
developed, highly effective Ebner electric exploders. The effectiveness of
the torpedoes in preventing the Federal fleet from sweeping up the
James River to Richmond was now finally acknowledged by Secretary
of the Navy Mallory, who wrote Maury urging that he rush any additional information he had on torpedoes.[94] Remembering Mallory's having laughed at his torpedo proposal early in the summer of 1861, Maury
wrote Jansen to tell of Mallory's total conversion to torpedoes: "The

'prejudices' of which the Secretary speaks [in his letter] as existing in the outside world were as strong in Richmond and with him as they were anywhere. He thought nothing of the plan when I proposed it and would give me no encouragement till I prevailed on him one day to go and see me explode a keg of powder under water." [95]

Having worked closely with Britain's Wheatstone and Whitworth, Maury intensified his scientific investigations, rented a spare room at Bowdon, and set up his own laboratory. In order to make some large-scale tests of submarine explosives he went to London and, while he was experimenting at a shop there, General Sir John Burgoyne came to observe, as the British were then "moving upon the question of submarine mining and torpedoes." [96] Because of his co-operation with the British, Maury was given access to information received by Her Majesty's government at that time concerning the experiments in "Seeminen" of Baron von Lenk, a major general in the Austrian Army.[97]

Maury had closely followed the British study and manufacture of guncotton for military purposes and now advised the Confederate Navy that guncotton should be used in torpedoes to be floated near the surface as this explosive was only one third the weight of gunpowder. The latter, he warned, should still be used for mines to be placed on the bottom of a river or bay. In late August, 1864, Maury shipped a great deal of torpedo equipment to the Navy Department in Richmond, and in October he sent further information and supplies back by Captain Raphael Semmes, who was to take command on the James River.[98] He also wrote General Robert E. Lee, Secretary of War James A. Seddon, and Secretary of the Navy Mallory, urging that the Confederacy use torpedoes on land as well as under the water.[99]

Maury's hope that a negotiated peace might be reached was dashed by Lincoln's re-election in November. He was further saddened at news of hardships that were the lot of his wife and daughters, who had for nearly two years been living in the former infirmary of the University of Virginia at Charlottesville. Because most of the university students were off at war, the Maurys had been allowed to rent this refuge.[100] Diana's husband was still a prisoner at Fort Donelson and Dick was too crippled to walk.

Hopeful that the tide of war might once again turn in favor of the South, Maury labored on with his torpedo investigations. His main findings in those months were thus described by him to a British electrical engineer:

> My own experiments show that the electrical torpedo or mine has not hitherto been properly appreciated as a means of defense in war.

It is as effective for the defense as ironclads and rifled guns are for the attack. . . . These experiments have resulted in some important improvements and contrivances, not to say inventions and discoveries, which have been fully made known to you verbally.

The points upon which this system hangs and which give special value to the information imparted to you concerning it are mainly these: 1. A plan for determining by cross bearings when the enemy is in the torpedo field of destruction and for "making connections" among the torpedo wires in a certain way and by which the concurrence of each of two operators becomes necessary for the explosion of any one or more torpedoes. This plan requires each operator to be so placed or stationed that a line drawn straight from them to the place of the torpedoes may intersect as nearly as practicable at right angles. And it requires the connection to be such that each operator may put his station in or out of circuit at will. When the torpedoes are laid, a range for each station is established for every torpedo or group of torpedoes. When either operator observes an enemy in range with any torpedo, he closes his circuit for that torpedo. If the enemy before getting out of this range should enter the range for any torpedo from the other station, the operator there closes his circuit and discharges the igniting spark. Consequently, if the ranges belong to the same torpedo, its explosion takes place. But if not, there will be no explosion. Hence, here is an artifice by which explosion becomes impossible when the enemy is not in the field of destruction and sure when she is. 2. The Electrical Gauge, a contrivance of my own which you perfectly understand and some of which you have already made; by means of it one of the tests which the igniting fuse has to undergo before it is accepted is applied. By means of it, the operators can telegraph through the fuse to each other without risk to the torpedoes and by which the torpedoes may without detriment to their explosibility be tested daily or as often as required. And thus the operators can at all times make sure that all is right. 3. A plan for planting torpedoes where the water is too deep for them to lie on the bottom and explode with effect, by which they will not interfere with the navigation of the channels and by which, when the enemy makes his appearance, they may by the touch of a key be brought instantly into the required position at the required depth.[101]

While in London early in 1865 Maury suffered a severe kidney attack and was operated on at that time.[102] In spite of this, he quickly returned to his torpedo experiments and to getting in order all financial accounts

of his official transactions in England. Because there was no hope of purchasing more ships for the Confederacy or of achieving diplomatic recognition, Maury had been granted permission by Secretary Mallory to
return to the Confederacy whenever he judged it the best course.[103] In
late March Maury acknowledged that Richmond was likely to fall but
thought he had a sufficient supply of the improved torpedo equipment
to assist the Confederacy somewhere else. As the only way into the Confederacy was by that time through Texas ports, he planned to go by
that route. His departure was delayed, however, when the old kidney
pain returned, and on April 8 he was forced to submit to another operation, which he hoped would put him in shape for the voyage to the
South.[104] Maury wanted to leave Brave in England to complete his education, but the expense forbade his doing this. Besides, Brave wished
to go with his father to Texas and to volunteer there. By April 20 Maury
had received word of the fighting around Farmville, Virginia, and that
Lee's army was breaking up.[105] Still he felt he should continue his plan
to sail on May 2, as his torpedoes might be used to keep Galveston harbor open for the Confederates.[106]

Finally, six days later, Maury received a long-awaited statement from
Thomas Bold that all of his accounts, which had earlier been settled
with Commodore Barron, had now been audited by Captain Bulloch
"who, after examination, passed them all as correct without the alteration of a single figure." To this Bold felt constrained to add, "Although
the custom here would have sanctioned your receiving a large per cen-
tum in the way of commission on contracts, purchases and disburse-
ments made by me, yet you consistently set your face against it and never,
to my certain knowledge, received a shilling." [107]

On May 1 Commissioner Mason drafted a dispatch for Maury to take
to Secretary of State Judah P. Benjamin. Mason stated that the evacuation of Richmond and the surrender of General Robert E. Lee, which
had taken place at Appomattox Courthouse, Virginia, April 9, had made
Europe feel the South could not continue the war elsewhere. Mason went
on to state that he did not accept this as true and would remain in
England to await orders.[108]

Maury sailed on May 2, bearing this and other dispatches, and carrying with him some $40,000 worth of torpedo equipment for the desper-
ate attempt to keep Galveston harbor open. Brave was by his side as
they steamed across the Atlantic on the Royal Mail steamer *Atrato*. Two
weeks later, when they put in at St. Thomas in the West Indies, Maury
obtained Northern newspapers and learned of the further collapse of
the Confederacy.[109]

When the *Atrato* docked in Havana on the morning of May 22 Maury learned authoritatively that General Joseph E. Johnston had surrendered the Army of the Tennessee. That settled Maury's course. There was no possible service he could render by going on to Texas. He grounded his arms by ordering ashore the torpedo equipment he had been taking to Galveston. He left it in custody for Captain Bulloch, who had paid for it out of Confederate funds. The material actually belonged to no one, the Confederate States of America having ceased to exist. Maury could probably have realized $20,000 from selling the torpedo equipment in Havana, but he felt it improper for him to make such a sale.[110]

This disposition of the torpedo material was the first step in a plan Maury had worked out during the Atlantic crossing, to put into effect if the news at Havana confirmed that all effective Confederate resistance was at an end.[111] Having faced the fact that his own future was uncertain and offered little hope of systematic education for Brave, Maury immediately booked passage for his son on a steamer scheduled to sail within a few days for New York.[112] Although Maury heard in Havana that feeling in the North had risen to a new pitch of bitterness toward Southerners because of the tragic assassination of President Lincoln by the mad actor John Wilkes Booth, Maury did not believe that United States authorities would turn back a 16-year-old boy who had taken no part in the war.

During his crowded two and a half days in Cuba Maury learned that Flag Officer Samuel Barron, and his party of officers who had preceded him to Havana, intended to wait there for a general amnesty. There were two factors that militated against Maury's remaining with them. He hoped that recently inaugurated President Andrew Johnson would issue such an amnesty but was far from sanguine about it. Maury remembered all too clearly that the amnesty President Lincoln had offered in December of 1863, made when the South was still in fighting posture, had spelled out six categories of Confederates not eligible to the amnesty. It was impossible for Maury to forget that the duties to which he had been ordered by the Confederate government had placed him in three of the six excepted categories: "all who are or shall have been civil or diplomatic officers or agents of the so-called Confederate government" (his propaganda work would doubtless include him as an agent); "all who are or shall have been military or naval officers of said so-called Confederate government above the rank of colonel in the army or lieutenant in the navy"; "all who resigned commissions in the [U.S.] army or navy . . . and afterwards aided the rebellion." [113] Even if the new President decided to follow an extremely generous policy of conciliation, Maury suspected that a *general* amnesty would not be issued for some time to come. And as he had no friend in authority in Cuba to

419

help him secure work, he felt he must go where he had such a friend in the hope that he could earn a living.

After giving Brave final instructions for his venturesome return to the United States, Maury said a quick farewell to him on May 24 and once more boarded the *Atrato,* bound for Mexico.[114] As soon as the ship reached the open sea, Maury began composition of a letter he considered necessary to declare himself no longer a belligerent. At sea, on May 25, 1865, Maury wrote a note to the United States consul at Vera Cruz, Mexico, asking him to transmit the enclosed letter addressed "To the officer in command of the U.S. Naval forces in the Gulf of Mexico." It read:

> In peace as in war I follow the fortunes of my native old state (Virginia). I read in the public prints that she has practically confessed defeat and laid down her arms. In that act mine were grounded also. I am here without command, officially alone, and am bound on matters of private concern abroad. Nevertheless, and as I consider further resistance worse than useless, I deem it proper formally so to confess, and to pledge you in the words of honor that, should I find myself before the final inauguration of peace within the jurisdiction of the United States, to consider myself a prisoner of war, bound by the terms and conditions which have been or may be granted to General Lee and his officers. Be pleased to send your answer through my son (Colonel R. L. Maury), a prisoner of war on parole in Richmond. In the meantime, and until I hear to the contrary, I shall act as though my surrender had been formally accepted on the above named terms and conditions.
>
> M. F. Maury
> Commander, C.S. Navy [115]

With that signature Maury closed his naval career.

CHAPTER XXI

Starting Over—New Virginia, Mexico

On the short voyage from Havana to Vera Cruz, Maury took stock of his situation. He was virtually a man without a country. He was certainly a man without job, salary, or private income—and owning no home anywhere to serve as shelter for his family.[1] His Confederate bonds, into which he, like every dedicated Southerner, had converted his savings, were worthless.[2] His situation would not have been pleasing to any self-respecting individual, and to Maury it seemed intolerable. He was able to see only one plan of action that might offer him an honorable way out of his dilemma—to continue on to Mexico City and offer his services to Maximilian. Feeling confident that he would receive a warm personal welcome from the Emperor by whom he had been honored for his scientific work, Maury was less sure of the reception that would be given to the proposals he planned to make.[3]

Faced with the fact that the South had gone down to defeat in everything but spirit, and in desperate need of a course of action that offered hope for the future, Maury had conceived the idea that many families, whose fortunes had been ruined in the war, might like to emigrate to Mexico and make a fresh start. He knew well the pride of Southern men and believed that a good many of them would prefer expatriation to being governed by their conquerors. He also thought that planters whose homes had been burned or destroyed by bombardment during the war, whose fields had earlier been depleted by too-constant planting to one crop and had suffered four years without fertilization, might prefer new homes on fertile, comparatively untouched land in Mexico. He had begun thinking of this possibility in London when he had heard of General Lee's surrender, and he had developed the idea into a plan on the long voyage from England to Cuba.[4] He was satisfied that it had been wise for him to leave Havana, where he had no prospect of employment, and he was glad he was nearing the coast of Mexico.

While still at sea, Maury had written to the Reverend Francis W.

Tremlett in England, "If 'Max' is wise and will encourage my New Virginia schemes, these people will establish his empire and make him great." [5]

But even while planning a "New Virginia" colony in Mexico Maury found it hard to suppress his yearning to go home to old Virginia. When he reached the end of the completed section of the railroad line that Colonel Andrew Talcott, former engineer of the commonwealth of Virginia, had contracted to build from the coastal city of Vera Cruz to Mexico City, Maury, on May 29, 1865, wrote a Northern well-wisher to ask what would happen if he should come to New York. [6] It was a question dictated by his emotions, for in his mind Maury could not have deceived himself as to the answer—his departure from Havana had proved that.

The truth was that Maury's letter to the officer in command of the United States naval forces in the Gulf of Mexico, offering to consider himself a prisoner of war should he find himself within the jurisdiction of the United States, was—however clever—an act of desperation. He well knew how small was the likelihood of the United States' granting him, who had been a foreign agent, the same terms as were granted the soldiers who had surrendered with Lee. Maury did not actually expect that the United States would send him a reply in care of his son Dick. He didn't really anticipate an answer when he wrote the letter. He wrote because he felt the situation required some such formality.

Maury's enthusiasm for his plan to bring former Confederates to Mexico was increased by his first days in that land. "On the way from Vera Cruz to the capital," Maury stated, "I saw corn in all its stages, from the time of its scattering by the hand of the sower, till it was gathered in the arms of the reaper. But agriculture is in a rude state. I saw them ploughing with a stick, and sawing with an axe, hoeing their corn with a shovel, and grinding it with a pebble. A few of our clever farmers, bringing with them their agricultural apprentices, would give new life and energy to the country. By sprinkling the Empire with settlers of this sort, they and their improved implements of husbandry and methods of culture would serve as so many new centres of agricultural life, energy, and improvement."

On reaching Mexico City, Maury put up at the Hotel Iturbide and drafted a letter to His Excellency General de la Peza, Minister of War in Maximilian's government. In this communication Maury outlined his system for the use of electric torpedoes and the results that had been achieved by the Confederates through their use of these submarine mines. He concluded by offering his knowledge of the defensive use of torpedoes to the Emperor of Mexico.[7]

The wait for definite news concerning the policy of the United States government toward the defeated South seemed interminable to Maury, but on the night of June 16 Colonel Andrew Talcott reached Mexico City after a 17-day trip from New York. The next day he gave to Maury a copy of the amnesty proclamation that had been issued by President Andrew Johnson on May 29.[8] Instead of reducing the number of categories of former Confederates excluded from the amnesty proclaimed by Lincoln, President Johnson had added eight more excepted categories, making a total of fourteen.

Of the eight additional categories three applied to Maury: "all persons who have been or are absentees from the United States for the purpose of aiding the rebellion"; "all persons who left their homes within the jurisdiction of the United States to aid the Confederacy"; and "all persons who have been engaged in the destruction of the commerce of the United States." [9]

President Johnson added in his proclamation that an individual in the excepted classes could make a special application for executive pardon. After reading the President's concluding statement that "clemency will be liberally extended as may be consistent with the facts of the case and the peace and dignity of the United States," [10] Maury had no illusions as to how the facts of his case would be regarded in Washington.

In addition, Maury was faced with the haunting question of whether— even if there was any likelihood of its being granted—he could, in honor, apply for a pardon. Like tens of thousands of other men who had felt that secession was a constitutional right and not treason to the United States, and that a state's secession automatically carried with it its citizens, Maury pondered how a man could ask pardon for following what he considered the course of moral principle.[11]

On June 19, in somber mood, he wrote Ann: "I have read the so called 'Amnesty' proclamation. Horrid. According to it, I can't come to you. I remained in the house all day yesterday and was in deep meditation." [12]

A letter from Ann's brother Dr. Brodie S. Herndon, written on May 1 from Richmond, where he had served as a surgeon in Confederate hospitals, did nothing to lighten Maury's distress:

> In view of the state of the public mind in the North at present, I think it would be decidedly unsafe for you to return to this country. Your absence abroad in a semi-diplomatic character, your prominence, and the earnest part taken by you in the cause, would make you a decided object of that "vengeance against leaders" so

openly proclaimed and so plainly visible. In time, I hope, these vindictive feelings will subside, and then, and only then, would it be safe and prudent for you to return.

A good many of the young men of the South will go abroad, and this is one of the gloomy features of our future. Dick was here last night. . . . He is implacable, and declares that he cannot live in this country. He and Betty are greatly opposed to your return. They have just written their mother begging her to go to you. I believe sister Ann will be embarrased in her mind to decide what to do. But I think she will try to possess her soul in patience, and wait to hear directly from you, and know your plans and wishes.[13]

At that point in his reading Maury must surely have stopped to think of his wife and her embarrassment of mind to which her brother had alluded. Much as he longed to have his wife with him, Maury had no idea of suggesting that she join him until he had a definite salaried position that would ensure his staying in Mexico. And he knew just how difficult it would be even then for Ann to come to a foreign land. He was aware that, despite her many wonderful qualities, she was not a person who transplanted well. She had grown up in Virginia. Her only move in her life had been fifty miles up the road from Fredericksburg to Washington, and she had gone back to Fredericksburg to visit whenever she could, although Washington in the prewar years had been full of Virginians and quite Virginian in flavor.

When he continued with his reading of Brodie's letter, the words of his doctor brother-in-law gave Maury much-desired information about his eldest son.

Dick's health and strength in his legs are much improved. He now walks pretty well without his crutches. You know he went with Lee, in spite of his lameness, to Appomattox Court House, and was paroled [as a prisoner of war following General Lee's surrender] there.[14]

Brodie, who was deeply religious, concluded:

May God give His Holy Spirit to His people, to animate their hearts and minds and guide them aright. . . . May He grant that we come forth from our sore trials a wiser and better people—a nation fearing God and working righteousness. If the North deals kindly with the South, I do not think it impossible in time to heal the deep wounds that have pierced so many hearts. It took more than a generation to efface the animosities we bore England; but they were effaced.

We shall not live to see the changes in character wrought in the old dominion [Virginia] and the other slave States by the abolition of slavery; but our children will. We shall no doubt gain much; I am full of hope myself. . . . I believe the balance-sheet will be much in our favour.[15]

Dick advised his father not to return, bluntly stating, "I do not think that duty does call you. . . . What good can you do the State by coming here and hanging or suffering a long imprisonment only to be banished at the expiration of it?"[16] Dick's letter had been written after it was learned that Jefferson Davis was manacled in a casemate at Fortress Monroe, Virginia. The former Confederate President was held under threat of trial for treason.

Equally disheartening was the warning from Maury's daughter Betty, who, with her husband, Will Maury, had been given shelter by James H. Grant in Richmond. "Don't trust to any parole or any promise. General Curtis of the U.S. Army, who is staying here, said to me this morning that you ought not to come under any circumstances. General Lee said to me the other day, 'Mrs. Maury, tell your father from me not to think of coming home.' "[17]

Rutson Maury, who had been a staunch supporter of the Union cause throughout the war, in spite of a ten weeks' imprisonment for an unwise business trip south early in the hostilities, wrote in reply to Maury's query about going to New York, "I think you'd find a *prison* all ready to receive you and find yourself inside of it within 24 hours. . . . What would be done with you afterwards is more than I can say."[18] Rutson did hold out hope that four years might change the situation and enable Maury to return then to his homeland.

From England Frank Tremlett counseled against return, reporting that Minister Adams had expressed the hope that Maury would not risk it because the people of the North were more incensed against him than against any other Confederate. Tremlett added, "Adams said this at a dinner party just after your letter to Godon appeared."[19] Maury's letter of surrender had—unknown to him—been transmitted to the United States by Acting Admiral Sylvanus W. Godon, U.S.N., who had been ringleader of the anti-Maury members of the 1855 Navy Retiring Board. The letter had been published in the Washington *National Intelligencer* without comment. The New York *Times* had printed it but with accompanying condemnatory remarks.[20]

Rutson sent Maury a clipping of the New York *Times* copy of his surrender letter and explained that Maury's application to be considered a prisoner of war on parole would be automatically rejected. "Parole would not be granted unless you came home and then you would be a State Prisoner." [21]

In Virginia General Robert E. Lee, who had considered himself on military parole, had been excluded from the amnesty. He had decided to make application for individual pardon but waited for a reply to his application. Lee continued to wait. Pardon was never granted. Lee's move toward conciliation, however, led many Southerners, whose prominence was not such as to make the granting unacceptable to President Johnson, to apply for pardon.[22]

To the numerous opinions warning Maury not to attempt a return to the United States was added a succinct "don't come yet" in a letter from his nephew, Major General Dabney H. Maury.[23] The unanimity of opinion confirmed for Maury the instinctive impression he had had in Havana—that he had no reasonable alternative to exile.

Maury, however, had not waited for letters from home before starting his campaign to persuade Maximilan to set up an immigration program that would give new opportunity to Confederates. Never one to remain idle, he was eager for work; furthermore, he was genuinely in need of the pay it would bring.

Maximilian was absent from the capital in the mid-June weeks but sent for Maury to join him at Puebla. The message was so worded that Maury did not realize it was a direct invitation and waited in Mexico City for the Emperor's return.[24] He made use of this time to write to his powerful friend in France, Admiral Octave de Chabannes, to whom he outlined his immigration plan, asking that the Admiral lay the proposal before Napoleon III in order that the French Emperor might urge Maximilian to adopt the program. Maury received a prompt answer from Chabannes, who reported his belief that Napoleon would act.[25]

In the last week of June Maximilian returned to Mexico City and received Maury. The Emperor listened with interest to the immigration proposal sketched by Maury during three short conversations. On June 27 Maury was received and granted time to present his full plan. Maximilian asked him to leave the written draft he had brought so that further study might be given to the whole concept.[26]

On the following morning an invitation was presented to Maury to come that afternoon to Maximilian's palace at Chapultepec, some three miles from the city. He was expected at three o'clock for dinner with the Emperor and Empress.[27] On this occasion the Emperor extended unusual courtesies to Maury. He requested that Maury, unlike others, would from that time forward remain seated when the Emperor was in the room. Maury felt flattered and a little uncomfortable at this dispensation and honor. He was further flattered when the Empress Carlotta, daughter of Leopold I of Belgium and first cousin of Queen Victoria, expressed the wish to have his photograph for her album.[28]

Soon after this dinner Maximilian sent one of his ministers of state to ask what position Maury would consider most acceptable of those in the imperial power to grant. Maury's reply was, "Wherever I can be of most service to His Majesty and the Empire." [29]

Maury continued to use every opportunity to convince the Emperor of the merits of his colonization plan. In a letter to Tremlett in mid-July he reported joyfully, " 'Max' enters heartily into my ideas." [30]

Even Maury's enthusiasm must have quailed some, however, when later in the month he received a letter from Marin Jansen pleading with him to give up the scheme of a New Virginia colony in Mexico. Jansen, out of the depths of loyalty, wrote, "Let your imagination which has been a blessing of God, not become a curse in your old age." [31]

The plan that Maury had worked out was an imaginative one, and the Emperor and Empress both liked it, especially approving the idea of drawing to Mexico men like Maury.

Late in August Maximilian decided to commit his government to the program of seeking immigration from the states of the late Confederacy. He informed Maury that he would soon issue an imperial decree appointing him to the post of imperial commissioner of colonization at a salary of $5,000 a year. The pay was to be retroactive to June.[32]

Maury was elated that he could now support his family in comfort and give a suitable education to his four youngest children. The prospect of a full scope for his energies, a position of dignity, and sufficient means did wonders for his health.

His pleasure over the appointment, however, was not shared by any member of his family except Dick. Even the approving Dick sent a communication that was upsetting to Maury—a letter to Dick from Robert E. Lee that the weary General had written from his place of quiet retreat in a borrowed Virginia farmhouse.

Col. Richard L. Maury   near Cartersville
My dear Colonel: July 30, 1865
   I received by the last packet from Richmond your letter of the 22d enclosing an extract from a letter of your Father to you dated June 27 and a project of a decree of the Emperor of Mexico to encourage emigration of the planters of the South to that country.
   I was very glad to learn of the well being of your Father and of his safe arrival in Mexico and had felt assured wherever he might be that he deeply sympathized in the suffering of the people of the South and was ready to do all in his power to relieve them. I do not

know how far their emigration to another land will conduce to their eventual prosperity although their prospects may not now be cheering.

I have entertained the opinion that it would be better for them and the country to remain at their homes and share the fate of their respective States. I hope however the efforts of your father will facilitate the wishes and promote the welfare of all who find it necessary or convenient to expatriate themselves but should sincerely regret that either he or his should be embraced in that number.

I beg that you will present him my most cordial thanks for his sympathy and interest in our behalf and my best wishes for his happiness. For your own kind expression towards me and mine please accept my grateful thanks. My daughters unite with me in kindest regards to Mrs. Maury.

I am most truly yours,

R. E. Lee [33]

Soon afterward Maury received a letter from Lee expanding these views, "I shall be very sorry if your presence will be lost to Virginia. She has now sore need of all her sons, and can ill afford to lose you. I am very much obliged to you for all you have done for us, and hope your labours in the future may be as efficacious as in the past, and that your separation from us may not be permanent." [34]

Still working to dissuade Maury from the colonization plan, Marin Jansen wrote from Holland: "As long as Maximilian tries to make what is called a civilized government his position is unstable and I should not like you to stay there, however sweet and pleasant it may be in the shade of an Emperor's crown." [35] Jansen continued by pointing out that if Maximilian assumed absolute power Maury might well lose his head.

Even more vehemently Rutson Maury urged from New York that Maury accept the still open invitation of the Grand Duke Constantine to go to Russia and pursue his scientific studies or take advantage of Napoleon III's invitation for him to go to France to live. [36]

Maury took time to explain to Rutson that he did not wish to be a royal pensioner but wanted to earn a living. He added: "I have come here to provide a home for such of the conquered people as like to emigrate. Suppose they do not thank me—well, there is still useful and honourable occupation for me here. There are many things here with which I may identify myself and do good, such as organizing the census, a land-survey for the Empire, a system of internal improvements; and though last, not least, the introduction of chinchona cultivation." [37]

Early in August Dick, who had decided not to ask for pardon, wrote his father that he and his wife Sue would come to Mexico in October. He also advised that the University of Virginia authorities would have to have possession of the infirmary by October.[38] This latter news put an end to any idea that Maury's family could stay on in their Charlottesville refuge, as they had agreed to move when the building was needed for students. Maury wrote impulsively urging his wife to come to Mexico with Dick. Then, after further consideration, the lonely man faced up to the fact that no suitable schooling was available in Mexico City for his daughters or for Brave. He quickly wrote again and instructed his wife to pack their belongings, vacate the Charlottesville refuge, and take the younger children to England. In outlining this plan Maury expressed confidence that Rutson would arrange in New York for his family's steamer tickets, Brave would guard them on the journey, and Thomas Bold would meet them in Liverpool. Meanwhile, he explained, he would work as hard as he could to get the immigration program launched and, as soon as the Emperor felt he could be spared, would seek a leave of absence and come to England to see his wife and children.[39]

It was well that Maury changed his proposal, for he might have met with the first refusal of his life from Ann had he insisted on her going to Mexico. She was opposed to his colonization plan. She had heard discussions by her brothers and by her son-in-law Wellford Corbin that the United States government had no intention of allowing Maximilian to establish a strong government on its southern flank and might even go to war with Mexico rather than permit the Emperor's French troops to remain there. She knew that most of Maury's friends and relatives felt his position was fraught with grave danger because of the precariousness of Maximilian's throne. She also felt that if Maximilian's government was to endure, it would mean her husband had exiled himself for life from his native land. She was opposed to his setting up a colony that he could not honorably leave if the United States eventually did modify its position toward men who had served the Confederacy. Furthermore, she was appalled at the thought of taking her young daughters and Brave to live in a country whose language they did not speak, and whose customs were at variance to the way of life she loved.[40]

Ann also dreaded a trip to England, but she preferred it to going to Mexico. She began preparations to leave Virginia.

Maximilian completed the organization of Maury's program with the issuance, on September 5, 1865, of a decree that began with these words:

> We, Maximilian, Emperor of Mexico, in consideration of the sparseness of the population in the Mexican territory, in proportion

to its extent, desiring to give to immigrants all possible security for property and liberty . . . do decree as follows: Mexico is open to immigrants of all nations. Immigration agents shall be appointed, whose duty it will be to protect the arrival of immigrants, install them on the lands assigned them, and assist them in every possible way in establishing themselves. These agents will receive the orders of the Imperial Commissioner of Immigration, especially appointed by us, and to whom all the communications relative to immigration shall be addressed.[41]

Imperial Commissioner Maury[42] was most pleased with Article 9 of the decree, which declared, "Liberty in the exercise of their respective forms of religious worship is secured to immigrants by the organic law of the Empire."[43]

A presentation of general information on Mexico's climate, topography, agricultural opportunities, and mineral wealth had been written by Maury, and this also received imperial approval for distribution to prospective immigrants.[44]

Under the regulations of the program, free passage to Mexico and travel cost to certain government-owned lands that had not previously been cultivated were to be granted to Class A immigrants, persons who had lost all in the war. Under this category a man with a family would receive 320 acres and a single man 160 acres of Mexican soil. Those Southern immigrants who still possessed means were categorized as Class B and were to purchase lands that had been under cultivation, the price to be approximately one dollar an acre. These wealthier settlers could also acquire haciendas that had long been established.[45] Maury received many offers of land from Mexicans who wished to sell to Class B settlers.[46]

The program was now launched, but Maury realized that its implementation would not be easy. Strong opposition was inevitable from the United States government,[47] and from the followers of former President Benito Juárez, whose republican forces had been defeated by the French in 1862. Juárez had established his capital at El Paso del Norte (Cuidad Juárez) and continued his fiery resistance to the Emperor's regime. Maury also learned that some of Maximilian's own official family desired to obstruct the immigration plan. This difficulty he dealt with while dining with Maximilian and Carlotta at Chapultepec on September 11. He described the event to his wife:

There were present the Empress, and one of her ladies, four German naval officers, and a Mexican—all were of his household, I believe. It was mail-day for Europe; the Emperor had been busy at the palace writing (he told me) seventeen letters for the steamer. I got there a moment before he did, so he went into the sitting-room which joins the Empress's chamber. He opened her chamber-door and said "Carlotta, here's Mr. Maury." She came out immediately and commanded me to be seated, the Emperor and the other gentlemen standing. Presently her lady-in-waiting came in; I rose, but she touched me gently on the arm and said, "The Emperor wishes you always to be seated." The lady stood also. In a few minutes dinner was announced. The Emperor led off, and we all followed in single file. As I passed through the door, one of the "aides"—a baron —whispered in my ear, "On the Empress's left." The dinner—excepting the wines, the number of servants, and the liveries—reminded me very much of those Lucy Ellen [Ann's sister-in-law] used to give us in our summer visits to Fredericksburg.

After dinner (say three-quarters of an hour) we, the gentlemen, led by the Emperor, went into the smoking-room. Gilt cigars were handed round; the Emperor did not smoke. Here he drew an armchair up into the corner, and seated me again, he and the others standing until their cigars were nearly finished. Then he took a seat, and commanded the others to be seated. Despatches were handed him, some of which he handed to me to look into. Presently he dismissed the gentlemen, and said, "Mr. Maury, you have something to say to me?" "Yes, sire; I can't manage immigration through the Ministers. I must transact business with you directly, and not through them; nor must they have anything to do with it." "That's what I intend," said he. Said I, "I have not seen my wife and children for three years; I want to be quick, organize immigration, and take the steamer of 13th November for France." "Certainly," said he. Then he said, "I wish you to continue the conversation with the Empress; I have something pressing to do. She will make notes, give me verbal explanations, and have it all ready for me by four o'clock in the morning, when I will attend to it." Carlotta was walking in the garden. He referred me to some books on the table, and went to look for her. She came, and we commenced discussing matters, she making notes nearly as fast as I could talk. Among other subjects, I mentioned that of an office; that I had sent for Dick and family, who would be the first immigrants under the Decree, and that a house had been offered me which would answer the purpose of an office and a dwelling as well. "Certainly." Then we discussed, with approbation, my going to see you; the appointments of agents in the South and their salaries, and the organization of a land-office.

She is very clever, practical and business-like. I told her I thought she could do more business in a day than all of the Ministers put together could do in a week. She said, "I believe I could." She told me she had recently received a letter from the Empress of France about me, and enclosing a copy of a long letter I wrote in June to Admiral Chabannes about my new "Virginia," commending the plan as a grand idea, and asking Carlotta if she did not know me." [48]

Admiral le Vicomte de Chabannes approved Maury's plan because he thought settlers from the Southern planter class would help to stabilize Maximilian's position in Mexico. But Maury's family continued to pour out their criticism. Two carefully reasoned arguments against his continuing with the colonization effort, written by kinsmen—Franklin Minor and Law Professor John B. Minor of the University of Virginia—reached Maury at this time. They did not disturb him as much, however, as did a thoughtful letter from Wellford Corbin in which the younger man declared that, if Maury definitely decided to live in Mexico, he would come there—but that any new colonists from the South would be unable to bring with them any labor force. Corbin said, "Some of the New York journals are already inciting the popular mind against your scheme and characterizing it as 'Slavery in Disguise.' " [49] Dick Maury also told his father that he did not think any Negroes would come with white settlers because "they expect the Yankees to divide up Southern farms and give them land." [50]

Those last two criticisms pinpointed one totally unrealistic feature of Maury's plan. Not having been in the United States since Lincoln's Emancipation Proclamation, Maury possessed no firsthand knowledge of the way the Negroes of the South had responded to their freedom. Having known that slaves manumitted by their owners prior to the war had frequently stayed on to work as freedmen for their former masters, Maury had thought that many Southern Negroes would follow that procedure in 1865. He had, therefore, made a part of his colonization plan a proposal for the Negroes to come to Mexico as apprentices. All Southerners who could persuade their former servants—the term usually employed in the South for slaves—to accompany them as apprentices for not less than seven years were offered 150 acres and $150 for each apprentice. The employer was to pay the wages of the apprentice in a lump sum at the expiration of his apprenticeship and in addition to give him 45 acres of land.[51] The plan was very similar to that by which great numbers of Englishmen had bound themselves to come to America in early colonial days, but circumstances were different in 1865. As Corbin flatly stated, "Emigrants will not be able to induce a single freedman to go." [52]

While Maury's plan did not propose slavery and could not have done so, as that institution was forbidden by Mexican law, it was a reactionary plan, unlike Maury's usual line of thinking. So was his service under an emperor—an emperor brought in to rule over a country of which he was not a native. Maury, who believed in the freedom of the individual, who believed that the inherent superiority of government by the people would eventually triumph over the monarchical system [53]—that Maury had been temporarily eclipsed by a man whose world had crumbled around him, a man who was trying to create a haven for people who, like himself, wanted desperately to make a new start.

The decree making Maury imperial commissioner of colonization was signed on September 27, 1865,[54] only five days after he had been appointed director of the National Observatory, which Maximilian expected to build soon in Mexico City.[55] To enable Maury to hold these two posts Maximilian's government had issued naturalization papers to Maury on September 23.[56]

When this news of Maury's "naturalization as a Mexican" reached New York, Rutson Maury was more distressed than ever because former Confederate Secretary of the Treasury George A. Trenholm and some other Southern leaders had just been released from prison and placed on parole by order of President Johnson.

Rutson "advised immediately and strongly" against Ann's taking an action she had planned without consulting her husband in Mexico. Unaggressive but courageous Ann Herndon Maury had originally planned to stop one day in Washington en route to New York to sail for England to see President Johnson to try to obtain permission for her husband to return to the United States.[57] When Maury heard of Ann's plan, he was relieved that she had not gone through with it. He stated, "The greatest mortification that they [his family] can cause me is to talk about asking Mr. Johnson for anything for me, or to talk about pardon." [58]

Ann had yielded to Rutson's plea and had not stopped in Washington to see the President but had gone straight through to New York and with her younger children had sailed for England.

Meanwhile in Mexico a number of Maximilian's ministers who opposed the colonization plan carried on a stalling program, and Maury had to face the possibility that delay might cause failure to the undertaking.[59] He admitted:

> I am by no means sanguine about my "New Virginia"; not but
> that there are plenty of people in the South who are dying to come
> . . . for there are now about one hundred first-rate men, some of

them with their families, from various parts of the South, looking for homes. Some of them have been sent by their neighbors and friends to look at the country and report. The Government is not yet prepared to offer them lands on any terms. We are not ready. Some of them have gone home in disgust, and the golden, precious moments are passing by. I am not yet in harness; but if I can't carry colonization, this is no place for me. And this the Emperor also understands, for I have told him I could not stay if immigration fails. At any rate, I now almost despair of seeing it well in motion before this time next year.[60]

Many of Maury's official arrangements for the immigration program were handled by the Empress Carlotta. On September 26 she agreed to Maury's request to have Major General John Bankhead Magruder appointed as head of a land office at a salary of $3,000 a year, with a large force of surveyors under him.[61] They were needed to assist in the clarification of land titles. Magruder, a native of Virginia, had graduated from West Point and served the United States Army with distinction until 1861. He had been made a major general in the Confederate Army after winning an early battle at Big Bethel and, while serving as head of the Department of Texas from 1862 to 1864, had captured Galveston. Maury felt it promised well for the future of immigration when General Magruder announced he would bring his family to Mexico to live.[62]

In mid-October Maury was able to inform the Empress that he expected, within a week, to be joined by his son Dick. He explained that he would not go to see his wife until he had organized the office of colonization, which he had now opened in two of the rooms of an apartment he had rented in mid-September. The apartment occupied the whole upper story of a building at 13 San Juan de Laterán.[63]

Carlotta approved Maury's plan for an eventual trip to England to see his wife and his wish to train Dick to handle the office during his absence.[64] Dick and Sue reached Mexico City on the evening of October 24, 1865, and Maury was overjoyed to see his eldest son after a separation of more than three years.[65]

Within a month Maury was writing proudly to his wife:

Dick is a great help and comfort to me. Bless his heart, he wins upon me every day: so crippled yet so patient, so devoted to his new duties, and so hard-working, he surprises and delights me with his business tact and capacity. He is so handsome too, and in his new clothes looks, as he is, every inch a gentleman. He was consulting me to-day about buying some Cordoba lands. I have it in my mind to bring Corbin here and induce him to settle upon them; and though

I believe he and Nannie [Diana] would come, if I had urged them, yet, in the face of so much opposition [from home] I had not the heart to do it.

In the olden times, Cordoba was the garden spot of New Spain. There stands on one side, and but a little way off, the Peak of Orizaba, with its cap of everlasting snow, and on the other the sea in full view. These lands were heavily in debt to the Church, and as the Church property has been confiscated (not by the Emperor, though) Max. took possession of these lands for colonization. The railway hence to Vera Cruz passes right through them; and I am now selling these lands to immigrants, as fast as they can be surveyed, at $1 the acre on 5 years' credit. There are about 40 of our people already there. [Judge] Perkins [from Louisiana] has bought himself a house and has sent for his family; so has [Confederate General] Shelby, and so have a number of others. Mr. Holdham, an Episcopal clergyman, with his family—nice people—has been engaged by the settlement as pastor and teacher. I am going to reserve land for a church, cemetery, and school-house. Thus, you see, my sweet wife, colonization is a fact, not a chimera. By the time these lands are paid for they will be worth, even if no more settlers come to the Empire, $20, $30, or even $100 the acre, for they produce everything under the sun, and yield perpetual harvests. . . .

Lafayette Caldwell, who used to be draughtsman at the Observatory, has sent for his family, Newmarket for his, and there are a number of nice families already there, some of them established in the city; but those are all going to break up and go down to the new, dear old Spotsylvania.

Now, if I can only get lands surveyed in time—for there are plenty of them—here is your "New Virginia." There are other settlements forming in other parts of the Empire. Colonization is a success, if we can only get instruments and surveyors to bring the land into market. The people of the South are restrained by political considerations from speaking of their intentions; but we have letters. Thousands are dying to come; and I hope to have a decree this week which will put them in motion.[66]

It is likely that one reason Maury called his proposed colony New Virginia was to induce reluctant Virginians, like Ann, to think of Mexico as similar to the land they loved—and hence their move there less of an upheaval. At any rate because of his wife's opposition to his being in Mexico and attempting to draw Southerners there, Maury always reported his successes to her.

To Frank Tremlett he felt free to reveal the real difficulties of his undertaking. On October 29 Maury mentioned: "I had a long and touching conversation with 'my Carlotta' yesterday. I told her that 'Max' had false friends about him—that she knew." [67] The Empress, Maury added, asked his help against disloyal associates. Maury was undoubtedly referring to some of the Mexican conservative leaders who had originally sought Napoleon III's aid in founding a Mexican empire. These men had found Maximilian too liberal in his policies and were seeking to counteract these tendencies and mold the policy of the Empire according to their convictions.[68]

Even while not pleasing the Mexican conservatives Maximilian was certainly winning no converts to his policy among the followers of Indian-born Benito Juárez, who continued the hero of the masses of the Mexican people. They fervently backed Juárez in his desire to drive all foreigners from Mexico and take over the government with his program of reforms designed to better the lot of the people.[69]

Maury's position was, as he had been warned, one to put him in jeopardy, for he had been created honorary councilor of state by imperial decree on September 18, 1865.[70] He was also the trusted counselor of both Emperor and Empress, known to have great personal influence with them.[71] The opposition that he encountered in Mexican circles, however, did not prove as wearing to him as that constantly expressed by family and friends. He admitted that the latter disapproval made his path hard to follow even though he personally believed he had chosen the right course.[72] In spite of this assertion, Maury must surely have had to stifle many an inner whisper of doubt. Though unwilling to admit it, he was aware that Maximilian lacked decision and forcefulness and that the Emperor's vacillating policy had discouraged some Southerners who had emigration to Mexico under consideration. Maury urged the Emperor to take a more decisive stand with his ministers to prevent their blocking his imperial orders.[73]

In the late fall and early winter of 1865 Maury continued to work to overcome obstacles and advance the immigration program. Much literature was sent to Southern states, and agents were appointed there to make arrangements for those who decided to make the move to Mexico.[74] United States Secretary of State Seward, however, ordered that all Southerners who applied for passports to Mexico should take an oath *never to return*.[75] That requirement naturally discouraged many prospective citizens of New Virginia.

By late February, 1866, however, Maury felt enough settlers had come for him to leave the colonization effort in the hands of Dick and his other assistants. At that time, Maury wrote to Ann and his children in England:

> Two shiploads of immigrants have just arrived. [Major General Philip H.] Sheridan had refused to let them embark at New Orleans as he was "determined to break up that Maury nest of Confederates which was agitating the public mind of the South, and preventing the people there from quietly submitting to subjugation." [So the emigrants went to Cuba and thence to Mexico.]
>
> I thank him for the encouragement. We are going to have happy times, a fine country and a bright future here. Dick has got land in my Carlotta Colony—640 acres, he has sent to China for labourers —12 or 15—to work it, and to Virginia for young Crutchfield to take charge of it. I have such good irons in such good fires, that some of them will surely be got to welding heat.[76]

Other Confederate leaders were at this time working to establish colonies in Sonora, Chihuahua, San Luis Potosí, and Jalisco.[77]

Late in January, 1866, leave was granted to Maury to make his long projected trip. The Emperor wrote:

> My dear Counselor Maury,
>
> I have the pleasure of answering your kind letter of the 22nd of January in which you express your just desire to see your family again. If on the one hand, I behold with regret your absence for some time from the Capital, where you are so effectively helping us with your intelligence; on the other hand, I realize that it is quite necessary to fulfill one's most sacred duties toward one's family, and in consideration of this I cannot oppose your voyage, and my only wish is that you carry it out successfully and that you return with your family. I hope furthermore on returning from my journey to Cuernavaca to see you in Mexico [City] before you undertake yours, in order to take leave of you in person.
>
> Your most affectionate,
> Maximilian [78]

The Emperor, sure of Maury's personal loyalty, had been reluctant to have his counselor leave the country, but he had been persuaded by the Empress to grant the permission. With Maximilian's letter she sent one of her own in which she reported to Maury that in addition to granting "you a complete leave of absence to arrange your affairs in England . . . he quite agrees with your purchasing the instruments for studying the rainy season; and thirdly, that he approves of any effort you may make

437

to introduce the chinchona tree, and authorizes you to have sent from Kew a few specimens of this valuable plant." [79]

Maury had made some meteorological observations in Mexico and was glad to have the authorization to secure instruments needed for further studies of the weather.[80]

It was a matter of personal satisfaction to Maury that he had finally been able to interest Maximilian in his long-nourished idea of introducing the cultivation of the chinchona (or cinchona) tree to Mexico. The bark of this tree, variously called calisava, Jesuit's or Peruvian bark, was the source of quinine vitally needed in the treatment of malaria. Before leaving England in 1865 Maury had discussed with Clements R. Markham, English traveler, geographer, and successful developer of chinchona plantations in India, the possibility that chinchona might grow in Mexico.[81] Since arriving in Mexico, Maury had studied soil and weather conditions and become convinced that the forest-covered slopes above the Tierra Caliente would grow the chinchona. This had led him to ask imperial permission to secure chinchona plants for a pilot study.[82]

Maury sailed from Vera Cruz in early March, officially on leave—without salary—but entrusted with funds for two projects that the Emperor had authorized him to carry out in England.[83]

At midnight of March 29, 1866, Maury arrived at 30 Harley Street, Cavendish Square, London, and walked in on his family.[84] He had not seen his wife for three and a half years. After the first few minutes of joyful reunion he realized that, while her hair still retained its lovely auburn shade, Ann's general appearance was that of a woman of more than fifty-four years. Sorrow over John's death, Dick's crippling, poverty, and the vicissitudes of war had left their stamp on her face.[85] Maury must have been startled, however, when his youngest child blurted out, "This is not my papa! This is an old man with a white beard." [86]

Maury had indeed changed in appearance since young Lucy had last seen him. But he had written to prepare his wife for the fact that his mustache and short beard, grown in the early part of the war, had turned white after he learned of John's disappearance.[87] Maury looked considerably older than his sixty years but possessed more physical vigor than had been his prior to his departure from England in 1865.

Maury rediscovered his children: Mary, a pretty girl of 21, Eliza, serious and unusually quiet for 19, Matthew Jr. (Brave), a handsome youth of 17, and Lucy, who, though nearing 14, still seemed a baby to her father.[88]

After some days of the heart-warming family reunion, Brave had to return to Rose Hill School, where he had again enrolled on arriving in England. Maury now made plans for the girls to study in London. He busied himself with his personal business affairs and wrote William C. Hasbrouck to see if Harper and Brothers had on hand any funds for him from sales of *The Physical Geography of the Sea*. He had received no royalties from the American publishers for a long time but knew that any sum they might have would be small, as his leaving the United States Navy and becoming a Confederate officer had caused American sales of his book to drop badly from 1861 on.[89]

Maury soon set about his official missions in London. He began negotiations for the meteorological instruments that he planned to take back to Mexico and was able to order them at an advantageous price.[90] His next move was to call on Clements R. Markham at the "India Office" in London. Markham welcomed Maury's proposal to introduce the chinchona tree into Mexico. He agreed to make arrangements at once to have seeds of the tree sent to Maury from India.[91]

In Mexico, during these weeks Maximilian was encountering increased opposition and enmity. Ministers whose hostility had been countered by Maury as long as he was present in the country now brought great pressure on the Emperor to abolish the program of immigration. Thus it was that on a mid-May day in London Maury received the following communication from the Emperor of Mexico:

April 19, 1866

My dear M. F. Maury,

Impelled by motives of economy and convenience to abolish the Imperial Commission of Colonization which in the month of September of last year I confided to your loyalty and superior knowledge, I must on informing you of this measure express the pleasure and satisfaction I feel for the exertions you have so successfully made in the Empire to augment its population, without which the various sources of wealth contained in its fruitful soil cannot be made productive.

If your talents cannot for the present be made available in that way, I am convinced that they will be eminently useful in the direction of the Observatory which situation I formerly conferred on you, and in which I trust you will continue, that our beautiful firmament examined by your intelligent eye may procure us the means of profiting by the knowledge which science has already acquired and of making even new discoveries to increase the fame which you have already so justly attained.

Whenever circumstances will permit a new development of colo-

439

nization, I intend making appeal to your advice and activity and I will now direct the necessary localities to be prepared in the Palace for the Observatory in order to be able to have you always near me.

Believe me,

Your affectionate,
Maximilian [92]

Maury had always known there was a chance that the program could not be carried out. However, receipt of the letter from Maximilian telling him that the colonization project had collapsed was undoubtedly a severe blow. It left him again without country, occupation, or salary. He had put much of himself into creating the plan, persuading Maximilian to accept it, and especially into the organizational work of the project. He had believed the colony would preserve many of the good features of Southern plantation life without the evil of human slavery. He had apparently planned that Dick would take over the running of the colonization office while he organized the new observatory the Emperor planned to build. He had made his first small step toward a meteorological program in Mexico.

But Maximilian's letter ended all those hopes for Maury. It also proved that his friends and his wife had been more right than he in their appraisal of his undertaking in Mexico. That was not helpful to Maury's already bruised pride—the pride of a man who believes himself still capable of large-scale accomplishment but who is blocked from the opportunity to prove it.

Maury must have been disheartened indeed, for he waited about six weeks before he wrote his answer to Maximilian:

> I read, in your letter of April 19th, fresh proof of your Majesty's confidence and friendly consideration; I am touched by them. I am grieved to learn that your Majesty should be compassed with difficulties so serious as must be those which made it necessary to abandon such a cherished policy as I know that of colonization to have been. . . . Colonization being suspended, I fear that my return to Mexico would tend rather to increase the embarrassments than to smooth any of the difficulties by which your Majesty is surrounded. . . .
>
> In stating this conclusion I hope I may not be considered unmindful of obligations or insensible to kindness. Far from it. Proof that I recognize both in their highest sense is found in the fact, that in homage to them I forego the high and honourable position so

kindly offered me near the person of your Majesty in the service of your Empire.

Connected with this subject, I beg leave to report, that, of the sum placed in my hands for the purchase of seeds and instruments a balance will remain. H. B. M.'s Government has kindly ordered chinchona seeds from India, because they were required for your Majesty's service. Defraying the cost of their transportation out of this fund, I shall be glad to account for it, and pay over the balance due to any person here that may be designated.

That God may ever have your Majesties in His holy keeping is the constant prayer of your earnest well-wisher and humble friend,

M. F. Maury [93]

CHAPTER XXII

Another Start—England

Maury had gone to England with a good many objectives in mind over and above the very important one of being reunited with his wife and children. In January he had passed his sixtieth birthday. He had become increasingly anxious to build up a fund for the completion of the education of his children and to support his wife in case of his death or an incapacitating illness. He had decided that the time had come for him to realize financially on some of the technological studies he had made earlier. The study that would produce most quickly, he had decided, was the system he had developed for the military use of torpedoes or electrically detonated mines. Believing that nations would pay for this knowledge, Maury had, on April 25, 1866, less than a month after his arrival from Mexico, sent to various representatives of foreign countries stationed in London a circular advising that he would give courses of complete instruction in the use of the torpedo or electric mine. He had suggested that each government send one military engineer, one naval officer, and one electrician to take the course, for which the charge would be £500. At that time Maury had pointed out that his stay in England was limited but that officers could begin the course until the middle of August. In the circular Maury had given a résumé of the history of electric torpedoes and outlined the improvements he had made in this instrument of war.[1]

The first government to respond to Maury's offer of torpedo instructions had been that of Napoleon III. The French had requested that Maury come to Paris to lecture late in May and had agreed to pay him 25,000 francs. The initial lecture in France had been delivered by Maury on May 21.[2] The next day he had been received by the Emperor at 2 P.M., whereafter Maury had demonstrated one of his electric mines in the Seine at Saint-Cloud before Napoleon III, various military and naval officers, and members of the court. The Emperor had closed the circuit and exploded the torpedo.[3] The final lecture of the French series had been given on May 28. As a result of this visit, Maury was invited to become a French citizen [4] and subsequently asked to occupy a post in the Meteorological Observatory, with promise of eventual promotion to director of the Imperial Observatory.[5] But after the collapse of his Mexican colonization effort, Maury was not eager to commit himself again to foreign service of a permanent nature.

The next government to accept Maury's offer of torpedo instruction was that of the kingdom of Sweden and Norway, which sent officers to London to take the course. On July 8 Maury wrote of the Scandinavian officers, "They will graduate in 'sea mining' this week. Monday the school opens again for the Dutch at £500." [6] This covered board and tuition for three officers. The King of Württemberg wanted Maury to assist him by laying down a system of land mines to keep the Prussians out of his small kingdom, but Maury considered this an uncertain proposition and delayed action on it.[7]

In his torpedo school in London Maury started the course with the history of the development of submarine mines or torpedoes, gave detailed instructions on the use of torpedoes by the Confederacy in the recent war, and emphasized that the improvements that he had made on electric torpedoes in 1864-1865 gave enormous power for defense, even against ironclads.[8] Maury also gave detailed instructions in the use of electric torpedoes for guarding mountain passes and roadways, for the protection of strongholds, and for the defense of fortified positions:

> Forts may be protected against assault, and your own rifle-pits from occupation by an enemy, simply by the proper distribution of these new engines of war. They may be planted line within line, and one row above another, and so arranged that volcanoes may be sprung at will under the feet of assaulting columns.
>
> The only attempt that was made in the late American war to bring the electrical torpedo into play on the land was made by the Confederates at Fort Fisher, in 1865, just before its fall. . . . The officer in charge used the magneto exploder. . . . The instrument used on this occasion was just such a one as this before you. It was the first that had reached the Confederacy.[9]

Maury offered his courses to several other countries, but no other governments sent officers to study under him, apparently because considerable knowledge of his system had leaked out through his British agent, who had proved singularly unaggressive on Maury's behalf.[10] Also, facts concerning the improvements that Maury had devised were naturally taken home by the officers he had taught, and these became a part of the general fund of knowledge. In this way Maury's special contribution

443

to torpedo development was lost sight of and not recorded in histories of the technology of electric mines.

Between Maury's torpedo instructions in France and the similar courses that he gave in England, he received a high tribute in London. On June 5, 1866, a dinner was given at Willis Rooms in London at which leaders gathered to pay tribute to him. Chairman of the occasion was Sir John Pakington, First Lord of the Admiralty, who made the address of the evening in which he described the benefits that all maritime nations had gained from Maury's *Wind and Current Charts,* his *Sailing Directions,* and the worldwide marine meteorological co-operation brought about by the Brussels Conference of 1853.[11] It was appropriate that two guests at the dinner were men who had been delegates to that conference and had continued their active support of the universal system agreed on there. They were one of Britain's delegates, Colonel Sir Henry James, and Holland's delegate, Captain Marin H. Jansen.

The guests for the occasion were all men. Inasmuch as the dinner was given in recognition of his scientific work, Maury yielded to the urging of his family and wore all his decorations and medals. For once his breast glittered—as did those of others present, including the Danish, Mexican, and Argentine ministers, six British admirals, and high-ranking officers of the Russian and Swedish navies. Maury was pleased to see among the dignitaries from overseas his wartime friend General P. G. T. Beauregard, whose career as a Confederate general was well known in England. Among the scientists who came to honor Maury was physicist John Tyndall, who had succeeded Faraday as director of the Royal Institution, and Alexander Keith Johnston, royal geographer of Scotland. Maury's shipbuilding friend and member of Parliament John Laird was there as was another member of Parliament, A. J. B. Beresford-Hope, with whom Maury had worked for a cessation of hostilities in the war. Of all the hosts of the occasion, none had done more to bring it about than Captain Jansen of Holland and the Reverend Francis W. Tremlett, for they had been leaders in the move to raise a testimonial fund and present it to Maury at this gala dinner.[12]

The fund had reached the total of 3,000 guineas, of which £1,000 had been sent by the Grand Duke Constantine of Russia, £1,100 by admirers in Holland, and most of the balance by donations of individual Britishers. The purse was presented to Maury in a handsome silver-gilt casket, with a testimonial signed by all the donors.

> We the undersigned beg your acceptance of the accompanying purse of Three Thousand Guineas in appreciation and acknowledgment of the eminent and disinterested service which through

years of untiring zeal in the cause of science you have rendered to the maritime nations of the world. Receive from us this public testimony of our regard with every wish for your future welfare and happiness.[13]

At this particular juncture in his career Maury doubtless was almost as much fortified by the tribute of this event as by receipt of the fund itself. And there was certainly no doubt that he needed the latter—since the money he was earning by torpedo instruction was to be invested for the sole purpose of providing a law education for Dick.[14] The testimonial fund, Maury rejoiced, would assure completion of Brave's preparatory and college education, plus completing that of Maury's younger daughters.

Midsummer of 1866 found Maury again taking stock of his situation. The money he had brought from Mexico had been lost when a banker to whom he had entrusted it for investment failed financially. There seemed no likelihood of other governments accepting his offer to instruct officers in torpedo warfare. However, he had received a letter from a New York publisher asking him to prepare a series of school geographies for sale in the United States. In the face of a lack of other offers, Maury decided he had better undertake the work, to provide "bread and butter." [15] The financial results from the books, however, would not be reaped for a long time to come, and so Maury decided he and his family must move from Harley Street to less expensive accommodations.[16]

Maury secured lodgings at 41 Clarendon Terrace, Belsize Road, on the outskirts of London and moved the family there before he started work on the textbooks. He was very relieved that the lodgings cost only 48 shillings a week for his family of six, but he admitted that they were "very humble." [17] They were apparently too uncomfortable for Ann, who was extremely unhappy over being in England with no prospect of going home. She was sensitive to surroundings and also suffered from the hard beds in their rented rooms.[18] To try to make Ann happier and everyone more comfortable, Maury not long afterwards moved his family to less crowded lodgings at 3 Belsize Square, N.W. There the cost to him "for all hands" amounted to $40 a week for food and lodging.[19] The great advantage was that the Maurys were now located near the home of Frank Tremlett and his sister, Miss Louisa Tremlett, and were able to see them often.[20]

Once he had entered into an agreement with Charles B. Richardson of Richardson and Company, a New York publishing house, to write five school geographies,[21] Maury set to work to present geography in a way that would stimulate the interest of youngsters. He applied his im-

445

agination to the problem and decided to use one method he had found useful with his own children. He would write *First Lessons in Geography* so that the youngest students would feel they were on an imaginary trip around the world, visiting different countries and the peoples of those countries. This device is familiar, even old-fashioned now, but in Maury's day it was considered a startling innovation. Maury ended the preface to this little book with a warning to the instructor: "The teacher should *teach* as well as hear *recitations*." [22] That August Maury wrote a friend: "I am hard at work on Geography No. 1, Brave drawing the maps. Well, I could not wind up my career more usefully—and usefulness is both, honor and glory—than by helping to shape the character and mould the destinies of the rising generations." [23]

His second geography, *The World We Live In,* was written for slightly older children. In future years Maury's first two school texts were combined and called *Elementary Geography,* later retitled *New Elements of Geography.*[24] Mary and Eliza were the scribes who copied the pages after their father had worked out rough copies.[25] Maury was subsequently to add more titles to the series. His presentation of geography was branded by some teachers as too radical a departure from the schoolbooks then in use. However, his geographies were widely used in the United States, especially in the schools of the South.[26]

One of Maury's hopes, on his return to England, had been to become associated with Cyrus Field and his coworkers in the new effort to lay a successful cable across the North Atlantic. However, Field and his brothers were inimical to men who had sided with the South and offered Maury no active role in their organization.[27] When the Atlantic Telegraph Company, instead, offered Maury £1,000 for the use of his name, he refused the tender.[28] He could well have used the money, but he did not like the idea. His talents were available for worthwhile projects, but his name alone was not for sale.

Following the successful laying of the North Atlantic Cable in August, 1866, by Field and his associates, Maury received a letter from Maximilian stating:

> It is with pride that I heard of the scientific triumph just achieved, and due to your illustrious labors. The Transatlantic Cable, while uniting both hemispheres, will continually recall to their minds the debt of gratitude they owe to your genius. I congratulate you with all my heart, and I am pleased at announcing to you that I have appointed you Grand Cross of the Order of Guadalupe. Receive the assurance of the good wishes of your affectionate Maximilian.[29]

The Emperor undoubtedly had chosen to honor Maury for his discovery of the telegraphic plateau and his work with Cyrus Field on behalf of the cable from 1854 to 1861. Certainly the Emperor of Mexico knew that Maury had not been long enough in England to have played a major role in the successful 1866 undertaking. Maury, however, felt that Maximilian's generosity had led him to an excess of good will, and he wrote the Emperor that he had had no hand in the recent achievement and would, therefore, for the present, not wish to receive the Grand Cross of the Order of Guadalupe. He said the telegraphic cable in which he was specifically interested would be laid later and he would hope at a future date to deserve the imperial "well done." [30] Maury referred to negotiations he was carrying on with a British electrical engineer, Nathaniel Holmes, who planned to lay a cable to the West Indies. [31]

At about the time that Maximilian was sending this commendation to Maury the latter dispatched to Mexico three large parcels of chinchona seeds that had been secured for him by direction of the Secretary of State for India. [32] These were planted on the mountain slopes of Mexico, under the supervision of the Mexican Society of Geography and Statistics, which later that year reported that several thousand of the seeds sent from Madras had germinated satisfactorily. [33] The cultivation was carried on, and this gave Maury much satisfaction. Samples of chinchona bark from Mexico were shown at the Philadelphia International Exhibition in 1876. [34]

Meanwhile, however, tides of adversity were sweeping strongly against the throne of Maximilian. Early that summer of 1866 the Emperor of Mexico had received word from Napoleon III that the French troops would soon be withdrawn from Mexico. This was the move for which the republicans under Juárez had worked, and now they and other Mexicans brought into the open their hostility to Maximilian. The opposition of the government of the United States to Maximilian also was strengthened by Napoleon's pronouncement.

Empress Carlotta could not believe that Napoleon III would go back on his promise to support Maximilian in Mexico for five years. As Maximilian could not leave the country, she sailed for France to see the Emperor and plead with him personally to keep his promise to her husband. Having been confident that she could shame Napoleon III into this action, Carlotta was horrified and desolate when the Emperor flatly refused to continue his support. Carlotta turned to Pope Pius IX in the belief that she could obtain papal intervention to avert a move that would topple her husband from the Mexican throne. The Pope declared he could take no action.

The Empress, who possessed a very able and perceptive mind, could not stand the shock of these refusals, which seemed acts of betrayal. On October 1, 1866, her reason gave way under the strain and grief, and she became hopelessly insane. In Mexico, when Maximilian was told of the refusal of further support by Napoleon III and of his wife's insanity, he decided to abdicate the throne. This pleased Napoleon III, and he sent word through General Bazaine, in command of the French troops in Mexico, that Maximilian should leave with the troops. However, priests possessing influence with Maximilian persuaded this deeply religious man that it was his duty to stay on in his adopted country. The final chapter of Maximilian's tragedy did not take place until after the withdrawal of the last French troops in March, 1867. Subsequently, Juárez was able to extend his power very quickly, and a colonel betrayed Maximilian into the hands of the republican leaders. The Emperor was given a hasty court-martial and, with his two loyal native Mexican generals, Miramón and Mejía, was shot at Querétaro on June 19, 1867.[35]

Maury was greatly saddened by the tragedy that had befallen his friends. In the last letter that Carlotta had written him she had enclosed photographs of herself and Maximilian; and Maury was always to retain a personal affection for these two ill-fated people.[36]

After the first shock of the news of Maximilian's death Maury expressed a realization of his own good fortune in not being in Mexico. He wrote Jack Maury, who had assisted him in the laying of torpedoes in the waters of Virginia in 1861: "But for my good luck in having J. D. and Mal [Jefferson Davis and Secretary of the Navy Mallory] for enemies to send me here into banishment [wartime duty in England] and then kind Mexican villains to intrigue me out of Mexico, you see the rocks, that but for enemies, I should have split upon." [37]

Maury could never regard his having been ordered to England as other than a device to place him where he could have no active part in the administration of Confederate affairs. He continued to believe that he could have rendered the Confederacy more effective service at home.

As the summer of 1867 gave way to autumn, Maury made up his mind to take a step that was to give him great happiness. In childhood he had been baptized in the Protestant Episcopal Church and had throughout his life regularly attended Episcopal services. However, when he had come to "years of discretion" he had not received the laying on of hands from a bishop as is required of Episcopalians before they may receive Holy Communion. Maury had long had the matter under consideration, and his wife had been urging him to be confirmed ever since the early years of their marriage.[38] During the period when he had served the Confederacy in England and had come to value the friendship of Frank

Tremlett, this Anglican clergyman had sought to persuade his friend to come into the full communion of the church. After one such talk Maury had written Tremlett's sister: "Last night Frank and I had a long and interesting conversation about the sacrament. He thinks I ought to take it, but I think I am not 'fitten.' " [39]

Tremlett finally persuaded Maury that personal worthiness was not the issue for, if it were, no human being could ever presume to receive Holy Communion. Maury, who had declared his faith in 1862, when he commenced his will with the words "By the grace and mercy of my blessed Lord and savior, Jesus Christ," [40] now made the decision to be confirmed with his children, Lucy and Matthew Jr. The confirmation took place in Tremlett's church, St. Peter's, and the officiating bishop was the Right Reverend Charles Todd Quintard of Tennessee, successor to Maury's old friend Bishop Otey.[41] Quintard had come to London with other American bishops to attend the Pan-Anglican Congress at Lambeth Palace, September 24 to 27, 1867.[42]

Since the end of the war Maury had been receiving tentative inquiries whether he would accept a chair of astronomy at the University of Virginia [43] and in December, 1867, Bishop Quintard began a campaign to persuade Maury to succeed him as vice-chancellor (equivalent to president) of the University of the South at Sewanee, Tennessee.[44] Maury had been interested in this Episcopal college from its inception as an idea by Bishop Otey, and he had made an address when the cornerstone had been laid at Sewanee in 1860. The possibility of playing a leading role in creating a university was a proposal large enough in scope to make Maury give serious thought to Quintard's repeated urgings.[45]

However, an inquiry from his native state was also commanding Maury's interest. In mid-February, 1868, Maury received a letter from General Francis H. Smith, superintendent of the Virginia Military Institute, proposing that he become a professor at that college, which specialized in scientific training.[46] This possibility particularly interested him because he admired Smith, with whom he had served on the Governor's Advisory Council in 1861, and because he had always had a passionate belief in scientific education for young Americans.

On April 18 Maury received an official letter from Sewanee's chancellor, the Right Reverend William Mercer Green, asking him, on behalf of the Board of Trustees and executive committee, to come to Sewanee as vice-chancellor.[47] Maury deliberated but decided to decline. The main reason for his refusal was his conviction that Sewanee would have to raise more funds to become well established, and he knew he could not successfully solicit them in the North.[48]

449

On April 21, 1868, Maury, still in England, decided to go to the Virginia Military Institute.[49] He would become professor of physics and superintendent of the Physical Survey of Virginia. A decisive factor in Maury's decision to accept the Virginia Military Institute Board of Visitors' offer was General Smith's assurance that he would not be expected to hold daily classes but would lecture to the cadets when feasible. He was to apply the main portion of his energies to the survey. Smith pointed out the need of accurate information on the soil and climate of the various belts of Virginia, the minerals, metal ores, crop potential, water power, means of transportation, and other assets that might lure outside capital to assist the rebuilding of the war-scarred state. Maury was anxious to undertake the task, for he longed to have a part in restoring Virginia.[50]

He believed that some of the bitterness the North had felt toward him had subsided in the three years since the surrender at Appomattox but admitted, "I'm not sure whether I'll be interfered with on landing in the United States." [51] He was one of about three hundred former Confederates still not included in the amnesty by the second amnesty proclamation which President Johnson had issued on September 7, 1867.[52]

Maury had received a letter from Betty reporting that a judge in Virginia had advised that he should not attempt to return to the United States until autumn.[53] However, when cautious, knowledgeable Rutson Maury of New York advised that he believed Maury could return safely because General Magruder, who had assisted Maury in Mexico, had been allowed back in the country without arrest, Maury determined to take the risk.[54] He felt it was vital for him to put an end to this period of inadequate use of time and energy—and important for him to be at home.

For some time Maury had known that he was to receive a doctor of laws degree from Cambridge University. It was a happy circumstance that the award of this honor was to be the last major event of Maury's years in England. He spoke of the coming occasion as the coronation and jokingly said to a friend, "So you don't know what I mean by the 'coronation,' eh? Why boy, I'm a Cambridge LL.D. and am going there, I and Max and the Queen on the 28th—she to unveil the Prince Consort and I to be rigged up in 'dyed garments from Bozra' in a gown and a cap and a beautiful red silk cowl and hear myself all done up in Latin!" [55] The "Max" Maury mentioned as another who was going to receive the degree of LL.D. *honoris causa,* was Frederick Max Müller, professor of comparative philology at Oxford. Müller had won scholarly fame as an authority on Sanskrit. A second acquaintance of Maury's who was to receive the degree was William Wright, who had rendered distinguished service to the British Museum in the translation of early Egyptian manuscripts.

At nine o'clock on the morning of May 28, 1868, Maury, accompanied by his wife, daughters Mary and Lucy, and Frank Tremlett, took the train from London to Cambridge. At 1:15 P.M. they were entertained at an official luncheon, where Maury enjoyed chatting with Max Müller and William Wright, who possessed a keen sense of humor.[56]

From the luncheon the party went to the Senate House, where the ceremonies took place. The presentation address was, of course, in Latin; and Maury, who had never forgotten his years of training in that classical tongue, had no difficulty in following the meaning as W. G. Clark, public orator of the university, rolled out the words, "Presento vobis Mattheum Fontaine Maury . . ." In translation the remarks read:

> I present to you, Matthew Fontaine Maury, who while serving in the American Navy did not permit the clear edge of his mind to be dulled, or his ardor for study to be dissipated, by the variety of his professional labors, or by his continual change of place, but who, by the attentive observations of the course of the winds, the climate, the currents of the seas and oceans, acquired these materials for knowledge, which afterwards in leisure, while he presided over the Observatory at Washington, he systematized in charts and in a book —charts which are now in the hands of all seamen, and a book which has carried the fame of its author into the most distant countries of the earth.
>
> Nor is he merely a high authority in nautical science. He is also a pattern of noble manners and good morals, because in the guidance of his own life he has always shown himself a brave and good man. When that cruel Civil War in America was imminent, this man did not hesitate to leave home and friends, a place of high honor and an office singularly adapted to his genius—to throw away, in one word, all the goods and gifts of fortune—that he might defend and sustain the cause which seemed to him the just one. "The victorious cause pleased the gods," and now perhaps, as victorious causes will do, it pleases the majority of men, and yet no one can withhold his admiration from the man who, though numbered among the vanquished, held his faith pure and unblemished even at the price of poverty and exile.[57]

The words must have been grateful ones to a man who had received such a torrent of abuse for having taken this action. The great meaning of the day for Maury was, however, that in spite of his lack of college education, for which he had been condemned by rival "scientifics"

451

in Washington, one of the great universities of the world had thought him worthy of this degree.

Mention of the "coronation" was made by Wright later when he wrote Maury: "I have not been at Cambridge lately, but I know that all our friends there are well. Max Müller is now in Germany; I hope to see him at Kiel at the end of September, when we shall both attend the gathering of the German Orientalists. Lord, what a figure we three of us looked, dressed up like lobsters, in the midst of that big hall, gazed at by such a host of people, 'when shall we three meet again?' Certainly never under the like circumstances." [58]

During the last weeks before he left England Maury gave a lecture at Cambridge on "Science and the Bible: Educational Ideals of the South." [59]

Having received authorization from General Smith, Maury bought scientific instruments to be used by the V.M.I. surveyors in mapping out the commonwealth of Virginia. Included in the purchase were some pocket barometers invented by G. F. Loseby, who had made chronometers for Maury when he was superintendent of the U.S. Naval Observatory.[60] Maury greatly admired skilled craftsmanship such as Loseby possessed but he particularly valued a letter Loseby had written him, declaring: "It must be a source of gratification for you to know, that, although you are not now young, your life has chiefly been spent in the good work of enabling mankind to cross the ocean with less risk from the elements than formerly. I have never met with a scientific man, who did not bear testimony to the great services you have rendered to mankind." [61]

With his business concluded, Maury spent as much time with Brave as was possible since the boy was to remain in England to complete his studies at the Royal School of Mines in London, where he had commenced courses in chemistry, geology, and mining engineering the preceding January.[62] Dick was in Nicaragua as a supervisor at the Javala Gold Mines, but Maury hoped his eldest son would soon decide to return to Virginia.[63]

Going back with Maury, in addition to his wife and unmarried daughters, was Diana Maury Corbin, who had come over to join the family the preceding year following the destruction by fire of her house at Farley Vale.[64] Diana had brought her little daughter and had given birth to a son, John Maury Corbin, during her stay in London. On July 1, 1868, the Maury family sailed from Liverpool on the *France*.[65]

Fifteen days at sea gave the long-absent Maury time to try to prepare himself for whatever reception was to be his when he landed in the United States.

CHAPTER XXIII

Professor on the March

Memories crowded in on Maury as the *France* approached the outer harbor of New York on July 16, 1868. How very different was this homecoming from his previous returns to this port. He could recall a summer day like this in 1830 when a band had played "Hail, Columbia, Happy Land" as the *Vincennes* sailed into the harbor as the first United States Navy ship to have circumnavigated the globe. There would be no band today; there might even be officers waiting to arrest him. But whatever the reception, Maury was glad that he had come. He was not cut out for exile. He had cared too deeply and too long about his native land. And now her shores were again in sight.

His reflections were cut short by the need to strap luggage for Ann, daughters Diana, Mary, Eliza, and Lucy, and Diana's two small children.

When a tug brought out the harbor pilot Diana's husband, Wellford Corbin, came on board with the pilot. Corbin had come out to welcome his wife and children but more especially to report to Maury that on July 4 President Johnson had issued a proclamation granting pardon "for the offense of treason against the United States" to all former Confederates except those under court presentment or indictment. Corbin's words greatly heartened Maury for the landing.[1]

At the New York customs Maury was both surprised and relieved by the consideration shown him and the fact that his luggage and that of his family was passed without difficulty. However, intensity of emotion and the heat of the midsummer sun combined to threaten Maury with prostration. A physician was called. After taking a restorative and remaining quiet for a short while, Maury was able to leave the hot, uncovered wharf. No effort was made to stop him.[2] His chief emotion must have been one of thankfulness that he had risked returning when he did.

Maury took his family at once to 17 East Fourth Street, the home of first cousins Ann and Rutson Maury.[3] There they found a letter from Dick in Nicaragua. Instead of the hoped-for news that Dick and Sue were returning to the United States, the letter brought word of the death of their young son, Richard Launcelot Maury, III.[4] There was also a letter reporting that Maury's oldest child, Betty, was quite ill in Richmond.[5] None could ignore the absence of John, nor did Maury forget how hard Rutson and Ann had worked to assist in the long unfruitful search for John in Union prisons. The happiness of the home-coming and reunion was clouded by realization of all that the war had cost.

Mary, Eliza, and Lucy Maury had been invited to stay with their first cousin, Ellen Herndon Arthur, and her husband, Chester Alan Arthur. Maury was deeply appreciative of this conciliatory move on the part of Chester Arthur, who had been quartermaster general of New York during the war and was soon to become collector of the port of New York. Maury may have suspected that the way had been smoothed for him at customs by Arthur, who was already launched on his political career.[6]

In spite of these evidences of the determination of relatives to try to heal the wartime breach, Maury was under no illusions as to his official status. He was in the country on sufferance, a man with no political status and no guarantee of protection.[7] He was on his way to becoming a professor and making a physical survey for Virginia, considered by the United States government—not a state, but Military District No. 1. He had but to read one of the many Northern newspapers that Rutson subscribed to for a full realization of the intensity of antagonism still felt by most Northerners toward the South. He realized how strong feeling was toward him when his publisher told him that no Northern schools had bought or seemed likely to buy the geographies Maury had written for elementary education. However, Charles B. Richardson said that sales of the texts were expected to increase throughout the South and West.[8]

After conferences with his publisher Maury fulfilled one wish that was very close to his heart. He felt he might never have another chance to see his friend since Harpeth Academy days—William C. Hasbrouck. Maury wanted to express in person his gratitude to this man who had thought enough of him to attempt to pass through the lines in 1861 in the hope of persuading Maury to return to the Union.[9] When he had paid that tribute to loyal friendship Maury was ready to go to Virginia.

It was nearing the end of July when Maury reached Richmond. The capital of Virginia was under martial law—the state legislature under the control of Radicals and Negroes. Wherever Maury went in the business part of the city or in the section along the James River he saw grim reminders of the evacuation fire set just before the Confederate troops had yielded the city to the Federals in 1865.[10] In the residential sections he noted many once-proud residences in serious need of repair and paint.

454

Richmonders were trying to make a living, but Maury observed the desperate poverty of the people in spite of their efforts to hide it.

On the streets of Richmond Maury saw a strange medley—handsomely uniformed Federal soldiers carrying out the orders of the military governor of Virginia; civilians in shabby suits; men with empty sleeves, artificial legs, or crippled and swinging along on crutches; prosperous-looking men who had come from the North to invest money or start in business in the South; countrymen from nearby Hanover County offering small stocks of vegetables at prices beyond the pocketbook of many native Richmonders; Negroes, wandering constantly, savoring the taste of being free to move around, free to do nothing; Negro leaders talking purposefully with Radical Republicans, planning how to ensure continuance of their joint control of the Virginia General Assembly. In church on Sunday the number of women, especially young women, in widow's black and the noticeable scarcity of young men were mute reminders that of the white men who had been physically able to bear arms for the Confederacy one fourth were dead or permanently incapacitated.[11] Maury observed and felt deeply. However, he had come not to mourn but to rebuild, and he set immediately about his task.

Maury dedicated himself to silence on any subject connected with politics or government policies.[12] His task was to work quietly with the element of Virginians who believed their state could and must rise from the devastation of war. The call to conduct a physical survey of Virginia had struck a responsive chord in him because he knew that Virginians must turn to the industry to which they had been so largely indifferent prior to 1861 and must utilize the state's water power for mills. It was imperative that Virginia link herself with the West by expanded railroads that would carry the grain of the plains and the coal of war-born West Virginia to Norfolk for export. It was vital to establish a trans-Atlantic steamship line from that city's large harbor to put the state into international commerce.[13] Maury was eager to ascertain accurately the potential of iron ore and coal in the mountains of Virginia, to discover what crops the soils in the state were best suited for, to help farmers learn scientific methods that would compensate for the loss of Negro labor on the former plantations. Maury knew that such a survey was overdue. During the war Harvard's professor of geology, Josiah Dwight Whitney, with William H. Brewer, had conducted a geological survey of California, and qualified scientists were busy making other state surveys.[14]

Maury's reception by the people of Virginia was heart-warming to a man who had been under such long and steady criticism. His act of rejecting the high scientific post offered him by the French Emperor to return to work for his native state at a pittance of salary was hailed publicly and privately as an act of self-sacrificing patriotism.[15] Maury could live without praise, but he could certainly work better with it.

In Richmond in early August Maury informed himself of the economic condition of the state. He conferred with the old conservative leaders, spending much of his time with the presidents of railroads to learn how much had been done in restoring the rails and rolling stock of the lines so severely damaged during the war. He wished to have as many facts as he could before going on to the Virginia Military Institute for his official installation, scheduled to take place shortly after the beginning of the fall term.

General Smith wrote Maury authorizing him to draw an advance of $500 on his yearly salary of $2,000. "Draw in your own name as Professor of Physics," advised the superintendent of V.M.I.[16] The salary was admittedly ridiculous for a man of Maury's stature and inadequate for his needs, but it was an assured income considerably larger than many former Confederate leaders were able to earn in those years when the South was financially prostrate.[17]

As a part of his welcome-home, Maury received invitations from proprietors of several of "the springs of Virginia" to take his family as guests to these watering resorts located in the mountains. For generations Southerners who could afford it had made a custom of going to the mountains in the summer to avoid seasonal attacks of malaria. Maury's favorite resort was the Greenbrier White Sulphur Springs, located just across the Virginia border in West Virginia.[18] "The White," as it was called by its devotees, had long drawn a distinguished clientele from all the Southern states, from Washington and Baltimore. Leaders from other sections also came to take part in the fashionable August season for which the resort high in the Alleghenies was noted. Guests filled every room in the large central hotel structure and the cottages that faced the spacious and well-kept lawns.[19] In the summer of 1868 The White had a particular appeal for Southern men. There in that privately owned establishment in West Virginia, which had broken away from Virginia during the war to remain with the Union,[20] Southerners could foregather and discuss politics in a way that was impossible to them in their home states under martial law.

Therefore, Maury gratefully accepted an invitation from the owners of the Greenbrier White Sulphur Springs to bring his family to that resort to be guests of the management.[21] In mid-August Maury, and his family went from Richmond to The White.[22] Maury was welcomed and made much over by friends from Washington and all over the South. He enjoyed the sociability, but he had gone to the resort with two serious objectives. He wanted to discuss the condition of the South with the leaders he knew he would find gathered there and he wished to interest Washington capitalists and prominent Virginians in the Physical Survey of Virginia he was about to undertake. Maury met with a favorable response to his plans for the survey, securing from many the assurance of their backing for the project.[23] Of particular value to Maury were conversations with his distant cousin, Edmund Fontaine, president of the Chesapeake and Ohio Railroad, and General Joseph R. Anderson, president of the Tredegar Iron Works, both of whose companies were industrially important to the rebuilding of Virginia. Maury was also able to discuss his coming work with the chairman of the Board of Visitors of the Virginia Military Institute, John Letcher, former Virginia governor under whom Maury had served in 1861.

Other Confederate acquaintances with whom Maury renewed friendships were General P. G. T. Beauregard, whom Maury had last seen at the testimonial dinner in London, and former Vice-President of the Confederacy Alexander H. Stephens, who, after earlier imprisonment, had just completed the first volume of his *A Constitutional View of the Late War Between the States*. Maury also talked with Charles Magill Conrad of Louisiana, who as chairman of the House Committee on Naval Affairs in the Confederate Congress had backed him in the building of his gunboat fleet. Most meaningful to Maury was the opportunity again to be with General Robert E. Lee, whom he held in the utmost respect. The two men had been friends since the days when Lee was on Army duty in Washington and living at Arlington, just across the Potomac from the Naval Observatory where Maury was carrying out his oceanic research.[24]

By the first of September Maury had learned that these men, as well as many other former Confederate leaders at The White held views similar to his own about the South's position in this difficult postwar period.

These views were fully expressed in a letter signed at The White on August 26 by General Lee and thirty other Southerners who had experienced the three years of postwar Federal rule in the South. Their views had been solicited by General W. S. Rosecrans, one of the managers of the campaign to elect a Democratic President in the coming national election.[25] The portions of the letter that were probably most meaningful to Maury read:

> At the close of the war the Southern people laid down their arms and sought to resume their former relations to the United States government. Through their State conventions, they abolished slavery and annulled their ordinances of secession, and they returned to

their peaceful pursuits with a sincere purpose to fulfill all their duties under the Constitution of the United States, which they had sworn to protect. If their action in these particulars had been met in a spirit of frankness and cordiality, we believe that ere this old irritations would have passed away and the wounds inflicted by the war would have been in a great measure healed. . . .

The great want of the South is peace. The people earnestly desire tranquillity and the restoration of the Union. They deprecate disorder and excitement as the most serious obstacles to their prosperity. They ask a restoration of their rights under the constitution. They desire relief from oppressive misrule. Above all, they would appeal to their countrymen for the re-establishment in the Southern States of that which has justly been regarded as the birth-right of every American—the right of self-government.[26]

There was much talk at The White about the letter; there was to be more when it was subsequently published in newspapers.

On September 2 Maury left White Sulphur Springs to go to the Rockbridge Baths, a modest mountain inn located only 11 miles from Lexington.[27] General Smith had suggested that Maury go there to be near the Virginia Military Institute, since the house that V.M.I. was preparing for him would not be finished for some months.[28]

Maury and his family got off the eastbound train at Goshen, Virginia, and took the stage for the Rockbridge Baths.[29] The way lay through Goshen Pass, a gorge in the Allegheny Mountains at the bottom of which rushed a sparkling blue-water stream. The North River, one day to be renamed for Maury, made up for its lack of width by following a bold course over large boulders. The sound of the swift-flowing water delighted Maury as did the shiny leaves of rhododendron and laurel bushes that grew on the mountain slopes. The damp, cool smell of woods refreshed the travelers after their tiresome trip. But to Maury, whose life for years had been so filled with strife and uncertainty, this secluded vale seemed a place of peace, a place that offered nature's healing to the bruises of the human spirit. From that day forward Goshen Pass was to possess special meaning for him.

During the next week at Rockbridge Baths, General Smith came often from V.M.I. so that he and Maury could lay their initial plans for the Physical Survey of Virginia.[30] Maury was expected to concentrate his efforts on the survey and to lecture at V.M.I. only when it should prove feasible.

On September 10, 1868, Maury went to Lexington to report to the Virginia Military Institute.[31] He found the turreted main building standing forth boldly on a high bluff but still showing signs of damage inflicted by General David Hunter in his valley raid. Thomas Jonathan Jackson had gone forth from his professorial duties here to win fame as one of history's greatest military commanders and the unforgettable nickname of Stonewall. From these barracks the V.M.I. cadets had marched forth to fight at Newmarket.[32] In front of the main V.M.I. structure stretched a parade ground, and along one side of this stood a handful of houses, including one that had been severely damaged by General Hunter and was being restored for occupancy by Maury. These buildings, of military-Gothic architecture, were constructed of brick, faced with stucco to harmonize with the college's turreted main building.

In front of the superintendent's house a platform had been built, and rows of chairs stood ready for the guests who would attend Maury's installation. At five o'clock that afternoon, September 10, when the heat of the day had passed, the ceremony was begun. General Robert E. Lee, president of nearby Washington College, had come to join the institute's Board of Visitors, professors, and leading citizens of Lexington in welcoming Maury.[33] Behind these seated guests stood the cadet corps.

The installation ceremonies were opened by the Reverend William N. Pendleton, rector of Grace Episcopal Church in Lexington, but still called "General" and possessed of the booming voice that he had used as Lee's chief of artillery. General Francis H. Smith, superintendent of V.M.I., made the welcoming address, pointing out that the installation of Maury was of high interest "to the cause of scientific development, which it is the special object of this institution to promote." [34]

At the conclusion of Smith's speech the president of the Board of Visitors, former Governor John Letcher, read the commission from the Board of Visitors installing Maury as professor of physics and charging him with the task of making a Physical Survey of Virginia. Governor Letcher concluded, "In handing you this commission, I may in truth say, you confer more honor upon Virginia than Virginia confers on you." [35]

According to the Richmond *Whig*, "Commodore Maury then arose, and with a feeling which found expression in every lineament of his countenance" [36] gave an "extended commentary" on the sciences, outlined the work of the Physical Survey of Virginia and asked for the fullest assistance without which, he declared, he would lack courage for the work. Maury had been persuaded by his daughters to wear the orders bestowed on him by foreign governments, and this pleased the cadets, as did the fact that the scientist of whom they had heard so much spoke in unaffected language they could understand and remember.

459

Following the installation ceremonies Maury released to the press his official appeal to the people of the state to supply needed information to the office of the Physical Survey of Virginia. Maury had drawn up a questionnaire that asked for specific information on the four divisions or belts of Virginia: the Seaboard; from the Seaboard to the head of the Tidewater (belt extending 100 miles from coast); between Tidewater and the Blue Ridge; and west of the Blue Ridge Mountains. The queries were phrased in simple language so that they could be understood by any moderately intelligent farmer or businessman.[37] Maury's method of going to the people to make them collaborators in the undertaking was reminiscent of the technique he had used in the forties and fifties to persuade sailors to gather and send in information about the sea. The printed forms, with questions and blank spaces for answers, resembled his early Abstract Logs.

Maury stayed on in Lexington for ten or twelve days, working with General Smith and discussing with other V.M.I. professors the needs of the survey.[38] Because lack of building supplies and labor had delayed rebuilding of the house for Maury, it was agreed that he should set up a temporary office in Richmond. Both General Smith and Maury thought this sensible in view of two major efforts that the survey was about to make. One of these was a campaign to establish a direct steamship line between Virginia's port of Norfolk and Flushing, Holland. The people of Flushing were active in support of the proposal, and efforts in the Netherlands were directed by Commodore Marin Jansen.[39] The other major enterprise was to be backing expansion of rail facilities both within Virginia and to the west. Richmond was much nearer Norfolk and was a railroad center, while Lexington was 23 miles from any rail line and dependent on stage lines and packet boat travel over the James River and Kanawha Canal.

Maury, therefore, went to Richmond and there established his office for the winter. He kept close liaison with General Smith and also with John Mercer Brooke, of the faculty of V.M.I., who did mathematical work needed for the survey, such as computing the distance that steamers would travel on the great circle route from Norfolk to Flushing.[40] It was a matter of great personal satisfaction to Maury to be working again with Brooke.

General Smith was anxious for Maury, in addition to gathering information, to make as many speeches as he could to promote the survey. To enable Maury to do this required traveling on his small professorial salary, the V.M.I. superintendent secured railroad passes for Maury's use. The presidents of all the rail lines operating in the state also supplied the survey with the economic statistics that they had accumulated over the years.[41]

Maury's first speech in his new capacity was made on October 28, 1868, at a large agricultural fair held at Staunton, Virginia. In this he reported that the impression had developed in England and New England that the South was lacking in energy and enterprise. Maury admitted that war always left an aftermath of fatigue in the land where it had been waged and that there was no way ever to replace the great number of young men who had given their lives in battle. He also recognized that there was desperate need of capital and a way had to be found to make easier the shift from slave to free labor. With these premises acknowledged, Maury offered his positive program for Virginia. He painted a picture of Virginians harnessing their unused water power and using it to create industry equal to that of the North. He urged that better roads be built and begged farmers to band together to do this, as they had in Europe, to get their produce to market more easily.

Finally, Maury recommended that Virginia organize a drive to persuade hard-working German, Dutch, and Danish farmers to come to the state to settle. He pointed out that these people, with their thrift, could make productive some of the lands lying idle because of death in battle of the men who used to farm them. But, Maury challenged his fellow Virginians, real effort would have to be put forth to persuade Europeans to come to the South; concrete encouragement would have to be given.[42]

Maury and Smith had earlier agreed that it would not do to keep the information they gathered until the entire Physical Survey could be completed. Maury had, therefore, announced in his installation address at V.M.I. that a preliminary report would be put out as soon as possible. This was completed and published late in December, 1868.[43] One of the first copies of Maury's *Preliminary Report Number 1, Physical Survey of Virginia,* was sent by General Smith to the Washington philanthropist W. W. Corcoran with the statement: "The report is one of the *first fruits* of your kind interest for V.M.I. in subscribing $2,000 of its bonds and I am sure you will be gratified to learn that it has been received everywhere with an interest which the high authority from which it emanates is so well calculated to give." [44] Smith knew of Corcoran's admiration for Maury's abilities.[45]

When the report had been widely distributed and commented on editorially, General Smith wrote from the Virginia Military Institute to Maury in Richmond that the consensus on the Report was one of "unqualified approbation."

"We have steadily kept before us our legitimate work as a *state scientific* school, have never allowed ourselves to be diverted from it and

461

leaving to W. C. [Washington College] experiments upon university pro-
gramme—or manual labor schools, etc., we shall press steadily upon our
specific work—sure that we shall have as much patronage as we want." [46]

After publication of the Preliminary Report, the office of the Physical
Survey received so many inquiries from the North and such favorable
press response in Washington and Chicago that Maury sought and received authorization to send out agents to sell the Report in those areas.
He welcomed this opportunity to stir up interest in the investment of
capital to build a Virginia where industry would develop side by side
with a new scientific agriculture. Out-of-state distribution for the *Physical Survey of Virginia Preliminary Report* and accompanying maps was
also necessary to direct "attention to the Virginia through-routes, as the
true lines of trade from the Mississippi basin to the Atlantic." [47] A first
objective of the survey was to bring about completion of the Chesapeake
and Ohio Railroad from Hampton Roads to the Ohio River. The westward extension of that rail line would greatly increase the area shipping
goods to the port of Norfolk for transshipment to Europe via the proposed direct steamship line to Holland. Toward achievement of this two-
fold aim Maury also sent an agent to concentrate his promotional efforts in Norfolk and the adjoining city of Portsmouth. [48]

In the early months of 1869 Maury was hard at work in Richmond on
production of a second Preliminary Report that would concern itself
primarily with climate, soil, and products. By his own enthusiasm and
by the success of his first report he had stirred the men of the state to
compile information for him and send samples of ore. The value of the
reports varied greatly, from the systematic data sent by Robert Beverley
of Fauquier County to the frank admission of insufficient knowledge on
the part of Major General William Henry Fitzhugh ("Rooney") Lee,
struggling to learn how to farm White House Plantation, from which
his great-great-grandmother Martha Custis had gone forth as the bride
of George Washington. Rooney Lee suggested that Maury come to visit
him and gain the needed facts, a device resorted to by many planters
including Maury's former Navy colleague, Robert R. Carter of Shirley. [49]

The Richmond, Fredericksburg, and Potomac Railroad and other railroads of the state helped to finance the second Preliminary Report in
order that Maury might proceed with the work. [50] Maury prepared an
address on railroad extension to be delivered at the Commercial Convention to be held in Memphis. General Smith wanted Maury to go to
Tennessee to deliver his speech. But Maury felt that work on the Report was too pressing, and he sent his chief agent, Colonel Thomas H.
Ellis, who delivered his address on May 19, 1869, before delegates from

all the Southern states seeking to set up an adequate system of railroads and improve the economy of the entire region.[51]

After his work hours, however, Maury did find time in Richmond to sit for a bust by the sculptor Edward V. Valentine. This pleased General Smith, who wrote Maury in an unusually light vein, "Look your prettiest and see to it that it graces our [V.M.I.] cabinet." [52]

At last Maury received word that the house in Lexington was ready and he left Richmond on May 25, 1869, going by the C and O Railroad to Goshen and thence by stage through Goshen Pass, where the blooms of the rhododendron had made the mountain gorge even more beautiful than on his visits the preceding fall.[53] When Maury, Ann, and their daughters Mary, Eliza, and Lucy reached the house they were to occupy at V.M.I., his chief delight was finding he was to have his own study, the first in his sixty-three years of life. Of this Eliza wrote to Marin Jansen: "He has a nice large, well lighted office at our house in Lexington which he delights in, plenty of room to throw his papers about and lose them too and then have all the household stirred up to come and hunt for them." [54]

Maury had taught the children to protect their never robust mother, and Eliza reported, "Mary and I keep the house for Mama—she one month and I one month—on opposite months we take turns writing for Papa." [55]

Maury had earlier received an invitation from a committee of the First Class (seniors) of the Virginia Military Institute to make their graduation address.[56] On July 2, 1869, at the commencement exercises, Maury, feeling in top form, delivered the speech with a quiet earnestness that commanded the interest of his audience. He urged the graduates to regard the work they had done at V.M.I. as the foundation for an education and declared:

> The character of your studies as you engage in the battle of life will be changed; but you will be learners still; therefore, there must be no relaxation as to intensity of application; for whatever be the specialty you may fancy most, you can neither excel nor shine in your calling, or even win the respect of the good, unless you master it in all its details, for remember, that the mental activity of the world is such that all the arts, all the departments of human knowledge, all the avocations of human life, in which the forces of matter are brought to bear upon practical affairs, all, all are progressive. Among the industrial pursuits of man there is not a single calling that has not, since the date of recorded history, received from the hand of progress the marks of improvement. . . . The potter's

463

wheel of the present day is the potter's wheel of Biblical times. The exception proves the rule. . . . All other implements and machinery employed in the affairs of men, from the nail to the ship, from the pot to the steam-boiler and engine, show improvement and indicate progress.

These improvements and this progress are simply the result of an increase of man's knowledge as to the forces of nature and the properties of matter. That sort of knowledge is accumulating daily, for the discovery of every new fact in physics, the development of every new principle in nature, the detection of every new property in matter, is a fresh clue placed in our hands. It leads into chambers of knowledge; it guides us through labyrinths into which our fathers could not find their way, and about the doors of which they groped in the dark; but it brings *us* out into the presence of everlasting truth.[57]

Maury then turned to the presentation of some facts concerning scientific discoveries. He referred to the vista opened up by Gustav Robert Kirchhoff's recent discovery that the dark lines in the solar spectrum provided a clue to similarities between the earth, sun, stars, and planets. With fervor he asked:

When those around you are achieving such conquests, and signalizing the age in which you live by such glorious triumphs of the human intellect, are you, gentlemen, after having laid such firm foundations for knowledge as you have been doing here, going to fling away study, shut your books and your eyes to the wonders of creation, and live in ignorance of all fresh knowledge that your contemporaries in other parts of the world are gathering and recording for future generations? . . .

What is it but the increase and diffusion of knowledge that has given us our arts, our sciences, our manufactures, our comforts, our luxuries, our civilization—in short, everything that raises us above the savage, who, by his ignorance, is degraded to the level of the brutes with which he be herded? And from what did this increase of knowledge arise but from observing the operations and studying the laws of nature? [58]

Fully aware that all the graduates had lived through a stirring chapter of history in which some had seen battle, Maury stated that "the heroic deeds of the brave men and noble women of the past are of themselves trumpet-tongued. . . . Treasure them up. They are a precious legacy—heirlooms of inestimable value in the eyes of every true man among us." But since Maury knew that there was no danger of these young Southerners' forgetting the past, he moved into his main theme, stressing that investigation of the physical world was necessary to create a better future.

> Every physical fact, by whomsoever observed, is, when placed in its true connections, a discovery, an invention; and all such facts are like the sheaf of magic wheat—the more it is threshed the more it yields. Therefore, take up, let me entreat you, for observation and study in your leisure moments, some one branch of the physical sciences. You will find it a never-failing source of pleasure and enjoyment. Always keep in reserve points of inquiry relating to it upon which you desire information. The practice begets habits of inquiry, and fosters the observing faculties. The pursuit of knowledge and especially of this kind of knowledge, is the noblest of all occupations that engage the energies of man; it ennobles his mind and dignifies his nature.[59]

General Smith was not surprised when the cadets besieged Maury with requests for copies. To meet the demand the Virginia Military Institute proudly had the speech printed in pamphlet form.

Maury had no sooner settled into his work at V.M.I. than he received an offer of the presidency of the University of Alabama. The Tuscaloosa authorities were insistent, and correspondence on the subject continued throughout the summer and fall.[60]

The salary Alabama proposed was much larger than Maury was receiving and he knew that state-supported V.M.I. was in no position to grant him a raise. It would be years before the state treasury would be able to meet state needs. For four years armies had fought across Virginia. Public buildings, mansions, business houses, and barns had been reduced to ruins by bombardment or put to the torch. Flourishing enterprises that had paid taxes no longer existed. Productive plantations were going back to weed and brier for lack of labor. New banks had been chartered from 1865 on, but in the spring of 1865 every bank in the state had ceased to exist when their assets—Confederate securities—had become worthless. Citizens who had been wealthy prior to the fall of the Confederacy could not use their valueless bundles of Confederate money or bonds to rehabilitate their property or to pay taxes.[61] Virginians were trying to make an economic comeback, but Maury knew how difficult it was for them to pay even the modest tuition fees at V.M.I. and how hard it was for General Smith to balance the budget there.[62] But he also knew that he had been unable to collect royalties from the publisher of his school geographies, whose firm was suffering financial difficulties.[63] The

465

University of Alabama offer was a temptation to Maury. But he decided that his commitment to serve Virginia was one that he should not set aside.[64]

On July 13, 1869, Maury gathered with the leaders of higher education in the state to plan the modernization and increase of intellectual training for Virginia youth. The occasion was the fourth annual meeting of the Educational Association of Virginia held at Washington College in Lexington.[65]

That autumn of 1869 was a happy time for Maury on the personal level. Matthew Jr. arrived from London with diplomas in hand from the Royal College of Chemistry and the Royal School of Mines.[66] Also Maury received a visit from his sister Betsy, Mrs. Kemp S. Holland of Mississippi.[67]

In these months Maury concentrated on the next report of the Physical Survey of Virginia and on the effort to lure European immigrants to the South. Both the Memphis Commercial Convention and one held at Louisville, with delegates from twenty-nine states, endorsed this immigration effort. Maury's agent, Colonel Ellis, wrote asking him to try to persuade General Lee to lend his name to immigration promotion.[68] Lee responded with a most helpful favorable statement.[69] But months later Maury had to admit to Frank Tremlett that "Immigration is very hard to be turned this way." [70]

When cold weather set in late in October Maury was seized with severe rheumatism. His fingers became so swollen and stiff that his handwriting grew almost illegible. Even more serious was the pain he suffered in "the broken knee," and this forced him to use crutches. In December, Maury was still not well and wrote wistfully to his sister, who had returned to her home: "All hands busy getting ready for Christmas —wish I had a pig tail with the old appetite." [71]

Maury was well enough, however, to complete, on December 16, 1869, the drafting of a 40-page speech he had agreed to deliver to the Educational Association of Virginia. It was a plea for Virginia to establish a polytechnic school where all the life sciences would be taught.[72]

It was fortunate that V.M.I. had given Maury an office in his house, for during the severe winter of 1869-70 he was seldom able to go outside but could hobble on crutches to his own sanctum. There he dictated to his daughters all business correspondence and material for the next survey report. To his much-loved nephew, Dabney Herndon Maury, struggling to build an insurance business in Louisiana, Maury made the effort to pen his own notes. In mid-March, he wrote Dab two short paragraphs in pitifully shaky script and admitted that the effort had taken him nearly an hour.[73]

466

Letters that Maury always answered, no matter how he felt, were those from men who were desperately trying to find work amidst the troubles of Reconstruction in the South. Full of compassion for their plight, Maury tried to help them secure jobs but usually found it impossible. He had not even been able to assist Matthew Jr. in finding work. He himself needed more income.[74]

Maury adhered strictly to his policy of not discussing anything of a political nature, but to a railroad president who was finding it difficult to carry on business under the limitations imposed on Southerners, he wrote his own philosophy: "Storms will come and with the vicissitudes of life, changes in the affairs of men. These have been forced upon us, and it becomes us to adjust ourselves to the assumptions, on the part of our new rulers, of these new powers and attributes, as best we may." [75]

At that time, however, Maury was full of rejoicing that Virginia had been readmitted to the Union on January 26, 1870, with military government giving away to civil authority the following day.[76] This had been brought about largely through an act by President Ulysses S. Grant. On April 17, 1868, the Constitutional Convention of Virginia, led by Radicals and Negroes, had voted their approval of a new state constitution with a clause that disfranchised the entire leadership group of the state and another clause that set up a test-oath by which "all persons before entering office were required to swear that they had not voluntarily aided the Confederacy or held office under it." [77] Upon taking office in Washington President Grant had seen that these clauses would block acceptance by the majority of Virginians of the state constitution that provided for universal male suffrage. In his first message to Congress, April 7, 1869, Grant had recommended that Virginians be allowed to vote on the body of the constitution separately from these two clauses.[78] Congress had passed a bill to permit this and on May 14 President Grant had issued a proclamation setting a day for that voting.[79] The citizens of Virginia had on July 6, 1869, voted for the constitution and against the disfranchisement clause and the test-oath clause.[80] Conservative Virginians had voted for Republican Gilbert C. Walker to be governor and defeated the more radical candidate H. H. Wells.[81] These steps had paved the way for Virginia to resume her place in the Union.

In his work for the Physical Survey Maury had written a pamphlet stating the need for extension of a railroad or canal from Virginia to the West. This won the approval of General Lee who, though already ill in the midwinter of 1870, took time to send it to a friend in Baltimore.[82] So unwell was Lee, in fact, that everyone in Lexington was glad when he went, that spring, on a tour to try to improve his health. In

Savannah the General dined with Ann Maury's brother, Brodie Strachan Herndon, who was practicing medicine there.[83] However, the end was already approaching for Lee, the man who to Maury, as well as to so many others, exemplified all that a man should be. The following autumn, after superintending the opening of the new term at Washington College, the revered Confederate leader died on October 12, 1870.

At the Virginia Military Institute, the banners of the fifteen Southern states were hung at half-mast. On the morning of October 15 Maury joined the Board of Visitors, General Smith, the entire V.M.I. faculty, and cadet corps to take part in the funeral procession for Lee. In the chapel at Washington College Maury heard General Pendleton read the Episcopal burial service and stood at attention as the remains of the Confederate chieftain were carried to the vault below.[84]

The death of Lee probably played a part in persuading Maury that he should listen to his physician's pleas that he go south for the winter months.[85] A few weeks earlier Maury had been obliged to admit to himself that winter cold made it necessary for him to turn down the presidency of St. John's College, Annapolis, Maryland, though they offered him an increase of one third over his V.M.I. salary.[86] General Smith was not heartily in favor of Maury's making the trip to the deep South, but he gave him authorization to go. Late in November Maury left for Richmond to conclude some work for the Physical Survey of Virginia.[87]

From Richmond, Maury went to Holly Springs, Mississippi, where he and his sister Betsy sat down to their first Christmas dinner together in forty-eight years. Maury next went to New Orleans to see nephew Dab. He visited for a while on a Louisiana sugar plantation and made his way via Mobile to Savannah.[88] There a welcoming committee was waiting at the station for him, but he managed to slip by them and avoid a public reception. He was delighted, however, the next morning to receive a call from General Joseph E. Johnston and later to be honored with various entertainments.[89]

The relaxation and the milder weather did wonders for Maury, and he returned to Lexington freed of rheumatic pain. In the late winter of 1871, he resumed his duties at the institute with zest and lectured to the cadets on "Man's Power-giving Knowledge." [90] He continued his efforts to arouse an interest in the physical sciences and to convince the young men of the satisfactions to be derived from accurate study. He emphasized his belief that science led man to religion and not away from it. He also enjoyed talking privately with cadets such as young Bennehan Cameron, whom former Secretary of the Navy William A. Graham sent with an introductory note.[91] Reading that note Maury must have thought back to Graham's backing, which had made possible his planning for the Brussels Conference.

Now came another spate of offers to Maury to leave V.M.I. On April 15, 1871, a regent of the University of Alabama offered him the presidency of that institution at $3,500 salary. Almost this same offer had been rejected once before and was so treated now.[92] The superintendent of public instruction in Alabama wrote in June informing Maury that he had been unanimously elected university president with salary of $5,000, a comfortable house, full power to select his own faculty, no requirements to undertake regular class instruction but authority to lecture when he wished.[93] For Maury, with four women dependent on his support, these were tempting terms as was the thought of working in a milder climate than the mountains of Virginia. Maury was loath to leave V.M.I., but on July 30 he telegraphed to Alabama, "I will come."[94] In a matter of weeks, however, Maury learned that the terms on which he had accepted the presidency could not be met by the university, and in August he informed Alabama authorities of his probable withdrawal. Final word of his resignation went to them on September 11.[95] During this short period, however, the university had sent out literature listing Maury as president; his New York publisher had used the presidential title on his *Manual of Geography,* which went to press at this time; and Alabama's naval hero, Admiral Raphael Semmes, had eulogized Maury in an article that appeared that September in the Montgomery *Advance.*[96]

In October the Right Reverend Charles Todd Quintard once more tried to persuade Maury to go to Sewanee at a salary of $4,000 or $5,000 and a house, declaring, "We must have you as Vice-Chancellor of the University of the South."[97] The embarrassing episode about Alabama had had its effect on Maury. But because of the sad postwar state of finances in all Southern institutions, he decided that a college presidency was not for him, at his age, though he was briefly tempted by a subsequent inquiry from the University of Tennessee.[98] In these years Maury was almost pitifully anxious to make a larger salary so that he could set aside savings to leave his wife. He was now within a few months of his sixty-sixth birthday and, because of his early injuries and various illnesses, was older in body than in mind.

For Maury this was a time of stock-taking and of decision for the future. He had hoped that by now funds would be available to publish the *Second Preliminary Report of the Physical Survey of Virginia,* which he had completed the previous May.[99] V.M.I. had no money for this and none with which to push the survey through to completion.[100] This fact, Maury saw, gave him the time to throw his energies into a wider effort that his fighting blood longed to make, a cause that would reap him no money but would benefit all Americans.

In the autumn of 1871 Maury decided again to enter the meteorological arena because he felt dissatisfaction over the incompleteness of a recent national development. During the preceding year Congress, by joint resolution, had voted the country's first full-time weather service. This had been organized by General Albert James Myer in the Signal Office of the Army [101] but had not absorbed into the program various observations that continued to be made by other agencies. Maury decided that the time had come for the citizens of the United States to rise up and demand the over-all meteorological service that the government could provide if it would establish a central weather bureau to handle all land meteorology for the United States. He also wanted crop reports issued to assist farmers.

General Smith still wished Maury to speak as often as possible to agricultural and mechanical interests as an extension of the work of the Physical Survey of Virginia. Therefore, that fall Maury made addresses to agricultural societies and to large audiences at fairs in Rockbridge County, Virginia, Shelby County, Tennessee, Nashville, Memphis, and St. Louis.[102] Each address varied with the audience, but always the subject was the same. Maury called for a United States Weather Bureau and crop reports. He explained the need for an international conference of leading meteorologists and agriculturists detailing the benefits that would flow to all countries from co-operative effort.

"By associating in one large and comprehensive system of meteorological research 'the weather and the crops' we may reasonably expect to find among the early and most important results of the system a series of 'crop forecasts' that will add to the stability of commerce, check speculation in the price of agricultural produce, encourage producers and benefit consumers," he declared.[103]

These great fairs attracted both leaders and the general public. Maury appealed to Americans to urge their lawmakers to press for an international conference and for Congress to pass an act combining the Signal Corps weather service with the crop studies of the Agricultural Bureau. His enthusiasm was contagious, and the farmers went home and wrote their state legislators to recommend that Congress act on the proposals. The Governor of Rhode Island wrote Maury that he would, at the next session, urge his state's General Assembly to petition Congress on the subject. The Governor of Massachusetts said he would refer the matter to his successor. Connecticut refused to take action, but West Virginia, New York, and Tennessee agreed to do so.[104] On December 13, 1871, the General Assembly of North Carolina passed a resolution recommending to the Congress of the United States that the legislators approve Maury's suggestion for international meteorological observations.[105]

The campaign continued to gain powerful support and Maury rejoiced to receive a copy of the Edinburgh *Courant* of January 26, 1872, which reported favorable reaction evinced by the Scottish Meteorological Society at a meeting presided over by Admiral Sir William Hope Johnstone.[106] Alexander Buchan, secretary of the Society, wrote giving his backing and asking Maury if the United States government was going to propose the international conference to other nations. If it was, Scottish meteorologists would bring pressure on the British government.[107]

In Brussels, Quetelet was delighted that Maury was again battling for their long-time dream. The distinguished Belgian urged Maury to come in May to the hundredth anniversary of the founding of the Royal Academy of Science, Letters and Fine Arts, of which he had long been a member.[108] In March *Le Messager de Paris* published a laudatory account of Maury's scientific work and reported that French savants such as Hippolyte Marié-Davy, P. F. Zurcher, and Elie Margollé were happy to work with the American scientist for an international meteorological conference and general system of observations.[109] The International Congress of Geographical, Cosmographical and Commercial Sciences, meeting in St. Petersburg, endorsed Maury's proposal for a meteorological conference.[110]

In Washington, however, it was a different story. Senator John W. Johnston of Virginia received a very cool reception from Secretary of State Hamilton Fish, who said he could do nothing about the proposal until Congress had taken action.[111] Maury had hoped that Fish would send notes to other nations proposing an international meteorological gathering as had his predecessor, Daniel Webster, in 1851, when no Congressional action had been deemed necessary.

In view of Fish's attitude, Senator Johnston tried another tack:

> I therefore called upon Mr. Watts, the Commissioner of Agriculture, who scarcely had the civility to hear me. He made the conversation very short, and said that he had just ordered the meteorological reports, which his predecessor had been collecting and publishing, to be discontinued. I ventured mildly to suggest that if meteorology did not appertain to his Department, at least Agriculture did. He gave this a qualified assent, but told me very positively that he would have nothing to do with the proposed scheme. I met with the same rebuff in other quarters and fancied that I saw a premeditated and arranged plan of resistance. Under these circumstances, it was manifestly useless to move now, and so I have not offered the

amendment [to provide funds for delegates to the International Agricultural Congress] and will not do so at this session. I am sorry indeed that a scheme so useful should be so treated.[112]

Maury was fully aware that Joseph Henry, secretary of the Smithsonian Institution, which was continuing its meteorological observations, was opposing all the plans that he was advocating.

Henry and his group of scientific friends had increased their power in Washington during the war, when they had organized the National Academy of Sciences with the immediate purpose of aiding President Lincoln's prosecution of the war. In the eyes of its chief organizer, Alexander Dallas Bache, the ultimate purpose of the organization was that it should be the "high tribunal" of science for which Bache had called since 1851.[113] Essaying this role, the National Academy of Sciences on January 9, 1864, had approved a resolution declaring that "the volumes entitled *Sailing Directions,* heretofore issued to navigators from the Naval Observatory and the Wind and Current charts which they are designed to illustrate and explain, embrace much which is unsound in philosophy and little that is practically useful, and that therefore these publications ought no longer to be issued in their present form." [114]

Maury knew that this resolution, which had been proposed by a committee of six of Henry's closest scientific friends, would cause lasting damage to his work and reputation. It made no difference that tens of thousands of navigators had found his philosophy sound and his instructions eminently useful. Neither these men of the sea nor prominent scientists who believed in his work had been present to defend it in this wartime academy meeting.

It was futile for Maury to seek to combat either this particular derogation or the oblique insults in memorials written by members of this group of Northern scientists.[115] In prewar days Jefferson Davis had advised Bache and Henry to "ignore" Maury with silence; and he, in turn, now tried to follow this policy toward Joseph Henry and his associates. At Memphis in October, 1871, however, Maury momentarily lost his usual restraint and made an intemperate blast at Henry, warning the farmers that the Smithsonian chief would seek to block his meteorological proposals.[116] Henry's opposition was a fact, but Maury's remarks were unworthy of him and served to reveal how much the ceaseless criticism had worn him down. Especially difficult for him was the hostility that he experienced from pro-Joseph Henry scientists at meetings outside the former Confederate states. In the spring of 1872 the tired old campaigner finally admitted to a daughter, "I am timid about such gatherings and it requires me severe mental effort to screw my courage up to the sticking point of mixing in with them." Then, as if ashamed of such weakness where the meteorological effort was involved, he declared, "I'll carry it in spite of them." [117]

And so, though he had been ill most of the winter and had already sent his address to General W. H. Jackson, of Nashville, to deliver for him, Maury "screwed up his courage" and went to St. Louis and there, on May 29, 1872, he made a powerful speech before the National Agricultural Association. Concerning a general system of weather and crop reports among all nations Maury said that "It is too big for any nation to handle alone." He reported how many nations had given indications of co-operating if the United States would take the lead. "In all moves like this, first the people and then the government have to be educated up to it." [118]

As to the carrying out of the work that would be outlined at the international conference, the United States had the preliminary machinery for this, Maury advised:

> The Signal Office or Bureau was got up last year with an appropriation of $25,000 especially for the benefit of Lake meteorology and navigation [Great Lakes] and to carry it on for another year an appropriation of ten times that amount is recommended by the committee in Congress. Instruct your Representatives then to adopt this plan, to go for an act making that establishment and the Agricultural Bureau co-operative offices and then, this appropriation will have a double value and be made as beneficial to Agriculture as to Commerce and its Atlantic outposts will watch in the interest of the farmer as well as the sailor. Will you press it upon Congress? [119]

The National Agricultural Association passed a resolution urging the Congress and other branches of the general government to carry out the plan proposed by Maury. They also ordered 10,000 copies of the speech to be printed at once and distributed to all governments and scientific societies.[120]

That summer letters about the proposed conference reached Maury from Henry Toynbee, successor to Admiral Fitzroy as head of the Meteorological Bureau, Board of Trade, British Admiralty, and from Alexander Buchan of Scotland. The British Association for the Advancement of Science sent an urgent invitation to Maury to come over for their annual meeting in August.[121] He was even advised that the Cunard line would give him half fare, but still he found it financially impossible to go.

His school geographies had proved successful but, of the $30,000 cleared on them by the publisher in 1871, Maury received only a small share.[122] Charles B. Richardson, who had for some time been in financial difficulties, changed his firm's name from Richardson and Company to the University Publishing Company, and on January 1, 1872, the latter firm bought outright the copyright to Maury's school geographies and wall maps.[123]

Though much of Maury's effort was devoted to his meteorological crusade in 1872, still he found time to give one or more lectures to the V.M.I. cadets on "What We Owe to Science." [124]

Another work that Maury carried on was a drive to have the state establish an agricultural college in conjunction with the Virginia Military Institute. After his first proposal Maury had drafted a memorial to the General Assembly of Virginia asking that Congressional land grants be assigned to V.M.I. to provide agricultural and mechanical education on a college level. This memorial had been approved by the Academic Board and signed by General Smith on December 18, 1871.[125] Maury lost the battle for the establishment of this school at V.M.I., but his chief objective was achieved when the Virginia Polytechnic Institute was subsequently established at Blacksburg and effectively provided the much-needed courses.[126]

In spite of the work he was able to do, Maury grew increasingly restive because funds had still not been found to prosecute the Physical Survey of Virginia. He felt he was not earning his proverbial salt at V.M.I. He considered himself only half a professor. On May 5, 1872, Maury wrote one of his daughters: "I have given Smith 'notice' and everybody's talking about it. They don't want me to quit a bit. The 'Gov' [Letcher, president of the Board of Visitors]—the Gov's a good old fellow—he protests and sends word . . . that I am, just as I am, worth more to V.M.I. than an entire professor." [127] The Board of Visitors refused to accept Maury's resignation and told him that in working for his meteorological plan he was doing just the kind of work they had brought him to Lexington to do.[128]

After his illness the preceding winter, Maury frankly dreaded another mountain winter. He was therefore mildly interested when a group of New Orleans men asked if he would head a polytechnic school there, but he declined that request.[129] He had to admit to himself that he was in no shape to organize and head a college. He was having occasional fainting spells and even in the warm weather of July his foot was giving him such severe pain that he was forced to use crutches.

At this time, however, came an invitation to speak which he was determined to accept at any cost. The associate editor of the Boston *Daily Globe* asked him to come to Boston in September to speak to the Farmers Club at Norfolk, Massachusetts. This sign of the healing of the wartime breach was balm to Maury's soul, since, as he put it, he was still "under the bans of the nation." [130] Maury mentioned in a letter to Frank Tremlett in England: "Only think that Boston, which offered a ransom for my head in 1861, called me traitor and treated my portrait with indignity, now asks me to come there and tell the Massachusetts farmers how they can help to 'roll' [the meteorological ball]." [131]

In early September, 1872, Maury left for Boston. In his speech there he was his most tactful self. He made allusions to John Quincy Adams, who had helped him in his early career, vigorously presented his meteorological proposals, and won the backing of the Massachusetts farm group.[132]

Back in New York, Maury spent a week of hard work with his publisher, making decisions about his school geographies and doing revision of texts. The effort exhausted him. Eliza tried to dissuade her father from continuing his trip to St. Louis, but he felt he must go as the Missouri people were among the staunchest backers of his crusade for a weather bureau. He was sick on the way west but on October 9, when he should have been in bed, Maury gave his speech before the agricultural fair in St. Louis. The text was masterly, but his delivery was very feeble.[133]

Now father and daughter headed east as Maury was scheduled to speak in Norfolk, Virginia, the port for which he had such vision. Here he would breathe the sea air and feel the stiff breeze coming in off the Atlantic, and he was sure that that would make him feel better. But by the time he got as far as Fredericksburg, Virginia, he was too ill to continue the journey and had to telegraph the directors of the Seaboard Agricultural Society that he could not deliver the address.[134] Maury's crusade was over.

As soon as he was well enough to leave Fredericksburg Maury, with his faithful Elie (Eliza), returned to Lexington and was welcomed by Ann. The suffering man said quietly, "My dear, I am come home to die." [135]

In December Maury's brother-in-law, Dr. Brodie S. Herndon, came from Savannah for a visit. Herndon agreed with the V.M.I. physician that Maury was suffering constant gastric pain and nausea, occasional hematemesis, feeble pulse, cool extremities, and a resulting depression of spirit. Dr. R. L. Madison of Lexington had placed Maury on medication and the blandest of diets to alleviate the pain caused by a bleeding stomach ulcer, and Herndon urged his brother-in-law to stick to this regimen.[136]

One of the greatest comforts to the ill man was that his son Dick could come often to sit with him. Dick had returned to the United States late in 1868, had studied law as hoped for by his father, and had been asked to come to Lexington to practice law with Governor Letcher's firm. On January 21, 1873, Maury had Dick rewrite his will so that he could leave some token to each member of the family since he had so little money to bequeath.[137]

Maury's gastric pain increased daily, and on January 28, when Dr. Madison came the sick man asked if he had come to torment him by trying to make him eat. Dr. Madison said no, only to take his pulse. Maury said to him, "You have done your duty like a man and a Christian. You have done all that a skillful physician could do and I thank you and pray that you will not disturb me any more but leave me alone with my God." There was a moment of shocked silence, so Maury added, "I am in very sane mind and I know what I am saying." [138]

Maury was full of gratitude that his mind remained clear in spite of his suffering. He told his children, who had gathered around him, "You see how God has answered my prayers for I know you every one; I shall retain my senses to the last." [139] He prepared for his death as he had for every event in life. He remained quiet in his bed for hours at a time and reviewed his life, his sins of omission and commission, and communed with God. Well before his death he spoke of experiencing a great sense of God's forgiveness.[140]

Maury asked Wellford Corbin to write to Marin Jansen and express his devotion.[141] Maury also instructed one of the children to "Write to Tremlett and tell him I think with gratitude of him as the means of bringing me to the communion." [142] In spite of weakness he insisted on dictating for his children's use the prayer he had said nightly for the thirty-four years he had lived since his crippling stagecoach accident in 1839:

> Lord Jesus, thou Son of God and Redeemer of the world, have mercy upon me! Pardon my offences, and teach me the error of my ways; give me a new heart and a right mind. Teach me and all mine to do Thy will, and in all things to keep Thy law. Teach me also to ask those things necessary for eternal life. Lord, pardon me for all my sins, for Thine is the kingdom and the power and the glory, for ever and ever. Amen.[143]

When some of his family had earlier inquired where his body should lie after death, Maury stated then, as he always had, that this was of no importance to him. But when Ann asked that she be permitted to bury him in Richmond, he replied, "Very well, my dear, then let my body remain here until the spring, and when you take me through the Goshen

Pass you must pluck the rhododendrons and the mountain ivy and lay them upon me." [144]

On the evening of January 31 Maury asked the family to sing him verses from two favorite hymns, a request he had made often during his illness. At the conclusion of the singing Maury said in a clearly audible voice, "The peace of God which passeth all understanding be with you all—all!" [145]

The next morning, realizing that he was about to embark on his last voyage, Maury asked his eldest son, "Are my feet growing cold? Do I drag my anchors?" Dick replied, "They are firm and secure." His father murmured, in the term he had used long before on many a lonely watch at sea, "All's well." [146]

With the perception that had always been his Maury knew when the end was near and sent Ann and his daughters from the room fifteen minutes before his death. He wished to spare them the sight of a struggle should one take place. But he was to go peacefully, with Dick holding one hand and Brave the other. The hour was 12:40 P.M., Saturday, February 1, 1873.[147]

A telegram was sent by the V.M.I. authorities to the President of the United States asking that, in view of Maury's renown in foreign countries, news of his death be delivered to the Diplomatic Corps in Washington. From Monday, February 3, until Wednesday, February 5, his body lay in state in the hall of the Virginia Military Institute library.[148]

In the weeks to come newspapers, magazines, and scientific journals in many countries were to publish accounts or evaluations of Maury's career. A paragraph from a long article in the New York *Herald* of February 3, 1873, is typical of the opinions generally expressed:

> The death of this distinguished physical geographer will create a profound sensation both at home and abroad. As the founder and most successful prosecutor of the benign system of oceanic researches, which has illumined the perilous paths of the mariner and taught commerce how to make the winds and currents of the sea do its bidding, his labors will long be gratefully remembered. As a marked type of an American scientist his career deserves careful study.[149]

At twelve o'clock on Wednesday, February 5, the Reverend Dr. William N. Pendleton, rector of Grace Episcopal Church, of which Maury had been a member since moving to Lexington, began the funeral service. At the conclusion, members of the First Class of V.M.I. carried the casket outside to the waiting hearse, and the procession moved off from the library, the hearse being drawn by four horses, led by

477

grooms. Behind the hearse marched the full battalion of the cadets of the Virginia Military Institute. The faculties of V.M.I. and Washington and Lee University (as Washington College had been renamed after General Lee's death) were in the procession, as were most of the citizens of Lexington and students of the university.

All the business houses of Lexington were closed. The bells of the churches and public buildings tolled, and guns were fired at regular intervals at the institute as the cortege moved through the town to the cemetery. There in a vault, lent by Maury's fellow professor, Colonel Gilham, Maury's body was laid to rest opposite the tomb of Stonewall Jackson.[150]

General Smith urged that Maury's body receive permanent burial in Lexington,[151] but Ann resolved to carry out the plan made during her husband's last days. She was not ready, however, to move to Richmond in June, when the rhododendron was in bloom in Goshen Pass, and so one portion of her husband's request could not be fulfilled. On September 22 Ann, with her sister Mary Herndon, and her daughters Betty and Diana and their children left for Richmond.[152] In the next three days, Dick, Mary, Eliza, Matthew Jr., Lucy, and Wellford Corbin packed the family's furniture and had it hauled to the packet boat of the James River and Kanawha Canal for transportation to Richmond. When the house had been cleaned thoroughly enough to deserve their father's old commendation "shipshape," they turned over the keys to General Smith.[153]

On the morning of September 26, 1873, General Orders No. 41 were issued at the Virginia Military Institute suspending academic exercises that day in order that the cadet corps might serve as an escort for the removal of Maury's remains from Lexington.

The procession formed at noon, and the cadet corps marched with the cortege to the North River, which bounded Lexington on the east.[154] General Smith continued on in the procession of carriages that proceeded along the route designated by Maury. After they had entered Goshen Pass and reached a particularly beautiful spot the procession halted, and Maury's children pulled branches of the green mountain laurel and rhododendron, of bright yellow maple and dogwood already turned crimson by September chill. They covered the casket with these boughs and decked the horses' bridles. Except for the absence of rhododendron blooms, the scene was just as Maury would have liked it, for the sun was shining, the birds were singing, and to their music was joined that of the tumbling river below.[155] At Goshen, the nearest railroad station to Lexington, the young Maurys saw their father's body placed on the train for Richmond, which they then boarded after bidding farewell to General Smith, who returned to the Virginia Military Institute.[156]

By family wish the reinterment in Richmond was private. On Saturday, September 27, 1873, Maury's remains were taken from the Chesapeake and Ohio Station to Hollywood Cemetery.[157] There he was given his final resting place on a knoll close to the grave of President John Tyler and that of James Monroe, who had been President when Maury received his midshipman's warrant. His work and his travels were over.

To the future belonged the development of the science of the sea. Maury had set the course.

Notes

CHAPTER I

A Challenging Heritage

1. Matthew Fontaine Maury (cited hereafter as MFM) tombstone, Hollywood Cemetery, Richmond, Va.; family records in Bible of Richard and Diana Maury, owned by Herndon Maury Gatewood of Richmond. The incorrect date of January 24 given in Diana Maury Corbin, *Life of Matthew Fontaine Maury, U.S.N. and C.S.N.* (cited hereafter as Corbin, *Maury*), p. 7, was one of the typographical errors that Maury's daughter was unable to correct because no proofs were sent to her before her book was published in London in 1888. This fact was stated by Diana's collaborator, her sister, Mary Maury Werth, in a letter to Virginia State Librarian H. R. McIlwaine, October, 1917. I have a copy of this letter and partial list of errata detected by Mrs. Werth.

2. The Richard Maury property is now a part of the Spotsylvania National Military Park that includes three Civil War battlefields—Wilderness, Chancellorsville, and Spotsylvania Court House. A plaque on a boulder on the north side of Jackson Trail, halfway between Lee-Jackson bivouac and the remains of Catharine iron furnace, marks the nearby birthplace of MFM.

   Oscar F. Northington, Jr., Superintendent, Fredericksburg and Spotsylvania National Military Park, tells me that the Richard Maury house was occupied until shortly after the Civil War but abandoned then because of disrepair. Pillagers removed the bricks and used them elsewhere.

3. James Fontaine, *A Tale of the Huguenots, or Memoirs of a French Refugee Family* (cited hereafter as Fontaine, *Tale of the Huguenots*), translated and compiled from the original manuscripts by one of his descendants, Ann Maury of New York, published without her name in 1838, pp. 15-16.

4. Ibid., pp. 16-22.

5. Ibid., pp. 23-24.

6. Ibid., pp. 25-31. Jacques Fontaine II has been confused with both Jacques I and III by various writers, who have thus overlooked one generation of Fontaines.

7. Ibid., pp. 32-111. See also Article 4 of Revocation of Edict of Nantes in *Memoirs of a Huguenot Family,* published in 1853 by Ann Maury of New York (hereafter cited as Ann Maury, *Huguenot Family*), pp. 508-509; this volume consisted of the memoirs of the Rev. James Fontaine that she had translated and published in 1838 (see Note 3), the journal of John Fontaine (see Note 16), a sermon preached in Virginia by the Rev. Peter Fontaine, letters of Mary Anne Fontaine Maury, the Rev. Peter Fontaine, Peter Fontaine, Jr., the Rev. James Maury, John Fontaine, and Colonel William Fontaine, as well as the Edict of Nantes, Secret Articles, Grants and Proclamations by the King of France to the Huguenots, the Revocation of the Edict of Nantes, and the Confession of Faith required by those who abjured Protestantism.

8. Fontaine, *Tale of the Huguenots,* pp. 111-127.

9. Ibid., pp. 128-134.

10. Ibid., pp. 137-161.

11. The Rev. James Fontaine went to Cork, Ireland, to serve without salary as minister of a church for Huguenot refugees and to support himself by

the manufacture of cloth. He resigned this pastorate to avoid a split in the church threatened by one parishioner. Ibid., pp. 162-172.

12. At Bear Haven, Fontaine served as justice of the peace. Ibid., pp. 175-234.
13. Ibid., pp. 235-240.
14. Ibid., pp. 241-242, 244-248.
15. Ibid., p. 235.
16. John Fontaine kept a diary from Sept. 16, 1710, the day he obtained his ensign's commission in Lord Shaw's regiment, through his preparations to go to America, his trip there, and his return to Ireland in January, 1719. For start of his military service, see Ann Maury, *Huguenot Family,* p. 245.
17. Matthew Maury was born in France, 1685/1686. See Fontaine, *Tale of the Huguenots,* pp. 249-250. See also Robert Alonzo Brock, *Documents, chiefly unpublished, relative to the Huguenot emigration to Virginia . . . with an appendix of genealogies presenting data of the Fontaine, Maury . . . and other families* (cited hereafter as Brock, *Documents*), pp. 121-122; Horace E. Hayden, *Virginia Genealogies* (cited hereafter as Hayden, *Genealogies*), pp. 159, 257, 385, 386.
18. "Journal of John Fontaine" in Ann Maury, *Huguenot Family,* pp. 247-265. For Gov. Spotswood, see Richard Morton, *Colonial Virginia* (cited hereafter as Morton, *Colonial Va.*), Vol. II, pp. 410-489.
19. The "Journal of John Fontaine" supplies the only complete account by a member of Gov. Spotswood's transmontaine expeditionary party. See journal in Ann Maury, *Huguenot Family,* pp. 281-292. See also *Executive Journals of the Council of Colonial Virginia,* Vol. III, p. 428; *William and Mary College Quarterly Historical Magazine* (cited hereafter as *Wm. and Mary Q*), Ser. 2, Vol. III, pp. 43, 145-153; Fairfax Harrison, *Landmarks of old Prince William,* p. 223; Hugh Jones (ed. Richard Morton), *The Present State of Virginia,* pp. 58, 166, 167.
20. James Maury was born in Dublin, Apr. 8, 1717/1718. Records in Maury family Bibles cited in Notes 1 and 26, and a genealogical chart of Fontaines and Maurys begun by Ann Maury of New York in the late 1840's and lithographed later (copies owned by many present-day Maury-Fontaine descendants) are the most accurate basic source for comparative studies with other sources such as *Virginia Magazine of History and Biography* (cited hereafter as *Va. Mag.*), Vol. XII, p. 156; *Va. Mag.,* Vol. II, pp. 217, 218; *Va. Mag.,* Vol. XXVII, p. 376; *Wm. and Mary Q,* Ser. 1, Vol. IX, p. 176; *Wm. and Mary Q,* Ser. 1, Vol. X, pp. 122-123; *Wm. and Mary Q,* Ser. 1, Vol. I, p. 220; *Wm. and Mary Q,* Ser. 2, Vol. II, p. 279; Brock, *Documents,* pp. 119-150.
21. The plantation, containing the headsprings of Jack's Creek (which empties into Pamunkey River on the north side), was spelled Fontainebleu in contemporary references; apparently it was not named for Fontainebleau, France. See Malcolm H. Harris, *History of Louisa County, Virginia* (cited hereafter as Harris, *Louisa*), p. 389.
22. Ann Maury to Mrs. Martha Harris, Dec. 6, 1852, quoted in Anne Fontaine Maury, *Intimate Virginiana* (cited hereafter as A. F. Maury, *Virginiana*), p. 253; see also sermon by the Rev. Peter Fontaine in Ann Maury, *Huguenot Family,* pp. 111-124.
23. Bishop William Meade, *Old Churches, Ministers and Families of Virginia,* Vol. I, p. 315; Elizabeth Valentine Huntley, *Peninsula Pilgrimage,* p. 118.

24. *Va. Mag.*, Vol. XI, pp. 289-304; Brock, *Documents*, p. 122.

25. Lt. Gov. Gooch to Bishop of London, Feb. 4, 1742, in Fulham MSS, Virginia, Box II, No. 225, No. 234, MS Div., Library of Congress (library cited hereafter as LC); Richard L. Maury, *The Huguenots in Virginia* (cited hereafter as R. L. Maury, *Huguenots*), p. 113.

26. Mary Walker Maury, born Nov. 22, 1724, died Mar. 20, 1798, *Va. Mag.*, Vol. XXVII, pp. 376, 377; records in "Our family Bible—No. 2, M. F. & A. H. Maury, Xmas, 1858," owned by Herndon Maury Gatewood of Richmond, Va.

27. *Wm. and Mary Q*, Ser. 2, Vol. I, p. 279; Fredericksville Parish (Louisa) Vestry Book, 2 vols., photostat in Virginia State Library (library cited hereafter as VSL).

28. The Rev. E. L. Goodwin, revised by the Rev. G. M. Brydon, *Parish Lines in the Diocese of Virginia*, p. 8.

29. James Maury to his uncle, John Fontaine, in Ann Maury, *Huguenot Family*, p. 379; Henry Stephens Randall, *The Life of Thomas Jefferson*, Vol. I, p. 18.

30. Maury's wife, Mary Walker Maury, was niece of Kentucky explorer Dr. Thomas Walker, who became chief agent of the Loyal Company in 1750. The Rev. James Maury received a grant of 10,000 acres, Mar. 3, 1752; see *Va. Mag.*, Vol. V, p. 179.

31. James Truslow Adams, *The Living Jefferson*, p. 5; Dumas Malone, *Jefferson the Virginian*, p. 40; Claude G. Bowers, *The Young Jefferson*, pp. 12-13; Sarah N. Randolph, *Domestic Life of Thomas Jefferson*, Vol. I, p. 27.

32. The Rev. James Maury to his uncle, John Fontaine, in London, Jan. 10, 1756, quoted and commented on by his grandson, MFM, in *Physical Survey of Virginia, Preliminary Report Number 1* (1869 ed.), pp. 22-24.

33. Helen D. Bullock, "A Dissertation on Education in the form of a letter from James Maury to Robert Jackson, July 17, 1762," *Albemarle County Hist. Soc. Papers*, Vol. II (1941-1942), pp. 36-60. Bishop Meade, *Old Churches, Ministers . . . Virginia*, pp. 11, 44. Mary Newton Stanard, *Colonial Virginia, Its People and Customs*, p. 274.

34. Consul James Maury to Mrs. Elizabeth Herndon, June 1, 1827, quoted in A. F. Maury, *Virginiana*, p. 13. Letter by unnamed grandson of Consul James Maury, ibid., p. 2.

35. The Rev. James Maury's will revealed his library contained 400 books, 44 pamphlets; see *Va. Mag.*, Vol. XXVI, p. 318.

36. The Rev. James Maury to his uncle, John Fontaine, quoted in Ann Maury, *Huguenot Family*, pp. 386-400.

37. Peter Fontaine, Jr., to his uncle, John Fontaine, in Great Britain, ibid., p. 363.

38. Since establishment of the colony in May, 1607, Virginia had been a little England across the Atlantic. Church and state were united. The growth of Dissenters (nonconformists) to the Established Church had occurred after 1710. Governor Spotswood to Board of Trade, Oct. 24, 1710, *Official Letters of Spotswood*, Vol. I, p. 26.

    Puritanical New Light congregations, Scotch-Irish Presbyterians, Quakers, and Baptists stoutly opposed the Anglican Church. For modern authoritative account, see Morton, *Colonial Va.*, Vol. II, pp. 465-471, 501, 583-596, 754-758.

39. W. W. Hening (ed.), *Statutes at Large . . . of Virginia* (cited hereafter as

Hening, *Statutes*), Vol. VI, pp. 568-569; Hening, *Statutes,* Vol. VII, pp. 240-241; Ann Maury, *Huguenot Family,* p. 402.

40. Minutes of Vestry, Mar. 24, 1761, Fredericksville Parish Vestry Book, Vol. I, p. 64; the Rev. James Maury was entitled to 50 shillings per 100 lbs. of tobacco for 16,000 lbs. of tobacco but received only £144; he instituted suit April 1, 1762, and was represented by Peter Lyons; the defendants were represented by John Lewis. After preliminary hearing, followed by argument of demurrer, Nov. 5, 1763, trial began Dec. 1, 1763, with new lawyer for defendants, Patrick Henry; court presided over by Patrick Henry's father, Colonel John Henry. See *Wm. and Mary Q,* Ser. 1, Vol. XIX, p. 21; Harris, *Louisa,* pp. 160-161; William Henry Foote, *Sketches of Virginia,* Vol. I, pp. 142, 161; William Wirt Henry, *Patrick Henry,* Vol. I, pp. 37-43; James Maury-John Camm Letterbook, University of Virginia Alderman Library (library cited hereafter as UVAL).

41. The Rev. James Maury to the Rev. John Camm, Dec. 12, 1763, UVAL. Maury wrote that Patrick Henry declared "his sole view in engaging in the cause, and in saying what he had, was to render himself popular." See also Ann Maury, *Huguenot Family,* pp. 420-423. But Henry's views were much the same that he consistently expressed later. For good modern accounts, see Robert Douthat Meade, *Patrick Henry,* pp. 114-138, and Morton, *Colonial Va.,* Vol. II, pp. 751-819.

42. The Rev. James Maury to the Rev. John Camm, Dec. 12, 1763, UVAL.

43. Views of the Rev. James Maury as quoted in Bishop William Meade, *Old Churches, Ministers and Families of Virginia,* Vol. I, p. 429.

44. Extracts from records in Bible of Richard's brother, Consul James Maury, show Richard as the twelfth child of his parents, preceded by Matthew, James, Leonard Hill (died as an infant), Ann, Mary, Walker, Catherine, Elizabeth, Abraham, Fontaine, and Benjamin; *Va. Mag.,* Vol. XXVII, pp. 375-376. Matilda Hill Maury was born three years after Richard.

45. Fredericksville Parish Vestry Book, 1769-1808.

46. Ann Maury to Mary H. Maury, Aug. 8, 1873, MFM Papers, MS Div. (cited hereafter as MP), LC, Vol. XLIV.

47. *Va. Mag.,* Vol. X, p. 204; *Va. Mag.,* Vol. XXXIII, p. 158; *Va. Mag.,* Vol. XXXVIII, p. 361; *Wm. and Mary Q,* Ser. 1, Vol. VIII, p. 198; *Wm. and Mary Q,* Ser. 1, Vol. IX, pp. 52, 53, 181; *Wm. and Mary Q,* Ser. 1, Vol. XXIV, p. 227; John Gwathmey, *Twelve Virginia Counties,* pp. 210, 211, 273, 345.

48. Errors in various sources concerning Minor family have been eliminated or reduced by careful comparative studies of court records of Lower Norfolk, Lancaster, Middlesex, Caroline counties of Virginia in VSL, with Lottie Wright Davis's *Records of Lewis, Meriwether and Kindred Families* (cited hereafter as Davis, *Families*); with John B. Minor, *The Minor Family* (many errors); and with sources cited in this chapter's Notes 47, 49, 50, 51, and 52.

49. Maindort Doodes undoubtedly came first to Virginia as a sea captain engaged in the purchasing and transporting of tobacco to Holland, where a high price was obtained. Lower Norfolk County, Va., records include his power of attorney with his name spelled Meindert; *Wm. and Mary Q,* Ser. 1, Vol. VIII, p. 196. See also Davis, *Families;* L. Minor Blackford, *Mine Eyes Have Seen the Glory* (cited hereafter as Blackford, *Mine Eyes*), p. 26.

50. Minor (Anglicization of Maindort, Meindort, Meindert) Doodes of Lancaster County, Mariner, with consent of wife Mary (probably nee Johnson) in 1665 deeded 200 acres to Peter Montague; *Wm. and Mary Q*, Ser. 1, Vol. VIII, p. 196.

51. Ibid.

52. Hening, *Statutes,* Vol. II, pp. 308-309; Vol. III, p. 479.

53. Will of Maindort Doodes, Mariner, dated Dec. 13, 1677, sealed with wax impression of a galley, recorded at clerk of court's office, Middlesex County.

54. Doodes Minor's will supplies wife's name, Elizabeth. Genealogists dispute whether she was the daughter of Nicholas Cock (also spelled Cocke), a Dutchman naturalized in 1672 (*Wm. and Mary Q*, Ser. 1, Vol. VIII, pp. 199-200); daughter of Maurice Cock, son of Nicholas (Davis, *Families*); or whether after Minor's death she became Elizabeth Cock by marrying Maurice Cock (*Wm. and Mary Q*, Ser. 1, Vol. IX, p. 52).

55. *Wm. and Mary Q*, Ser. 1, Vol. IX, p. 52.

56. Diana Vivian Minor died Apr. 16, 1718; Garrett Minor died Feb. 2, 1720. See Christ Church, Middlesex County, Parish Register; also see *Wm. and Mary Q*, Ser. 1, Vol. IX, p. 52.

57. *Va. Mag.,* Vol. II, p. 222; *Va. Mag.,* Vol. XI, p. 100; *Va. Mag.,* Vol. XXXIII, p. 158; *Va. Mag.,* Vol. X, pp. 97-98; *Wm. and Mary Q*, Ser. 1, Vol. VIII, pp. 107, 130, 131, 197, 198; *Wm. and Mary Q*, Ser. 1, Vol. IX, pp. 46, 52, 53, 179-182; *Wm. and Mary Q*, Ser. 1, Vol. XXI, p. 50; *Wm. and Mary Q*, Ser. 2, Vol. X, pp. 217, 218. John Minor's will was proved in Spotsylvania County, Sept. 2, 1754; will of wife, Sarah Carr Minor, was dated Sept. 25, 1772.

58. Maj. Thomas Carr was born in 1678 in England, died Apr. 29, 1738, in Virginia. He married Mary Dabney (born Jan. 22, 1680, died Sept. 17, 1748), daughter of Corneille Dabney (D'Aubigné) and Susanne (surname unknown). See Davis, *Families;* Edgar Woods, *Albemarle County in Virginia* (cited hereafter as Woods, *Albemarle*), p. 7.

59. Sarah Carr was born Nov. 14, 1714, married John Minor, 1732, died 1772. The use of the word "castle" in a plantation name was not then unusual. Sarah's brother John called his plantation in Louisa County "Bear Castle." There was also "Roundabout Castle" in Louisa. "Castle" was originally used in Virginia to designate fortified property, such as "Bacon's Castle."

60. The largest property owners were called great planters; others were called planters, small planters, homesteaders, according to the size of their properties.

61. John Minor II's birth date is also given as Nov. 13, 1735, and year as 1736 (the latter because of change from Old Style to New Style calendar in 1752); see *Wm. and Mary Q*, Ser. 1, Vol. IX, p. 52; sources cited in Note 57; *Va. Mag.,* Vol. X, p. 204; ibid., Vol. XX, pp. 320, 423; *Wm. and Mary Q*, Ser. 1, Vol. XXII, p. 128; ibid., Vol. XXVII, p. 161; ibid., Ser. 2, Vol. X, p. 30.

62. David Cosby was a vestryman of Fredericksville Parish. See Fredericksville Parish Vestry Book, VSL; Harris, *Louisa*, p. 303.

63. *Va. Mag.,* Vol. X, p. 204; State Enumerations of Virginia, 1782-1785, VSL.

64. John H. Gwathmey, *Historical Register of Virginians in the Revolution,* p. 553; T. E. Campbell, *Colonial Caroline: A History of Caroline County, Virginia,* pp. 231, 233, 244, 263, 274, 345, 348, 349.

65. Family records in Maury Bible cited in Note 1. Walker's full name was James Walker Maury, but he was never called by his first name.

66. The Rev. James Maury had not lived on the glebe (parish) farm but on his own farm on border of Albemarle and Louisa. In 1767 he had purchased nearly 700 acres southwest of Ivy Depot. Latter property sold in 1797 by the Rev. Matthew Maury to the Rev. William Woods and Richard Woods. See Woods, *Albemarle*, p. 268; Albemarle court records from 1748 to 1783 were lost during the Revolution.

67. Virginia County Records, Spotsylvania County Deed Book P, 1797-1802, deed of sale, Aug. 31, 1797, pp. 6-8, on microfilm 01000, reel 8, VSL. The error of using the name of Richard Henry Lee as vendor in deed of sale, Deed Book P, p. 6, is corrected by all subsequent references to Henry Lee; by fact it was land General Henry Lee had purchased from Gen. Spotswood, Dec. 4, 1794, as recorded in Spotsylvania County Deed Book O, 1794-1797, p. 63; by fact of statement, "John M. Herndon, S. S. C. surveyed for Richard Maury 103 acres of land—which he purchased of Gen'l Henry Lee and which is bounded agreeable to said plat. Recorded Spotsylvania Court House, 5 Sept. 1797, (signed) Jos. Chew, C. S. C.," Deed Book P, p. 8. For easier reference, see William Armstrong Crozier (ed.), *Spotsylvania County Records, 1721-1800, Being Transcriptions from the Original Files at the County Court House of Wills, Deeds . . .* , p. 497.

68. Lease, Deed Book P, Spotsylvania County, 1797-1802, with plat, pp. 9-11, microfilm 01000, reel 8, VSL.

69. The terms of payment probably meant Richard Maury was to pay the value of 1,000 lbs. of crop tobacco in tobacco or cash.

70. For an interesting account of Gov. Spotswood's early mining operations, see "A Progress to the Mines," in J. S. Bassett (ed.), *Writings of Colonel William Byrd II.*

71. The hematite ore of the area is mentioned in J. P. Lesley, *Iron Manufacturer's Guide*, pp. 63, 445.

72. Joseph Martin in his *New and Comprehensive Gazetteer of Virginia and District of Columbia, 1836* (cited hereafter as Martin, *Gazetteer VaDC*), pp. 279-280, spoke of this area as "lands exhausted by injudicious cultivation."

73. Ann Maury of New York to Mary H. Maury, Aug. 8, 1873, MP, Vol. XLIV, LC.

74. John Minor III had studied law under George Wythe of Williamsburg. Launcelot Minor successfully managed "Minor's Folly" plantation in Louisa County, Virginia.

75. Spotsylvania County Deed Book R, 1806-1809, deed of sale, Feb. 13, 1808, p. 411, microfilm 01000, reel 9, VSL.

76. His widowed sister, Mrs. Elizabeth Maury Lewis, was married to Edward Herndon on July 13, 1809, by the Rev. Samuel Wilson.

77. Statement about farming in this area made to me by Oscar F. Northington, Jr., Superintendent, Fredericksburg and Spotsylvania National Military Park. For general study of problem, see Avery Craven, *Soil Exhaustion as a Factor in the Agricultural History of Virginia . . .* , University of Illinois Studies.

78. John Minor III had seen some service in last months of the Revolution. He became brigadier general of the 1st Brig., 2nd Div., Virginia Militia, and served around Norfolk in the War of 1812. He was a vestryman of

St. George's, Fredericksburg, a successful lawyer and member of the Virginia General Assembly.

79. Spotsylvania County Records, Aug. 1, 1808, Deed Book R, pp. 399-400, microfilm 01000, reel 9, VSL.

80. Midshipmen were warranted in U.S. Navy in this period. An appointment was granted to a youth to serve as acting midshipman for a trial period of six months at sea. When he had successfully passed that probation, he received his warrant as a midshipman dated retroactively to the date of his appointment. The term "midshipman" was, however, generally used to refer to both the acting midshipman and the warranted midshipman. See Navy Records (cited hereafter as NR), Letters to Officers, Ships of War, Vol. VIII, pp. 9, 242, National Archives, Navy Records Branch (cited hereafter as NAn).

81. NR, Acceptances G-N, 1804-1823, NAn.

82. Fontaine Maury (1761-1824) married Elizabeth Brooke in 1785. Abraham Maury (1763-1814) married Mildred Thornton and continued to live in Virginia; he should not be confused with Abram (or Abraham) Maury, who moved to Tennessee.

83. Richard Maury's uncle, Abraham Maury, born 1731 at "Fontainebleu," King William County, Va., moved to the southern frontier of Virginia, where on Dec. 20, 1775, in Mecklenburg County, he was appointed commissary to supply the militia of the area. He was appointed adjutant of Minute Men, July 18, 1776, and later rose to be a colonel in the Revolution. See John H. Gwathmey, *Historical Register of Virginians in the Revolution . . .* , p. 509.

84. Abram (also Abraham), son of Richard's uncle Abraham, was born in Virginia, Jan. 17, 1766, and died in Tennessee, Jan. 2, 1825. He was first cousin to Richard Maury, not brother or uncle as has often been stated.

85. For general development, see William Stevens Perry, *The History of the American Episcopal Church, 1587-1883*, Vols. I, II; George MacLaren Brydon, *Virginia's Mother Church and the Political Conditions under Which It Grew*, Vol. II; Edward L. Goodwin, *The Colonial Church in Virginia;* Philip Slaughter, *History of St. George's Parish*, Spotsylvania County, Va.

86. St. George's (Spotsylvania) Parish records were lost during the Civil War, but Richard and Diana Maury recorded in their Bible (cited in Note 1) the date of birth for each of their children and the names of the sponsors in baptism for all but their last child.

  The Book of Common Prayer and Administration of the Sacraments and Other Rites and Ceremonies of the Church According to the use of the Protestant Episcopal Church in the United States of America (1952 printing of 1928 revision, p. 273) states, "There shall be for every Male-child to be baptized, when they can be had, two Godfathers and one Godmother; . . . and Parents shall be admitted as Sponsors, if it be desired." The latter step was not necessary at MFM's baptism. Four sponsors, instead of the required three, made the solemn promises in his behalf. They were Miss Elizabeth Hull, Miss E. Herndon, John M. Herndon, and Jacob Herndon. The date of MFM's baptism is not recorded in the Bible, but the latest date possible for the event is established by the fact that his first-listed godmother ceased to be Miss Elizabeth Hull on Nov. 17, 1806, when she married Dabney Herndon. It is probable that MFM was baptized before July, 1806, when ill health forced the Rev. Abner Waugh to resign as rector of St. George's, after which the parish was without a rector for two years.

87. Richard Maury is listed in the U.S. Census, 1810, Spotsylvania County, Va., with his name spelled as many people pronounced it, Murry. The record shows that when the census taker visited his home, Richard possessed 12 slaves.

88. Relinquishment of trust with sale of slave included, Spotsylvania County, Deed Book S (film, VSL), pp. 159-160.

89. Ibid., pp. 160-161.

90. Ibid., p. 161.

91. Abram Maury's great-grandson, Maury T. Reid, wrote to Judge Walter W. Faw, Mar. 14, 1947, "Richard Maury came over to Tennessee in 1810 to join the Abram Maury Colony." Quoted in W. W. Faw, "Boyhood Home of MFM," typescript in Tennessee State Library and Archives (cited hereafter as TSLA). The Spotsylvania court order combined with deed of sale indicate the departure date as between mid-September and early November, 1810.

92. For route, see: William and Mary College President James Madison's Map of Virginia, 1807; Map of Spotsylvania County, 1820; Martin, *Gazetteer VaDC*. For Salem, see Writers' Program, Virginia, WPA (compilers), *Roanoke, Story of County and City*.

93. Letter about Matilda Maury from her granddaughter, Frances Virginia Guthrie, to Charles Lee Lewis, Mar. 19, 1928, TSLA; Corbin, *Maury*, p. 7.

94. Map issued by "Tennessee Government," 1810, showing only one practicable route from Virginia to Franklin, Tenn.

95. Range Map Middle Tennessee c. 1810. Williamson County was created by Tennessee legislature in 1799. Franklin was incorporated in 1799.

96. "Tree Lawn" property, including the Maury graveyard on Del Rio Pike, 2 miles northwest of Franklin, was visited by me in 1957, through courtesy of the owner, Will Reese, Sr.

97. As samples of Abram Maury's land transactions, see Land Grant Book A, pp. 426, 429; Book C, pp. 50, 51, 443; Deed Record Book B, pp. 536, 592, 637, 647 at Franklin Court House, Tenn.

98. F. A. Michaux, M.D., *Travels to the Westward of the Allegany Mountains in 1802*, p. 94.

99. Previous MFM biographers have incorrectly placed the Richard Maury family on their own farm on arrival in Tennessee; actually it was not acquired until 1813. Judge John H. Henderson, authority on local history, unveiling plaque to MFM at high school, Franklin, Tenn., in 1910, stated, "His father came first to the farm now owned by our venerable townsman H. S. Ewing where he remained for about two years. He then purchased the farm in the 5th Civil District." See Deed cited in Note 101.

The Ewing property was about 2 miles southeast of Franklin, now a suburb called Ewingville, on Tennessee State Highway 96. Mrs. Ewing Roberts Green, a great-granddaughter of grantee Alexanderia Ewing, lives on part of that property, with Ewing's original log house incorporated in her home. She permitted me to have a true copy made of her photostat of the original grant, No. 659, Dec. 8, 1797, Military Grants of North Carolina.

100. Corbin, *Maury*, pp. 7-8.

101. John and Launcelot (also spelled Lancelot) Minor signed document in Virginia on Oct. 13, 1813; deed of sale recorded at Franklin Court House, Tenn., on Nov. 2, 1813. See Williamson County, Tenn., Deed Book C, pp. 459-460.
102. Ibid.
103. William Nisbet Chambers, *Old Bullion Benton,* pp. 18, 19, 31, 32, 35, 42, 48, 51, 53.
104. Williamson County, Tenn., Deed Book C, pp. 459-460.
105. An account of MFM's boyhood, as told by him to his children, was written by his daughter, Mary H. Maury Werth in the form of a letter to her children, July 26, 1879; MP, Vol. XLII, LC.
106. Corbin, *Maury,* p. 8.
107. Richard Maury's slaves listed in U.S. Census, 1820, Williamson County, Tenn., p. 144.
108. Charles M. Maury to Mary H. Maury, Sept. 14, 1873, MP, Vol. XLIV, LC.
109. Article on the Rev. Gideon Blackburn in *Twentieth Century Dictionary of Notable Americans,* Vol. I (pages are not numbered); Walter W. Faw, "History of Harpeth Academy," TSLA. Tennessee historical markers, Franklin; plaque, St. Paul's Episcopal Church, Franklin, Tenn.
110. Account by John M. Maury's son, Dabney H. Maury (when serving as U.S. minister to Colombia), in letter to Mary H. Maury, Aug. 7, 1873, MP, Vol. XLIV, LC; Corbin, *Maury,* pp. 10-12.
111. Lewis was trained by Commodore Preble in the war with Tripoli. See Mary Lewis Cooke and Charles Lee Lewis, *An American Naval Officer in the Mediterranean, 1802-7,* reprinted from *U.S. Naval Institute Proceedings* (cited hereafter as *USNIP*), Vol. LXVII, No. 11, Whole No. 465 (November, 1941), pp. 1533-1539.
112. In that era the number of guns a man-of-war had been designed to carry was written immediately after her name, that is, *Essex,* 32. She was theoretically rated as a 32-gun ship but mounted more than her rating, as did virtually all warships. In this work each man-of-war will be mentioned once with her rating and subsequently by name only.
113. The *Epervier,* commanded by John M. Maury's former captain, William Lewis, sailed one day before John reached Norfolk; the ship was never heard from again.
114. David Porter, *Journal of a Cruise made to the Pacific Ocean in U.S. Frigate Essex, 1812-1814,* Vol. II, pp. 19-163; Archibald Douglas Turner, *Commodore David Porter, 1780-1843,* pp. 176-237; NR of the *Essex* and the *Essex Junior,* also of David Porter, John Downes, S. D. McKnight, David G. Farragut, John M. Maury, NAn.
115. Mary H. Maury Werth to her children, July 26, 1879, MP, Vol. XLII, LC; Corbin, *Maury,* pp. 12-13.
116. John M. Maury's voyage in the *Pennsylvania Packet* was made possible because in an era of too few Navy ships, the U.S. Navy granted long furloughs to naval officers to make such merchant marine voyages. See Charles Lee Lewis, professor U.S. Naval Academy, "Our Navy in the Pacific and the Far East Long Ago," *USNIP,* Vol. LXIX, No. 6, Whole No. 484 (June, 1943), pp. 857-858.

CHAPTER II

Education—A Burning Desire

1. MFM, *The Annual Address delivered before the Maryland Institute for the Promotion of the Mechanic Arts, Maryland Agricultural Society,* Oct. 25, 1855, p. 4.
2. Sketch of MFM's boyhood written from his reminiscences by his daughter, in Mary Maury Werth to her children, July 26, 1879, MP, Vol. XLII, LC.
3. An account of the history of Harpeth Academy and its leading students was written in 1951 by Judge Walter W. Faw, who had carefully researched the subject; typescript in TSLA.
4. Sketch of Blackburn in *Twentieth Century Dictionary of Notable Americans,* Vol. I (pages not numbered). See also article on Cherokee Indians, *Encyclopedia Americana* (1948 ed.), Vol. VI, p. 415.
5. Mary Maury Werth sketch of MFM cited in Note 2.
6. Alex (Ellick) C. Maury was son of Philip P. Maury, who was a brother of Abram Maury.
7. Arthur Benjamin Chitty, Jr., *Reconstruction at Sewanee,* p. 46; Garden Study Club (compilers), *History of Homes and Gardens of Tennessee,* p. 235.
8. Nashville *Whig,* Dec. 12, 1821.
9. James H. Otey was ordained a priest of the Episcopal Church in 1827 and was consecrated Bishop of Tennessee on Jan. 14, 1834. MFM wrote to him with considerable frequency during his early years at sea and later.

For use of term "preceptor," see "Commander Maury's Address at the Laying of the Cornerstone, October 10, 1860," the Rev. Telfair Hodgson, D.D., Vice-Chancellor (ed.), in *Reprints of the Documents and Proceedings of the Board of Trustees of the University of the South, University of the South Papers, Series A, No. 1,* p. 63.
10. MFM to daughter, Elizabeth (Betty) H. Maury, June 14, 1863, MP, Vol. XVIII, LC.
11. MFM to W. C. S. Ventress, Feb. 6, 1825, MP, Vol. I, LC.
12. Sketch of A. P. Maury in *Biographical Directory of the American Congress, 1774-1949,* House Doc. No. 607, 81st Cong., 2nd Sess. (cited hereafter as *Biog. Directory Cong.*), p. 1515; sketch in *Twentieth Century Dictionary of American Notables,* Vol. VII.
13. Sketch of Samuel Houston in *Biog. Directory Cong.,* p. 1334.
14. Williamson County, Tenn., Franklin Court House, Record of Wills and Inventories, Vol. IV, pp. 7-8.
15. Memorandum by Rutson Maury attached to MFM letter to Rutson Maury, Aug. 31, 1840, MP, Vol. II, LC.
16. MFM to Ann Maury of New York, Sept. 27, 1839, Maury Collection (hereafter cited as MC), UVAL.
17. Rutson Maury statement cited in Note 15.
18. Mary Maury Werth sketch of MFM cited in Note 2.
19. Ibid.
20. Report of J. S. Ellick, June 25, 1823, and report of Surgeon Cowdery, June 26, 1823, to Secretary of Navy in Captains' Letters for 1823, Vol. III, NAn. The date of John's death is indicated in these reports as June 23 but given as June 24 in records in Bible of Richard and Diana Maury. He died either

just before midnight of the 23rd or in the first hours of June 24. The *Decoy* reached Norfolk late in the evening of June 24. The date of John's death has been incorrectly stated as June 25 in Edward William Callahan (ed.), *List of Officers of the Navy of the United States and of the Marine Corps, 1775-1900* (cited hereafter as Callahan, *List of Officers*), p. 357.

21. Statement by John M. Maury's son, Dabney H. Maury, in note to MFM attached to entry for Jan. 25, 1872, MP, Vol. XLIV, LC.
22. Mary Maury Werth sketch cited in Note 2.
23. MFM to Rutson Maury, Aug. 31, 1840, MP, Vol. II, LC.
24. Memorandum by Rutson Maury, ibid.
25. MFM letter cited in Note 23.
26. Commodore David Porter to Secretary of Navy Smith Thompson, June 14, 1823, Captains' Letters for 1823, Vol. III, NAn.
27. Tombstone in family graveyard, "Tree Hill," on Del Rio Pike, about 2 miles northwest of Franklin, Tenn.
28. MFM letter cited in Note 23.
29. Ibid.
30. MFM letter cited in Note 11.
31. NR, Appointments, Orders and Resignations (cited hereafter as AOR), Vol. XIII, p. 235, NAn.
32. MFM letter cited in Note 23.
33. MFM to his wife, Oct. 12, 1863, MP, Vol. XVIII, LC.
34. MFM sometimes incorrectly spelled the name of his youngest sister, but it is properly spelled in the records in his Bible and on her gravestone at Richard Maury farm, about 6 miles from Franklin, on Blazer Road. Matilda had almost certainly already married and left home by this date. See MFM to Lucian Minor, his first cousin and Commonwealth's Attorney for Louisa County whom MFM addressed as Lucien, July 15, 1843, MP, Vol. II, LC.
35. Mary Maury Squires, 23-year-old widow, was married to Noah Miller Ludlow on Sept. 1, 1817, in Nashville. She later lived in Mobile, Ala., but settled in St. Louis, Mo. See Noah Miller Ludlow, *Dramatic Life as I Have Found It*, pp. 106-108, 118, 218; MFM to N. M. Ludlow, July 26, 1858, MSS Collection of Missouri Historical Society, St. Louis, Mo.; see also MFM to Rutson Maury, Mar. 17, 1848, MC, UVAL.
36. MFM letter cited in Note 23.
37. Ibid.
38. Mary Maury Werth sketch of MFM cited in Note 2; Corbin, *Maury*, pp. 14-15.
39. This was the average day's ride for MFM's first cousin William Maury, son of Consul James Maury, on a horseback tour of Southern states. William visited the Richard Maury family in Tennessee in May, 1821. See William Maury to his sister Ann Maury, Nov. 20, 1820, and May 29, 1821, quoted in A. F. Maury, *Virginiana*, pp. 81, 83.
40. Matthew Maury, son of Consul James Maury, to his mother, Mrs. Margaret Rutson Maury, Aug. 8, 1825, quoted in A. F. Maury, *Virginiana*, p. 61. Reuben Maury was the son of Richard's eldest brother, the Rev. Matthew Maury and Elizabeth Walker Maury.
41. Mary Maury Werth sketch of MFM cited in Note 2.
42. Thomas Walker Maury, lawyer, magistrate, and later head of a classical

school at his home "Midmont," near the University of Virginia. See A. F. Maury, *Virginiana,* pp. 61, 63, 321, 325.

43. "Laurel Hill," the home of Edward Herndon (1761-1837) and his wife Elizabeth Maury Lewis Herndon (1756-1834), was located on north side of Virginia state road 627 (formerly known as Gordon Road), about 1½ miles northeast of Goshen Church and about 1½ miles west of Ny (Ni) River. The house was pulled down in 1923. John Waterhouse Herndon visited the property and described it to Col. James Douglas Fife in a letter dated Dec. 16, 1950, of which I have a photostat sent me by Col. Fife's niece, Anne Freudenberg.

44. After the death of her first husband, who was either James Lewis of "Portland" or T. Lewis, Elizabeth married Edward Herndon in July, 1809. See *Va. Mag.,* Vol. XI, p. 100; MFM to Ann Maury of New York, May 28, 1842, MC, UVAL.

45. Brodie S. Herndon to Mary H. Maury, Aug. 8, 1873, MP, Vol. XLIV, LC.

46. Ann Hull Herndon, the third child of her parents, was born Aug. 8, 1811; John Goodwin Herndon, *The Herndons of the American Revolution,* Part Two: "Edward Herndon of Spotsylvania County, Virginia, and His Descendants" (cited hereafter as Herndon, *The Herndons*), p. 116.

47. MFM to B. Franklin Minor, Mar. 21, 1855, MP, Vol. IV, LC.

48. Elizabeth Hull Herndon was born Jan. 12, 1789, to Col. John Hull and Ann Strachan Hull. She married Dabney Herndon Nov. 17, 1806, died Apr. 20, 1825. See Spotsylvania County Records, Nov. 12, 1806, Marriage Licenses, p. 28; Herndon, *The Herndons,* pp. 114-115.

49. Dabney Herndon was born Apr. 14, 1783, to Joseph Herndon and his second wife, Mary Minor Herndon (sister of Maj. John Minor of "Topping Castle," Louisa County). Dabney Herndon died Dec. 20, 1824. His will was probated Jan. 13, 1825, Fredericksburg, Va., Hustings Court. See 1817-1828 Will Book B, p. 201; Herndon, *The Herndons,* p. 114. The Farmer's Bank of Fredericksburg, which Dabney Herndon headed, was one of twelve banks of the powerful Farmer's Bank of Virginia.

50. Mary Maury Werth sketch of MFM cited in Note 2.

51. MFM's uncle Abraham Maury had served in the Revolution: 2nd Lieut., 14th Va. Reg., Nov. 14, 1776; 1st Lieut., Dec. 8, 1777; Regimental Adjutant, Jan. 1, 1778. His regiment, 14th Va., was designated as 10th Va. from Sept. 14, 1778. Abraham Maury resigned, 1781. Francis B. Heitman, *Historical Register of the Officers of the Continental Army* . . . (cited hereafter as Heitman, *Register*), p. 385.

52. John T. Goolrick, *Historic Fredericksburg,* pp. 140, 141.

53. Mary Maury Werth sketch of MFM cited in Note 2.

54. Advertisement for steamboat and stage line between Richmond, Fredericksburg, and Washington, Washington *Daily National Intelligencer* (cited hereafter as *National Intelligencer*), June 1, 1825, p. 4.

55. Martin, *Gazetteer VaDC,* pp. 499-502.

56. Irving S. and Nell M. Kull, *A Short Chronology of American History,* p. 95.

57. For Washington and the Capitol at that period, see: Lieut. the Hon. Frederick Fitzgerald de Roos, Royal Navy, *Personal Narrative of Travels in the United States and Canada in 1826 with Remarks on the Present State of the American Navy in early 1826* (cited hereafter as De Roos, *American*

Navy), pp. 14-16. For general accounts, see Wilhelmus Bogart Bryan, *A History of the National Capital . . .* , Vols. I and II; Martin, *Gazetteer VaDC;* William Elliott, *The Washington Guide,* 1822 and 1826 editions.

58. The term "White House" was not used during MFM's lifetime. See Peter Force, *A Directory for the Public Offices in Washington, 1820,* p. 3; Martin, *Gazetteer VaDC,* pp. 500-501.
59. Richard B. Morris (ed.), *Encyclopedia of American History,* pp. 163-164.
60. Judah Delano, *Washington Directory* for 1820, p. 85; Charles Oscar Paullin, "Washington City and the Old Navy," *Columbian Historical Society Records,* Vols. XXXIII-XXXIV, pp. 174-175.
61. A few months later Richard B. Maury was made Register (registering clerk, not then called Registrar). See *Navy Register, 1826;* see also *Navy Register, 1824,* S. A. Elliott, *Washington Directory* for 1827.
62. Judah Delano, *Washington Directory* for 1820, p. 8.
63. *Navy Register, 1824.*
64. Sketch of Samuel L. Southard in *Dictionary of American Biography* (cited hereafter as *DAB*), Vol. XVII, p. 25.
65. Commodore David Porter to Secretary of Navy (second letter of day), June 14, 1823, Captains' Letters, 1823, Vol. III, NAn.
66. MFM letter cited in Note 23.
67. *Rules, Regulations and Instructions for the Naval Service of the United States,* 1818 (cited hereafter as *Navy Regulations,* 1818), known as the Blue Book in the service.
68. Leland P. Lovette, *Naval Customs, Traditions, and Usage* (cited hereafter as Lovette, *Naval Customs*), pp. 225, 253; *Navy Regulations,* 1818, p. 29.
69. De Roos, *American Navy,* p. 197.
70. Statement by Dabney H. Maury, son of Eliza and John M. Maury, cited in Note 21.
71. For an account of the Capitol and its stages of growth, see Glenn Brown, *History of the United States Capitol,* Vol. II, pp. 404, 426.
72. Howard Irving Chapelle, *The History of the American Sailing Navy, The Ships and Their Development* (cited hereafter as Chapelle, *Sailing Navy*), pp. 336, 534.
73. NR, Log No. 1, U.S.S. *Brandywine,* 44 guns (cited hereafter as *Brandywine* Log), entry for June 17, 1825, NAn.
74. Theodore Roscoe and Fred Freeman, *A Picture History of the United States Navy* (cited hereafter as Roscoe-Freeman, *Pictorial USN*), p. 426.
75. NR, *Brandywine* Log, entry for July 1, 1825, NAn.
76. Order to MFM dated July 8, 1825, NR, AOR, Vol. XIII, p. 266, NAn.
77. Statement by Lafayette's secretary, Auguste Levasseur, quoted in Sophie Radford de Meissner, *Old Naval Days—Sketches from the Life of Rear Admiral William Radford, U.S.N.* (cited hereafter as De Meissner, *Naval Days*), p. 21.
78. Daniel Ammen, Rear Admiral, U.S.N., *The Old Navy and the New. Personal Reminiscences* (cited hereafter as Ammen, *Old Navy*), p. 27; George Jones, *Sketches of Naval Life with Notices of Men, Manners and Scenery on the Shore of the Mediterranean in a Series of Letters from the Brandywine and Constitution Frigates* (cited hereafter as Jones, *Naval Life*), Vol. II, p. 271.

Nathaniel Bowditch's famous work was first published in 1802 with the lengthy title *The New American Practical Navigator, An Epitome of Navigation and Nautical Astronomy.* The full title was almost never used in the early Navy.

79. Richard B. Maury to W. C. S. Ventress, Nov. 4, 1825, MP, Vol. I, LC.

80. Ventress evidently had difficulty securing the $200 to send MFM because his check did not reach Washington until a few weeks after MFM had left. There may have been a letter (not preserved) from Ventress informing MFM that the check would come in due time because MFM instructed his cousin Richard B. Maury how to disburse the sum when it arrived. The uniforms were undoubtedly charged, with Navy clerk Richard B. Maury serving as MFM's credit reference.

CHAPTER III

The Navy Gains a Midshipman

1. In 1825 the ship of the line *North Carolina* was rated as a 74-gun ship, this being the number of guns she theoretically mounted according to her design. In practice she mounted 94 guns or more. The *Brandywine*'s additional guns above her rated number of 44 were carronades, short-chambered ordnance pieces of large caliber, especially valuable for fighting at close quarters. For details of ships' paint colors, see Chapelle, *Sailing Navy,* pp. 417-418.

2. NR, Muster Roll of *Brandywine,* 1825, entry Aug. 13, 1825, large Vol. I, pp. 1-2, NAn.

3. MFM to Rutson Maury, Aug. 31, 1840, MP, Vol. II, LC.

4. H. D. Smith, Article on Uniform of 1820, *United Service,* New Series, Vol. II (October, 1889), p. 377; Ammen, *Old Navy,* pp. 26-27.

5. Lieut. Francis H. Gregory, executive officer, was in command of the *Brandywine* until Sept. 5, 1825, when Capt. Charles Morris joined the ship.

6. The term "steerage" used in the sailing Navy has its modern counterpart in "junior officers' mess." See firsthand account of *Brandywine* steerage in Jones, *Naval Life,* Vol. I, pp. 5-12.

7. Lovette, *Naval Customs,* p. 252.

8. De Meissner, *Naval Days,* pp. 8, 9, 16, 21.

9. NR, Pay Roll of *Brandywine,* large Vol. I, pp. 19-45, 1-2, NAn.

10. Auguste Levasseur, *Lafayette in America in 1824 and 1825* (cited hereafter as Levasseur, *Lafayette*), Vol. II, pp. 258-259.

11. Ibid., pp. 230-254. See also accounts of Lafayette in *National Intelligencer,* Aug. 19, 1825, p. 3; Aug. 26, 1825, p. 2; Aug. 31, 1825, p. 3; Sept. 3, 1825, p. 3.

12. For nautical terms used often in quotes, see: Stewart's *Naval Magazine for 1836,* Vol. I; William Brady, Sailing Master, U.S.N., *The Kedge Anchor: or Young Sailor's Assistant* (cited hereafter as Brady, *Kedge Anchor*); John V. Noel, Jr., Commander U.S.N., *Naval Terms Dictionary.*

13. Jones, *Naval Life,* Vol. I, p. 37.

14. *Navy Regulations,* 1818, p. 68.

15. *Navy Regulations,* 1920, p. 53.

16. NR, *Brandywine* Log, entries for Aug. 14, 15, 16, 1825, NAn.

17. Jones, *Naval Life,* Vol. I, p. 9.

18. The pennant, a long narrow piece of bunting carried at masthead of a ship-of-war, was spelled by naval officers—pendent, pendant, or pennon. *Navy Regulations* of 1818 spelled it pendent.

19. NR, *Brandywine* Log, entry for Sept. 5, 1825, NAn. For source of subsequent facts about Morris, see: *The Pictorial Field Book of War of 1812*, pp. 443-445; Roscoe-Freeman, *Pictorial USN*, pp. 301, 305, 325, 326.

20. The account of Lafayette's departure is a synthesis of reports in: NR, *Brandywine* Log, entry for Sept. 8, 1825, NAn; accounts in *National Intelligencer*, Sept. 9, 1825, p. 3, and Sept. 10, 1825, p. 2; Levasseur, *Lafayette*, Vol. II, pp. 255-256; Jones, *Naval Life*, Vol. I, p. 15.

21. Jones, *Naval Life*, Vol. I, pp. 15-16.

22. NR, *Brandywine* Log, entry for Sept. 9, 1825, NAn.

23. *National Intelligencer*, Sept. 14, 1825, p. 3.

24. NR, *Brandywine* Log, entries for Sept. 10 through 14, 1825, NAn; Jones, *Naval Life*, Vol. I, p. 16; Charles Lee Lewis, *David Glasgow Farragut, Admiral in the Making* (cited hereafter as Lewis, *Farragut*), pp. 174-175.

25. Jones, *Naval Life*, Vol. I, pp. 17-18.

26. Auguste Levasseur, Lafayette's secretary, as quoted in De Meissner, *Naval Days*, p. 29; Jones, *Naval Life*, Vol. I, p. 22.

27. Corbin, *Maury*, pp. 16-17.

28. Jones, *Naval Life*, Vol. I, pp. 5-6, 19-20; Lawrence Fasano, *Naval Rank, Its Inception and Development* (cited hereafter as Fasano, *Naval Rank*), p. 145.

29. Jones, *Naval Life*, Vol. I, pp. 20-21.

30. Ibid., pp. 34-35.

31. Radford quoted by his daughter in De Meissner, *Naval Days*, p. 28.

32. Ibid.

33. Jones, *Naval Life*, Vol. I, pp. 34-90, and Vol. II, pp. 90, 240-241.

34. NR, *Brandywine* Log, entries for Oct. 3 and 4, 1825, NAn.

35. Levasseur, *Lafayette*, Vol. II, p. 260; Lewis, *Farragut*, pp. 174-175.

36. NR, *Brandywine* Log, entries for Oct. 4 and 5, 1825, NAn; Levasseur, *Lafayette*, Vol. II, p. 260; Jones, *Naval Life*, Vol. I, pp. 27-28.

37. The silver urn could not have been presented to Lafayette on board ship as has been stated by some writers. It was not made until later in Paris. See Levasseur as quoted in De Meissner, *Naval Days*, pp. 29-30.

38. Levasseur, *Lafayette*, Vol. II, p. 261.

39. Jones, *Naval Life*, Vol. I, pp. 28, 30-31.

40. MFM to W. C. S. Ventress, Nov. 13, 1825, MP, Vol. I, LC.

41. MFM and his contemporaries wrote the title of Bowditch's work as *Practical Navigator* or sometimes called it Bowditch's *Navigation*. The *Brandywine* Log referred to the text as Bowditch's *Navigator*. The fact of MFM's purchase is recorded in sketch of MFM's youth, from his reminiscences, written by his daughter Mary Maury Werth to her children, July 26, 1879, MP, Vol. XLII, LC.

42. MFM letter cited in Note 40.

43. NR, *Brandywine* Log, entry for Oct. 22, 1825, NAn. The call is quoted from William Francis Lynch, *Naval Life or Observations Afloat and Ashore: The Midshipman* (cited hereafter as Lynch, *Naval Life*), p. 18.

44. Fasano, *Naval Rank*, p. 88; Lovette, *Naval Customs*, p. 253.

45. MFM, "Scraps from the Lucky Bag," *Southern Literary Messenger* (cited hereafter as *SLM,* Vol. VI, No. 4 (May, 1840), p. 316.
46. Jones, *Naval Life,* Vol. I, pp. 45, 101; Hanson Baldwin, "The End of the Wine Mess," *USNIP,* Vol. LXXXIV, No. 8, Whole No. 666 (August, 1958), p. 83.
47. Jones, *Naval Life,* Vol. I, p. 46.
48. Ibid., p. 94.
49. Jones, *Naval Life,* Vol. II, p. 261.
50. Ibid., pp. 263-264.
51. MFM's dissatisfaction with Bowditch's *American Practical Navigator* as a textbook for midshipmen was later to lead him to write the kind of text he thought they needed.
52. Jones, *Naval Life,* Vol. I, p. 55.
53. Ibid., pp. 55-57; William Francis Lynch, *U.S. Expedition to the River Jordan and the Dead Sea,* p. 26.
54. Corbin, *Maury,* p. 16.
55. Jones, *Naval Life,* Vol. I, p. 58.
56. NR, *Brandywine* Log, entry for Nov. 17, 1825, NAn.
57. Ibid., entries for Nov. 28 and Dec. 3, 1825.
58. MFM, "Scraps from the Lucky Bag," *SLM,* Vol. VI, No. 4 (May, 1840), p. 316; Ammen, *Old Navy,* p. 103.
59. William Francis Lynch, U.S.N., *U.S. Expedition to the River Jordan and the Dead Sea,* pp. 18, 29-30; *Army and Navy Chronicle and Scientific Repository,* Feb. 9, 1843; *Encyclopaedia Britannica* (1957 ed.), Vol. XV, p. 562.
60. Jones, *Naval Life,* Vol. I, p. 86.
61. NR, *Brandywine* Log, entry for Dec. 6, 1825, and subsequent entries in log through Feb. 21, 1826, NAn.
62. Jones, *Naval Life,* Vol. I, p. 85.
63. MFM, "Scraps from the Lucky Bag," *SLM,* Vol. VI, No. 4 (May, 1840), p. 315.
64. Jones, *Naval Life,* Vol. I, p. 77, and Vol. II, p. 227; De Meissner, *Naval Days,* p. 45.
65. Maj. Gen. Dabney H. Maury, *Address to Reunion of Confederate Veterans, Maury Camp, No. 2* (named in honor of MFM), delivered Fredericksburg, Va., Aug. 23, 1883, pp. 5-6.
66. De Meissner, *Naval Days,* pp. 44-45.
67. Jones, *Naval Life,* Vol. I, p. 88.
68. NR, *Brandywine* Log, entry for Feb. 21, 1826, NAn; Jones, *Naval Life,* Vol. I, pp. 88-90.
69. NR, *Brandywine* Log, entry for Feb. 26, 1826, NAn.
70. Ibid., entry for Mar. 8, 1826.
71. MFM to Rutson Maury, Aug. 31, 1840, MP, Vol. II, LC.
72. NR, *Brandywine* Log, entries for Apr. 17 and 18, 1826, NAn.
73. Ibid., entries for Apr. 17-25, 1826.
74. Ibid., Apr. 26-30, 1826.
75. Ibid., Apr. 30-May 18, 1826.
76. Secretary of Navy Southard to MFM, Apr. 27, 1826, and MFM to Secretary Southard, May 2, 1826, NR, AOR, Vol. XIII, p. 303.
77. MFM to Secretary Southard, May 2, 1826, NR, AOR, Vol. XIII, p. 303.

CHAPTER IV

Around the World by Sail

1. MFM's two weeks' leave was the normal period granted a midshipman after less than a year's service. He did not go to Tennessee to visit parents during this leave as has been incorrectly stated by various writers. See orders for leave: NR, AOR, Vol. XIII, pp. 284, 303, NAn.

2. Ibid., p. 303.

3. See Richard B. Maury to William C. S. Ventress, Nov. 4, 1825, MP, Vol. I, LC.

4. See NR, AOR, Vol. XIII, pp. 298, 335; see also U.S.S. *Macedonian* Pay Roll, 1826-1828, Vol. I, p. 112; U.S.S. *Macedonian* Muster Roll, 1818-1838, Vol. II, p. 198, NAn.

5. Dick and MFM spelled the abbreviation "Mat" although many other members of the family wrote it "Matt." Dick carried out his proposal to name his first son for MFM. See MFM to Richard L. Maury, Nov. 4, 1834, MP, Vol. I, LC.

6. William D. Gordon, Commanding Pro Tem, U.S. Navy Yard, New York, to Secretary of Navy Southard, June 16, 1826, NR, Captains' Letters, May-June, 1826, p. 73, NAn.

7. Isaac Newton Phelps Stokes, *New York Past and Present,* pp. 30-31; prints of New York harbor of period in New York Public Library (cited hereafter as NYPL); Marine Section collection, Museum of City of New York; Richard C. McKay, *South Street, A Maritime History of New York* (cited hereafter as McKay, *South St.*), pp. 15-16.

8. Howard Irving Chapelle, *History of American Sailing Ships* (cited hereafter as Chapelle, *Sailing Ships*), pp. 278-281; Bernhard, Duke of Saxe-Weimar, *Reise durch, Nord-Amerika, 1825-1826, Plan von der Stadt, New York;* William Hooker, *Map of New York, 1831;* De Roos, *American Navy,* p. 6.

9. NR, Pay Roll of *Brandywine,* 1825-1826, payments until June 30, 1826, large Vol. I, p. 2, NAn.

10. McKay, *South St.,* pp. 1-30.

11. J. Ernest Brierly, *The Streets of Old New York,* pp. 104, 122; Stephen Jenkins, *The Greatest Street in the World: The Story of Broadway Old and New,* pp. 145-146; McKay, *South St.,* pp. 20, 145.

12. Thomas Dornin, U.S.N., personal journal kept on board the U.S.S. *Brandywine,* 1826-1830, Jacob Jones Commanding (cited hereafter as Dornin, Journal, *Brandywine*), p. 1, NAn.

13. Fasano, *Naval Rank,* p. 69.

14. The letter *T* was used in naval muster rolls to indicate transferred. Master Mate Aaron Woodwright and other petty officers had been transferred May 7, 1826, to the *Macedonian,* but the *T* was used routinely June 30, 1826, to show MFM transferred from completed period of duty in *Brandywine* to a new period of duty in the *Brandywine.* See NR, over-all Muster Roll of *Brandywine* for 1825-1836, pp. 29-30, 124, 148-149, NAn.

15. NR, Letters to Officers, Ships of War, Vol. XVII, Orders to Commodore Jacob Jones, Aug. 21 and 23, 1826; also Commodore Jacob Jones to Secretary of Navy Southard, Aug. 25, 1826, Captains' Letters, July-August, 1826, p. 99, NAn.

16. Ibid., Aug. 26, 1826, p. 104.
17. NR, Commodore Isaac Chauncey, Commanding U.S. Navy Yard, New York, to Secretary of Navy Southard, Aug. 31, 1826, Captains' Letters, July-August, 1826, p. 115; see also p. 108, NAn.
18. NR, Commodore Jacob Jones to Secretary of Navy Southard, Sept. 3, 1826, Captains' Letters, September-October, 1826, p. 4, NAn.
19. The official records of the *Brandywine* prove conclusively that MFM was on board that vessel when she sailed from New York, Sept. 3, 1826, when she arrived in Rio de Janeiro, Oct. 28, 1826, when she sailed from Rio on Nov. 18, 1826, and when she reached Valparaiso, Dec. 26, 1826. Additional proof of the fact is to be found in a letter MFM wrote Robert Clinton Wright of Baltimore in May, 1848: "Your letter brings you to mind as an old acquaintance whom I had the pleasure of seeing when I was in Rio in the *Brandywine* in 1826. I was quite a youngster at the time." Further proof is available in an autobiographical sketch in MFM's handwriting, prepared by him in 1852 for a German publication. MFM wrote that he made his first cruise "in the *Brandywine* and returned home in her in 1826 . . . and went in her to the Pacific whence transferred to the *Vincennes* for circumnavigation of the globe."

    These facts incontrovertibly prove that MFM biographers Charles Lee Lewis, John W. Wayland, and other writers have erred in stating that MFM sailed for South America in the *Macedonian*. They have confused MFM with his cousin Alex C. Maury, who did sail in the *Macedonian*. See: NR, *Brandywine* Log, Pay Roll, Muster Roll for 1826 and 1827; MFM to Robert Clinton Wright, May (between 19 and 22), 1848, in bound books Naval Observatory Letters Sent (hereafter cited as NOLS), Vol. III; MFM handwritten 1852 sketch of his life in Naval Observatory printed envelope, filed loose in NOLS, Vol. VI, all in NAn. For Alex C. Maury, see: NR, *Macedonian* records as cited in Note 4; and letter of Alex C. Maury cited in Note 32.
20. MFM, "Scraps from the Lucky Bag," *SLM*, Vol. VI, No. 4 (May, 1840), p. 315.
21. Dornin, Journal, *Brandywine*, p. 1; NR, over-all Muster Roll *Brandywine*, 1825-1836; see also "A Correct List of the Officers and Men Attached to the U.S. Ship *Brandywine* on the 31st Sept. 1826," p. 109, all in NAn.
22. NR, Commodore Jacob Jones to Secretary of Navy Southard, Sept. 8, 1826, Captains' Letters, September-October, 1826, p. 16, NAn.
23. *Navy Regulations*, 1818, pp. 107-110.
24. Ammen, *Old Navy*, p. 49.
25. NR, Commodore Jacob Jones to Secretary of Navy Southard, Oct. 30, 1826, Captains' Letters, September-October, 1826, p. 28; *Brandywine* Log, entry for Sept. 15, 1826, NAn.
26. Archibald Douglas Turnbull, *Commodore David Porter*, p. 109.
27. Lynch, *Naval Life*, pp. 18-22.
28. NR, *Brandywine* Log, entries for Oct. 25, 26, 27, 1826, NAn; Charles Samuel Stewart, *A Visit to the South Seas in the U.S. Ship Vincennes during the years 1829-1830* (cited hereafter as Stewart, *South Seas*), Vol. I, pp. 47-51.
29. NR, *Brandywine* Log, entry for Oct. 28, 1826, NAn.
30. NR, Commodore Jacob Jones to Secretary of Navy Southard, Oct. 30, 1826,

Captains' Letters, October-November, 1826, p. 28; *Brandywine* Log, entries for Oct. 28, 29, 30, 31, Nov. 1, 1826, NAn.

31. NR, *Brandywine* Log, entries for Nov. 8-15, 1826; *Macedonian* Log, entry for Nov. 8, 1826, NAn.

32. A letter written by Alex C. Maury to W. C. S. Ventress, Jan. 26, 1827 (MP, Vol. I, LC) has been mistakenly attributed by previous biographers to MFM. It was written by his cousin, whose initials A.C. can be deciphered before the surname Maury on the letter. Alex C. Maury continued to serve in the *Macedonian,* which remained on the "Brazilian Station," east coast of South America, until her return to the United States, Oct. 29, 1828. The letter that has caused the confusion was written by Alex C. Maury some weeks after MFM had sailed in the *Brandywine* from Rio for the Pacific.

33. NR, Captains' Letters, October-November, 1826; Letter Collection No. 82, translated copy of letter of the Counsellor, Minister and Secretary of State for Foreign Affairs, the Marquis of Inhambupé to Condy Raguet, Chargé d'Affaires of the United States at Rio de Janeiro, Nov. 13, 1826; Condy Raguet to Commodore Jacob Jones, Nov. 14, 1826, NAn.

34. NR, Captains' Letters, October-November, 1826; Letter Collection No. 82, Commodore Jacob Jones to Condy Raguet, Nov. 14, 1826, NAn.

35. Ibid., letter of Inhambupé to Raguet, Nov. 15, 1826.

36. Ibid., letter of Raguet to Inhambupé, Nov. 15, 1826; Raguet to Commodore Jacob Jones, Nov. 15, 1826; Commodore Jacob Jones to Captain of the Port, Nov. 15, 1826.

37. Ibid., Inhambupé to Raguet, Nov. 16, 1826; Raguet to Commodore Jacob Jones, Nov. 17, 1826; Commodore Jacob Jones to Secretary of Navy Southard, Nov. 17, 1826.

38. NR, *Brandywine* Log, entries for Nov. 18 to Dec. 5, 1826, NAn.

39. MFM, "On the Navigation of Cape Horn," *American Journal of Science and Arts* (cited hereafter as *Am. Journ. Science*), Vol. XXVI, Art. V (July, 1834), p. 54.

40. Ibid., p. 61.

41. Ibid., pp. 54-55.

42. NR, Captains' Letters, January, 1827, Commodore Jacob Jones to Secretary of Navy Southard, Jan. 2, 1827, NAn.

43. NR, *Brandywine* Log, entries for Dec. 5, 1826 to Dec. 26, 1826, NAn.

44. Stewart, *South Seas,* Vol. I, pp. 130-134.

45. NR, Captains' Letters, January, 1827, Commodore Jacob Jones to Secretary of Navy Southard, Jan. 12, 1827; *Brandywine* Log, entries for Dec. 26, 1826, to Jan. 8, 1827, NAn.

46. NR, *Brandywine* Log, entry for Jan. 9, 1827, NAn.

47. Ibid., entries for Jan. 19 to Feb. 9, 1827.

48. Stewart, *South Seas,* Vol. I, pp. 150, 153, 157.

49. Samuel M. Smucker (also spelled Schmucker), *Life of Dr. Elisha Kent Kane and Other Distinguished American Explorers* (cited hereafter as Smucker, *American Explorers*), see sketch of naval officer Charles Wilkes, pp. 337-344.

50. Ammen, *Old Navy,* pp. 295, 323.

51. MFM, "Scraps from the Lucky Bag," *SLM,* Vol. VI, No. 4 (May, 1840), p. 315.

52. MFM to W. C. S. Ventress, June 18, 1829, in MP, Vol. I, LC; MFM to Courtland Cushing, U.S. Chargé d'Affaires, Guayaquil, Ecuador, Feb. 10, 1853, MP, Vol. IV, LC.
53. MFM was detached from *Brandywine*, Mar. 9, 1827, and transferred to *Vincennes;* see NR, *Brandywine* Muster Roll, 1826-1829, large vol., p. 149; small vol., p. 1. MFM appeared on board *Vincennes* on March 10, 1827, Muster Roll, U.S.S. *Vincennes*, 1826-1836, p. 20, NAn.
54. *Vincennes* was a ship-sloop, 2nd class, 18 guns. For facts on her design and designer, see: Chapelle, *Sailing Ships*, pp. 112, 115-116, 105-109; also Chapelle, *Sailing Navy*, pp. 349, 358, 466, 501.
55. Stewart, *South Seas*, Vol. I, p. 140.
56. William Bolton Finch later changed his name to William Compton Bolton and under that name was promoted captain, Feb. 21, 1831; see Callahan, *List of Officers*, pp. 193, 65.
57. Stewart, *South Seas*, Vol. I, p. 140.
58. Article on Simón Bolívar, *Encyclopaedia Britannica* (1957 ed.), Vol. III, p. 809; article on Ecuador, ibid., Vol. VII, pp. 936-945; article on Peru, ibid., Vol. XVII, pp. 619-628; article on José Antonio Paez, ibid., Vol. XVII, p. 26; article on Antonio José de Sucre, ibid., Vol. XXI, pp. 503-504; article on Venezuela, ibid., Vol. XXIII, pp. 51-56.
59. MFM to the Rev. James H. Otey, Feb. 18, 1828 (date possibly 1829), MP, Vol. I, LC.
60. MFM, "Scraps from the Lucky Bag," SLM, Vol. VI, No. 4 (May, 1840), p. 315.
61. MFM to Rutson Maury, Aug. 31, 1840, MP, Vol. II, LC.
62. MFM to the Rev. James H. Otey, Feb. 18, 1829, MP, Vol. I, LC.
63. Ibid.
64. MFM to W. C. S. Ventress, June 18, 1829, MP, Vol. I, LC.
65. Ibid.
66. Ibid.
67. Charles Oscar Paullin, *Diplomatic Negotiations of American Naval Officers, 1778-1883* (cited hereafter as Paullin, *Diplomatic Negotiations*), p. 182.
68. NR, *Vincennes* Log, entry for July 4, 1829, NAn; Stewart, *South Seas*, Vol. I, pp. 209-210.
69. Captain Finch undoubtedly went to Nukuhiva because Commodore David Porter had claimed that island in the northern Marquesas for the United States in 1814, during his stay there to refit his ships for action in the War of 1812. The *Vincennes* anchored in the same harbor Porter had used although he had called it Anna Maria harbor. See Archibald Douglas Turnbull, *Commodore David Porter*, p. 187.
70. Stewart, *South Seas*, Vol. I, pp. 215-216.
71. The island's name is today written Nuku Hiva, but I have used the form used by Chaplain Stewart. MFM and other naval officers spelled it Nukahiva, doubtless the way the spoken word sounded to them. Taihoae is the modern capital of the northern district of the Marquesas.
72. NR, *Vincennes* Log, entries for July 28, 29, 1829; MFM to N. P. Willis, Sept. 24, 1859, MP, Vol. VIII, LC.
73. Stewart, *South Seas*, Vol. I, pp. 277-281, 292.
74. Ibid., pp. 346-351.
75. MFM to N. P. Willis, Sept. 24, 1859, MP, Vol. VIII, LC.

76. Stewart, *South Seas*, Vol. I, p. 352.
77. For Finch's official reports on his negotiations, see bound volume of letters: NR, Captain Finch's Cruise in U.S.S. *Vincennes*, 1826-1830, NAn.
78. Stewart, *South Seas*, Vol. II, pp. 7, 15, 19, 42-43, 46-50.
79. NR, Captain Finch's Cruise in U.S.S. *Vincennes*, 1826-1830, Finch to Secretary of Navy, Oct. 30, 1829, NAn.
80. Stewart, *South Seas*, Vol. II, pp. 100-105.
81. Ibid., pp. 118-132.
82. Kathleen Dickinson Mellen, *The Gods Depart, A Saga of the Hawaiian Kingdom, 1832-1873*, pp. 3-15; article on Hawaii, *Encyclopaedia Britannica* (1957 ed.), Vol. XI, p. 264.
83. Captain Finch letter cited in Note 79; Stewart, *South Seas*, Vol. II, pp. 171-234.
84. Stewart, *South Seas*, Vol. II, pp. 249-283.
85. Ibid., pp. 283-290; NR, *Vincennes* Log, entries for Dec. 19-30, 1829, NAn.
86. Stewart, *South Seas*, Vol. II, pp. 291-294; NR, *Vincennes* Log, entries for Dec. 31, 1829, Jan. 1, 1830, NAn.
87. Map, *Die Chinesiche Küste von Macao* (from 1834 Berghaus, *Atlas von Asia*); B. L. Ball, *Rambles in Eastern Asia*, pp. 98-100; *Encyclopaedia Britannica* (1957 ed.), Vol. XIV, p. 544; Vol. IV, p. 771.
88. Paullin, *Diplomatic Negotiations*, p. 183.
89. Stewart, *South Seas*, Vol. II, p. 294.
90. Ibid., pp. 295-296; Paullin, *Diplomatic Negotiations*, pp. 170-172, 183-185.
91. NR, *Vincennes* Log, entries for Jan. 21, 22, 1830, NAn.
92. Ibid., Jan. 26-29, 1830; Stewart, *South Seas*, Vol. II, pp. 300-303; *Encyclopaedia Britannica* (1957 ed.), Vol. XIV, p. 806. For descriptions of Manila in mid-nineteenth century, see: Henry Thomas Ellis, *Hong Kong to Manilla . . . 1856*, pp. 48-77; see especially John Glendy Sproston, U.S.N., *Private Journal*, pp. 94-95, 141.
93. Stewart, *South Seas*, Vol. II, pp. 300-316.
94. Ibid., pp. 317-320; illustrated map of Philippine Islands, Manila, *Campo Santo, Pueblo de Paco, 1812-1823*, LC; Michael Meyers Shoemaker, *Quaint Corners of Ancient Empires*, p. 145.
95. NR, Captain Finch's Cruise in U.S.S. *Vincennes*, 1826-1830, a collection of various letters of Captain Finch to Secretary of Navy, written in 1830, NAn.
96. NR, *Vincennes* Log, entries for February-March, 1830; Stewart, *South Seas*, Vol. II, p. 323.
97. Corbin, *Maury*, p. 17.
98. William Leigh to Mary H. Maury, Sept. (n.d.), 1873, MP, Vol. XLIV, LC.
99. NR, *Vincennes* Log, entries for Apr. 7, 8, 1830, NAn.
100. Stewart, *South Seas*, Vol. II, pp. 323-327; *Encyclopaedia Britannica* (1957 ed.), Vol. IV, pp. 790-791.
101. Stewart, *South Seas*, Vol. II, pp. 334-347.
102. NR, *Vincennes* Log, entries for May 5 to June 8, 1830, NAn.

CHAPTER V

Climbing the Rungs of the Ladder

1. NR, Bureau of Navigation, Record of Officers, September, 1825-December, 1831, Vol. G, p. 55, NAn.
2. The requirement was that a midshipman should take examinations after five years of service, three of which had been active duty at sea. Jones, *Naval Life,* Vol. II, p. 263.
3. In 1830 there were in the United States 1,277 miles of canal, 73 miles of railroad. See *Columbia Encyclopedia* (1935 ed.), article on Erie Canal, pp. 580-581.
4. Ibid., article on Peter Cooper, p. 419.
5. MFM to Ann Maury of New York, Nov. 27, 1838, MC, UVAL.
6. See Elliott's *Washington Directory, 1830;* also *Navy Register, 1831.*
7. MFM to Richard L. Maury, July 3, 1830, MP, Vol. I, LC.
8. Ibid.
9. For account by one of Eliza's sons who made the trip, see p. 6 of Dabney H. Maury to Mary H. Maury, Aug. 7, 1873, MP, Vol. XLIV, LC.
10. P. 43 of sketch of MFM by Mary Maury Werth written in letter to her children, Aug. 7, 1873, MP, Vol. XLII, LC.
11. Dabney H. Maury letter cited in Note 9.
12. Mary Maury Werth sketch cited in Note 10.
13. Entry in 1832 diary of Ann Maury, daughter of Consul James Maury, as quoted in A. F. Maury, *Virginiana,* pp. 206-208.
14. Blackford, *Mine Eyes,* pp. 10-12, 14, 33.
15. NR, Bureau of Navigation, Record of Officers, September, 1825-December, 1831, Vol. G, p. 337, NAn.
16. For an interesting account of naval education of the period, see Henry Leslie Burr, *Education in the Early Navy, A Dissertation . . . for the Degree of Doctor of Education in . . . Temple University, Philadelphia* (cited hereafter as Burr, *Education*).
17. Article on Jacob Jones, *DAB,* Vol. X, p. 176.
18. Fletcher Pratt, *The Navy: A History; The Story of a Service in Action* (cited hereafter as Pratt, *The Navy*), p. 238, et sqq.
19. Charles Lee Lewis, *Matthew Fontaine Maury, Pathfinder of the Seas* (cited hereafter as Lewis, *Maury*), p. 21.
20. McKay, *South St.,* pp. 172, 173, 178, 179; Stephen Jenkins, *The Greatest Street in the World . . . Broadway Old and New,* p. 145; Isaac Newton Phelps Stokes, *New York Past and Present,* pp. 1-70; Hooker's Map of New York, 1830-1831.
21. NR, Bureau of Navigation, Record of Officers, September, 1825-December, 1831, Vol. G, p. 351, NAn.
22. Richard B. Maury was the brother of Eliza Maury (Mrs. John M. Maury) and had his widowed sister and her small sons spending the winter of 1830-1831 in his home. See Dabney H. Maury to Mary H. Maury, Aug. 7, 1873, MP, Vol. XLIV, LC.
23. Ibid.
24. Burr, *Education,* p. 181.
25. NR, Bureau of Navigation, Record of Officers, September, 1825-December, 1831, Vol. G, p. 361, NAn.

26. MFM, "Scraps from the Lucky Bag," *SLM*, Vol. VII (December, 1840), p. 120.
27. William O. Stephens and C. Alphonso Smith, *Two Early Proposals for Naval Education*, reprinted from *USNIP*, Vol. XXXIX, No. 1, Whole No. 145 (March, 1913), p. 127, et sqq.
28. NR, Bureau of Navigation, Record of Officers, September, 1825-December, 1831, Vol. G, p. 361, NAn; Lewis, *Maury*, p. 21.
29. NR, Bureau of Navigation, Record of Officers, September, 1825-December, 1831, Vol. G, p. 433, NAn.
30. MFM to Franklin Minor, Mar. 21, 1855, MP, Vol. IV, LC.
31. On the standing collar of MFM's midshipman's blue jacket was a "foul anchor in gold under oak leaf and acorns. When he became a passed midshipman, the anchor was backed with a five-pointed star in white cloth." W. M. Schoonmaker, "Naval Uniforms—Origin and Development," *USNIP*, Vol. LVIII, Whole No. 350 (April, 1932), p. 519.
32. MFM to Richard L. Maury, Nov. 17, 1831, MP, Vol. I, LC.
33. The marriages between Maurys, Minors, and Herndons were numerous. Perhaps the clearest way of expressing Ann and Matthew's relationship is to say that her paternal grandmother and his maternal grandfather were sister and brother. Mary Minor (1741-1822), the sister of Maj. John Minor of "Laurel Hill," was second wife of Joseph Herndon (1737-1810), whose home was "Mattapony," Spotsylvania County. Their ninth child was Dabney Herndon. Dabney Herndon was half brother to Edward Herndon of "Laurel Hill," who was the son of Joseph Herndon by his first wife, Philadelphea Foster Herndon (1736-1764). Thus Edward Herndon was Ann's uncle, while his wife, Mrs. Elizabeth Maury (Lewis) Herndon, was Matthew's aunt.
34. MFM to Diana Maury Corbin, May 9, 1858, as quoted Corbin, *Maury*, p. 164.
35. MFM to Richard L. Maury, Apr. 10, 1833, MP, Vol. I, LC.
36. NR, Bureau of Navigation, Record of Officers, September, 1825-December, 1831, Vol. G, p. 409, NAn.
37. A naval officer's billet, or post of duty on a ship, does not change his status as to rank. On this cruise in the *Falmouth* MFM's fixed rank was passed midshipman, but he was assigned to serve as acting sailing master, the head of a department of the ship.
38. Corbin, *Maury*, p. 20.
39. The old Navy term "master" or "sailing master" is not to be confused with the higher rank of master commandant (now commander). See Fasano, *Naval Rank*, pp. 23, 75.
40. NR, Bureau of Navigation, Record of Officers, September, 1825-December, 1831, Vol. G, p. 433, NAn.
41. Corbin, *Maury*, p. 23.
42. The designation master commandant had been adopted in 1806 for a captain of the second rank, one who commanded a ship mounting 20 to 40 guns. "The Act of March 3, 1837, changed the title master commandant to commander (permanent rank), although the pay act of March 3, 1835, recognized the title." See Fasano, *Naval Rank*, pp. 135-136.
43. NR, *Falmouth* Muster Roll, June, 1831, NAn; statement by W. S. W. Ruschenberger, Surgeon of the *Falmouth*, MP, Vol. I, fourth entry, LC.

44. Officer in command of a ship was addressed as captain regardless of his statutory rank.

45. NR, *Falmouth* Log, entries for June 6 to July 5, 1831.

46. Chapelle, *Sailing Ships,* pp. 116, 108; Chapelle, *Sailing Navy,* p. 539.

47. Fasano, *Naval Rank,* pp. 23, 26, 58-59.

48. Ibid., pp. 69-71, 75.

49. Ibid., pp. 72-74.

50. Journal of Thomas Dornin, kept on board the *Falmouth,* commencing Apr. 1, 1831, NAn.

51. MFM, "On the Navigation of Cape Horn," *Am. Journ. Science,* Vol. XXVI, Art. V (July, 1834), pp. 60-61.

52. Ibid., p. 56.

53. Ibid., p. 59.

54. Ibid., p. 61.

55. Ibid., pp. 61-62, also pp. 55, 59-60.

56. Journal of Thomas Dornin, kept on board the *Falmouth;* see entries for October, 1831, NAn.

57. MFM to Richard L. Maury, Nov. 17, 1831, MP, Vol. I, LC.

58. MFM to Miss M. S. Herndon, Dec. 14, 1831, MP, Vol. I, LC.

59. Ibid.

60. Fasano, *Naval Rank,* p. 73.

61. Whiting was a midshipman in the *Falmouth* when assisting Maury on this survey but wrote the account when a commodore on the U.S.N. Retired List. William B. Whiting to Capt. John M. Brooke, May 31, 1873, MP, Vol. XLIV, LC.

62. MFM to W. C. S. Ventress, Jan. 14, 1833, MP, Vol. I, LC.

63. MFM to Richard L. Maury, Apr. 10, 1833, MP, Vol. I, LC.

64. MFM to T. Averett Berkeley, May 28, 1853, MP, Vol. IV, LC.

65. MFM to Capt. Thomas A. Dornin, July 3, 1839, MP, Vol. I, LC.

66. Mrs. Ann Herndon Maury to Richard Launcelot Maury, Oct. 15, 1859, MP, Vol. VIII, LC.

67. William B. Whiting to Capt. John M. Brooke, May 31, 1873, MP, Vol. XLIV, LC.

68. MFM to James H. Otey, Feb. 18, 1828 (possibly 1829), MP, Vol. I, LC.

69. MFM to Richard L. Maury, Apr. 10, 1833, MP, Vol. I, LC.

70. MFM to Courtland Cushing, U.S. Chargé d'Affaires, Guayaquil, Feb. 10, 1855, MP, Vol. IV, LC.

71. Jones, *Naval Life,* Vol. II, p. 271; see also pp. 261, 263-264.

72. Article on Nathaniel Bowditch, *Columbia Encyclopedia* (1935 ed.), p. 219.

73. Corbin, *Maury,* p. 23.

74. MFM to Richard L. Maury, Apr. 10, 1833, MP, Vol. I, LC. This letter was incorrectly dated as Apr. 16, 1835, by MFM's daughter Diana; see Corbin, *Maury,* pp. 23-24.

75. "Acting Lieutenant M. Maury, Acting Sailing Master S. Godwin . . . reported for duty" Aug. 21, 1833; see NR, *Dolphin* Log for June 13, 1833-Dec. 2, 1835, entry for Aug. 21, 1833, NAn.

76. NR, *Potomac* Log for 1833, entries for Aug. 26-27, 1833, NAn. For data on frigate *Potomac,* see: William Harwar Parker, Captain, U.S.N., *Recollections of a Naval Officer, 1841-65,* p. 35; Chapelle, *Sailing Navy,* pp. 324, 496, 497, 508, 550.

77. Charles Lee Lewis, "Our Navy in the Pacific and Far East Long Ago," *USNIP,* Vol. LXIX, No. 6, Whole No. 484 (June, 1943), p. 861. For a complete account of this adventurous cruise of the *Potomac,* see Francis Warriner, *Cruise of the United States frigate Potomac round the World, during the years 1831-34.*

78. MFM appeared on board the *Potomac* on Nov. 5, 1833, with 43 others who were similarly transferred from the *Dolphin.* See NR, *Potomac* Muster Roll, 1831-1833, p. 27, NAn.

79. For another authoritative account of the *Potomac*'s cruise, see Jeremiah N. Reynolds, *Voyage of the U.S. Frigate Potomac under the command of John Downes during the circumnavigation of the Globe in 1831-1834.*

80. NR, Journal of U.S.S. *Potomac,* 50 guns, John Downes Commanding, Nov. 1, 1833, to May 19, 1834 (cited hereafter as *Potomac* Journal), entries for Nov. 22 through Dec. 17, 1833, NAn.

81. Ibid., *Potomac* Journal, entry for Feb. 10, 1834.

82. William B. Whiting to Capt. John M. Brooke, May 31, 1873, MP, Vol. XLIV, LC.

83. NR, *Potomac* Journal, entries for Mar. 10-16, 1834; *Potomac* Log, entries for May 19, 1833-June 7, 1834, entries for March 10-16, NAn.

84. NR, *Potomac* Journal, entries for Mar. 27 to Apr. 9, 1834, NAn.

85. NR, *Potomac* Log, entries for Apr. 9 to May 27, 1834, NAn.

86. Whiting letter cited in Note 82.

87. NR, AOR, Vol. XV, entry for May 27, 1834, NAn.

CHAPTER VI

Marriage, a Scientific Book, and an Accident

1. See Dabney Herndon's will, probated Jan. 13, 1825, Fredericksburg, Va., Hustings Court Will Book B, 1817-1828, p. 201; see also inventory of his possessions entered in same book on Apr. 4, 1825. He left 12 slaves over fourteen years of age, 6 under fourteen, a good supply of mahogany furniture, horse, cart, saddle, bridle, cow, more than 130 books, and some stocks and bonds, but mostly uncollectable notes on loans made to friends.

2. MFM to Mrs. William Maury of Liverpool, England, Nov. 14, 1846, MP, Vol. III, LC.

3. Ibid.

4. Ann's father, Dabney Herndon, was son of Joseph Herndon (1737-1810) and his second wife, Mary Minor Herndon (1741-1822), who was a sister of MFM's maternal grandfather, Maj. John Minor (1735-1800) of "Topping Castle."

5. MFM, sketch in his own handwriting, in an envelope bearing imprint of the U.S. Naval Observatory, filed loose in NR, NOLS, Vol. VI, NAn.

6. MFM recorded in his Bible that the ceremony took place at 10 A.M. The marriage was reported in the Fredericksburg (Va.) *Herald,* July 23, 1834, but the writer incorrectly cited the place as Hay Farm. MFM's courtship and marriage were described in a letter written by his nephew, Dabney H. Maury, to Molly (Mary H.) Maury, Aug. 7, 1873; MP, Vol. XLIV, LC.

7. John W. Wayland, address delivered at ceremonies held by Washington-Lewis Chapter, D.A.R., to dedicate grave marker of Revolutionary soldier

Edward Herndon, at "Laurel Hill," Fredericksburg *Free Lance-Star,* July 3, 1931; John T. Goolrick, *Historic Fredericksburg,* p. 125.

8. Dr. Brodie S. Herndon to Mary H. Maury, Aug. 9, 1873, MP, Vol. XLIV, LC.

9. MFM to Ann Maury of New York, June 30, 1850, MC, UVAL.

10. MFM, "On the Navigation of Cape Horn," *Am. Journ. Science,* Vol. XXVI (July, 1834), pp. 54-63.

11. MFM to Richard L. Maury, Sept. 24, 1834, MP, Vol. I, LC.

12. Ibid.

13. NR, AOR, Vol. XV, entry for Nov. 5, 1834, NAn.

14. MFM letter cited in Note 11. Willia G. Gregory was the daughter of Abraham (Abram) Maury, brother of Richard, not of Abram Maury of Tennessee.

15. MFM to Richard L. Maury, Nov. 4, 1834, MP, Vol. I, LC.

16. MFM, "Plan of an Instrument for finding the true Lunar Distance," *Am. Journ. Science,* Vol. XXVI, Art. VI (July, 1834), pp. 63-65.

17. MFM, *A New Theoretical and Practical Treatise on Navigation, in which the Auxiliary Branches of Mathematics and Astronomy . . . are treated of, Also the Theory and most simple methods of finding Time, Latitude and Longitude . . .* (cited hereafter as Maury, *Navigation*).

18. Ibid.

19. Ibid.

20. MFM to Ann Maury of New York, Jan. 19, 1836, MC, UVAL.

21. MFM to James Maury, Nov. 19, 1834, MP, Vol. I, LC.

22. This house at 214 Caroline Street, which was to have great future significance to MFM, had been purchased by Mrs. Minor following General Minor's death. Caroline Street was the original and is the present name for the street, but it was called Main Street for a time after the Revolution when there was resentment against the use of royal names. For account of Minors and Blackford, see Blackford, *Mine Eyes,* pp. 10, 12, 33.

23. Blackford, *Mine Eyes,* pp. 16-47, 63-68, 84-87. MFM's first cousin, the Rev. Launcelot Minor, an Episcopal minister, personally took a group of freed slaves to Liberia and served there as a missionary until his early death. See MFM to Richard L. Maury, Sept. 9, 1836, MP, Vol. I, LC.

24. The British abolition soon freed 800,000 slaves, but slaves in Britain's West Indies colonies were not given freedom until 1838 and those in British India not until 1843. See *Encyclopaedia Britannica* (1957 ed.), Vol. XX, p. 782; *Encyclopedia Americana* (1962 ed.), Vol. XXV, p. 88b.

25. S. J. Quinn, *History of the City of Fredericksburg, Virginia,* pp. 226-227; David Franklin Houston, Harvard Historical Studies, Vol. III, *A Critical Study of Nullification in South Carolina* (cited hereafter as Houston, *Nullification*), pp. 65-105.

26. Houston, *Nullification,* pp. 106-131.

27. Article on secession, *Encyclopedia Americana* (1962 ed.), p. 501.

28. MFM's first cousin Ann Maury wrote of her father's and former President James Madison's feeling: "My father abhorred sectional feeling—so did Mr. Madison. We were at Mr. Madison's when the first streak of secession, no bigger than a man's hand, arose. It was all talked over & I now have the memorandums of the conversations, written at night in my room, while memory was fresh. Mr. Madison felt sure that Nullification would die out,

he spoke of the many difficulties that had been overcome in bringing the old 13 States to agree to the Constitution." From Ann Maury to Mrs. Sally C. M. Reid, Feb. 23, 1870, quoted in A. F. Maury, *Virginiana,* p. 3.

29. Consul James Maury's son, Matthew, wrote Aug. 12, 1829, from Virginia to his mother in Liverpool about his father's dismissal, "Mr. Madison and Mr. Monroe I learn are quite disgusted." Both former presidents were personal friends of his father's. The letter is quoted in A. F. Maury, *Virginiana,* p. 14; see also p. 13.

30. A. F. Maury, *Virginiana,* pp. 15-21, 162-209.

31. John T. Goolrick, *Historic Fredericksburg,* pp. 28-31.

32. Douglas Southall Freeman, *George Washington,* Vol. I, p. 267.

33. C. O'Conor Goolrick, "A Brief History of Fredericksburg, Virginia," *The New Approved Guidebook of Fredericksburg, Virginia,* p. 12; W. Edwin Hemphill, "His [James Monroe's] Course Fixed for Life?" *Virginia Cavalcade,* Spring issue, 1958, Vol. VII, No. 4, pp. 40-48.

34. Samuel Eliot Morison, *John Paul Jones, A Sailor's Biography,* pp. 7, 12-14, 27.

35. Article on President Madison, *Columbia Encyclopedia* (1935 ed.), p. 1095.

36. Douglas Southall Freeman, *R. E. Lee* (cited hereafter as Freeman, *Lee*), Vol. I, pp. 2-12, 33, 44.

37. MFM later wrote his eldest daughter, "Your Mother and I commenced housekeeping when my pay was $40 a month." MFM to Betty Maury, Nov. 26, 1856, as quoted in Corbin, *Maury,* p. 162. The annual pay for a passed midshipman awaiting orders was in 1835 increased to $600 by "An Act to regulate the pay of the Navy in the United States." See Benjamin Homans (compiler and arranger), *Laws of the United States in relation to the Navy and Marine Corps,* p. 162.

38. MFM to his daughter Betty Maury, Nov. 26, 1856, as quoted in Corbin, *Maury,* p. 162.

39. Ibid.

40. These expressions run through his letters to his wife and are especially to be found in letters written from England during the American Civil War.

41. MFM to his daughter Diana Maury Corbin, May 8, 1838, as quoted in Corbin, *Maury,* p. 165.

42. MFM to Richard L. Maury, Nov. 16, 1834, MP, Vol. I, LC. Ann was a member of St. George's Episcopal Church, Fredericksburg, where her father had been a vestryman; Bishop William Meade, *Old Churches, Ministers and Families of Virginia,* Vol. II, pp. 68-72.

43. MFM had received this information in a letter from his cousin and schoolmate Ellick (A. C.) Maury, who had gone home to Franklin, Tenn., on Navy leave. The term "Campbellite" was derived from Thomas and Alexander Campbell, who founded the Disciples of Christ; see *Columbia Encyclopedia* (1935 ed.), p. 284.

44. MFM letter cited in Note 42.

45. MFM to James Maury, Nov. 19, 1834, MP, Vol. I, LC.

46. See Preface of first edition (1836), Maury, *Navigation.*

47. MFM to Ann Maury of New York, June 12, 1835, MC, UVAL.

48. Ibid.; also July 15, 1835.

49. For facts about MFM's 7½ year tenancy of this house, see his testimony in Court File No. 93, Office of Town Clerk, Fredericksburg. After MFM's de-

parture, the widowed Mrs. Ellis sold the house in July, 1844, to Mrs. Eliza Johnston, from whom it then derived the name the Johnston house. See further facts on MFM's occupancy of house in Mary Maury Werth to her children, July 26, 1879, MP, Vol. XLII, LC.

50. I was taken to see this house in my childhood, but it has since been torn down and replaced by a scrap yard. A stone marker in the sidewalk formerly indicated this house where Maury did his early scientific writing, but I could not find the marker on a recent visit.

51. MFM to Ann Maury of New York, Sept. 26, 1835, May 31, Sept. 23, Dec. 23, 1836, Dec. 22, 1837, MC, UVAL; letter of Mary Maury Werth cited in Note 49; MFM to Richard L. Maury, Sept. 9, 1836, MP, Vol. I, LC.

52. MFM to Richard L. Maury, Oct. 29, 1835, MP, Vol. I, LC.

53. Mary Maury Werth to her children, July 26, 1879. MP, Vol. XLII, LC.

54. MFM letter cited in Note 52.

55. Nathaniel Bowditch to MFM, Apr. 21, 1835, as quoted in Maury, *Navigation* (3rd ed., 1845), p. 337.

56. Alexander Dallas Bache to MFM, Apr. 14, 1835, as quoted in Maury, *Navigation* (3rd ed., 1845), p. 337.

57. NR, *Brandywine* Muster Roll, 1825, NAn.

58. MFM to Ann Maury of New York, Jan. 19, 1836, MC, UVAL.

59. Ibid., June 18, 1836; MFM to Prof. Benjamin Silliman, June 16, 1836, in Boston Public Library.

60. The Catharine iron furnace, about 12 miles west of Fredericksburg (near MFM birthplace), was chartered in 1836, operative in 1837. There were also other iron mines and the U.S. Gold Mine in Spotsylvania County.

61. MFM letter cited in Note 58.

62. After serving on the Board of Navy Commissioners, Commodore Charles Stewart spent three years on his farm in New Jersey, from 1833 to 1836; he received his next naval orders in 1836, *Biographical Sketch, and services of Commodore Charles Stewart, of the Navy of the United States*, p. 41.

63. The publishers' registration of title for copyright made on April 29, 1836 (with transfer of copyright Sept. 25, 1843, to MFM written on the back), is filed under date of Apr. 29, 1836, MP, Vol. I, LC.

64. MFM to Ann Maury of New York, May 11, 1836, MC, UVAL.

65. Ibid.

66. Edgar Allan Poe review, *SLM*, Vol. II, No. 7 (June, 1836), pp. 454-455.

67. Letters of recommendation, Maury, *Navigation* (3rd ed., 1845), pp. 338-340.

68. Ibid.

69. Ibid. Schools at New York and Norfolk Navy Yards had in 1829 been declared by Secretary of Navy Branch to be temporary arrangements providing a limited education in elementary mathematics, House Doc. No. 2, 21st Congr., 1st Sess., p. 39.

70. *Am. Journ. Science*, Vol. XXXII, No. 1 (July, 1837), p. 208.

71. Bernard Jaffe, *Men of Science in America* (cited hereafter as Jaffe, *Men of Science*), p. 213.

72. Copies of the book were placed on every Navy ship by 1837. The book sold well enough to justify an enlarged second edition in 1843, published by E. C. Biddle, successor to Key and Biddle. MFM added much new ma-

terial for the third edition in 1845, by which time the publishing firm had become E. C. and J. Biddle.

73. The authorizing Navy General Order of Sept. 4, 1844, was published in a review of the second edition of Maury's *Navigation* in the *National Intelligencer,* Sept. 10, 1844, p. 3.

74. MFM to Prof. B. Silliman, June 16, 1836, Public Library of the City of Boston.

75. MFM, Address before the Geological and Mineralogical Society of Fredericksburg, May 13, 1836, published in the Fredericksburg *Political Arena,* May 20 and 24, 1836.

76. MFM to Ann Maury of New York, June 18, 1836, MC, UVAL.

77. NR, AOR, Vol. XV, p. 613, NAn.

78. U.S. Gold Mine was reached by proceeding west on the Fredericksburg-Orange turnpike and north on the curving U.S. Ford Road; letter of Jan. 14, 1959, to me from Ralph Happel, Park Historian, Fredericksburg and Spotsylvania National Military Park.

79. MFM to Richard L. Maury, Sept. 9, 1836, MP, Vol. I, LC.

80. Benjamin Silliman, "United States Gold Mine Near Fredericksburg, Virginia," *Am. Journ. Science,* Vol. XXXII, No. I, Art. 5 (July, 1837), in Miscellanies, p. 183.

81. Ibid., p. 184; MFM, "Description of an Alembic for Distilling Amalgam of Gold, contrived by M. F. Maury, U.S.N.," *Am. Journ. Science,* Vol. XXXIII, No. II, Art. V (January, 1838), p. 66.

82. MFM, "Description of an Alembic . . ." cited in Note 81, pp. 68-69.

83. Benjamin Silliman, "United States Gold Mine . . ." cited in Note 80, p. 184.

84. MFM, "Notice of the Gold Veins of the United States Mine near Fredericksburg, Virginia," *Am. Journ. Science,* Vol. XXXII, No. II, Art. XIV (July, 1837), p. 329; see also pp. 325-328.

85. Benjamin Silliman, "Remarks on some of the Gold Mines and on parts of the Gold Region of Virginia founded on personal observation, August-September, 1836," *Am. Journ. Science,* Vol. XXXII, No. I, Art. X (July, 1837), pp. 98-109, 117, 126.

86. MFM, "Description of an Alembic . . ." cited in Notes 81, 82.

87. MFM wrote his brother that he had been on shore two years and felt it was time to go to sea. See MFM to Richard L. Maury, Sept. 9, 1836, MP, Vol. I, LC. See also Lewis, *Farragut,* p. 203.

88. Lewis, *Farragut,* pp. 202-203.

89. Articles on arctic regions, Sir John Barrow, Sir James Clark Ross, Sir John Ross, and Sir William Edward Parry, *Columbia Encyclopedia* (1935 ed.), pp. 87, 145, 1533, 1348.

90. A contemporary presentation of the difficulties and animosities connected with the organization of the expedition is in *Exploring Expedition, Correspondence between John N. Reynolds and the Hon. Mahlon Dickerson [Secretary of the Navy] under Signatures of Citizen and Friend to the Navy, Originally published in the New York Times of July, August, and September, 1837, and in the New York Courier of December and January, 1837-38,* published as a book in New York in 1838 (cited hereafter as *Exploring Expedition*).

91. Sketch of Mahlon Dickerson, *DAB,* Vol. V, pp. 289-290.

92. Thomas ap Catesby Jones had been born in Virginia in 1790, the son of Maj. Catesby Jones and Lettice Corbin (Turberville) Jones, of the Virginia family who to this day retain the Welsh custom of using ap (son of) before the name. The family spell ap with a small *a;* books often capitalize the *a.* See sketch of Thomas Ap Catesby Jones, *DAB,* Vol. X, p. 201.

93. *Report on the Exploring Expedition, 1838* (bound book), House Exec. Doc. No. 147, 25th Cong., 2nd Sess. (cited hereafter as *Expl. Exped.,* House Exec. Doc. No. 147), p. 74.

94. MFM letter cited in Note 79.

95. Ibid.

96. MFM to Ann Maury of New York, Sept. 23, 1836, MC, UVAL.

97. Ibid.

98. Ibid.

99. MFM to Capt. Thomas A. Dornin, Sept. 29, 1836, MP, Vol. I, LC; see also letter of Sept. 18, 1836.

100. Ibid., Sept. 24, Sept. 26, 1836.

101. Ibid., Oct. 9, 1836.

102. See letters of MFM October-December, 1836, January-March, 1837, MP, Vol. I, LC, and MC, UVAL.

103. MFM ordered to *Macedonian* Mar. 18, 1837; NR, AOR, Vol. XV, p. 201, NAn. For quotation, see MFM to Ann Maury of New York, July 5, 1837, MC, UVAL.

104. MFM granted 12-month furlough Mar. 21, 1838; NR, AOR, Vol. XV, p. 205, NAn.

105. MFM to Ann Maury of New York, July 5, 1837, MC, UVAL.

106. Ordered to the Exploring Expedition; NR, AOR, Vol. XV, p. 300, NAn; quotation is found in letter of MFM to Capt. Thomas A. Dornin, Sept. 19, 1837, MP, Vol. I, LC.

107. Orders, in letter of Secretary of Navy Dickerson to MFM, Oct. 21, 1837, *Expl. Exped.,* House Exec. Doc. No. 147, p. 494; also see MFM to Capt. Thomas A. Dornin, Oct. 18, 1837, MP, Vol. I, LC.

108. MFM to Capt. Thomas A. Dornin, Oct. 25, 1837, MP, Vol. I, LC.

109. MFM to Secretary of Navy Dickerson, Oct. 23, 1837, *Expl. Exped.,* House Exec. Doc. No. 147, pp. 498-499.

110. *Expl. Exped.,* House Exec. Doc. No. 147, p. 76; *Exploring Expedition,* p. 74.

111. The question of the authorization was discussed in a review of the situation by the Secretary; see Secretary Dickerson to Commodore Thomas ap Catesby Jones, Nov. 14, 1837, *Expl. Exped.,* House Exec. Doc. No. 147, p. 562.

112. Commodore Thomas ap Catesby Jones to Secretary of Navy Mahlon Dickerson, Nov. 4, 1837, *Expl. Exped.,* House Exec. Doc. No. 147, p. 503.

113. MFM refers to the fact that he had shown Commodore Jones's letter of Nov. 12, 1837, to Secretary Dickerson on the morning of Nov. 14, 1837, and then quoted this portion of it in writing the Secretary later that day; MFM to Secretary of Navy Dickerson, Nov. 14, 1837, *Expl. Exped.,* House Exec. Doc. No. 147, pp. 560-561.

114. MFM to Commodore Thomas ap Catesby Jones, Commanding South Sea Surveying and Exploring Expedition, Nov. 29, 1837, *Expl. Exped.,* House Exec. Doc. No. 147, pp. 583-585.

115. Commodore Thomas ap Catesby Jones to Secretary of Navy Dickerson, Dec. 1, 1837; Secretary Dickerson to Charles Wilkes, Lieut. Commanding, U.S.S. *Porpoise*, Dec. 5, 1837; Lieut. Wilkes to Secretary Dickerson, Dec. 2, 1837; to be found in *Expl. Exped.*, House Exec. Doc. No. 147, pp. 595, 599-600, 601.

116. Commodore Thomas ap Catesby Jones to Secretary of Navy Dickerson, Nov. 14, 1837, *Expl. Exped.*, House Exec. Doc. No. 147, pp. 562-564.

117. Ibid. A review of Commodore Jones's letters of Nov. 30 and Dec. 4, with report of Fleet Surgeon Ticknor, is given in Dickerson's acceptance of Jones's resignation; Secretary of Navy Dickerson to Commodore Thomas ap Catesby Jones, Dec. 6, 1837, *Expl. Exped.*, House Exec. Doc. No. 147, pp. 600-601.

118. The next day, Dec. 7, 1837, a resolution was passed in the House of Representatives demanding full information on the causes of delay in departure of the Exploring Expedition. A report was read to the House on Feb. 7, 1838. This, in complete form, was published as House Exec. Doc. No. 147, already cited. Dickerson reported to the President that Kearny, Perry, and Gregory had been offered command of the expedition; *Expl. Exped.*, House Exec. Doc. No. 147, p. 10; also see William Shubrick, ibid., p. 603.

119. Martin Van Buren, when he had taken office Mar. 4, 1837, had kept Mahlon Dickerson on as Secretary of Navy but replaced him July 1, 1838, with James K. Paulding. Joel R. Poinsett was Van Buren's Secretary of War from 1837 to 1841. For Poinsett's handling of the appointment, see MFM to Capt. Thomas A. Dornin, Mar. 23, 1838, MP, Vol. I, LC.

120. MFM to Ann Maury of New York, Jan. 25, 1872, MP, Vol. XLII, LC; see also MFM to Ann Maury of New York, Apr. 5, 1838, MC, UVAL.

121. An article reprinted from the *North American Review* in the *Army and Navy Chronicle and Scientific Repository* stated that a captain from Massachusetts who had been offered the command said that he could not take it unless a scientific officer was assigned him. He designated Lieut. Charles Wilkes, who "declined to serve in this capacity." After Wilkes was given the command, he chose "Lieutenant Hudson . . . as his second but that officer refused to serve under a lieutenant lower on the list than himself." See *Army and Navy Chronicle and Scientific Repository*, Apr. 27, 1843, pp. 503-504. Quotation is from Daniel Carl Haskell, *The U.S. Exploring Expedition, 1838-42, and Its Publications*, introduction, p. 3.

122. MFM to Capt. Thomas Dornin, Mar. 23, 1838, MP, Vol. I, LC. Secretary of War Poinsett evidently informed Secretary of Navy Dickerson of the promise he had made Maury. Officers were supposed to be allowed to withdraw from duty with the expedition without prejudice to their careers.

123. Maury was relieved from duty with the Exploring Expedition, June 8, 1838; NR, AOR, Vol. XVI, p. 453, NAn. The next day he acknowledged receipt of his release and applied for active service with hydrographic surveys or orders to sea; MFM to Secretary of Navy Dickerson, June 9, 1838; see MFM's copy, MP, Vol. I, LC.

124. A typical remark by MFM in this period was, "I am still hanging by the eyelids here expecting every mail to bring a requisition from Washington for my services." MFM to Ann Maury of New York, Apr. 5, 1838, MC, UVAL.

125. "Harry Bluff" articles appeared in Richmond *Whig and Public Advertiser,* Aug. 10, 13, 14, 17, 18, 25, 27, 28, 1838, and Sept. 4, 1838. Report of reactions is in MFM letters to Ann Maury of New York, Aug. 28, Aug. 30, Sept. 6, 1838, MC, UVAL.
126. See especially letters from "Will Watch" to "Harry Bluff" in Richmond *Whig and Public Advertiser,* Dec. 21, 25, 28, 1838.
127. Ordered to repair to Washington and report at Department Dec. 6, 1838; and on Dec. 13, 1838, MFM was ordered to steamer *Engineer* on survey of Southern harbors. NR, AOR, Vol. XVII, pp. 112, 116, NAn.
128. MFM to Matthew Maury of New York, Jan. 4, 1839, MC, UVAL.
129. Message to Matthew Maury of New York in MFM letter to Matthew's sister Ann Maury, Dec. 12, 1838, MC, UVAL.
130. MFM to F. R. Hassler, Superintendent of Coast Survey, Feb. 11, 1839, in NYPL.
131. MFM to Ann Maury of New York, Aug. 28, 1838, MC, UVAL.
132. MFM to Ann Maury of New York, Jan. 26, 1839, MC, UVAL.
133. MFM was detached from the *Engineer* on July 31, 1839, and granted leave of one month. After that he was "awaiting orders" to report to the *Consort,* orders that were not issued until Sept. 10, 1839; NR, AOR, Vol. XVII, pp. 246, 270, NAn. Quotation is from MFM to Ann Maury of New York, Aug. 25, 1839, in MC, UVAL.
134. MFM to Ann Maury of New York, Sept. 27, 1839, MC, UVAL. The copy of this letter in Corbin, *Maury* (pp. 30-31), has been edited.
135. MFM had not seen his parents since his leave in 1830, when he had gone with Eliza Maury and her sons by stage to Tennessee. MFM to Ann Maury of New York, Sept. 27, 1839, MP, Vol. I, LC.
136. Facts of the accident are a summation of the testimony in court case of *M. F.* (incorrectly recorded as M. T.) *Maury* v. *D. Talmadge,* stage line proprietor, heard before the U.S. Circuit Court, Columbus, Ohio, July session, 1840. MFM made his deposition about the accident in Virginia and was represented by Thomas Ewing, U.S. Senator from the section of Ohio in which MFM was injured. See John McLean (ed.), *U.S. Circuit Court Reports, 1829-1855* (cited hereafter as McLean, *Reports*) Vol. II, pp. 157-167.
137. Mary Maury Werth to her children, July 26, 1879, MP, Vol. XLII, LC.
138. Because of the condition of the road, it had taken the stagecoach nearly a half hour for the run from Somerset to the point of the accident, so MFM certainly had a wait of over an hour before arrival of the men to take him back to Somerset.
139. The fact that MFM had suffered "a vertical fracture of the *patella,* or kneepan" and that "the joint is greatly deformed" was added to the diagnosis of the Ohio physicians by surgeons in Philadelphia on MFM's return from Ohio. See *Maury* v. *Talmadge,* McLean, *Reports,* Vol. II, p. 164.
140. MFM to Ann Maury of New York, Nov. 6, Nov. 17, 1839, MC, UVAL.
141. MFM letter of Nov. 6, 1839, MC, UVAL.
142. Continuation on Dec. 17 of MFM letter to Ann Maury of New York, Dec. 16, 1839, MP, Vol. II, LC.
143. MFM letter of Dec. 16, 1839, cited in Note 142.
144. MFM to Ann Maury of New York, Nov. 6, 1839, MC, UVAL.
145. Ibid.

146. MFM to Lieut. (fixed rank, had ceased to be addressed as captain because no longer commanding a ship) Thomas A. Dornin, Nov. 3, 1839, MP, Vol. II, LC.
147. MFM to Ann Maury of New York, Nov. 17, 1839, MC, UVAL.
148. MFM to Matthew Maury, Nov. 26, 1839, MC, UVAL.
149. Ibid.
150. Ibid.
151. MFM letter cited in Note 147.
152. In Dec. 17, 1839, continuation of MFM letter cited in Note 142.
153. MFM to Ann Maury of New York, Dec. 7, 1839, MC, UVAL.
154. MFM letter of Dec. 16, 1839, cited in Note 142.
155. MFM to Ann Maury of New York, Dec. 25, 1839, MC, UVAL.
156. MFM's uncle was within two weeks of his 93rd birthday, which occurred Feb. 3, 1840. Matthew and Rutson Maury were primarily exporters of cotton from the Southern states to England. Their office was at 57 Wall Street. The home of Consul James Maury, where his daughter and son, Ann and Rutson, were to live out their lives, was numbered 349 at the time of this visit of MFM. In 1850 the number was changed to 365 and by 1867 had become 17 East 4th Street. Six doors from the Maury residence stood an almost identical house—the home of their friends, the Seabury Treadwells. I visited this "Old Merchant's House," 29 East 4th Street, in 1959; and because it contains the original furnishings, books and clothing, I felt as if I were in the Maury home as MFM saw it.
157. MFM to Ann Maury of New York, Jan. 26, 1840, MC, UVAL.

CHAPTER VII

Campaign for Naval Reform

1. MFM to Ann Maury of New York, Feb. 15, 1840, MC, UVAL.
2. When he dictated this prayer to his children for their use on Jan. 30, 1872, MFM stated that he had formulated and used it every night subsequent to his accident. See account of MFM's last weeks in Mary H. Maury to Marin H. Jansen, Apr. 9, 1873, MP, Vol. XLII, LC.
3. MFM letter cited in Note 1.
4. Consul James Maury (1747-1840) had in 1796 married Margaret Rutson (1764-1830) in England. They sent their youngest son, Rutson (1805-1882), to Charter House School and their daughter Ann (1803-1876) to Miss Bushnell's Boarding School in England. From an early age Ann was taken on trips to various parts of the British Isles. In 1827 she traveled widely on the Continent with her brother William. Her diary entries describing the visit with her father to President Madison are quoted in A. F. Maury, *Virginiana*, pp. 176-177.
5. Ann translated from French the memoirs of the Rev. James Fontaine, French Huguenot émigré, and early in 1838 sent this manuscript to MFM for his criticism prior to its publication. See MFM to Ann Maury of New York, Apr. 5, 1838, MC, UVAL. The correspondence between MFM and his cousin was often about education or writing. For examples, see MFM to Ann Maury, Aug. 28, 1836, May 20, 1838, Aug. 28, 1838, July 4, 1841, MC, UVAL.
6. See Ann Herndon Maury (Mrs. MFM) to Ann Maury of New York, May

12, 1844, MC, UVAL; to B. Franklin Minor, Sept. 15, 1855, MP, Vol. IV, LC; to her son, Richard L. Maury, Oct. 15, 1859, MP, Vol. VIII, LC.

7. "I fell in love with my sweet, gentle Nannie [Ann]," MFM wrote to B. Franklin Minor, Mar. 21, 1855, MP, Vol. IV, LC. For her diffidence, see MFM to his wife, Nov. 23, 1858, MP, Vol. VII, LC, Sept. 23, 1865, MP, Vol. XXIII, LC.

8. Ann Herndon Maury's health problems were undoubtedly increased by the bearing of eight children. She must, however, have possessed an essentially strong constitution for, although only five years younger than MFM, she outlived him by twenty-eight years and her daughter Diana by a year.

9. MFM to Ann Maury of New York, Feb. 27, 1840, MC, UVAL.

10. Ibid.

11. Ibid.

12. MFM to Ann Maury of New York, Mar. 29, 1840, MC, UVAL.

13. Another series of letters criticizing Navy failures appeared in the same issues of the Richmond *Whig and Public Advertiser,* in August, 1838 (cited in Note 125, Chapter VI) in which MFM's first "Harry Bluff" articles had been published. This series has also been attributed to MFM but was more likely written by William F. Lynch. For a review of the perennial problem of slow promotion, see MFM report to Secretary of Navy William A. Graham, Oct. 7, 1850, NR, NOLS, Vol. VI, NAn.

14. MFM to Matthew Maury of New York, March 3, 1840, MC, UVAL.

15. Ibid.

16. MFM, "A Scheme for Rebuilding Southern Commerce: Direct Trade with the South," *SLM,* Vol. V, No. 1 (January, 1839), pp. 3-12.

17. "Harry Bluff" (MFM), "Scraps from the Lucky Bag," *SLM,* Vol. VI, No. 4 (April, 1840), p. 233.

18. He told his first cousins in New York because he sent them some of the articles for criticism. See MFM to Matthew Maury, Mar. 3, 1840, MC, UVAL, and MFM to Ann Maury, May 27, 1840, MC, UVAL.

19. "Harry Bluff" (MFM), "Scraps from the Lucky Bag," *SLM,* Vol. VI, No. 4 (April, 1840), p. 234.

20. Ibid., p. 235.

21. MFM to Ann Maury of New York, May 24, 1840, MC, UVAL.

22. "Harry Bluff" (MFM), "Scraps from the Lucky Bag," *SLM,* Vol. VI, No. 5 (May, 1840), p. 318.

23. Ibid., p. 319.

24. MFM to Ann Maury of New York, May 4, 1840, MC, UVAL.

25. Ibid., June 29, 1840.

26. Ibid.

27. MFM to Rutson Maury, Aug. 31, 1840, MP, Vol. II, LC.

28. John T. Goolrick, *Historic Fredericksburg,* p. 32.

29. For an example of this, see MFM to Matthew Maury, Oct. 12, 1840, MC, UVAL.

30. Benjamin Homans (compiler), *Laws of The United States in relation to the Navy and Marine Corps* (1841), p. 161.

31. Testimony of MFM in Court File No. 93, Office of Town Clerk, Fredericksburg, Va.

32. MFM to Matthew Maury of New York, Jan. 30, 1840, and to Ann Maury of New York, Feb. 15, 1840, both in MC, UVAL.
33. Verdict for the plaintiff, *M. F. Maury* v. *D. Talmadge*, U.S. Circuit Court, Columbus, Ohio, in McLean's *Reports*, Vol. II, p. 167.
34. NR, Acting Secretary of Navy C. Morris to MFM, Aug. 27, 1840; Capt. Thomas H. Stevens to U.S.N. Surgeons John A. Kearney and Bailey Washington, Sept. 2, 1840; NR, Report of Surgeons Kearney and Washington to Capt. Thomas H. Stevens, Sept. 4, 1840, Record Group No. 125 (hereafter cited as RG 125), Records of the Office of the Judge Advocate General (Navy) [hereafter cited as JAGen (Navy)]: "Courts of Inquiry, Act of January 16, 1857," Vol. XXI, pp. 37-39, NAn.
35. MFM to Secretary of Navy Paulding, Feb. 24, 1840; certification of U.S.N. Surgeon John C. Mercer, Feb. 3, 1840, both in NR cited in Note 34, pp. 35, 39.
36. Record that MFM was granted a $12.50 pension is in NR, cited in Note 35, p. 39.
37. MFM to Ann Maury of New York, Oct. 12, 1840, MC, UVAL.
38. Richard Launcelot Maury tombstone, Hollywood Cemetery, Richmond, Va.; ibid., Jan. 10, 1841.
39. MFM had been pleased that his brother Dick had named his eldest son for him, and he reciprocated later by having his fatherless nephew Mat spend the winter of 1849-1850 with him in Washington and go to school there.
40. MFM to Lucian Minor (whom MFM addressed as Lucien), Nov. 8, 1840, MP, Vol. II, LC.
41. MFM, "Scraps from the Lucky Bag," *SLM*, Vol. VI, No. 12 (December, 1840), pp. 786-800. The quotation is from MFM's further discussion of this subject in "Letter to Mr. Clay," *SLM*, Vol. VII, No. 10 (October, 1841), p. 726.
42. Numerous officers and secretaries of Navy had wanted an academy, Fasano, *Naval Rank*, pp. 150-151. For officers giving article to congressmen, see MFM to Ann Maury of New York, June 21, 1841, MC, UVAL.
43. For Maury's role, see Jaffe, *Men of Science*, pp. 214-215. For developments leading to U.S.N.A. at Annapolis, see Burr, *Education*, pp. 154-161; Ammen, *Old Navy*, pp. 94-97.
44. Works Progress Administration in Maryland (compilers), *A Guide to the United States Naval Academy* (American Guide Series), Service Academy Series, Sponsored by the United States Naval Academy (hereafter cited as U.S.N.A.), pp. 25-26, 120.
45. James Russell Soley, *Historical Sketch of the United States Naval Academy;* sketch of George Bancroft, *DAB*, Vol. I, pp. 564-570; sketch of Franklin Buchanan in *Columbia Encyclopedia* (1935 ed.), p. 248.
46. White's statement reported in MFM letter to Lucian Minor, Dec. 14, 1840, MP, Vol. II, LC.
47. Ibid.
48. MFM to Ann Maury of New York, Aug. 28, 1836, MC, UVAL.
49. Ibid., June 21, 1841.
50. MFM told what the officer stationed in Norfolk, Va., had written him in MFM letter cited in Note 49.
51. Summation of MFM charges on shipbuilding and repair, "Scraps from the

Lucky Bag," *SLM,* January, 1841, Vol. VII, No. 1, pp. 3-25; *SLM* (May-June [combined]), Vol. VII, Nos. 5-6, pp. 345-379; *SLM,* Vol. VII, No. 10 (October, 1841), pp. 724-729. See also "Lieutenant M. F. Maury of U.S. Navy," by "A Brother Officer," *SLM,* Vol. VII, No. 7 (July, 1841), p. 561.

52. Commodore Charles Morris, *Autobiography,* p. 110; Lovette, *Naval Customs,* p. 293.

53. MFM to Ann Maury of New York, Jan. 10 and June 21, 1841, MC, UVAL.

54. "A Brother Officer" in his article, "Lieutenant M. F. Maury of U.S. Navy," revealed MFM's authorship of "Scraps from the Lucky Bag" and reported proposals for MFM to be Secretary of Navy, *SLM,* Vol. VII, No. 7 (July, 1841), pp. 560-563.

55. Ibid., pp. 561-562.

56. MFM to Ann Maury of New York, Jan. 10, 1841, MC, UVAL.

57. MFM to Richard and Diana Maury, Jan. 26, 1841, as quoted in Corbin, *Maury,* p. 37.

58. MFM to Ann Maury of New York, Nov. 27, 1838, Aug. 25, 1839, MC, UVAL.

59. MFM's assumption of responsibility as general guardian of Sally Fontaine Maury and John M. Maury is evidenced by entries in MFM account book for Nov. 11, 1841, Mar. 31 and May 29, 1842, filed under date of Nov. 2, 1841, MP, Vol. II, LC; receipt from J. J. Chew, Clerk of Hustings Court, Fredericksburg, Va., for bond posted by MFM as general guardian, filed under date of May 10, 1842, MP, Vol. II, LC.

60. MFM to Ann Maury of New York, Sept. 23, 1836, May 26, June 21, 1841, Jan. 22, 1842, MC, UVAL.

61. MFM to Richard and Diana Maury, in Corbin, *Maury,* p. 38.

62. Editor White stated that "C.S." had given "no address and no means of communication" but that it was believed C.S. was "one high in authority." See article by C.S., "Reply to Harry Bluff," *SLM,* Vol. VII, No. 3 (March, 1841), pp. 209-213.

63. "A Brother Officer," "Lieut. M. F. Maury of U.S. Navy," *SLM,* Vol. VII, No. 7 (July, 1841), pp. 560-563. Maury called this laudatory article revealing his authorship his obituary and believed an enemy had written it.

64. MFM to Matthew Maury, Oct. 12, 1840, and to Ann Maury of New York, June 21, 1841, both in MC, UVAL.

65. MFM (his copy) to Secretary of Navy George E. Badger, June 10, 1841, MP, Vol. II, LC.

66. MFM to Ann Maury of New York, July 4, Aug. 14, and Oct. 10, 1841, MC, UVAL.

67. Order issued Oct. 4, 1841, NR, AOR, Vol. XVIII, p. 380, NAn.

68. MFM's will, dated Nov. 2, 1841, is in his small account book, filed under date of Nov. 2, 1841, MP, Vol. II, LC.

69. Ibid.

70. Ibid.

71. Press copies of the physicians' letter and of Judge John Tayloe Lomax's letter to Secretary of Navy Upshur, Nov. 11, 1841, NR, Miscellaneous Records of the Hydrographic Office—"Correspondence Relating Chiefly to Lt. M. F. Maury, U.S.N., and the 'Plucking Board' of 1855," No. 54, letters unarranged.

72. Judge Lomax letter cited in Note 71; MFM to Rutson Maury, Nov. 13, 1841, in Corbin, *Maury,* p. 39.

73. Secretary of Navy A. P. Upshur to MFM, Nov. 15, 1841, MP, Vol. II, LC.

74. MFM (his copy) to Secretary of Navy A. P. Upshur, Nov. 18, 1841, MP, Vol. II, LC.

75. Secretary of Navy A. P. Upshur to MFM, Nov. 22, 1841, MP, Vol. II, LC; order to frigate *United States* revoked, Nov. 22, 1841, NR, AOR, Vol. XVIII, p. 451, NAn.

76. *Constitution of The National Institution for the Promotion of Science* (printed in 1841), p. 16.

77. Ibid., pp. 1-18.

78. MFM to National Institution for the Promotion of Science, Dec. 5, 1840, in *Proceedings of the National Institution for the Promotion of Science,* Bulletin No. 1, p. 17; letter read at April, 1841, meeting, ibid., Bulletin No. 2; both in the *Papers Relative to the National Institute,* collected and arranged by Francis Markoe, Jr., corresponding secretary, p. 78. (15 pamphlets in 1 vol.)

79. "Union Jack," (MFM) "Letters to Mr. Clay," *SLM,* Vol. VII, No. 10 (October, 1841), p. 727.

80. Ibid.

81. MFM discussed these needs in Letter No. 4 to Mr. Clay, *SLM,* Vol. VII, No. 10 (October, 1841), p. 729, and in greater detail in an article he wrote in 1842, published later. See MFM, "The Navy and the West," *SLM,* Vol. IX, No. 1 (January, 1843), pp. 1-5.

82. MFM to Rutson Maury, Feb. 20, 1842, MC, UVAL.

83. MFM to Rutson Maury, Feb. 22, 1842, attached to and filed in the letter cited in Note 82.

84. Ibid.

85. MFM to Professor John B. Minor, Jan. 28, 1856, MP, Vol. V, LC.

86. "Harry Bluff," (MFM) "The Right of Search," *SLM,* Vol. VIII, No. 4 (April, 1842), pp. 289-301.

87. Ibid., p. 301.

88. The order for MFM to take charge of the Depot of Charts and Instruments was issued June 29, 1842; NR, AOR, Vol. XIX, p. 170, NAn.

89. MFM to Ann Maury of New York, May 17, 1842, MC, UVAL.

90. Ibid., May 28, 1842.

CHAPTER VIII

Scientific Opportunity at Last

1. MFM to Ann Maury of New York, Aug. 4, 1842, MC, UVAL.

2. John Spencer Bassett, *The Life of Andrew Jackson* (new ed., 1916), Vol. I, pp. 584-655, 693-699, 723-727, 730-734.

3. By 1841 there were already about 300 Americans in California, but they had not gone there by wagon train. Independence was the starting point of the Santa Fé trail and is considered the point of origin for this 1841 wagon train. The California-bound emigrants had assembled at a camp at nearby "Sapling Grove, a few miles west of the present site of Kansas City," according to James Truslow Adams, in *Dictionary of American History* (cited hereafter as Adams, *Dict. Am. History*), Vol. I, p. 269.

Sketch of John Charles Frémont, *Columbia Encyclopedia* (1935 ed.), p. 668.

4. Wilkes's expedition reached New York in mid-June. See sketch of Charles Wilkes, *DAB,* Vol. XX, pp. 217-218. For a full account of the expedition's achievements, see Charles Wilkes, *Narrative of the U.S. Exploring Expedition, 1838-1842.*

5. The officers were tried by a "grand court martial" held on board the U.S.S. *North Carolina,* moored off the New York Navy Yard. The *National Intelligencer* carried numerous accounts of the courts; for examples, see issues of Aug. 15, Sept. 24, 27, 1842; see also MFM to Ann Maury of New York, Aug. 4, 1842, MC, UVAL. Later in 1842 Wilkes was himself court-martialed for having illegally punished some of his men, and the court ordered that he be publicly reprimanded; sketch of Charles Wilkes, *DAB,* Vol. XX, p. 217.

6. Article on steamships, *Columbia Encyclopedia* (1935 ed.), p. 1683.

7. Secretary of Navy A. P. Upshur statement, Senate Doc. No. 1, Ser. 395, 27th Cong., 2nd Sess., p. 386; Fasano, *Naval Rank,* p. 161; *Navy Register,* 1842; Pratt, *The Navy,* p. 238.

8. MFM memorandum from *Navy Register, 1841,* filed as Folio 972, MP, Vol. VI, LC.

9. Brief historical sketch giving officers in command, Records of the Naval Observatory, 1840-1929, RG 78, NAn; Henry P. Beers, *Survey of Federal Archives: Bibliography of the Navy Department and the Naval Shore Establishments, The National Archives* (17-page typescript), passim; Gustavus A. Weber, *The Hydrographic Office, Its History, Activities and Organization,* Service Monograph of U.S. Government No. 42, Institute for Government Research (cited hereafter as Weber, *Hydrographic Office*), (depot history) pp. 1-14, (depot moved to Pennsylvania Avenue) pp. 16-17; Rear Admiral B. F. Sands, *Astronomical and Meteorological Observations Made During the Year 1871 at the U.S. Naval Observatory,* (address of depot) errata sheet.

10. MFM to Ann Maury of New York, Aug. 4, 1842, MC, UVAL.

11. MFM to John Quincy Adams, Nov. 17, 1847, in *SLM,* Vol. XIII, No. 1, p. 9; Weber, *Hydrographic Office,* p. 18.

12. MFM letter to Ann Maury cited in Note 10; MFM letter to John Quincy Adams, cited in Note 11, p. 9.

13. Weber, *Hydrographic Office,* pp. 17-18.

14. Ibid., pp. 11-13; see MFM's urging bureau system in "Scraps from the Lucky Bag," *SLM,* Vol. VII, No. 1 (January, 1841), pp. 24-25; House Rep. No. 449, Ser. 408, 27th Cong., 2nd Sess.; U.S. Statutes at Large, Vol. LVIII, p. 576. For MFM's following the progress of bills, see his letter cited in Note 10.

15. John Carroll Brent (ed.), *Letters on the National Institute, Smithsonian Legacy, the Fine Arts* (cited hereafter as Brent, *Letters on Nat. Institute*), pp. 56-58; Richard Rathbun, *The Columbian Institute for the Promotion of Arts and Sciences,* Smithsonian Institution Bulletin 101 (cited hereafter as Rathbun, *Columbian Institute*), pp. 62-64.

16. Rathbun, *Columbian Institute,* p. 63; see also pp. 62, 64.

17. See definition of prime meridian under meridian, Funk and Wagnall's *New Standard Dictionary of the English Language* (1940 ed.), p. 1554.

18. The quotation is from *Memoirs of John Quincy Adams* (cited hereafter as

J. Q. Adams, *Memoirs*), Vol. XI, p. 336. For his recommendation that an observatory be built, see *Memoirs*, Vol. VII, p. 55, Vol. X, pp. 25, 44, 57, Vol. XI, p. 112.

19. Benjamin Homans (compiler and arranger), *Laws of the U.S. in relation to the Navy and Marine Corps*, p. 161.
20. MFM letter cited in Note 10.
21. Ibid.
22. Ibid.
23. "An Act to Reorganize the Navy Department of the United States" (setting up five bureaus), Aug. 31, 1842, *Register of the Commission and Warrant Officers of the United States*, 1842, pp. 126-128, NAn.
24. House Rep. No. 449, Ser. 408, 27th Cong., 2nd Sess.; U.S. Statutes at Large, Vol. LVIII, p. 576.
25. Brent, *Letters on Nat. Institute*, p. 58.
26. "An Act . . . ," cited in Note 23.
27. MFM letter cited in Note 10; Commodore Charles Morris, *Autobiography*, p. 110.
28. Lewis J. Darter, Jr., "The Federal Archives Relating to Matthew Fontaine Maury," *American Neptune*, Vol. I (April, 1941), p. 154.
29. MFM to Secretary of Navy John Y. Mason, Nov. 18, 1844, NR, NOLS, Vol. I, NAn.
30. MFM to William M. Blackford, Nov. 19, 1843, MP, Vol. III, LC; Corbin, *Maury*, p. 53.
31. On Aug. 25, 1842, the *National Intelligencer* announced a dispatch had been received proclaiming the cessation of hostilities on Aug. 14 in the "second war with the Seminoles."
32. MFM to Ann Maury of New York, Aug. 14, 1841, MC, UVAL.
33. William Lewis Herndon, born in Fredericksburg in 1813, became a midshipman in 1828, a passed midshipman in 1834, and a lieutenant in 1841.
34. MFM to Ann Maury of New York, Oct. 15, 1842, MC, UVAL.
35. Ibid.; record of births in MFM's Bible.
36. MFM to Maj. W. B. Scott, Navy Agent, Washington, NR, NOLS, Vol. I, NAn.
37. Sketch of the Hydrographic Office, in *Guide to the Material in the National Archives* (1940), p. 123; Lovette, *Naval Customs*, p. 293.
38. Sketch of William Montgomery Crane in *DAB*, Vol. IV, p. 510.
39. MFM to William M. Blackford, U.S. Chargé d'Affaires, Bogotá, Nov. 19, 1843, MP, Vol. III, LC.
40. MFM to Commodore William M. Crane, Chief, Bureau of Ordnance and Hydrography, Nov. 9, 1842, NR, NOLS, Vol. I, NAn.
41. MFM, *Physical Geography of the Sea*, introduction, pp. v, vi.
42. MFM retained memory of the Psalms from his boyhood to his death. He used verses therefrom often in his writing and in his speeches.
43. For facts concerning the development of charts, see Nils Adolf Eric Nordenskiold (trans. by Francis Bather), *Periplus . . . Early History of Charts and Sailing Directions*. The fact that the 8th Psalm influenced MFM's thinking in this way was stated to me by his granddaughter, Mrs. N. Montgomery Osborne, of Norfolk, Va.
44. Orrin E. Klapp, "Matthew Fontaine Maury, Naval Scientist" (cited here-

after as Klapp, *MFM*), *USNIP*, Vol. LXXII, No. 11, Whole No. 513 (November, 1945), p. 1317.

45. MFM to Ann Maury of New York, Feb. 16, 1843; see also MFM to Rutson Maury, Nov. 13, 1842, both in MC, UVAL.

46. Gravestone of Richard Maury, MFM section, Hollywood Cemetery, Richmond, Va.

47. *Army and Navy Chronicle and Scientific Repository,* Jan. 19, 1843, p. 58, Feb. 16, 1843, p. 182, and subsequent issues.

48. James Pollard Espy (1785-1860) had been in England and France expounding his theory of storms to scientific societies. See article on Espy, *DAB,* Vol. VI, pp. 185-186; Jaffe, *Men of Science,* p. 202.

49. MFM to Commodore William M. Crane, Chief, Bureau of Ordnance and Hydrography, March 9, 1843, NR, NOLS, Vol. I, NAn.

50. For "storm king" title, see article on Espy, *DAB,* Vol. VI, p. 185. Espy was constantly trying to get a better government sponsorship for his studies. There are conflicting statements about his having worked under the aegis of both Army and Navy between 1842 and 1844. In February, 1844, Adams stated, "Mr. Espy, the storm-breeder came with a complaint"; J. Q. Adams, *Memoirs,* Vol. XI, p. 506. See also Eric R. Miller, "The Evolution of Meteorological Institutions in the United States," *Monthly Weather Review,* Vol. LIX, No. 1 (January, 1931), p. 2.

51. MFM to Ann Maury of New York, Feb. 16, 1843, MC, UVAL.

52. Account of this bill reported in the U.S. Senate, Jan. 25, 1843; *Army and Navy Chronicle and Scientific Repository,* Feb. 2, 1843, p. 126.

53. MFM to Commodore William M. Crane, Chief, Bureau of Ordnance and Hydrography, Mar. 16, 1843, NR, NOLS, Vol. I, NAn.

54. Ibid., Mar. 13, 1843.

55. *Army and Navy Chronicle and Scientific Repository,* Mar. 30, 1843, pp. 365, 375.

56. The word "institution" in the organization's name was changed to "institute" in 1843; *Proceedings of the National Institute for the Promotion of Science,* Bulletin No. 3, pp. 278, 279, in Francis Markoe, Jr. (collector), *Papers Relative to the National Institute.* See membership list of National Institute, *Army and Navy Chronicle and Scientific Repository,* May 25, 1843, pp. 637-638.

57. Possibly because of a sore throat, MFM had the Corresponding Secretary read his paper "proposing a plan for collecting information for the purposes of navigation, by means of blank charts furnished to all nations"; Francis Markoe, Jr. (collector), *Papers Relative to the National Institute,* p. 308.

58. MFM, "Blank Charts on Board Public Cruisers," *SLM,* Vol. IX, No. 8 (August, 1843), p. 458.

59. Ibid., pp. 458-461.

60. MFM also called for water gauges to be installed on Western rivers; "The Navy and the West," *SLM,* Vol. IX, No. 1 (January, 1843), pp. 1-5.

61. MFM always thanked each officer who sent him observations. His official correspondence in 1843 shows how few officers sent observations in this period. For typical MFM thanks, see MFM to Capt. Samuel Barron, Nov. 14, 1843, NR, NOLS, Vol. I, NAn.

62. MFM to Capt. F. H. Gregory, Aug. 29, 1843, NR, NOLS, Vol. I, NAn.
63. MFM to Commodore William M. Crane, Chief, Bureau of Ordnance and Hydrography, Sept. 25, 1843, NR, NOLS, Vol. I, NAn.
64. MFM to Ann Maury of New York, Nov. 4, Dec. 6, 1843, MC, UVAL.
65. Gravestone of Diana Minor Maury (Mrs. Richard Maury), MFM section, Hollywood Cemetery, Richmond, Va.
66. For MFM's settling estate, see MFM to Lucian Minor, July 15, July 29, 1843, Apr. 21, 1847; letters to MFM from F. F. Reid, of Franklin, Tenn., Dec. 13, 1843, Jan. 5, 1844; letter from Franklin lawyer Thomas N. Fiquers, Aug. 31, 1844; letter from Matilda Maury Guthrie, Mar. 27, 1845; receipt from Peggy Ann Maury, Apr. 29, 1845; letter from James Walker Maury, Aug. 18, 1846, all in MP, Vol. III, LC.
67. MFM, *Physical Geography of the Sea* (1855 ed.), pp. 59-64.
68. Continuing this statement, Marcus Benjamin described the congress as "the first cosmopolitan assemblage of the kind which in any respect foreshadowed the great congresses of the American Association [for the Advancement of Science] in later years." Marcus Benjamin, "Address to the 48th Annual Meeting [1899] of the American Association for the Advancement of Science" (organization cited hereafter as AAAS), *The Early Presidents of the American Association,* p. 3.
69. "Proceedings of the Meeting of April, 1844," *Proceedings of the National Institute,* Bulletin No. 3, in Francis Markoe, Jr. (collector), *Papers Relative to the National Institute,* p. 430.
70. Ibid., also pp. 278, 279, 375, 376, 428-434. See also Rathbun, *Columbian Institute,* pp. 2-3.
71. This is a joint letter from MFM and E.M.A. The quotation is from the first portion written by the visiting relative. In the section written by MFM, he urged Lucian Minor to leave Louisa Court House as he thought Lucian should use his talents where he had a wider scope. Lucian Minor later became professor of law at William and Mary College, Williamsburg. See letter of E.M.A. and MFM to Lucian Minor, June 13, 1844, MP, Vol. III, LC.
72. MFM, "The Gulf Stream and Currents of the Sea," SLM, Vol. X, No. 7 (July, 1844), pp. 393-409.
73. MFM, "On the currents of the Sea as Connected with Meteorology," paper on *Proceedings of Association of American Geologists and Naturalists,* 1844; see proceedings of May 14, 1844.
74. Carleton Mabee, *The American Leonardo: A Life of Samuel F. B. Morse,* pp. 275-279; Adams, *Dict. Am. History,* Vol. V, p. 238; MFM to Ann Maury of New York, June 1, 1844, MC, UVAL.
75. MFM to William M. Blackford, U.S. Chargé d'Affaires, Bogotá, Nov. 19, 1843, MP, Vol. III, LC.
76. Ibid.
77. Ibid. Dornin was made a commander Sept. 8, 1841.
78. MFM letter cited in Note 75.
79. MFM to Lucian Minor, July 14, 1844, MP, Vol. III, LC.
80. J. Q. Adams, *Memoirs,* Vol. XII, p. 189; MFM, writing in his capacity as president of the National Institute, to Dr. Mercer, Apr. 4, 1856, MC, UVAL; *Army and Navy Chronicle and Scientific Repository,* June 1, 1844, p. 639; Lewis, *Maury,* p. 44; letter of Lieut. Col. Floyd M. Johnson, Jr.,

U.S.M.C., to me, Feb. 16, 1959. For history, see W. S. Hughes, Lieut. U.S.N., *Founding and Development of the U.S. Naval Observatory.*

81. Keim's *Illustrated Handbook* (Washington, 1844), p. 163.
82. MFM to Ann Maury of New York, Apr. 17, 1844, MC, UVAL; joint letter of E.M.A. and MFM to Lucian Minor, June 13, 1844, MP, Vol. III, LC.
83. As early as November 19, 1843, MFM had written William M. Blackford that there was speculation about who would be made superintendent of the Observatory when it was completed, "Who is to have it I do not know —I suppose the competitors will be multitudinous and I shall not swell the list. I am trying to leave my mark before they wipe me out." MP, Vol. III, LC. As late as Sept. 12, 1844, MFM was writing to Ann Maury of New York, "I have been officially informed that the new observatory will be ready on 1st October. . . . I have not been told whether I would be continued in charge. . . . I shall await events." MC, UVAL. One of those who favored Gilliss for the superintendency of the Observatory was John Carroll Brent who, in 1844, published *Letters on the National Institute, Smithsonian Legacy, The Fine Arts.* Even after William C. Bond had gone to head Harvard's new observatory, there was talk about offering him the direction of the Naval Observatory.
84. The General Order issued Sept. 4, 1844, was printed, and the second edition of MFM's book was reviewed by the *National Intelligencer* on Sept. 10, 1844, p. 3. MFM commented on his pleasure at the book's official adoption in a letter to Ann Maury of New York, Sept. 11, 1844, MC, UVAL.
85. About John Young Mason (1799-1859) *DAB* says, "As Chairman of the House committee of foreign affairs, he advocated naval preparedness in the face of France's dilatory attitude over the spoliation claims." Sketch of Mason, *DAB,* Vol. XII, pp. 369-370.
86. The order was not issued in usual form and is not recorded in NR, AOR, NAn. Secretary Mason evidently considered the appointment a continuation of Maury's superintendency of the Depot of Charts and Instruments. When Maury learned that he was to head the new Observatory, he had already committed himself to a duty trip to Northern port cities in connection with nautical instruments of ships in harbor. He returned to Washington from that trip on Oct. 5, 1844. MFM to Commodore William M. Crane, Chief, Bureau of Ordnance and Hydrography, Oct. 12, 1844, NR, NOLS, Vol. I, NAn.

CHAPTER IX

Superintendent of the U.S. Naval Observatory

1. NR, MFM to Commodore William M. Crane, Chief, Bureau of Ordnance and Hydrography, Oct. 12, 1844, NOLS, Vol. I, NAn.
2. Report of Lieut. J. M. Gilliss to the Secretary of Navy, Nov. 23, 1843, in Brent, *Letters on Nat. Institute,* pp. 58-59.
3. NR, MFM letter cited in Note 1.
4. Ibid.
5. Ibid.
6. Lieut. Gilliss had followed a practice not uncommon in that period. Concerning such use of sulphur, a modern college chemistry textbook states,

"It is sometimes employed as a cement, as in fastening iron rods in stone. . . . It is easily melted at a temperature slightly higher than boiling water. . . . If exposed to air it will very slowly form an acid gas, sulphur dioxide. This will dissolve in moist air to form sulfurous acid which would be corrosive to metals such as iron." Lem B. Richardson and Andrew J. Scarlett, *General College Chemistry* (4th ed.), p. 216.

7. For a list of the astronomical instruments and their makers, see MFM to John Quincy Adams, quoted in full in *SLM,* Vol. XIV, No. 1 (January, 1848), pp. 5-6; see also report of Lieut. Gilliss, Brent, *Letters on Nat. Institute,* pp. 59-60.

8. NR, MFM to Prof. Benjamin Peirce (which MFM spelled Pierce), Cambridge, Mass., March 20, 1845, NOLS, Vol. I, NAn.

9. MFM quoted Barnard's request in his reply; NR, MFM to F. A. P. Barnard, Univ. of Alabama, Dec. 23, 1844, NOLS, Vol. I, NAn.

10. Ibid., Rathbun, *Columbian Institute,* p. 63.

11. Lieut. Charles Henry Davis had passed on a message from Prof. Peirce to MFM. In his letter MFM extended "the civilities of the Observatory" to Peirce and through him to Harvard. He declared that when the instruments should be ready, "I shall be glad to open a broadside with you upon the stars." MFM letter cited in Note 8.

12. NR, MFM to Commodore William M. Crane, Chief, Bureau of Ordnance and Hydrography, April 17, 1845, NOLS, Vol. I, NAn.

13. The chief damage had been done when the moist air rising from the river and the flats affected the sulphur with which the base of the astronomical instruments had been fastened to their bases, and the resulting sulphurous acid started a corrosive process in the metal. However, Maury was still writing about the miasma to the Secretary of Navy as late as the fall of 1855.

14. For placement of the instruments, see MFM letter cited in Note 7.

15. J. Q. Adams, *Memoirs,* Vol. X, pp. 25, 44, 57; Vol. XI, p. 112.

16. Adams was still discussing his proposed observatory with Secretary of Treasury Spencer in March, 1843, some months after the Naval Observatory had been authorized (on Aug. 31, 1842). See entry in Adams's diary for March 10, 1843, J. Q. Adams, *Memoirs,* Vol. XI, p. 336.

17. Adams stated his opinions about the Observatory and praised MFM in his diary entry for Apr. 1, 1845; ibid., Vol. XII, p. 189.

18. Ibid. J. Q. Adams, *Memoirs,* Vol. XII, p. 189. NR, MFM to J. Q. Adams, July 28, 1846, NOLS, Vol. II, NAn.

19. J. Q. Adams, *Memoirs,* Vol. XII, p. 195.

20. MFM used this term for the Observatory at the head of many of his letters, and the press used it almost exclusively. For use of this name, see *SLM,* Vol. XIV, No. 1 (January, 1848), p. 4, *SLM,* Vol. XV, No. 5 (May, 1849), p. 304. See Note 45, this chapter, for order to stop using that term.

21. Report on Observatory in the form of a letter from MFM to J. Q. Adams cited in Note 7.

22. Ibid., p. 5.

23. Ibid.

24. Ibid., p. 4.

25. MFM and his family remained in the Pennsylvania Avenue house until July 1, 1845; NR, MFM to Mr. Adler, May 31, 1845, NOLS, Vol. I, NAn.

Birth of Mary was recorded in MFM Bible. For nickname, see Corbin, *Maury*, p. 152.

26. Ann Herndon Maury to Ann Maury of New York, May 12, 1844; MFM to Ann Maury of New York, Oct. 31, 1847, both in MC, UVAL; Corbin, *Maury*, p. 153.

27. Mary Maury Werth to her children, July 26, 1879, MP, Vol. XLII, LC.

28. Ibid.; Corbin, *Maury*, pp. 151-152.

29. On April 24, 1845, MFM wrote to several Washington contractors requesting bids from them for building a slate-roofed house with basement, two stories high, to have a "back building" and "wash house." MFM to "Builders," April 24, 1845, NR, NOLS, Vol. I, NAn.

30. This dwelling was owned by a Mr. Adler and had been rented by the late Fully Wise; MFM to Mr. Adler, May 31, 1845, NR, NOLS, Vol. I, NAn.

31. Callahan, *List of Officers*, p. 280. See also *Navy Register, 1845;* MFM letter cited in Note 7, p. 5.

32. Callahan, *List of Officers*, p. 308. See also *Navy Register, 1845;* MFM letter cited in Note 7, p. 5.

33. NR, MFM to Secretary of Navy George Bancroft, March 6, 1846; to Prof. Heinrich C. Schumacher (ed.), *Astronomische Nachrichten*, March 31, 1846, both in NOLS, Vol. II, NAn; MFM letter cited in Note 7, p. 5.

34. MFM to Ann Maury of New York, Sept. 13, 1845, MC, UVAL.

35. MFM, "The National Observatory," an address delivered by him to annual meeting of the Virginia Historical Society, Richmond, Dec. 14, 1848, in *SLM,* Vol. XV, No. 5 (May, 1849), p. 307.

36. MFM letter cited in Note 7, p. 7.

37. MFM letter cited in Note 7, pp. 7, 8.

38. Official order from Secretary of Navy Bancroft to MFM, March 6, 1846, quoted in MFM, "The National Observatory," *SLM,* Vol. XV, No. 5 (May, 1849), p. 307.

39. Bernard de Voto, *The Year of Decision, 1846,* p. 3.

40. Ibid.

41. Ibid., pp. 3-4.

42. MFM, "Duplicity of Biela's Comet," *Royal Astronomical Society Monthly Notices,* 1845-1847, Vol. VII, pp. 90-91. MFM's official reports on Biela are in his letters to Commodore Crane, Chief, Bureau of Ordnance and Hydrography, Jan. 13, Jan. 15, Jan. 19, 1846, and to Secretary of Navy Bancroft, Feb. 19, 1846. MFM also wrote an account to Prof. G. B. Airy, Astronomer Royal, Greenwich, England, Jan. 23, 1846, all in NR, NOLS, Vol. II, NAn.

43. NR, MFM to Secretary of Navy Bancroft, Feb. 19, Mar. 6, 1846, NOLS, Vol. II, NAn.

44. Ibid., July 28, 1846; Capt. J. F. Hellweg, U.S.N., address delivered in Washington 1935 when Superintendent of Naval Observatory, *Memorial Windows in the Washington Cathedral to Lieutenant Matthew Fontaine Maury . . . ,* p. 7.

45. In reply to a request from the Chief of the Bureau of Ordnance and Hydrography for an official decision upon the name of the Observatory, Secretary of Navy J. C. Dobbin wrote, "My opinion is that it should be styled 'The U.S. Naval Observatory and Hydrographical Office.' . . . It is a Navy affair and its reputation is the property of the Navy. If it assumes another

name and character the next step will be to place a civilian at its head."
See NR, Secretary Dobbin to Commodore Charles Morris, Dec. 12, 1854,
Letters to Heads of Bureaus, Dec. 2, 1853-July 8, 1861, Vol. 3, NAn.

46. Review of *Astronomical Observations: Made under the direction of M. F.
Maury, Lieut. U.S. Navy, during the year 1845, at the U.S. Naval Observatory, Washington,* in Notices of New Works, SLM, Vol. XIII, No. 4 (April,
1847), pp. 251-252; MFM to Ann Maury of New York, Sept. 13, 1845, MC,
UVAL.

47. MFM to William M. Blackford, Jan. 1, 1847, MP, Vol. III, LC.

48. MFM told Blackford of having said this to Secretary of Navy John Y.
Mason; ibid.

49. Article on Mexican War, *Columbia Encyclopedia* (1935 ed.), pp. 1162-1163;
Freeman, *Lee*, Vol. I, p. 201; sketch of President James Knox Polk, *DAB*,
Vol. XV, pp. 34-39; sketch of John Slidell, *DAB*, Vol. XVII, pp. 209-211.

50. NR, MFM to Secretary of Navy Bancroft, May 11, 1846, NOLS, Vol. II,
NAn.

51. Sketch of Dabney Herndon Maury, *DAB*, Vol. XII, p. 427; MFM to Mrs.
Kemp S. Holland, Hudsonville, Miss., Jan. 10, 1847, MP, Vol. III, LC.

52. MFM to Mrs. William Maury, Jan. 31, 1847; to Ann Maury of New York,
Sept. 30, 1847, both in MC, UVAL.

53. Sarah Mytton Maury, *The Statesmen of America in 1846* (American ed.,
1847), pp. 167-168.

54. MFM wrote Prof. Benjamin Peirce of Harvard on Jan. 26, 1846, "The
Secretary promised me today to appoint Walker. I think highly of him,"
NR, NOLS, Vol. II, NAn. MFM's first assignment of observations to
Walker; NR, MFM to Secretary of Navy Bancroft, Feb. 28, 1846, NOLS,
Vol. II, NAn; sketch of Sears Cook Walker, *DAB*, Vol. XIX, p. 359.

55. NR, MFM to Secretary of Navy Mason, Feb. 8, 18, 26, March 25, 1847,
NOLS, Vol. II, NAn.

56. John Y. Mason had been the only member of Tyler's Cabinet given a
Cabinet position by Polk when he was inaugurated President in 1845.
Mason was made Attorney General. After eighteen months in that position Mason was asked by Polk to take the Navy post for the second time
on Sept. 10, 1846.

57. By March 1, 1847, MFM had learned that Sears Walker planned to sever
his connection with the Naval Observatory. Between that date and March
11, 1847, Walker left the Observatory, apparently after an unpleasant exchange of words with MFM. Walker then circulated the story that Alexander Dallas Bache had "a message to him [Walker] from Mr. Bancroft
while Secy. of the Navy substantially offering him the Observatory." Bache
denied that he was involved in the matter. See NR, MFM to Commodore
Lewis Warrington, Chief, Bureau of Ordnance and Hydrography, Mar. 1,
1847; to Alexander Dallas Bache, Mar. 11, July 1, 1847, NOLS, Vol. II,
NAn.

58. NR, MFM to Prof. (Elias) Loomis, Union College, New York, April 20,
1847, NOLS, Vol. II, NAn.

59. Sketch of Sears Cook Walker, *DAB*, Vol. XIX, p. 359.

60. Thomas Coulson, *Joseph Henry, His Life and Work* (cited hereafter as
Coulson, *Henry*), pp. 1-181; sketch of Joseph Henry, *Encyclopaedia Britannica* (1957 ed.), Vol. XI, pp. 444-445.

61. NR, MFM to Joseph Henry, Oct. 20, 1847, NOLS, Vol. II, NAn.
62. A copy of the *Astronomische Nachrichten* article (No. 605 [August, 1847], pp. 66-79) is filed in NR, October, 1847, NOLS, Vol. II, NAn. See also copy in the compilation of 1847 issues of that journal bound as Vol. XXVI, 1848 (Altona, Germany).
63. Ibid.
64. MFM's belief that Henry's signature had been forged is in MFM letter cited in Note 61.
65. Coulson, *Henry*, pp. 4, 5, 91, 93, 106, 146, 147.
66. MFM letter cited in Note 61.
67. MFM advised Henry of this fact in his letter cited in Note 61.
68. NR, MFM to Joseph Henry, Sept. 20, 1847, NOLS, Vol. II, NAn.
69. The excerpts from Henry's reply are quoted by MFM in his reply to this letter of Oct. 11, 1847. The letters from Henry in this particular correspondence are missing in NR, Naval Observatory Letters Received (NOLR), because many of the letters received in 1847 were ruined by water, I am told by Navy Branch, National Archives officials. Similarly, Joseph Henry's letterpress or true copies of the letters he wrote MFM are missing for this period because of a fire at the Smithsonian. There is also no Joseph Henry Journal for the period. I greatly regret not being able to present Henry's letters. However, MFM's quotations from those letters are unquestionably accurate as MFM would have been precise when quoting Henry's words back to him.
70. NR, MFM to Joseph Henry, Oct. 20, 1847, NOLS, Vol. II, NAn.
71. Ibid.
72. Henry's letter of Nov. 9, 1847, is not given in full for the reasons described in Note 69. This quotation from Henry's note was made by MFM in his reply to that communication; NR, MFM to Joseph Henry, Nov. 15, 1847, NOLS, Vol. II, NAn.
73. NR, MFM letter cited in Note 72.
74. Jules Marcou, the biographer of Agassiz, said, "Bache was a rather ambitious man, full of academic distinctions and a lover of power." Jules Marcou, *Louis Agassiz*, Vol. II, p. 157. A study of Bache's personal correspondence in the Bache Papers (MS Division, LC), of Henry's letters, abstracts, and journals (in the Smithsonian Institution Archives, cited hereafter as SIA), and of the printed writings of the two scientists, reveals their jointly held belief in their mission to establish a criterion for American scientists and their determination to deny authority to those who did not meet their criterion.
75. A. D. Bache letter to Joseph Henry, Dec. 4, 1846, in Merle Middleton Odgers, *Alexander Dallas Bache* (cited hereafter as Odgers, *Bache*), p. 165.
76. This theory of Bache's and Henry's had undoubtedly been greatly strengthened by their travels in Europe, where they became acquainted with the leaders of such scientific organizations as England's Royal Society and Royal Institution; Coulson, *Henry*, p. 117.
77. [Varina Howell Davis] *Jefferson Davis, Ex-President of the Confederate States. A Memoir by His Wife* (cited hereafter as Varina Davis, *Jefferson Davis*), Vol. I, p. 260; sketch of Alexander Dallas Bache, *DAB*, Vol. I, p. 461.
78. Hudson Strode, *Jefferson Davis, American Patriot, 1808-1861* (cited here-

after as Strode, *J. Davis to 1861*), pp. 36, 154, 304-306, 308; Odgers, *Bache,* pp. 102, 152, 203.

79. Odgers, *Bache,* pp. 13-15; sketch of Alexander Dallas Bache, *DAB,* Vol. I, p. 461.
80. Sketch of Bache, *DAB,* Vol. I, p. 461; Odgers, *Bache,* p. 137.
81. Sketch of Bache, *Encyclopaedia Britannica* (1957 ed.), Vol. II, p. 876; Odgers, *Bache,* pp. 91-92.
82. Odgers, *Bache,* pp. 91-102, 130, 134.
83. Ibid., pp. 91-92, 145.
84. Gustavus A. Weber, *The Coast and Geodetic Survey, Its History, Activities and Organization, Service Monograph* (cited hereafter as Weber, *Coast Survey*), pp. 2-5; sketch of Ferdinand Rudolph Hassler, *Columbia Encyclopedia* (1935 ed.), p. 800.
85. Coulson, *Henry,* p. 106; Odgers, *Bache,* pp. 61, 137-145.
86. Odgers, *Bache,* p. 146.
87. Ibid., p. 147.
88. Ibid.; sketch of John Canfield Spencer, *Columbia Encyclopedia* (1935 ed.), p. 1669.
89. Weber, *Coast Survey,* pp. 2-7; Odgers, *Bache,* pp. 155-156.
90. NR, 27-page MS Report of MFM to Secretary of Navy William A. Graham, Oct. 7, 1850, NOLS, Vol. VI, NAn.
91. A. D. Bache to MFM, April 21, 1835, published in Maury's *Navigation* (3rd ed., 1845), p. 337.
92. NR, MFM to A. D. Bache, Mar. 6, July 28, 1846, June 8, 1847, NOLS, Vol. II, NAn.
93. See letter signed "A" to A. D. Bache, June 4, 1858, in Bache Papers, Letters Received—1858, LC.
94. A. D. Bache and his wife, who were childless, adopted a six-year-old boy after Lieut. George M. Bache was washed overboard from the surveying brig *Washington* off Nag's Head, N.C., Sept. 8, 1846. See Callahan, *List of Officers,* p. 33.
95. Bache was successful in winning personal loyalty from many—Sears Cook Walker, Charles Henry Davis, Jefferson Davis, and Bache's coterie of friends, whom Merle Odgers speaks of as his "cronies." See Odgers, *Bache,* p. 204.
96. The letters of Bache to Henry are filled with veiled allusions. For this habit of Bache's and his scornful attitude, see especially his letters in The Dudley Observatory Book, Bache Papers, LC.
97. Henry acknowledged one such letter from Bache: "I do not like the expression in your letter relative to the separation which the enemy may make in our ranks." Joseph Henry to A. D. Bache, Oct. 18, 1858, SIA.
98. James Ferguson, former assistant in the Coast Survey, to Freeman Hunt, editor, Hunt's *Merchants' Magazine,* Vol. XX, No. 6 (June, 1849), p. 595.
99. Joseph Henry to A. D. Bache, Oct. 25, 1851, Jan. 12, 1859, SIA.
100. This emphasis is to be found in many of Bache's writings. See *Address of Professor Alexander Dallas Bache, President of the American Association* [for the Advancement of Science] *for the Year 1851, on Retiring from the Duties of President* (cited hereafter as *Bache Address,* AAAS, 1851), reprinted from *Proceedings, American Association for the Advancement of Science, 6th meeting held at Albany* [N.Y.], *August, 1851,* pp. xli-lx.

101. "The labors of his office were so onerous that Henry found it impossible to continue his researches in pure science." Sketch of Joseph Henry, *DAB*, Vol. VIII, p. 553. See also Odgers, *Bache*, pp. 164-165; Coulson, *Henry*, p. 251; sketch of Joseph Henry, *Columbia Encyclopedia* (1935 ed.), p. 817.

102. Franklin left school at ten years of age, and was apprenticed in a printing shop at twelve. Despite his lack of a formal education, Benjamin Franklin became a learned man through a rigorous program of self-education. See sketch of Benjamin Franklin, *Columbia Encyclopedia* (1935 ed.), p. 660.

103. Albany Academy emphasized mathematics and science, while Harpeth Academy emphasized a classical education. The course of studies at Albany is given in a pamphlet, *The Celebration of the Centennial of the Albany Academy*, May, 1913, p. 18.

104. The Georgetown College Observatory, built from private donations, was completed in 1844. Some of the astronomical instruments had been ordered from Europe. "Professor, the Reverend James Curley" was in charge. The Depot of Charts and Instruments and Georgetown College Observatory were the "International and Domestic Exchanges" for scientific information in Washington in 1844; Brent, *Letters on Nat. Institute*, pp. 60, 56.

105. MFM, *Address before the Philodemic Society, Georgetown College, Washington, D.C., Aug. 28, 1846, at the commencement.* See also MFM to Ann Maury of New York, July 9, 1846, to Mrs. William Maury, July 17, 1846, both in MC, UVAL.

106. Polk and Mason, both UNC graduates, had received honorary degrees in 1845. Thomas J. Wilson, Jr., Registrar, Univ. of North Carolina, to Charles Lee Lewis, Feb. 14, 1922, Tennessee Historical Society papers, TSLA; William S. Powell, Librarian, North Carolina Collection, Univ. of North Carolina Library, to George D. Griffin, Nov. 1, 1962; Archibald Henderson, *The Campus of the First State University*, pp. 92-93.

107. James Russell Soley, *Historical Sketch of the United States Naval Academy*, pp. 1-20.

108. A. F. Maury, *Virginiana*, p. 322.

109. Corbin, *Maury*, p. 152.

110. MFM to William M. Blackford, July 12, 1847, MP, Vol. III, LC; to Ann Maury of New York, Sept. 30, Oct. 31, 1847, MC, UVAL.

111. MFM to Mrs. William Maury, July 23, 1847, MC, UVAL.

112. Ibid.; MFM to Ann Maury of New York, July 23, April 6, 1847, MC, UVAL.

113. NR, MFM to Professor (Elias) Loomis, Union College, Apr. 20, 1847, NOLS, Vol. II, NAn.

114. This problem was a leading reason for the fact that the *Astronomical Observations made under the direction of M. F. Maury, Lt. U.S. Navy, during the year 1846, at the National Observatory* (Vol. II of observations) was not published until 1851; and the observations made in 1847 were not published until 1853.

115. MFM letter cited in Note 7, p. 7.

116. Ibid., p. 8.

117. NR, MFM to George Bancroft, Minister to the Court of St. James's, Nov. 1, 1847, NOLS, Vol. II, NAn.

CHAPTER X

Charting the Winds and Currents of the Sea

1. Commodore William B. Whiting to Capt. John M. Brooke, May 31, 1873, MP, Vol. XLIV, LC. The quotations are from MFM to John Quincy Adams, Nov. 14, 1847, *SLM*, Vol. XIV, No. 1 (January, 1848), pp. 9-10.

2. Maury's *Explanations and Sailing Directions to Accompany the Wind and Current Charts* (cited hereafter as MFM, *Sailing Directions*) (4th ed., 1852), p. 41. Also see letter of William B. Whiting cited in Note 1.

3. MFM, *The Physical Geography of the Sea* (1st ed., 1855), introduction, pp. ix-xi; MFM, *Sailing Directions* (4th ed., 1852), pp. 304-305; MFM to Ann Maury of New York, Jan. 21, 1848, MC, UVAL; to Mrs. William Maury, Jan. 22, 1848, MP, Vol. III, LC.

4. MFM, "The Routes to Rio" and "Comparison of passages by old and new route," MFM, *Sailing Directions* (4th ed., 1852), pp. 288-291, 306. The quotation is from account of MFM's work written by Gen. Francis H. Smith but unsigned, *Proceedings Academic Board of the Virginia Military Institute, Lexington, Virginia, on the occasion of the death of Commodore Matthew Fontaine Maury, LL.D., Professor of Physics, V.M.I.* (cited hereafter as *V.M.I. In Memoriam*), p. 15.

5. Ibid., p. 14; NR, MFM to Secretary of Navy Isaac Toucey, Oct. 29, 1858, NOLS, Vol. XVI, NAn; MFM to Matthew Maury of New York, July 14, 1848, MC, UVAL.

6. MFM, *Sailing Directions* (4th ed., 1852), pp. 41-42; John Lyman, Lieut. Commander, U.S.N.R., Inactive, "The Centennial of Pressure-Pattern Navigation," *USNIP*, March, 1948, Vol. 74, No. 54 (cited hereafter as Lyman, *Navigation, USNIP*), p. 310.

7. Baltimore *American*, May 18, 1848, editorial page.

8. MFM, *Sailing Directions* (4th ed., 1852), p. 42; MFM, "On the Winds and Currents of the Ocean," *Proceedings, AAAS,* 1848, pp. 64-68.

9. Explaining the use of the abstract logs, MFM wrote: "It is the custom to keep a log-book on board of every ship, and to enter in that log-book remarks and observations upon the winds, the weather, and the sea; and all that is requisite to impart a new and a greater value to these observations, is that they should be made all at the same time, recorded in a stated journal—the 'abstract log' kept for the purpose—and then be made available by being returned to the office [Naval Observatory] appointed to receive them." MFM, *Sailing Directions* (4th ed., 1852), p. 19. Also see sample pages of abstract log in same book, pp. 412-413.

   See: *"Abstract Log for the Use of American Navigators.* By Lt. M. F. Maury, U.S.N., superintendent, National Observatory, Washington, C. Alexander, printer, 1848." A second edition with some changes was printed the same year, and a reprint of that issued in 1849.

10. "Navigators who are disposed to try these routes should have the 'Pilot Charts' on board, which 'Pilot Charts' will be furnished to them on application either at the National Observatory, at Washington, or to George Manning, no. 142 Pearl Street, New York, provided the applicant will agree to furnish this office an abstract of his log according to the form with which he will also be gratuitously supplied. . . ." From "Notice to

Mariners," issued Dec. 14, 1849, reprinted in MFM, *Sailing Directions* (4th ed., 1852), pp. 289-291.

See: "Conditions on which charts are furnished to Navigators" and "Receipt," including promise to keep abstract log that had to be signed by a captain; MFM, *Sailing Directions* (4th ed., 1852), p. 411.

11. The quotation is the explanatory note printed on: Sheets Nos. 2 and 3, Wind and Current Charts of the North Atlantic, by M. F. Maury, A.M., Lieut., U.S. Navy, Superintendent of the U.S. Naval Observatory, Washington, compiled from materials in the Bureau of Ordnance and Hydrography, Commodore Lewis Warrington, Chief of Bureau. These sheets published in 1848 followed sheet No. 1 published in 1847. A complete set of MFM's *Wind and Current Charts* is in the U.S. Naval Oceanographic Office, Suitland, Md.

12. For a study of the development of the clipper ship, see Octavius T. Howe and Frederick C. Matthews, *American Clipper Ships, 1833-1858,* Vol. I, pp. v-vii.

13. Björn Landström, *The Ship, An Illustrated History,* pp. 196-197.

14. MFM to William M. Blackford, July 17, 1848, MP, Vol. III, LC.

15. MFM, *Sailing Directions* (4th ed., 1852), p. 305. As late as 1854, MFM was writing, "My observations have impressed me with the notion that navigators are very slow to give up old works for new." NR, MFM to Lieut. S. Phillips Lee, Nov. 20, 1854, NOLS, Vol. XI, NAn. The quotation is from a conversation with a midshipman repeated in letter of MFM to Ann Maury of New York, Apr. 19, 1848, MC, UVAL.

16. MFM to Matthew Maury, July 14, 1848, MC, UVAL.

17. First quotation, ibid. Second quotation is from MFM to Mrs. William Maury, Liverpool, England, Jan. 22, 1848, MP, Vol. III, LC.

18. Lord Wrottesley (Sir John Wrottesley prior to 1841, when he succeeded to his father's baronetcy), speech in the House of Lords, British Parliament, April 26, 1853, Hansard's *Parliamentary Debates,* Ser. 3, Vol. CXXVI (cited hereafter as Wrottesley, *Hansard,* Ser. 3, CXXVI), cols. 526-527. See also cols. 522-539.

19. "The charts are going ahead bravely. They are quite as much admired on the other side as on this and they do turn out exceedingly rich." MFM to William M. Blackford, Mar. 12, 1849, MP, Vol. III, LC. Roscoe-Freeman, *Pictorial U.S.N.,* pp. 453, 484; MFM to Ann Maury of New York, June 10, 1848, MC, UVAL.

20. Annual Report of the Secretary of Navy, 1847, p. 12.

21. MFM to Ann Maury of New York, April 19, 1848, MC, UVAL.

22. Ibid., Aug. 25, 1848.

23. Writing about the charts, MFM declared, "I am very much encouraged in this undertaking by [Robert Bennett] Forbes of Boston who has taken the matter up in good earnest and who is pouring tracks in upon me." MFM to Rutson Maury, March 17, 1848, MC, UVAL. Captain Forbes copied for MFM the logbooks of ships that had sailed out of Boston or Salem to the Orient or those that had cruised widely in the Pacific, later delegating the copying of journals of Salem ships to A. H. Bancroft, L. Heflin, Lieut., U.S.N. "Comments and Notes," *USNIP,* Vol. LXXIV, No. 6, Whole No. 544 (June, 1948), p. 759.

24. MFM reported this development in full to William M. Blackford, who

had left the U.S. diplomatic service and become a newspaper editor in Lynchburg, Va.; MFM letter, July 17, 1848, MP, Vol. III, LC.

25. Ibid.

26. MFM never forgot the troubles politicians had caused Commodore Thomas ap Catesby Jones while commander of the Exploring Expedition.

27. Sarah Mytton Maury, *Statesmen of America in 1846,* p. 167; MFM to Mrs. William Maury, July 17, 1846, MC, UVAL.

28. MFM to John C. Calhoun, March 29, 1848, on the best route for a railroad to the Pacific coast; DeBow's *Review,* Vol. VI, No. 3 (September, 1848), pp. 205-214.

29. MFM letter cited in Note 27. MFM secured an appointment for John M. Maury, son of the former Navy Register Richard B. Maury, as third assistant engineer, March 23, 1848; Callahan, *List of Officers,* p. 357.

30. MFM to William M. Blackford, Jan. 1, 1847, MP, Vol. III, LC.

31. MFM to Ann Maury of New York, Jan. 29, 1849. For help to other young men, ibid., Oct. 10, 1841, Dec. 6, 1843, July 27, Aug. 12, 1844, Sept. 30, 1847, Feb. 9, 1851, all in MC, UVAL.

32. "The Wind and Current Charts come on famously, as rich as famous. I find that tracks of vessels at sea are full of meaning." MFM to Ann Maury of New York, Apr. 19, 1848, MC, UVAL. While merchant captains had not responded to the circular issued in 1842 (only one direct response and that in 1851), MFM did receive track charts from shipowners through the Maurys of New York and directly from owners such as R. B. Forbes of Boston (see MFM letter, Note 23), and Robert Clinton Wright of Baltimore (see NR, MFM to Robert Clinton Wright, May [n.d.], 1848, NOLS, Vol. III, NAn). Captains of men-of-war sent the major portion of the information needed to MFM up until 1851.

33. In the name of the AAAS, "promotion" was first used and later "advancement" was substituted; Address to the AAAS, 48th annual meeting, 1899, in Marcus Benjamin, *The Early Presidents of the American Association,* p. 274.

34. Ibid., p. 4; Jaffe, *Men of Science,* p. 201.

35. MFM, Report, *Proceedings, AAAS, First Meeting,* pp. 64-67. Quotations are from p. 67.

36. *Proceedings, AAAS, First Meeting,* p. 67.

37. Ibid. Sketch of William Barton Rodgers, *DAB,* Vol. XVI, p. 115.

38. *Proceedings, AAAS, First Meeting,* p. 7. For success of work of this committee, see MFM, *Sailing Explanations* (4th ed., 1852), p. 41.

39. Lynch did not return to the United States until some time after publication of MFM's article for which he had supplied the facts from the Holy Land. For the story of this naval exploration, see William Francis Lynch, Lieut. Commanding, *U.S. Expedition to the River Jordan and the Dead Sea;* also MFM, "Dead Sea Expedition," SLM, Vol. XIV, No. 9 (September, 1848), pp. 547-553.

40. MFM, "The Track Charts," "The Trade Wind Charts," "The Pilot Charts," MFM, *Sailing Directions* (4th ed., 1852), respectively pp. 217-218, 218-230, 193-198.

41. Jaffe, *Men of Science,* p. 217.

42. MFM, "Thermal Charts," MFM, *Sailing Directions* (4th ed., 1852), pp. 198-216.

The Wind and Current Charts, Series E, Storm and Rain Charts, were published somewhat later—Atlantic Ocean, North, 1853; Atlantic Ocean, South, 1854; Pacific Ocean, North, Sheet 1, 1860; Pacific Ocean, South, not issued, probably because of outbreak of the Civil War.

43. MFM to William M. Blackford, March 12, 1849, MP, Vol. III, LC.

44. Convinced of his obligation to gain knowledge and use it for mankind, MFM was proud of being a practical scientist and laughed off criticism on this point. On March 12, 1849, he wrote William M. Blackford, "Lewis Herndon has the whales in hand. That chart will be of such practical importance to the whale men that they might well afford to give us a perpetual say [?] in all their ships." Ibid. See MFM, "The Whale Charts," "Letters from Whalemen," MFM, *Sailing Directions,* respectively pp. 234-236, 237, 239. See also NR, MFM to Prof. Louis Agassiz, Harvard College, April 30, 1852, NOLS, Vol. VIII, NAn; to Prof. S. F. Baird, Smithsonian Institution, Oct. 29, 1853, NOLS, Vol. X, NAn.

45. In addition to other scientific works, Alexander von Humboldt (1769-1859) wrote *Kosmos,* a five-volume description of the physical universe, considered "one of the world's greatest scientific writings." *Columbia Encyclopedia* (1935 ed.), p. 859.

46. MFM to Baron Alexander von Humboldt, Sept. 6, 1849, MP, Vol. III, LC.

47. Sketch of Robert John LeM. McClure (1807-1873), *Columbia Encyclopedia* (1935 ed.), p. 1085. See MFM, "The Open Sea in the Arctic Ocean," in *Physical Geography of the Sea* (1st ed., 1855), pp. 146-147.

48. MFM to Mrs. William Maury, Mar. 22, 1848, MP, Vol. III, LC.

49. Family records, MFM Bible.

50. "The mania for California gold rages here." MFM to Ann Maury of New York, Jan. 29, 1849, MP, Vol. III, LC. Also see MFM, "The California Passage," in *Sailing Directions* (4th ed., 1852), pp. 368-370.

51. Act of March 3, 1849 [Naval Appropriations Bill], Sec. 2, 31st Cong., 1st Sess., U.S. Statutes at Large, Vol. IX, p. 378.

52. MFM applied repeatedly to have assigned either all three ships that had been authorized or two, but he never persuaded the Navy Department to order more than one small ship at a time on this duty. See MFM to Secretary of Navy, Senate Exec. Doc. No. 1, 32nd Cong., 1st Sess., pp. 60-61.

53. NR, MFM to J. C. Walsh, Lieut. Commanding, U.S. Schooner *Taney,* Oct. 1, 1849, NOLS, Vol. IV, NAn. See also MFM, "The Cruise of the Taney," in *Sailing Directions* (4th ed., 1852), pp. 125-127.

54. MFM, "The Isthmus Line to the Pacific," *SLM,* Vol. XIV, No. 5 (May, 1849), pp. 441-457. MFM letter opposing the Tehuantepec Railroad, Mexico, as unwise compared to railroad across Isthmus of Panama, was published in DeBow's *Review,* Vol. VII, No. 1 (July, 1849), pp. 16-17. Also see MFM, "Panama Railway and the Gulf of Mexico," *SLM,* Vol. XV, No. 8 (August, 1849), pp. 441-457.

55. The Memphis Convention, which convened Oct. 23, 1849, was one of the large economic conventions held in that period. See MFM in *National Intelligencer,* Nov. 4, 1849, p. 3, and MFM to William M. Blackford, Sept. 20, Nov. 20, 1849, MP, Vol. III, LC. Dabney H. Maury's story of MFM's refusing the money is quoted in Corbin, *Maury,* pp. 104-105.

56. *Proceedings, AAAS, Third Meeting, 1850,* pp. 17-20, 53, 74-80, 126-147.

57. MFM report to Secretary of Navy William A. Graham, in *Annual Report of the Secretary of Navy for 1851,* pp. 13, 61.
58. Abstract Log of the *Flying Cloud,* J. P. Creesy, New York to San Francisco, June 2-Aug. 30, 1851, in MFM, *Sailing Directions* (4th ed., 1852), pp. 380-384; account of passage, MFM, *Physical Geography of the Sea* (1st ed., 1855), p. 263.
59. MFM, *Sailing Directions* (4th ed., 1852), p. 386; (6th ed., 1854), p. 710. Octavius T. Howe, M.D., and Frederick C. Matthews, *American Clipper Ships, 1833-1858,* Vol. II, pp. 507, 570; see also facts on other clippers using MFM Wind and Current Charts, Vol. I, pp. 98, 306; Vol. II, pp. 540, 595, 597, 598, 639.
60. MFM, *Physical Geography of the Sea* (1st ed., 1855), p. 263.
61. Ibid., pp. 263-266.
62. MFM described this race from the abstract logs and reports sent him by each of the captains. The abstract log of the *John Gilpin* ended when the pilot came on board and so that time was cited by him. See MFM, *Physical Geography of the Sea* (1st ed., 1855), pp. 263-269, quotation is from p. 269. See also MFM, *Sailing Directions* (6th ed., 1854), pp. 724-730.
63. MFM, *Physical Geography of the Sea* (1st ed., 1855), p. 270.
64. NR, MFM to Secretary of Navy James C. Dobbin, May 9, 1853, NOLS, Vol. IX, NAn. After reporting the passage of the *Flying Cloud* in 89 days from New York to San Francisco, N. L. Canfield continued: "But the utility of Maury's 'directions' was better shown by the consistency with which fast passages were made. Eighteen separate voyages required less than 100 days, though the average of the clippers was somewhat greater." *Weather and the Navigation of the Sea,* reprinted from *Weekly Weather and Crop Bulletin,* National Summary of Jan. 9, 1956.
65. Columbus O'Donnell Iselin, (then) Director of the Woods Hole Oceanographic Institution, *Matthew Fontaine Maury (1806-1873), "Pathfinder of the Seas," The Development of Oceanography,* Address to the Newcomen Society in North America, Falmouth, Mass., June 6, 1957 (cited hereafter as Iselin, *Maury*), p. 8; MFM, *Sailing Directions* (6th ed., 1854), p. 730.
    Observations required were listed in ten pages of instructions, *Abstract Log for the Use of American Navigators* (1848), predecessor of MFM, *Sailing Instructions.*
66. NR, MFM to Commodore William M. Crane, Chief, Bureau of Ordnance and Hydrography, Nov. 19, 1851, NOLS, Vol. VII, NAn; or see MFM, *Sailing Directions* (4th ed., 1852), p. 19.
67. Letter of Capt. Phinney to MFM, Jan. (n.d.), 1855, in MFM, *Physical Geography of the Sea* (8th Amer. ed., 1861), pp. xii-xiii.
68. NR, MFM to Commodore Charles Morris, Chief, Bureau of Ordnance and Hydrography, Jan. 12, 1853, NOLS, Vol. VIII, NAn.
69. MFM, *Physical Geography of the Sea* (1st ed., 1855), pp. 57-58; Corbin, *Maury,* p. 57.
70. NR, MFM to Capt. F. W. Beechey, Royal Navy (cited hereafter as R.N.), Board of Trade, London, and to Adolphe Quetelet, Astronomer Royal, Brussels, both Jan. 17, 1853, NOLS, Vol. VIII, NAn.
71. MFM, *Sailing Directions* (8th ed.), Vol. II (1859), pp. 585-605; see also pp. 605-678; MFM, *Physical Geography of the Sea* (8th ed., 1861), p. 358.
72. MFM, *Physical Geography of the Sea* (1st ed., 1855), pp. vii, viii, and viii,

fn.; Sir John Pakington, First Lord of the Admiralty, speech at a dinner to honor MFM, June 5, 1866, Willis Rooms, London, in Corbin, *Maury*, p. 57.

73. Inaugural Address of the Earl of Harrowby, President of the British Association [for the Advancement of Science], Liverpool, 1854, *Proceedings of the British Association, 24th Meeting, 1854;* see also *Annual Report of the (U.S.) Secretary of the Navy, 1854,* pp. 401-402.

74. Senate Rep. No. 443, Ser. 775, Vol. I, Report of Senate Naval Affairs Committee to accompany Senate Bill 657, 33rd Cong., 2nd Sess.

75. The calculation of annual saving to the United States was published in Hunt's *Merchants' Magazine,* Vol. XXX, No. 5 (May, 1854), reprinted in MFM, *Physical Geography of the Sea* (1st ed., 1855), p. viii, fn.

For MFM's appreciation of gifts, see NR, MFM to Messrs. Walter P. Jones, W. H. Aspinwall, Edwin Bartlett, R. C. Minturn, Sidney Brookes et al., Merchants and Underwriters of New York, July 14, 1853, NOLS, Vol. IX, NAn.

76. For examples of MFM's acceptance of criticism and statement that he was constantly recasting and trying to improve the charts, see NR, MFM to Prof. Elias Loomis, New York Univ., Nov. 22, 1859; to Lieut. Edouard Vaneechout, French Navy, Martinique, March 12, 1860, NOLS, Vol. XVII, NAn.

77. MFM, *Sailing Directions* (8th ed., 1858), p. iii.

78. MFM believed that the Gulf Stream, "as well as all the *constant* currents of the sea, is due *mainly* to the constant difference produced by temperature and saltness in the specific gravity of water in certain parts of the ocean." He stated that these agents "reach from the equators to the poles" but "are not the *sole* cause of currents. The winds *help* to make currents . . . so do the rains . . . and so does the atmosphere." (MFM's italics) MFM, *Physical Geography of the Sea* (8th U.S. ed., 1861), p. 20. For MFM's refutation of Sir John Herschel's theory, ibid., pp. 20-48. For Herschel's statement of the trade winds as cause of the Gulf Stream and his denial of MFM's theory of the cause of the great *constant* currents of the sea, see Herschel's article, "Physical Geography," signed J.F.W.H., *Encyclopaedia Britannica* (8th ed., 1859), Vol. VII, pp. 569-642, but especially pp. 577-579. The criticism is easier read in abstracted form in MFM, *Physical Geography of the Sea* (8th U.S. ed., 1861), pp. 22, 23, 29 footnotes. The quotation is from editorial on MFM, New York *Herald,* Feb. 3, 1873, p. 6.

79. For Sir Charles Lyell's denial of MFM's theory that an under-current flowed out from the Mediterranean and returned to the Atlantic the large amount of salt carried into the Mediterranean by a surface current flowing from the Atlantic into the Mediterranean, and for MFM's refutation of Lyell's theory, see MFM, *Physical Geography of the Sea* (8th U.S. ed., 1861), pp. 182-188. "His [MFM's] views of submarine circulation once so steadily opposed by Sir Charles Lyell, have been verified by the late and extensive deep sea and surface current observations of Carpenter, Thomson and others, while his reasoning in favor of an open polar sea so warmly espoused by Petermann, Bent, Von Middendorf and other living geographers, has rather been confirmed than invalidated by the latest Arctic explorations." New York *Herald,* February 3, 1873, p. 6.

80. The statement of the hydrographer-meteorologist chief of the Board of

Trade, Vice-Admiral Fitzroy, R.N., is found in reprint of a British article, *Eclectic Magazine of Foreign Literature, Science and Art,* New Series, Vol. XVIII, No. 1 (July, 1873), p. 116. See especially Marin H. Jansen, "The Gulf Stream," *Ocean Highways: Geographical Review* (London), Vol. I, No. 3, pp. 98-101.

81. Lyman, *Navigation, USNIP,* pp. 311-312.

82. MFM was awarded a medal of honor for the Wind and Current Charts exhibited at the Paris Universal Exhibition of 1855. Concerning the display, Alexandre Vattemare wrote to MFM: "The charts were placed under my care in the scientific department formed by me in the Palace of Industry . . . and while I was showing them to the Sovereigns of France and England, the Emperor exclaimed, 'Is it possible that such a work could have been undertaken and enacted by one man?' and her Majesty [Victoria], expressing her gratification to the Emperor thanked him for the opportunity offered to her of seeing these wonderful charts." Letter of Alexandre Vattemare, Jan. 26, 1856, MP, Vol. V, LC. See complete collection of Pilot Charts, U.S. Naval Oceanographic Office.

CHAPTER XI

For Scientific Co-operation Between Nations

1. MFM rarely made any reference in his letters to the social functions he attended. He mentioned one dinner given by the British Minister, John F. Crampton, because there he met Sir Charles Lyell, whose scientific work he esteemed. On file is one invitation to a reception given by the President typical of many attended by MFM, NR, Dec. 30, 1858, NOLS, Vol. XVI, NAn. Joseph Henry, Secretary of the Smithsonian Institution, recorded in his Journal on Jan. 24, 1852, "Saw Maury at the supper of the Secretary of War. . . ." For an account of seeing Maury at various entertainments at the home of Justice Campbell of the Supreme Court, see [Mrs. Virginia Clay-Clopton], Ada Sterling (ed.), *A Belle of the Fifties, Memoirs of Mrs. Clay of Alabama* (hereafter cited as *Memoirs of Mrs. Clay*), p. 76. MFM wrote, "I enjoy the family circle and my leisure so much, I never feel like going out and when I have to go, the going is an endurance." Letter to Ann Maury of New York, Dec. 1, 1854, MC, UVAL.

2. The Tennessee delegation brought Maury's ideas to the attention of Congress on numerous occasions. For examples, see House Doc. No. 33, Ser. 408, 28th Cong., 1st Sess., Vol. III, pp. 20-48; extract from treatise by Lieut. Maury on subject of a Western depot and armory and touching generally the maritime interests of the South and West, House Rep. No. 120, Ser. 488, 28th Cong., 1st Sess., Report from House Committee on Naval Affairs, Jan. 31, 1844, *Concerning Building a Naval Depot at Memphis.* For his recommending reclaiming the "drowned lands" of the Mississippi Valley, see MFM to William M. Blackford, July 17, 1848, MP, Vol. III, LC.

3. A Virginia-Tennessee railroad and direct trade between Europe and Southern ports were among the subjects MFM discussed with Virginia congressmen. See MFM, "To Congress and the Memphis Convention. Maritime Interests of the South and the West," *SLM,* Vol. XI, No. 11 (November,

1845), pp. 651-661; MFM, *The Commercial Prospects of the South,* Address to the Virginia Mercantile Convention, Sept. 10-11, 1851; MFM, "Extending Commerce of South and West," *DeBow's Review,* Vol. XII, No. 4 (April, 1852), pp. 381-399.

4. John Walker Maury succeeded General John P. Van Ness as president of the Bank of the Metropolis (later the National Metropolitan Bank), founded in 1814. He was elected to the Common Council in 1835 and served on that body (with the exception of 1840, when he declined to be a candidate) until elected an alderman. He was elected mayor in 1852 and served until 1854; Wilhelmus B. Bryan, *A History of the National Capital,* Vol. II, pp. 404, 426.

5. William A. Maury, *John Walker Maury—His Lineage and Life,* pp. 13-14.

6. John Walker Maury had been an active member of the National Institute. Subsequent to Walker's death MFM, when president of the National Institute, in April, 1856, formed a Committee of Three composed of himself, Dr. Gale of the Patent Office, and W. W. Corcoran to put the Washington scientific organization on "a proper footing."

7. MFM to B. Franklin Minor, Nov. 24, 1855, MP, Vol. V, LC; Corbin, *Maury,* p. 148.

8. Corbin, *Maury,* p. 149.

9. MFM to B. Franklin Minor, Nov. 20, 1855, MP, Vol. V, LC.

10. Ibid.; Corbin, *Maury,* p. 150.

11. Sketch of William Ballard Preston, *DAB,* Vol. XV, pp. 206-207.

12. William A. Graham was Governor of North Carolina in 1847, when MFM received an honorary degree from the Univ. of North Carolina. On that occasion, Secretary of Navy John Y. Mason introduced MFM to Graham. Graham and Mason were, in MFM's opinion, the two secretaries of the Navy who did most to make possible his scientific achievements. For facts on MFM's role in planning the Herndon-Gibbon exploration of the Amazon, see NR, statement of MFM, Apr. 17, 1856, NOLS, Vol. XIII, NAn; MFM to Capt. William F. Lynch, U.S.N., June 17, 1852, NOLS, Vol. VIII, NAn.

13. MFM, *Valley of the Amazon and the Atlantic Slopes of South America* (cited hereafter as MFM, *Valley of Amazon*), p. 22; William Lewis Herndon, Hamilton Basso (ed. of modern abridged edition), *Exploration of the Valley of the Amazon* (cited hereafter as Basso-Herndon, *Exploration of Amazon*), p. xvi.

14. MFM, *Valley of Amazon,* p. 22; William Lewis Herndon, *Exploration of the Valley of the Amazon,* Vol. I, pp. 10-37.

15. Under Navy Department orders of Oct. 30, 1850, Herndon reached Lima, Feb. 6, 1851, and was joined there on April 4 by Lardner. Under Navy Department orders of Feb. 15, 1851, they left Lima together on May 21, 1851, for the first portion of the journey; *Exploration of the Valley of the Amazon,* Vol. I, pp. 10-44.

16. "Inca" (MFM), "The Amazon and the Atlantic Slopes" (letters), published in the *National Intelligencer,* No. 1 Nov. 17, No. 2 Nov. 19, Nos. 3 and 4 Nov. 27, No. 5 Nov. 29, No. 6 Dec. 1, and No. 7 Dec. 3, 1852.

17. This pamphlet, published by Franck Taylor, not Frank or French Taylor as often stated, announced that it was "A Series of Letters Published by the *National Intelligencer* and *Union* Newspapers under the signature of

'Inca.'" I found the letters only in the *National Intelligencer*. Title of pamphlet on cover is *Valley of the Amazon*, while title on title page is *The Amazon and the Atlantic Slopes of South America;* see citation of same in Note 13 as MFM, *Valley of Amazon*.

18. For a comprehensive discussion of effect on Brazilians, see Percy Alvin Martin, *The Influence of the United States on the opening of the Amazon to the World's Commerce*, read before the Pacific Coast branch of the American Historical Association, 1917, and by title to meeting of American Historical Association, Philadelphia, Dec. 29, 1917. Reprinted from *Hispanic American Historical Review*, Vol. I, No. 2 (May, 1918).

19. NR, MFM to J. Randolph Clay, U.S. Minister to Republic of Peru, March 15, 1853, NOLS, Vol. IX, NAn. For a readable abridged version of Herndon's account of the trip, see Basso-Herndon, *Exploration of Amazon*. For decision to separate and make two explorations, see William Lewis Herndon, *Exploration of the Valley of the Amazon*, Vol. I, p. 94.

20. Herndon was thirty-eight when he made the trip. Gibbon was in his early twenties, having been a passed midshipman on duty with MFM at the Observatory when ordered to South America for the exploration. On March 15, 1853, MFM wrote, "Gibbon is at my house well, Herndon ill." MFM letter cited in Note 19. The quotation is from MFM, *Valley of Amazon*, p. 22.

21. William Lewis Herndon, journal entry, quoted in MFM, *Valley of Amazon*, p. 34.

22. Herndon's report was sent to Secretary of Navy John P. Kennedy, Jan. 26, 1851, and to Congress on Feb. 10. On March 3, 1853, the Senate ordered 10,000 additional copies printed. Herndon's account was published in 1853 as Senate Exec. Doc. No. 36, 32nd Cong., 2nd Sess., *Exploration of the Valley of the Amazon*, Vol. I.

23. Lardner Gibbon's account of his exploration was published in 1854 as House Exec. Doc. No. 53, 33rd Cong., 1st Sess., *Exploration of the Valley of the Amazon*, Vol. II.

24. "Inca" (MFM), "Shall the Valleys of the Amazon and Mississippi Reciprocate Trade?" *DeBow's Review*, Vol. XIV, No. 2 (February, 1853), pp. 136-145; "Valley of the Amazon" (No. 1), *DeBow's Review*, Vol. XIV, No. 5 (May, 1853), pp. 449-460; "Valley of the Amazon" (No. 2), *DeBow's Review*, Vol. XIV, No. 6 (June, 1853), pp. 556-567; "Valley of the Amazon" (No. 3), *DeBow's Review*, Vol. XV, No. 1 (July, 1853), pp. 36-43. MFM, under the pseudonym "Manco-Capac" (first of the Incas), was author of *El rio Amazonas y las comarcas que forman su hoya vertientes hacia el Atlantica*, a 68-page booklet published in Lima, Peru. For statement about Humboldt, see MFM, *Valley of Amazon*, p. 22.

25. Booklet of 41 pages about MFM's efforts for free navigation, *Maury on South America and Amazonia*, reprint of an article signed "H" in *Southern Quarterly Review*, October, 1853, p. 11. The author of this work was very critical of MFM's earlier proposal that the surplus of slaves that would eventually become a problem in the United States be sold to Brazilians for development of Amazonia. "H" was opposed because he felt MFM was working toward gradual elimination of slavery in the United States. See earlier "safety valve" proposal in MFM, "The Commercial Prospects of

the South," *SLM,* Vol. XVII, Nos. 10 and 11 (October-November, 1851), pp. 686-698.

26. MFM to William M. Blackford, Sept. 20, 1852, MP, Vol. IV, LC.

27. From November, 1851, to September, 1852, Brazil was represented in Washington by Luis Pereira Sodre, who was chargé d'affaires. He was succeeded in September, 1852, by Francisco Ignacio de Carvalho Moreira in the rank of minister; memorandum of information by Mrs. Margarette de Andrade, sent me by Mrs. Fowler Wahl, both of Brazilian Embassy, Washington, Jan. 8, 1962.

28. House Misc. Docs., No. 22, Ser. 741, Vol. I, *Free Navigation of the Amazon River, Memorial of Lt. Maury in behalf of the Memphis Convention in favor of free navigation of the Amazon,* 33rd Cong., 1st Sess.; this is MFM's 31-page memorial presented to Congress in February, 1854. House Rep. No. 95, Ser. 808, Vol. I, Report by Representative Ingersoll, Feb. 23, 1855, on *Memorial of Lt. M. F. Maury in behalf of Memphis Convention and favoring free navigation of Amazon.*

29. "H," *Maury on South America and Amazonia,* pp. 16-17.

30. Ibid., pp. 19, 29.

31. Joaquim Nabuco, *Um Estadista Do Imperio, Nabucio De Aranjo,* by his son, Vol. III, p. 12; see also Pedro de Angelis, *De la navegación del Amazonas. Respuesta á una memoria de M. Maury*—Reimpreso . . . 1857.

32. Basso-Herndon, *Exploration of Amazon,* p. xix.

33. MFM letter cited in Note 19. Thomas Jefferson Page described three years of rigorous duty at the Observatory under MFM and his subsequent exploration of the La Plata in "Autobiographical Sketch of Thomas Jefferson Page," submitted by Commander R. S. Crenshaw, *USNIP,* Vol. 49, No. 248 (October, 1923), pp. 1672, 1687-1690; Page's report in *Annual Report of the Secretary of the Navy for 1856,* pp. 430-465; sketch of Thomas Jefferson Page, *DAB,* Vol. XIV, pp. 140-141; Thomas Jefferson Page, *La Plata: The Argentine Confederation and Paraguay.*

34. Lieut. Edwin J. De Haven was on duty with MFM at the Naval Observatory from 1848 until he was ordered to New York in the early spring of 1850 to prepare for an arctic expedition. His expedition sailed from New York May 22, 1850, returned there Sept. 30, 1851. In his official report made Oct. 4, 1851, De Haven stated: "Between Cornwallis Island and some distant high land visible in the North, appeared a wide channel leading to the westward. A dark, misty-looking cloud which hung over it (technically termed frost smoke), was indicative of much open water in that direction. This was the direction to which my instructions, referring to the investigations at the National Observatory concerning the winds and currents of the ocean, directed me to look for open water. Nor was the open water the only indication that presented itself in confirmation of this theoretical conjecture [of Maury's] as to a milder climate in that direction. . . . Thus these admirably drawn instructions, deriving arguments from the enlarged and comprehensive system of [Maury's] physical research . . . pointed with emphasis to an unknown open sea into which [Sir John] Franklin had probably found his way. . . . To the channel which appeared to lead into the open sea over which the cloud of frost smoke hung as a sign, I have given the name of *Maury,* after the distinguished gentleman at the head of our National Observatory, whose theory with

regard to an open sea to the north is likely to be realized through this channel." Official Report of Edwin J. De Haven, Lieutenant, U.S.N. Commanding Arctic Expedition to Secretary of Navy William A. Graham, Oct. 4, 1851, in Elisha Kent Kane, M.D., U.S.N., *The United States Grinnell Expedition in Search of Sir John Franklin, A Personal Narrative,* pp. 498-499; map showing Maury Channel, ibid., opposite p. 13. See also NR, MFM to Prof. Alexander Keith Johnston, Edinburgh, Nov. 2, Dec. 13, 1853, NOLS, Vol. X, NAn.

35. Kane, who had been senior medical officer for the First Grinnell Expedition, was fully aware of the belief of his former commanding officer, Lieut. De Haven, in MFM's open polar sea theory. When given command of the Second Grinnell Expedition, "Dr. Elisha Kent Kane spent some time [with MFM] receiving instruction how to proceed to reach the open Polar Sea. He was an interesting looking but silent little man with dark hair and keen black eyes," Diana Maury Corbin wrote in a memorandum of reminiscences, filed as Folio 8327, MP, Vol. XLII, LC. For MFM's assistance to Kane, see NR, MFM to Dr. Elisha K. Kane, Nov. 26, 1852, Feb. 3, 1853, NOLS, Vol. VIII, NAn.

36. Smucker, *American Explorers,* p. 97. See also discoverer's own description, "William Morton's Report to Kane of Journey to North and East during the months of June and July, 1854," in Elisha Kent Kane, *Arctic Exploration: The Second Grinnell Expedition in Search of Sir John Franklin, 1853, '54, '55,* Vol. II, p. 278, and Kane's comments thereon, ibid., Vol. I, pp. 304-306.

37. Referring to Maury and evaluation of this discovery, Kane wrote: "In this recapitulation of facts I am not entering upon the question of a warmer climate impressed upon this region in virtue of a physical law which extends the isotherms towards the Pole. Still less am I disposed to express an opinion as to the influence which ocean-currents may exert on the temperature of these far northern regions; there is at least one man, an officer in the same service with myself whose scientific investigations do it honor, with whom I am content to leave that discussion." Ibid., p. 309. The quotation about naming the waters is from NR, MFM to Dr. Elisha Kent Kane, Oct. 7, 1856, NOLS, Vol. XIII, NAn.

38. This volume did not create the same stir as had Vol. I published in 1846 because that had been the first work published by an observatory in the United States. See *Astronomical Observations made under the direction of M. F. Maury, Lt. U.S. Navy, Superintendent,* Vol. II (Washington: C. Alexander, printer, 1851).

39. In the *Appendix to the Observations made during the year 1846* (separate pamphlet), MFM stated that he had three lieutenants and six passed midshipmen on duty at the Observatory. He also stated that the passed midshipmen came and went too rapidly to be made trained observers but that they would take with them the scientific information they had absorbed and spread it in the Navy. That MFM worked the lieutenants hard is evidenced by this description by Thomas Jefferson Page of his tour of duty at the Observatory from 1844 to 1847: "It was not an easy berth, for day and night in good weather I was at work with the Muriel Circle. The Observatory was in its infancy and its character before the world was to be established. Placed thus upon our mettle, we all labored diligently in

consequence." From autobiographical sketch cited in Note 33. After the Mexican War, MFM secured an increase in the number of officers at the Observatory, but he also multiplied the work being done there by launching the Wind and Current Charts. On July 30, 1852, he reported to the Secretary of Navy that he was shorthanded at the Observatory as five professors of mathematics assigned to duty at the Observatory were ill and that that left only two for observations at night, one fourth the force needed to man the instruments. NR, MFM to Secretary of Navy John P. Kennedy, July 30, 1852, NOLS, Vol. VIII, NAn.

40. A volume of the observations made during each year from 1846 to 1849 was subsequently published and a combined volume for the observations made in 1849 and 1850. Vol. 1, part 1, of the catalogue, *Zones of Stars observed at the National Observatory, Washington . . . Containing the zones observed with the meridian circle in 1846,* by Commander M. F. Maury, LL.D., Superintendent, was published in 1860.

41. MFM also prepared a 33-page circular in relation to the U.S. Astronomical Expedition to Chile, by direction of Secretary of Navy William Ballard Preston; this was published in 1849.

42. MFM, "Circulation of the Atmosphere," "On the Probable Relation Between Magnetism and the Circulation of the Atmosphere," "Red Fogs and Sea Dust," all first published in MFM, *Sailing Directions* (3rd ed., 1851), pp. 143-172, 157-172, 149-157.

43. MFM, "On the Geological Agency of the Winds," "Of Clouds and the Equatorial Cloud Ring," *Proceedings, AAAS, 6th Meeting held at Albany* [N.Y.], *August, 1851,* pp. 277-296, 160-167.

44. A. D. Bache, *Address of the President of the Association, AAAS, Albany, N.Y., August, 1851* (reprinted from *Proceedings, AAAS, 6th Meeting held at Albany* [N.Y.], *August, 1851,* pp. xli-lx), pp. xliv-xlv, xlv-xlvi.

45. Ibid., pp. xlvi-xlvii.

46. The Navy did not relinquish the idea of getting the Coast Survey under Navy Department control, and the Navy's campaign for this transfer was intensified in 1850-1851. The Secretary of Navy asked MFM to give his views on this subject, which he did in a report on the Navy, NR, report of MFM to Secretary of Navy William A. Graham, Oct. 7, 1850, NOLS, Vol. VI, NAn. See also Weber, *Coast Survey,* p. 7.

47. Bache Address cited in Note 45, p. lviii.

48. Committee listings, *Proceedings, AAAS, 6th Meeting held at Albany* [N.Y.], *August, 1851.*

49. NR, MFM to Prof. Joseph Henry, Secretary, Smithsonian Institution, June 1, 1852, NOLS, Vol. VIII, NAn.

50. *Proceedings, AAAS, 6th Meeting held at Albany* [N.Y.], *August, 1851,* pp. 167-168.

51. NR, MFM to Commodore Charles Morris, Chief, Bureau of Ordnance and Hydrography, Nov. 21, 1851, NOLS, Vol. VII, NAn; MFM, *Sailing Directions* (4th ed., 1852), p. 63. For an apparent contradiction, see statement that observations were being made by "more than a thousand American seamen." *Annual Report of the Secretary of the Navy, 1852,* p. 342. The word "seamen" may have inadvertently been used instead of "navigators," the term used by MFM in *Physical Geography of the Sea* (1st ed., 1855), p. xii.

52. British Chargé d'Affaires John F. Crampton to Secretary of State Daniel Webster, Nov. 13, 1851; Secretary of State Daniel Webster to Secretary of Navy William A. Graham, Nov. 14, 1851, in published correspondence, MFM (compiler), *On the Establishment of An Universal System of Meteorological Observations By Sea and Land* (cited hereafter as MFM, *On Establishment of Universal System*), pp. 1-2.

53. Commodore Charles Morris, Chief, Bureau of Ordnance and Hydrography, to Lieut. M. F. Maury, Superintendent of U.S. Naval Observatory, etc., Nov. 19, 1851, in MFM, *On Establishment of Universal System*, pp. 2-3.

54. NR, MFM to Commodore Charles Morris, Chief, Bureau of Ordnance and Hydrography, Nov. 21, 1851, NOLS, Vol. VII, NAn; see also in MFM, *On Establishment of Universal System*, pp. 3-5.

55. MFM letter cited in Note 54 in NAn, or see this portion of letter in MFM, *On Establishment of Universal System*, pp. 6-8.

56. Ibid.

57. Commodore Charles Morris, Chief, Bureau of Ordnance and Hydrography, to Secretary of Navy William A. Graham, Dec. 5, 1851, in MFM, *On Establishment of Universal System*, pp. 9-10; Secretary of Navy Graham to Secretary of State Daniel Webster, Dec. 6, 1851, NR, Executive Letter Book, No. 7, p. 220, NAn.

58. Letter of Secretary Graham to Secretary Webster, ibid.

59. See authorizing letter of Secretary of Navy William A. Graham to Lieut. M. F. Maury, Superintendent, United States Naval Observatory, Dec. 6, 1851, in MFM, *On Establishment of Universal System*, p. 13. NR, MFM to Abbott Lawrence, Envoy Extraordinary and Minister Plenipotentiary "near" the Court of St. James's, Dec. 10, 1851; to William Cabell Rives, American Minister to France, Dec. 12, 1851, NOLS, Vol. VII, NAn.

60. Quotation is from MFM letter to William Cabell Rives, ibid.

61. NR, MFM to heads of missions in Washington, Dec. 10, 15, 16, 18, 19, 1851, NOLS, Vol. VII, NAn.

62. NR, MFM to Lewis Cass, Jr., U.S. Chargé d'Affaires, Pontifical States, Rome, Dec. 20, 1851, NOLS, Vol. VII, NAn.

63. NR, MFM to George P. Marsh, Dec. 20, 1851; to Luther Severance, U.S. Commissioner to Sandwich Islands, to Peter Parker, U.S. Commissioner to China, both Dec. 31, 1851; to G. R. Clark, U.S. Chargé d'Affaires to Peru, Jan. 2, 1852; to U.S. Chargé d'Affaires to Ecuador, Jan. 3, 1852, and to foreign representatives in Washington, Dec. 23, 24, 1851, all in NOLS, Vol. VII, NAn.

64. NR, MFM to Baron von Gerolt, Envoy Extraordinary and Minister Plenipotentiary of Prussia to U.S., Dec. 15, 1851, NOLS, Vol. VII, NAn.

65. NR, MFM to Baron Alexander von Humboldt, Apr. 1, 1851, NOLS, Vol. VI, NAn.

66. Walsh was consul general through 1851 and then remained on in Paris as a private citizen. See NR, MFM to Robert Walsh, Paris, Dec. 30, 1851, NOLS, Vol. VII, NAn.

67. NR, MFM to these foreign scientists dated Dec. 29, 1851, Jan. 5, Jan. 6, Jan. 13, April 1, 1852, all in NOLS, Vol. VII; also April 5 and April 10, 1852, NOLS, Vol. VIII, NAn.

68. NR, MFM to Father Curley, Georgetown College, Jan. 20, 1852, NOLS, Vol. VII, NAn.

69. NR, MFM to Prof. Joseph Henry, Smithsonian Institution, Jan. 14, 1852, NOLS, Vol. VII, NAn.
70. NR, MFM to American scientists, service leaders listed, and Cabinet members, Jan. 14, 15, 17, 20, 1852, NOLS, Vol. VII, NAn.
71. NR, MFM to Prof. Joseph Henry, Smithsonian Institution, Jan. 22, 1852, NOLS, Vol. VII, NAn.
72. Joseph Henry Journal, entry for March 2, 1852, SIA.
73. At the meeting of the AAAS held in 1852 after these letters had been sent out by MFM, a "Committee to Arrange the Details of a System of Combined Meteorological Observations for North America" was appointed with the following members: Prof. A. D. Bache, William C. Redfield, Prof. Joseph Henry, Capt. J. H. Lefroy, Prof. A. Guyot, Dr. T. R. Beck, Prof. A. Caswell, Hon. William Mitchell, Prof. Elias Loomis, Prof. J. H. Coffin. MFM was not appointed to the committee. Captain J. H. Lefroy was the man through whom Joseph Henry handled the question of co-operation with Canadian observers.
74. If MFM suspected Henry's opposition on this point, he never revealed it in any of the voluminous correspondence he carried on prior to the Brussels Conference.
75. Joseph Henry Journal, entry for May 6, 1852, SIA.
76. The anglicization of "savants" to "savans" was widely used in the period and did not indicate ignorance of the French word. Bache was expressing his opinion on another scientific project that called for the identical type of intergovernment co-operation called for by MFM; see A. D. Bache to Joseph Henry, May 30, 1853, Smithsonian letter collection, SIA.
77. Secretary of State Webster had sent his inquiries on the Cabinet level to the Secretary of War and the Secretary of Navy. The reply from the Secretary of War played no role in the issue. Secretary of Navy Graham stated in his Dec. 6, 1851, reply to Secretary of State Webster, "And in connection with this subject I have the honor to transmit with this communication a letter from the Chief of the Bureau of Ordnance and Hydrography with one from the Superintendent of the Naval Observatory and one from Professor Henry of the Smithsonian Institution, also, Lieutenant Maury's *Sailing Instructions* and his Wind and Current Charts and Professor Espy's second and third reports on Meteorology." NR, Executive Letter Book No. 7, p. 220. Henry's chance had been coequal with that of MFM.
78. "It was Sabine, you know, who in the council of the R.S. [Royal Society] defeated land observations in the original proposition for the Brussels Conference. He quoted you, Dove et al. as against it, you recollect." NR, MFM to Adolphe Quetelet, Director, Royal Observatory, Brussels, Dec. 7, 1860, NOLS, Vol. XVIII, NAn. Sabine had quoted incorrectly, as both Quetelet and Dove favored having land meteorology included in the discussions at the proposed conference. Sabine was known for his significant contributions in the study of terrestrial magnetism; sketch of Sir Edward Sabine (1788-1883), *Dictionary of National Biography* (hereafter cited as *DNB*), Vol. XVII, pp. 563-567.
79. Details of the Report of the Royal Society and the quotation from that report are in NR, MFM to Secretary of Navy John P. Kennedy, Nov. 6, 1852, NOLS, Vol. VIII, NAn.
80. Wrottesley, *Hansard*, Ser. 3, Vol. CXXVI, cols. 534, 535.

81. Ibid., cols. 522, 523; NR, MFM to Robert Walsh, Paris, June 25, 1853, NOLS, Vol. IX, NAn.

82. NR, MFM to Secretary of Navy John P. Kennedy, Nov. 6, 1852, NOLS, Vol. VIII, NAn.

83. NR, MFM to Dr. Johann von Lamont, Munich, Nov. 10, 1852; to Prof. A. Secchi, Collegio Romano, Rome, Nov. 11, 1852; to the Envoy Extraordinary and Minister Plenipotentiary of Brazil to the United States, Feb. 21, 1853, all in NOLS, Vol. VIII, NAn.

84. NR, MFM to Capt. Henry James, Royal Engineers (cited hereafter as R.E.), April 19, 1853, NOLS, Vol. IX, NAn.

85. Following his father's death and his accession to the baronetcy and the family estate, Lord Wrottesley in 1841 moved his astronomical observatory from Blackheath to Wrottesley Hall, near Wolverhampton. For Wrottesley's scientific work and honors, see *DNB*, Vol. XXI, pp. 1082-1083. For accounts of England's scientific societies and leaders, see Dr. H. G. Thornton, F.R.S., D.Sc., "The Invisible College that became The Royal Society," *The English-Speaking World*, Vol. XLII, No. 2 (March, 1960), pp. 9-15; *History of the Royal Astronomical Society, 1820-1920*, published by the Society in 1923, no author given; Osbert John Radcliff Howarth, *The British Association: A Retrospect, 1831-1921*. In Howarth see especially p. 219 for action of Parliamentary Committee of the British Association for the Advancement of Science in backing MFM's proposal.

86. Quotations from Lord Wrottesley's speech in House of Lords, British Parliament, Wrottesley, *Hansard*, Ser. 3, Vol. CXXVI, col. 521.

87. Ibid.

88. Ibid., cols. 521-522.

89. The first paragraph is an excerpt from Report of the Royal Society in Wrottesley, *Hansard*, Ser. 3, Vol. CXXVI, col. 534. The first portion of the second paragraph in the quotation is an interpolation by Lord Wrottesley, while the latter portion is a continuation of the quotation from the report of the Royal Society; ibid., cols. 534-535.

90. Ibid., cols. 523-534, 536-544.

91. NR, MFM to Lieut. Marin H. Jansen, Dutch Navy, Delft, Holland, May 7, 1853; to George Folsom, U.S. Chargé d'Affaires to the Netherlands, The Hague, May 7, 1853; to Chevalier Hulsemann, Austrian Chargé d'Affaires to U.S., New York, June 16, 1853; and especially MFM to Secretary of Navy James C. Dobbin, June 18, 1853, all in NOLS, Vol. IX, NAn.

92. NR, MFM to the head of mission for Russia, for Sweden and Norway, and to British Minister John F. Crampton, June 25, 1853; to head of mission for Spain, Portugal, France, Austria, Belgium, Brazil, Prussia, June 27, 1853, all in NOLS, Vol. IX, NAn.

93. Letter of MFM to Crampton cited in Note 92; NR, MFM to Capt. William H. Smyth, R.N., June 28, 1853, to Capt. Henry James, R.E., Edinburgh, June 29, 1853, NOLS, Vol. IX, NAn.

94. Corbin, *Maury*, p. 155.

95. NR, MFM to the Rt. Rev. James H. Otey, Bishop of Tennessee, Nashville, June 30, 1853, NOLS, Vol. IX, NAn.

96. The lack of the $1,000 that MFM estimated the trip would cost was obviously also a factor in Bishop Otey's inability to make the trip.

97. The size of the purse as well as the gift of a handsome 5-piece silver serv-

ice and tray indicate the savings that these New York men felt MFM's Wind and Current Charts and *Sailing Directions* had realized for New York shipping from 1848 to 1853. In this pre-Brussels Conference period, Americans had enjoyed the chief benefit from MFM's oceanic investigations. Following the conference the benefit was shared by the shipping of all maritime nations.

98. NR, MFM to "Messrs. Walter P. Jones, W. H. Aspinwall, Edwin Bartlett, R. C. Minturn, Sidney Brookes et al., Merchants, Underwriters, Shipmasters and Others Engaged in foreign trade at New York," July 14, 1853, NOLS, Vol. IX, NAn.

99. Writers have often stated that this degree was given MFM by Columbia College. It was granted by Columbian College in the District of Columbia, which by an act of Congress of March 3, 1873, changed its name to Columbian University and by another Congressional act in 1904 changed its name to George Washington University. For granting of degree, see Notes of the Board of Trustees, July 13, 1853, when the faculty recommended the degree be given MFM by July 15, Archives of Columbian Univ., in George Washington Univ. Archives, Washington.

100. The University of North Carolina had conferred a second honorary degree on MFM at the commencement of 1852; Thomas J. Wilson, Jr., Registrar, Univ. of North Carolina, to Charles Lee Lewis, Feb. (n.d.), 1922, TSLA.

101. "Lieut. Maury left this A.M. for Europe." Statement of Lieut. George Minor, Acting Superintendent, Observatory, July 20, 1853, NR, NOLS, Vol. IX, NAn. Also see NR, MFM to Capt. William H. Smyth, R.N., June 28, 1853, and Lieut. George Minor, Acting Superintendent, Observatory, to Lieut. Commanding Thomas Jefferson Page, U.S.S. *Water Witch,* mission to the valley of the La Plata, Sept. 21, 1853, NOLS, Vol. IX, NAn.

102. Corbin, *Maury,* p. 155.

103. Washington *Union,* Sept. 6, 1853, p. 3; MFM, *Sailing Directions* (8th ed., 1859), Vol. II, p. 591.

104. Ibid.; Corbin, *Maury,* pp. 155-156. Lord Wrottesley at this time warned MFM of jealousy on the part of high-ranking British naval officers; NR, MFM to Adolphe Quetelet, Aug. 13, 1860, NOLS, Vol. XVIII, NAn.

105. Washington *Union,* Sept. 6, 1853, p. 3. NR, Notice of Thomas Challis, Mansion House, London, to The Shipowners of London, August 18, 1853; MFM from London to Lieut. George Minor, Acting Superintendent, National Observatory, Washington, Aug. 14, 1853, both in NOLR, 1853, NAn.

106. NR, MFM to Sir Charles Lyell, June 22, 1853; to Joseph Ingersoll, U.S. Minister to England, London, June 29, 1853, NOLS, Vol. IX; to Colonel Edward Sabine, Royal Artillery, March 22, NOLS, Vol. X, NAn; MFM, *Sailing Directions* (8th ed., 1859), Vol. II, p. 591.

107. This was reported to MFM by his second-in-command at the Observatory; NR, Lieut. George Minor, Acting Superintendent, to MFM, Sept. 8, 1853, NOLS, Vol. IX, NAn.

108. MFM, *Sailing Directions* (6th ed., 1854), pp. 54-88; (8th ed., 1858), Vol. I, pp. xxv, 338.

109. Beechey was at that time member of the Naval Department of the Board of Trade, London. See sketch of Frederick William Beechey, *DNB,* Vol. II, pp. 121-122.

110. Capt. Henry James, R.E., Fellow of the Royal Society, was sent as a delegate to the conference because he was the author of the *Instructions for Taking Meteorological Observations—Drawn up by Order of the Inspector General of Fortifications, Maj. Gen. Sir John Burgoyne, R.C.B.,* which had been proposed by the British in 1851 as the basis for co-operation on land meteorology. See excerpts therefrom printed in MFM, *On Establishment of Universal System,* pp. 14-16.

111. MFM, *Sailing Directions* (6th ed., 1854), pp. 54-55; (8th ed., 1858), Vol. I, p. 350.

112. MFM, *Sailing Directions* (8th ed., 1858), Vol. I, p. 330.

113. A history of the Brussels Conference is given in Adolphe Quetelet, *Notice sur Le Capitaine M. F. Maury, Associé de l'Académie Royale de Belgique,* a 55-page booklet published by the Academy, Brussels, 1874.

114. The first portion of MFM's speech is quoted in an address delivered by C. Alphonso Smith, Head of Department of English, U.S. Naval Academy, Annapolis, at unveiling of MFM portrait at Annapolis, Nov. 20, 1923; repeated at unveiling of MFM memorial in Goshen Pass, Va., June 9, 1923; and at University of Virginia Summer School, Aug. 10, 1923; reprinted as pamphlet *Matthew Fontaine Maury* from *University of Virginia Alumni Bulletin,* January, 1924. See also C. Alphonso Smith, "Matthew Fontaine Maury," *Southern Literary Studies,* pp. 168-181.

115. MFM, *Sailing Directions* (6th ed., 1854), pp. 55-88.

116. On March 16, 1853, MFM received a letter from Chevalier George de Sibbern, Chargé d'Affaires of Sweden and Norway (then a united kingdom) to the United States, informing MFM that the King had referred the question of participation in the proposed conference to a Navy Board and the Academy of Sciences, had ordered the Swedish Navy to keep the Abstract Logs, submit them to the Academy of Sciences at Stockholm, there to be discussed, and information sent on to the Observatory at Washington. The King did not include the Swedish merchant marine at that time but reserved that "for future consideration." MFM, *Sailing Directions* (8th ed., 1859), Vol. II, p. 593.

MFM thereupon recommended to the Navy Department that the Wind and Current Charts be supplied to foreign co-operators on same basis as to U.S. co-operators; NR, MFM to Secretary of Navy James C. Dobbin, March 17, 1853, NOLS, Vol. IX, NAn.

MFM wrote that he had been authorized by the Navy to send charts for merchant marine as well as the Navy if the King wished this to be done; NR, MFM to Chevalier George de Sibbern, March 26, Apr. 4, 1853, NOLS, Vol. IX, NAn. See also declaration he could supply charts to their merchant marine on same basis as to U.S. ships, MFM to representatives in Washington of Prussia, England, France, Holland, Russia, Denmark, Brazil, Mar. 30, 1853; to representatives of Spain, Belgium, Portugal, Sardinia, Austria, the Two Sicilies, Apr. 5, 1853, all in NOLS, Vol. IX, NAn.

117. MFM, *Sailing Directions* (8th ed., 1858), Vol. I, pp. 331-332. The quotation is from NR, Lieut. George Minor, Acting Superintendent, Naval Observatory, to MFM, Sept. 4 and 5, 1853, NOLS, Vol. IX, NAn.

118. On April 26, 1853, Lord Wrottesley declared in the British Parliament, "However, the Dutch have in this instance been beforehand with us; they

have already adopted Maury's plan." Wrottesley, *Hansard,* Ser. 3, Vol. CXXVI, col. 535.

119. MFM, *Sailing Directions* (8th ed., 1858), Vol. I, pp. 332-356; also see abstract logs (6th ed., 1854), pp. 88-96; MFM, *Physical Geography of the Sea* (1st ed., 1855), pp. 272-273.

120. MFM, *Sailing Directions* (6th ed., 1854), p. 88.

121. The newspaper account was quoted by George Minor in his account of MFM's success at Brussels to his former associate at the Observatory, "Jeff" Page, who was exploring the La Plata River. NR, Lieut. George Minor to Lieut. Commanding Thomas Jefferson Page, U.S.S. *Water Witch,* Mission to the Valley of the La Plata, Sept. 21, 1853, NOLS, Vol. IX, NAn.

122. "The papers of the country have treated the Brussels Conference with consideration and my countrymen generally are proud of it." NR, MFM to Prof. Adolphe Quetelet, Brussels, Feb. 9, 1854, NOLS, Vol. X, NAn. Also see Lieut. George Minor letter to MFM cited in Note 107; *Washington Union,* Sept. 6, 1853, p. 3.

123. MFM, *Physical Geography of the Sea* (1st ed., 1855), p. xiii.

124. NR, MFM to Prof. F. G. W. von Struve, Director of Central Observatory, Pulkovo near St. Petersburg, July 18, 1853, NOLS, Vol. IX, NAn. See authorizing letter of Secretary of Navy: "Under orders for this Department, Lieut. M. F. Maury, U.S. Navy, will probably visit England, France, Holland, Russia &c. To meet his expenses while abroad, he has been authorized to draw upon you from time to time for such sums as he may require. Be pleased therefore to honour his drafts to an amount not exceeding one thousand dollars and charge the same to this department." NR, Secretary of Navy James C. Dobbin to Messrs. Baring Brothers and Co., Temporary Agents for the U.S. Navy Dept., London, July 8, 1853, Navy Agent Record Book No. 8, NAn.

125. Before this visit several letters had been exchanged between Humboldt and MFM. On the preceding May 5, 1853, MFM had sent Humboldt a copy of his most recent edition of *Sailing Directions.*

126. When MFM called on Humboldt, he found the German scientist studying the reports on deep-sea soundings in the *Sailing Directions* that he had sent him some months before. MFM wrote to Commander Cadwalader Ringgold that Humboldt "thought them the most interesting contributions as to the crust of our planet." NR, MFM to Commander C. Ringgold, Commanding Surveying Expedition North Pacific and China Seas, Nov. 10, 1853. See also MFM to Francis Lieber, Columbia, S.C., Oct. 27, 1853; MFM to Baron Alexander von Humboldt, Nov. 10, 1853, all in NOLS, Vol. X, NAn.

127. Corbin, *Maury,* p. 156. Ehrenberg's name is misspelled, and in the list of European scientists seen by MFM the name Lieber is given instead of von Liebig—more typographical errors Mrs. Corbin had no opportunity to correct because she was not sent proofs.

128. "Maury is back at the Observatory—travel worn, but will in a few days resume his arduous labors." NR, note by Lieut. George Minor, Acting Superintendent, Oct. 21, 1853, NOLS, Vol. IX, NAn.

129. On Oct. 22, 1853, MFM sent the Secretary of Navy a copy of the proceedings of the Brussels Conference (printed in both French and English) and the abstract form adopted there. He asked official approval of the abstract

form for use by the U.S. Navy. NR, MFM to Secretary of Navy James C. Dobbin, Oct. 22, 1853, NOLS, Vol. IX, NAn. Also see NR, General Order of Nov. 3, 1853, NOLS, Vol. X, NAn; MFM, *Sailing Directions* (8th ed., 1859), Vol. II, p. 870.

130. "You will see by the accompanying order commanding the American men of war to keep an abstract log according to the Brussels form that I have safely arrived and not been idle." NR, MFM to A. de la Marche, Hydrographic Engineer, Imperial Marine, Paris, Nov. 9, 1853. Also see MFM letters to delegates of Brussels Conference, James Buchanan, American Minister to England, Secretary of the American Legation in Paris, U.S. Chargé d'Affaires at Copenhagen, Nov. 9, 1853, all in NOLS, Vol. X, NAn.

131. Baron von Grabow, representing Baron von Gerolt, the Prussian Minister, called on Maury to bring this official message on Nov. 8, 1853; NR, MFM to Adolphe Quetelet, Director, Royal Observatory, Brussels, Nov. 10, 1853, NOLS, Vol. X, NAn.

132. NR, MFM to Señor José M. Mugalla, Spanish Envoy Extraordinary and Minister Plenipotentiary, Nov. 22, 1853, NOLS, Vol. X, NAn.

133. NR, MFM to Rudolph Schleiden, Minister Resident of Republic of Bremen, Nov. 25, 1853; to Lieut. Marin H. Jansen, March 9, 1854, both in NOLS, Vol. X, NAn.

134. MFM, *Sailing Directions* (8th ed., 1858), Vol. I, p. xi.

135. *Monthly Notices of the Royal Astronomical Society* (London, 1874), Vol. 34, p. 157; sketch of Robert Fitzroy (1805-1865), *DNB*, Vol. VII, pp. 207-209.

136. MFM, on Nov. 18, 1853, wrote how delighted he was to hear that the "Minister of Marine and H.E. the Minister of the Interior of the Netherlands intend to establish a Meteorological Institute" and to have Lieut. Jansen in charge of the marine department; NR, MFM to I. C. Zimmerman, Consul General of the Netherlands, New York; also see MFM letters to Lieut. Marin H. Jansen, Jan. 17, March 9, 1854, all in NOLS, Vol. X, and MFM to Royal Meteorological Institute, Holland, Feb. 21, 1855, NOLS, Vol. XI, NAn; MFM, *Sailing Directions* (8th ed., 1858), Vol. I, p. 375. For a sketch of Marin H. Jansen, see "Obituary, Admiral Jansen," *Geographic Journal* (London), Vol. II, No. 5 (November, 1893), pp. 465-468.

137. MFM, *Sailing Directions* (8th ed., 1858), Vol. I, pp. iv, v, vi, vii. When this co-operation had first been sought, MFM had written Quetelet, "I agree with you entirely as to the importance which His Holiness and his missionaries may render to our undertaking. To enlist their services would be an achievement indeed." NR, MFM to Adolphe Quetelet, Brussels, Feb. 9, 1854, NOLS, Vol. X, NAn.

138. The new issues of the Wind and Current Charts and of *Sailing Directions* were the chief means of keeping all participants informed as to the findings made by the observers of other nations. On Feb. 21, 1855, MFM wrote the representatives of all participating nations to inform them that he would bring out the 7th edition of the *Sailing Directions* in the spring or early summer and suggesting that they send in any of their findings "which you deem not sufficient for separate publication" to be included with full credit to be given therefor; NR, MFM to representatives of Denmark, Prussia, Austria, Russia, Bremen, Spain, Holland, Portugal, Eng-

land, NOLS, Vol. XI, NAn. The best summary of the spread of the program in the first five years after the conference is to be found in MFM, *Sailing Directions* (8th ed., 1858), Vol. I, pp. i-xxv, 339-382, Vol. II, pp. 593-595. This program continued among the participating nations after MFM's separation from active participation in it in 1861, and continues today in issuance of charts of the U.S. Naval Oceanographic Office and in continued international co-operation.

139. C. Alphonso Smith, "Matthew Fontaine Maury," cited in Note 114.

140. MFM wrote to Lieut. Nils Ihlen, R.N., Norway, Nov. 2, 1854, that "Quetelet backed by James, Dove, Kupffer et al. is trying hard to induce the British Government to head a move for another Congress for the land." See also MFM to Adolphe Quetelet, Dec. 12, 1853, Jan. 17, Feb. 9, 1854, all in NR, NOLS, Vols. XI and X, NAn.

141. NR, MFM to Lieut. Marin H. Jansen, Utrecht, Jan. 17, 1854, NOLS, Vol. X, NAn.

142. NR, MFM to Adolphe Quetelet, Director, Royal Observatory, Brussels, Dec. 12, 1853, NOLS, Vol. X, NAn.

143. Ibid.

144. Ibid.

145. NR, MFM to Adolphe Quetelet, Director, Royal Observatory, Brussels, Feb. 9, 1854, NOLS, Vol. X, NAn.

146. NR, MFM to Lieut. Nils Ihlen, R.N., Norway, Nov. 2, 1854, NOLS, Vol. X, NAn.

147. NR, MFM to Capt. Henry James, R.E., Edinburgh, Dec. 12, 1853, NOLS, Vol. X, NAn.

148. Diana Corbin Maury gave a list of her father's chief decorations and honors, as well as letters that accompanied them, in Appendix A, Corbin, *Maury*, pp. 291-292. The list is not complete, as many of MFM's certificates of membership in learned societies were lost during the Civil War. Most of MFM's medals are on permanent display in the National Museum of the United States, Smithsonian Institution, Washington.

149. When MFM received an order or medal from abroad, he immediately notified the Secretary of Navy. For examples, see NR, MFM to Secretary of Navy James C. Dobbin, Dec. 29, 1855, March 12, 1856, reporting medals from Republic of Bremen and the King of the Netherlands (NOLS, Vol. XIII), and to Secretary of Navy Isaac Toucey reporting gold medal from Emperor Napoleon III, June 8, 1859 (NOLS, Vol. XVI, NAn).

150. For examples of Congress's passing resolutions authorizing MFM's acceptance of the medals, see: Gold Medal from King of Sweden, U.S. Statutes at Large, Vol. X, p. 830, Jan. 29, 1854; gold medals from governments of Prussia, of Holland, and of the Republic of Bremen, U.S. Statutes at Large, Vol. XI, p. 151, Aug. 30, 1856; gold medal from Emperor of Austria, U.S. Statutes at Large, Vol. XI, p. 271, June 5, 1858; gold medal from Sardinian government, U.S. Statutes at Large, Vol. XI, p. 441, Feb. 14, 1859.

151. Odgers, *Bache*, p. 198.

152. Coulson, *Henry*, pp. 146-147.

153. Henry's closest professional friend, A. D. Bache, worked to see that Henry's contribution to science was recognized and his leadership acknowledged beginning with Henry's election to the American Philosophical Society in Philadelphia in 1835, through their years of leadership of the AAAS, and

their part in founding the National Academy of Sciences early in the Civil War. Henry became vice-president of the Academy in 1866 and in 1867 succeeded Bache as its president, which office Henry held until his death in 1878.

154. NR, MFM to Lieut. Marin H. Jansen, Dutch Navy, Batavia, June 22, 1857, NOLS, Vol. XIV, NAn.

155. NR, MFM to Adolphe Quetelet, Director, Royal Observatory, Brussels, May 3, 1858, NOLS, Vol. XV, NAn.

156. MFM's last important letter on the subject while serving as superintendent of the Naval Observatory was written December 7, 1860, to Adolphe Quetelet, Director, Royal Observatory, Brussels, with whom MFM was in the post-Civil War years to renew correspondence on the need for a general meteorological conference; NR, NOLS, Vol. XVIII, NAn.

CHAPTER XII
Maury and the Atlantic Cable

1. *The Atlantic Telegraph* (cited hereafter as *Atl. Teleg. History*), a descriptive history published by the directors of The Atlantic Telegraph Co. in England (no author given), pp. 5-6.

2. Ibid., p. 6; Sir William Howard Russell, *The Atlantic Telegraph* (cited hereafter as Russell, *Atlantic Teleg.*), pp. 3-5.

3. Ibid., p. 5.

4. Henry M. Field, *The Story of the Atlantic Telegraph* (cited hereafter as Henry Field, *Telegraph*), pp. 11-12.

5. Henry M. Field, in his book about the cable project of his brother Cyrus West Field, states that Gisborne first talked to Matthew D. Field, an engineer, who arranged for his brother Cyrus to see Gisborne and hear his proposal; ibid., pp. 15-16.

6. Isabella Field Judson, *Cyrus W. Field, His Life and Work* (cited hereafter as Judson, *Cyrus W. Field*), p. 61.

7. Henry Field, *Telegraph*, pp. 17-18.

8. NR, MFM to Cyrus W. Field, Nov. 3, 1853, NOLS, Vol. X, NAn.

9. MFM had described the start of his deep-sea sounding program in MFM, *Sailing Directions* (4th ed., 1852), pp. 125-190, and had published the first depth map of the North Atlantic in MFM, *Sailing Directions* (5th ed., 1853).

10. See second section of act of Congress, March 3, 1849, providing funds for the Navy. U.S. Statutes at Large, Vol. IX, pp. 374-379.

11. MFM instructions to Lieut. J. C. Walsh for investigations to be made on deep-sea sounding expedition of U.S. schooner *Taney*; MFM, *Sailing Directions* (4th ed., 1852), p. 127.

12. MFM, *Physical Geography of the Sea* (1st ed., 1855), pp. 200-201.

13. MFM, *Annual Address delivered before the Maryland Institute, October 25, 1855*, pp. 21-23.

14. MFM, *Physical Geography of the Sea* (1st ed., 1855), pp. 201-206.

15. Ibid., p. 206. See also MFM, *Sailing Directions* (5th ed., 1853), pp. 286-287, 290-291, 296.

16. MFM, *Sailing Directions* (4th ed.), 1852, pp. 125-139; the quotation is from p. 139.

17. Ibid., pp. 174-176, 190. See article (describing results of the cruise of the U.S.S. *Dolphin,* 1851-1852, S. Phillips Lee, Lieut. Commanding, under instructions from MFM) by Julius A. Palmer, Jr., an American shipmaster, reprinted from Boston *Transcript* in Richmond (Va.) *Times,* Nov. 20, 1892.

18. MFM, *Sailing Directions* (4th ed., 1852), pp. 139-140, 177, 187-190.

19. Plate XIV, Plate XV, in MFM, *Sailing Directions* (5th ed., 1853).

20. NR, MFM to Secretary of Navy Isaac Toucey, Sept. 4, 1858, NOLS, Vol. XVI, NAn.

21. NR, MFM to Otway H. Berryman, Lieut. Commanding U.S.S. *Dolphin,* Sept. 1, 1852; to Secretary of Navy Isaac Toucey, Sept. 4, 1858, respectively in NOLS, Vols. VIII and XVI, NAn.

22. NR, MFM to Otway H. Berryman, Lieut. Commanding U.S.S. *Dolphin*, March 14, 1853, NOLS, Vol. IX, NAn.

23. MFM, *Address . . . Maryland Institute,* cited in Note 13, p. 23.

24. Ibid., p. 24.

25. Ibid.; see sketch of John Mercer Brooke in Lyon Gardiner Tyler (ed.), *Encyclopedia of Virginia Biography,* Vol. III, pp. 48, 49. NR, MFM to Commodore John Rodgers, Commanding North Pacific Surveying Expedition, Nov. 17, 1855, NOLS, Vol. XII, NAn.

26. MFM, *Physical Geography of the Sea* (1st ed., 1855), pp. 206-207; (8th ed., 1861), pp. 313-314.

27. NR, MFM to Secretary of Navy Isaac Toucey, Sept. 4, 1858, NOLS, Vol. XVI, NAn.

28. Ibid.

29. Ibid., MFM, *Physical Geography of the Sea* (1st ed., 1855), pp. 210, 216. See sketch of Christian G. Ehrenberg, *Larousse du XXᵉ Siècle,* Vol. III, 82; sketch of Jacob Whitman Bailey (1811-1857), *DAB,* Vol. I, 498.

30. Prof. Jacob Whitman Bailey to MFM, Nov. 29, 1853, is in MFM, *Physical Geography of the Sea* (1st ed., 1855), pp. 210-211; for bathymetrical map, see description thereof, ibid., pp. 208-209, and Plate XI at back of book.

31. MFM, *Physical Geography of the Sea* (1st ed., 1855), pp. 210, 212; MFM, *Sailing Directions* (8th ed., 1858), Vol. I, pp. 113-166, 167-179.

32. Prof. Jacob Whitman Bailey to MFM, Nov. 29, 1853, in *Physical Geography of the Sea* (1st ed., 1855), pp. 210-211. See also NR, MFM to Prof. Jacob Whitman Bailey, Dec. 1, 1853, NOLS, Vol. X, NAn.

33. NR, MFM to Secretary of Navy James C. Dobbin, Feb. 22, 1854, NOLS, Vol. X, NAn, printed in full in Henry Field, *Telegraph,* pp. 18-21.

34. Ibid.

35. MFM wrote Field on Feb. 24, 1854, and enclosed with that letter his report commenced on Feb. 22, 1854, to the Secretary of Navy in which he had made the recommendation of the prize as quoted. NR, MFM to Cyrus W. Field, Feb. 24, 1854; to Secretary of Navy James C. Dobbin, Feb. 22, 1854, both in NOLS, Vol. X, NAn.

36. NR, MFM to Prof. S. F. B. Morse, Feb. 23, 1854, NOLS, Vol. X, NAn.

37. Henry Field, *Telegraph,* pp. 22-27; Russell, *Atlantic Teleg.,* pp. 6-7. The quotation is from Judson, *Cyrus W. Field,* p. 62.

38. Henry Field, *Telegraph,* pp. 27-35.

39. Ibid., p. 34; Russell, *Atlantic Teleg.,* p. 8.

40. NR, MFM to Cyrus W. Field, Apr. 21, 1854, NOLS, Vol. X, NAn.

41. Ibid.

42. The transportation of British and French troops by sea to the Crimea was a phase of this war closely observed by the Mediterranean Squadron of the U.S. Navy. See account of Crimean War, *Encyclopaedia Britannica* (1957 ed.), Vol. VI, pp. 706-708.

43. NR, MFM to Cyrus W. Field, Apr. 24, 1854, NOLS, Vol. X, NAn.

44. This was an extreme case (cited in NR, MFM to Prof. Charles Piazzi Smyth, Oct. 28, 1853, NOLS, Vol. X, NAn), but MFM worked to hold down postage costs. His shipments of books and charts to scientists in Berlin were channeled through Baron von Gerolt, the Prussian Minister in Washington, and MFM also sent information abroad through other diplomatic representatives. As early as 1847 MFM wrote Bache, "I am making up a box for the Russian Observatory and there is room in it, at your service, for as much as you may want to send." As late as 1858 MFM wrote Joseph Henry that he wished to place at his disposal a copy of the meterological papers of the Board of Trade received from London. See NR, MFM to A. D. Bache, Nov. 27, 1847, and to Joseph Henry, Jan. 9, 1858, NOLS, Vols. II and XV, NAn.

45. Henry Field, *Telegraph*, pp. 43-44. For an account of John Watkins Brett's earlier telegraphic work, see Arthur C. Clarke, *Voice Across the Ocean*, pp. 12-17; sketch of John Watkins Brett, *DNB*, Vol. II, p. 1191.

46. MFM to Cyrus W. Field, June 20, 1855, MP, Vol. IV, LC.

47. Cyrus W. Field to MFM, June 22, 1855, and copy of Extract from Minutes, Resolutions passed by the Board of Directors, New York, Newfoundland and London Telegraphy Company, June 22, 1855, MP, Vol. IV, LC. Also see MFM's official copy of Resolutions filed loose in NR, NOLS, Vol. XII, under date of June 22, 1855, NAn.

48. In the summer of 1856 Field's cable company had nearly completed building the telegraph line across the island of Newfoundland from St. John's to Cape Ray that was to serve as the cablehead for the submarine cable to be laid across to Cape Breton; Henry Field, *Telegraph*, pp. 38-44.

49. Ibid., p. 45; Cyrus W. Field to MFM, July 27, 1855, MP, Vol. IV, LC.

50. MFM to Prof. John B. Minor, July 28, 1855; to B. Franklin Minor, July 28, 1855, both in MP, Vol. IV, LC.

51. MFM to Lucian Minor, Aug. 9, 1855, MP, Vol. IV, LC; to Ann Maury of New York (who was in England), Aug. 13, 1855, MC, UVAL.

52. NR, MFM to Cyrus W. Field, June 13, 1856, NOLS, Vol. XIII, NAn; Russell, *Atlantic Teleg.*, p. 33.

53. MFM repeated this statement that he had made to Field in May, 1856, in a later letter. See NR, MFM to Cyrus W. Field, July 21, 1858, NOLS, Vol. XV, NAn.

54. NR, MFM to Cyrus W. Field, June 13, 1856, NOLS, Vol. XIII, NAn.

55. Ibid.

56. Study of the records of employees of the Coast Survey and of its supervising department, the Treasury, for 1856 reveals no employee by the name of Ripley. Nor was there any topographical engineer by that name and rank. From MFM's remark it is clear that Field knew Ripley, so he may have been a prominent citizen with government connections. It is possible that this may have been Major Roswell Sabine Ripley, who had worked for the Coast Survey before serving in the Mexican War. He had resigned from the Army in 1853, gone into business in Charleston, S.C., but served

as an officer of South Carolina militia, kept up his Army contacts, and made trips to Washington.

57. NR, MFM to Secretary of Navy Dobbin, May 5, 1856, NOLS, Vol. XIII, NAn.

58. MFM was prevented from making comparative scientific studies with other observatories by one such action of Bache's. MFM wrote Prof. Hugh D. Vail, West Haverford, Pa.: "With regard to a telegraphic communication between us I hope in the course of the summer to be able to have it complete. The Telegraphic wires formerly came to the Observatory but the posts were cut down by the authority of the superintendent of the coast survey for what purpose I do not know. I am now endeavoring to have them returned when they will be placed beyond the reach of any such wantonness and then I shall be most happy to exchange signals with you and to co-operate with your observatory for all other good and useful purposes you may suggest." NR, MFM to Prof. Hugh D. Vail, Feb. 21, 1854; see also MFM, same date, to Hon. John Cabell Breckinridge, House of Representatives, both in NOLS, Vol. X, NAn.

59. Odgers, *Bache,* pp. 39, 146, 158, 201. For detailed study, see A. D. Bache Papers, private correspondence, Vol. I, and Dudley Observatory correspondence, Vol. X, LC.

60. Coulson, *Henry,* pp. 236, 282; Joseph Henry to A. D. Bache, March 19, 1858, SIA; Odgers, *Bache,* pp. 102, 149, 204; Strode, *J. Davis to 1861,* pp. 36, 154.

61. Sketch of Jefferson Davis, *Encyclopaedia Britannica* (1957 ed.), Vol. VII, pp. 84-85; William E. Dodd, *Jefferson Davis,* pp. 63-67.

62. George Brown Goode (ed.), *The Smithsonian Institution, 1846-1896, The History of Its First Half Century.*

63. Joseph Henry to A. D. Bache, Oct. 25, 1851, SIA.

64. The Secretary of Navy in his Annual Report for 1846 recommended that a nautical ephemeris be part of the work of the Naval Observatory; Weber, *Hydrographic Office,* p. 22. See also MFM to John Quincy Adams, Nov. 17, 1847, printed under title "The National Observatory," *SLM,* Vol. XIV, No. 1 (January, 1848), p. 9; Lieut. Charles Henry Davis, Office of the Coast Survey, to Hon. Horace Mann, Member of Congress, May 4, 1848, Harvard University Library.

65. The work was begun at Cambridge in the latter part of 1849, and the first volume of the *American Ephemeris and Nautical Almanac* was published in 1852. The office was moved to Washington in 1866 and on Oct. 20, 1893, was moved to the Naval Observatory; Weber, *Hydrographic Office,* pp. 26-27.

66. Charles H. Davis, *Life of Rear-Admiral Charles Henry Davis* (cited hereafter as Davis, *C. H. Davis*), pp. 75, 87-89.

67. Ibid., pp. 75-85, 89.

68. Ibid., p. 84.

69. Ibid.

70. For examples of friendly relationship, see NR, MFM to Charles Henry Davis, Dec. 26, 1850, March 11, 1851, NOLS, Vol. VI, NAn.

71. Davis, *C. H. Davis,* p. 86.

72. MFM and Charles Henry Davis traveled to Charleston together, stopping en route for Davis to see Richmond, Va.; Davis, *C. H. Davis,* p. 92. Their

report was published as a 30-page pamphlet, *Report on the Harbor of Charleston,* by Prof. A. D. Bache, Lieuts. C. H. Davis, J. N. Maffitt, M. F. Maury, U.S.N., S. D. Kurtz, U.S.E., to the Chamber of Commerce, Charleston, S.C.

73. There are a number of letters on this subject in MFM's official correspondence. For an example, see NR, MFM to Lieut. Charles H. Davis, Superintendent, Nautical Almanac, Cambridge, Mass., June 29, 1853, NOLS, Vol. IX, NAn.

74. Lieut. Charles H. Davis to Prof. Joseph Henry, July 2, 1852, SIA.

75. NR, MFM to Lieut. Charles H. Davis, Cambridge, Mass., Feb. 9, 1853, NOLS, Vol. VIII, NAn.

76. Ibid., Feb. 19, 1853.

77. Ibid., Feb. 22, 1853.

78. Secretary of Navy James C. Dobbin to Commodore Charles Morris, Chief of Bureau of Ordnance and Hydrography, in *Sailing Directions from Sea to Sandy Hook,* Published Separately by Authority of Hon. J. C. Dobbin, Secretary of Navy (Philadelphia: E. C. and J. Biddle, May, 1855), p. 8.

79. Second Annual Message of President Franklin Pierce, James D. Richardson (ed.), *A Compilation of the Messages and Papers of the Presidents, 1789-1897* (cited hereafter as *Messages and Papers of the Presidents*), Vol. V, pp. 288-289.

80. Commodore Charles Morris, Chief of Bureau of Ordnance and Hydrography to MFM, Jan. 9, 1855, in *Sailing Directions from Sea to Sandy Hook* (cited in Note 78), p. 8.

81. NR, MFM to Commodore Charles Morris, Chief of Bureau of Ordnance and Hydrography, Jan. 11, 1855, and to R. B. Forbes, March 5, 1855, both in NOLS, Vol. XI, NAn; also see *Sailing Directions from Sea to Sandy Hook;* MFM to B. Franklin Minor, Dec. 25, 1855, MP, Vol. V, LC.

82. Charles Henry Davis worked out at least two other plans that he laid before A. D. Bache and for which he secured Bache's leadership in implementing the plans. One plan was for the creation of the National Academy of Sciences; see Davis, *C. H. Davis,* p. 290; Odgers, *Bache,* p. 170. Davis's son quotes his father's account of another joint plan described by Charles Henry Davis in a letter to his wife, Aug. 28, 1861; "And when Bache learned from me that the Army had made no progress whatever in the matter you wot of, he danced round, jumped up and down in his chair and tore his hair and I could really have sat down in my chair and cried when I saw that our plan for seizing and occupying the coast of Georgia was about to be anticipated by the authorities of the State." Davis, *C. H. Davis,* p. 129. For veiled terminology, see Odgers, *Bache,* pp. 158, 165, 201.

83. Odgers, *Bache,* p. 198; A. D. Bache to Joseph Henry, June 30, 1853, in Bache Papers, LC; Joseph Henry to "My dear friend Pierce," May 31, 1854, SIA. Bache's habit of using veiled phraseology did not apply only where MFM was concerned. A study of his letters reveals his penchant for indirect reference; see Bache Papers, LC.

84. The original handscript index was in the book of Private Correspondence, 1855-1856, Bache Papers, LC, when Catherine Cate Coblentz was doing research some years ago for a biography of Maury that was never published but of which the typescript of text and source notes are in MP, LC. The Bache Letter Books have been rebound since I first searched them in 1957.

The original handscript index indicating the letters that were withdrawn from the collection was not retained in the rebound volumes. Although I was unable to find where these Charles Henry Davis letters are now preserved, Bache's replies to Davis give a clear indication of the content of the letters.

85. Alexander D. Bache to Commander Charles Henry Davis, written from New York, Nov. 9, 1855, Bache Papers, Vol. I, LC.

86. Ibid.

87. Ibid. Note reference on p. 239 to Bache's habit of using an initial in lieu of a name, as opposed to the forthright use of Mr. Dobbin's name by Commander Davis when he answered this letter.

88. Sketch of Jefferson Davis, *Encyclopaedia Britannica* (1957 ed.), Vol. VII, p. 84.

89. In his article on Bache, "Alexander Dallas Bache and His Connection with the American Philosophical Society" (*American Philosophical Society Proceedings,* Feb. 14-15, 1941, Vol. LXXXIV, pp. 143-144), Edwin G. Conklin quoted from an editorial in *Living Age,* a Philadelphia newspaper, Feb. 19, 1867, the statement that Bache "owes everything to him who is now a prisoner at Fortress Monroe." Also see Odgers, *Bache,* p. 152; Strode, *J. Davis to 1861,* p. 304; Varina Davis, *Jefferson Davis,* Vol. I, pp. 581-582.

90. Lieut. Charles Henry Davis to Alexander D. Bache, Nov. 12, 1855, Bache Papers, Vol. I, LC.

91. Ibid.

92. This portion of basic law of the Coast Survey, quoted by MFM to Prof. Benjamin Silliman et al., is in NR, MFM to editors of *Am. Journ. Science,* Sept. 15, 1858, NOLS, Vol. XVI, NAn.

93. During their years together in the Pierce Cabinet, Secretary of War Jefferson Davis substituted a number of times for Secretary of Navy James C. Dobbin. Written permissions for this substitution were signed by President Pierce. For examples of these permissions, see NR, Executive Letter Book for 1853, NAn. See especially "Decision," June 9, 1853, signed by Jefferson Davis, Acting Secretary of Navy, followed by a General Order, October 17, 1853, signed by J. C. Dobbin, Secretary of Navy, *Navy Register, 1855,* p. 134.

94. MFM's work had been singled out for praise in the annual report of President Fillmore, Dec. 2, 1851, and in the following annual reports of secretaries of Navy: Secretary Graham, Nov. 30, 1850, and again Nov. 29, 1851; Secretary Kennedy, Dec. 4, 1852; Secretary Dobbin, Dec. 5, 1853, and again Dec. 4, 1854. In addition to having praised MFM in his annual reports, Secretary Dobbin had on Jan. 23, 1855, replied to a query from Senator Stephen R. Mallory, chairman of the Senate Naval Affairs Committee, that MFM had "added to the honor of his country" and saved her large sums of money. For these commendations of MFM, see Senate Rep. No. 443, Ser. 775, 33rd Cong., 2nd Sess., pp. 3-5.

95. NR, MFM to Secretary of Navy Dobbin, May 5, 1856, NOLS, Vol. XIII, NAn.

96. NR, Secretary of Navy Dobbin to MFM, May 7, 1856, Letters to Officers, Ships of War, Vol. LIII, NAn.

97. NR, Cyrus W. Field to MFM, with copies of Cooper-Dobbin correspondence, May 31, 1856, NOLR, May-June, 1856, NAn.

98. "My son and I set out for Minnesota in the A.M. We think of returning

via New York City and will be there by the middle of July." NR, MFM to Cyrus W. Field, June 13, 1856, NOLS, Vol. XIII, NAn. See MS. copy of MFM's speech delivered in St. Paul, on occasion of laying of cornerstone of the Minnesota Historical Society, June 24, 1856, MP, Vol. XLVII, LC.

99. NR, Secretary of Navy Dobbin to Secretary of Treasury Guthrie, May 1, May 27, and quotation in letter of June 23, 1856, Executive Letter Book No. 10, NAn.

100. "You knew before the *Arctic* put to sea in 1856 that she was sent under the law of '49 to 'assist in perfecting the discoveries made by Lieut. Maury' etc. You recollect you obtained her orders from her commander in New York and showed them to me, in which it was so stated, and that you concurred with me that it would be highly improper for the results of her soundings to be published except through me." NR, MFM to Cyrus W. Field, May 17, 1859, NOLS, Vol. XVI, NAn.

101. MFM arrived in Washington on July 9, 1856. He may not have reached the city in time to see Secretary Dobbin that day because he took a room at Willard's Hotel and had breakfast at the hotel on the morning of July 10, after which he probably went immediately to the nearby Navy Department Building to see the Secretary. Having seen the Secretary. MFM then went to his residence at the Observatory. See MFM to B. Franklin Minor, July 11, 1856, MP, Vol. VI, LC.

102. NR, Secretary of Navy Dobbin to O. H. Berryman, U.S.N., Lieut. Commanding U.S.S. *Arctic,* New York, July 10, 1856, Letters to Officers, Ships of War, Vol. LIII, NAn.

103. Article, "Deep Sea Sounding," by George E. Belknap, U.S.N., *A Naval Encyclopaedia* (L. R. Hamersly and Co., 1881), p. 201.

104. Ibid., pp. 201-202. W. P. Trowbridge, like A. D. Bache, was a West Point graduate. As an Army engineer he did work for the Coast Survey from 1849 to 1856, and he became assistant superintendent for the Coast Survey in 1857. He invented an instrument to register depth in soundings; *DAB,* Vol. XVIII, p. 656. Although a proponent of the Massey Indicator or "patent log attached to the sounding lead," Trowbridge later admitted that the Massey Indicator in the *Baltic* was "off" (inaccurate); W. P. Trowbridge, "On Deep Soundings," *Am. Journ. Science,* 2nd Series, Vol. XXVI, No. 77 (September, 1858), p. 171.

105. George E. Belknap article, "Deep Sea Sounding," *A Naval Encyclopaedia,* pp. 201-204.

106. Abstract Log, U.S.S. *Arctic,* O. H. Berryman, Lieut. Commanding, cruise July-September, 1856; see entries for July 18, July 31, Aug. 1, 1856, all soundings recorded, in MFM, *Sailing Directions* (8th ed., 1858), Vol. I, pp. 147-154.

107. Ibid., pp. 147-151; see especially entries for Aug. 4, 5, 8, 13, 15, 19, 21 and 23, 1856.

108. Ibid., pp. 151-154; see especially entries for Sept. 11 to Oct. 14, 1856. On reaching New York, Lieut. Berryman and his men were ordered back to the *Vixen* to continue their regular work for the Coast Survey.

109. Acting Secretary of Navy Welsh notified Secretary of Treasury Guthrie that he had carried out instructions in strict compliance with Guthrie's stipulations that the steam reel and other instruments be returned to the *Vixen* on completion of the *Arctic*'s deep-sea sounding cruise; NR, Acting

Secretary of Navy Welsh to Secretary of Treasury Guthrie, Oct. 24, 1856, Executive Letter Book No. 10, NAn.

110. MFM to Secretary of Navy Dobbin, Nov. 15, 1856, MFM, *Sailing Directions* (8th ed., 1858), Vol. I, p. 161; NR, MFM to Augustus Maverick, *Daily Times* office, New York, Sept. 9, 1858, NOLS, Vol. XVI, NAn.

111. NR, MFM to Cyrus W. Field, Feb. 28, Apr. 28, and May 7, 1857, NOLS, Vol. XIV, NAn.

112. Berryman drew three conflicting profiles of bottom of the sea sounded by him; profiles are given in MFM, "Das Telegraphen Plateau des Nord-Amerikan Atlantischen Ozeans," Petermann's *Mittheilungen* (December, 1857), p. 507.

113. MFM to Cyrus W. Field, May 7, 1857, NOLS, Vol. XIV, NAn.

114. MFM had lavished praise on Berryman's earlier, more carefully made soundings in letter cited in Note 22, and in all his previously published writings about deep-sea soundings. MFM repeated this praise of Berryman's earlier soundings in NR, MFM to Secretary of Navy Isaac Toucey, Sept. 4, 1858, NOLS, Vol. XVI, NAn.

115. MFM letter to Cyrus W. Field cited in Note 113.

116. NR, MFM letter in rebuttal of article signed "B," written Dec. 29, 1856 (published in *Union,* Jan. 1, 1857); MFM to Cyrus W. Field, May 7, 1857, both in NOLS, Vol. XIV, NAn.

117. NR, MFM to Cyrus W. Field, Dec. 27, 1856, NOLS, Vol. XIV, NAn.

118. Henry Field, *Telegraph,* pp. 112-113.

119. Ibid., pp. 93-111; Judson, *Cyrus W. Field,* pp. 70-73, 75-76. For Bache's ability to secure liberal aid from Congress, see sketch of Bache in *Encyclopaedia Britannica* (1957 ed.), Vol. II, p. 876.

120. Philip B. McDonald, *A Saga of the Sea,* pp. 30-31, 42.

121. Russell, *Atlantic Teleg.,* p. 9; Henry Field, *Telegraph,* pp. 81-83.

122. Judson, *Cyrus W. Field,* pp. 76-77.

123. NR, Cyrus W. Field to MFM, March 7, 1857, NOLR, 1857, NAn.

124. *Nautical Directions for Sailing from Valentia to Newfoundland,* being a letter of MFM to Cyrus W. Field, March 28, 1857, printed in London as a pamphlet, also published in MFM, *Sailing Directions* (8th ed., 1858), Vol. I, pp. 183-189.

125. Ibid.

126. NR, MFM to Cyrus W. Field, Feb. 28, 1857, NOLS, Vol. XIV, NAn.

127. Ibid., May 7, 1857,

128. NR, MFM to Secretary of Navy Toucey, May 11, 1857, NOLS, Vol. XIV, NAn.

129. Apparently Secretary Toucey felt that three highly experienced men at the Observatory could do the job as well as anyone else, and the order was channeled through Maury to Werden, Aulick, and Hubbard. Aulick had had much experience in soundings and charting while serving as an officer under William Francis Lynch on the Navy's exploration of the Dead Sea and River Jordan before coming to duty at the Observatory. Hubbard had been on duty at the Observatory since the commencement of MFM's hydrographic work. See NR, order of MFM to Lieuts. Werden and Aulick and Prof. Hubbard, July 10, 1857, NOLS, Vol. XIV, NAn.

130. The report of the three men detailed the discrepancies in the soundings made from the *Arctic* and concluded, "It is our opinion, therefore, that the

work is unreliable and that any results derived from such data would be of little value." MFM, *Sailing Directions* (8th ed., 1858), Vol. I, pp. 154-155. See also Plate XII at back of volume.

131. MFM, *Sailing Directions* (8th ed., 1858), Vol. I, pp. 165-166.

132. The telegraphic plateau extended from Cape Race, Newfoundland, to Cape Clear, Ireland, between the 48th and 55th parallel of north latitude, further north than the first soundings had indicated but as indicated by the intervening soundings; *Atl. Teleg. History,* p. 31.

133. NR, MFM to Dr. Christian G. Ehrenberg, Berlin, Nov. 8, 1857; to Capt. Joseph Dayman, Royal Navy, London, March 22, 1858, both in NOLS, Vol. XV, NAn. See also quotations from Dayman's official report of his soundings and remarks on his findings by MFM in 68-page manuscript by MFM bearing title "The Atlantic Cable—1857," pp. 34 and 46 of manuscript, MP, Vol. XLVII, LC.

134. The Atlantic Telegraph Company was organized in London on Dec. 9, 1856, with Cyrus W. Field subscribing for 100 shares of the stock ($500,000). Of these shares he was able to sell only 21 shares to other Americans on his return to the United States; Judson, *Cyrus W. Field,* pp. 69-70. The quotations are from *Atl. Teleg. History,* p. 33.

135. Ibid., p. 49.

136. As quoted in *Atl. Teleg. History,* pp. 49-50.

137. In the party that had sailed with Cyrus W. Field from New York bound for Newfoundland on Aug. 7, 1855, there had been an unusually large number of clergymen. Among the prominent journalists had been John Mullaly of the New York *Herald,* who wrote an account of that cruise in John Mullaly, *The Laying of the Cable, or the Ocean Telegraph, Being a Complete and Authentic Narrative of the attempt to Lay the Cable Across the entrance to the Gulf of St. Lawrence in 1855, and of the Three Atlantic Telegraph Expeditions of 1857 and 1858,* pp. 51-75. For quotations from newspapers of the time, see Judson, *Cyrus W. Field,* pp. 72-73, 77, 78-82; Henry Field, *Telegraph,* pp. 118-120, 127-128.

138. Russell, *Atlantic Teleg.,* pp. 20-22.

139. Ibid., pp. 22-23.

140. For decline of public faith in cable, see Henry Field, *Telegraph,* pp. 142-143; the quotation is from NR, MFM to Adolphe Quetelet, July 9, 1857, NOLS, Vol. XIV, NAn.

141. MFM, "Das Telegraphen Plateau des Nord-Amerikan Atlantischen Ozeans," Petermann's *Mittheilungen* (December, 1857), pp. 507-508.

142. Russell, *Atlantic Teleg.,* p. 24.

143. Ibid., pp. 24-25. Cyrus W. Field's brother stated they had lost 300 miles of cable; Henry Field, *Telegraph,* p. 164.

144. Henry Field, *Telegraph,* pp. 162-164.

145. Ibid., pp. 165-174; the quotation is from p. 174.

146. Russell, *Atlantic Teleg.,* p. 25.

147. Ibid., p. 26, for practice messages sent. Field states the Queen's message was received Aug. 16, 1858, and supplies text; Henry Field, *Telegraph,* p. 198.

148. Sir William Howard Russell incorrectly stated the date of the Queen's message as being received August 18 but a few lines later gives the President of the United States's reply to Victoria under its correct date, August

16. For both and quoted message sent by the directors of the Atlantic Telegraph Company in England, see Russell, *Atlantic Teleg.*, p. 26.

149. For popular rejoicing and religious thanksgiving, see Henry Field, *Telegraph*, pp. 199-202 and 203-205. For religious reaction, see Judson, *Cyrus W. Field*, pp. 88, 95, 99-103; for public rejoicing, see pp. 96, 98, 104-107.

150. The collision between the two Cunarders occurred the night of August 14, but the *Europa* had to steam back to St. John's before the news could be telegraphed to New York. The news was reported in the New York morning papers of August 17; see New York *Times*, Aug. 17, 1858, p. 1. Delay in sending the news to England was caused by Field's absence from New York. Upon his return, he authorized use of the Atlantic cable to transmit the message, which was received by Sir Samuel Cunard on August 20. Some messages took hours to transmit across the first Atlantic cable, but one message was sent from the office at Trinity Bay, Newfoundland, to Ireland, and an answer came back in two minutes; Henry Field, *Telegraph*, pp. 219, 220-221.

151. For concern about cable, see Judson, *Cyrus W. Field*, p. 106; for quotation, see Russell, *Atlantic Teleg.*, p. 27.

152. Joseph Henry to A. D. Bache, Aug. 31, 1858, SIA.

153. Coulson, *Henry*, p. 234; *Army and Navy Chronicle*, June 21, 1844, pp. 795-797; Carleton Mabee, *The American Leonardo, A Life of Samuel F. B. Morse*, pp. 309-311, 377; communication from Prof. Joseph Henry to the Board of Regents of the Smithsonian Institution, March 16, 1857, in "Extracts from the Proceedings of the Board of Regents of the Smithsonian Institution in relation to the Electro-Magnetic Telegraph, 1861," *Smithsonian Miscellaneous Collections 1862*, Vol. II, pp. 7-38.

154. Modern hero welcomes in New York City are pale compared to this one celebrating the laying of the cable and honoring the men who had achieved it. A solemn service of thanksgiving led by Bishop Doane of New Jersey, assisted by 200 clergy and attended by 1,000 persons, started the celebration at 10:00 A.M., Sept. 1, 1858, at Trinity Church. Cyrus W. Field and officers of the ships that had laid the cable landed at noon at Castle Garden, the Battery. See Judson, *Cyrus W. Field*, pp. 107-110, 114-116; New York *Times*, Sept. 2, 1858, p. 1.

155. The parade formed at the Battery, took five hours to reach the Crystal Palace, 42nd Street and Sixth Avenue. See Judson, *Cyrus W. Field*, p. 115; Henry Field, *Telegraph*, pp. 206-207; New York *Times*, Sept. 2, 1858, pp. 1, 5.

156. Speech of David Dudley Field in New York *Times*, Sept. 2, 1858, pp. 5, 8.

157. This banquet was most elaborate, with a three-page menu; Judson, *Cyrus W. Field*, pp. 117-120. For Field's toast, see New York *Times*, Sept. 3, 1858, p. 4.

158. New York *Times*, Sept. 3, 1858, p. 5.

159. "I have this A.M. your note of September 8 in relation to an article about the Telegraphic Plateau by the Coast Survey in the September number of Silliman's *Journal*. I have not seen the article itself . . ." and the quotation in the text are in NR, MFM to Augustus Maverick, *Daily Times* office, New York, Sept. 9, 1858, NOLS, Vol. XVI, NAn.

160. The article could not have been published without permission of the Coast Survey superintendent. See *Am. Journ. Science*, 2nd Ser., Vol. XXVI,

No. 77 (September, 1858), Article XVII, pp. 157-175. Editors Benjamin Silliman, Sr., Benjamin Silliman, Jr., and James B. Dana, with their associate editors, Profs. Asa Gray, Louis Agassiz, and Dr. Wolcott Gibbs, all of whom were friends of A. D. Bache and Joseph Henry, also published in the same issue an unsigned article attacking MFM's position on Berryman's soundings made from the *Arctic;* "The Telegraph-Plateau—Remarkable Discrepancies in the Published Statement of Soundings," ibid., Article XXVI, pp. 219-223.

161. NR, MFM to editors of the *American Journal of Science and Arts,* New Haven, Conn., Sept. 15, 1858, NOLS, Vol. XVI, NAn.

162. Ibid.

163. NR, MFM to Messrs. Silliman and Dana, editors of the *American Journal of Science and Arts,* Sept. 21, 1858, NOLS, Vol. XVI, NAn.

164. NR, MFM to Secretary of Navy Toucey, Sept. 24, 1858, NOLS, Vol. XVI, NAn.

165. NR, MFM to Secretary of Treasury Howell Cobb, Sept. 20, 1858, NOLS, Vol. XVI, NAn.

166. NR, MFM to Secretary of Navy Toucey, Sept. 24, 1858, and to Cyrus W. Field, Sept. 28, 1858, both in NOLS, Vol. XVI, NAn.

167. The need for the determination of longitude had been a prime argument for building the Observatory in Washington. See Richard Rathbun, *Columbian Institute,* pp. 63-64. See also statement about Naval Observatory's establishing longitude in Notice of New Works, *SLM,* Vol. XIII (April, 1847), p. 252. In 1848, ten years before A. D. Bache opposed the Naval Observatory's making a comparison of longitude with Greenwich, MFM had written Bache informing him that the Observatory had made arrangements for a comparison of longitude over the "magnetic telegraph" with certain inland cities; NR, MFM to A. D. Bache, July 17, 1848, NOLS, Vol. III, NAn. This letter did not please Bache, who had asked and obtained the facilities of the Naval Observatory for determination of longitude of the stations of the Coast Survey and certain other cities. Subsequent to this exchange of letters in 1848, and prior to 1854, Bache gave orders for the telegraph posts carrying the wire to the Observatory (necessary for the comparisons of longitude) to be cut down, according to statements by MFM in NR, MFM to J. C. Breckinridge, member of Congress (Representative), and to Prof. Hugh D. Vail, Feb. 21, 1854, NOLS, Vol. X, NAn. Following those letters MFM had the posts put back and wires run again, and in 1855 the leading Washington directory of the day reported, "The National [usual name used for Naval] Observatory . . . has already become one of the most celebrated institutions of our Government. Lieutenant Maury, its superintendent, enjoys a world-wide reputation as a scientific and practical man, and it is principally to his exertions and skill that its celebrity is due. Already it ranks among the first institutions of the kind in the world. By it is regulated the time of the city and Government, and from it is calculated the latitude and longitude of the Western Hemisphere." *Ten Eyck's Washington and Georgetown Directory,* 1855. The determination of longitude was a function of the Coast Survey; it was also considered a function of the Naval Observatory but not so considered by Bache.

168. Joseph Henry to A. D. Bache, Sept. 28, 1858, SIA.
169. Ibid.
170. For Bache's position in the long drawn-out Dudley Observatory quarrel, see Dudley Observatory correspondence, Bache Papers, Vol. X, LC. For the position of the Trustees of the Observatory, see *Statement of the Trustees*, Albany, 1859, and article, "The Dudley Observatory Feud—Statement of the Trustees," New York *Times*, Sept. 6, 1858, p. 2. For the position of Bache's protégé, Gould, see Benjamin Apthorp Gould, Jr., *Reply to the "Statement of the Trustees,"* published in Albany, N.Y., 1859.
171. The article in the New York *Times* (cited in Note 170) stated that in August, 1855, "The purchase of a heliometer [was] urged by Dr. C. H. F. Peters, an Assistant in the Coast Survey. Further urged by Superintendent Bache, who proposed to furnish a transit instrument and observers from the Coast Survey, free of expense to the Trustees, if they would procure the heliometer, the use of which was of the utmost importance to his labors. The proposal [was] acceded to by Dr. Ormsby; and Mr. Olcott induces Mrs. Dudley to advance $6,000 for the purpose. Prof. Peirce proproses a Scientific Council, as an aid to the Trustees. Proposal accepted; Messrs. Gould, Bache, Peirce and Davis being named, the latter name being afterwards struck out at the request of Mr. Gould, a personal enemy, and that of Prof. Henry substituted." Bache placed the transit instrument at the Dudley Observatory and a Coast Survey crew.
172. Julius Hillyer, Solicitor of Treasury, to A. D. Bache, Aug. 10, and Sept. 14, 1858; A. D. Bache to Julius Hillyer, Solicitor of Treasury, Sept. 18 and Sept. 21, 1858; Thomas Olcott, President of the Board of Trustees, Dudley Observatory, Albany, N.Y., to Howell Cobb, Secretary of Treasury, Sept. 2, 1858; Howell Cobb, Secretary of Treasury, to A. D. Bache, Oct. 5, 1858, all in Dudley Observatory correspondence, Bache Papers, Vol. X, LC. See also Joseph Henry to A. D. Bache, Jan. 11 and Jan. 12, 1859, SIA.
173. Joseph Henry to A. D. Bache, Oct. 4, 1858, SIA.
174. The first quotation, ibid.; the second quotation, Joseph Henry to A. D. Bache, Oct. 18, 1858, SIA.
175. Joseph Henry, A. D. Bache, and Charles Henry Davis referred to Jefferson Davis as "the General," and when using that term did not refer to General Winfield Scott as did many Washingtonians of the day. See Joseph Henry to A. D. Bache, March 19, 1858, SIA.
176. Jefferson Davis to A. D. Bache, Oct. 27, 1858, Bache Papers, Vol. X, LC.
177. Ibid., Oct. 22, 1858.
178. Henry Field, *Telegraph,* pp. 213-230.
179. NR, MFM to Cyrus W. Field, May 17, Aug. 8, 12, 26, 1859, NOLS, Vols. XVI, XVII, NAn; MFM, "The Atlantic Telegraph-Cable," *Journal of the Royal Society of Dublin,* 1858-59, Vol. II, pp. 221-229; *Maury's Letter to John Locke, Esq., Read before the Royal Dublin Society, Friday, January 28, 1859* (16-page pamphlet), p. 15.
180. NR, MFM to Cyrus W. Field, May 17, 1859, NOLS, Vol. XVI, NAn.
181. Ibid., Aug. 8, 1859, Vol. XVII.

CHAPTER XIII

The Physical Geography of the Sea

1. Maury's dedication to the dissemination of knowledge is best evidenced by his writings, which are listed in a separate bibliography at the back of this book. For his work on 6th ed. *Sailing Directions,* see NR, MFM to G. I. A. D. Pegado, Professor of Physics, Lisbon, Portugal, Nov. 9, 1853; to Baron Alexander von Humboldt, Nov. 10, 1853; to Adolphe Quetelet, Astronomer Royal, Brussels, Feb. 9, 1854, all in NOLS, Vol. X, NAn.

2. MFM, *Physical Geography of the Sea* (1st ed., 1855), p. xiii.

3. Dabney Herndon Maury, who had lost his naval officer father, John Maury, when he was one, had grown up in his uncle MFM's home, entered the University of Virginia at 17, and then studied law briefly before going to West Point, from which he graduated. Dabney was made a first lieutenant, U.S. Army, Jan. 27, 1853. He recounted the episode when he received the advice for MFM from the Biddles; Gen. Dabney Herndon Maury, Ex-United States Minister to Colombia, *Recollections of a Virginian in the Mexican, Indian, and Civil Wars,* p. 18.

4. Dabney H. Maury to Molly (Mary) Maury, Aug. 7, 1873, MP, Vol. XLIV, Folio 8654, LC.

5. Ibid.; Corbin, *Maury,* pp. 149-150.

6. Ann Herndon, before her marriage, often visited her aunt, Mrs. Dabney Minor, at "Woodlawn," on the North Anna River in Orange County, Va. Mrs. Minor's granddaughter, Mrs. Lucy Minor Scales Humphries, re-counted this family story to her granddaughter, Miss Lucy H. Ewin of Mis-sissippi, who wrote it to me Jan. 12, 1962.

7. Corbin, *Maury,* p. 149.

8. MFM to Ann Maury of New York, June 21, 1854, MC, UVAL.

9. Ibid., Dec. 1, and 12, 1854.

10. At the Observatory in December, 1854, MFM wrote the dedication: "As a token of friendship, and a tribute to worth, this volume is dedicated to George Manning of New York."

11. MFM, *Physical Geography of the Sea* (1st ed., 1855), p. xv.

12. Ibid., p. 25.

13. Article by John F. W. Herschel (signed with initials) on "Physical Geog-raphy," *Encyclopaedia Britannica* (8th ed., 1859), Vol. VII, pp. 569-642, especially 577-579; MFM, *Physical Geography of the Sea* (8th U.S. ed., 1861), pp. 22, 23, 29 fns. 20-48, 182-188. See also editorial, New York *Herald,* Feb. 3, 1873, p. 6; reprint of article from *Temple Bar* (London) in *Eclectic Magazine of Foreign Literature, Science and Art,* New Ser., Vol. XVIII, No. 1 (July, 1873), pp. 116-117.

14. Quotation from Carpenter in editorial on MFM, New York *Herald,* Feb. 3, 1873, p. 6.

15. MFM, *Address to the Graduating Class of the Virginia Military Institute, July 2, 1869,* p. 9.

16. MFM, *Physical Geography of the Sea* (1st ed., 1855), p. 53.

17. Ibid., p. 68.

18. Ibid., pp. 91-92.

19. Ibid., pp. 124-145; for investigations of undercurrents by Lieuts. Lee and Walsh, pp. 141-142.

20. Ibid., pp. 146-147.
21. Ibid., pp. 153-154.
22. Ibid., p. 70. For the statement on number of observations, see reprint of article on MFM from British publication *Temple Bar* in *Eclectic Magazine of Foreign Literature, Science and Art,* New Ser., Vol. XVIII, No. 1 (July, 1873), pp. 116-117.
23. MFM, *Physical Geography of the Sea* (1st ed., 1855), The Winds, pp. 217-229, and Plate VIII, back of book; The Climates of the Ocean, pp. 231-243; Isothermal Chart, p. 230; Storms, pp. 257-261; Hurricane Chart, Plate X, back of book; Drift of the Sea, pp. 244-256, Plate IX, back of book; Probable Relation between Magnetism and the Circulation of the Atmosphere, pp. 104-123; Red Fogs and Sea Dust, pp. 97-103; Equatorial Cloud Ring, pp. 171-180; Depths of the Ocean, pp. 200-207; Basin of the Atlantic, pp. 208-216.
24. Ibid., Sketch of Apparatus, p. 207; pp. 206-216, Plates XI and XII at back of book.
25. Ibid., Routes and Race of Clipper Ships, pp. 262-270; conclusion about launching of science of marine meterology at Brussels Conference, pp. 271-273.
26. "*The Physical Geography of the Sea* had gone into a 3rd Edition before I knew the 2nd was out. I shall not think of recasting it for some time." MFM to Ann Maury of New York, Aug. 13, 1855, MC, UVAL. The second, third, fourth and fifth editions would today be termed "printings" as MFM made no revision until December, 1855, and early January, 1856. The first revised and enlarged edition was published in 1856, followed by further revised and enlarged editions in 1857, 1859, 1861 and 1871, with a reprint of the 1857 edition in 1858.
27. Sampson Low, Son and Company, London, published all but one of the English editions, and that was published by T. Nelson and Sons, London, 1859. The last British edition was published in 1883 and was marked "19th edition."
28. *Natuurkundige Beschrijving der Zeen, door M. F. Maury. . . .* (Vertald door M. H. Jansen) P. K. Braat, Dordrecht, 1855.
29. French editions: *Géographie Physique de la Mer* (traduit par P. A. Terquem) J. Correard, Paris, 1858; rev. et completée 2nd ed., 1861. The reconstructed and enlarged 8th British edition was also translated and published in France as *Géographie Physique de la Mer* (traduit par MM. Zurcher et Margollé) Hetzel, Paris, 1865, 2nd ed., 1868. German editions: *Die Physische Geographie des Meeres* (Deutsch bearbeitet von Dr. C. Boettger) G. Mayer, Leipzig, 1856, 2nd ed., 1859. Italian edition: *Geografia Fisica del mare e sua Meteorologica di M. F. Maury,* Versione Italiana dalla 14th ed. inglese, autorizzata dell'autore (del luogotenente Luigi Gatta) . . . E. Lotscher, Rome, 1872. MFM's daughter stated that the book was also translated into Swedish and Spanish, but I have not been able to find that the translations were published; see Corbin, *Maury,* p. 72.
30. Corbin, *Maury,* p. 71.
31. E. François Jomard to MFM, Nov. 18, 1855, MP, Vol. V, LC.
32. *Edinburgh Review* as quoted in Corbin, *Maury,* p. 71.
33. *Royal Astronomical Society Monthly Notices* (London), Vol. XXXIV, No. 4 (February, 1874), p. 157.

34. *Revue des Deux Mondes,* Paris, 1855, as quoted in Lewis, *Maury,* p. 74.
35. A comparison of the 1st American edition, 1855, and the 8th, 1861, reveals the amount of knowledge Maury and his associates had gained about the sea in the intervening years. See editions cited in Notes 26 and 27; see also bibliography of MFM's works in this book.
36. *The Physical Geography of the Sea* is often today referred to as "the first textbook of modern oceanography" or the "first classic book on ocean-ography." See H. A. M. (Harry A. Marmer) sketch of MFM, *DAB,* Vol. XII, pp. 428-431. For Dr. Smith's quotation, see C. Alphonso Smith, address at Univ. of Virginia, June 9, 1923, *UVa. Alumni Bulletin,* January, 1924, p. 7.
37. Hugh Robert Mill and D. Wilson Barker, "The Air" in G. Herbert Fowler (ed.), *Science of the Sea* (1st ed., 1912), p. 3.
38. MFM stated in his *Lanes for the Steamers Crossing the Atlantic* that "approximately 300 died," but the loss is placed at 350 lives in article on shipwrecks, *Columbia Encyclopedia* (1935 ed.), p. 1622. See also Second Annual Message of President Franklin Pierce, *Messages and Papers of the Presidents, 1789-1897,* Vol. V, pp. 288-289.
39. MFM wrote about Robert Bennett Forbes's suggestion and the plan he had developed from that suggestion in NR, MFM to Walter R. Jones, president Atlantic Mutual Insurance Co., New York, Nov. 8, 1854, NOLS, Vol. XI, NAn.
40. NR, MFM to Robert Bennett Forbes, Boston, Dec. 14, 1854, NOLS, Vol. XI, NAn.
41. MFM received a letter dated Jan. 8, 1855, from Messrs. John S. Sleeper, C. W. Cartwright, J. Ingersoll Bowditch, R. B. Forbes and other under-writers, shipowners and merchants of Boston, saying they had been in-terested by MFM's proposal in his letter of Nov. 8, 1854, to Walter R. Jones of New York, and requested that MFM proceed to chart the one-way trans-Atlantic lanes he had proposed. See MFM, *Sailing Directions* (8th ed., 1859), Vol. II, pp. 71-73. See letter also in *Steam Lanes Across the Atlantic,* U.S. Navy Hydrographic Office Publication No. 40, pp. 7-8.
42. MFM to Messrs. Sleeper, Cartwright, Bowditch, Forbes et al., Feb. 15, 1855, and subsequent statements, MFM, *Sailing Directions* (8th ed., 1859), Vol. II, pp. 73-80.
43. Ibid.; *Steam Lanes Across the Atlantic,* U.S. Navy Hydrographic Office Publication No. 40, p. 19.
44. MFM, *Lanes for the Steamers Crossing the Atlantic,* 12-page pamphlet published by the Board of Underwriters of New York, 1855, Scrap Book, MP, LC.
45. The original chart drawn at the Observatory was sent by MFM with his letter of Feb. 15, 1855 (cited in Note 42) and was printed for distribution in 1855.
46. NR, MFM letter written from steamer at sea to the Rt. Rev. James H. Otey, Bishop of Tennessee, Nov. (n.d.), 1860, NOLS, Vol. XVIII, NAn.
47. NR, MFM to Commodore Charles Morris, Chief of Bureau of Ordnance and Hydrography, May 18, 1855, NOLS, Vol. XII, NAn. See *Steam Lanes Across the Atlantic,* U.S. Navy Hydrographic Office Publication No. 40.
48. London *Times* as quoted in Corbin, *Maury,* p. 142 fn.
49. Statement of Julius A. Palmer, Jr., shipmaster, reprinted from Boston

Transcript in Richmond *Times*, Nov. 20, 1892. The steamship company was the Cunard Line. For a modern account, see an article in a publication of the Cunard Steamship Co., Phillip Vyle, "Maury's Lanes Across the Atlantic," *The Running Tide,* March, 1930, reprinted in *The Neptune Log,* April, 1930, pp. 5-6 (good except for incorrectly giving year 1854, instead of 1855, for publication of plan).

50. Editorial in New York *Herald*, Oct. 26, 1889.

51. Phillip Vyle, "Maury's Lanes Across the Atlantic," *The Neptune Log,* April, 1930, pp. 5-6.

52. MFM, ("Rules of Conduct") *Address delivered before the Literary Societies of the University of Virginia on the 28th June, 1855;* first paragraph, p. 7; balance of quotation, p. 21.

53. Ibid.; the quoted phrase, p. 23; the quoted paragraph, p. 22.

Chapter XIV

The Plucking Board

1. MFM's pay as superintendent of the Naval Observatory and Hydrographical Office was $3,000, not $3,500 as stated in Lewis, *Maury,* p. 114. See salary statement in report by Senator Stephen R. Mallory, chairman, Senate Naval Affairs Committee, Senate Rep. No. 443, 33rd Cong., 2nd Sess., p. 5. His kinsman and friend, B. Franklin Minor, who visited MFM "two or three times a year," wrote to a Virginia senator, "He [MFM] told me that his fuel and lights were quite a heavy item of his expenses; over $300, I think; and laughed at the idea of the government paying one cent of it." B. Franklin Minor to Senator R. M. T. Hunter, May 11, 1860, MP, Vol. IX, LC.

2. Since publication of his early articles for naval reform, MFM had publicly urged the creation of more officer grades. He had believed that the United States Navy should have admirals as did the navies of other nations. On these points he had been outspoken, but study of his voluminous correspondence, both personal and official, does not reveal complaint about the Navy Department's failure to promote him. When the Treasury had refused to pay the salary of $3,000 voted him by Congress because the bill had termed him the "Superintendent of the Marine," MFM had to wait for months for the matter to be clarified. Near the end of the period he complained to his first cousin, Ann Maury of New York, "This poverty is a terrible weight upon one's will and wants," but he made no complaint about not receiving promotion.

3. NR, Lieut. George Minor to George Manning of New York, Oct. 8, 1853, NOLS, Vol. IX, NAn.

4. Senate Report No. 443, to accompany bill S. 567, made by Senator Mallory in the Senate, Jan. 29, 1855, 33rd Cong., 2nd Sess., p. 6.

5. Ibid.

6. Ibid., first quotation, p. 7; second quotation, p. 9.

7. Facts on McClure (also spelled M'Clure) in article on arctic regions, *Encyclopaedia Britannica* (1957 ed.), Vol. II, p. 298; sketch of McClure, *Columbia Encyclopedia* (1935 ed.), p. 1085.

8. Because of the number of programs in progress, MFM had the largest staff in 1855 that he ever had associated with him at the Observatory. This

fact helped to make possible his enormous productivity that year. There were 9 lieutenants, 7 U.S.N. professors of mathematics, and two passed midshipmen on Observatory duty. Some of this staff were completing the time-consuming reductions or mathematical calculations of observations made in 1848 and preparing the text of *Astronomical Observations made during the Year 1848 at The United States Naval Observatory, Washington, under the direction of M. F. Maury, LL.D., Lt., U.S.N. superintendent,* Vol. IV, which was published in Washington in 1856.

9. *Abstract Log for Men of War* (E. C. and J. Biddle, 1855). The same firm had published *Abstract Log for the Merchant Service* in 1854.

10. *Chart showing two steamer lanes each twenty miles wide, North Atlantic* (published at expense of New York Board of Underwriters, New York, 1855); MFM, *Lanes for the Steamers Crossing the Atlantic* (published by Board of Underwriters, New York, 1855), 12 pp., map, and chart.

11. MFM supplied much of the information contained in Rep. No. 95, Ser. 808, Vol. I, Report by Representative Ingersoll, Feb. 23, 1855, on *Memorial of Lt. M. F. Maury in behalf of Memphis Convention and favoring free navigation of Amazon.*

12. MFM, "On the Construction of a Submarine Telegraph," *Annual of Scientific Discovery, 1855,* pp. 161-162.

13. MFM, "Barometric Anomalies about the Andes," *Am. Journ. Science,* Ser. 2, Vol. XIX, Art. XXXVIII (May, 1855), pp. 385-391.

14. MFM, *Annual Address delivered before the Maryland Institute for the Promotion of the Mechanic Arts, Maryland Agricultural Society, October 25, 1855* (published as a 26-page pamphlet, Baltimore, 1856).

15. MFM, "The Bible and Science," *Southern Churchman,* Jan. 22, 1855.

16. MFM, "Meteorology for the Farmers," *American Farmer,* Vol. XI, No. 2 (August, 1855), pp. 33-35.

17. MFM, "An Appeal to the Agricultural Interests of Virginia," *Southern Planter and Farmer,* Vol. XV, No. 6 (June, 1855), pp. 161-163; report of meeting and resolution of the Virginia State Agricultural Society, *Southern Planter and Farmer,* Vol. XV, No. 12 (December, 1855), pp. 353-355.

18. A typical comment of MFM in these letters was, "There is little or no chance this session for the Navy Bill I think. The sentiment among officers here appears to be as it is with you—objectionable and faulty though the bill be it cannot bring about a state of things worse than we have; therefore let us have it now." NR, MFM to Lieut. Stephen C. Rowan, Jan. 15, 1853, NOLS, Vol. VIII, NAn.

19. In a letter to Hamilton Fish, whom he still addressed as "Dear Governor," although Fish had for two years been U.S. senator from New York, MFM wrote: "I am in hopes to have a leisure day next Saturday and I suppose you will not have one before—if so—I am entirely at your service for that day—after 12. In the meantime I send you a note—from Capt. Mumford . . . he is very zealous and warm in the cause [of securing a bill to improve the naval service]." NR, Washington, Dec. 14, 1853, NOLS, Vol. X, NAn. Earlier Secretary of Navy Graham had asked MFM to submit a report giving his views "concerning the Navy and the reforms requisite to place it in a more efficient state." See NR, report of MFM to Secretary William A. Graham, Oct. 7, 1850, NOLS, Vol. VI, NAn. Also see NR, MFM to Capt. S. F. Du Pont, Nov. 1, 1850, NOLS, Vol. VI, NAn.

20. NR, MFM to Capt. Thomas A. Dornin, July 20, 1851, NOLS, Vol. VII, NAn.

21. As early as 1853 MFM wrote: "Mallory—for it appears to be his bill—asked me as he has done, I suppose, everybody else here, to work over it and suggest amendments. I did so—upon the basis of preserving the principles of the bill as it was originally proposed." NR, MFM to Lieut. Stephen R. Rowan, Jan. 15, 1853, NOLS, Vol. VIII, NAn.

22. "An Act to Promote the Efficiency of the Navy," 32nd-33rd Cong., 1851-1855, U.S. Statutes at Large, Vol. X, pp. 616-617.

23. MFM to B. Franklin Minor, Oct. 16, 1855, MP, Vol. V, LC.

24. MFM, his daughter Betty, Dick, and John, had suffered one attack of malarial chills after their return from the brief trip to New York when MFM found that the cable expedition to Newfoundland would not sail on Aug. 1, as planned, but on Aug. 7, and that it was to be a more extended trip than he had anticipated.

25. "I want to talk to you about agricultural meteorology and show you how as much may be done through that for the agricultural interests of the country as the winds and currents have done for commerce." MFM to B. Franklin Minor, March 21, 1855, MP, Vol. IV, LC.

26. Secretary of Navy James C. Dobbin's letter, dated Sept. 17, 1855, and addressed to MFM in Washington, had evidently gone to the Observatory and been forwarded to Virginia; MP, Vol. IV, LC.

27. NR, MFM to Secretary of Navy Dobbin, Sept. 20, 1855, NOLS, Vol. XII, NAn.

28. NR, Secretary of Navy Dobbin to MFM, Sept. 24, 1855, NOLS, Vol. XII, NAn.

29. MFM to Rt. Rev. James H. Otey, Bishop of Tennessee, Sept. 21, 1855, and to William M. Blackford, Sept. 23, 1855, both in MP, Vol. V, LC.

30. NR, MFM to Robert Hatton, Nashville, Tenn., Dec. 10, 1855, NOLS, Vol. XII, NAn.

31. MFM to William M. Blackford, Oct. 17, 1855, MP, Vol. V, LC.

32. NR, MFM to Secretary of Navy Dobbin, Oct. 1, 1855, NOLS, Vol. XII, NAn.

33. NR, Miscellaneous Records of the Hydrographic Office—"Correspondence Relating Chiefly to Lt. M. F. Maury, U.S.N., and the 'Plucking Board' of 1855" (1 vol.), No. 54. Press copies unarranged (cited hereafter as NR, Miscellaneous . . . Lieut. MFM and Plucking Board, No. 54), NAn.

34. MFM to Franklin Minor, Nov. 13, 1855, MP, Vol. V, LC.

35. S. Phillips Lee, who had made the second deep-sea sounding expedition for MFM in 1851-1852, was acting superintendent of Observatory while MFM was absent. MFM extracted the paragraphs pertaining to him from Lee's letter and sent copy to William M. Blackford, stating, "The enclosed extract is from Lee to Lewis Maury." MFM to William M. Blackford, Sept. 23, 1855, MP, Vol. V, LC. On the extract neither Lee's name nor that of Lewis Maury is given, probably because of the kinship of Lewis and MFM. See extract from "——— at Observatory, Washington, to officer U.S.N. in New York," Sept. 18, 1855, MP, Vol. V, LC.

36. When MFM wrote Ann in mid-August he had not the slightest suspicion that he had been overslaughed by the Navy Retiring Board, but he was already condemnatory of its methods of procedure; MFM to Ann Maury

of New York, who was visiting relatives in England, Aug. 13, 1855, MC, UVAL.

37. William Lewis Maury (son of William Grymes Maury, whose father was the Rev. Walker Maury, son of the Rev. James Maury) was born in Virginia, Oct. 13, 1813. His first wife's death left him with three children. He and Anne Fontaine Maury (born Oct. 20, 1832) became engaged on Sept. 9, 1855, and she reported this news to her aunt and guardian, Ann Maury, who was still abroad, in a letter written Sept. 10, 1855, published in A. F. Maury, *Virginiana*, p. 255.

38. In issuing his instructions to the Navy Retiring Board on June 20, 1855, Secretary James C. Dobbin had instructed them to confine all information concerning their decisions exclusively to the Board and the Executive Department of the government until the President had approved or disapproved the Board's findings. This was necessary and right, but it had not been anticipated that the Board would pledge themselves to silence after the President had acted. MFM wrote to his esteemed cousin Ann Maury: "I *know* that neither the President or Secretary thinks him [Lewis] under any obligations officially [to remain silent longer]. The former [the President] has sent me word that he doubted the propriety of his ordering them [members of the Board] to tell their reasons [for placing MFM on Reserved List], but I could ask them and they could do as they pleased." MFM to Ann Maury of New York, Nov. 3, 1855, MC, UVAL.

39. Such a resignation would undoubtedly have been viewed by the Navy Department as similar to an attempt on the part of an officer to resign while on a mission. That resignation from the Navy would have been necessary to avoid going on the Board is indicated by MFM's statement that one member of the Board (possibly Lewis Maury) "has told me that it was the mistake of his life, his connection with that Board and his regret amounts to remorse that he did not resign and fling up his commission rather than be a member of it." MFM to B. Franklin Minor, Oct. 11, 1855, MP, Vol. V, LC.

40. On April 3, 1856, Lewis Maury married Anne Fontaine Maury, niece and adopted daughter of Ann Maury of New York, and this was another strengthening of the family bond between MFM and Lewis. Lewis Maury occasionally received his mail in care of MFM and on one occasion in 1857, when a letter came for Lewis, MFM informed him of the arrival of the letter and suggested that Lewis accompany him to Fredericksburg to visit MFM's family vacationing there. During the Civil War MFM secured the services of Lewis Maury to work with him in laying the electric mines or torpedoes in the James River, worked very closely with him in England, and had Lewis live with him there when Lewis was waiting for completion of the cruiser he was to command.

41. NR, Secretary of Navy Dobbin to MFM, Oct. 25, 1855, NOLS, Vol. XII, NAn.

42. Ibid.

43. NR, MFM to Secretary of Navy Dobbin, Oct. 29, 1855, NOLS, Vol. XII, NAn.

44. MFM to the Rt. Rev. James H. Otey, Bishop of Tennessee, Sept. 21, 1855, MP, Vol. V, LC.

45. NR, letters sent to each member of Board identical to that of MFM to

Commodore M. C. Perry, Nov. 8, 1855; see also Secretary Dobbin to MFM, Nov. 9, 1855, all in NOLS, Vol. XII, NAn. For MFM's expression of resentment and hurt, see letters of MFM to B. Franklin Minor, Oct. 3, Oct. 5, Oct. 9, Oct. 12, Oct. 16, Oct. 21, Oct. 23, Nov. 3, Nov. 8, 1855; to William M. Blackford, Nov. 3, 1855, all in MP, Vol. V, LC; see also NR, MFM to James T. Earle, Oct. 22, 1855; to Marin H. Jansen, Oct. 24, 1855; to Admiral F. W. Beechey, R. N., Oct. 28, 1855; to Commodore John Rodgers, Nov. 17, 1855, all in NOLS, Vol. XII, NAn.

46. NR, M. C. Perry to MFM, Nov. 13, 1855; see also letters of William B. Shubrick, Charles S. McCauley, Abraham Bigelow, G. J. Pendergrast, Franklin Buchanan, Samuel F. Du Pont, Samuel Barron, Andrew H. Foote, John S. Missroon, Richard L. Page, S. W. Godon, William L. Maury, James S. Biddle, Nov. 9 to Nov. 15, 1855, NOLS, Vol. XII, NAn.

47. NR, Lieut. James S. Biddle to MFM, Nov. 13, 1855, NOLS, Vol. XII NAn.

48. MFM to Franklin Minor, Oct. 3, 1855, in MC, UVAL. The quoted phrase is from NR, MFM to Marin Jansen, Oct. 24, 1855, NOLS, Vol. XII, NAn.

49. NR, petition of MFM to U.S. Senate and House of Representatives, Dec. 1, 1855, in NR, Miscellaneous . . . Lieut. MFM and Plucking Board, No. 54, NAn.

50. MFM to B. Franklin Minor, Nov. 15, 1855, MP, Vol. V, LC.

51. Charles Stewart, No. 1; Charles Morris, No. 2; T. ap Catesby Jones, No. 7 on list, *Navy Register, 1855*, p. 18; see also facts on Stewart's Navy career, Callahan, *List of Officers*, p. 521.

52. *National Intelligencer* as quoted in Corbin, *Maury*, p. 113.

53. *Scientific American*, November, 1855.

54. New York *Herald* as quoted in Lewis, *Maury*, pp. 112-113.

55. In spite of this statement MFM rallied his energies and delivered the speech to a crowd of nearly 5,000 people on the night of Oct. 25, MFM to Franklin Minor, Oct. 26, 1855, MP, Vol. V, LC. See MFM, *The Annual Address delivered before the Maryland Institute for the Promotion of the Mechanical Arts, Maryland Agricultural Society, October 25, 1855* (published as a 26-page pamphlet, Baltimore, 1856).

56. MFM's position is perhaps best described by a statement of Commander H. K. Thatcher, then serving as superintendent of the Naval Asylum, Philadelphia (naval hospital and home for retired naval men): "Tell me what you think of the treatment of the retiring board to our friend Maury. I think it must have caused him grief and mortification. The Naval service cannot do without him. He has given character to the Navy and the country both at home and abroad such as it could not have from any other source. It is true he will always remain at the head of that department, but if he is removed from the line of promotion it will throw a damper over his spirits, I feel, so he will be disposed to leave us altogether and seek in civil life that distinction which should be reflected upon the Naval service through him." H. K. Thatcher to George Manning, New York, Nov. 1, 1855, MP, Vol. V, LC. Secretary Dobbin had informed MFM in his letter of Sept. 17, 1855 (cited in Note 26) that MFM would receive leave of absence pay. For a lieutenant that pay was $1,200; Benjamin Homans (compiler), *Laws of the U.S. in Relation to the Navy and Marine Corps* (published in 1841 but still in effect), p. 161.

57. Exactly one month after Secretary Dobbin had informed MFM of his

change of Navy status, MFM wrote: "I have a letter from the Dutch minister informing me that the King of Holland has ordered a gold medal to be struck in my honor—Hurrah for the Dutchman!" MFM to B. Franklin Minor, Oct. 17, 1855, MP, Vol. V, LC. The medal was a recognition of MFM's pioneering role in marine meteorology that had led Holland to establish a marine meteorological department at their Meteorological Institute and also of his *Physical Geography of the Sea* (just published in Holland, having been translated by Marin H. Jansen). See also letter of Baron Alexander von Humboldt to MFM, Feb. 3, 1855, that had accompanied Gold Medal and the Kosmos Medal from the King of Prussia when presented earlier that year, published in Corbin, *Maury,* Appendix A, pp. 292-293; document of the Imperial Academy of Sciences of Russia, making MFM a corresponding member, Dec. 29, 1855, MP, Vol. V, LC.

58. The visit to MFM of the Russian chargé d'affaires (later minister) "to deliver, by command of his government, an autographed letter from the Grand Duke Constantine who, it will be remembered, is the Commander in Chief of the Russian Navy," was reported in an article in the *National Intelligencer* entitled "Honor to an American Officer." The quotation is from Constantine's letter published in the same article with editorial comments on MFM's being retained at the National Observatory; see *National Intelligencer,* Oct. 5, 1855, p. 3.

59. Ibid. For acknowledgment of the honor, see MFM to His Imperial Highness, the Grand Duke Constantine, Lord High Admiral of the Russian Navy, Oct. 22, 1855, NOLS, Vol. XII, NAn, also in MP, Vol. V, LC.

60. New York *Herald,* Dec. 15, 1855.

61. NR, Rudolph Schleiden, Minister Resident, Republic of Bremen, to MFM, Dec. 28, 1855, NOLS, Vol. XIII, NAn.

62. New York *Journal of Commerce* as quoted in Corbin, *Maury,* p. 113.

63. MFM to B. Franklin Minor, Nov. 15, 1855, MP, Vol. V, LC.

64. "I don't complain of the law and Congress has done me no wrong. My complaint is against the conduct of the Board, its secret proceedings, its partiality and injustice." MFM to B. Franklin Minor, Oct. 10, 1855, MP, Vol. V, LC. "My complaint is not against the Secretary or President, but against the Board . . . that I have been set aside on the grounds of professional *incompetency* [Maury's italics]." NR, MFM to the Hon. Neill S. Brown, Nov. 29, 1855, NOLS, Vol. XII, NAn.

65. NR, MFM to Robert Hatton, Dec. 11, 1855, NOLS, Vol. XII, NAn.

66. The petition of MFM was 17 pages of printed text and 18 pages of appendix containing the act of Feb. 28, 1855, and correspondence; *The Petition of Matthew Fontaine Maury to the Senate and House of Representatives in Congress Assembled,* presented by Senator Bell, Jan. 21, 1856.

67. Senate Rep. No. 443, to accompany bill S. 567, made by Senator Mallory in the Senate of the U.S., Jan. 29, 1855, 33rd Cong., 2nd Sess.

68. *Congressional Globe,* Jan. 10, 1856, 34th Cong., 1st Sess., p. 203, also pp. 400-404; Ulrich Bonnell Phillips, *The Life of Robert Toombs* (cited hereafter as Phillips, *Robert Toombs*), pp. 145-146.

69. *Congressional Globe,* Feb. 4, 1856, 34th Cong., 1st Sess., p. 343.

70. Ibid., Feb. 6, 1856, p. 367.

71. Ibid., Feb. 4, 1856, p. 343.

72. Ibid., Feb. 4, 1856, p. 346. See also Phillips, *Robert Toombs,* p. 146.
73. *Congressional Globe Appendix,* May 15, 1856, 34th Cong., 1st Sess., p. 577.
74. Senator Crittenden in an attack on the Board's secrecy said, "No record is kept . . . all information is refused when applied for." Ibid., May 16, 1856, p. 589; see also March 31, p. 312.
75. Ibid., Feb. 13, 1856, p. 409.
76. Ibid.
77. Ibid., p. 403.
78. Ibid.
79. Ibid., p. 407.
80. Ibid., p. 405.
81. Ibid.
82. The fact that C. H. Davis had been promoted but MFM put on the Reserved List confirmed for many the belief that there had been a determination on the part of some members of the board to "get Maury." According to his son, Charles Henry Davis completed a cruise in 1840, studied at Harvard, took his degree and "in April, 1842, was appointed an assistant on the Coast Survey, and for a period of fifteen years he had very little connection with the active duties of the Navy." From 1849 to 1856 Charles Henry Davis was in Cambridge, Mass., as superintendent of the American Ephemeris and Nautical Almanac; Davis, *C. H. Davis,* pp. 73, 75, 80, 83-84, 86-87, 89. The appropriation bill of March 3, 1849, set Davis's salary at $3,000, the same as MFM's, but like the latter he also at first had a hard time collecting it. Thus his case very closely paralleled MFM's in that since 1842 he had been engaged primarily in land-based scientific duty that served the interests of the Navy. Davis, promoted June 12, 1854, was still on shore duty in the spring of 1856 but was not accused of having avoided sea duty.
83. *Congressional Globe,* Feb. 13, 1856, 34th Cong., 1st Sess., p. 405.
84. Ibid.
85. Mallory was quoted by Senator Bell in *Speech of Senator John Bell of Tennessee on the Naval Retiring Board delivered in the Senate April 28 and 29, 1856,* p. 4.
86. The rebuttal of Senator Butler is found in *Congressional Globe,* Feb. 14, 1856, 34th Cong., 1st Sess., p. 418. For Senator Toombs's remark, ibid., Feb. 13, 1856, p. 409.
87. Joseph T. Durkin, S.J., *Stephen R. Mallory, Confederate Navy Chief* (cited hereafter as Durkin, *Mallory*), p. 76.
88. MFM to B. Franklin Minor, Feb. 27, 1856, MP, Vol. VI, LC.
89. Ibid., Jan. 23, 1856, Vol. V.
90. This laudatory report of the Board's procedure by its ranking member was published in the New York *Herald,* March 14, 1856.
91. For resumption of debate on March 11, see Senator Clayton's speech in Executive Session of the Senate, *Congressional Globe Appendix,* March 11, 1856, 34th Cong., 1st Sess., pp. 170-173. Senator Samuel Houston made an extended speech mainly in defense of MFM on March 18. The quotation from Senator Iverson, ibid., March 31, 1856, pp. 310-311.
92. Ibid., p. 311; see also p. 312.
93. In protesting "the hot haste" of the Board in having devoted only "12 minutes and 28 seconds" to consideration of each officer, Senator Iverson

stated that the exact number of officers reviewed by the Board had been 697; ibid., p. 310.

94. Senator Crittenden stated that, according to the report of the Naval Affairs Committee, "We learn that a copy of the Navy Register and of the act of Congress establishing the board were placed in the hands of each of the fifteen officers of the board; and, as I understand, each from his knowledge marked upon that Register the names of those who he thought were objectionable and ought to be removed. We are told by the president of the board that such was the obvious and known incapacity of these men, that one hundred and fifty of them were unanimously fixed upon at the first guess." Ibid., May 16, 1856, p. 587.

95. This surmise was based on the fact of Lewis Maury's known devotion to his cousin, MFM, on the tone of the letters Page and Barron had sent to MFM in reply to his inquiry to them of Nov. 8, 1855 (cited in Note 45), and the long-standing professional friendship between the men. MFM had served with Barron on his first cruise in the *Brandywine* in 1825. More recently, Barron had made deep-sea soundings from his ship at MFM's request and sent records of them to MFM at the Observatory.

96. Senator Samuel Houston began his speech by introducing a (nonofficial) memorial signed by members of the legislature of Maryland endorsing a recent resolution passed by the legislature of Virginia urging Congress to see that the harm done by the 1855 Board was rectified. Houston related a story indicating that certain members of the Navy Retiring Board had decided in advance of their meeting which officers would be overslaughed. He also alleged that a clique of men on the Board consisting of Du Pont, Missroon, Godon, and Pendergrast had worked against MFM. Houston stated that Du Pont had been "associated with Missroon, Godon and Pendergrast when they were arraigned in 1838, 1839, 1840, and 1841 and when they lay under censure" and that the bond between the officers had continued. See *Congressional Globe Appendix*, March 18, 1856, 34th Cong., 1st Sess., pp. 244, 245, 248.

97. Ibid., March 18, 1856, p. 250. In connection with this debate of March 18, 1856, it is pertinent to comment on Joseph T. Durkin's statement that in that debate, "Mallory proposed on the floor of the Senate that Maury be reimbursed for his wind and sailing charts and sailing directions." Durkin, *Mallory*, p. 76. The source cited for this statement was "34 Cong., 1 Sess., March 18, 1856 (Cong. *Globe* Appendix, 245)." The closest scrutiny of the records for that period reveals no such move on the part of Senator Mallory. Durkin must have had reference to the offer that was made by Mallory in January, 1855, cited in Note 4, this chapter. In the same footnote 59 on p. 76 of his work, Durkin quotes Diana Corbin Maury's statement that Jefferson Davis and Senator Mallory were inimical to MFM both before and "after" (during) the Civil War. Durkin refers to Mrs. Corbin as "this not completely reliable source." There were errors in Mrs. Corbin's book but not on this point, as Father Durkin could have ascertained by a careful study of the Maury and Bache papers in the LC and the Henry papers in the SIA.

98. Durkin, *Mallory*, p. 76.

99. MFM to William M. Blackford, March 24, 1856, and to B. Franklin Minor, April 1, 1856, MP, Vol. VI, LC.

100. On March 26 MFM wrote to three former secretaries of the Navy under whom he had served who lived near enough to give a quick reply. Former Secretary John Y. Mason was in Paris as U.S. Minister, and no query went to him as no answer could be received in less than a month. See the letters of MFM to William A. Graham, John P. Kennedy, and William Ballard Preston, March 26, 1856, and their replies printed in *Speech of Senator John Bell of Tennessee on the Naval Retiring Board delivered in the Senate, April 28 and 29, 1856,* p. 12.

101. *Congressional Globe Appendix,* March 31, 1856, 34th Cong., 1st Sess., pp. 310-325.

102. *Speech of Senator John Bell of Tennessee on the Naval Retiring Board delivered in the Senate, April 28 and 29, 1856,* p. 12.

103. Ibid., p. 9.

104. Ibid.

105. *Congressional Globe Appendix,* May 1, 1856, 34th Cong., 1st Sess., p. 510.

106. Ibid., May 15, 1856, pp. 572-573, 584.

107. Senator Butler of South Carolina, as quoted in Durkin, *Mallory,* p. 78.

108. *Congressional Globe Appendix,* May 15, 1856, 34th Cong., 1st Sess., p. 585.

109. Ibid.

110. Ibid.

111. Ibid.

112. Ibid.

113. "The Board has found me incompetent. It is cruel and cowardly treatment, could they not have said what was the reason of my incompetency instead of making it so broad, that envy, hatred and malice may lay hold of me under the general charge and bite me for it, saying that it is anything that is infamous, everything that is vile." NR, MFM to Commodore John Rodgers, Commanding North Pacific Surveying Expedition, Nov. 17, 1855, NOLS, Vol. XII, NAn.

    "I am therefore bound—I owe it to myself, my children and my friends to pursue this matter and never let it rest until the grounds of my alleged 'incompetency' be known. If it be lameness—let it be so stated, that no one may say it is drunkenness or any 'immorality.'" MFM to Ann Maury of New York, Nov. 3, 1855, MC, UVAL.

114. Senator Mallory repeated this statement on July 10, 1856, *Congressional Globe, Part 2,* July 10, 1856, 34th Cong., 1st Sess., p. 1594.

115. NR, MFM to Senator John Bell, Feb. 25, 1856, in NR, Miscellaneous . . . Lieut. MFM and Plucking Board, No. 54, NAn.

116. *Congressional Globe, Part 2,* July 10, 1856, 34th Cong., 1st Sess., p. 1594.

117. NR, MFM to the Hon. Neill S. Brown, Nov. 29, 1855, NOLS, Vol. XII, NAn.

118. NR, MFM to Senator John Bell, NR, Miscellaneous . . . Lieut. MFM and Plucking Board, No. 54, NAn.

119. *Congressional Globe, Part 2,* July 15, 1856, 34th Cong., 1st Sess., p. 1638. Also see report of passage in *National Intelligencer,* July 18, 1856, p. 3.

120. *National Intelligencer,* July 16, 1856, p. 3. This newspaper reported that the Senate on July 17 confirmed the promotion of all but three or four out of the 200 officers up for promotion as a result of the action of the 1855 board; *National Intelligencer,* July 18, 1856, p. 3.

121. Mr. Clingman introduced the act in the House of Representatives, *Congressional Globe,* Feb. 21, 1856, 34th Cong., 1st Sess., p. 487. On March 24, 1856, Representative J. S. Millson made a strong speech in the House in favor of MFM, *Congressional Globe Appendix,* March 24, 1856, 34th Cong., 1st Sess., pp. 266-270.
122. *Congressional Globe, Part 2,* July 28, 1856, 34th Cong., 1st Sess., pp. 1795-1796.
123. Report on Lieut. O. H. Berryman's imminent departure for deep-sea soundings in U.S.S. *Arctic, National Intelligencer,* July 19, 1856, p. 3.
124. NR, telegram of Secretary of Navy J. C. Dobbin to Charles Henry Davis, Superintendent, Nautical Almanac, Cambridge, Mass., Nov. 7, 1856, Letters to Officers, Ships of War, Vol. LIV, NAn.
125. NR, letter of Secretary of Navy Dobbin to Charles Henry Davis, Nov. 15, 1856, ibid.
126. Davis, *C. H. Davis,* p. 99.
127. Representative Samuel P. Benson of Maine had asked consent of the House to report the bill for printing and that it then be recommitted to committee. This was not granted and there was no debate, *Congressional Globe, Part 2,* Aug. 13, 1856, 34th Cong., 1st Sess., pp. 2159-2160. For passage of the bill in House, see *Congressional Globe,* Jan. 12, 1857, 34th Cong., 3rd Sess., pp. 301-302.
128. "An Act to amend 'An Act to promote the Efficiency of the Navy,'" Jan. 16, 1857, *Navy Register, 1857,* pp. 126-127.
129. Precept from Secretary of Navy Dobbin to Capt. E. A. F. Lavalette, setting up Naval Court of Inquiry, Feb. 12, 1857, and Feb. 6 orders to Capt. Lavalette, Feb. 12 orders to Capts. S. H. Stringham and William I. McCluney to report for duty on the court; NR, RG 125, Records of the Office of the JAGen. (Navy): "Courts of Inquiry, Act of January 16, 1857," Vol. XXI, pp. 2-5.

CHAPTER XV

Court of Inquiry

1. NR, MFM to Prof. John B. Minor, Feb. 25, 1857, NOLS, Vol. XIV, NAn. A naval court of inquiry did not carry with it the imputation of blame as did a court-martial. Many of the Navy's crack officers had been before courts of inquiry. See, for instance: NR, Hull, Isaac, 1773-1843, defendant, Minutes of proceedings of the court of inquiry into official conduct of Capt. Isaac Hull at U.S. Navy Yard, Charlestown, Mass., Aug. 12, 1822; also same on Capt. James Biddle, Oct. 7, 1822, NAn.
2. NR, MFM to Secretary of Navy Isaac Toucey, Apr. 6, 1857, NOLS, Vol. XIV, NAn.
3. Navy Department Circular filed in *Navy Register, 1857,* following p. 134, Search Room, NAn.
4. Order for court to convene Feb. 20, 1857—see "Precept" of Secretary of Navy Dobbin to Capt. E. A. F. Lavalette, U.S. Navy, Feb. 12, 1857, NR, RG 125: Records of the Office of the JAGen (Navy): "Courts of Inquiry, Act of January 16, 1857," Vol. XXI, p. 2.
5. "When I entered upon my duties in this Department [March 7, 1857] I found a Naval court of inquiry already organized under the act of

January 16, 1857. Deeming it important that the investigation directed by that act should be brought to an early conclusion, I immediately organized two additional courts. These three courts have prosecuted their labors with great assiduity." This statement in one section of Secretary of Navy Toucey's first annual report was concluded by remarks indicating the Secretary's desire to shed all responsibility for the courts or for their actions. See *Annual Report of the Secretary of the Navy, 1857*, p. 583.

6. Captain E. A. F. Lavalette was president, Capts. S. H. Stringham and William J. McCluney were members, and J. M. Carlisle was judge advocate of the first court of inquiry; see Precept of Secretary Dobbin cited in Note 4. On March 21, 1857, Charles H. Winder was appointed judge advocate of the court and replaced J. M. Carlisle on the court presided over by Lavalette. On April 6, 1857, Capt. Henry A. Adams was ordered to relieve Capt. Stringham at the conclusion of case then being heard. On Aug. 8, 1857, Capt. William J. McCluney was relieved from duty on the court, and on Sept. 1, 1857, Capt. Samuel Mercer was ordered to report for duty on the court. NR, RG 125, Records of the office of the JAGen (Navy): "Courts of Inquiry, Act of January 16, 1857," Vol. XXI, pp. 2-10, NAn.

7. Circular of Secretary of Navy Toucey, May 4, 1857, filed in *Navy Register, 1857*, following p. 134, Search Room, NAn.

8. MFM to B. Franklin Minor, June 1 and 10, 1857, MP, Vol. VII, LC.

9. NR, MFM to Secretary of Navy Toucey, Oct. 15, 1857, NOLS, Vol. XV, NAn.

10. He had written this after reading in the *Congressional Globe* that "they have been overhauling the files of the Department to see what they can rake up against me." MFM to B. Franklin Minor, Jan. 23, 1856, MP, Vol. V, LC.

11. Following a severe late-June storm that knocked his fruit, flowers, and vegetables in the garden at the Observatory "into the middle of next week," MFM suffered a chill. He said he was making preparations to go to "the White," as he and other Southerners called the Greenbrier White Sulphur Springs in Greenbrier County, Va. (later W. Va.). Ibid., June 27, 1857, Vol. VII.

12. "I embrace the opportunity at this same time to express the gratification with which I have observed this honorable tribute from so distinguished a source to the merits and labors of a citizen of the United States." Secretary of State Lewis Cass to MFM, "Superintendent of National Observatory, now at White Sulphur Springs, Greenbrier County, Va.," Aug. 24, 1857, and enclosed copy of letter of Count Walewski, Minister of Foreign Affairs of France, to John Y. Mason, U.S. Minister to France, July 17, 1857, all in MP, Vol. VII, under date of Aug. 24, 1857, LC.

13. John Y. Mason, U.S. Minister to France, to Count Walewski, Minister of Foreign Affairs, July 27, 1857, in reply to that of Count Walewski to him of July 17, 1857—copies of both in MP, Vol. VII, LC.

14. Count Walewski wrote about the Emperor's wishing to honor MFM to M. le Compte de Sartiges, French Minister to the U.S. on Nov. 6, 1858, copy in MP, Vol. VII, LC. MFM did not immediately receive this honor but was eventually made a commander of the Legion of Honor, Corbin, *Maury*, Appendix A, p. 291.

15. MFM was particularly absorbed at this time in a study of the abstract log of an extended cruise of a British ship, the *Gloriana,* commanded by Capt. Henry Toynbee. The captain had been accompanied by his wife. Mrs. Toynbee had decorated the log with "exquisite microscopic drawings of the insects of the sea." MFM published these in color in the 8th edition of *Sailing Directions.* For his description of these, see MFM to Ann Maury of New York, Dec. 9, 1857, MC, UVAL.

16. It had been brought out in the debates in the U.S. Senate in 1856 that all U.S. mail steamers of the period had to be commanded by a U.S. naval officer, yet this was not technically counted as sea duty for an officer. William Lewis Herndon was a commander by rank, having been promoted in July, 1856.

16. Lovette, *Naval Customs,* p. 16.

17. *Report of Lt. Matthew F. Maury on the loss of the United States Mail Steamer Central America under the command of William Lewis Herndon,* written Oct. 19, 1857, published in Washington, 1884. Lewis Herndon's wife "Mit" and his daughter Ellen had spent part of the preceding winter with the Maurys; Goolrick, *Historic Fredericksburg,* p. 125.

18. NR, MFM to Secretary of Navy Toucey, Oct. 10, 1857, NOLS, Vol. XV, NAn.

19. Secretary of Navy Toucey to MFM, Oct. 13, 1857, in NR, RG 125: Records of the Office of the JAGen (Navy): "Courts of Inquiry, Act of January 16, 1857," Vol. XXI, pp. 16-17.

20. NR, MFM to Secretary of Navy Toucey, Oct. 15, 1857, NOLS, Vol. XV, NAn.

21. "The Case of Lieut. M. F. Maury, Naval Court of Inquiry, No. 1," in NR, RG 125: Records of the Office of the JAGen (Navy): "Courts of Inquiry, Act of January 16, 1857," Vol. XXI, pp. 1-13, NAn.

    For consistency I have standardized as Lieut. all abbreviations for Lieutenant used in the record of the court.

22. Duties and procedure as explained by Capt. W. J. Murphy, U.S.N., Director of Litigation and Claims Division, Office of the JAGen, Department of the Navy, in letter to Commander R. H. Maury, U.S.N. (Ret.), June 22, 1962, in answer to questions asked for me by Commander Maury. Capt. Murphy also sent copies of Articles 23-25, Articles for the Government of the Navy, approved July 17, 1862, and Articles 55-60 from *Regulations for the Government of the Navy of the United States,* as approved by Secretary of the Navy on Aug. 7, 1876, Washington, 1876; and Instructions for Courts and Boards, Articles 505-509, from *Naval Courts and Boards* as approved by Secretary of Navy, Aug. 18, 1917, Washington, 1917.

23. From this note through Note 61, all citations refer to "The Case of Lieut. M. F. Maury . . . Court of Inquiry . . ." cited in Note 21. For this specific reference, see p. 13 of that record.

24. Ibid., pp. 15-17.

25. Ibid.; first five paragraphs of quotation, pp. 17-18; sixth paragraph, p. 21.

26. Ibid., p. 21; see also p. 19.

27. Ibid., pp. 1-68 for complete method of procedure.

28. Ibid., p. 22.

29. **Ibid.,** p. 23.

30. Ibid., pp. 23-25.

31. Ibid., p. 25.
32. Ibid., p. 26.
33. Ibid., pp. 26-29.
34. Ibid., p. 29.
35. Ibid., p. 30.
36. Ibid., p. 31.
37. Ibid., pp. 31-32.
38. Ibid., p. 32.
39. Ibid., pp. 56-57.
40. Ibid., p. 32.
41. Ibid., p. 33.
42. Ibid., p. 34.
43. Ibid., p. 34.
44. Ibid., p. 34.
45. Ibid., pp. 35-40.
46. Ibid.; first six paragraphs of quotation, pp. 41-42; balance of quotation, pp. 44-46.
47. Ibid., pp. 46-47.
48. Ibid., pp. 47-48.
49. Ibid., pp. 50-51.
50. Ibid., pp. 51-52.
51. Ibid., pp. 52-53.
52. Ibid., pp. 54-55; quotations on p. 55.
53. Ibid., p. 55.
54. Ibid., p. 55.
55. Ibid., pp. 56-57.
56. Ibid., pp. 57-58.
57. Ibid., p. 58.
58. Ibid., pp. 58A (incorrectly numbered 57 on record) and 58B (incorrectly numbered 58 on record).
59. Ibid., p. 58B.
60. Ibid., pp. 58B-59.
61. Ibid., p. 59.
62. This was the first year in a decade that there had been no specific mention in the annual report of the Secretary of Navy of work achieved by Maury at the Observatory. For comment on the Secretary's failure to mention, see MFM to William M. Blackford, Dec. 17, 1857; see also Dabney H. Maury to MFM, Dec. 16, 1857, both in MP, Vol. VII, LC.
63. Although Secretary Toucey failed to mention Herndon, a monument was erected at Annapolis in 1860 to commemorate Commander William Lewis Herndon's heroic death at sea. It is located near the chapel, just off Chapel Walk at the United States Naval Academy.
64. President Buchanan's nomination of MFM for promotion to commander on active list of Navy, Dec. 22, 1857, *Journal of the Executive Proceedings of the Senate of the United States of America from December 3, 1855, to June 16, 1858,* Vol. X, p. 268.
65. Ibid., p. 277.
66. Ibid., p. 285.
67. Ibid., p. 291 (Senate confirmation, Jan. 18, 1858).
68. *National Intelligencer,* Jan. 23, 1858, p. 3.

69. Secretary of Navy Toucey to MFM, Jan. 29, 1858, MP, Vol. VII, LC. MFM's commission as a commander in the Navy is in MP, Miscellaneous File, LC.

70. MFM to William C. Hasbrouck, March 29, 1858, MP, Vol. VII, LC. MFM's belief that further efforts would be made against him was to come true. Others realized this, too. To try to prevent MFM's being removed from his post at the Observatory and to urge that he be promoted, resolutions were passed by the General Assembly of New Jersey on March 18, 1858, by the General Assembly of Virginia on April 8, 1858. Similar resolutions were passed by the legislatures of Tennessee, Louisiana, Maryland, and Alabama. See MFM letter to Hasbrouck, this note; resolutions filed by date in MP, Vol. VII, LC; and Virginia resolution printed in *Acts of the Virginia General Assembly of 1857-1858*, p. 287.

71. Navy Department Circular filed in *Navy Register, 1857*, following p. 134, Search Room, NAn.

72. There can be no debating the fact that a balance between shore duty and sea duty has always been accepted procedure in the U.S. Navy. In the case of MFM, however, the senators in their debates and MFM in his correspondence brought out the fact that the Navy Retiring Board had not been authorized by law to make any distinction between service afloat and service ashore, as well as the fact that MFM was an officer of inferior rank whom the Navy Department could have ordered to sea at any moment the authorities decided sea duty more important for him than his service at the Observatory.

Among the reforms brought about in the reorganization of the Navy in the Civil War years was the creation of the rank of admiral and other grades long urged by MFM and other officers. Retirement rules were established in 1861, and in 1862 the first advisory board on promotions was appointed by the Secretary of Navy. See the *Retirement Rules of December 21, 1861, U.S. Navy* and "An Act to Establish and Equalize the Grade of Line Officers of the United States Navy," U.S. Statutes at Large, Vol. XII, pp. 329-330; also see the *Navy Registers* for 1863 and 1865. For establishment of an examining board of three naval officers, see *Annual Report of Secretary of Navy, 1862*, pp. 40-41; and U.S. Statutes at Large, Vol. XIII, pp. 53-54, 420.

CHAPTER XVI

Crusade for a U.S. Weather Bureau

1. *Army and Navy Chronicle and Scientific Repository*, Jan. 19, 1843, p. 58, Feb. 16, 1843, p. 182, and subsequent issues. See also MFM to Ann Maury of New York, Aug. 4, 1842, MC, UVAL.

2. Weber, *Hydrographic Office*, p. 18; MFM to John Quincy Adams, Nov. 17, 1847, *SLM*, Vol. XIII, No. 1 (January, 1848), p. 10.

3. NR, MFM to the Earl of Rosse, July 27, 1854, NOLS, Vol. XI, NAn. See also MFM, Sailing Directions (8th ed., 1858), Vol. I, pp. ix-xiii.

4. MFM, *On the Establishment of a Universal System of Meteorological Observations by Sea and Land;* NR, MFM to Prof. Joseph Henry, Smithsonian Institution, Jan. 14, 1852, and to American scientists and service leaders, Jan. 14, 15, 17, 20, 1852, NOLS, Vol. VII, NAn.

5. William J. Rhees, *The Smithsonian Institution, Journal of the Board of Regents, Reports of Committees* . . . , 1879, p. 43.

6. Quoted from Smithsonian Report for 1848 by Marcus Benjamin in "Meteorology"; George Brown Goode (ed.), *The Smithsonian Institution, 1846-1896, The History of its First Half Century* (cited hereafter as **Goode,** **Smithsonian**), p. 653.

7. Eric R. Miller, "The Evolution of Meterological Institutions in the United States," *Monthly Weather Review,* Vol. LIX, No. 1 (January, 1931), p. 2; *Smithsonian Report, 1851,* p. 68.

8. Goode, *Smithsonian,* p. 654.

9. Ibid.

10. Quotation from Joseph Henry Journal (notebook), Feb. 9, 1849, quoted in Goode, *Smithsonian,* p. 146.

11. Ibid., quotation of entry in Joseph Henry Journal, March 12, 1849.

12. Goode, *Smithsonian,* p. 654 (150 monthly returns in 1849).

13. James H. Coffin, professor of mathematics and astronomy at Lafayette College, Easton, Pa., had furnished the names of possible observers to whom the circular had been sent in the winter of 1848-1849. In his *Treatise on the Winds of the Northern Hemisphere* (1853), he pointed out the existence of three important wind zones in the Northern Hemisphere. Arnold Guyot's first service to the Smithsonian was the selecting and ordering of more accurate instruments that were distributed to observers making meteorological observations for the Smithsonian. He prepared a pamphlet, *Directions for Meteorological Observations,* issued by the Smithsonian in 1850, and compiled *A Collection of Meteorological Tables,* issued in 1852. See Goode, *Smithsonian,* pp. 654-656.

14. Joseph Henry Journal, entry for Jan. 3, 1852, SIA.

15. Goode, *Smithsonian,* p. 143.

16. Joseph Henry Journal, entry for Jan. 24, 1852, SIA.

17. Ibid., Jan. 27, 1852.

18. Ibid., March 2, April 16, April 17, 1852.

19. Ibid., May 1, May 6, May 31, 1852.

20. NR, MFM to Secretary of Navy James C. Dobbin, Nov. 7, 1854, **NOLS,** Vol. XI, NAn.

21. "Lieutenant Maury's New Enterprise," *National Intelligencer,* Sept. 18, 1855, p. 3.

22. For MFM's proposals, see MFM, "An Appeal to the Agricultural Interests of Virginia," *Southern Planter and Farmer,* Vol. XV, No. 6 (June, 1855), pp. 161-163; MFM, "Meteorology for the Farmers," *American Farmer,* Vol. XI, No. 2 (August, 1855), pp. 33-35. The quotation is from MFM to B. Franklin Minor, Nov. 20, 1855, MP, Vol. V, LC.

23. Message of MFM in letter written for him by Diana Maury to B. Franklin Minor, Dec. 18, 1855, MP, Vol. V, LC.

24. MFM to B. Franklin Minor, Jan. 11, 1856, MP, Vol. V, LC.

25. MFM letter published in New York *Daily Tribune,* Dec. 25, 1855, p. 3.

26. MFM, *Physical Geography of the Sea,* pp. 91-92.

27. *U.S. Agricultural Society Journal for 1856, Part I, Vol. III, Journal of 4th Annual Meeting, January, 1856,* pp. 1-38. The quotation is from p. 38.

28. MFM to B. Franklin Minor, per Nannie Curly (Diana), in Corbin, *Maury,* p. 79.

29. *U.S. Agricultural Society Journal for 1856, Part I, Vol. III, Journal of 4th Annual Meeting, January, 1856,* pp. 39-43, 48.

30. Ibid., pp. 48-51.

31. Ibid., pp. 51, 52.

32. Ibid., p. 52.

33. Ibid., pp. 52, 53.

34. Ibid., p. 53.

35. *Bache Address,* A.A.A.S., 1851; see also Joseph Henry, "Meteorology in Its Connection with Agriculture," *Scientific Writings of Joseph Henry,* 2 vols. bound as one. See Vol. II, pp. 85-86, in *Smithsonian Miscellaneous Collections,* Vol. XXX.

36. MFM to B. Franklin Minor, Jan. 11, 1856, MP, Vol. V, LC.

37. Ibid., Jan. 21, 1856.

38. Ibid.

39. MFM worked with Senator James Harlan, supplying ideas to be incorporated in the bill and in the report. See Orrin E. Klapp, "Matthew Fontaine Maury, Naval Scientist," *USNIP,* Vol. LXXI, Whole No. 513 (November, 1945), pp. 1323-1324.

40. A copy of Senator Harlan's report, dated Dec. 18, 1856, is in MP, Vol. XLVI, LC. See *Senate Rep. No. 292, made Dec. 18, 1856, on behalf of Senate Committee on Agriculture, to accompany bill S. 481, 34th Cong., 3rd Sess.*

41. Even while MFM was representing the United States at the Brussels Conference, one of these critical letters signed only by an initial had appeared in a Washington paper. MFM's second-in-command had reported it to MFM in Belgium, commenting that MFM would recognize "the paternity of it." Following the meeting of the U.S. Agricultural Society in January, 1856, MFM wrote about such a piece in a Washington paper, "You scented Henry I see. I was told his piece meant as you read it. So you are right." MFM to B. Franklin Minor, Jan. 16, 1856, MP, Vol. V, LC.

42. Letter to the editor, dated Feb. 18, 1857, signed "X," published in the Boston *Atlas* between Feb. 19 and 24, 1857. The original clipping from the *Atlas* that was sent to B. Franklin Minor, Feb. 26, 1857, is filed under latter date, MP, Vol. VII, LC.

43. Ibid.

44. In 1854 MFM stated that Col. Edward Sabine, vice-president and treasurer of the Royal Society, Sir George Biddell Airy, Astronomer Royal, Capt. Henry James, R.E., F.R.S., M.R.I.A., F.G.S., of England, Johann von Lamont, of Munich, C.H.D. Buys-Ballot, director of the Meteorological Institute of Holland, Adolphe Quetelet, director of the Royal Observatory of Belgium, Wilhelm Heinrich Dove of Berlin, and A. T. Kupffer, leading Russian meteorologist, favored a conference to take up extension to the land of the system of marine meteorological observations agreed on at the Brussels Conference. In 1858 MFM reminded Secretary of Navy Toucey of his having long urged this and informed the Secretary that Holland had just taken this step. See NR, MFM to Marin H. Jansen, Jan. 17, 1854, NOLS, Vol. X; to Nils Ihlen, R.N., Norway, Nov. 2, 1854, NOLS, Vol. XI; to Secretary of Navy Toucey, Feb. 4, 1858, NOLS, Vol. XV, NAn.

In 1859 MFM wrote Irish scientist John Locke in Dublin, "You are right. The system of meteorological research which we have established for the sea, *must* be extended to the land also. . . . You know that Le Verrier in Paris is in receipt daily by telegraph of all parts of the Continent. These he prints immediately and circulates—but they get no discussion—and it is discussion—instantaneous discussion, that we want. If you succeed with your government, I have no doubt Le Verrier will send to your office every day his reports, for he gets them as far off as St. Petersburg, Moscow, Vienna etc." NR, Nov. 17 (first half of quotation), Nov. 23 (last half), 1859, NOLS, Vol. XVII, NAn.

"The British Association [for the Advancement of Science] has asked the British Government to carry out my plan of daily weather reports by telegraph," MFM to B. Franklin Minor, Dec. 4, 1859, MP, Vol. VIII, LC.

Adolphe Quetelet, director of the Royal Observatory, Brussels, in 1860 stated, "I am persuaded that in all these countries [France, Holland, England, Spain, Portugal, Sweden and Norway, Italy, Belgium, Austria, the republic of Bremen, Prussia, Denmark, Chile and Brazil—co-operating in marine meteorological program] my colleagues concur with me, equally in the interest of science as well as industry, that we should enlarge the circle of our observations, to extend the researches on land and thus to make the system universal." *De la Nécessité d'un Système Général d'Observations Nautique et Météorologiques,* Extract from the *Bulletins of the Royal Academy of Science . . . of Belgium,* Ser. 2, Vol. IX, No. 5 (1860), 20-page pamphlet.

45. In the satiric tone he adopted in speaking of Joseph Henry after the latter attacked him at the U.S. Agricultural Society meeting in January, 1856, MFM wrote, "Your friend Henry and the Patent Office are now making arrangements so a Member of Congress told me today, with the companies for daily reports of the weather through Telegraph!" He concluded that they were "villains" who would "steal your brains." MFM to B. Franklin Minor, June 11, 1856, MP, Vol. VI, LC. That MFM was wrong in this belief is shown by Marcus Benjamin's statement that Joseph Henry borrowed the idea of using telegraphy in connection with meteorology from Elias Loomis, who had got the idea from an article by William C. Redfield published in 1846, Goode, *Smithsonian,* p. 656, fns 3, 4. It is true that the identical idea of a weather map had been a part of MFM's plan as proposed in Senator Harlan's Senate bill.

46. Joseph Henry stated that the telegraphic weather information was first exhibited daily on the Smithsonian weather map in 1856 and that, "At the same time publication of telegraphic despatches was made in the newspapers," *Scientific Writings of Joseph Henry* (as cited in Note 35), Vol. II, p. 453.

The brilliance of Joseph Henry's intellect, his achievements as a physicist, his contribution to the advancement of meteorology and other sciences through his leadership of scientific societies, and especially through his administration of the Smithsonian Institution, have been most ably reported in a wide variety of publications. In this book the limitations of space have forced me to confine myself to the story of Joseph Henry as it affected the achievements and reputation of MFM, the subject of this biography. For more information on Joseph Henry, see Thomas Coulson, *Joseph Henry, His Life and Work;* Goode, *Smithsonian,* especially pp. 115-156, 647-678; also see *Annual Reports of the Board of Regents of the Smith-*

sonian Institution to Congress (*Smithsonian Reports*) for the years 1846-1878; William J. Rhees, *The Smithsonian: Journals of the Board of Regents, Reports of Committees, Statistics* . . . ; also *The Scientific Writings of Joseph Henry*, 2 vols.; S. P. Langley, "The Meteorological Work of the Smithsonian Institution," Bulletin No. 11 of the U.S. Weather Bureau; William B. Taylor, "The Scientific Work of Joseph Henry," *Bulletin of the Philosophical Society of Washington, 1878*, Vol. II, pp. 230-238.

47. See quotation from MFM letter to John Locke cited in Note 44.
48. Orrin E. Klapp, "Matthew Fontaine Maury, Naval Scientist," cited in Note 39, this chapter, p. 1315.
49. Of the scientific clique that opposed him, MFM said, "They are dogs in the manger, and require everything that is done [in American science] to be subsidiary to their will," NR, MFM to Prof. C. H. D. Buys-Ballot, director of the Meteorological Institute, Utrecht, Holland, Sept. 13, 1859, NOLS, Vol. XVII, NAn.
50. NR, MFM to Lieut. Félix Julien, Imperial Navy, Toulon, France, July 18, 1859, NOLS, Vol. XVII, NAn.
51. MFM requested leave, to begin Nov. 17, 1858, for "three or four weeks" for his "personal affairs." NR, MFM to Secretary of Navy Toucey, Nov. 10, 1858, NOLS, Vol. XVI, NAn. On the 15th he wrote, "I go off lecturing in a day or two . . . I am hard up and have to resort to this to make the two ends meet," MFM to John Minor, Fredericksburg, Nov. 15, 1858, MP, Vol. VII, LC. For description of lecture tour, see MFM to his wife from Chicago, Nov. 20, from Kalamazoo, Mich., Nov. 23, from Chicago, Nov. 27, from Cleveland, Dec. 1, 1858, MP, Vol. VII, LC; also quoted with account of his lectures from Chicago *Press and Tribune*, Nov. 23, 1858, in Corbin, *Maury*, pp. 166-173.
52. MFM to William C. Hasbrouck, Nov. 2, 1858, in MP, Vol. VII, LC.
53. Senator Bell had informed the Senate that the late Navy Retiring Board had not left MFM in the "enjoyment of his position as superintendent of the Observatory, and of the emoluments attached to it . . . the extent of their generosity towards him, distinguished as he is by eminent service, will be told when it is stated that they recommended him to be placed on the leave-pay list, with a salary of $1,200, without the hope of promotion or of any increased compensation whatever," *Speech of Senator John Bell . . . April 28 and 29, 1856*, p. 11.
54. MFM to B. Franklin Minor, written from Tremont House, Boston, Dec. 7, 1856, MP, Vol. VI, LC.
55. Catherine Cate Coblentz, unpublished biography, "Naval Lieutenant Matthew Fontaine Maury: First Citizen of the World, 1853-1953," Chapt. XVII, "Deep Sea Soundings," fn 14, MP, LC.
56. Accounts of his speeches, Buffalo *Commercial Advertiser*, Nov. 28, 1856, in Lewis, *Maury*, pp. 103-104; Cleveland *Plain Dealer*, Nov. 22, 1858, in Maury, *Corbin*, p. 166. See also articles in Cleveland *Plain Dealer*, Nov. 30, Dec. 2, Dec. 3, 1858; Detroit *Daily Advertiser*, Dec. 17, 1858.
57. These facts were given in MFM's speech at Chicago, reported in Chicago *Press and Tribune*, Nov. 23, 1858, quoted in Corbin, *Maury*, p. 172.
58. NR, MFM to Capt. E. P. Dorr, Buffalo, N.Y., Dec. 28, 1858, NOLS, Vol. XVI, NAn.

59. Ibid.
60. Capt. E. P. Dorr to Thompson B. Maury, Feb. 25, 1873, MP, Vol. XLIII, LC. See also R. H. Heywood to Mary H. Maury, May 6, 1873, MP, Vol. XLIV, LC.
61. MFM, Address delivered before North Alabama Mechanical and Agricultural Society, Oct. 19, 1859, MP, Vol. XLVII, LC.
62. Speech of Representative Vest of Missouri, delivered on Dec. 14, 1880, in the 46th Cong., 3rd Sess., as quoted in Corbin, *Maury*, pp. 96-97.
63. NR, MFM to Adolphe Quetelet, Dec. 7, 1860, NOLS, Vol. XVIII, NAn. For Henry's criticism of using ordinary seamen to make meterological observations, see *Scientific Writings of Joseph Henry* (cited in Note 35 this chapter), Vol. II, p. 37.
64. MFM letter to Quetelet cited in Note 63.
65. NR, MFM to Heinrich Wilhelm Dove, May 29, 1860, NOLS, Vol. XVII, NAn.
66. MFM to Rutson Maury, March 3, 1861, to Prof. Charles Piazzi Smyth, Edinburgh, March 4, 1861, MP, Vol. XI, LC.
67. MFM to B. Franklin Minor, April 2, 1861, MP, Vol. XI, LC.

CHAPTER XVII

Maury the Man

1. The personal correspondence of MFM, in MP, LC; the written reminiscences of Diana, Mary, and Eliza, in MP, Vols. XLII, XLIV; Diana's account in her book, and Betty Herndon Maury's Diary in MP, LC—all reveal the role that the giving and receiving of affection played in the life of MFM. Even in MFM's official correspondence, in NR, NOLS, NAn, this is evident in letters to and from professional associates who through their work together became friends.

   The fact that Ann's petite and feminine type of woman continued to be MFM's ideal of womanly beauty is revealed by a comparison he made of two young cousins. He admired Harriet, who was small of stature. "I think Harriet beautiful though most persons like Nan's appearance better. Nan is quite tall," MFM to Ann Maury of New York, May 6, 1849, MC, UVAL.

   The closest approach to Ann's arguing with MFM was recounted by her to her eldest son. She wrote that even after marriage she worried over the possibility that MFM should have married someone else (the implication was that an intellectual woman might have suited him better). She reported that she had often told MFM this but that he always assured her that she was wrong; Mrs. Ann Herndon Maury to her son, Richard Launcelot Maury, Oct. 15, 1859, MP, Vol. VIII, LC.
2. MFM wrote to Ann's brother, "Her gentleness has blessed us all—for with God's help it was her goodness, her teachings and her example that made my Davy Jones [John] the lovely character and the faultless son that he was." MFM to Dr. Brodie S. Herndon, Apr. 22, 1863, MP, Vol. XVIII, LC.
3. MFM described his wife, Ann, whom he started calling Nannie after their first months of marriage, as "my first and only love, my charming Nannie, who has helped and who now cheers and comforts me." MFM to Mrs. William Maury, Liverpool, England, Nov. 14, 1846, MP, Vol. III, LC.

To Ann he wrote "[your] noble spirit of firmness and of resolution, which has borne you up so manfully," MFM to his wife, Sept. 16, 1865, MP, Vol. XXIII, LC.

In addition to calling his wife Nannie, MFM gave their daughter Diana the nickname Nannie Curly, which was shortened to Nannie when she grew up. In citing letters I have employed the name used in the salutation, placing the actual name immediately after in parentheses.

4. MFM mentioned Ann's quality of gentleness so often that it must have had a very great influence on him. A man who suffered attack carried on in such secrecy that he had no way to confound his critics had need of the unswerving loyalty of a woman like Ann Herndon Maury. MFM fought back against his opponents and remembered those who had attempted to reduce him to a position of professional impotence, but after each attack he moved on to new action instead of making a career of recrimination. A study of all available evidence on MFM's life has convinced me that Ann played a subtle but substantial role in helping her husband cast off what temptation may have been his, after 1855, to become a permanently angry man. He wrote Ann later of his efforts "to show myself worthy of you . . . and do homage to the great ambition that I have to deserve your . . . praise and love." Sept. 23, 1865, quoted in Corbin, *Maury*, p. 245.

5. MFM to Ann Maury of New York, Sept. 20, 1851, MC, UVAL. Before moving into the house he had written "Nannie [Ann] will be in Fredericksburg for some weeks yet . . . till the house be ready, with which I am very busy—carpeting, building, painting, etc., etc." Ibid., Sept. 30, 1847.

6. Ann, who had lost both parents before she was 14 years old, had in the following years often been invited for extended visits in the homes of Virginia relatives. Her aunt, Mrs. Lucy Herndon Minor (Mrs. Dabney Minor, Jr.), welcomed her at all times to her home "Woodlawn," on the North Anna River in Orange County and wrote of 16-year-old Ann to a relative, "Ann will remain here as long as she pleases. I have told her to consider it a home" (Sept. 20, 1827); "Ann Herndon and Cordelia [Mrs. Minor's 17-year-old daughter] have established themselves in the schoolroom [outside building] and they would be quite happy but for their proximity to Violet [elderly maid] whose tongue is a great annoyance" (Dec. 15, 1827). "Henry [Mrs. Minor's son] went to Fredericksburg last week & John [Ann's brother] returned with him in a gig to carry Ann down. Her friends in George Town [Washington] were so urgent for her to visit them [that] Mr. Roberts thought she had better go, & she has gone down with the expectation of doing so. . . . We all miss Ann very much; she had endeared herself to everyone by her sweetness of disposition and sprightliness of manners—Cordelia seems quite in the cellar now —they had intended to go to the Ball at L. C. House [Louisa Court House] on the 22nd [George Washington birthday ball] but I believe Cordelia has declined attending it now" (Feb. 17, 1828). These excerpts from the letters of Mrs. Lucy Herndon Minor, sent me by her great-great-granddaughter, Miss Lucy Herndon Ewin, reveal the affection with which Ann's relatives and friends surrounded her. It was natural for a person of her diffidence to prefer to be with those who had shown her so much kindness in her youth. Ann and her brother, Brodie S. Herndon, were particularly

close. Each was deeply religious and neither placed great value on worldly possessions. After practicing medicine in Culpeper, Va., for a period, Brodie returned to Fredericksburg to practice. Ann and the children often visited in his home in Fredericksburg.

7. "Nannie [Ann], Mary [her sister who lived with them] and I 'out-did' ourselves in visiting yesterday by making some fifteen calls. The first time Nannie has been in the mood and health for junketing for a long time." MFM to Ann Maury of New York, May 6, 1849, MC, UVAL. For MFM's urging her to make calls, see MFM to his wife, Nov. 23, 1858, in Corbin, *Maury*, pp. 167-168.

8. For MFM's evaluation of the qualities he admired and believed a married woman should possess, see the letter he wrote his eldest daughter, Betty, Dec. 26, 1856, just after she became engaged, and the letter he wrote his daughter Diana immediately after her marriage, in Corbin, *Maury*, pp. 161-165.

9. MFM to Lucian Minor, July 14, 1844, MP, Vol. III, LC.

10. "I agree with you about . . . the shallowness of female education in the United States." MFM to Ann Maury of New York, Aug. 28, 1836, MC, UVAL; MFM to Mrs. William M. Blackford, Apr. 2, 1849, MP, Vol. III, LC.

11. "The school is getting on pretty well," said MFM of his teaching but admitted that teaching and planting the 17 acres of the Observatory grounds (which he called "the plantation") took much time; MFM to Ann Maury of New York, March 17, 1851, MC, UVAL; Corbin, *Maury*, pp. 152-153.

12. Mrs. Mary Maury Werth to her children, July 26, 1879, MP, Vol. XLII, LC.

13. Diana recounted the episode of her winning the telescope in her book; Corbin, *Maury*, pp. 154-155.

14. MFM's third daughter, Mary, who was first called Tots and later Molly, gave a good description of her father's method of interesting them in a study of nature on walks and visits to the garden while "talking all sorts of lovely nonsense to us." Mrs. Mary Maury Werth to her children, July 26, 1879, MP, Vol. XLII, LC.

15. Corbin, *Maury*, pp. 153-154.

16. MFM to his nephew Richard L. Maury in Tennessee, Jan. 18, 1858, MP, Vol. VII, LC.

17. As a youth, MFM had felt strongly that the curriculum at Harpeth Academy had overemphasized Latin and Greek and that he had not received sufficient schooling in mathematics and science. He had hoped to go to West Point to receive advanced training in those subjects. In his mature years he held the view that the same imbalance in the curriculum was general in U.S. preparatory schools. He continued to believe that the U.S.M.A. at West Point gave a boy the best college education then available in the United States because it stressed science and mathematics instead of a classical course. He did not want to eliminate a study of the classic languages, but "the system, if it could be brought down to my wishes would soon attain to the happy middle—Latin to *some* but English to all." MFM to Ann Maury of New York, July 4, 1841; see also his letter to her Aug. 28, 1836, and letter to Mrs. William Maury, March 22, 1848, all in MC, UVAL.

18. NR, MFM to Edward Everett, Nov. 1, 1853, NOLS, Vol. X, NAn.
19. NR, MFM to Prof. Charles Piazzi Smyth, Edinburgh, Oct. 28, 1853, NOLS, Vol. X, NAn.
20. MFM to Ann Maury of New York, Dec. 1, 1854, MC, UVAL. J. M. D. Meiklejohn, M.A., later ran Rose Hill, preparatory school for boys in Bowdon, a suburb of Manchester, England, attended by Matthew Jr. See MFM to his wife, Jan. 1, April 15, April 16, April 19, 1863, MP, Vol. XVII, LC.
21. In December, 1859, when MFM was revising and enlarging his *Physical Geography of the Sea* for a new edition, he wrote, "I read Shakespeare to the children o' nights and work 'Physical Geography.'" MFM to B. Franklin Minor, Dec. 7, 1859, MP, Vol. VIII, LC.
22. Letter of Mrs. Mary M. Werth to her children cited in Note 12.
23. This remark is preceded by a statement of MFM's pleasure at having heard high praise for the daughter of the William M. Blackfords. "I hope she has a code of rules for study which are unbending and which she follows up daily with great diligence and that she does not often take doses of *poison* from those things called novels." MFM to Mrs. William M. Blackford, April 15, 1844, MP, Vol. III, LC.
24. Diana told this episode: "Betty borrowed 'Helen,' one of a very handsome and complete set of Miss Edgeworth's novels, from cousin Sally Fontaine in Washington, thinking or persuading herself, that Papa would not object, as that was so mild a type of fiction, and we both read most of it." However, MFM found them reading it and burned the book in the open fireplace of their mother's room. They wept over not being able to return the novel and did not learn until years later that he had replaced the book for the owner; Corbin, *Maury,* pp. 153-154.
25. MFM to A. Hamilton Lieber, who was about to enter the U.S. Naval Academy, May 30, 1850. Rear Admiral Henry B. Wilson, U.S.N., when Superintendent of the U.S.N.A., Annapolis, had this letter "published for the information of the Regiment," N.A. Dist. "B" & "E," U.S.N.A., 9-4-24-10933; and these quotations are taken from my copy of MFM's letter issued by Admiral Wilson to the midshipmen, U.S.N.A.
26. Ibid.
27. MFM to nephew Richard L. Maury, Tennessee, Jan. 13, 1858; to John Minor, Fredericksburg, Apr. 20, 1859, MP, Vol. VII, LC.
28. For MFM's dislike of lecturing for a fee, see MFM to B. Franklin Minor, Dec. 7, 1856, MP, Vol. VI, LC. For MFM's wanting the money for Dick's education, see MFM to Diana Maury Corbin, Apr. 12, 1858, in Corbin, *Maury,* p. 166.
29. The love and admiration that MFM's children felt for him are perhaps most clearly revealed in the personal diary kept by his daughter Betty in 1861-62. Betty could write of family feelings in a private diary in a way that her sister Diana could not in her published life of their father. There are two MS volumes to the Diary of Betty Herndon Maury (Mrs. William A. Maury) in MP, LC. The girls, who had excellent handwriting, had good grounds on which to tease their father about his. He accepted the joking in good grace and wrote, "Proof sheets of the Geological Gulf Stream were sent me yesterday. There were only two words and one of them a Latin and the other a *French* one that the printer could not make

out." MFM to Ann Maury of New York, May 24, 1844, MC, UVAL. For a daughter's grumbling about looking for MFM's lost papers, see Elie (Eliza) Maury to Marin H. Jansen, Aug. 4, 1870, MP, Vol. XXXV, LC.

30. "Betty our eldest daughter was married to Wm. A. son of John W. Maury at 1 P.M. of 24 Feb. 1857 by the Rev. Mr. Cummings [name not clear] at the Observatory." Entry in records in Holy Bible inscribed "our family Bible—No. 2, M. F. & A. H. Maury" (Matthew Fontaine and Ann Herndon Maury). For MFM's feeling about marrying a cousin, see MFM to Betty Maury, Nov. 26, 1856, in Corbin, *Maury*, p. 161.

31. John Walker Maury, who had been a trustee of Columbian College (now George Washington University) and a regent ex officio of the Smithsonian Institution when mayor of Washington, 1852-1854, had died Feb. 2, 1855, at the age of 46. Following his death, his widow found it necessary to sell his collection of paintings to add to her funds. Of her fifteen children, twelve lived to maturity. See William A. Maury, *John Walker Maury, His Lineage and Life*.

32. For praise of Will's character, see MFM to Betty Maury, Nov. 26, 1856, in Corbin, *Maury*, p. 161; for account of wedding, see Nannie (Diana) Maury to Nannie Maury (cousin), March 12, 1857, MP, Vol. VII, LC.

33. On March 1, 1858, in a letter to a nephew, MFM reported the birth of his first grandchild, a little girl born to Betty Maury five weeks earlier, and announced "Nannie [Diana] is to be married in May to Wellford Corbin." MFM to Dick F. Holland, March 1, 1858, MP, Vol. VII, LC. For approaching marriage, see also MFM to William C. Hasbrouck, Apr. 23, 1858, MP, Vol. VII, LC. Corbin wrote the name of his plantation "Farley Vale"; his wife wrote it "Farleyvale" in later years. When he purchased the property it consisted of about 1,500 acres but by 1865 consisted of 930 acres, 500 for cultivation and the balance in woods or duck marshes; S. Wellford Corbin to MFM, Sept. 29, 1860, Aug. 10, 1865, MP, Vols. IX and XXII, LC.

34. MFM to Diana Maury Corbin, May 9, 1858, quoted in full in Corbin, *Maury*, pp. 163-165.

35. MFM to William C. Hasbrouck, Oct. 24, 1859; to B. Franklin Minor, Oct. 30, 1859, MP, Vol. VIII, LC; and Mrs. Mary Maury Werth to Charles Lee Lewis, Dec. 17, 1921, TSLA.

36. Speaking of doing their homework study assignments, Diana stated, "He always expected and required that we should not prepare them at night, but should then come into the parlour to receive and entertain and be entertained by the distinguished men and women who frequently gathered round him. He considered this a most important part of our education." Corbin, *Maury*, p. 152.

37. "When there were no visitors he encouraged us to chatter and talked to us himself." Mrs. Mary Maury Werth to her children cited in Note 12.
    "Le Verrier spent several weeks with him at the Observatory. . . ." Diana Maury Corbin's reminiscences of her father, written about 1890, MP, Vol. XLII, Folio 8327, LC.

38. In Diana Maury Corbin's reminiscences of her father cited in Note 37.

39. Most nations were then still kingdoms or empires with a royal or imperial observatory. The United States Naval Observatory in Washington was then generally called the National Observatory and considered by foreign

visitors as such. While the number of visitors to the Observatory was large, it was nothing in comparison with the number of people with whom MFM corresponded. MFM might write one letter to the captain of a whaling ship and the next to the King of Siam, to whom he sent charts. Sir James Brooke, Raja of Sarawak, Borneo, received information from him. People not connected with the sea gathered abstract logs from mariners and sent them to him; such a one was Nathaniel Hawthorne, American writer and U.S. consul at Liverpool. The wide range of people with whom MFM was in touch is easily seen by a study of the index of the volumes of NOLS, NAn. See also NOLR, 1842-1861, NAn.

40. Among the diplomats who came to the Observatory to see MFM especially mentioned by him or by newspaper accounts were Rudolph M. Schleiden, Minister Resident of the Republic of Bremen, Edward de Stoeckl, Russian Minister to the United States, Baron Franz von Gerolt, Prussian Minister, Baron Grabow, of the Prussian Legation, Torbin Bille, Danish envoy to the U.S., Blondeel van Cuelbrouk, Belgian Minister to the United States, and Charles F. Loosey, Consul General of Austria.

41. MFM to Ann Maury of New York, June 10, 1848, Apr. 25, 1851, MC, UVAL; to the Rt. Rev. James H. Otey, May 28, 1859; to John Minor, Nov. 6, 1859, MP, Vols. VII and VIII, LC.

42. T. C. De Leon, *Belles, Beaux and Brains of the 60's*, pp. 33-39; Durkin, *Mallory*, pp. 45-46; *Memoirs of Mrs. Clay*, pp. 116-142.

43. *Memoirs of Mrs. Clay*, p. 76.

44. Ibid., pp. 76-77.

45. Description of MFM's appearance from study of all available photographs, magazine illustrations, engravings, and the bust of him modeled from life by E. V. Valentine, as well as from the word picture of him by his daughter; Corbin, *Maury*, p. 147.

46. "In early youth he was careless in his dress, and expressed contempt for those who judged of a man by his outward appearance. 'But,' he said, 'I soon perceived the folly of this carelessness'; and in later years he became scrupulously neat in his attire." Corbin, *Maury*, p. 148.

47. See the picture of MFM in civilian dress in the group picture taken in London, 1868 in picture section of this book. See also "copy of an engraving of Maury which hangs in the Superintendent's office at the United States Naval Observatory" in Lewis, *Maury*, opposite p. 66; and frontispiece picture in Corbin, *Maury*.

48. MFM took his daughters to visit the Hasbroucks as early as 1851 on his way to attend the A.A.A.S. meeting at Albany. For the Hasbroucks's coming to Washington, see, for example, MFM to William C. Hasbrouck, April 1, 1852; Hasbrouck to MFM, April 28, 1852, both in MP, Vol. IV, LC.

49. MFM to William C. Hasbrouck, July 3 and 10, 1859; John H. Maury to William C. Hasbrouck, Aug. 5, Aug. 8, Aug. 29, 1859, all in MP, Vol. VIII, LC; for a visit of MFM, MFM to William C. Hasbrouck, Nov. 13, 1858, MP, Vol. VII, LC; a visit of MFM, Ann, and two children to the Hasbroucks, see NR, MFM to the Rt. Rev. James H. Otey, Sept. 15, 1860, NOLS, Vol. XVIII, NAn.

50. MFM to William C. Hasbrouck, Apr. 29, May 5, and June 6, 1859, MP, Vol. VII, LC.

51. William Francis Lynch, born 1801, was five years older than MFM and

had entered the Navy six years before him. Lynch was promoted to lieutenant in 1828 and captain in 1856. There had been expeditions to explore the Sea of Galilee and the River Jordan prior to the one he led in 1848; but, as *DAB* says, Lynch's was the "most successfully executed and the most productive of scientific results."

Lynch's popular *Narrative of the United States Expedition to the River Jordan and the Dead Sea* was first published in 1849, with several other editions. His *Official Report of the United States Expedition to Explore the Dead Sea and the River Jordan* was published by the U.S. Naval Observatory in 1852. See sketch of William Francis Lynch, *DAB*, Vol. XI, pp. 524-526.

52. The book that Lynch dedicated to MFM was *Naval Life; or Observations Afloat and on Shore: The Midshipman.* See inscribed copy Lynch gave MFM in VSL.

53. MFM wrote the facts to his very understanding friends William and Mary Minor Matthews in Lynchburg and asked that they extend their friendship to Lynch, who was to be in that community; MFM to William M. Blackford, Oct. 1, 1849, MP, Vol. III, LC.

54. NR, MFM to Secretary of Navy Toucey, Oct. 19, 1857, NOLS, Vol. XV, NAn; Corbin, *Maury*, pp. 133-141.

55. Charles Lee Lewis, *David Glasgow Farragut, Admiral in the Making*, pp. 252-253 (see also pp. 269-270); NR, MFM to J. A. Dahlgren, June 20, 1853, NOLS, Vol. IX, NAn; reminiscences of Thomas A. Dornin's daughter about MFM's frequent visits to her father when he was stationed at the Washington Navy Yard, Nannie Seddon Barney of Norfolk to Mary H. Maury, Oct. 13, 1873, MP, Vol. LXIV, LC.

56. MFM to Ann Maury of New York, Feb. 15, 1840, MC, UVAL; NR, MFM to J. A. Dahlgren, June 20, 1853, NOLS, Vol. IX, NAn.

57. NR, MFM to Charles Henry Davis, March 1, 1856, in NR, Miscellaneous . . . Lieut. MFM and Plucking Board, NAn.

58. NR, MFM to Marin H. Jansen, Dec. 3, 1859, NOLS, Vol. XVII, NAn.

59. MFM to B. Franklin Minor, Jan. 23, 1856, MP, Vol. V, LC.

60. Corbin, *Maury*, pp. 150-151.

61. William Leigh, Falling Waters, Berkeley County, W.Va., Sept. 23, 1873, to Mary H. Maury, MP, Vol. XLIV, LC.

62. Ibid.

63. This evaluation of Maury was written by N. P. Willis about six weeks after a trip in July, 1859, in which they had both been among the celebrities whom the Baltimore and Ohio Railroad took on a pleasure trip in a special train from Baltimore to Wheeling, W.Va., and return. Among the other guests on the excursion were former Secretary of Navy John P. Kennedy, Bayard Taylor, and John R. Thompson, poet and editor of the *Southern Literary Messenger.* This account in the third person is in Corbin, *Maury*, p. 148; but for the same statement written directly to MFM, see N. P. Willis to MFM, Sept. 18, 1859, MP, Vol. VIII, LC. In connection with this statement about MFM, it is interesting to note that Willis wrote and published the only piece of personal journalism about MFM that ever disturbed MFM enough to demand a retraction. During the B. and O. excursion in July, 1859, MFM had recounted an anecdote of his early experience on Nukuhiva Island in the Pacific and the offer of the Happa

chief to give him "his sceptre, his own wife and the daughter of a neighboring chief" if he would remain on Nukuhiva. In the Sept. 10, 1859, edition of the *Home Journal,* Parker reported the story but incorrectly placed the happening in the Sandwich (Hawaiian) Islands instead of the Marquesas and stated the princess involved was the "Princess of Owhyhee [Hawaii]." MFM was shocked at a journalist's reporting a private, off-the-record conversation and even more shocked at N. P. Willis's having involved the Princess of Hawaii in such a way. MFM wrote Willis, "How could you do such a thing? There is not a word of truth in it. . . . The Princess of Owhyhee . . . was a highly educated, refined, and accomplished lady and what do you make her out to be," MFM to N. P. Willis, Sept. 12, 1859, in MP, Vol. VIII, LC; Willis replied, "Your letter is this moment received [it had been forwarded promptly]. I promise to repair the wrong I have done you. In the *Home Journal* of next week (this week's having gone to press) you will find a correction of the error." Willis added that on the four or five days of the excursion "to support the unusual fatigues of that trip, I drank much more than I am accustomed to and I may therefore have an unreliable memory of the matter." N. P. Willis to MFM, Sept. 18, 1859, MP, Vol. VIII, LC. John P. Kennedy was in agreement with MFM in the matter; the Associated Press published a denial of the story, and Stephen C. Rowan, who had been with MFM on the cruise of the *Vincennes,* wrote Willis to validate MFM's account of what had happened in the Marquesas and to deny that the Princess of Hawaii was involved in any way. Willis published an apology and praised MFM. Probably the prompt denial prevented the story's being considered an affront to Hawaii's royal family. See *Home Journal,* Sept. 10, Oct. 1, 1859, letters previously cited in this note and letters of MFM to Hon. John P. Kennedy, Baltimore, Sept. 12, Sept. 28, 1859; to John Minor, Sept. 18, 1859, all in MP, Vol. VIII, LC.

64. Francis H. Smith, "Matthew Fontaine Maury, 1806-1873," in Edwin A. Alderman (ed.) *Library of Southern Literature,* Vol. VIII, p. 3440.
65. MFM to B. Franklin Minor, July 25, 1855, MP, Vol. IV, LC. Francis H. Smith, a West Point graduate, was superintendent of the Virginia Military Institute.
66. Recollection of her father, MS memorandum written about 1890, by Diana Maury Corbin, MP, Vol. XLII, Folio 8327, LC.
67. Rutson Maury to MFM, Sept. 6, 1872, MP, Vol. XLI, LC.
68. Prof. John B. Minor to Mary H. Maury, July 30, 1873, MP, Vol. XLIV, LC.
69. John Barbee Minor was professor of common and statute law at the University of Virginia and the author of a number of legal textbooks. He chaffed MFM with remarks like, "Who knows but that . . . you may by degrees slough off some of the other paradoxical whimsies which I have so long had occasion to deplore." John B. Minor to MFM, May 17, 1870, MP, Vol. XXXV, LC. See also John B. Minor to MFM, Aug. 12, 1865, MP, Vol. XXII, LC.
70. MFM to Prof. John B. Minor, July 4, 1859; to William C. Hasbrouck, July 15, 1859, both in MP, Vol. VIII, LC.
71. MFM to R. T. W. Duke, secretary of the Board of Visitors, Univ. of Virginia, July 7, 1859, NR, NOLS, Vol. XVII, LC.
72. As early as 1848, "B. B. M." (Benjamin Blake Minor, lawyer and later

president of the Univ. of Missouri), writing in the *SLM* had proposed that MFM be made the president of the College of William and Mary, B. B. M., "Stars and Streamers," *SLM*, June, 1848, Vol. XIV, No. 6 (June, 1848), p. 348.

73. B. Franklin Minor was the son of Peter Minor, who bought "Ridgeway" in 1809. MFM addressed letters to him as Franklin Minor and called him Frank. Minor signed his name B. F. Minor. I have used B. Franklin Minor in these notes to combine the two and to avoid confusion with Francis Minor, who was also called Frank. B. Franklin Minor first established a classical school for boys at the "Rigory" near Charlottesville but later exchanged that property with his brother Hugh for "Ridgeway" (often spelled Ridgway) in Albemarle County. A considerable portion of his acreage was in upland woods and pasture. Minor's most productive farming was carried on in 180 acres of very fertile low ground. His wife was Lucy Ann Gilmer Minor, who had grown up at "Edgemont." Franklin Minor served on the Board of Visitors of the University of Virginia and from 1861 to 1863 was a member of the House of Delegates of the Virginia General Assembly. He gave up his school when war and ill-health forced him to do so. MFM's admiration for his friend and cousin is revealed by this statement to B. Franklin Minor, "I agree with you in your philosophizing about life. But, my dear friend, count your blessings. Do you not know that we are all a set of most ungrateful scamps? . . . The position in life I should most like to occupy . . . [the] position of *true* greatness which has been one of lifelong longing is occupied, Frank, by you . . . a farmer with enough for him and his with a little to spare for a friend in need and whose counsels are sought by old and young and in whom his neighbors repose confidence and esteem. Such is the outward skeleton of the real great man and yours are the fillings up. Put that in your pipe and smoke it." MFM to B. Franklin Minor, Aug. 18, 1859, MP, Vol. VIII, LC. In 1836 MFM had written, "I am trying to turn the attention of farmers to their marl beds the nature of which is not understood by many Virginia farmers who might profit by them." MFM to Ann Maury of New York, June 18, 1836, in MC, UVAL.

74. MFM to B. Franklin Minor, March 21, 1855, MP, Vol. IV, LC; see other MFM letters on this subject to B. Franklin Minor, in 1855, 1856, MP, Vols. V and VI, LC.

75. For Minor's visits, see B. Franklin Minor to Senator R. M. T. Hunter, May 11, 1860, MP, Vol. IX, LC; for "shots in the locker" expression, see MFM to Diana Maury, Apr. 12, 1858, MP, Vol. VII, LC; for chilling champagne for Minor, see MFM to B. Franklin Minor, Nov. 24, 1855, MP, Vol. V, LC.

76. The dream of Bishop Otey and other founders of Sewanee was to build the university on the Sewanee plateau of the Cumberland Mountains, Tennessee, 2,000 feet above sea level, far from city activities that could divert the students from their studies. On July 29, 1859, Otey came to visit MFM at the Observatory. "His visit was a great treat—we enjoyed it much and regretted his stay was so short . . . We talked over his three million dollar university. They have raised $500,000 and are going to work with the interest." MFM to B. Franklin Minor, July 31, 1859, MP, Vol. VIII, LC. Bishop Otey returned in late August and MFM went with

him to call on the President, Secretary of State and others; diary of MFM's son, John H. Maury, entry Aug. 30, 1859, MP, Vol. XLVI, LC.

77. MFM to the Rt. Rev. James H. Otey, June 7, Nov. 10, 1859, MP, Vol. VIII, LC.

78. NR, MFM to the Rt. Rev. James H. Otey, Sept. 15, 1860, NOLS, Vol. XVIII, NAn.

79. Arthur Ben Chitty, Jr., in his *Reconstruction at Sewanee* gives a graphic picture of this extraordinary event held Oct. 10, 1860, in a place that was extremely difficult to reach. The crowd was estimated at between 4,000 and 10,000 people, many of whom came by foot, wagon, or muleback, others in carriages, omnibuses or by narrow-gauge mining company train. A religious service, in which the eight bishops participated, was held in the morning and concluded by Bishop Leonidas Polk striking the cornerstone three times and announcing the university dedicated. After that the choir sang the Benedicite to instrumental accompaniment. It was the singing of this ancient hymn of praise to which MFM made reference in his speech delivered that afternoon after a midday banquet. There were also speeches by other notables.

80. "Commander Maury's Address at the Laying of the Cornerstone, October 10, 1860," in the Rev. Telfair Hodgson, D.D., Vice-Chancellor (ed.), *Reprints of the Documents and Proceedings of the Board of Trustees of the University of the South, University of Sewanee Papers*, Ser. A, No. 1, pp. 63-68.

81. See long answer to a query about his views on the "Harmony of Science and Revelation." MFM to Ann Maury of New York, Jan. 22, 1855, MC, UVAL. See also MFM "The Bible and Science," *Southern Churchman*, Jan. 22, 1855.

82. MFM believed that God was profoundly interested in man, had made the earth for man, and was more eager to reveal than to withhold the secrets of nature for man's benefit. MFM never turned aside from the convictions he expressed in 1834 to his brother, "Learn your duties, Dick, from the Bible. There you have them laid down in example, law, and precept. I love to see Christians after the Bible and according to their own consciences, and not according to the opinions of other men." MFM to Richard L. Maury, Tennessee, Nov. 16, 1834, MP, Vol. I, LC.

83. See MFM to B. Franklin Minor cited in Note 73, this chapter. See Note 89 for MFM's conviction that he was unworthy to be confirmed and receive Holy Communion. For MFM's awareness of the dangers of pride of position and haughtiness, see MFM letter to his daughter Diana cited in Note 34 of this chapter.

84. MFM believed that a clergyman who bewailed or "whined" did Christianity a disservice, that a preacher also better reached the heart and mind of his listeners if he delivered his sermons quietly and reasonably and concluded in 23 minutes. See MFM's wife, Ann Herndon Maury, to Ann Maury of New York, May 12, 1844, MC, UVAL; MFM to the Rev. Francis W. Tremlett, Jan. 6, 1869, July 29, 1872, MP, Vols. XXVIII and XL, LC.

85. In his protracted and painful final illness MFM still held to this belief and pointed out to his children how God had sustained him by allowing his senses to remain clear to the very end. See recollections of the last

words of Commodore M. F. Maury to S. Wellford Corbin, Jan. 24 to Feb. 1, 1873, MP, Vol. XLII, Folio 8348, LC.

86. Prayer dictated by MFM, Jan. 30, 1872, "which he had used every day . . . since that 29th Oct. [1839] when he was laid upon the bed at Somerset, Ohio," in memorandum written Jan. 30, 1872, MP, Vol. XLII, Folios 8228-8229, LC.

87. MFM took the family to the morning service at St. John's and held a service at home every Sunday night in which each member of the family or house guest took part; Corbin, *Maury,* p. 153.

88. Letter of Ann Herndon Maury to Ann Maury of New York cited in Note 84; MFM to Louisa Tremlett, Feb. 3, 1864 or 1865 [year not given on letter but indicated by contents], in Confederate Museum, Richmond, Va.

89. Letter of MFM to Louisa Tremlett, sister of MFM's English clergyman friend, the Rev. Francis W. Tremlett, cited in Note 88. Douglas Southall Freeman suggests that Robert E. Lee's similar wait to be confirmed until he was past 45 years old may have been caused by the fact that the theology preached in his youth and the emotionalism of much faith in that period was alien to Lee's nature. These same reasons probably played an unconscious role in MFM's thinking on the issue. See Freeman, *Lee,* Vol. IV, p. 502.

90. An example of this is that after all the efforts that Alexander Dallas Bache had made since 1846 to obstruct MFM's scientific work, it was not until 1858 that MFM finally admitted to a first cousin, "There is much villainy going on. Your idea of my being set upon is a new one but I reckon a true one. Bache's jealousy and envy surpass my comprehension. He is a bad man." MFM to John Minor, Nov. 15, 1858, MP, Vol. VII, LC.

91. Concerning his eldest daughter's debut party he wrote, "Bettie [this spelling for Betty's name was used occasionally for some reason] is getting ready for a turnout party and sends you an invitation, I hope you will accept." NR, MFM to Lieut. Marin H. Jansen, Netherlands, Jan. 17, 1854, NOLS, Vol. X, NAn. "This is little Lucy's birthday—seven years old. It will be ten years, I reckon, before she will be coming out." MFM to Diana Maury Corbin, May 9, 1858, in Corbin, *Maury,* p. 163. For description of Betty's wedding reception, see Diana Maury's letter to Nannie Maury cited in Note 32.

92. MFM urged a former shipmate who had retired from the Navy to come from Nashville to the Greenbrier White Sulphur Springs for a summer vacation "and you shall have the nicest society sprinkled with enough of the Navy to excite pleasant reminiscences." MFM to M. G. L. Claiborne, Nashville, Feb. 20, 1858, in a collection of 37 pieces of correspondence between Claiborne, MFM and others in MP, Ac 9036, LC. For MFM's going to "the White," see MFM to B. Franklin Minor, June 27, 1857; Secretary of State Lewis Cass to MFM "now at White Sulphur Springs, Greenbrier Co., Va.," Aug. 24, 1857, both in MP, Vol. VII, LC.

93. Percival Reniers, *The Virginia Springs,* pp. 27-29, 59, 62-63, 73-74, 78, 91, 94, 98, 112, 120, 131, 136, 140-143, 180, 184-185, 189, 198, 208-209, 211, 216-217, 227-228, 262-263, 277. See also William Alexander McCorkle, *The White Sulphur Springs, West Virginia, The Tradition, History, Social Life.*

94. Families from New Orleans and other far Southern communities often

stayed for eight or ten weeks. Virginians who could afford it frequently spent the month of August at "the White" and often extended their stay into September. While MFM favored "the White," each of the "'Springs" of Virginia had its devotees, and it was fashionable to make a pilgrimage that also included the Virginia Hot Springs and the Warm Springs in not far distant Bath County. For letter to former Navy colleague, see MFM to M. G. L. Claiborne cited in Note 92.

95. Before MFM left home he had heard family genealogy and history discussed in his home and in that of other Maurys for 19 years. Between 1834 and 1842 he spent a great deal of time in Fredericksburg and frequently saw aunts, uncles, and cousins of every degree. He also saw his uncle Consul James Maury a number of times before James's death in 1840. All of these people were interested in their family history, and MFM heard the subject thoroughly discussed. See MFM to Ann Maury of New York, May 20, 1838, MC, UVAL. MFM was greatly interested in his cousin Ann's translating the memoirs of their great-great-grandfather, the Rev. James (Jacques) Fontaine, from the French in which they had been written in 1722 and rejoiced when they were published as a book, *Tale of a Huguenot Family*, in 1838. After his crippling stagecoach accident MFM read the diary of John Fontaine, which Ann sent him from New York for his opinion on publishing it. He advised favorably, stating that John Minor said to "un-Irish-cize the English." (See MFM to Ann Maury of New York, Jan. 30 and May 4, 1840, MC, UVAL.) This was published in 1852 in *Memoirs of a Huguenot Family*. For two of MFM's rare written references to his forebears, see his description of his grandfather's role in the Parson's Cause, MFM to William C. Hasbrouck, Nov. 3, 1852, MP, Vol. IV, LC; and MFM to the Rev. Dr. Proudfit, Professor of Classical Languages, Rutgers University, New Brunswick, New Jersey, May 2, 1855, NR, NOLS, Vol. XII, NAn.

96. The text of this book gives evidence of his active interest in living people. For some references to his living relatives, see MFM to Ann Maury of New York, June 12, July 15, Aug. (n.d.), 1835; May 11, Aug. 28, 1836; Apr. 5, Sept. 6, Oct. 10, Nov. 27, Dec. 12, 1838; Jan. 26, 1839; May 4, 1840; Jan. 22, May 17, May 28, 1842; Dec. 6, 1843, MC, UVAL; to Lucian Minor, July 15, July 29, 1843, MP, Vol. II, LC.

97. The story was circulated in Washington, where a man who heard the story asked one of MFM's Minor relatives "if it were really a fact." MFM to Ann Maury of New York, Jan. 31, 1842, MC, UVAL.

98. NR, MFM to Cyrus W. Field, March 26, 1860, NOLS, Vol. XVII, NAn.

99. "Godon was just below me [on the Navy Register]. He is the one I told you who said he had had eyes upon me ever since I entered the service and his ambition it was to get above me. He has succeeded, Bueno!" Note of MFM to B. Franklin Minor on bottom of letter from S. W. Godon, written from Philadelphia, Nov. 13, 1855, MP, Vol. V, LC.

100. "I have waited with impatience for your return from Africa to put into execution a plan which I have devised for discussing, developing and combining the various nautical experiences of naval men and I want you to forego the usual leave of absence given to officers after a foreign cruise and accept orders at once to the Observatory. Hard work is glorious." This statement referring to beginning the Wind and Current Charts was

written by MFM to William B. Whiting, who quoted it in a letter to Capt. John M. Brooke, May 31, 1873, MP, Vol. XLVI, LC. This approach appealed to Whiting, to William Lewis Herndon, and to other dedicated officers but certainly not to all ordered to duty at the Observatory.

101. For example of MFM's criticism, see NR, MFM to Charles Henry Davis, Feb. 9, Feb. 19, June 29, 1853, NOLS, Vols. VIII, IX, NAn. The fact that earlier proposals calling for the American Ephemeris and Nautical Almanac to be produced at the Naval Observatory in Washington had not been followed and that Charles Henry Davis and his close friends in the Bache-Henry group of scientists had caused a separate office to be established at Cambridge, Mass., undoubtedly played a part in MFM's irritation about Davis's method of producing the astronomical work. MFM had never believed that one superintendent could direct the Naval Observatory and Hydrographical Office as well as the Nautical Almanac. He did think the Naval Observatory was the place where the Almanac should be produced and that the direction of it should be handled by an officer who would be assistant superintendent of the Naval Observatory. However, MFM's papers do not reveal that he worked to have the Almanac office moved from Cambridge to Washington.

102. As has been stated in the text of Chapter XVI, much of the criticism of MFM was made in letters to editors signed with disguised initials rather than names and other indirect methods; but for Henry's open derogation of MFM, see *U.S. Agricultural Society Journal for 1856, Part I, Vol. III, Journal of 4th Annual Meeting, January, 1856,* pp. 48-51.

103. NR, MFM to Adolphe Quetelet, Dec. 7, 1860, NOLS, Vol. XVIII, NAn.

104. MFM to B. Franklin Minor, June 11, 1856, MP, Vol. VI, LC.

105. The outstanding example of this was the letter written by MFM to Charles Henry Davis, Feb. 9, 1853, cited in Note 101.

106. NR, MFM to Prof. Elias Lewis, Nov. 22, 1859, NOLS, Vol. XVII, NAn.

107. NR, MFM to Lieut. Edouard Vaneechout, March 12, 1860, NOLS, Vol. XVII, NAn.

108. "He wore his honors easily, but while he valued the public tributes he received, he was not fond of displaying the insignia which came with them. He would put on those jewels sometimes in the privacy of home to gratify his children." Gen. Francis H. Smith, "Matthew Fontaine Maury, 1806-1873" (Edwin A. Alderman, ed.), *Library of Southern Literature,* Vol. VIII, p. 3440.

Chapter XVIII

Efforts to Save the Union

1. "Let every good man do what he can to preserve the Union," MFM wrote to the Rt. Rev. James H. Otey, Oct. 22, 1860, NR, NOLS, Vol. XVIII, NAn. See also letters to B. Franklin Minor, Dec. 30, 1859, Oct. 22, 1860; to Commodore Robert F. Stockton, Dec. 14, 1860, all in MP, Vols. VIII-XI, LC; to Gen. William Giles Harding, Nashville, Tenn., Dec. 20, 1860, in Mary Harding Ragland Collection of Gen. Harding's papers, Vanderbilt University Library (cited hereafter as Harding Collection, VUL), Nashville, Tennessee.

2. Describing the formation of the Union, MFM pointed out that, "The com-

pact had for its corner-stone the aforementioned rights. With the assertion of these precious rights—which are so dear to the hearts of all true Virginians—fresh upon their lips, each one of these thirteen States signatories to this compact, delegated to this new Government so much of her own foreign powers as were deemed necessary for the accomplishment of its objects, reserving to herself all the powers, prerogatives, and attributes not specifically granted or specially enumerated." "A Vindication of Virginia and the South," *SHSP*, Vol. I, No. 2 (February, 1876), pp. 49-50; reprinted in Corbin, *Maury*, pp. 302-314.

3. MFM had stated his position in 1851 to a first cousin who had been shocked by his proposal that the surplus of slaves (which would be built up by the slave population's roughly doubling itself every thirty years) be transported to work the rich forests of the Amazon River Valley. "No, my dear cousin, I am not seeking to make slave territory out of free, or to introduce slavery where there is none. Brazil is as much of a slave country as Virginia, and the valley of the Amazon is Brazilian.

"I am sure you would rejoice to see the people of Virginia rise up to-morrow and say, from and after a future day—say 1st January, 1855—there shall be neither slavery nor involuntary servitude in Virginia. Although this would not strike the shackle from off a single arm, nor command a single slave to go free, *yet it would relieve our own loved Virginia of that curse* [Maury's italics]. Such an act on the part of the State would cause slave-owners generally either to leave the State with their slaves, or to send them off to the Southern markets. But they would be still slaves in your own country. . . . We must take things as we find them, and if we would be practical and do good, we must deal with mankind as they are, and not as we would have them." MFM to Mrs. Mary Minor Blackford, Dec. 24, 1851, MP, Vol. IV, LC. MFM owned one slave, the family cook, who stayed with the family until the last months of the Civil War, when she left the Maurys with no argument on either side; Col. Richard L. Maury to Beverley B. Munford, June 1, 1907, in Virginia Historical Society collection, Richmond, Va. I found no record of the purchase of this woman in MFM's account books, MP, LC, and this suggests that she was one of the young slaves left by Ann's father, Dabney Herndon, at his death in 1824. She may have been Ann's maid before her marriage to MFM.

MFM acted and wrote on this issue without the daring hope of revolutionary change that he believed in and worked for in the field of science. For some of the economic difficulties involved in emancipating slaves that influenced MFM's thinking, see Beverley B. Munford, *Virginia's Attitude Toward Slavery and Secession* (cited hereafter as Munford, *Slavery and Secession*), pp. 159-177.

4. "The graves of my ancestors are in Virginia. It was there I drew my first breath; and in that dear old commonwealth are the homes of some of my nearest of kin and best of friends." MFM to Frederick W. Coleman, Senate, Virginia General Assembly, Feb. 21, 1860, NR, NOLS, Vol. XVII, NAn.

5. "Virginia is closest to me but I grew up in Tennessee." MFM to Jabez Lamar Curry, Republic of Alabama, Feb. 11, 1861, MP, Vol. XI, LC.

6. MFM to the Rt. Rev. James H. Otey, Feb. 23, 1861, MP, Vol. XIII, LC. MFM, "A Vindication of Virginia and the South" (cited hereafter as

MFM, "Vindication"), printed as Appendix C in Corbin, *Maury,* pp. 307-308. The title in Corbin places the word "South" first.

7. MFM, "Vindication," Corbin, *Maury,* p. 309.

8. Bruce Catton, *The Coming Fury,* p. 84. See also Avery Craven, "The Coming of the War Between the States: An Interpretation," *Journal of Southern History,* Vol. II, No. 3, p. 305.

9. MFM, "Vindication," Corbin, *Maury,* pp. 305-307; MFM to Rutson Maury, March 29, 1861, MP, Vol. XIII, LC.

10. Roy Basler, *The Collected Works of Abraham Lincoln,* Vol. IV, pp. 146, 160. The Northern position on this whole issue is admirably presented in James Ford Rhodes, *History of the United States from the Compromise of 1850 to the Final Restoration of Home Rule in the South in 1877,* and in John Bach McMaster, *A History of the People of the United States from the Revolution to the Civil War.*

11. MFM but echoed a statement made by many Southerners when he wrote in 1851, "The New England States and the Middle States did not emancipate their slaves; they banished them. They passed their post-natal and prospective laws of emancipation it is true; but they did not command the master to let the slave go free; before the time came round for the slave to go free [some of the laws were not effective for 20 years], he had, in most cases, been taken off to the South and sold there; so that the so-called emancipation at the North was simply a transfer to the South of the slaves of the North—an act of banishment, nothing more." MFM, "The Commercial Prospects of the South," *SLM,* Vol. XVII, Nos. 10 and 11 (issued together) (October-November, 1851), p. 697.

12. For a well-documented account of the opposition of many Virginians to slavery and work for the American Colonization Society to repatriate Negroes to Africa, see Munford, *Slavery and Secession,* pp. 15-124.

   MFM's first cousins Matthew, Rutson, and Ann Maury, whose mother was English, had been reared and educated in England and held strong antislavery views. Following in the tradition of Maindort Doodes, the progenitor of the Minor family in Virginia who had stipulated in his will that his slaves be manumitted, MFM's Minor first cousins (especially Mrs. Mary Minor Blackford) were vitally interested in freeing slaves and sending them to the Liberian colony of the American Colonization Society. See Blackford, *Mine Eyes,* pp. 23-33. These cousins could not understand MFM's not taking a position of strong opposition to slavery. His failure to do so seemed to them totally out of keeping with his enlightened attitude on other moral issues. See Mrs. Mary B. Minor Blackford to MFM, Jan. 7, 1851 (misdated, should have been dated 1852), MP, Vol. IV, LC; MFM to Ann Maury of New York, Dec. 14, 1845, MC, UVAL.

13. MFM had not altered his opinion stated in 1845, "I say not a word for or against slavery as expressing my own notions about it. Suffice it to say the Bible does not condemn it, nor will I." MFM to Ann Maury of New York, Dec. 14, 1845, MC, UVAL.

14. MFM to Governor William F. Packer, of Pennsylvania, written Jan. 3, 1861 (The statements made by MFM about events then in progress conclusively establish the date of this letter as 1861 rather than the year 1860 —the date given by Mrs. Corbin and followed by subsequent writers. The

letter could not have been written on Jan. 3, 1860, as no states had then withdrawn from the Union or were on the point of so doing.), Corbin, *Maury*, pp. 183-184; MFM to Gen. William G. Harding, Dec. 20, 1860, cited in Note 1.

15. *Captain Maury's Letter on American Affairs. Letter to Rear Admiral Robert Fitzroy, R.N.*, August, 1861; MFM, "Vindication," Corbin, *Maury*, p. 303.

16. George Bancroft, *History of the United States*, Vol. IV, p. 198.

17. For a clear summarized statement, see the article on Secession, which points out that the most notable example of secessionist sentiment in the North was the Hartford Convention, *Columbia Encyclopedia* (1935 ed.), p. 1598.
    For a work presenting background material on this subject, see Dwight L. Dumond, *The Secession Movement, 1860-1861*.
    Dr. Ulrich Bonnell Phillips, then professor of American history in the University of Michigan, in his *The Life of Robert Toombs* (p. 194, fn), supplied this statement useful to the student who wishes to pursue the subject of earlier threats of secession in the United States, "The narrative of these sectional struggles is related with interpretation favorable to the North in Schouler's, Von Holst's, McMaster's and Rhodes's histories of the United States and with interpretations favorable to the South in such less known books as W. C. Fowler, *The Sectional Controversy*, 1863; S. D. Carpenter, *The Logic of History*, Madison, Wis., 1864; G. Lunt, *The Origin of the Late War*, N.Y., 1866; A. Harris, *The Political Conflict in America*, N.Y., 1876."

18. Ulrich B. Phillips, *The Life of Robert Toombs*, pp. 49-166; for a specialized study, see Ulrich B. Phillips, *The Course of the South to Secession;* see also Hinton Rowan Helper, *The Impending Crisis of the South; How to Meet It.*

19. "The love of money by the people and the lust for place by politicians have been the chief causes of this terrible infliction upon the country." MFM to the Rt. Rev. James H. Otey, Feb. 23, 1861, MP, Vol. XIII, LC.
    MFM explained to the head of the Meteorological Department of the Board of Trade, Admiralty, London, his opinion of the popular emphasis on log cabins, hard cider and rail splitting as requisites for high office and concluded, "Thus the great men of the country Calhoun, Webster, Clay &c were proscribed, and the populace came down below mediocrity for rulers. . . .
    "In this way, the government ceased to be managed for the good of the people; it became the instrument of party for the reward of partizans, consequently its checks and balances became first deranged, then destroyed; with this derangement, high sectional interests were involved." MFM to Admiral Robert Fitz Roy (Fitzroy), Aug. 4, 1861, the original 23-page MS letter is in MC, UVAL. This is the copy that eventually went to the London *Times* for publication and is marked by the editor "Not to be cut or soiled," with Fitzroy's name marked out. Apparently the *Times* gave it back to MFM, and he sent it to Rutson and Ann Maury.
    For presentations of other views on the causes of the Civil War, see: Howard K. Beale, *What Historians Have Said About the Causes of the Civil War: Theory and Practice in Historical Study;* a Report of the

Committee on Historiography, Bulletin 54, 1946, Social Science Research Council; Thomas J. Pressly, *Americans Interpret Their Civil War;* French Ensor Chadwick, *The Causes of the Civil War;* Avery Craven, *The Coming of the Civil War* (2nd rev. ed., 1957).

20. For MFM's remarks on John Brown's raid and the North's admiration of Brown, see MFM to Ann Maury of New York, Nov. 17, 1859, MC, UVAL; MFM, "Vindication," Corbin, *Maury,* p. 311. For an account of the event much as MFM heard it in Washington, see Douglas Southall Freeman, *R. E. Lee,* Vol. I, pp. 394-403.

21. MFM to B. Franklin Minor, Dec. 30, 1859, MP, Vol. VIII, LC.

22. MFM was very proud of the role Virginia had played in helping to form the Union and in her generosity in 1784 in ceding to the new federal government the whole of her Northwest Territory "to be held by it in trust for the benefit of all the States alike." MFM, "Vindication," Corbin, *Maury,* p. 307. New York, Massachusetts, and Connecticut made similar cessions to the general government.

23. MFM to the Rt. Rev. James H. Otey, March 13, 1860, MP, Vol. IX, LC.

24. About the only quoted phrase that MFM used repeatedly was the old saw, as he called it, " 'T is wise and brave to hope the best." After some of his meager savings were lost because of developments beyond his control, he said, "I do not suffer these losses to disturb me for I value peace of mind more than I do the lucre." MFM to Rutson and Ann Maury, Jan. 22, 1842, MC, UVAL. He had a strong awareness of the role that thought and emotions play in the well-being and productivity of a human being. He made numerous references to the effect on the health of his sister-in-law, Eliza Maury, of her worrying and tendency to see the dark side of things. See MFM to Ann Maury of New York, Jan. 26, 1839, and Feb. 27, 1840; note by Mrs. Eliza Maury added to letter of MFM to Ann Maury of New York, May 4, 1840, all in MC, UVAL.

25. "When I became old enough to reflect, it was the aim at which all my energies were directed to make myself a useful man. I soon found that occupation, for some useful end or another, was the true secret of happiness." MFM to Rutson Maury, Aug. 31, 1840, MP, Vol. II, LC.

   "My health is good and I stand the labour like a regular son of Adam. A glorious privilege is that of labour." MFM to Ann Maury of New York, Sept. 13, 1845, MC, UVAL.

26. Quotation of statement by Admiral Fitzroy in article on MFM, *Eclectic Magazine,* New Series, Vol. XVIII, No. 1 (July, 1873), p. 116.

27. NR, MFM to Secretary of Navy Toucey, March 31, 1860, NOLS, Vol. XVII, NAn.

28. MFM, map of Antarctica, dated June, 1860, MP, Miscellaneous File, LC.

29. Lewis, *Maury,* p. 124.

30. Ibid. MFM is one of the distinguished sons of Tennessee whose likeness is painted on the frescoed ceiling of a room at the Tennessee State Capitol in Nashville. For a sketch of "Prince of Fire Eaters" Yancey's approach to the North-South crisis, see Dwight Dumond's sketch of William Lowndes Yancey, *DAB,* Vol. XX, pp. 592-595.

31. "I sailed from New York 28th Oct., arrived in London 14th Nov., left again Nov. 27th, and sailed from Southampton Nov. 28th, having accomplished the immediate object of my visit, which was to copyright the

new edition of the 'Physical Geography of the Sea and Its Meteorology.' This is almost a new work." MFM to William C. Hasbrouck, Dec. 7, 1860, MP, Vol. X, LC. See also NR, MFM to Commodore Wullerstorf, Imperial Navy, Trieste, Austria, Oct. 3, 1860, NOLS, Vol. XVIII, NAn.

32. The growing sectional strife and likelihood of war, added to the financial and technical difficulties connected with making a new cable, had prevented any attempt to lay another cable across the Atlantic after the 1858 cable had ceased to transmit messages.

33. Letter of MFM to William C. Hasbrouck cited in Note 31.

34. Bruce Catton has given a vivid picture of South Carolina's reaction to Lincoln's election and the actions taken by that state, Alabama, Mississippi and Georgia. He also gives Lincoln's reactions to the moves made by those states. See *The Coming Fury*, pp. 111-118.

35. In the national election in the autumn of 1860 Lincoln won 1,865,593 popular votes; his nearest rival, Stephen A. Douglas, had 1,382,713 popular votes. Other votes that Douglas might have garnered were the 848,356 that went to John C. Breckinridge and the 592,906 votes for John Bell. W. D. Burnham, *Presidential Ballots, 1836-1892* (Baltimore, 1955).

36. MFM delivered his address at a dinner given by the Royal Geographical Society. For speeches, see MFM, "On the Physical Geography of the Sea in Connection with the Antarctic Region," *Royal Geographical Society Proceedings,* 1861, Vol. V, pp. 22-26; MFM, "On the Climates of the Antarctic Regions as indicated by observations upon the height of the barometer and direction of the winds at sea," *British Association* (for the Advancement of Science) *Reports 1860,* Part 2, pp. 46-48.

37. NR, MFM to Lord Ashburton, Dec. 1, 1860; to Marin H. Jansen, Dec. 1, 1860; to Captain A. Gorkovenko, Russian Imperial Navy, St. Petersburg, March 15, 1861, all in NOLS, Vol. XVIII, NAn.

38. "Jansen joined me in London . . . and we left Fitz Roy quite as much in favor of another go [at international co-operation for meteorology of land and sea] as you or I could wish," (and then more about scientists seen). NR, MFM to Adolphe Quetelet, written on board the steamer *New York,* Dec. 7, 1860, NOLS, Vol. XVIII, NAn.

39. Account of dinner at Lord Ashburton's with Carlyle and Ruskin is in Memoirs of Marin H. Jansen, "Het Leven van een blooshoude Gedenk Schriften van M. H. Jansen," an original MS annotated by S. P. L. Honoré-Naber, professor of history, Univ. of Utrecht, Holland, *Historisch Genootschap te Utrecht,* L Series III, No. 49, 1925 (cited hereafter as Memoirs of Jansen—annotated by Honoré), translated by Annette Scheltema for Catherine Cate Coblentz, who made reference to this in her MS biography of MFM, Chap. XX, p. 16, source note 23, MP, LC.

40. MFM to Commodore Robert Field Stockton, Dec. 14 and 24, 1860, MP, Vol. X, LC.

41. Ibid.

42. Other pleas MFM wrote urging Southern men to attempt to procure mediation were to William M. Blackford, Dec. 16, 1860, H. Owen, Judge John Tayloe Lomax, the Rt. Rev. James H. Otey, Dec. 17, 1860, William Leigh, Dec. 20, 1860, and B. Franklin Minor, Dec. 21 and 24, 1860, all in MP, Vol. X (see also letters in Vol. XI), LC.

43. MFM to Gen. William G. Harding, Dec. 20, 1860, Harding Collection, VUL.
44. MFM to William C. Hasbrouck, Dec. 7, 1860, MP, Vol. X, LC. The dedication read, "To William C. Hasbrouck, of Newburgh, New York, this Volume is Inscribed as a Token of the Friendship and Esteem, From Boyhood till Now, of His former Pupil, The Author." MFM, *Physical Geography of the Sea* (8th American ed., 1861).
45. *Journal of the Convention of the People of South Carolina, Held in 1860-1861*, pp. 46-47, 53.
46. *The War of the Rebellion: a Compilation of the Official Records of the Union and Confederate Armies* (cited hereafter as *O.R.*), Ser. I, Vol. I, pp. 68-90; Samuel Wylie Crawford, *The Genesis of the Civil War; the Story of Sumter, 1860-61* (cited hereafter as Crawford, *Civil War*), pp. 6-7, 54-55, 71-74, 95, 142-144, 146, 148.
47. Bruce Catton, *The Coming Fury*, pp. 160-164.
48. MFM to B. Franklin Minor, Jan. 16, 1861, MP, Vol. X, LC.
49. This letter quoted in full in Corbin, *Maury*, pp. 183-184, was incorrectly dated Jan. 3, 1860, in Mrs. Corbin's life of her father. It may have been a typographical error she would have caught had proofs been sent her by her English publishers. The content of the letter will prove to the reader that this letter was written Jan. 3, 1861.
50. Ibid.
51. MFM to Lord Wrottesley, Jan. 1861, MP, Vol. X, LC.
52. A description of the tense atmosphere in Washington is in T. C. De Leon, *Belles, Beaux and Brains of the 60's*, pp. 37-40; see also Durkin, *Mallory*, pp. 118-121.
53. The joint resolution of the General Assembly carefully avoided use of the word "secession" but called for consideration of the problems and dangers of the hour, but no one had any illusions as to the chief subject that would be discussed by the convention. See *Journal of the House of Delegates of the State of Virginia for the Extra Session, 1861*, p. 25.
54. Historian James Ford Rhodes wrote, "Virginia, whose share in forming the Union had been greater than that of any other one state, was loath to see that great work shattered, and now made a supreme effort to save it." *History of the United States*, Vol. III, p. 290. Rhodes was referring to the action of the Virginia General Assembly in adopting a series of resolutions inviting all such states "as are willing to unite with Virginia in an earnest effort to meet on the fourth day of February next, in the City of Washington." Other resolutions were passed providing for the immediate appointment of former President John Tyler as a commissioner to the President of the United States, and Judge John Robertson as a commissioner to the state of South Carolina and to any other state that had seceded or might secede, to urge them to refrain from committing any acts that might precipitate armed conflict between such states and the United States.
   The Senate passed the resolutions with only one vote against their adoption. The House voted 112 ayes to 5 noes; *Journal of the House of Delegates of the State of Virginia for the Extra Session, 1861*, p. 10. Ibid., pp. 65-67, for the vote authorizing Peace Conference, Jan. 19, 1861.
55. In his message to the General Assembly, convened in extra session on Jan. 7, 1861, Governor John Letcher declared, "If the judgments of men were

consulted, if the admonitions of their consciences were respected, the Union would yet be saved from overthrow." *Journal of the House of Delegates of the State of Virginia for the Extra Session, 1861*, Doc. No. 1. Letcher's efforts to keep Virginia in the Union without sacrifice of the state's principles were so strenuous that rabid Virginia secessionists vilified him.

56. Varina Davis, *Jefferson Davis*, Vol. I, pp. 694-695.
57. *Memoirs of Mrs. Clay*, pp. 147-148.
58. Ibid., p. 148. See also Hudson Strode, *J. Davis, to 1861*, p. 389. For an account of the farewell speech of Senator Davis, see Varina Davis, *Jefferson Davis*, Vol. I, pp. 696-698; also *Congressional Globe*, Jan. 21, 1861, *Part I*, p. 487, 36th Cong., 2nd Sess.
59. MFM to M. G. L. Claiborne, Jan. 21, 1861, MP, Ac 9036, LC; to W. C. Whithorne, Speaker, House of Delegates, Nashville, Tenn., Jan. 4, March 21, 1861, MP, Vols. X, XI, LC.
60. MFM to Rutson Maury, Jan. 24, 1861, MP, Vol. XI, LC.
61. Rutson Maury to MFM, Jan. 27, 1861, MP, Vol. XI, LC.
62. Proposal that there be sent an ultimatum of the views of the actual people of the South to the actual people of the North; MFM to His Excellency John Tyler, former President of the United States, Brown's Hotel, Washington, Jan. 26, 1861; and report of visit to Tyler in MFM to B. Franklin Minor, Jan. 28, 1861, both in MP, Vol. XI, LC.
63. MFM to Lord Wrottesley, Jan. 28, 1861, MP, Vol. XI, LC.
64. In addition to writing and seeing John Tyler, MFM wrote another Virginia delegate to the Peace Conference just before it began. See MFM to the Hon. James A. Seddon, Richmond, Va., Jan. 28, 1861, MP, Vol. XI, LC.
65. MFM thought the "sub clave" meetings unwise. He said that there were good men in the Congress but that the majority of delegates came from free states and had nothing to complain of and the minority delegates from the South were "divided among themselves as to what will satisfy their people and give quiet to the country." MFM to the Rt. Rev. James H. Otey, Feb. 23, 1861, MP, Vol. XIII, LC. See also criticism of Peace Congress in MFM to Jabez L. M. Curry, Feb. 11, 1861, MP, Vol. XII, LC.
66. MFM wrote a series of letters to the Virginia Convention setting forth his views on possible ameliorating steps that might be taken in the national crisis. For this quotation, see MFM, letter No. 5 to the Virginia Convention, Feb. 7, 1861, MP, Vol. XII (see preceding letters in Vols. XI and XII), LC.
67. MFM to Jabez L. M. Curry, Republic of Alabama, Feb. 11, 1861, MP, Vol. XII, LC.
68. Hudson Strode, *J. Davis, to 1861*, pp. 403, 410. See also article on Confederate States of America, *Encyclopaedia Britannica* (1953 ed.), Vol. VI, p. 227.
69. MFM to the Rt. Rev. James H. Otey, Memphis, Feb. 23, 1861, MP, Vol. XIII, LC.
70. Another development that gave moderate Southerners encouragement for a compromise settlement between North and South was the vote of the U.S. House of Representatives on Feb. 28, 1861, approving an amendment that sanctioned continuance of slavery in the states that had it. The Senate voted in favor of this amendment by a two-thirds vote on March 2, 1862.

For facts in the text and on this amendment, see Rhodes, *History of the United States,* Vol. III, pp. 296, 306-313.

71. "The new President is now on his way to the capitol, and the *Express* reports 'All Quiet,' as I took it for granted it would be. I have no idea of any disturbance, or any attempt even at a plot." MFM to William C. Hasbrouck, March 4, 1861, MP, Vol. XIII, LC.

72. The sword was described by his daughter Mary, who had it in her possession. She also told of accompanying MFM to the White House for this reception by President and Mrs. Lincoln in March, 1861, as well as to an earlier reception given by President Buchanan in honor of H. R. H. The Prince of Wales; Mrs. Mary Maury Werth to Charles Lee Lewis, Dec. 17, 1921, Tennessee Historical Society collection, TSLA.

73. MFM to B. Franklin Minor, March 8, 1861, MP, Vol. XIII, LC.

74. Ibid., March 26, 1861.

75. MFM to B. Franklin Minor, Jan. 31, 1861, MP, Vol. XI, LC.

76. Ibid., Feb. 11 and 14, 1861, Vol. XII.

77. Letter of J. G. Willoby (or Willoughby) filed under date of March 3, 1861; see also letters of Charles Piazzi Smyth, Astronomer Royal of Scotland, March 4, 1861, of Rudolph Schleiden, Minister Resident for Hanseatic Republic, to MFM ("My dear Captain"), March 12, 1861, all in MP, Vol. XIII, LC.

78. "You were the originator of a maritime conference which met in Brussels in 1853 for the purpose of establishing a uniform system of meteorological observations at sea." Blondeel van Cuelebrouck, Belgian Minister to United States, to MFM, Apr. 1, 1861, MP, Vol. XIII, LC.

79. NR, MFM to Capt. A. Gorkovenko, Russian Imperial Navy, March 15, 1861, NOLS, Vol. XVIII, NAn.

80. Ibid.

81. Proposal of international antarctic expedition, NR, MFM to Lord Lyons, British Minister, Henri Mercier, French Minister, Edward de Stoeckl, Russian Minister, and other heads of missions in Washington, Apr. 10, 1861, NOLS, Vol. XVIII (see especially pp. 345-363), NAn.

    The American Geophysical Union of the National Academy of Sciences in 1961 held a centennial symposium at the Tenth Pacific Congress of the Pacific Science Association to pay tribute to Maury for his contributions to Antarctic research. For summaries of his research and tributes to Maury at the symposium and scientific papers on modern Antarctic research read there, see Harry Wexler, Morton J. Rubin, J. E. Caskey, Jr. (eds.), *Antarctic Research: The Matthew Fontaine Maury Symposium, Geophysical Monograph Number 7* . . . American Geophysical Union of the National Academy of Sciences—National Research Council, Publication No. 1036, 1962.

82. "Lettre de M. F. Maury à M. Mercier, Ambassadeur de France aux Etats-Unis, datée du 10 Avril, 1861, et traitant principalement la question du climat au pole sud," *Annales Hydrographiques,* 1862, p. 150. See also Belgian publication of portions of MFM's proposal, "Une Page d'Histoire et d'Actualité," *Extrait du no. 12, 1903, du Bulletin de la Sócieté Belge d'Astronomie.*

83. In the Public Record Office in London MFM's 48-page MS proposal to Lord Lyons of an international exploring expedition is filed under Foreign Office 5/762, Folios 395 to 444; for letter of MFM, Apr. 8, 1861, sending

four copies of monograph "On the Barometer at Sea," see Foreign Office 5/762, Folio 250 et sqq.; for letter of Lord Lyons advising Lord Russell not to thank Maury, Foreign Office 5/763, Folio 230 et sqq.—abstracted by Philip Van Doren Stern and sent me by him.

84. The hope was general as late as April 3, Rhodes, *History of the United States*, Vol. III, p. 337. Virginians continued to hope because on April 4 a test vote in the Virginia Convention was 2 to 1 against secession, *Journal of the Committee of the Whole, Virginia Convention, 1861*, pp. 31-33. In addition, John B. Baldwin, a pro-Union member of the Virginia Convention, met with President Lincoln on April 4, 1861, and urged the President to proclaim that the federal government had no intention of coercing the seceded states. "Only give this assurance to the country in a proclamation of five lines, and we pledge ourselves that Virginia will stand by you as though you were our own Washington." President Lincoln declined to give the assurance and urged adjournment *sine die* of the Virginia Convention without adoption of an ordinance of secession; the Rev. R. L. Dabney, "Memoir of a Narrative Received of Col. John R. Baldwin of Staunton, Touching the Origin of the War," in *SHSP*, Vol. I, No. 6, pp. 443-455.

On April 8, 1861, the Virginia Convention in Richmond resolved to send a committee of three delegates "to wait upon the President of the United States . . . and respectfully ask him to communicate to this convention the policy which the Federal Executive intends to pursue in regard to the Confederate States." *Journal of the Acts and Proceedings of a General Convention of the State of Virginia, 1861* (cited hereafter as *Journ. of Va. Convention*), p. 143. William Ballard Preston, Alexander H. H. Stuart, and George W. Randolph formed the committee but were unable to see the President until April 13, 1861, when they learned that their hopes were ill-founded and that Lincoln was firm in his determination to repossess all property and places belonging to the U.S. government; *Journal of the Virginia Convention of 1861*, Doc. No. XVII.

85. See April records in *Journ. of Va. Convention*.

86. MFM to B. Franklin Minor, March 26, 1861, MP, Vol. XIII, LC.

87. Frank Moore, *The Rebellion Record; A Diary of American Events*, Vol. I, p. 47.

88. Sketch of William Henry Seward in *Columbia Encyclopedia* (1950 ed.), p. 1799.

89. "Papers of the Hon. John A. Campbell, 1861-1865," *SHSP*, New Series, Vol. IV, Whole Number XLII (October, 1917), pp. 31-37. See also Hudson Strode, *Jefferson Davis, Confederate President* (cited hereafter as Strode, *Davis, Confederate President*), p. 27.

90. Sketch of John Archibald Campbell, *Columbia Encyclopedia* (1935 ed.), p. 284; Bruce Catton, *The Coming Fury*, pp. 291-295, 299-301.

91. *O.R.*, Ser. I, Vol. I, pp. 13, 14, 18, 19, 22-24, 237-238, 249, 273, 292, 294, 297, 299, 301, 305, Vol. IV, pp. 249-250. Rhodes, *History of the United States*, Vol. III, p. 355; Abner Doubleday, *Reminiscences of Forts Sumter and Moultrie in 1860-61*, Diary of Edmund Ruffin, Vol. IV, LC, especially pp. 797-798.

92. *O.R.*, Ser. III, Vol. I, pp. 67-68, Roy Basler, *The Collected Works of Abraham Lincoln*, Vol. IV, pp. 331-332.

93. MFM to "My dear Cousin [Mrs. B. Franklin Minor]," Apr. 17, 1861, MP, Vol. XIV, LC.

94. MFM, being alone at the Observatory, had undisturbed time for his study of the antarctic and urging of exploration of that area. He wrote, "I am in the Antarctic regions." MFM to B. Franklin Minor, Apr. 12, 1861. On April 16 he wrote his northern friend, Hasbrouck, "My wife is in Fredericksburg. Frank Minor's visit to you is knocked in the head as he is a candidate for the [Virginia] Legislature," MFM to William C. Hasbrouck, Apr. 16, 1861, both in MP, Vol. XIV, LC.

   Betty and her husband had lived in the home of his mother on Capitol Hill until Aug. 29, 1859, when they had moved into their own house at 379 3rd Street, West, a long way from the Observatory.

95. "The line of duty . . . is to me clear—each one to follow his own State, if his own State goes to war; if not, he may remain to help on the work of reunion.

   "If there be no war between the sections, we must hoist the flag of reannexation, to carry the elections of '64 upon that issue, bring back the seceding States and be happier and greater, and more glorious than ever." MFM to William C. Hasbrouck, March 4, 1861, as quoted in Corbin, *Maury,* p. 186.

96. MFM's friends in the Navy knew exactly where he stood. Published articles in magazines and newspapers had carried his views, and his letters to the Peace Congress and to the Virginia Convention had certainly not gone unnoticed in Washington.

97. This was the course that his friend Thomas Aloysius Dornin subsequently followed, but Dornin was a native of Ireland, not of Virginia. He had married a Virginia girl and established her and their daughter in Fredericksburg, where they lived while he was at sea on long cruises, but his attachment to Virginia was not the same as MFM's. Dornin received a noncombat post in Baltimore and thus avoided actual fighting against Virginia.

98. "Officers of the Army and Navy—should war come between the sections —will have a hard time; and indeed, who will not? No military man can permit himself to accept service with a mental reservation." Letter of MFM to William C. Hasbrouck cited in Note 95.

99. It was not until April 18 that the Washington *Star* carried an unsubstantiated report that the Virginia Convention had passed an ordinance of secession. This was offset by publication on the same day in the Alexandria *Gazette* of a dispatch sent from Richmond at 5:00 P.M. of the 17th stating that up to that hour the Virginia Convention was still in secret session and had not passed an ordinance of secession.

100. Letter of MFM to Mrs. B. Franklin Minor cited in Note 93.

101. Joseph E. Johnston, *Narrative of Military Operations during the late War Between the States,* p. 10.

102. "All who are foes of his flag, and whom his country considers enemies of hers, are enemies of his; therefore, if we have war between the sections, every man who continues in Uncle Sam's service, is, in good faith, bound to fight his own, if his own be on the other side." Letter of MFM to William C. Hasbrouck, March 4, 1861, cited in Note 95. Neither MFM nor any of his close Southern-born friends could "fight their own." One Virginia-born naval officer, Otway H. Berryman, with whom MFM had

come into disagreement about deep-sea soundings, remained with the Union, to the great admiration of Cyrus W. Field and his brothers. Approximately one fourth of the officers of the U.S. Navy resigned to follow their seceded states in the War Between the States.

103. NR, MFM to Flag Officer Samuel L. Breese, Commandant, Navy Yard, New York, Apr. 20, 1861; see also letter to Capt. William L. Hudson, Commandant, Navy Yard, Boston, Apr. 19, 1861, both in NOLS, Vol. XVIII, NAn.

104. NR, MFM to John D. Defrees, Superintendent, Public Printing, Washington, D.C., Apr. 18, 1861, NOLS, Vol. XVIII, NAn. MFM, *Nautical Monograph No. 3, The Southeast Trade Winds of the Atlantic* (Washington, 1861). His quoted evaluation of the work is from MFM to William C. Hasbrouck, May 12, 1861, MP, Vol. XIV, LC.

105. Letter of MFM to William C. Hasbrouck cited in Note 104.

106. The fact that MFM gave up the sword he had worn as an officer of the U.S. Navy was substantiated by a letter from James Gilliss, Jr., the son of Capt. James M. Gilliss, who was ordered to fill MFM's place at the Observatory. The younger Gilliss sent the sword to MFM's daughter after the war and followed the gift with a letter, "The sword sent to you was found at the Naval Observatory by Captain James M. Gilliss and given to me by him with the information that it had been left there by Commander M. F. Maury." James Gilliss, Jr., to Mrs. Mary Maury Werth, Apr. 24, 1898, from copy of letter sent by Mrs. Werth to Charles Lee Lewis, Dec. 17, 1921, Tennessee Historical Society collection, TSLA.

107. Corbin, *Maury,* p. 190.

108. Of the millions of words MFM had written at the United States Naval Observatory and Hydrographical Office during his long tenure of office there, his last letter was very brief. Dated April 20, 1861, and addressed to "His Excellency, Abraham Lincoln, President of the United States," it read, "I beg leave herewith to resign into your hands my commission as a Commander in the Navy of the United States." It was signed "Respectfully, M. F. Maury." The Observatory's true copy of the resignation is the last letter in NR, NOLS, Vol. XVIII, NAn. That the resignation was received is attested by the fact that Lincoln's Secretary of the Navy, Gideon Welles, subsequently wrote MFM in Richmond to inquire the reason for MFM's resignation and MFM replied in letter of MFM to Secretary Welles, April 26, 1861, MP, Vol. XIV, LC. The record of MFM's service in the U.S. Navy carries the entry "Dismissed 26 April, 1861." NR, Record of Officers, Bureau of Navigation, January, 1859, to December, 1863, Vol. LI, entry made on May 15, 1861, NAn. Since someone has drawn a line through the incorrect day of the month and changed it to the date on which MFM sent in his resignation, perhaps some day the word "dismissed" will be changed to "resigned" in MFM's official U.S. Navy record.

109. MFM's daughter stated, "When he left [the Observatory], he left his uniform, his sword and epaulettes behind him." Mrs. Mary Maury Werth to Charles Lee Lewis, Nov. 16, 1922, Tennessee Historical Society Papers, TSLA. There is no picture of MFM in civilian clothes of the prewar period that shows him in anything but a black broadcloth suit.

110. MFM admitted that he had left the Observatory "with a heart full and eyes

overflowing on the 20th." MFM to William C. Hasbrouck, Apr. 29, 1861, MP, Vol. XIV, LC.

111. MFM could have gone by rail on the Alexandria and Orange Railroad to Gordonsville and then by the Virginia Central Railroad into Richmond, the route taken by R. E. Lee two days later. The probability is, however, that MFM went by steamer to Aquia Creek railhead on the Potomac, and possibly saw his family in Fredericksburg briefly, thence by the Richmond, Fredericksburg and Potomac early train to Richmond the following morning. That would have put him in Richmond about 9:00 A.M., April 21.

CHAPTER XIX

War Comes to Virginia

1. The world renown of such military leaders as Robert E. Lee, Stonewall Jackson, and J. E. B. Stuart was yet to be made in the war that lay ahead. Lee had had a distinguished record in the U.S. Army and had been offered its command, but in April, 1861, his name was not known in the United States or abroad in the way that MFM's was, nor had he received the medals and orders that had been bestowed on the naval scientist by the leaders of other nations. Virginia's outstanding son to remain with the Union, Winfield Scott, Commanding General of the United States Army until November 1861, enjoyed a very high national reputation but was not famous in Europe or the Orient.

2. Message of Governor John Letcher to the Virginia Convention, April 21, 1861, *Journ. of Va. Convention.* See also *Calendar of Virginia State Papers,* arranged by H. W. Flournoy (cited hereafter as *Calendar of Va. State Papers*), Vol. XI, p. 110.

3. Richard L. Maury, "The First Marine Torpedoes," *Southern Historical Society Papers,* 1903, Vol. XXXI (cited hereafter as R. L. Maury, "Torpedoes," *SHSP*), p. 327.

4. T. C. De Leon, *Four Years in Rebel Capitals: An Inside View of Life in the Southern Confederacy from Birth to Death,* p. 104; George Cary Eggleston, *A Rebel's Recollections,* pp. 22-24; Mrs. Sally Ann Brock Putnam, *Richmond During the War; Four Years of Personal Observations,* pp. 24-26; *O.R.,* Vol. LI, Part 2, p. 24.

5. *Journ. of Va. Convention,* pp. 178-179.

6. *Journ. of Va. Convention,* Ordinances Adopted . . . in Secret Session in April and May, 1861, rear section, p. 9; *O.R.,* Vol. LI, Part 2, p. 21.

7. Proceedings of the Advisory Council of Virginia, 1861 (cited hereafter as Proceedings of Advisory Council), a bound volume of MS minutes of the meetings of the council from April 21 through June 19, 1861 (the minutes were signed daily by those present), in the Archives of Virginia, VSL, pp. 1-2. There is also a second volume of rough minutes that do not cover entire period but supply the pay record for the Council in back of book. MFM received $4 per day in addition to his Navy pay.

8. Freeman, *Lee,* Vol. I, Appendix I-3, pp. 637-638.

9. MFM to B. Franklin Minor, July 19, 1861, MP, Vol. XIV, LC.

10. Ibid., May 16, 1861.

11. Robert A. Brock, *Virginia and Virginians,* Vol. II, pp. 416-417; *Official*

Records of the Union and Confederate Navies in the War of the Rebellion (cited hereafter as *O.R.N.*), Ser. I, Vol. VI, pp. 278, 288-291, 300-309.

12. Robert A. Brock, *Virginia and Virginians*, Vol. II, pp. 416-417.

13. On February 1, 1832, the U.S. Secretary of War had caused to be issued Order No. 11, A.G.O., to the effect that the military post at Old Point Comfort, Va., was to be called Fort Monroe and not Fortress Monroe, Robert Arthurs, *History of Fort Monroe*, p. 69. It was an order that was more ignored than obeyed. Virginians continued to use the old name and while some officers used the official name, the majority did not. In 1861 Secretary of the U.S. Navy Gideon Welles and Flag Officer G. J. Pendergrast, commanding the U.S.N. Home Squadron with his flagship anchored off the post, both termed it Fortress Monroe in official communications; *O.R.N.*, Ser. I, Vol. IV, pp. 357-358, Vol. V, pp. 719, 721.

14. The Russians had experimented with electric submarine mines in the Baltic in 1854 but had not been successful. The Austrians had used floating torpedoes to mine partially the approaches to Venice in what Bradford called the French-Austrian war and MFM called the Italian war. These torpedoes, however, were not used because Venice was not attacked. See R. B. Bradford, Lieut. Commander, U.S.N., *History of Torpedo Warfare;* sketch of the history of electric torpedoes in talk given by MFM in France, May 21, 1866, MP, Vol. XXV, Folios 4552-4559, LC.

15. This information is found in a sketch dated Nov. 18, 1865, undoubtedly written by MFM in Mexico. MFM had no records with him in Mexico, and the sketch advances the date of MFM's departure from Washington and of his beginning duty on the Governor's Advisory Council by one day. The sketch incorrectly gives April 20 (instead of April 21, 1861) as the date when he began duty on the Council and states, "The same day he [MFM] sent an agent to New York to purchase a quantity of insulated wire to be used in this new system of defense." Other evidence points to the fact that MFM dispatched this agent on Monday, April 22, rather than Sunday, April 21, 1861, and I have accordingly used this date. See account of MFM's development of C.S.N. torpedoes, Nov. 18, 1865, MP, Vol. XXIII, LC.

16. Lee's acceptance was, of course, subject to confirmation by the Virginia Convention. There is no official record of the conversation between Governor Letcher and Lee, but see record of Letcher's original tender sent by messenger, Letcher's nomination to the convention in the entries of the Executive Minute Book (MS), entries for April 20 and 23, 1861, in Archives of Virginia, VSL. For unanimous approval of the Virginia Convention, see *Journ. of Va. Convention*, pp. 184-185.

17. Ibid., p. 186.

18. MFM to B. Franklin Minor, May 9, 1861, MP, Vol. XIV, LC.

19. The Lynchburg *Virginian*, April (day not stated), 1861, as reprinted in Richmond *Enquirer*, April 25, 1861, p. 2.

20. Fasano, *Naval Rank*, p. 136, fn.

21. *Journ. of Va. Convention*, Ordinance No. 9, Ordinances Adopted . . . in Secret Session in April and May, 1861, rear section, p. 6.

22. *Journ. of Va. Convention*, p. 209. For correction of the statements, "At Richmond, Maury was at once made a commodore in the Virginia Navy," (John W. Wayland, *The Pathfinder of the Seas, The Life of Matthew*

Fontaine Maury, p. 112), and "he was granted a commission as commodore in the Virginia Navy," (Jaquelin Ambler Caskie, *Life and Letters of Matthew Fontaine Maury,* p. 135), see MFM's commission as commander, Virginia Navy, dated April 23, 1861, in MP, Vol. XV, Folio 2423, LC.

23. MFM to U.S. Secretary of Navy Gideon Welles, Apr. 26, 1861, in NR, Executive, Letters Received, April-May, 1861, NAn; letter quoted in Lewis, *Maury,* p. 143.

24. *Journ. of Va. Convention,* Ordinances Adopted . . . in Secret Session in April and May, 1861, rear section, pp. 4-5.

25. Ordinance of April 27, 1861, established Virginia Navy, *Journ. of Va. Convention,* p. 209.

26. The *Patrick Henry* of the New York and Old Dominion Steamship Line was renamed the *Yorktown* and the steamer *Jamestown* of the same line was rechristened the *Thomas Jefferson,* but both were usually referred to by their original names. The Virginia Navy also had one small tug, the *Teaser,* Brock, *Virginia and Virginians,* p. 423; see also Virginius Newton, "The Confederate Navy," *Southern Historical Society Papers,* 1894, Vol. XXII, p. 90.

27. *O.R.N.,* Series I, Vol. V, p. 803.

28. In connection with MFM's duties in advising Governor Letcher about placing batteries to defend the strategic points of Virginia rivers, it is interesting to note that one of the two main laboratory buildings of the Virginia Institute of Marine Science, located on Gloucester Point, is named for MFM and MFM's chart table is on view there. The battery on the point was commanded by one of MFM's former Observatory associates, Commander T. J. Page, explorer of the La Plata River in South America. For assignment of Leigh and Page to West Point and Gloucester Point, respectively, see report of Samuel Barron, Captain in Charge of Naval Detail and Equipment to Governor Letcher, June 10, 1861, *O.R.N.,* Ser. I, Vol. V, pp. 803-806; see also *O.R.N.,* Ser. I, Vol. VI, pp. 724, 746.

29. I have used the form and the spelling for Sewell's Point used by MFM and in the official atlas to accompany the official records of the Civil War. This strategic point, however, was called Sowels Point by Joshua Frye and Peter Jefferson in their 1751 map, and Sewall Point on the 9-sheet map by Herman Böyë, of 1825 corrected to 1859. Hearne Brothers' Map of Greater Norfolk 1945 shows it as Sewall Point.

For information on William Lewis Maury's commanding battery on Sewell's Point, see *O.R.N.,* Ser. I, Vol. V, pp. 801, 805, Vol. VI, pp. 740, 768, 772; MFM to B. Franklin Minor, June 19, 1861, MP, Vol. XIV, LC.

In fairness it seems advisable to state at this point that it was not MFM, as frequently stated, but William Lewis Maury, former U.S.N. lieutenant, commander in the Virginia Navy and later lieutenant and commander in the Confederate Navy, who took heavy guns to be installed on Jamestown Island on Sunday, May 5, 1861. By not stating the officer's first name, the official records have confused previous writers, who took the reference to "Commander Maury" and two references to "Lieutenant Maury" in a postcript on the report as references to MFM. The references were to MFM's cousin, William Lewis Maury, who was at that time assigned to the specific duty of placing guns in batteries at points considered important to the defense of Virginia; *O.R.N.*, Ser. I, Vol. IV, pp. 772-773.

MFM could not have transported the guns by boat to Jamestown on Sunday, May 5, 1861, because he was in Fredericksburg that day to see his ill wife. On Monday, May 6, while waiting in the Advisory Council Chamber in Richmond for Governor Letcher to return from Norfolk, MFM wrote, "I went to [my] wife's house [John Minor's house lent her in Fredericksburg] Saturday night and returned to my post here this morning at 9. I left my wife sick abed." MFM to B. Franklin Minor, May 6, 1861, MP, Vol. XIV, LC.

In the general sense, MFM had a part in the establishment of the battery on Jamestown Island through his work on the Governor's Advisory Council. However, for the actual work of William Lewis Maury's transporting guns to Jamestown of May 5, 1861, see Report of Lieut. Catesby ap R. Jones, Virginia Navy, Commanding Battery, Jamestown Island, to Capt. Samuel Barron, Virginia Navy, Richmond, May 6, 1861, *O.R.N.*, Ser. I, Vol. VI, pp. 701-702.

30. The order extending the blockade to the ports of Virginia and North Carolina was issued by President Lincoln, April 27, 1861, *O.R.N.*, Ser. I, Vol. VI, p. 340; see also p. 356. For Pendergrast's stating he had successfully blockaded, see Brock, *Virginia and Virginians,* p. 422.

31. Proceedings of Advisory Council, minutes for Apr. 30, 1861.

32. I have used the spelling *Merrimac* in this book because it was the spelling used by the Governor's Advisory Council in its recommendation that the wreck of the steam frigate *Merrimac* be raised. See vote and MFM's signature to minutes of May 11, 1861, Proceedings of Advisory Council, p. 68. This is also the spelling used by E. G. Swem in his *Virginia Historical Index.* MFM was well aware that the 40-gun steam frigate was named *Merrimack* (for a New England river) and had used that spelling in a letter about the ship long before he left the U.S. Naval Observatory in Washington. He used the spelling with a *k* in his private letters in the early part of the war, but in published letters for popular consumption MFM wrote the name in the way that was used by most people other than naval officers.

33. MFM, "Man's Power Giving Knowledge," lecture to V.M.I. students, MS in MP, Vol. XLVIII, Folios 9690-9691, LC.

34. Boston *Daily Evening Traveller,* May 4, 1861, p. 1.

35. MFM wrote from Richmond, "and here I am contending, as the fathers of the Republic did, for the right of self-government, and those very principles for the maintenance of which Washington fought when this, his native State, was a colony of Great Britain." Letter to H.I.H. the Grand Duke Constantine, Grand Admiral of Russia, St. Petersburg, Oct. 29, 1861, MP, Vol. XV, LC.

36. Boston *Daily Evening Traveller,* May 2 and 3, 1861.

37. MFM to William C. Hasbrouck, Newburgh, N.Y., May 12, 1861, MP, Vol. XIV, LC.

38. Ibid., May 11, 1861.

39. For Mallory's appointment and confirmation, see Durkin, *Mallory,* pp. 131-135; for Secretary Mallory's arrival in Richmond, see letters of Capt.

Samuel Barron to Lieut. Catesby ap R. Jones, May 29, June 1 and 2, 1861, *O.R.N.,* Ser. I, Vol. VI, pp. 706, 708, 709.

40. Proceedings of Advisory Council, minutes for June 3, 1861.
41. Ibid., minutes for June 7, 1861.
42. Letter of Capt. Samuel Barron to Lieut. Catesby ap R. Jones, June 2, 1861, *O.R.N.,* Series I, Vol. VI, p. 709.
43. Proceedings of Advisory Council, minutes for June 14, 1861.
44. MFM to B. Franklin Minor, June 11, 1861, MP, Vol. XIV, LC.
45. Ibid.
46. For details, see account of the "Steamer Plan" in "Maury and the Atlantic Cable," Chap. XII, this book. For the role of Jefferson Davis (or the "General" as Bache and Charles Henry Davis called him) in this plan, see Alexander Dallas Bache to Charles Henry Davis, Nov. 9, 1855, Bache Papers, Vol. I, LC.
47. Jefferson Davis to Alexander Dallas Bache, Oct. 22 and 28, 1858, Bache Papers, Vol. X, LC.
48. Corbin, *Maury,* p. 112.
49. See the full story of Senator Mallory's leadership of the fight to prevent MFM's being restored to the Active List of the Navy in "The Plucking Board," Chap. XIV, this book. Mallory also spoke against MFM's receiving an increase in pay when the matter came before the Senate in the winter of 1859-1860; B. Franklin Minor to Senator R. M. T. Hunter, May 11, 1860, MP, Vol. IX, LC.
50. Prior to the Virginia Navy's being incorporated in the C.S. Navy, Samuel Barron was the captain in charge of the Office of Naval Detail and Equipment, Virginia Navy, and was continued in the same position that summer and early fall, 1861, in the C.S.N. Office of Orders and Detail. See orders issued by Barron, June 3, Oct. 5, 1861, *O.R.N.,* Ser. I, Vol. V, p. 803; Vol. VI, p. 709.
51. Franklin Buchanan, Captain in Charge, Office of Orders and Detail, C.S.N., to Lieut. Robert D. Minor, *O.R.N.,* Ser. I, Vol. VI, p. 304A.
52. Robert H. Maury had before the war handled MFM's small investments. His place of business was at 1328 East Main Street. Among other activities, Robert H. Maury represented a London banking firm. His residence at 1105 East Clay Street was a typical Richmond town house of the period and consisted of an English basement and three stories. The front bedroom on the second floor was turned over to MFM. See Mary Wingfield Scott, *Houses of Old Richmond,* p. 245.
53. MFM to John Minor, Apr. 28, 1861, MP, Vol. XIV, LC.
54. Dr. Brodie S. Herndon to MFM, May 29, 1861, MP, Vol. XIV, LC.
55. Betty Herndon Maury's Diary, 2 MS vols., Vol. I, entry for June 3, 1861, MP, LC.
56. Ibid.
57. William C. Hasbrouck to MFM, May 8 and June 21, 1861, MP, Vol. XIV, LC.
58. Ibid., Apr. 29, May 10, 11, 13, 1861.
59. Betty Herndon Maury's Diary, Vol. I, entry for June 3, 1861, MP, LC.
60. Ibid.
61. Ibid.
62. Ibid., entry for June 6, 1861.

63. The Richmond, Fredericksburg and Potomac Railroad had run its first train in 1836. The line's tracks extended from Richmond to Fredericksburg. In 1842 the tracks were extended to the Potomac at the point where Aquia Creek enters the river. At that railhead the train made connection with the river steamer running to and from Washington. In Richmond the R. F. and P. train ran down Broad Street to its depot on Broad between 7th and 8th Streets, only a few blocks from where MFM was staying and an even shorter distance from the Capitol, where MFM was in daily attendance at the meetings of the Governor's Advisory Council.

64. MFM to John Minor, Sept. 18 and 26, 1861, MP, Vol. XIV, LC; Betty Herndon Maury's Diary, Vol. I, entry for Jan. 12, 1862, MP, LC.

65. On April 26, 1861, Governor Letcher nominated and recommended to his Advisory Council the appointment of 20½-year-old "Richard L. Maury to be 1st Lieut. of Volunteers for service in Council Chamber." The council advised unanimously that young Maury be appointed. This was temporary duty for Dick, who shortly thereafter secured active duty in the field. See Proceedings of Advisory Council, minutes for Apr. 26, 1861. See also R. L. Maury, "Torpedoes," *SHSP*, p. 329.

66. *O.R.N.*, Ser. I, Vol. V, pp. 553-555.

67. MFM to B. Franklin Minor, June 26, 1861, MP, Vol. XIV, LC; Betty Herndon Maury's Diary, Vol. I, entry for July 1, 1861, MP, LC.

68. MFM to B. Franklin Minor, June 26, 1861, MP, Vol. XIV, LC.

69. Ibid.

70. Ibid., Betty Herndon Maury's Diary, Vol. I, entries for June 27, 28, July 1, 1861, MP, LC; *O.R.N.*, Ser. I, Vol. V, pp. 553-555. MFM to Gen. William G. Harding, July 3, 1861, Harding Collection, VUL.

71. Proceedings of Advisory Council, minutes for June 19, 1861. These final minutes of the council are on p. 154; there is a copy of the ordinance that terminated the life of the council on p. 155 of this interesting volume detailing Virginia's mobilization.

72. Proceedings of Advisory Council, minutes for May 27, 1861.

73. MFM to Dr. James L. Cabell, professor, Univ. of Virginia, May 31, 1861, MP, Vol. XIV, LC.

74. MFM's son Richard L. Maury spoke of an "ordinary washtub" having been used in his article "Torpedoes," p. 328. Mrs. Francis W. Upshur wrote me in 1961 that her aunt Belle (Isobel Maury), the daughter of Robert H. Maury, told her that it was the tub in which the Robert H. Maury children took their baths and that she remembered the family's butler carrying the tub up to MFM's bedroom when he wished to experiment.

The Negro butler greatly disapproved of MFM's experiments and declared that "Marse Mat" would blow up the house and all of them with it, according to a family anecdote handed down to Mrs. Upshur and told me by her.

75. The brothers, Charles and James M. Talbott, were partners not only in Richmond's iron industry but also in building houses. Their firm was then sometimes called Talbott and Brother, sometimes Talbott Brothers, but not Talbott and Son as stated by Richard L. Maury in his article cited in Note 3. The business was located at 1541 East Cary Street according to Mills and Starke's 1866 publication, *The City of Richmond, Business Directory and City Guide*, p. 6.

76. MFM to B. Franklin Minor, June 26, July 8 and 19, 1861, MP, Vol. XIV, LC; Betty Herndon Maury's Diary, Vol. I, entry for July 10, 1861, MP, LC.
77. Betty Herndon Maury's Diary, Vol. I, entry for July 10, 1861, MP, LC.
78. MFM to Dr. Brodie S. Herndon, Apr. 22, 1863, MP, Vol. XVIII, LC.
79. Betty Herndon Maury's Diary, entry for July 10, 1861, MP, LC.
80. MFM's description quoted in R. L. Maury, "Torpedoes," p. 329.
81. Betty Maury, who had so long served as an amanuensis for her father before her marriage to William A. Maury, wrote the full story of this expedition as recounted by MFM in her diary on the third day after the expedition; Betty Herndon Maury's Diary, Vol. I, entry for Wednesday, July 10, 1861, MP, LC.
82. Ibid., MFM's statement as quoted in account cited in Note 80.
83. Betty Herndon Maury's Diary, Vol. I, entry for July 17, 1861, MP, LC.
84. The expression "your man" was ironic as Minor had held a low opinion of Mallory since 1855. The quotation is from MFM to B. Franklin Minor, Aug. 11, 1861, MP, Vol. XIV, LC.
85. MFM's early experiments in June, 1861, and his struggle in June and July, 1861, to persuade Secretary Mallory to recognize the potential of torpedo warfare refute such statements as this in an article by R. O. Crowley: "The idea of using torpedoes on the Confederate side originated, I believe, with the Hon. S. R. Mallory, Secretary of the Navy; and he directed the distinguished Captain M. F. Maury to make experiments, with a view to their general employment, if practicable. His [MFM's] work began in the spring of 1862, and continued for a few months only with electrical torpedoes." *Century Magazine,* June, 1898, reprinted in Philip Van Doren Stern, *Secret Missions of the Civil War,* p. 209.

    The intense opposition of Ann Herndon Maury to her husband's work in developing and laying torpedoes for the Confederacy was described to me by her granddaughter, Mrs. N. Montgomery Osborne of Norfolk. It was the first time Ann had opposed him. MFM asked her if she could not see that he was trying to make war so horrible that men would agree to sit down around a table to decide their differences. Interview with Mrs. Osborne in August, 1958.
86. MFM to B. Franklin Minor, July 19, 1861, MP, Vol. XIV, LC.
87. Ibid.
88. MFM to B. Franklin Minor, July 19, Oct. 8, 1861, MP, Vol. XV, LC; R. L. Maury, "Torpedoes," SHSP, p. 328.
89. R. L. Maury, "Torpedoes," p. 328.
90. MFM to B. Franklin Minor, Aug. 11, 1861, MP, Vol. XIV, LC.
91. Ibid. See also MFM to B. Franklin Minor, Aug. 19, 21, 1861, MP, Vol. XIV, LC.
92. *The American Navy, Its Organization, Ships, Armament and Recent Experiences,* reprint of "Report of meeting, June 1, 1868," *Journal of the Royal United Service Institution* (London), Vol. XIII, MP, Miscellaneous Pamphlets, LC.
93. MFM to B. Franklin Minor, Aug. 2, 1861, MP, Vol. XIV, LC. The original of MFM's Aug. 2, 1861, proposed peace message is in the Georgia Room, Confederate Museum, Richmond; a true copy is in MP, Vol. XIV, Folios 2351-2352, LC.
94. See Lieut. Isaac N. Brown, C.S.N., to Maj. Gen. Leonidas Polk, Aug. 2,

1861; Maj. Gen. Leonidas Polk to C.S. Secretary of War Judah P. Benjamin, Oct. 10, 1861; MFM to Maj. Gen. Leonidas Polk, Dec. 4, 1861, *O.R.N.*, Ser. I, Vol. XXII, pp. 791, 793, 806. For facts on writing letter, see Betty Herndon Maury's Diary, Vol. I, entry for Sept. 30, 1861, MP, LC.

95. Richmond *Enquirer,* September and October, 1861; see article referred to in issue of Oct. 3, 1861 (date obscured), on microfilm in VSL. In same paper, see letter from "prominent citizen of South Carolina" praising "Ben Bow's" articles urging the strengthening of the Confederate Navy. Article No. 1, "Ought We to Have a Navy," and article No. 2, "The Navy Again: Big Guns and Little Ships," are in MP, Scrap Book, Box marked Ac 7922, LC; reprint of article No. 1, in Corbin, *Maury,* pp. 204-209.

96. MFM to Maj. Gen. Leonidas Polk, Dec. 4, 1861, *O.R.N.*, Ser. I, Vol. XXII, p. 806.

97. MFM to B. Franklin Minor, Oct. 8, 1861, MP, Vol. XV, LC.

98. Ibid.

99. Ibid.

100. Orders from Franklin Buchanan, Captain in Charge, C.S.N. Office of Orders and Detail to Lieut. Robert D. Minor, Oct. 5, 1861, *O.R.N.*, Ser. I, Vol. VI, p. 304.

101. See MFM to B. Franklin Minor, Oct. 8, 1861, MP, Vol. XV, LC; Richard L. Maury from "Camp near Fairfax Station" to his mother, Mrs. Ann Herndon Maury, Oct. 10, 1861, MP, Vol. XV, LC; Betty Herndon Maury's Diary, Vol. I, entries for Sept. 6, 10, 20, 1861, MP, LC.

102. MFM to B. Franklin Minor, Oct. 8, 1861, MP, Vol. XV, LC. The dogma of "Big Guns and Little Ships" had been propounded by MFM in his "Ben Bow" articles in the Richmond *Enquirer* in weeks previous to this letter; Betty Herndon Maury's Diary, Vol. I, entry for Oct. 7, 1861, MP, LC.

103. Testimony of Commander John Mercer Brooke, C.S.N., "Report of Evidence Taken Before a Joint Special Committee of Both Houses of the Confederate Congress to Investigate the Affairs of the Navy Department." *O.R.N.*, Ser. II, Vol. I, p. 783.

104. Secretary Mallory is entitled to full recognition for his early and forceful urging of the importance of ironclads to the Confederate Navy. See *O.R.N.*, Ser. II, Vol. I, pp. 740-743; *Report of* [C.S.] *Secretary of Navy to* [C.S.] *Congress,* July 18, 1861. Testimony of Commander Brooke (cited in Note 103), *O.R.N.*, Ser. II, Vol. I, pp. 783-786. Brock, *Virginia and the Virginians,* Vol. II, pp. 423-424.

105. John Mercer Brooke testified that he submitted his proposal to Secretary Mallory and, receiving approval for his idea, asked for a skilled naval draftsman to be brought from Norfolk. When a man who was not a draftsman came to Richmond, Brooke drew his own plan but asked Secretary Mallory to send for Confederate Naval Constructor John L. Porter and the naval engineer for a consultation. Porter, who had been a U.S. naval constructor, brought with him a model. "The difference between the model [of Constructor Porter] and my drawing," Brooke testified, "consisted in the one I proposed having the ends prolonged and shaped like those of any fast vessel, and in order to protect them from the enemy they were to be submerged two feet under water, so that nothing was to be seen afloat but the shield." He further stated that his original plan had "supposed

that the projection beyond the shield submerged would be sufficient as a beak. The vessel was pretty well advanced when the beak was put on. The shield was up." He stated that a "ram has a strong cutwater stem but not necessarily a beak" and "Mr. Porter decided to put on the iron beak which she carried."

Both Brooke and Porter had conceived very much the same idea independently, but the fact that it was Brooke's plan that was approved by Secretary Mallory and that in Mallory's official report Brooke received credit for designing the *Virginia,* as the rebuilt *Merrimac* was christened, led to resentment on the part of the very able John L. Porter. *O.R.N.,* Ser. II, Vol. I, pp. 783-788.

106. Ibid. The testimony was given on Feb. 26, 1863. MFM was then in England and, there being no Atlantic cable, could not be asked for his opinion. There is, however, no doubt that MFM had proposed a mosquito fleet of gunboats that were not designed to be covered with iron plate.
107. MFM to B. Franklin Minor, Oct. 8 and 19, 1861, MP, Vol. XV, LC.
108. MFM to Governor John Letcher, Oct. 8, 1861, MP, Vol. XV, LC.
109. Ibid.
110. Betty Herndon Maury's Diary, Vol. I, entries for Oct. 7 and 13, 1861, MP, LC; MFM to B. Franklin Minor, Oct. 8, 1861, MP, Vol. XV, LC.
111. MFM to B. Franklin Minor, Oct. 19, 1861, MP, Vol. XV, LC.
112. Ibid.; Betty Herndon Maury's Diary, Vol. I, entry for Oct. 17, 1861, MP, LC.
113. Betty Herndon Maury's Diary, Vol. I, entry for Oct. 6, 1861, MP, LC.
114. Ibid., entry for Oct. 24, 1861.
115. Grand Duke Constantine to MFM, July 27, 1861, *Southern Historical Society Papers,* 1876, Vol. II, pp. 51-53.
116. Edward de Stoeckl, Russian Minister to the United States, Sept. 18, 1861, MP, Vol. XIV, LC.
117. Betty Herndon Maury's Diary, Vol. I, entry for Oct. 27, 1861, MP, LC.
118. MFM to the Grand Duke Constantine, Oct. 29, 1861; to B. Franklin Minor, Nov. 1, 1861, both in MP, Vol. XV, LC.
119. MFM to B. Franklin Minor, Nov. 5, 1861, MP, Vol. XV, LC.
120. Ibid., Nov. 16, 1861.
121. Ibid., Nov. 5, 1861.
122. Ibid., Nov. 21, 1861.
123. Charles M. Conrad, chairman of House Committee on Naval Affairs, Confederate Congress, to C.S. Secretary of Navy Stephen R. Mallory, Dec. 9, 1861; testimony of Charles M. Conrad before a joint Select Committee of the Senate and House of Representatives of the Confederate Congress "to investigate the administration of the Navy Department under its present head," Feb. 10, 1863, *O.R.N.,* Ser. II, Vol. I, p. 731.
124. *Journal of the Congress of the Confederate States of America, 1861-1865,* Vol. I, pp. 606, 612, 621.
125. Ibid.; Betty Herndon Maury's Diary, Vol. I, entries for Dec. 22, 1861, Jan. 5, 1862, MP, LC; MFM to Capt. William F. Lynch, Jan. 19, 1862, cited in Note 130; to William M. Blackford, Feb. 5, 1862, MP, Vol. XV, LC; testimony of Charles M. Conrad cited in Note 123.
126. Before passage of this bill Charles M. Conrad, chairman of the House Committee on Naval Affairs, Confederate Congress, used the title "com-

mander." He wrote, "The enclosed communication from Commander Maury," in a letter to C.S. Secretary of Navy Mallory, Dec. 9, 1861; *O.R.N.*, Ser. II, Vol. I, pp. 750-751. On Feb. 10, 1863, testifying in the investigation of Secretary Mallory's conduct of the C.S. Navy Department, Charles M. Conrad used the title "commodore" in a statement, "Commodore Maury had recommended to the Virginia Convention the construction of . . . small gunboats." On Sept. 9, 1862, earlier in the same investigation, Ethelbert Barksdale, member of the House of Representatives from Mississippi, Confederate Congress, in questioning Capt. William C. Whittle, C.S.N., who had been in command of defenses on the York River, Virginia, in 1861, asked, "Do you recollect when Commodore Maury was placed in charge of the business of supervising the construction of gunboats in Virginia waters?" *O.R.N.*, Ser. II, Vol. I, p. 447.

Richard L. Maury sometimes spoke of his father as "the captain" and sometimes as "the commodore." Gen. Francis H. Smith used the title "captain" until after the war, when he adopted use of the title "commodore." General R. E. Lee addressed MFM as "My dear Captain Maury" in a letter written, Sept. 8, 1865, Corbin, *Maury*, pp. 238-239.

In issuing official orders Secretary Mallory used MFM's statutory rank, which remained commander throughout the war. For substantiation, see MFM's giving his rank as commander in his letter of surrender, May 25, 1865, *O.R.N.*, Ser. I, Vol. III, pp. 546-547. For examples of usage by Southerners of title "commodore" for MFM, see James Morris Morgan, *Recollections of a Rebel Reefer* (cited hereafter as Morgan, *Rebel Reefer*), pp. 96, 98, 114; C.S. Secretary of State Judah P. Benjamin to C.S. Commissioner John Slidell, Paris, March 11, 1864, in *O.R.N.*, Ser. II, Vol. III, p. 1059.

127. MFM to his sister, Mrs. Elizabeth Maury Holland, Jan. 12, 1862, MP, Vol. XV, LC; to Gen. William G. Harding, Jan. 5, 1862, Harding Collection, VUL; Betty Herndon Maury's Diary, Vol. I, entries for Jan. 5, 12, 1862, MP, LC.

128. MFM to C.S. Secretary of Navy Mallory, Jan. 25, 1862, *O.R.N.*, Ser. II, Vol. II, p. 138.

129. For John's activities, see Betty Herndon Maury's Diary, Vol. I, entries for July 17, 28, Aug. 3, Oct. 4, 1861, Jan. 22, 1862, MP, LC.

130. MFM to Commodore William F. Lynch, Jan. 19, 1862, *O.R.N.*, Ser. I, Vol. VI, pp. 633-635.

131. Report of Appraisal Board to Commander S. C. Rowan, Commanding U.S. Naval Forces, Sounds of North Carolina, *O.R.N.*, Ser. I, Vol. VI, p. 622; Preliminary Report of Flag Officer L. M. Goldsborough, U.S.N., Commanding North Atlantic Blockading Squadron, to U.S. Secretary of Navy Gideon Welles, Feb. 14, 1862, *O.R.N.*, Ser. I, Vol. VI, p. 632; Betty Herndon Maury's Diary, Vol. I, entries for Feb. 12, 14, 18, 1862, MP, LC.

132. Betty Herndon Maury's Diary, Vol. II, entry for March 16, 1862, MP, LC.

133. Testimony of Capt. William C. Whittle before a Joint Select Committee of the Senate and House of Representatives of the Confederate Congress "to investigate the administration of the Navy under its present head," Sept. 9, 1862; *O.R.N.*, Ser. II, Vol. I, pp. 448-451. For MFM's original proposal on this point, see letter of MFM to Governor Letcher cited in Note 108.

134. MFM to Gen. William G. Harding, Dec. 11, 1861, Jan. 5, 1862, Harding Collection, VUL. General Harding's home still stands and is open to the public. Spacious grounds have been retained around the house, but the plantation has been absorbed in the fashionable Belle Meade residential section of Nashville.

135. MFM sent his son-in-law S. Wellford Corbin through the South to try to secure ships' carpenters; Betty Herndon Maury's Diary, Vol. II, entries for March 16 and 23, 1862. To secure iron and engines, an agent requested by MFM was sent by Secretary Mallory; testimony of Charles M. Conrad, Feb. 10, 1863, in investigation of Secretary Mallory's conduct of the Navy Department, *O.R.N.*, Ser. II, Vol. I, p. 732.

136. MFM's son John received an appointment as a master in the Navy and worked on the building of the gunboats on the Pamunkey River under the direction of Lieut. William Lewis Maury, C.S.N.

    For intelligence about gunboats reaching Washington, see report of R. H. Wyman, Lieut. Commanding Potomac Flotilla, to U.S. Secretary of Navy Gideon Welles, March 13, 1862, in *O.R.N.*, Ser. I, Vol. V, p. 25.

137. For story of the U.S.S. *Monitor*, which was laid down at Greenpoint, Long Island, Oct. 25, 1861, see Robert Stanley McCordock, *The Yankee Cheese Box*, (building) pp. 30-38, (launching Jan. 30, 1862) p. 52, (fitting for sea and trial run) pp. 55-56, (correcting technical problems) pp. 70-71.

138. Testimony of Commander John M. Brooke, Feb. 26, 1863, before Joint Committee of the Confederate Congress . . . , *O.R.N.*, Ser. II, Vol. I, p. 785. See also John M. Brooke, "The Virginia or Merrimac: Her Real Projector [Mallory]" in *Southern Historical Society Papers*, 1891, Vol. XIX, pp. 1-34.

139. John L. Porter was directed to perform all the duties of constructor in connection with the alterations of the former *Merrimac*. Chief Engineer William P. Williamson was directed to repair the engines for use. Both worked in Norfolk. Brooke was ordered to supervise the rolling of the plates and casting of guns at the Tredegar Iron Works, Richmond. Brooke stated in testimony cited in Note 138, "It was a difficult matter to get iron [plates] from Richmond to Norfolk, there being over 700 tons of iron sent down in the course of her construction." *O.R.N.*, Ser. II, Vol. I, p. 783. See also Report of Franklin Buchanan, Captain C.S.S. *Virginia*, to Navy Department, enclosure No. 2 in message of President Davis to Confederate Congress, Apr. 10, 1862; to Secretary Mallory, March 27, 1862, *O.R.N.*, Ser. I, Vol. VIII, pp. 44-45. Betty Herndon Maury's Diary, Vol. II, entry for March 16, 1862, MP, LC.

140. Report on the engagement by Franklin Buchanan, Captain C.S.S. *Virginia*, *O.R.N.*, Ser. I, Vol. IX, pp. 1-14; for a modern account, see Robert Stanley McCordock, *The Yankee Cheese Box*.

141. An excellent account of the battle and its naval significance, MFM to Capt. A. de la Marche, Dépôt de la Marine, France (29 pp.), March 15, 1862 (press copy of the original, signature has been cut out), MP, Vol. XV, LC.

    Even more interesting than MFM's description of the battle of the ironclads is a postscript that he added to this letter to Capt. de la Marche. It comprises the only reference that I have been able to find by MFM to a short-lived service he rendered the Confederacy: "P.S. I am engaged in assisting to prepare a system of weights and measures and coins for the Confederacy. We are sadly in want of the papers and documents about the French system. Please send to consul."

MFM was referring to service on a committee that had come about this way: The preceding Nov. 29, 1861, John Tyler, former President of the United States, had offered a resolution in the House of Representatives of the Confederate Congress instructing the Committee on Commerce to inquire into the expediency of providing a new system of weights and measures and of coin for the Confederate States of America. This was agreed to. (*Journal of the Provisional Confederate Congress*, p. 429.) The Committee on Commerce reported this resolution back to the House on Jan. 23, 1862, with the recommendation that it lie on the table. (Ibid., p. 694.) On Jan. 29, 1862, the Special Committee on Commercial and Financial Independence reported back to the House and offered the following Resolution: "*Resolved*, That Captain Matthew F. Maury and Professors A. T. Bledsoe and F. [Francis Henry] Smith, of the University of Virginia, be, and they are hereby, appointed by Congress to draw up a system of weights and measures and coins, to be presented to the Confederate Congress for its consideration."

The committee went to work, but I have been unable to find a copy of any report they made to the Confederate Congress or of legislative action on the part of that body on any recommendations of the committee on which MFM served.

It was because of his work on that committee that MFM formed a high opinion of A. T. Bledsoe's mental powers; this led MFM to introduce Bledsoe to his English friends when the former professor came to England on a mission in the autumn of 1863 (MFM to the Rev. Francis W. Tremlett, Oct. 27, 1863; to Mrs. Tremlett, Oct. 31, 1863, both in MP, Vol. XVIII, LC.)

There was not much that MFM, Bledsoe and Smith could do about a system of coinage for the Confederacy because of the South's shortage of metals. Only two Confederate coins were issued—a cent and a half dollar—and neither of these was issued in large quantity (Fred Reinfeld, *The Story of Civil War Money*, pp. 52, 53, 55, 57, 67, 68.)

Any contribution MFM may have made to a new system of weights and measures must have been extremely limited in view of the fact that in February and March, 1862, he was devoting his energies to the program of building 100 gunboats as rapidly as possible, and in May and June he was working long hours daily in mining the James River to prevent Union gunboats from reaching Richmond. His office was listed in the 1862 directory of Confederate government offices as "Commander M. F. Maury, C.S.N., Office of 'Special Service,' corner of Bank and 9th Sts, south side."

142. Testimony of Charles M. Conrad, chairman of House Naval Affairs Committee, Feb. 10, 1863, before Joint Committee of House and Senate, Confederate Congress, *O.R.N.*, Ser. II, Vol. I, p. 731.

143. Ibid., pp. 731-732; report on the resolution of the House of Representatives, Confederate Congress, passed March 17, in letter of Secretary of Navy Mallory to President Davis, March 29, 1862, ibid., p. 751.

144. Letter of Secretary Mallory to President Davis cited in Note 143.

145. "They talk in Congress of scrapping the gunboats because they are not

plated." MFM to B. Franklin Minor, Apr. 1, 1862, MP, Vol. XV, LC. "Papa came up yesterday. He looks very depressed." Betty Herndon Maury's Diary, Vol. II, entry for March 23, 1862. MFM's concern was not simply distress about his gunboat fleet but also dread of the approaching capture of Fredericksburg by the Union forces. In less than three weeks, "Papa has ordered the boat yards on the Rappahannock to be abandoned. There is one here and one a few miles below. They are destroying all they cannot take away." Ibid., entry for April 13, 1862.

"The gun boats on the Pamunkey that Papa was having built, and his Navy Yard there have had to be broken up and abandoned. The enemy have left him no water now to build upon. His occupation is gone. Oh that Congress had given him the appropriation sooner. The gun boats would have been done by this time and their service would have been invaluable." Ibid., entry for May 5, 1862.

146. MFM, Address to the Ladies' Defence Association urging the collection of all types of scrap and stating places to which it was to be delivered, Apr. 4, 1862, MP, Vol. XV, LC. The need was so great that MFM offered "to make a 'Lady–gun boat' speech" in Charlottesville to raise funds and scrap iron; MFM to B. Franklin Minor, April 7, 1862, MP, Vol. XV, LC.

147. Ibid., Apr. 19, 1862.

148. Ibid., Apr. 21, 1862.

149. "I send you the basis of such a treaty as in my judgment may be negotiated with France including a seven point memorandum of proposals to be made to France for assistance during the war and for a period of years thereafter." MFM to Col. James Lawrence Orr, chairman of Committee on Foreign Relations, Confederate Senate, March 6, 1862, MP, Vol. XV, LC.

150. This plaque was placed on the house in 1910 by the Confederate Memorial Literary Society, the organization that has preserved many treasures of the Confederacy and maintains the Confederate Museum in the White House of the Confederacy, one half block east from the house where MFM experimented on torpedoes.

151. Jaffe, *Men of Science in America*, p. 225; see also p. 224.

152. MFM, lecture on torpedo warfare to French officers and government officials, Paris, May 21, 1866, MP, Vol. XXV, Folios 4552-4559, LC.

153. MFM's will was drafted while he was preparing to mine the James River with his new electrically detonated torpedoes. See draft completed and witnessed by Robert H. Maury and Robert H. Maury, Jr., May 4, 1862. Two codicils were added to this will in 1869 and 1872, but it is filed under date of May 4, 1862, MP, Vol. XVI, LC.

154. Betty Herndon Maury's Diary, Vol. II, entries for March 23, Apr. 18, Apr. 25, May 4, May 5, May 16, June 12, 1862, MP, LC. Two of MFM's letter books were taken as souvenirs subsequent to this date.

155. *Calendar of Virginia State Papers,* Vol. XI, pp. 105, 107; Betty Herndon Maury's Diary, Vol. I, entry for July 20, 1861, in MP, LC; sketch of Dabney Herndon Maury, *DAB,* Vol. XII, p. 427.

156. Betty Herndon Maury's Diary, Vol. II, entries for May 17, 20, 22, 1862, MP, LC.

157. MFM spelled the name of the bluff Chapin as did most Virginians. It was spelled that way on the Civil War map, "Environs of Richmond for use

by Adjutant General's Office," by Maj. H. B. McClellan, A.A.G. and Chief of Staff, from *Campaigns of Stuart's Cavalry, 1861-1864*. Maj. Gen. J. F. Gilmer, Chief Engineer, C.S.A., issued a map of the "Vicinity of Richmond and Part of the Peninsula" in 1864 on which the bluff was spelled Chafin and another undated map of "The Country between Richmond and Petersburg" in which it was called Chaffin. The Federals preferred the latter spelling, and this was inserted when the records were compiled in Washington.

158. Orders of Secretary of C.S. Navy Mallory to Lieut. Hunter Davidson, June 20, 1862, *O.R.N.*, Ser. I, Vol. VII, p. 546.

159. MFM, lecture on torpedo warfare to French officers and government officials, Paris, May 21, 1866, MP, Vol. XXV, LC.

160. MFM to Count Charles Vilzhum d'Eckstaedt, Minister of Saxony, Apr. 25, 1866, MP, Vol. XXV, LC.

161. MFM, lecture on torpedo warfare cited in Note 159.

162. Ibid.

163. Once the effectiveness of ironclads had been proved by the *Virginia* and *Monitor,* MFM campaigned tirelessly for the use of torpedoes as the chief weapon to use against them. He was the pioneer, others followed. On May 1, 1862, MFM wrote C.S. Secretary of War George Wythe Randolph, "I beg to call your attention to our river defenses, and to say that the most effectual way of keeping off the enemy with his shot proof vessels is to mine the channel-ways, and blow up by means of electricity when he attempts the passage." *O.R.N.*, Ser. I, Vol. VI, p. 780.

164. Hunter Davidson's statement that Secretary Mallory favored the use of torpedoes is accurate if "the beginning" is taken to be 1862, when Davidson was ordered to assist MFM, but Davidson apparently had no knowledge of Mallory's opposition thereto in 1861. Davidson makes the rather extreme statement that the torpedoes he used were different in every particular from those devised by MFM. Davidson undoubtedly made improvements on MFM's system that was turned over to him in 1862. He also had the benefit of the new findings sent back to the Confederacy by MFM after his study of and experiments on torpedoes made in England from 1862 to 1865, as well as use of the Abel fuses and Wheatstone exploders that MFM secured, tested, and sent back for use in the Confederacy's torpedo warfare. For Davidson's claims for his work, see Hunter Davidson, "Electrical Torpedoes as a System of Defence," *Southern Historical Society Papers,* 1876, Vol. II, pp. 1-6. For an excellent account of torpedoes by a Union officer, published in 1869, see J. S. Barnes, Lieut. Commander U.S.N., *Submarine Warfare, Offensive and Defensive,* especially pp. 65, 78, 162, 168-169, 189. U.S. Secretary of Navy Gideon Welles made the statement about torpedoes in his December, 1865, Annual Report of the Navy.

165. MFM to B. Franklin Minor, June 1, 1862, MP, Vol. XVI, LC.

166. Freeman, *Lee,* Vol. I, p. 641, Vol. II, p. 74.

167. MFM to B. Franklin Minor, June 5, 1862, MP, Vol. XVI, LC.

168. Ibid., June 8, 1862.

169. *O.R.N.*, Ser. I, Vol. VII, pp. 790-791; MFM to B. Franklin Minor, June 29, 1862, MP, Vol. XVI, LC; Betty Herndon Maury's Diary, Vol. II, entry for July 27, 1862, MP, LC.

170. *O.R.N.*, Ser. I, Vol. VII, pp. 790-791; Charles C. Jones, Jr., *The Life and*

Service of Commodore Josiah Tattnall, pp. 192-217; sketch of Josiah Tattnall, *DAB,* Vol. XVIII, p. 310.

171. *O.R.N.,* Ser. I, Vol. VII, pp. 787-799.

172. MFM to Octave de Chabannes, Admiral, French Navy, July 4, 1862; to Rear Admiral Robert Fitzroy, R.N., Aug. 4, 1862, both in MP, Vol. XVI, LC. The original of latter is in MC, UVAL.

173. MFM to B. Franklin Minor, Aug. 25, 1862, MP, Vol. XVI, LC.

174. Action of House of Representatives, Aug. 27, of Senate, Confederate Congress, Aug. 28, 1862, *Journal of the Congress of the Confederate States of America, 1861-1865,* Vol. V, p. 322. See also *O.R.N.,* Ser. II, Vol. I, p. 431. For testimony in investigation, ibid., pp. 432-809.

175. MFM to Maj. Gen. George B. McClellan, Commanding Army of the Potomac, July 30, 1862 (sent through the lines by Gen. R. E. Lee); to B. Franklin Minor, July 31, Aug. 29, 1862, all in MP, Vol. XVI, LC. See also Betty Herndon Maury's Diary, Vol. II, entries for July 30, Aug. 4, 1862, MP, LC.

176. Dick's marriage to Susan Elizabeth Crutchfield took place at "Ridgeway," home of B. Franklin Minor, July 17, 1862, Betty Herndon Maury's Diary, entry for July 27; for other facts, see entries for June 25, 28, July 7, 9, 10, 27, Aug. 18, 27, 31, Sept. 5, 7, 11, 14, 1862, MP, LC; MFM to B. Franklin Minor, July 31, Aug. 25, 29, 1862, MP, Vol. XVI, LC.

177. Betty Herndon Maury's Diary, Vol. II, entry for Sept. 15, 1862, MP, LC; MFM to his wife, Sept. 17, 18, 1862, M. F. Maury, Jr., to his mother, Sept. 17, 1862, all in MP, Vols. XVI, XVII, LC.

178. Referred to in MFM to Lieut. Robert D. Minor, C.S.N., Apr. 21, 1863, MP, Vol. XVIII, LC.

179. MFM to his wife, Oct. 12, 1862, MP, Vol. XVII, LC; to Jack (John Minor Maury), July 24, 1867, MP, Vol. XXVI, LC.

180. M. F. Maury, Jr., to his mother, Sept. 24, 1862, MP, Vol. XVII, LC.

181. MFM to his wife, Sept. 24, 1862, MP, Vol. XVII, LC.

182. M. F. Maury, Jr., to Glum (his sister Eliza), Oct. 7, 1862, MP, Vol. XLIII, LC; Morgan, *Rebel Reefer,* pp. 93, 94, 96.

183. MFM to his wife, Sept. 25, 29, 30, 1862, also letter to her, Folios 2824, 2826; to B. Franklin Minor, Oct. 12, 1862, all in MP, Vol. XVII, LC. See also Betty Herndon Maury's Diary, Vol. II, entries for Sept. 29, Oct. 2, 8, 1862, MP, LC.

184. MFM to his wife, Oct. 8, 1862, MP, Vol. XVII, LC. See also Betty Herndon Maury's Diary, Vol. II, entry for Oct. 8, 1862, MP, LC.

CHAPTER XX

To England on Secret Service

1. The *Hero*'s repeated unsuccessful efforts to put to sea had made her too obvious a target for the blockading fleet. See Morgan, *Rebel Reefer,* pp. 85-86, 94, 96-98; Betty Herndon Maury's Diary, Vol. II, entry for Dec. 28, 1862, MP, LC; MFM to his wife (code used, "My dear friend"), Oct. 18, 1862, MP, Vol. XVII, LC.

2. Morgan, *Rebel Reefer,* p. 98.

3. Ibid., pp. 99-100.

4. Ibid., p. 102.

5. MFM to his wife, Oct. 18, 20, 21, 29, 1862; to B. Franklin Minor, Oct. 24, 1862, all in MP, Vol. XVII, LC; Betty Herndon Maury's Diary, Vol. II, entry for Dec. 28, 1862, MP, LC.

6. Sketch of Charles Wilkes, *DAB*, Vol. XX, pp. 216-217; sketch of James Murray Mason, *DAB*, Vol. XII, pp. 364-365; sketch of John Slidell, *DAB*, Vol. XVII, pp. 209-211; article on the *Trent* affair in James Truslow Adams (ed.), *Dictionary of American History*, Vol. V, pp. 321-322.

7. See Chap. VI of this book, especially the material covered by Notes 110-122.

8. Letter of MFM to B. Franklin Minor cited in Note 5.

9. Morgan, *Rebel Reefer*, pp. 102-103.

10. MFM to his wife, Nov. 10, 1862, MP, Vol. XVII, LC.

11. Morgan, *Rebel Reefer*, p. 103.

12. Ibid., pp. 104-105.

13. Ibid., pp. 101-102.

14. MFM to his wife, Nov. 25, 1862, MP, Vol. XVII, LC.

15. MFM had again given his wife this address for his mail when in Halifax, Nova Scotia; MFM to his wife, Nov. 10, 1862, MP, Vol. XVII, LC. For MFM's immediately reporting there, see Morgan, *Rebel Reefer*, p. 106.

16. Orders, C.S. Secretary of Navy Mallory to Capt. James D. Bulloch, chief Confederate naval representative in England, Sept. 20, 1862, *O.R.N.*, Ser. II, Vol. II, p. 270.

17. Morgan, *Rebel Reefer*, p. 107.

18. MFM to Marin H. Jansen, Dec. 13, 1862, Feb. 10, 1863; to his wife, Nov. 30, Dec. 29, 1862, all in MP, Vol. XVII, LC.

19. One week after landing in England MFM received a telegram from Marin H. Jansen saying he would come from Holland within a few days. Jansen was in London with MFM and Brave by Dec. 5, 1862; MFM to his wife, Nov. 30, with note added Dec. 5, 1862, MP, Vol. XVII, LC.

20. "As yet I have not set fairly in about my business—I am posting myself up —that has kept me busy." MFM to his wife, Nov. 30, 1862; see also note of Dec. 5, 1862, both cited in Note 19; M. F. Maury, Jr., to his mother, Dec. 8, 1862, MP, Vol. XVII, LC.

21. MFM to his wife, Dec. 8, 14, 1862, MP, Vol. XVII, LC; Betty Herndon Maury's Diary, Vol. II, entries for Feb. 1, 12, 1863, MP, LC.

22. MFM to Marin H. Jansen, Dec. 20, 1862, MP, Vol. XVII, LC.

23. MFM to editor of London *Times*, in London *Times*, Dec. 22, 1862, re-printed in New York *Times*, Jan. 8, 1863, in Richmond *Whig*, also in *O.R.N.*, Ser. II, Vol. II, pp. 335-336.

24. MFM had first asked this question, "Where are you? What I would not give to know," on Nov. 30, 1862; and as many letters failed to get through to him from his family, he continued to ask. See MFM to his wife, Nov. 30, Dec. 28, 1862, MP, Vol. XVII, LC.

25. News of Meiklejohn's visit is in letter of MFM to his wife, Jan. 1, 1863; the quotation is from MFM to his wife, Jan. 14, 1863, both in MP, Vol. XVII, LC.

26. James Dunwody Bulloch, *The Secret Service of the Confederate States in Europe or How the Confederate Cruisers were Equipped* (cited hereafter as Bulloch, *Secret Service*), Vol. II, p. 260.

27. MFM to B. Franklin Minor, Jan. 21, 1863, MP, Vol. XVII, LC.

28. MFM to "My dear Sir" (no name), Jan. 20, 1863, MP, Vol. XVII, Folio 2849, LC.
29. MFM to his wife, Jan. 23, 1863, MP, Vol. XVII, LC.
30. For the constant intelligence work carried out by U.S. agents against the Confederate officers and agents in England, see Morgan, *Rebel Reefer*, p. 111; also see MFM to Lieut. Robert D. Minor, Apr. 21, 1863, MP, Vol. XVIII, LC; Capt. James D. Bulloch to C.S. Secretary of Navy Mallory, *O.R.N.*, Ser. II, Vol. II, p. 583.
   For example cited, see extract from Consular Dispatch, Jan. 9, 1863, *O.R.N.*, Ser. I, Vol. XIII, p. 640. It seems likely that there was a connection between the Mr. Hope mentioned in the dispatch and Major J. E. Hope, Royal Artillery, who wrote a letter to William C. Hasbrouck from the Clarendon Hotel, New York, Dec. 13, 1862, sending on a letter to Hasbrouck from MFM. This letter is filed under Dec. 13, 1862, MP, Vol. XVII, LC.
31. News about the *Princess Royal's* being captured is written out, but MFM's orders are in cipher; C.S. Secretary of Navy S. R. Mallory to Commander M. F. Maury, London, Feb. 21, 1863, MP, Vol. XVII, LC. For fuller account, see Betty Herndon Maury's Diary, Vol. II, entries for Feb. 1, 12, 1863, MP, LC; also Betty Herndon Maury to B. Franklin Minor, Feb. 24, 1863, MP, Vol. XVII, LC.
32. M. F. Maury, Jr. (signed with his code, No. 7), to his mother and sisters, March 14, with notes added March 18, 19, 20, 21, 1863, MP, Vol. XVII, LC.
33. C.S. Secretary of Navy Mallory to MFM, Nov. 7, 1862, *O.R.N.*, Ser. II, Vol. II, p. 295; letter of MFM to Lieut. Robert D. Minor, C.S.N., Richmond, Apr. 21, 1863, cited in Note 30. For more about Lewis Maury's being expected and arriving in England, see MFM to his wife, Jan. 23, Feb. 12, 1863, MP, Vol. XVII, LC.
34. C.S. Commissioner James M. Mason to C.S. Secretary of State Judah P. Benjamin, Nov. 4, Dec. 10, 1862, *O.R.N.*, Ser. II, Vol. III, pp. 590-596, 617; MFM to Marin H. Jansen, Dec. 20, 1862, March 6, 1863, MP, Vol. XVII, LC; Marin H. Jansen to MFM, Nov. 8, 1863, MP, Vol. XIX, LC; MFM's Diary, April 27, 1863—Dec. 29, 1863 (cited hereafter as MFM's Diary, 1863), entry for Sept. 27, 1863, MP, LC; letter of MFM to Lieut. Robert D. Minor, Apr. 21, 1863, cited in Note 30.
35. Letter of MFM to Lieut. Robert D. Minor, Apr. 21, 1863, cited in Note 30.
36. U.S. Consular Dispatches, sent from Liverpool, Apr. 11, 1863, *O.R.N.*, Ser. I, Vol. XIV, p. 174.
37. Report of George M. Phillips, late captain of the *Dictator*, to U.S. Secretary of Navy Gideon Welles, June 23, 1863, *O.R.N.*, Ser. I, Vol. II, p. 355.
38. MFM to his wife, Feb. 12, 1863, MP, Vol. XVII, LC; MFM letter to Lieut. Robert D. Minor cited in Note 30.
39. "No, my friend, the only dangerous part I have played is in the G[eorgia] case in Scotland." Letter of Marin H. Jansen, from Delft, Holland, to MFM cited in Note 34. MFM later wrote in his diary, "Asked Jansen to do for the *Victor* what he did for the *Japan* [renamed the *Georgia*]," MFM's Diary, 1863, entry for Sept. 26, 1863, MP, LC.
40. MFM to Lieut. William Lewis Maury, Mar. 6, 1863, MP, Vol. XVII, LC.

41. Bulloch, *Secret Service,* Vol. II, p. 261; note of M. F. Maury, Jr., to his mother and sisters, March 21, 1863, added to letter of March 14, 1863, cited in Note 32.

42. Bulloch, *Secret Service,* Vol. II, p. 261.

43. Midshipman Morgan wrote an interesting account of receiving sudden orders in London to go to his hotel, get his belongings, and go to a place of meeting in Little St. James's Street, from which he and other C.S.N. officers went to the railroad station and took a train "for a little seaport about one hour from London." Writing years after the event, Morgan mistakenly called the port White Haven (near Scotland) instead of New Haven (English Channel), as reported by Capt. Bulloch, in command of Confederate naval activities in England. At a small inn at New Haven the party from London met their future captain, William Lewis Maury, who was at that time a lieutenant by rank, as word of his promotion to commander did not reach England until after he had sailed. For latter fact, see letter of MFM to C.S. Secretary of Navy Mallory, June 23, 1863, MP, Vol. XVIII, LC. See Morgan, *Rebel Reefer,* pp. 112-114. See also report of Capt. George M. Phillips to U.S. Secretary of Navy Gideon Welles, June 23, 1863, *O.R.N.,* Ser. I, Vol. II, p. 355.

44. Extracts from U.S. Consular Dispatches, *O.R.N.,* Ser. I, Vol. XIV, pp. 172-174.

45. Hoisted colors, April 9, 1863, Abstract Log of C.S.S. *Georgia, O.R.N.,* Ser. I, Vol. I, p. 811; Morgan, *Rebel Reefer,* pp. 115-116; Bulloch, *Secret Service,* Vol. II, p. 262.

46. Bulloch, *Secret Service,* Vol. II, pp. 261-262.

47. Morgan, *Rebel Reefer,* pp. 117-165; Report of O. S. Glisson, Capt., U.S.N., Commanding U.S.S. *Mohican,* to U.S. Secretary of Navy Gideon Welles, May 26, 1863, *O.R.N.,* Ser. I, Vol. II, p. 216; U.S. Secretary of Navy Welles to Capt. George M. Phillips, late captain of the *Dictator,* June 17, 1863, *O.R.N.,* Ser. I, Vol. II, pp. 354-355.

48. Abstract Log of C.S.S. *Georgia, O.R.N.,* Ser. I, Vol. I, pp. 811-818. Report of Commander William Lewis Maury to Flag Officer Samuel Barron, Dec. 27, 1863, *O.R.N.,* Ser. I, Vol. II, pp. 802-803.

49. The cruisers purchased by the Confederate Navy, manned by Confederate officers (but not by Confederate sailors), and owned by the Confederate States of America, are often confused with privately owned commerce raiders sailing under Confederate letters of marque but not directly commissioned by the Navy Department. The term "privateer" is correct for the latter type of ship.

    By the time MFM was ordered to purchase ships in England, the espionage of U.S. agents was so effective and the British government so anxious to avoid trouble with the United States that it was a great achievement for a Confederate agent to purchase a ship of any kind. The *Georgia* did not meet all the requirements MFM had listed but was the best ship he could find.

    The quotation about the C.S.N. cruisers is from James Russell Soley, *The Navy in the Civil War: The Blockade and the Cruisers,* p. 224.

50. Ibid., p. 229.

51. On Feb. 3, 1863, Gen. Dabney H. Maury wrote to Ann's brother, Dr. Brodie S. Herndon, that John was missing, "Don't tell Uncle Mat yet, till

certain." On March 3 William A. Maury wrote his mother-in-law that Robert H. Maury had sent the letter by Moncure Robinson and that the members of MFM's immediate family had therefore better write at once; letters of William A. Maury and his wife Betty, to Mrs. Ann Herndon Maury, March 3 and 20, 1863, all in MP, Vol. XVII, LC.

52. This was written the day MFM received the news about John in the letter of sympathy from Robert H. Maury; MFM to his wife, Apr. 8, 1863, MP, Vol. XVII, LC.

53. MFM to his wife, Apr. 15, 1863, MP, Vol. XVII, LC.

54. Ibid., Apr. 15, 16, 20, 1863; MFM to his daughter Molly (Mary) Maury, April 17, 1863; M. F. Maury, Jr., to his mother, Apr. 19, 1863, all in MP, Vol. XVII, LC.

55. MFM to his daughter Nannie (Mrs. Diana Maury Corbin), Apr. 20, 1863, MP, Vol. XVII, LC.

56. Gen. Dabney H. Maury to Dr. Brodie S. Herndon, Feb. 3, 1863; to his mother, Mrs. Eliza Maury, Feb. 4, 1863; to Capt. and Mrs. M. F. Maury, Feb. 14, 1863, all in MP, Vol. XVII, LC.

57. MFM to Ann Maury of New York, Oct. 22 and 29, 1863, MC, UVAL; to W. C. Hasbrouck, Oct. 31, 1863, MP, Vol. XVIII, LC; to his wife Nov. 14 and 29, 1863; Rutson Maury to MFM, Nov. 10, Dec. 2 and 7, 1863; Lieut. E. M. Underhill to Maj. Gen. Dabney H. Maury, Jan. 7, 1864, all in MP, Vol. XIX, LC.

58. MFM to Marin H. Jansen, Apr. 21, 1863, MP, Vol. XVIII, LC.

59. Ibid.

60. Letter of MFM to Lieut. Robert D. Minor, cited in Note 30.

61. For plans about ironclad, see MFM to Marin H. Jansen, Apr. 25, 29, 30, 1863; for MFM going to Paris, see M. F. Maury, Jr., to his aunt, Mrs. Eliza Maury, May 17, 1863, all in MP, Vol. XVIII, LC. For quotation, see letter of L. Arman to "Mr. Maury, Admiral of the Confederate States of America." *O.R.N.*, Ser. II, Vol. II, pp. 438-439.

62. C.S. Commissioner John Slidell to C.S. Secretary of State Judah P. Benjamin, March 4, 1863, *O.R.N.*, Ser. II, Vol. III, p. 356.

"Mr. Dayton [U.S. Minister to France] has also furnished [to the French Minister of Foreign Affairs] copies of letters and other papers which were stolen from Capt. M. F. Maury," C.S. Commissioner John Slidell stated in October, 1863, to C.S. Secretary of State Judah P. Benjamin in a report of the theft of a number of papers about the vessels ordered or under construction at Bordeaux and Nantes; *O.R.N.*, Ser. II, Vol. III, p. 960. See also MFM's Diary, 1863, entries for Apr. 29, May 1, 5, June 4, 15, 22, 1863, MP, LC.

63. MFM to C.S. Secretary of Navy Mallory (sent by Lieut. Whittle, C.S.N., returning to Confederacy via Halifax and Bermuda), July 6, 1863, MP, Vol. XVIII, LC.

64. Ibid.; MFM to C.S. Commissioner James M. Mason, Aug. 8, 1863, MP, Vol. XIX, Folio 3359, LC; orders from MFM to Lieut. William Fitzhugh Carter, July 24, 1863, *O.R.N.*, Ser. II, Vol. II, p. 471.

65. MFM's Diary, 1863, entry for Oct. 6, 1863, MP, LC; Bulloch, *Secret Service,* Vol. II, p. 265.

66. MFM decided on Nov. 23, "Shall have to send the ship off before she is

ready." See MFM's Diary, 1863, entries for Nov. 23, 25, 26, 1863, MP, LC; Bulloch, *Secret Service*, Vol. II, pp. 266-267.

67. *O.R.N.*, Ser. I, Vol. III, pp. 719-749; Lewis, *Maury*, p. 173.

68. For facts on the C.S.S. *Stonewall*, see *O.R.N.*, Ser. I, Vol. III, pp. 719-748; Bulloch, *Secret Service*, Vol. II, pp. 78-108.

69. MFM's Diary, 1863, entries for Aug. 21, 23, 1863, MP, LC.

70. MFM sent these to the Confederacy by Lieut. R. R. Carter, by whom he sent an account of the results of his torpedo investigations to C.S. Secretary of Navy Mallory; MFM's Diary, 1863, entries for Oct. 12, 14, 20, 21, 23, 29, 31, 1863, MP, LC.

71. MFM's 11-page MS letter to the editor of the London *Times*, "Prospects of the South," dated Aug. 17, 1863, is in MP, Vol. XVIII, LC. "My letter in Times Aug. 20," MFM wrote in his Diary, 1863, entry for Aug. 23, 1863, MP, LC.

72. M. F. Maury, Jr., to No. 1 (Betty Maury), Aug. 23, 1863; MFM to No. 5 (Mary Maury), from Newcastle, Sept. 3, 1863, both in MP, Vol. XVIII, LC; MFM's Diary, 1863, entry for Sept. 3, 1863, MP, LC.

73. The petition called for the end of hostilities without forcing the seceded states to rejoin the Union. See MFM, letter to accompany "Petition for Peace" and sermon preached by the Rev. Francis W. Tremlett, St. Peter's, London, Nov. 1, 1863, sent to "20,000 parishes," MP, Vol. XVIII, Folios 3196-3198, LC; petition in MP, Vol. XX, Folio 3688A, LC; MFM to Mrs. Francis W. Tremlett, Nov. 9, 12, 1863; a note to MFM from Southern Independence Association, Manchester; Lord Wharncliffe of Wortley Hall, Sheffield, to MFM, Nov. 12, 1863; MFM to the Rev. Francis W. Tremlett, Dec. 7, 1863, all in MP, Vol. XIX, LC; and many more letters throughout his stay on the subject.

74. MFM to his wife, Dec. 25, 1863, MP, Vol. XIX, LC.

75. Ibid., Jan. 20, 1864.

76. Ibid.

77. His anxiety over his family's lack of food was expressed in MFM to his wife, Dec. 10, 1863, MP, Vol. XIX, LC.

78. MFM to Commander J. N. Maffitt, Sept. 9, 1863, *O.R.N.*, Ser. I, Vol. II, p. 660; Flag Officer Samuel Barron to Commander William Lewis Maury, Jan. 19, 1864, *O.R.N.*, Ser. I, Vol. II, p. 810.

79. Orders from Flag Officer Samuel Barron to Lieut. Evans, Jan. 29, 1864, *O.R.N.*, Ser. I, Vol. II, p. 810.

80. U.S. Minister to France William L. Dayton to U.S. Secretary of State William H. Seward, *O.R.N.*, Ser. I, Vol. I, p. 605.

81. Report of Capt. James D. Bulloch to C.S. Secretary of Navy Mallory, Feb. 18, 1864, *O.R.N.*, Ser. II, Vol. II, pp. 588-590; MFM's Diary, 1864, entry for Feb. 22, 1864, MP, LC; MFM to Marin H. Jansen, Feb. 25, 1864, MP, Vol. XX, LC.

82. MFM wrote the Archduke Ferdinand Maximilian on Oct. 8, 1863, and although his copy of this letter was apparently either lost or destroyed, the sense of it is clear from Maximilian's reply. See Archduke Ferdinand Maximilian to MFM, Oct. 24, 1863, MP, Vol. XVIII, LC; MFM to S. Wellford Corbin, Dec. 21, 1863, to Mary Maury, Jan. 27, 1864, to his wife and children, May 12, 1864, all in MP, Vols. XIX, XX, LC; MFM's Diary, 1864, entries for Feb. 22, March 3, April 1, 8, and 10, 1864, MP, LC. For gen-

eral picture, see Jefferson Davis to Maximilian, appointment by President Davis of Gen. William Preston of Kentucky to be C.S. Minister (Commissioner) to the Court of Maximilian and Walker Fern as Secretary of C.S. Legation in Mexico City, *O.R.N.*, Ser. II, Vol. III, pp. 154-155; C.S. Commissioner John Slidell to C.S. Secretary of State Judah P. Benjamin, *O.R.N.*, Ser. II, Vol. III, postscript to letter on p. 1047.

83. MFM's Diary, 1864, entries for May 4, 10, 11, 17, 19, 1864, MP, LC.

84. Ibid., entry for May 27, 1864; MFM to the Rev. Francis W. Tremlett, May 15 and 31, 1864, MP, Vol. XX, LC.

85. *O.R.N.*, Ser. II, Vol. III, p. 962; the Rev. Francis W. Tremlett to MFM, May 30, June 1, 1864; MFM to his wife, June 28, 1864, all in MP, Vol. XX, LC.

86. MFM's Diary, 1864, entries for May 31, June 2 and 9, 1864, MP, LC; statement about deputation from Society for Obtaining the Cessation of Hostilities in America, June 11, 1864, MP, Vol. XX, LC.

87. MFM's Diary, 1864, entry for June 10, 1864. The quotation is from MFM to his wife, June 10, July 1, 1864, MP, Vol. XX, LC.

88. MFM to his wife, July 17, 1864, MP, Vol. XX, LC.

89. Ibid., Aug. 1, with notes added Aug. 2, 1864.

90. MFM to his wife and children, June 28, 1864; to Marin H. Jansen, July 23, 1864; M. F. Maury, Jr., to his brother Richard L. Maury, June 28, 1864, all in MP, Vol. XX, LC.

91. Letter of MFM to Marin H. Jansen cited in Note 90; letter of Lamar Fontaine to Ann Maury of New York, July 6, 1864, in A. F. Maury, *Virginiana*, pp. 285-286.

92. MFM's Diary, 1864, entries for June 20, 22, 1864, MP, LC; Bulloch, *Secret Service*, Vol. II, pp. 106-116. M. F. Maury, Jr., to Marin H. Jansen, June 20, 1864; to his brother Richard L. Maury, June 28, 1864, both in MP, Vol. XX, LC.

93. Letter of MFM to Marin H. Jansen cited in Note 90.

94. Excerpts from C.S. Secretary of Navy Mallory to MFM, June 18, 1864, MP, Vol. XX, Folios 3576-3577, LC.

95. MFM to Marin H. Jansen, Aug. 9, 1864, MP, Vol. XX, LC.

96. MFM's Diary, 1864, entries for Aug. 2 and 11, 1864, MP, LC; MFM to Marin H. Jansen, Sept. 28, Oct. 12, Nov. 17, 27, 1864, MP, Vols. XX, XXI, LC.

97. Postscript added to letter of MFM to Marin H. Jansen, Sept. 28, 1864, cited in Note 96; letter of MFM to Jansen, Oct. 12, 1864, cited in Note 96.

98. Letter of MFM to Gen. Dabney H. Maury, Oct. 2, 1864, MP, Vol. XX, LC; MFM's Diary, 1864, entry for Aug. 25, 1864, MP, LC.

99. MFM reported this in letters to his wife, Sept. 28, Oct. 21, 1864, MP, Vols. XX, XXI, LC.

100. Nannie (Diana) Maury Corbin to B. Franklin Minor, March 26, 1863, MP, Vol. XVII, LC; MFM to his wife, May 8, July 5, 30, 1863, Aug. 29, 1864, and to the Rev. Francis W. Tremlett, Nov. 18, 1864; Mary H. Maury to Mary Fontaine, March 14, 1865, MP, Vols. XVIII, XX, XXI, LC.

101. MFM to Nathaniel J. Holmes, Apr. 11, 1865, MP, Vol. XXI, LC.

102. MFM to Ann Maury of New York, to Marin H. Jansen, both Feb. 3, 1865; to Marin H. Jansen, March 17, 1865, all in MP, Vol. XXI, LC.

103. "Letters came this morning . . . I had some from the [C.S. Navy] Depart-

ment of 14 and 18 of June. . . . The Secretary tells me I 'have done and am doing us good serving abroad' and then leaves it to my discretion about coming home." Note added Aug. 2, 1864, to letter of MFM to his wife, Aug. 1, 1864, MP, Vol. XX, LC.

104. MFM to Marin H. Jansen, March 29, Apr. 8, 1865; to Cousin Bell (Maury), Apr. 14, 1865; to his wife and children, Apr. 14, 1865; Richard L. Maury to his mother, May 7, 1865, all in MP, Vol. XXI, LC.

105. MFM to his wife and children, Apr. 19, 20, 1865, MP, Vol. XXI, LC. The news of the fall of Richmond reached England April 15, and the news of Gen. R. E. Lee's surrender left New York April 22, 1865, according to letter of Rutson Maury to the Rev. Francis W. Tremlett, Apr. 29, 1865, MP, Vol. XXI, LC.

106. Richard L. Maury to his mother, May 7, 1865; the Rev. Francis W. Tremlett to Col. Richard L. Maury, May 12, 1865; Rutson Maury to MFM, June 27, 1865, all in MP, Vols. XXI, XXII, LC. Bulloch, *Secret Service,* Vol. II, p. 270.

107. Thomas Bold to MFM, Apr. 26, 1865, MP, Vol. XXI, LC.

108. Dispatch from C.S. Commissioner James M. Mason to C.S. Secretary of State Judah P. Benjamin, May 1, 1865, *O.R.N.,* Ser. II, Vol. III, p. 1277.

109. MFM to his wife, Oct. 15, 1865, MP, Vol. XXIII, LC; Bulloch, *Secret Service,* Vol. II, p. 270; MFM to B. Franklin Minor, written "Off San Domingo," May 19, with note added May 20, 1865, MP, Vol. XXI, LC; Capt. J. H. North to the Rev. Francis W. Tremlett, May 27, 1865, Confederate Museum, Richmond.

110. Rutson Maury to the Rev. Francis W. Tremlett, June 1, 1865, MP, Vol. XXI, LC; letter of MFM to his wife cited in Note 109.

111. "I do not want to countenance a vain prolongation of the war—neither do I wish to be outlawed." MFM to the Rev. Francis W. Tremlett, May 27, 1865, MP, Vol. XXI, LC; see also letter of MFM to B. Franklin Minor cited in Note 109.

112. Letter of MFM to the Rev. Francis W. Tremlett cited in Note 111; letter of Rutson Maury to Tremlett cited in Note 110.

113. Letter of MFM to B. Franklin Minor cited in Note 109; Rutson Maury to the Rev. Francis W. Tremlett cited in Note 105. Amnesty Proclamation of President Abraham Lincoln, Dec. 8, 1863; James D. Richardson (compiler), *Messages and Papers of the Presidents,* Vol. VI, pp. 213-215.

114. Letter of Rutson Maury to the Rev. Francis W. Tremlett cited in Note 110.

115. Letter of surrender of MFM to Officer in Command of U.S. Naval Forces in the Gulf of Mexico, enclosed in a covering letter, dated May 25, 1865, to U.S. Consul at Vera Cruz, *O.R.N.,* Ser. I, Vol. III, pp. 546-547.

CHAPTER XXI

Starting Over—New Virginia, Mexico

1. Two years earlier MFM had written, "I have no land of my own. Maybe if it should please God to give us peace and bring us all home together, maybe I will have enough left of the wreck to buy a little house somewhere of my own." MFM from London to his daughter Molly (Mary) Maury, May 17, 1863, MP, Vol. XVIII, LC. As a result of that longing

to own a home, MFM between May, 1863, and April, 1865, evidently instructed his relatives to purchase one, but it was not done in time. On May 7, 1865, his daughter Diana (Nannie) wrote, *"You lost everything.* Uncle John [Herndon, Ann's brother] had just settled on a house and lot in Fredericksburg that he was going to invest a part of your funds in when the smash up came." Diana Maury Corbin to her father, in MFM papers, Confederate Museum, Richmond.

2. Rutson Maury received a letter from Ann's brother, Dr. Brodie S. Herndon, who was in Richmond when the Confederacy fell, stating that in addition to MFM's pay as a naval officer having stopped, his "other means invested in Confederate bonds are now worthless." Rutson wrote this to Frank Tremlett (as MFM called his English clergyman friend, the Rev. Francis W. Tremlett in London) Apr. 29, 1865, MP, Vol. XXI, LC.

3. When Maximilian, as head of the Austrian Navy, had sent a diamond pin to MFM for his wife in 1857, the Archduke had written, " . . . since years I observed, with intense interest and admiration, your noble and unequaled efforts, in order to forward the improvement of the scientific part of our profession.

"I trust you will accept this little present as a token of my gratitude towards a man whom all seafaring nations are bound to look upon with respect and thankfulness." Archduke Ferdinand Maximilian to MFM, Dec. 10, 1857, printed in Corbin, *Maury*, p. 296.

For MFM's uncertainty of Maximilian's reception of his plan, see MFM to B. Franklin Minor, May 19, 1865, MP, Vol. XXI, LC.

4. As early as March 29, 1865, MFM had written, "Richmond I take it is likely to fall—if it does it will be more of a quarrel than a war. I have written through the North proposing my family should join me in Cuba." MFM to Marin H. Jansen, March 29, 1865, MP, Vol. XXI, LC.

Although MFM subsequently countermanded that proposal to his family, it suggests that MFM was at that time considering going to Mexico if the Confederacy was conquered. On April 28, before leaving London, he wrote his wife, "Brave may join you from Cuba depending on circumstances." This was in line with a letter MFM had written one week earlier saying he was sailing and his course would be decided later, "maybe May 23," after his arrival in Cuba. See MFM to his wife and children, April 19, 20, 28, 1865, MP, Vol. XXI, LC.

MFM's idea that a good many Confederates would emigrate was not a chimera. Commodore Josiah Tattnall went to Nova Scotia to live and did not return to his native Georgia until 1869; Charles C. Jones, Jr., *The Life and Services of Commodore Josiah Tattnall*, pp. 238-239. Robert Toombs, the senator who had campaigned in the U.S. Senate for MFM's restoration to active duty in 1856 and later been C.S. Secretary of State, thought for a time of locating in Mexico but gave up the idea; Phillips, *Life of Toombs*, p. 256. Capt. James D. Bulloch, C.S. Navy chief in England, remained in England for the rest of his life; sketch of Bulloch in *DAB*, Vol. III, pp. 257-258. C.S. Commissioner James M. Mason remained in England until 1866, then lived in Canada for nearly three years; sketch of Mason, *DAB*, Vol. XII, p. 365. A good many Confederates emigrated to Brazil while Maj. Gen. Thaddeus P. Mott, Brig. Gen. Charles P. Stone, Brig. Gen. W. W. Loring, and others, including former Midshipman James Morris

Morgan, became officers in the army of the Khedive of Egypt, Morgan, *Rebel Reefer,* p. 272.

5. MFM to the Rev. Francis W. Tremlett, May 25, 1865, MP, Vol. XXI, LC.

6. This query of MFM's of May 29 is referred to in Rutson Maury's reply to MFM written from New York, June 13, 1865, MP, Vol. XXII, LC.

7. Ten weeks later MFM explained to his English confidant, "The quickest way of making my opinion known to friends at home was, though not in the presence of the enemy, to lay down my arms and so inform him. I did so. The note fell into the hands of acting Rear Admiral Sylvanus W. Godon, of the United States Navy. . . ." MFM to the Rev. Francis W. Tremlett, Aug. 8, 1865, MP, Vol. XXII, LC. (The ranks of rear and vice-admiral, for which MFM had so long campaigned, had been established during the Civil War.)

For his vignette of the state of Mexican agriculture, ibid. For the offer of torpedo instruction, MFM to General de la Peza, Minister of War, Mexico City, June 6, 1865, MP, Vol. XXI, LC. See also Gen. Zamacona, June 23, 1865, MP, Vol. XXII, LC.

8. MFM to his wife, June 17, with note added June 19, 1865, MP, Vol. XXII, LC.

9. The text of President Andrew Johnson's first amnesty proclamation of May 29, 1865, is in *O.R.,* Ser. II, Vol. VIII, pp. 578-580.

10. Ibid.

11. MFM's nephew, Maj. Gen. Dabney H. Maury, was much troubled on this score. Dick Maury felt he could not ask for pardon.

Gen. Lee explained the reasoning that enabled him to apply: "I need not tell you that true patriotism sometimes requires of men to act exactly contrary, at one period, to that which it does at another, and the motive which impels them—the desire to do right—is precisely the same. The circumstances which govern their actions change, and their conduct must conform to the new order of things. History is full of illustrations of this: Washington is an example of this. At one time he fought against the French, under Braddock, in the service of the King and Great Britain; at another, he fought with the French at Yorktown, under the orders of the Continental Congress of America, against him [the King of England]. He has not been branded by the world with reproach for this, but his course has been applauded." Gen. R. E. Lee to General (P.) G. T. Beauregard, Oct. 3, 1865, in Rev. J. William Jones, D.D., *Personal Reminiscences, Anecdotes and Letters of General Robert E. Lee,* published by authority of the Lee family, and of the Faculty of Washington and Lee University (cited hereafter as Jones, *Personal . . . Letters of . . . Lee*), p. 207.

12. Note of MFM of June 19 appended to MFM letter of June 17, 1865, cited in Note 8.

13. Dr. Brodie S. Herndon to MFM, May 1, 1865, MP, Vol. XXI, LC; printed in Corbin, *Maury,* pp. 226-227.

14. Ibid.

15. Ibid.

16. Richard L. Maury to MFM, May 21, 1865, MP, Vol. XXI, LC.

17. Elizabeth Herndon Maury to MFM, June 19, 1865, MP, Vol. XXII, LC.

18. Rutson was not exaggerating the probability. For example, a few of those arrested—former C.S. Secretary of Navy Stephen R. Mallory; Benjamin

Hill, a Georgia political leader; and Maj. Gen. Howell Cobb, who had earlier been Speaker of the U.S. House of Representatives and Secretary of the Treasury—had been captured in Georgia, taken to Fort Lafayette, New York, and incarcerated there on June 4, 1865. Mallory was held prisoner in that damp stronghold until March 10, 1866. Former Senator Clement C. Clay was a prisoner until late April, 1866; Durkin, *Mallory,* pp. 344-383. Former C.S. Secretary of the Treasury George A. Trenholm was imprisoned in Fort Pulaski; Morgan, *Rebel Reefer,* pp. 245-252.

Strong Union man and Lincoln-backer Rutson Maury spoke with feeling about imprisonment because he and his brother and business partner, Matthew Maury, had both served short terms of imprisonment in the early part of the war when they had unwisely made a trip south after the outbreak of war. Rutson Maury had been arrested in Baltimore in 1861 as he was making his way south to Alabama. He declared that he was travelling to see members of his family; he was found to be carrying needles, an item that was scarce in the Confederacy. Matthew Maury was arrested and imprisoned for carrying 1,000 letters from New Orleans through the lines. The brothers were confined in Fort Lafayette, New York, and Fort Warren, Boston. See records of Claims Arising out of the Civil War, Madeira to Maury, Public Record Office, London, Foreign Office, Vol. 5/1267, no folios in volume; the correspondence about the Maury brothers is not in consecutive order; the first pertinent entry is that for Nov. 18, 1861.

These trips had evidently been made primarily in an effort to conclude outstanding business with Southern planters whose cotton Maury Brothers exported. However, there can be no question of the absolute hatred of and articulated opposition to slavery and secession, nor of the total loyalty to the U.S. government of Matthew, Rutson, and Ann Maury of New York. They did not, however, let their abhorrence of the Confederate cause prevent them from corresponding with MFM after his son John's disappearance, and they did all they could to find a trace of John in the Federal military prisons.

For the quotation, see Rutson Maury to MFM, June 13, 1865, MP, Vol. XXII, LC. MFM's son-in-law had written, "We and all of his friends think it worse than madness for him to think of coming now." William A. Maury to Rutson Maury, May 19, 1865, MP, Vol. XXI, LC.

19. The Rev. Francis W. Tremlett to MFM, July 30, 1865, MP, Vol. XXII, LC.
20. Rutson informed MFM that the article and accompanying acidulous comment had been published in the New York *Times,* June 14, 1865; Rutson Maury to MFM, June 14, 1865, MP, Vol. XXII, LC. The letter was published in *National Intelligencer,* June 16, 1865; Corbin, *Maury,* p. 225, fn.
21. Letter of Rutson Maury to MFM cited in Note 20.
22. In replying to a question from Gen. Beauregard on the proper course to follow, Gen. Lee wrote on October 3, 1865, that after the proclamation of President Johnson of May 29, 1865, "[I] determined to comply with its requirements, and applied on the 13th of June to be embraced within its provisions. I have not heard the result of my application." Letter of Gen. R. E. Lee to Gen. (P.) G. T. Beauregard, cited in Note 11. See also Freeman, *R. E. Lee,* Vol. IV, pp. 202-207.
23. In warning his uncle "don't come yet," Dab wrote that he had at first thought he himself "would exile" but had decided that he had "better plug

it out in Virginia." Maj. Gen. Dabney H. Maury to MFM, June 30, 1865, MP, Vol. XXII, LC.

24. MFM to his wife, June 17, 1865, also note added June 24, MP, Vol. XXII, LC.
25. Octave de Chabannes, Admiral, French Navy, to MFM, July 27, 1865, MP, Vol. XXII, LC. Carlotta later told MFM that the Empress of France had written her approving the colonization plan and had enclosed MFM's letter on the subject to Admiral de Chabannes; MFM to his wife, Sept. 12, 1865, MP, Vol. XXIII, LC.
26. MFM to Louisa Tremlett (sister of the Rev. Francis W. Tremlett), June 28, 1865, MP, Vol. XXII, LC. MFM had first outlined his plan in a letter, dated June 9, 1865, to be shown to Maximilian; Emmanuel Domenech, *Histoire du Mexique, Juárez et Maximilian* (cited hereafter as Domenech, *Juárez et Maximilian*), Vol. III, pp. 263-265.
27. Letter of MFM to Louisa Tremlett cited in Note 26.
28. Letter of MFM to his wife cited in Note 25.
29. MFM to the Rev. Francis W. Tremlett, July 16, 1865, MP, Vol. XXII, LC.
30. Ibid.
31. Marin H. Jansen to MFM, July 1, 1865, MP, Vol. XXII, LC.
32. By Aug. 27, 1865, MFM's whole colonization proposal was known by his family in Virginia and was reported in a letter of S. Wellford Corbin to William C. Hasbrouck, Aug. 27, 1865, MP, Vol. XXIII, LC. See also MFM to his wife, Sept. 23, 1865, MP, Vol. XXIII, LC; *Diario del Imperio,* issues of Oct. 7, 10, 1865.
33. Gen. R. E. Lee to Richard L. Maury, July 30, 1865, copy of which was sent with letter of Richard L. Maury to MFM, Aug. 6, 1865, MP, Vol. XXII, LC. This letter, with a slight variation in punctuation, is in Jones, *Personal . . . Letters of . . . Lee,* pp. 205-206.
34. Gen. R. E. Lee to MFM, Sept. 6, 1865, in Corbin, *Maury,* pp. 238-239; portion quoted is on p. 239. This letter is also in Jones, *Personal . . . Letters of . . . Lee,* pp. 206-207.
35. Marin H. Jansen to MFM, Aug. 19, 1865, MP, Vol. XXII, LC.
36. Rutson Maury to the Rev. Francis W. Tremlett, Aug. 29, 1865, MP, Vol. XXIII, LC.
37. For MFM's explanation, see MFM to Rutson Maury, Sept. (n.d.), 1865, quoted in Corbin, *Maury,* pp. 239-240.
38. Richard L. Maury to MFM, written from the Infirmary, Univ. of Virginia, Aug. 6 and 10, 1865, MP, Vol. XXII, LC.
39. Rutson Maury wrote to MFM's friend Frank Tremlett that he had received a letter from MFM on Aug. 8, 1865, with instructions for Ann and their unmarried children to join MFM in Mexico, but that on Aug. 22, 1865, he had received a letter from MFM changing the instructions to have Ann and the unmarried children go to England, where MFM would visit them; Rutson Maury to the Rev. Francis W. Tremlett, Sept. 8, 1865. However, as late as Aug. 27 S. Wellford Corbin wrote that MFM's wife was "expected to go out to Mexico." S. Wellford Corbin to William C. Hasbrouck, Aug. 27, 1865, both in MP, Vol. XXIII, LC. For plans for family to go to England, see Rutson's letter just cited and MFM to the Rev. Francis W. Tremlett, Aug. 18, 1865, MP, Vol. XXII, LC.
40. Diana Maury Corbin, in her life of her father, referred twice to the opposi-

tion of MFM's friends but avoided any direct reference to her mother's opposition to her father's Mexican plan. Ann's opposition, as well as that of the family, was clearly expressed in her letter to MFM, June 15, 1865, MP, Vol. XXII, LC, and in innumerable references in letters to MFM of B. Franklin Minor, June 30, 1865, John B. Minor, Aug. 12, 1865, Richard L. Maury, Aug. 17, 1865, as well as in letter of S. Wellford Corbin to William C. Hasbrouck, Aug. 27, 1865, MP, Vols. XXII, XXIII, LC.

The intensity of Ann's opposition is, however, more clearly revealed in a letter MFM wrote after receiving her letters written subsequent to getting his instructions for her to join him in Mexico. "My heart is as big as a mountain and as heavy as lead. Your letter is so sad at leaving friends behind and going to a strange land." MFM to his wife, Sept. 23, 1865, MP, Vol. XXIII, LC.

41. For the decree "given at Chapultepec on the 5th day of September 1865," see Maximilian's Decree, *Diario del Imperio*, issue of Sept. 9, 1865; MFM's copy in MP, Vol. XXIII, LC; also see *Decrees for the Encouragement of Immigration and Colonization,* a 16-page pamphlet printed by order of MFM, Office of Colonization, Mexico, November, 1865.

42. MFM created an Honorary Councillor of State and appointed Imperial Commissioner of Colonization; Imperial Decrees of Sept. 18 and 27, 1865, announced in *Diario del Imperio,* Oct. 7, Oct. 10, 1865.

43. For easy access, see the decree in Corbin, *Maury,* pp. 233-234, especially Article 9 on p. 234.

44. For MFM's 27 Regulations and Instructions as well as General Remarks to accompany the decree approved by H.M. the Emperor, Sept. 11, 1865, see MP, Vol. XXIII, LC; pamphlet cited in Note 41, or extracts therefrom in Corbin, *Maury,* pp. 234-236.

45. See pamphlet cited in Note 41.

46. See copies of letters to MFM in MP, Vol. XXIII, LC.

47. S. Wellford Corbin wrote his father-in-law that if MFM definitely decided to live in Mexico, he (Corbin) would come out to settle but warned of the almost absolute certainty of war between the U.S. and Mexico if Maximilian continued on the throne; S. Wellford Corbin to MFM, Aug. 10, 1865, MP, XXII, LC. On Aug. 27, 1865, Corbin explained to William C. Hasbrouck, "The Emperor defers issuing [colonization decrees] until he hears whether acceptable in Washington." S. Wellford Corbin to William C. Hasbrouck, Aug. 27, 1865, MP, Vol. XXIII, LC. See also the able article by A. J. Hanna, "The Role of Matthew Fontaine Maury in the Mexican Empire," *Virginia Magazine,* Vol. LV, No. 2 (April, 1947), especially pp. 113-114.

48. MFM to his wife, Sept. 12, 1865, MP, Vol. XXIII, LC.

49. Letters to MFM from Octave de Chabannes, Admiral, French Navy, July 7, 1865; from B. Franklin Minor, June 30, 1865; from John B. Minor, Aug. 12, 1865; from S. Wellford Corbin, Aug. 10, 1865, all in MP, Vol. XXII, LC.

50. This idea on the part of the Negroes was not without foundation. "The only sound policy was to confiscate the lands and divide them among the Negroes to whom, sooner or later, suffrage must be given," Thaddeus Stevens declared, according to Richard Taylor in *Destruction and Recon-*

struction, Personal Experiences of the Late War, p. 244; also see Richard L. Maury to MFM, Aug. 6, 1865, MP, Vol. XXII, LC.

51. MFM, "Project of a Design to Encourage the Immigration into Mexico of Planters from Virginia and the South with their Freed Slaves," submitted to Maximilian, June 29, 1865, MP, Vol. XXII, LC.

52. Quotation is from S. Wellford Corbin to William C. Hasbrouck, Aug. 27, 1865, MP, Vol. XXIII, LC; see also Corbin to MFM, Aug. 10, 1865, MP, Vol. XXII, LC.

53. MFM's views on the superiority of government by the people and his prediction of the end of European monarchies were expressed in letters to Sarah Mytton Maury of Liverpool, England, March 22, 1848, and to Ann Maury of New York, Apr. 19, 1848, both in MC, UVAL.

54. Decree of Maximilian of Sept. 27, 1865, in *Diario del Imperio*, Oct. 10, 1865.

55. Domenech, *Juárez et Maximilian*, Vol. III, pp. 266, 267; MFM to his wife, Sept. 23, 1865, MP, Vol. XXIII, LC.

56. "Yesterday, I received my appointment as Director of the Observatory and today my naturalization papers which qualify me to hold office—my salary is $5,000 to commence with June last." Letter of MFM to his wife cited in Note 55.

57. These facts are all from a letter of Rutson Maury to the Rev. Francis W. Tremlett, Oct. 2 (probably Oct. 20), 1865, MP, Vol. XXIII, LC.

58. MFM did not hear of Ann's proposed action until much later. He evidently became alarmed that even though Ann had sailed for England some relative might seek a pardon for him. The quotation is from MFM letter to S. Wellford Corbin, Oct. 31, 1865, MP, Vol. XXIII, LC.

59. The French, believing that Mexico needed 60,000 immigrants to realize the country's agricultural potential, had urged Maximilian to adopt a program of colonization. Because of this, in late April, 1865, Maximilian had created a Board of Colonization to direct immigration and placed it under the Minister of Development (Fomento). MFM found that he could make no progress on the colonization program by going through the channels of the Ministry of Development. He took the matter up with Maximilian after a dinner at the palace and received permission to discuss his office's problems of immigration in the future directly with the Emperor. This naturally aroused hostility to MFM within the Ministry of Development. See MFM to his wife, Sept. 12, 1865, MP, Vol. XXIII, LC, and Domenech, *Juárez et Maximilian*, Vol. III, pp. 266-267.

60. MFM considered that his program would bring about an emigration of people of ability such as had not occurred since the emigration of the Huguenots from France in 1685. Because he believed that the country would benefit enormously if these settlers came to Mexico, he expected Mexicans to welcome him as Virginians had welcomed his French-speaking forebears. Instead, many Mexicans considered him a foreigner who stood in the highest favor with a foreign ruler, Maximilian.

For the quotation, see MFM to his wife, Sept. 23, 1865, MP, Vol. XXIII, LC.

61. Of the Empress, MFM wrote, "She is very clever, practical, and business-like. I told her I thought she could do more business in a day than all of the Ministers put together could do in a week. She said, 'I believe I could.' " MFM to his wife, Sept. 12, 1865. "I saw the Empress yesterday, and ar-

ranged about my office and a land-office, at the head of which I asked her to place [former Confederate Maj. Gen. John Bankhead] Magruder, with a salary of $3,000 which she did." MFM to his wife, Sept. 27, 1865, both in MP, Vol. XXIII, LC. Announcement of the appointment of Richard B. Maury as Sub-Commissioner of Immigration at a salary of $2,500 appeared in *La Sociedad*, Mexico City, Nov. 5, 1865.

62. Ibid., Oct. 15, 1865.

63. The apartment was furnished and servants were provided. MFM's fellow Virginians, the Talcotts, rented a duplicate apartment across a courtyard. See note added Sept. 17 to MFM letter to his wife, Sept. 12, 1865, and MFM to his wife, Sept. 23, 1865, both in MP, Vol. XXIII, LC.

64. MFM's plan was to have Dick run the colonization office during his trip to England, to bring Molly (Mary) back with him, then in perhaps nine months to go again to England for a visit when he would take Molly back to her mother and bring Eliza to Mexico with him. After his third visit he hoped that his wife Ann and little Lucy would come back with him. He hoped that S. Wellford Corbin and Diana would come to Mexico and acquire one of the haciendas in the Cordoba area.

In spite of the failure of MFM's Mexican colonization idea, it cannot be said that he recommended it to other Southern families without practicing it himself. His plans for his family were outlined in letters to his wife cited in Notes 59, 60, and MFM to his wife, Oct. 15, Nov. 27, 1865, MP, Vol. XXIII, LC.

65. Rutson Maury to William C. Hasbrouck, Nov. 20, 1865, MP, Vol. XXIII, LC.

66. MFM to his wife, Nov. 27, 1865, MP, Vol. XXIII, LC.

67. MFM to the Rev. Francis W. Tremlett, Oct. 29, 1865, MP, Vol. XXIII, LC.

68. The Conservatives had apparently expected that they could dominate Maximilian and secure a restoration of the special privileges they had enjoyed in the pre-Juárez, pre-French invasion period. For an interesting general study of the problems encountered by Maximilian, see Count Egon Caesar Corti's 2-vol. work, *Maximilian and Charlotte of Mexico.*

69. Sketch of Benito Juárez (1806-1872), Mexican liberal statesman and national hero, in *Encyclopaedia Britannica* (1957 ed.), Vol. XIII, pp. 161-162; see also Herbert Ingram Priestley, *The Mexican Nation*, pp. 349-351, 353, 356, 359, 363.

70. Imperial Decree of Sept. 18, 1865, making MFM "Consejero Honorario de Estado," announced in *Diario del Imperio*, Oct. 7, 1865. During 1865 MFM was also made "Miembro honorario de la Sociedad Mexicana de Geografía y Estadística" and "Miembro de la Imperial Academia Mexicana de Ciencias." Corbin, *Maury*, p. 292.

71. Concerning MFM's personal influence with Maximilian and Carlotta, Rutson Maury wrote, "M. F.—as you will have seen has renounced his nationality and become a Mexican subject and he now stands nearer to the throne than anyone else; being equally in favor with the Emperor and Empress. As he said to me in a letter of 18 October, his position may be compared well with that of Joseph in Egypt. But I have told him in turn that Joseph was thirty years old when he stood before Pharaoh." Rutson Maury to William C. Hasbrouck, Nov. 20, 1865, MP, Vol. XXIII, LC.

72. MFM tried to persuade Ann to his view that "it becomes me to use whatever power for good I may have acquired in the world for the benefit of this people [former Confederates], who have suffered in the same cause with us, and who are so near and dear to us." MFM to his wife, Sept. 23, 1865, MP, Vol. XXIII, LC. Realizing that he had not removed the opposition to his Mexican venture felt by all in his family except Dick, MFM finally wrote that their letters of opposition had made it hard for him to tread the path he had chosen; MFM to his wife, Oct. 24, 1865, MP, Vol. XXIII, LC.

73. Corti, *Maximilian and Charlotte of Mexico*, Vol. II, pp. 539, 540, 561.

74. In addition to the almost impossible political situation, other obstacles to the success of MFM's immigration program were the wholly inadequate transportation system in Mexico and the difficulty of obtaining clear title to a majority of the estates desired by potential settlers.

    Believing that these difficulties could be overcome, MFM sent his appeal "To the People at Home," written Sept. 9, 1865 (MP, Vol. XXIII, LC), and later sent literature published by his authority to the former states of the Confederacy for distribution by the agents he appointed. He tried to secure his nephew Maj. Gen. Dabney H. Maury, his lawyer son-in-law, William A. Maury, or his former U.S.N.-C.S.N. friend, Capt. William F. Lynch, to act as agent in Richmond at $100 a month. Apparently because of opposition to the program, none of the three accepted the post, but others did. See Rutson Maury to the Rev. Francis W. Tremlett, Oct. 2, 1865, MP, Vol. XXIII, LC.

75. S. Wellford Corbin to (probably William C. Hasbrouck), Oct. 23, 1865, MP, Vol. XXIII, LC; Corbin, *Maury*, p. 250.

76. MFM to his children, March 1, 1866, MP, Vol. XXIV, LC.

77. Among the Confederates who went to Mexico but did not remain long were Gen. C. M. Wilcox and Gen. J. A. Early. See Gen. Robert E. Lee, Dec. 23, 1865, addressed to Wilcox in "City of Mexico" and addressed to Early in Ciudad de Mexico, March 15, 1866, in Jones, *Personal . . . Letters of . . . Lee*, respectively, pp. 207-208, 214-216. Others included Gens. Kirby-Smith (last Confederate general to surrender his command), Shelby, Slaughter, Walker, Terrell, and Hindman, former Governor Reynolds of Georgia, Henry W. Allen (former governor of Louisiana and Confederate general), Pierre Soulé of Louisiana, Maj. Mordecai of North Carolina, Col. Andrew Talcott of Virginia and his son.

    For colonies headed by Bryant of Arkansas, Mitchell of Missouri, and Terrell of Texas, see Lewis, *Maury*, p. 199.

    See also George D. Harmon, "Confederate Migration to Mexico," *Hispanic American Historical Review*, Vol. XVII (November, 1937), pp. 458-487; Lawrence F. Hill, "The Confederate Exodus to Latin America," *Southwestern Historical Quarterly*, Vol. XXXIX (October, 1935), pp. 98-134. For a firsthand account, see Ramón Eduardo Riz (ed.), *An American in Maximilian's Mexico—The Diaries of William Marshall Anderson*.

    Among those actively associated with MFM were former Confederate Generals John B. Magruder and Sterling Price, Judge John Perkins, and Isham G. Harris, former Governor of Tennessee; MFM to his wife, Oct. 15, 1865, MP, Vol. XXIII, LC.

78. Maximilian to MFM, Jan. 29, 1866, MP, Vol. XXIV, LC.

79. Carlotta to MFM, Jan. 29, 1866, MP, Vol. XXIV, LC. (I have used the name Carlotta as spelled by MFM, rather than Carlota or Charlotte, as the Empress signed her letters written in English to MFM.)

80. MFM, meteorological observations made at Hacienda of Mirador, near Cordoba, Mexico, height 3,600 feet, 1865, MP, Vol. LI, Folio 1284, LC.

81. In 1888 MFM's daughter Diana wrote, "Before leaving England in 1865, he [MFM] had conversed with Mr. Clements Markham on the subject, who is the introducer of chinchona cultivation into British India." Corbin, *Maury,* pp. 252-253; see also MFM to Rutson Maury, Sept. (n.d.), 1865, quoted in Corbin, *Maury,* p. 240.

82. Ibid., p. 253. Permission for this experiment was granted by Maximilian and transmitted to MFM by the Empress in letter from Carlotta cited in Note 79.

83. Rutson reported that the New York *Journal of Commerce,* March 14, 1866, stated that "Commodore Maury is on board [British mail steamer Conway] on public business of the Empire." Rutson Maury to William C. Hasbrouck, March 15, 1866; see also MFM to William C. Hasbrouck, March 13, 1866, both in MP, Vol. XXIV, LC.

84. MFM to William C. Hasbrouck, written from 30 Harley St., Cavendish Square, London, Apr. 14, 1866, MP, Vol. XXIV, LC.

85. See picture in this book of Ann Herndon Maury seated with her husband among those of their family who were with them in London, and MFM's friend, Captain Marin H. Jansen. This picture, taken in 1867, shows that Ann's hair had not lost its color. This fact was also stated by Mrs. Mary Maury Werth in a letter written in 1926 to Charles Lee Lewis, in Tennessee Historical Society papers, TSLA.

86. Corbin, *Maury,* p. 257.

87. "I was surprised yesterday to discover that my moustache had turned nearly all white. I looked at the hair of my head to discover what the month [since he had heard of John's loss] had wrought there. But I could not discover any silver marks . . . except a little from before." MFM to his wife, May 8, 1863, MP, Vol. XVIII, LC.

88. Writing from Mexico, he had referred to Lucy as "my little Loo." MFM to his wife, Sept. 12, 1865, MP, Vol. XXIII, LC.

89. Letter of MFM to William C. Hasbrouck cited in Note 84.

90. MFM to Maximilian, July 1, 1866, MP, Vol. XXV, LC.

91. Ibid.; Clements R. Markham to MFM, May 17, 1867, MP, Vol. XXVI, LC; Corbin, *Maury,* pp. 253-254.

92. Maximilian to MFM, Apr. 19, 1866, MP, Vol. XXV, LC.

93. Letter of MFM to Maximilian cited in Note 90.

Chapter XXII

Starting Over—England

1. For an example of information sent, see MFM to His Excellency Count Charles Vitzhum d'Eckstaedt, Minister of Saxony, Apr. 25, 1866, MP, Vol. XXV, LC.

2. MFM lecture, "Remarks before the French Commission," May 21, 1866, MP, Vol. XXV, Folios 4552-4559, LC.

3. MFM to his daughter Molly (Mary) Maury, written from Hotel de Glasgow, 418 rue St.-Honoré, Paris, May 22, 1866, MP, Vol. XXV, LC.

4. MFM, lecture to the French Commission, May 28, 1866, MP, Vol. XXV, Folios 4572-4576, LC. For French citizenship offer, see MFM to William C. Hasbrouck, July 28, 1866, MP, Vol. XXV, LC; Corbin, *Maury*, pp. 258-259.

5. Charles Pigeard to MFM, June 25, 1868, MP, Vol. XXVII, LC; Francis H. Smith, "Matthew Fontaine Maury," *Library of Southern Literature*, Vol. VIII, p. 3440.

6. MFM to Rutson Maury, July 8, 1866, MP, Vol. XXV, LC. For arrangements for Dutch officers to take the course, see MFM to Baron Bentinck, Minister of the Netherlands to Great Britain, May 12, 1866, MP, Vol. XXV, LC.

7. MFM to the consul of H.M. the King of Württemberg, June 30, 1866, MP, Vol. XXV, LC; MFM to Rutson Maury, July 8, 1866, cited in Note 6.

8. MFM lectures on torpedoes, July and August, 1866, to Swedes and Norwegians, and to Dutch officers, MP, Vol. XLVII, Folios 9192-9331, 9332-9355; see also questions asked by the Dutch and answers, Folios 9357-9380, LC.

9. Excerpt from MFM's lecture delivered July 28, 1866, to the Dutch officers taking his torpedo course, quoted in Corbin, *Maury*, p. 265.

10. MFM's agent was Nathaniel J. Holmes, electrical engineer, Universal Private Telegraph Co., 4 Adelaide Street, West Strand, London. See full explanation of system, MFM to Holmes, Apr. 11, 1865, MP, Vol. XXI, LC.

    In December, 1865, the Rev. Francis W. Tremlett, with whom MFM's contract with Holmes had been deposited, urged MFM to return to England because he was having difficulty protecting MFM's interests against "our electrical." Tremlett mentioned the details of MFM's work on torpedoes and the Confederate patent for one of his torpedo inventions secured before MFM left Virginia in 1862. This letter was written in 1865 to MFM in Mexico; but was incorrectly dated 1863 and filed under Dec. 14, 1863 (1865), in MP, Vol. XIX, LC.

    On arriving in London MFM wrote, "Nor has Holmes done anything in the torpedo line." MFM to Marin H. Jansen, May 8, 1866, MP, Vol. XXV, LC. MFM had earlier given information on his torpedo system to Marin H. Jansen in appreciation of Jansen's assistance to him and the Confederacy in supervising the fitting of the Confederate cruiser *Georgia*. MFM's idea was that Jansen was to make the information available to the Dutch government and retain any financial benefits derived thereby. See MFM to Marin H. Jansen, Aug. 9, 29, Sept. 28, Oct. 19, 25, Nov. 27, Dec. 10, 12, 18, 1864, Feb. 3, March 17, 1865, all in MP, Vols. XX, XXI, LC.

11. Picture and article on MFM and the testimonial dinner in *Illustrated London News*, June 23, 1866, MP, Vol. XXV, Folios 4578-4579, LC. See sketch of Sir John Pakington, later Baron Hampton, *DNB*, Vol. XV, pp. 94-95.

12. Special bound volume of letters sent to the Rev. Francis W. Tremlett by men giving to the MFM testimonial fund or attending the dinner; MP, Alphonso Smith collection, Ac 3219, LC; letters on the same subject from Sir Henry James and A. Keith Johnston, in Maury collection, Confederate Museum, Richmond. Date of dinner is established as June 5, 1866 in letters

cited, and erroneously stated as June 6 in his daughter Diana's account; see Corbin, *Maury,* pp. 257-258.

13. See letter of Capt. A. Gorkovenko (who had been Russia's delegate to the Brussels Conference) that accompanied gift from Archduke Constantine; also statement quoted in bound volume on the testimonial fund and dinner cited in Note 12.

14. MFM described his torpedo instruction as an effort "to make a little money and so keep off the Parish" but admitted, "Still I see nothing permanent and there's the rub." MFM to Rutson Maury, July 8, 1866; to his son Richard L. Maury, July 10, 1866, MP, Vol. XXV, LC.

    Following the receipt of the testimonial fund in London, MFM invested in some shares that he referred to as "Turkish" with no further explanation as to their nature.

15. Letter of MFM to William C. Hasbrouck, July 28, 1866, cited in Note 4.

16. He stated that he made the move "through motives of economy." MFM to his son Richard L. Maury, July 10, 1866, cited in Note 14.

17. Ibid.; letter to William C. Hasbrouck, July 28, 1866, cited in Note 4.

18. Ann Herndon Maury, accompanied by her unmarried children, had reached Liverpool on Oct. 20, 1865, and until her husband's arrival in England, March 29, 1866, had visited in the home of Thomas Bold, at Birkenhead across the Mersey from Liverpool. Bold, who had been MFM's agent for purchasing ships for the Confederacy, was not related to MFM but was a maternal cousin of Matthew, Rutson and Ann Maury. For Ann's unhappiness at being in England, see Rutson Maury to William C. Hasbrouck, Nov. 20, 1865, MP, Vol. XXIII, LC.

    Ann wrote about the "hard and uncomfortable" beds at their English lodgings to her daughter Betty in Virginia, who wrote in concern about it to her father; Mrs. Betty Maury to MFM, Nov. 25, 1866, MP, Vol. XLVI, Folio 9025, LC.

19. The Maurys move to 3 Belsize Square, N.W., was made in late November, 1866. In that area of London there was also Belsize Road, Belsize Lane, Belsize Park, Belsize Park Avenue. Dr. Tremlett's church, St. Peter's, was in St. Peter's Square, Belsize Park, a good distance to the northwest of Regent Park and not far from Hampstead Road. See *Reynold's Map of London 1860, Post Office Directory Map, 1866, Whitbread's New Plan of London 1869.* For cost of living in new lodgings, see MFM to Dabney H. Maury, Feb. 23, 1867, MP, Vol. XXV, LC.

20. The Rev. Francis W. Tremlett had at that time already received an M.A., LL.D., Ph.D., and been "made doctor of theology by the Patriarch of Antioch." In 1869, he was to receive the University of the South's first honorary degree, D.C.L., and in 1894 the D.D. degree from St. John's College, Annapolis; Mrs. Elizabeth N. Chitty, Sewanee, to me, March 29, 1960.

    A Low Church Anglican, Dr. Tremlett headed his letters with the address "The Parsonage, Belsize Park, Hampstead." In good weather the Maurys enjoyed playing croquet with the Tremletts. The lack of references to Mrs. Tremlett in this postwar period suggests that she had died and Miss Louisa Tremlett was keeping house for her brother.

21. Memorandum of Agreement between MFM and Charles B. Richardson,

Richardson and Co., Publishers and Booksellers, 540 Broadway, New York, Sept. 20, 1866, MP, Vol. XXV, Folios 4642-4647, LC.

22. Preface to MFM, *First Lessons in Geography,* published in New York, 1868. See preface to 1922 edition of MFM, *New Elements of Geography,* for description of MFM's plan for his textbooks.

23. Quotation from a letter written by MFM, in Corbin, *Maury,* p. 266.

24. *The World We Live In* was published separately in 1868 and 1871. The merged text *New Elements of Geography* was published in various editions from 1881 to 1925. MFM's *Manual of Geography*—a complete treatise on mathematical, physical and political geography—was first published in 1870, went through eight editions by 1925. For other texts written by him, see the section on geography in the bibliography of MFM's works in this book. The books were revised by other writers in later editions.

25. In contrast to their father's handwriting, the girls both had very clear handwriting, and their copies were sent direct to the publisher. On Nov. 21, 1866, one of the girls managed to copy fifty pages of manuscript. See memorandum (fragment of a family letter) dated Nov. 21, 1866, MP, Vol. XXV, LC.

26. MFM to Tots (Mary) Maury, March 10, 1872, MP, Vol. XXXIX, LC.

27. The attitude of the Fields toward men who in 1861 felt their first allegiance was to their native state rather than to the Union is revealed in the tribute paid Virginian Lieut. Otway H. Berryman and his wife for following the opposite course; Henry Field, *Telegraph,* pp. 58-59.

28. Lewis, *Maury,* pp. 211-212.

29. Maximilian to MFM, Aug. 16, 1866, MP, Vol. XXV, LC.

30. MFM to Maximilian, Oct. 11, 1866, MP, Vol. XXV, LC.

31. Nathaniel Holmes, representing the North Atlantic Telegraph Co., Ltd., to MFM, Oct. 5, 1866, MP, Vol. XXV, Folios 4652-4655, LC; S. Wellford Corbin to William C. Hasbrouck, June 8, 1867, MP, Vol. XXVI, LC.

32. Clements R. Markham to MFM, May 17, 1867, MP, Vol. XXVI, LC.

33. "Sir Stafford Northcote [then Secretary of State for India] has received the intelligence contained in the letter from the Secretary of the Society of Geography and Statistics, dated the 11th of December last, that several thousand of chinchona seeds sent from Madras according to your instructions have germinated satisfactorily in the Mexican mountains, with much gratification." Clements R. Markham to MFM, May 17, 1867, cited in Note 32.

34. Corbin, *Maury,* p. 254; see especially the footnote.

35. For an outline of the facts, see sketch of Maximilian, *Columbia Encyclopedia* (1935 ed.), p. 1139; for fuller accounts, see Corti, *Maximilian and Charlotte,* Vol. II, pp. 633-640, 743-822; Herbert Ingram Priestley, *The Mexican Nation,* pp. 349-363.

   The death of Maximilian and the fall of his empire apparently meant the end of Mexican citizenship to MFM.

36. MFM to Marin H. Jansen, July 7, 1867, MP, Vol. XXVI, LC; Corbin, *Maury,* p. 256.

37. MFM to Jack (John Minor) Maury, July 24, 1867, MP, Vol. XXVI, LC; Ann Herndon Maury to Ann Maury of New York, May 12, 1844, MC, UVAL.

38. Statements have been made that MFM did not join the Christian church

until he took this step. For example: "He was a firm believer in the Christian church but did not join the church til 1867 when he was confirmed with his children." Sketch of MFM, *Popular Science Monthly,* Vol. XXXVII, No. 3 (July, 1890), p. 407.

According to the teachings of the Episcopal Church as set forth in its service for Holy Baptism, MFM had been "grafted into the body of Christ's Church" when he was baptized as a small child in Spotsylvania County, Va. He had, however, not taken the second step of confirmation, which would have made him a communicant or fully participating member of the church.

There is no doubt that Ann did not consider anyone a full Christian until he or she was able to receive Holy Communion. For her great wish for MFM to make an adult acknowledgment of faith through being confirmed, see Ann Herndon Maury to Ann Maury of New York, May 12, 1844, MC, UVAL.

39. MFM to Miss Louisa Tremlett, Feb. 3 (either 1864 or 1865, no year on letter), Maury papers, Confederate Museum, Richmond. Quotation is from sketch of Cyrus W. Field, *Encyclopedia Americana* (1957 ed.), Vol. XI, p. 178.

40. MFM will signed May 4, 1862, MP, Vol. XVI, LC.

41. MFM's daughter Diana Maury Corbin, who was an eyewitness to the confirmation, states that her father was confirmed when Bishop Quintard "was then in London attending the Pan-Anglican Assembly at Lambeth" (Sept. 24-27, 1867); Corbin, *Maury,* p. 267. Her statement and other evidence point to the confirmation's having taken place just prior to the convening of the Lambeth Conference. MFM had written the Rt. Rev. Charles Todd Quintard, Aug. 21, 1867, on the latter's arrival in England; MP, Vol. XXVI, LC. The Rev. Francis W. Tremlett, who was to render valuable assistance to Quintard in soliciting funds for the University of the South, evidently welcomed Quintard to his home shortly after the Bishop of Tennessee reached London. Thus it appears that between Aug. 22 and Sept. 23, 1867, MFM became acquainted with Bishop Quintard at Tremlett's home and was confirmed by Quintard before the Bishop of Tennessee joined his fellow American bishops in attendance at Lambeth. This is the only period for which there is a gap in the diary (now in the Sewanee Archives) that Bishop Quintard kept in England.

Quintard soon formed a high opinion of MFM and by December, 1867, had tentatively proposed that MFM become the vice-chancellor (president) of the University of the South, Sewanee, Tenn.; MFM to Marin H. Jansen, Dec. 19, 1867; to Dr. James M. Minor, Dec. 22, 1867, MP, Vol. XXVI, LC; the Rt. Rev. Charles Todd Quintard to Maj. George Rainsford Fairbanks, Dec. 26, 1867, in Sewanee Archives. This proposal by Quintard in December tends to substantiate the fact that, prior to that date, MFM had become a communicant, because this would certainly have been a prerequisite for the top executive post in the university the Episcopal Church in the Southern states was attempting to build.

Bishop Quintard confirmed twenty-six people in St. Peter's, London, in a group Confirmation on Easter Day, April 12, 1868, and recorded the event in his diary. At that time Bishop Quintard was anxiously waiting for MFM to decide whether he would accept the proffered vice-chancellorship of the University of the South, Sewanee. Had MFM been confirmed in that group, Quintard would almost certainly have recorded the fact in his detailed diary. That he did not lends support to Diana Maury Corbin's statement that her father was confirmed in September, 1867, when Bishop Quintard was in London to attend the assemblage at Lambeth Palace. The date of 1866 in Lewis, *Maury*, p. 215, was probably a typographical error, as Bishop Quintard did not reach England until August, 1867.

Efforts to secure from England a record of MFM's confirmation were unsuccessful. In reply to inquiries made for me on this point, the Rt. Rev. Robert C. Mortimer, Bishop of Exeter, England, wrote the Rev. John Page Williams, Dean of Church Schools for the Diocese of Virginia, "I am afraid I simply cannot answer your question about Matthew Maury and his confirmation. No confirmation records were kept in England until this century. Ours here [Exeter] only date back to 1926." Dr. Williams to me, March 14, 1960.

Much of the information about Bishop Quintard used in this text is the result of painstaking search of his diaries, letters, and papers in the archives of the University of the South by the late university archivist, Mrs. O. N. Torian, the university historiographer, Arthur Ben Chitty, and his wife, Elizabeth, in March, 1960. This was supplied to me in copies of pertinent material and in letters from Elizabeth N. Chitty, March 22 and 29, 1960.

42. In telling of the election of the Rev. Charles Todd Quintard, chaplain of the Army of Tennessee, as Bishop of Tennessee, Arthur Ben Chitty, describes him as a man of "remarkable talents and unquenchable enthusiasm." For facts on Quintard and his attendance at the Pan-Anglican Conference of bishops at Lambeth Palace, his confirmation of MFM, and subsequent work in England, see Arthur Ben Chitty, *Reconstruction at Sewanee*, pp. 81 fn, 85, 86, 90-91, 99, 101-102, 105-106.

43. Diana Maury Corbin to MFM, May 7, 1865, Maury collection, Confederate Museum, Richmond; Prof. Schele de Vere, Univ. of Virginia, to Mary Maury, March 6, 1867, MP, Vol. XXV, LC; MFM to Marin H. Jansen, Aug. 5 and 22, 1867, MP, Vol. XXVI, LC.

44. The Rt. Rev. Charles Todd Quintard to Maj. George Rainsford Fairbanks, Dec. 26, 1867; to the Rt. Rev. J. P. B. Wilmer, Jan. 8, 1868; MFM to the Rt. Rev. Charles T. Quintard, Jan. 4, 1868, all in Sewanee Archives; MFM to Marin H. Jansen, Dec. 19, 1867; to Dr. James M. Minor, Dec. 22, 1867; to William A. Maury, Jan. 12, 1868, all in MP, Vol. XXVI, LC.

45. In 1860 MFM had written of Sewanee, "It is an institution in the success of which I feel the most lively interest." MFM to the Rt. Rev. James H. Otey, Sept. 15, 1860, MP, Vol. IX, LC. See also MFM to Bishop Otey, June 7, Aug. 30, Nov. 10, 1859, Aug. 20, 1860, MP, Vols. VIII, IX, LC; to B. Franklin Minor, July 31, 1859, MP, Vol. VIII, LC; entry in John Maury's diary, Aug. 30, 1859, MP, Vol. XLVI, Folio 9104, LC. For MFM's vision for the university in 1868, see letter of MFM to the Rt. Rev. Charles T. Quintard, Jan. 4, 1868, cited in Note 44.

46. MFM received a preliminary offer in February, 1868. This was sent by the Atlantic cable that Cyrus Field and his associates had succeeded in laying in 1866, the Rt. Rev. Charles T. Quintard to Maj. George R. Fairbanks, Feb. 26, 1868, Sewanee Archives. The formal announcement that the Board

of Visitors of the Virginia Military Institute had appointed MFM professor of meteorology (changed in July, 1868, to professor of physics) was dated Feb. 22, 1868, "under the seal of the State." See official announcement of John Letcher, president of the Board of Visitors, Virginia Military Institute, to MFM, Corbin, *Maury*, p. 270. For comment on proposal, see MFM note dated April 8 added to MFM letter to Rutson Maury, April 6, 1868, MP, Vol. XXVI, LC.

Francis H. Smith had served in the rank of major general, C.S.A. Volunteers from 1861 to 1865; but he was called General Smith after the war, and I have used that rather than the fuller title.

47. Bishop Green, who was interested in securing a clergyman for the position, delayed taking action on Bishop Quintard's urging of MFM for the vice-chancellorship. The delay worried Bishop Quintard, who wrote, "Of course I am feeling very anxious about Com^d Maury's appointment. If we lose him—I shall almost despair, & I do beg & pray you to be very *persuasive* with the dear Bp of Miss." The Rt. Rev. Charles T. Quintard to Maj. George R. Fairbanks, March 12, 1868, Sewanee Archives. The formal offer of the Sewanee position sent by Bishop Green reached MFM on April 18, 1868; Rutson Maury to Dr. Brodie S. Herndon, May 2, 1868, MP, Vol. XXVI, LC. The office of vice-chancellor could only be offered by the board of trustees or the executive committee of the university. It was the latter group meeting in Savannah, Ga., April 4, 1868, that voted their approval of the letter of tender presented by Bishop Green, chancellor of the university, Minutes of the Executive Committee for that day, Sewanee Archives.

48. MFM to the Rt. Rev. W. M. Green (MFM used Greene), Bishop of Mississippi, declining Sewanee offer, Apr. 21, 1868, and to Bishop Green, explaining some of his reasons for declining, Apr. 21, 1868, both in Sewanee Archives. MFM had faced the hopelessness of trying to raise money for Sewanee in the North after the Rev. Francis W. Tremlett had written bishops of the Episcopal Church in the North soliciting donations and had had no reply except from the Bishop of Rhode Island; MFM to Rutson Maury, Apr. 6, 1868, MP, Vol. XXVI, LC. This lack of response was a disappointment because the presiding bishop of the Episcopal Church and the bishops of Minnesota, Louisiana, Iowa, New Hampshire, and others attending the Lambeth Conference had given a letter of endorsement to Dr. Tremlett for the solicitation in England of funds for Sewanee. This situation in the winter of 1867-1868 was not to last, fortunately, and the university subsequently received generous assistance from the North. See MFM to William A. Maury, Apr. 22, 1868, MP, Vol. XXVI, LC. See also reception of MFM's refusal of the offer, Minutes of the Executive Committee, Univ. of the South, May 28, 1868, Sewanee Archives.

49. MFM to Gen. Francis H. Smith, Virginia Military Institute, Apr. 21, 1868, V.M.I. Archives, printed in Corbin, *Maury*, pp. 270-271; Gen. Francis H. Smith to William A. Maury, May 13, 1868, MP, Vol. XXVI, LC.

50. MFM to Rutson Maury, Apr. 22, 1868, MP, Vol. XXVI, LC.

51. MFM to William C. Hasbrouck, May 24, 1868, MP, Vol. XXVI, LC.

52. President Johnson's Second Amnesty Proclamation had excluded from eligibility for pardon the Confederacy's president, vice-president, heads of departments, foreign agents, those above the rank of brigadier general, and

the naval rank of captain, the governors of the Confederate states, and two categories of civilians that left a total of about 300 unpardoned Confederates; Richardson, *Messages and Papers of the Presidents*, Vol. VI, pp. 547-549.

53. Referred to in letter of Rutson Maury to Dr. Brodie S. Herndon cited in Note 47.

54. Ibid.

55. MFM to Dr. James M. Minor, May 10, 1868, MP, Vol. XXVI, LC.

56. MFM to Marin H. Jansen, May 24, 1868, MP, Vol. XXVI, LC; letter of MFM to William C. Hasbrouck cited in Note 51. Diana Maury Corbin was unable to go to Cambridge for the event because of an ill child, and this may account for the inaccuracy of her statement that "Alfred Tennyson received his degree on the same occasion." Corbin, *Maury*, pp. 267-269.

57. Extract from speech delivered in the Senate by W. G. Clark, public orator, Cambridge Univ., England, May 28, 1868, translated from the Latin by J. M. D. Meiklejohn, M.A., headmaster, Rose Hill School, MP, Vol. XXVI, Folio 4999, LC.

58. William Wright to MFM, Aug. 3, 1869, MP, Vol. XXXII, LC.

59. MFM lecture, "Science and the Bible Educational Ideals of the South," delivered at Cambridge Univ., June, 1868, MP, Vol. XLVII, Folios 9451-9481, LC.

60. MFM to Rutson Maury, Apr. 22, 1868, sent on by Rutson to Gen. Francis H. Smith, May 6, 1868, MP, Vol. XXVI, LC.

61. G. J. Loseby to MFM, July 2, 1864, MP, Vol. XX, LC.

62. MFM to Dr. James W. Minor, June 7, 1868, MP, Vol. XXVI, LC. For Matthew Jr.'s starting technical courses, see MFM to Dabney H. Maury, Feb. 23, 1867, MP, Vol. XXV, LC.

63. MFM to William C. Hasbrouck, May 24, 1868; to Marin H. Jansen, July 17, 1868, MP, Vols. XXVI, XXVII, LC.

64. S. Wellford Corbin to William C. Hasbrouck, June 8, 1867, MP, Vol. XXVI, LC.

65. Letter of MFM to Dr. James W. Minor cited in Note 62; Corbin, *Maury*, p. 271.

CHAPTER XXIII

Professor on the March

1. This third amnesty signed by President Andrew Johnson in Washington on July 4, 1868, was disapproved by the Radical Republicans, who wanted disfranchisement of all former Confederates. For President Johnson's proclamation, see Richardson, *Messages and Papers of the Presidents*, Vol. VI, pp. 655-656. For MFM's account of Corbin's reporting the amnesty, see MFM to Marin H. Jansen, July 17 and Aug. 5, 1868, MP, Vol. XXVII, LC.

2. Letter of MFM to Marin H. Jansen, July 17, 1868, MP, Vol. XXVII, LC.

3. This arrangement was made in advance by Rutson; Rutson Maury to MFM, May 1, 1868, MP, Vol. XXVI, LC.

4. Letter of MFM to Marin H. Jansen cited in Note 2.

5. Ibid.

6. The arrangement for the girls to stay with the Arthurs was reported in Rutson Maury to Mr. and Mrs. William A. Maury (Betty and her husband), May 2, 1868, MP, Vol. XXVI, LC. At the request of his wife, Chester A. Arthur had arranged for records of the Federal prison at Alton, Ill., to be searched for any trace of John Maury following his disappearance in the war; MFM to his wife, Nov. 29, 1863, MP, Vol. XIX, LC.

7. President Johnson's proclamation of July 4, 1868, meant that MFM would not be arrested for treason; but it had no effect upon MFM's qualifications for suffrage in the face of the Reconstruction Act passed by Congress on March 2, 1867, the supplementary Reconstruction Act of March 23, 1867, and the Constitution of Virginia adopted April 17, 1868, by the Radical-dominated Virginia constitutional convention. See John W. Burgess, *Reconstruction and the Constitution, 1866-1876 (American History Series)*, pp. 216, 220; Hamilton James Eckenrode, *The Political History of Virginia During the Reconstruction (Johns Hopkins University Studies in Historical and Political Science)*, June-July-August, 1904, Ser. XXII, Nos. 6-7-8 (cited hereafter as Eckenrode, *Virginia During Reconstruction*), pp. 52-53, 100-103.

8. MFM had received word from his publisher about Northern hostility to his text before he left England; MFM to Dr. James M. Minor, June 7, 1868, MP, Vol. XXVI, LC. For his spending a week working with his publisher, see letter of MFM to Marin H. Jansen, July 17, 1868, cited in Note 1.

9. Note added by one of his children to letter of MFM to Marin H. Jansen, Aug. 5, 1868, MP, Vol. XXVII, LC.

10. There is a good account of the devastation of the evacuation fire in Rembert W. Patrick, *The Fall of Richmond*, pp. 101-103.

    By the time of MFM's return to Richmond a substantial amount of building had obliterated the worst of the damage to downtown Richmond, but there were ample signs still to be seen. For pictures of the devastation of lower Richmond in 1865, see Frances Leigh Williams, *They Faced the Future, A Saga of Growth*, pp. 26, 27, 33, 39.

11. For a general picture of Richmond in the years from 1865 to 1873, see W. Asbury Christian, D.D., *Richmond, Her Past and Present*, pp. 256-341.

    The awareness of Richmonders of the number of men who had given their lives for the Confederate cause is best revealed by the emphasis laid on keeping the graves of these men decorated. In the postwar years the women of Richmond made a continuing effort to keep flowers or greens on the graves of Confederate soldiers and sailors buried in Hollywood and Oakwood Cemeteries. Two Memorial Days observed in late May were annual occasions of major importance in Richmond. For an account, see "The Southern Dead," Richmond *Whig*, May 24, 1877, p. 1. For the percentage of Southern men permanently incapacitated or killed, see Hodding Carter, *The Angry Scar, The Story of Reconstruction*, pp. 42-43.

12. The lack of expression of opinion about political leaders and government policies in MFM's correspondence subsequent to his return to Virginia is in marked contrast to his freedom of expression on the subject in previous years. I found only three paragraphs of such expression of opinion by MFM in those years; MFM to P. P. Borst, president of the Shenandoah Valley Railroad, Sept. 5, 1870, published in "Maury Visioned Develop-

ment of Great Virginia Port," Richmond *Times-Dispatch*, March 26, 1922, editorial and magazine section, Part II, p. 8.

13. Shortly before MFM's arrival in Richmond it had been announced, "The Board of Visitors [of the Virginia Military Institute] have established a 'School of Physics.' The chair will be filled by Commodore Maury, who is expected here by 15th instant. Commodore Maury will recommence the physical survey of the State, stopped by the war, and carry it on to completion. Too great praise can hardly be rendered the Institute for its energy and zeal in this important interest." Richmond *Whig*, July 7, 1868, p. 2.

   Not one of the state's many needs received more constant coverage in the postwar Richmond newspapers than that of extending the railroad from Covington, Va., to the Ohio River and on to the cities of the Middle West. For examples, see reprint from the New York *Herald* in Richmond *Whig*, July 3, 1867, p. 1; for the vote on whether Richmond should subscribe $2,000,000 toward construction of Chesapeake and Ohio Railroad, see Richmond *Whig*, Sept. 17 (p. 2), 18 (p. 1), Dec. 17, 28 (both p. 2), 1867; see also Richmond *Whig*, Jan. 24 (p. 2), and especially Sept. 2, 1868, p. 1.

   In promoting a steamship line from Norfolk to Holland, MFM was renewing the campaign he had waged long before the war in numerous articles written on direct trade between Southern markets and Europe. For the proposal of line to Holland, see Corbin, *Maury*, p. 272.

14. Thurman Wilkins, *Clarence King, A Biography*, pp. 55-80.
15. Virginia Military Institute (written by Gen. Francis H. Smith but not signed), *In Memoriam—Matthew Fontaine Maury, LL.D.*, p. 19.
16. For preliminary plans, see Gen. Francis H. Smith to MFM, July 25, 1868; for quotation, see Gen. Smith to MFM, July 30, 1868, both in MP, Vol. XXVII, LC.
17. In late August, 1865, the South's military commander Robert E. Lee had thought it not unbecoming his talents or position to accept the presidency of Washington College in Lexington at a salary of "$1,500 per annum, plus a house and garden and one-fifth of the tuition fees of the students, which were raised to $75 each." Freeman, *Lee*, Vol. IV, p. 215. General Lee's emoluments were gradually increased, but his financial reward continued to reflect the South's poverty. Shortly after Lee had accepted the college presidency, he had written, "I look forward to better days, and trust that time and experience, the great teachers of men, under the guidance of the ever-merciful God, may save us from destruction, and restore to us the bright hopes and prospects of the past," Robert E. Lee to MFM, Sept. 8, 1865, in Jones, *Personal . . . Letters . . . of Lee*, p. 206.
18. For a good account of the Greenbrier White Sulphur Springs, the other fashionable Virginia mountain resorts, and the society that frequented them, see Percival Reniers, *The Springs of Virginia*.
19. For a general account of the resort, see William Alexander McCorkle, *The White Sulphur Springs, West Virginia, The Tradition, History, Social Life*.

   An interesting description of life at "The White" in the summer of 1867, during Gen. Lee's first postwar visit and of Lee's insistence on friendliness being shown Northern guests, is in Freeman, *Lee,* Vol. IV, pp. 323-330.

20. After the citizens of Virginia ratified the ordinance of secession voted by the Virginia Convention in April, 1861, the trans-Allegheny delegates, who had disapproved the vote to sccede, met at Wheeling and declared void the secession ordinance of the Virginia Convention. They then called a convention to be held at Wheeling and in that convention, on June 11, 1861, declared independence of Virginia and set up a government for what had been western Virginia and became West Virginia. The new state was admitted to the Union on June 20, 1863. See article on West Virginia, *Columbia Encyclopedia* (1935 ed.), p. 1888.

21. MFM to Marin H. Jansen, Aug. 5, 1868, MP, Vol. XXVII, LC.

22. Corbin, *Maury,* pp. 271-272.

23. MFM found an able ally at "The White" in former Governor John Letcher, under whom he had served on the Governor's Advisory Council throughout its brief existence from April 21 to June 19, 1861. President of the Board of Visitors of the Virginia Military Institute and greatly interested in assisting MFM on the Physical Survey of Virginia, former governor Letcher was one of the men to whom Dr. Freeman had reference in telling of General Lee's arrival at the White Sulphur Springs in August, 1868. "He [Lee] found a large gathering of former Confederates there, including many of his old generals and not a few of the civil officials of the dead government." Freeman, *Lee,* Vol. IV, pp. 372-373.

24. MFM undoubtedly spent a good deal of time with Col. Edmund Fontaine because the extension of the Chesapeake and Ohio Railroad westward was to be a major objective of the Physical Survey of Virginia. MFM was at "The White" on Aug. 31, 1868, when the board of directors of the C. and O. Railroad Company resolved that the old Central Railroad that had run from Richmond to Covington and the newer Covington and Ohio Railroad Company, committed to extend the line to the Ohio River, "assume the name and style of Chesapeake and Ohio Railroad Company. The President of the company [Fontaine] was authorized to enter into a contract with the Tredegar Iron Works Company, of Richmond, for the rail and bridge iron for the entire road which he has done." Richmond *Whig,* Sept. 2, 1868, p. 1. In view of the speed with which the contract was consummated, it seems that Col. Fontaine and Gen. Joseph R. Anderson must have signed the contract at the White Sulphur Springs, where they were both guests, the day after the C. and O. line had been formally voted into existence. MFM was in the right place for his purposes.

While it was during this stay at "The White" that MFM saw General Lee for the first time after his return to Virginia, their subsequent relationship in Lexington was far more enjoyable and meaningful to both. Diana Maury Corbin states that Gen. Lee's presence in Lexington as president (she called him rector) "had no small influence in Maury's choice of Lexington for a home, so highly did he appreciate the pleasure of a renewal of the friendship which existed between them as neighbors in old times." Corbin, *Maury,* pp. 269-270.

Lee reciprocated MFM's feeling, according to the Rev. J. William Jones, D.D., former chaplain of the Army of Northern Virginia, who served as chaplain of Washington College during Lee's presidency. In his authorized publication of personal letters Jones referred to MFM as "the great scientist whom the whole world honored . . . who was General Lee's intimate friend, and in whose society in Lexington he seemed so much to delight." Jones, *Personal . . . Letters . . . of Lee,* p. 206.

25. Dr. Freeman gives a very clear picture of how Gen. Rosecrans persuaded Lee to break his self-imposed rule and take part in the expression of a political opinion. Not finding a MS copy of the Rosecrans letter, Dr. Freeman declared lost the text of General Rosecrans's formal letter to Lee requesting that the Southerners, with whom Rosecrans had conferred at Lee's cottage, issue a formal statement of their views; Freeman, *Lee,* Vol. IV, pp. 373-374, including fn 8 on p. 374. However, the letter sent Lee by Gen. Rosecrans was, strange to say, published subsequent to Lee's reply thereto and is available for study. See Gen. W. S. Rosecrans to Gen. R. E. Lee, Aug. 26, 1868, in Richmond *Daily Enquirer and Examiner,* Sept. 7, 1868, p. 3.

26. General Robert E. Lee and thirty other Southern leaders to General W. S. Rosecrans, Minister to Mexico, White Sulphur Springs, Aug. 26, 1868, released under Washington dateline of Sept. 4, 1868, published in full with names of signers in the Richmond *Daily Enquirer and Examiner,* Sept. 5, 1868, p. 1.

27. MFM to Marin H. Jansen, Sept. 1, 1868, MP, Vol. XXVII, LC.

28. Gen. Francis H. Smith to MFM, July 30, 1868, MP, Vol. XXVII, LC.

29. Gen. Smith had instructed MFM to take the train (eastbound from Covington—then nearest rail point to the White Sulphur Springs) to Goshen Depot and then the stage through Goshen Pass 10 miles to Rockbridge Baths, which they would reach "by 8 PM the same day." Ibid. to MFM, July 30, 1868.

30. Gen. Francis H. Smith, superintendent of the Virginia Military Institute, 1839-1889, was a West Pointer and apparently did not consider excessive an 11-mile ride from Lexington to Rockbridge Baths. (Until 1869 Gen. Lee often rode out and back on Traveller the same afternoon.) Gen. Smith had informed MFM that the cost for his family would not exceed $50 for a week's stay at the Rockbridge Baths; ibid.

31. Annual Report of Gen. Francis H. Smith, Superintendent of V.M.I. to the Board of Visitors, June 25, 1869, V.M.I. Archives.

32. William Couper, *One Hundred Years at V.M.I.,* Vol. II, pp. 266-342; Francis H. Smith, *The Virginia Military Institute, Its Building and Rebuilding,* pp. 196, 197. For a general sketch, see Joseph R. Anderson, Jr., *The Virginia Military Institute and Her Sons—In the Past,* March 15, 1904.

33. An excellent description of the V.M.I. buildings, including the house that was restored for MFM's use, may be found in William Couper, *One Hundred Years at V.M.I.,* Vol. III, p. 156.

For details of MFM's installation, see *Supplement to Richmond Semi-Weekly Whig,* Sept. 15, 1868, p. 1.

The information that Gen. Lee was present at MFM's installation is from the personal notes of Col. William Couper of V.M.I. Gen. Lee may have reached Lexington that day just in time for the ceremony. On Sept. 3 Lee and his family were at the Hot Springs, Virginia, for the last portion of their vacation, and by Sept. 14 Lee was back at work at Washington College; Richmond *Daily Enquirer and Examiner,* Sept. 5, 1868, p. 1;

Faculty Minutes, Washington College, Sept. 14, 1868, Washington and Lee Univ. Archives.

34. The Rev. W. N. Pendleton concluded his very lengthy prayer with thanks to God that "he [MFM] is restored in safety to the land of his love and has the ability and the heart to labor for the welfare of her suffering people." For this quotation and that of Smith, see *Supplement to Richmond Semi-Weekly Whig,* Sept. 15, 1868, p. 1.

35. Ibid.

36. Ibid.

37. MFM, *Office of the Physical Survey of Virginia, Virginia Military Institute, to the Public,* Sept. 10, 1868, printed folder in MP, Vol. XXVII, LC; published in Richmond *Whig,* Sept. 28, 1868, p. 3, see also editorial on p. 2; *Southern Planter and Farmer,* Vol. II, No. 10 (October, 1868), pp. 633-638.

38. MFM to Col. Edmund Fontaine, president of C. and O. Railroad, written from V.M.I., Sept. 17, 1868, MP, Vol. XXVII, LC.

39. The plan to establish a shipping line between Norfolk, Va., and Flushing, Holland, and MFM's belief in the advantage of Hampton Roads as a port over New York and other points are presented in MFM, *The Physical Survey of Virginia, Preliminary Report No. 1* (1st ed., 1868), pp. 23-39, 69, 75-76, 79-90.

40. Other V.M.I. professors associated with MFM in conducting the Physical Survey of Virginia were Gen. George Washington Custis (called Custis) Lee, Col. John Mercer Brooke and Col. Marshall McDonald. For work plans, see Gen. Francis H. Smith to MFM, Sept. 24, Oct. 14, 1868, MP, Vol. XXVII, LC.

41. Gen. Francis H. Smith to MFM, Oct. 14, 1868, and subsequent letters throughout autumn of 1868, MP, Vols. XXVII and XXVIII, LC.

42. MFM, "The Augusta County Fair Speech of Commodore M. F. Maury," *Southern Planter and Farmer,* Vol. II, No. 11 (November, 1868), pp. 698-704.

43. MFM, *The Physical Survey of Virginia, Geographical Position of; Its Commercial Advantages and National Importance; Preliminary Report No. 1* (1st ed.), published by W. A. R. Nye, Richmond, 1868.

44. Gen. Francis H. Smith to W. W. Corcoran, undated but obviously written in late December, 1868, MP, Vol. XLVI, Folios 9066-9067, LC.

45. MFM had first come to know W. W. Corcoran in the capital in the 1840's through John Walker Maury, who had served successively on the Common Council, the Board of Aldermen, and as mayor of Washington, D.C. Walker Maury and W. W. Corcoran had worked together closely for the public betterment of the city. When MFM had served as president of the National Institute, W. W. Corcoran had united with him in an effort to place that organization on a sound organizational basis.

46. Gen. Francis H. Smith to MFM, Feb. 4, 1869, MP, Vol. XXIX, LC.

47. Francis H. Smith, *The Virginia Military Institute, Its Building and Rebuilding,* p. 223.

48. After reading *The Physical Survey of Virginia, Preliminary Report No. 1,* a Norfolk citizen wrote MFM, "It did me good to see the old Borough [Norfolk] spoken of in such words of prophecy." F. M. Lewis to MFM, Jan. 26, 1869, MP, Vol. XXVIII, LC.

MFM was invited to visit Norfolk to explain the proposed Flushing-Norfolk steamer line; invitation of the directors of the Merchants and Mechanics Exchange of Norfolk, Feb. 22, 1869, MP, Vol. XXIX, LC.

See reports of MFM's chief agent, Col. Thomas H. Ellis, former president of the James River and Kanawha Canal, of survey work in Norfolk and nearby Portsmouth; Thomas H. Ellis to MFM, March 4, 9, 15, 1869, MP, Vols. XXIX, XXX, LC.

For a modern appreciation written since much of MFM's vision for the Hampton Roads area has come true, see "Maury Visioned Development of Great Virginia Port," Richmond *Times-Dispatch,* March 26, 1922, Editorial and Magazine Section, Part II, p. 8.

49. Letters of C. C. Baldwin, L. U. Mayo, M.D., James M. Buchanan, R. R. Carter, Hector Owens, M.D., William W. Minor, Cary C. Cocke, Frank G. Ruffin, Theodore S. Garnett, W. H. F. Lee, Robert Beverley, Thomas Leigh, Robert Binford, A. F. M. Rust et al. in period from Jan. 20 to June 17, 1869, MP, Vols. XXVIII through XXXI, LC.

50. The Seaboard and Roanoke Railroad from its home office, Norfolk, contributed $200 in advance of publication; after publication of *Preliminary Report No. 1,* the Richmond, Fredericksburg and Potomac Railroad subscribed to 260 copies of *Preliminary Report No. 2;* Thomas H. Ellis to MFM, March 15, 1869; Mary H. Maury to the Rev. Francis W. Tremlett, Aug. 30, 1869, MP, Vols. XXX, XXXII, LC.

51. Gen. Francis H. Smith to MFM, Feb. 22, March 29, 1869, MP, Vols. XXIX, XXX, LC; the Merchants and Mechanics Exchange of Norfolk to MFM, May 12, 1869, Thomas H. Ellis to MFM, June 1, 1869, both in MP, Vol. XXXI, LC.

52. Gen. Francis H. Smith to MFM, Feb. 19, 1869, MP, Vol. XXIX, LC.

53. "I feel every day the importance of having you near by and am pressing forward the mansion hoping to have you here early in May." Gen. Francis H. Smith to MFM, Feb. 15, 1869. Smith reported the second floor was painted in his letter of March 6, 1869, and on Apr. 9 wrote, "The painter is now finishing off the rose tint walls of the parlour and dining room as suggested by your daughter. The yard is enclosed—water in the house—cistern built—white-porcelain door knobs—all quite ready for the light of your good countenance." See also Gen. Smith on house, furnishings and servants, Apr. 20, 1869; MFM to his sister, Mrs. Elizabeth Maury Holland, May 20, 1869. Also see the report, "On Tuesday last the Commodore and family set out for Lexington whither they arrived on Wednesday afternoon after a ride in the hot sun of six hours [by stage or carriage from C. and O. depot at Goshen]." William A. Maury to William C. Hasbrouck, May 30, 1869. MFM reported on the house and his having settled in; MFM to the Rev. Francis W. Tremlett, June 13, 1869, all in MP, Vols. XXIX, XXX, XXXI, LC.

54. Eliza Maury to Marin H. Jansen, Aug. 4, 1870, MP, Vol. XXXV, LC.

55. Ibid.

56. Committee of Three, First Class, V.M.I., to MFM, May 5, 1869, MP, Vol. XXXI, LC.

57. *Address to the Graduating Class of The Virginia Military Institute, July 2, 1869, by Commodore M. F. Maury, published by request,* pp. 4-5. For easier reading I have divided the paragraph.

58. Ibid., pp. 6-7.
59. To try to give the essence of this speech in condensed form I have rearranged the sequence of sentences but have, of course, made no alteration in MFM's words. The first portion quoted is from p. 11 of MFM's *Address* (cited in Note 57); the first sentence of the indented paragraph is from p. 9; the next four sentences are from p. 11; and the final sentence from p. 7.
60. MFM to the Rev. Francis W. Tremlett, June 13, 1869; S. Wellford Corbin to William C. Hasbrouck, June 16, 1869, both in MP, Vol. XXXI, LC. See also plea that MFM accept the proposal in H. L. Owen, of Mobile, Ala., to MFM, July 16, 1869, and equally urgent plea that MFM not leave V.M.I. in the Rev. Francis W. Tremlett to MFM, July 30, 1869, both in MP, Vol. XXXII, LC.
61. Two examples within the Maury family illustrate one phase of the economic problem in Virginia. Jesse Maury, who owned "Piedmont," the 2,000-acre family estate one mile from the University of Virginia where MFM had been entertained in 1825 on his way to Washington to become a midshipman, could not borrow money in Virginia to rehabilitate his property damaged by Federal troop occupancy during the war. He wrote that he was trying to borrow funds in New York; Jesse Maury to MFM, Jan. 8, 1869, MP, Vol. XXVIII, LC. MFM's son-in-law had similarly tried to borrow money to finance a recommencement of farming at his plantation "Farley Vale," but not being successful had gone to New York to work as a salesman for a New York carpet firm, L. Edgerton and Co.; S. Wellford Corbin to William C. Hasbrouck, July 29, 1865, and MFM to Dabney H. Maury, Dec. 20, 1869, MP, Vols. XXII, XXXIII, LC.

The situation in Richmond in 1868 was described in these words, "The people had one great reason for believing that better times would come, and that was that they could not be worse than they had been." W. Asbury Christian, D.D., *Richmond, Her Past and Present,* p. 300.

For general accounts of the serious problems and difficulties of the Reconstruction period, see William A. Dunning, *Reconstruction, Political and Economic;* Robert Stiles, *Reconstruction in Virginia;* Eckenrode, *Virginia During Reconstruction;* James G. Randall, *Civil War and Reconstruction;* Whitelaw Reid, *After the War: A Southern Tour;* Richard Taylor, *Destruction and Reconstruction . . . ;* Hodding Carter, *The Angry Scar: The Story of Reconstruction;* Sally A. Pryor, *Reminiscences of Peace and War.*
62. Financial problems at V.M.I. prevented General Smith from travelling with MFM to promote the aims of the Physical Survey of Virginia. He wrote MFM, "Our deposits are $30,000 behind and I must stir up delinquents. We have to show indulgence to the patrons at such a time as this [Reconstruction era] but it works heavily against us in the last quarter of the fiscal year." Gen. Francis H. Smith to MFM, March 5, 1869, MP, Vol. XXIX, LC.

The tuition at V.M.I. in 1869 was only $100, board $180, with fuel, lights, surgeon's fee, and washing bringing cost to $350. In addition, a cadet was expected to have $150 for uniforms and incidental expenses. He was not allowed to receive more than $5 pocket money per month, and it is doubtful that many received that. See information on back of front cover of MFM, *The Physical Survey of Virginia, Preliminary Report No. 1* (2nd ed.), March, 1869.

Because of the lack of state funds, Gen. Smith had persuaded private donors such as W. W. Corcoran of Washington to give sufficient money to restore the barracks that had been damaged during the war. They were repaired by the fall of 1868 when MFM was installed; Richmond *Whig*, March 17, 1868, p. 2.

63. Rutson Maury to MFM, Apr. 23, 1869, MP, Vol. XXXI, LC.

64. The Alabama proposition tempted MFM partly because it would permit him to place Matthew Jr., with his newly earned London diplomas, on the faculty of the University of Alabama; MFM to the Rev. Francis W. Tremlett cited in Note 60. MFM was at this time engaged in writing a paper in behalf of railroad extension westward from Virginia, entitled "The Importance to Cincinnati of the Chesapeake and Ohio Railroad," dated June 17, 1869, MP, Vol. XXXI, LC.

65. *Minutes of the Educational Association of Virginia; Fourth Annual Session;* Freeman, *Lee,* Vol. IV, pp. 433-434.

66. Matthew Jr.'s subsequent business letterhead listed him as Fellow of the Geological Society of London, Graduate of the Royal College of Chemistry, London, Associate of the Royal School of Mines, and Graduate in Civil Engineering of the Virginia Military Institute. He had studied for the engineering degree at V.M.I. following his return to Virginia in the summer of 1869. See M. F. Maury, Jr., to his father, May 8, 1872, MP, Vol. XL, LC.

67. Mary H. Maury to the Rev. Francis W. Tremlett, Aug. 30, 1869, MP, Vol. XXXII, LC.

68. Both Memphis and Louisville commercial conventions had endorsed the promotion of European immigration to the South. Ellis asked MFM to see Gen. Lee and persuade him to lend his name as a patron of the effort in Virginia; Thomas H. Ellis to MFM, Oct. 25, 1869, MP, Vol. XXXII, LC.

69. A chief objective of the Physical Survey of Virginia was to interest German and Dutch immigrants to settle in Virginia. Gen. Lee, fully cognizant of the need to secure reliable labor for the state, gave his approval stating, "I believe this can only be secured by the introduction of a respectable class of labourers from Europe, for although a temporary benefit might be derived from importation of the Chinese and Japanese, it would result I fear in eventual injury to the country and her institutions. We not only want reliable labourers, but good citizens, whose interests and feelings would be in unison with our own. . . ." Robert E. Lee to Thomas H. Ellis, Dec. 30, 1869, original letter in the collection of James R. Gilliam, Jr., Lynchburg, Va.

70. Some success was achieved in the immigration effort, and MFM proudly reported that he had "never in any country tasted a grape more delicious for the table" than grapes he had bought from a German named Wiess, a vinedresser from the Rhine who had in the postwar period established a vineyard near Lexington; MFM, *Physical Survey of Virginia, Preliminary Report No. 2,* p. 119.

The quotation is from MFM to the Rev. Francis W. Tremlett, June 30, 1870, MP, Vol. XXXV, LC.

71. MFM to his sister, Mrs. Elizabeth Maury (Kemp S.) Holland, Dec. 22, 1869, MP, Vol. XXXIII, LC.

72. "Address Before the Educational Society [Association] of Virginia on the need of a more thorough study of natural science in the schools," the preparation of which was completed Dec. 16, 1869, MS in MP, Vol. XLVIII, Folios 9500-9540, LC. The speech was delivered by MFM the following July, *Minutes of the Educational Association of Virginia, Fifth Annual Session, Held in Warrenton, Va., July 12-15, 1870,* p. 6; *Educational Journal of Virginia,* Vol. I, No. 10 (August, 1870), pp. 304-313.

73. MFM to Dabney H. Maury, March 19, 1870, MP, Vol. XXXIV, LC.

74. For example, see an application for work with the Physical Survey from a former Confederate artillery colonel who, between 1842 and 1844, had worked on MFM's staff at the Depot of Charts and Instruments in Washington; J. B. Carter to MFM, July 1, 1870, MP, Vol. XXXV, LC.

75. Letter of MFM to Peter B. Borst, president, Shenandoah Valley Railroad, Sept. 5, 1870, cited in Note 12.

76. Eckenrode, *Virginia During Reconstruction,* pp. 126-127.

77. "Oath of office," *Constitution of Virginia, 1867-1868,* Art. III, Sec. VII, p. 10.

78. Richardson, *Messages and Papers of the Presidents,* Vol. VII, p. 11.

79. *Code of Virginia* (1873), p. 26.

80. For an account of the Virginia Constitutional Convention that assembled in the capitol in Richmond, Dec. 3, 1867, and voted a new state constitution on April 17, 1868, as well as for the vote of Virginia citizens thereon, see Eckenrode, *Virginia During Reconstruction,* pp. 87-125. For the disfranchising article, see *Constitution of Virginia, 1867-1868,* Art. III, Sec. I through VI, pp. 8-10.

81. Eckenrode, *Virginia During Reconstruction,* p. 125.

82. P. Wroth, M.D., Baltimore, to MFM, May 15, 1870, MP, Vol. XXXV, LC.

83. Dr. Brodie S. Herndon to MFM, Apr. 25, 1870 (incorrectly dated 1871 and filed by that date), MP, Vol. XXXVII, LC. See also Freeman, *Lee,* Vol. IV, pp. 444-453.

84. "Funeral Obsequies for General Lee," Oct. 15, 1870, MP, Vol. XXXVI, LC. For Lee's final illness and funeral, see also Freeman, *Lee,* Vol. IV, pp. 488-493.

85. Gen. Francis H. Smith to MFM, Sept. 24, 1870, MP, Vol. XXXVI, LC.

86. MFM was asked to become president of St. John's College at a salary of $3,000 and a suitable president's house; James S. Waddell to MFM, Sept. 24, 1870, MP, Vol. XXXVI, LC.

87. MFM from Richmond to the Rev. Francis W. Tremlett, Dec. 7, 1870, MP, Vol. XXXVI, LC.

88. Letter of Elie (Eliza) Maury to Marin H. Jansen, Dec. 29, 1870; MFM to Dr. Brodie S. Herndon, written from "The Lodge," near Holly Springs, Miss., Jan. 6, 1871, both in MP, Vol. XXXVI, LC.

89. Dr. Brodie S. Herndon to his sister Mrs. Ann Herndon Maury, Feb. 22, 1871, MP, Vol. XXXVI, LC.

90. MFM, "Man's Power-Giving Knowledge," MS copy dated Jan. 23 [1871?]; MP, Vol. XLVIII, Folios 9671-9702, 9690-9693, LC. The date that MFM delivered the talk after his return to V.M.I. is not on the MS.

91. Anecdote of MFM's receiving Benehan Cameron at his home at V.M.I. is recounted on editorial page, Richmond *News Leader,* June 4, 1925.

92. Joseph H. Speed, member of Board of Regents, Univ. of Alabama to MFM, Apr. 15, 1871, MP, Vol. XXXVII, LC.

93. Col. Joseph Hodgson, president, Board of Regents, Univ. of Alabama, to MFM, June 21, 1871, MP, Vol. XXXVII, LC.

94. The telegram is referred to in MFM to Col. Hodgson, July 31, 1871, MP, small bound letter book of letterpress copies marked April 4, 1871-March 19, 1872, LC.

95. MFM to Col. Hodgson, Sept. 11, 1871, in volume cited in Note 94; see also MP, Vol. XLVI, Folio 9138, LC.

96. A college prospectus listing "Matthew F. Maury, LL.D., President" was published by authority of Col. Hodgson, between the time MFM wired his acceptance and subsequently declined the position. See MP, Vol. XLVI, Folio 9138, LC. The eulogistic article about MFM by Raphael Semmes was published in Montgomery (Ala.) *Advance,* Sept. 25, 1871.

97. Bishop Quintard wrote from Baltimore, where the General Convention of the Episcopal Church was about to be held: "You know how ye [he wrote ye for the] heart of Tennessee has yearned after you. *We must have* you as Vice-Chancellor of ye University of ye South. May I propose your name? We will give you some sort of a house—a good one—with four of five thousand to live on.

"Now, my dear friend, we want you not to teach but to administer—& plan & execute. Will you not come to us?

"If you will drop me a line *at once.* I will propose your name at ye special meeting of ye Board to assemble in this city during ye session of ye genl Convention." The Rt. Rev. Charles T. Quintard, to MFM, Oct. 8, 1871, MP, Vol. XXXVIII, LC.

98. MFM to the Rev. Francis W. Tremlett, Feb. 2, 1872, MP, Vol. XXXIX, LC.

99. MFM expressed his awareness of the passage of time, "Yesterday was my birthday—sixty-six. Read my mercies in the first of the morning Psalms, 71st for the 14th day, and imagine the unction with which I joined in the reading at church. . . ." MFM to Rutson Maury, Jan. 15, 1872, in Corbin, *Maury,* p. 276.

100. MFM, *Physical Survey of Virginia, Preliminary Report No. 2,* rough notes and draft of text, MS, submitted to Gen. Francis H. Smith, MP, Vol. XLVIII, Folios 9541-9656; Vol. XLIX, Folios 9705-9925; Vol. L, Folios 9935-10083, LC.

A sign of the poverty of Virginia was the fact that this report prepared by MFM was not published until after his death. Richard L. Maury brought his father's text up to date, and it was finally published in 1878.

101. *Guide to Records of Weather Bureau in the National Archives,* p. 95. Although little mention is made of MFM's work for a central weather bureau, a good sketch of the developments leading to the bureau is Gustavus Adolphus Weber, *The Weather Bureau, Its History, Activities and Organization.*

102. For an example of his speeches, see MFM, Address before Congress of the National Agricultural Association held at St. Louis, Mo., May 27-30, 1872, MS in MP, Vol. LI, Folios 10143-10172, LC; published in *National Agricultural Association Proceedings, 1872,* pp. 40-54.

103. MFM, *Address before the Fair of the Agricultural and Mechanical Society of Memphis, Tennessee, Oct. 17, 1871,* pamphlet in MP, Ac7922, LC.

104. The resolutions passed by state legislatures and other groups recommend-

ing adoption of MFM's proposal for weather and crop are in MP, Vol. LI, LC. See also Charles H. Taylor, private secretary to Governor William Claplin of Massachusetts, to MFM, Nov. 26, 1871; letters from governors of Rhode Island, Connecticut, West Virginia, New York, and Tennessee, November and December, 1871, all in MP, Vol. XXXVIII; from the House of Representatives, State of Missouri, to MFM, Jan. (n.d.), 1872, from the St. Louis Agricultural Congress to MFM, May 27, 1872, and other letters or memorandums on subject in MP, Vols. XXXIX, XLIII, Folios 8420-8422, LC.

105. The General Assembly of North Carolina to MFM, Dec. 13, 1871, MP, Vol. XXXVIII, LC.

106. A copy of MFM's address proposing international meteorological and crop reports as delivered to the Rockbridge Agricultural and Mechanical Society, Oct. 13, 1871, was also read at a general meeting of the Scottish Meteorological Society. An account of the proceedings was published in the Edinburgh *Courant*, Jan. 26, 1872, reported in letter from Alexander Buchan, secretary of the Scottish Meteorological Society, to MFM, Jan. 26, 1872, MP, Vol. XXXIX, LC.

107. Letters of Alexander Buchan, secretary, Scottish Meteorological Society, Jan. 26, Aug. 5, 1872, MP, Vols. XXXIX, XL, LC.

108. Adolphe Quetelet, Le Secrétaire Perpétuel de l'Académie Royale des Sciences, des Lettres et des Beaux Arts, Bruxelles, to MFM, Feb. 15, 1872, MP, Vol. XXXIX, LC.

109. "The American Savant—Cm^{dr} Maury," *Le Messager de Paris*, March 21, 1872, filed by that date in MP, Vol. XXXIX, LC.

110. Adolphe Quetelet to MFM, Sept. 28, 1872; to MFM's family, Oct. 2, 1873, MP, Vols. XLI, XLIV, LC.

111. Secretary of State Hamilton Fish to Senator John W. Johnston, March 16, 1872; U.S. Senator John W. Johnston of Virginia to MFM, Apr. 25, 1872, MP, Vol. XL, LC.

112. Letter of Senator John W. Johnston to MFM, Apr. 25, 1872, cited in Note 111.

113. Merle Odgers describes Bache's "high tribunal" dream and gives an excellent account of Charles Henry Davis's interesting Bache and Henry in a plan for the three of them to form a permanent commission to report on matters of arts and sciences out of which grew the plan for the National Academy of Sciences. The planning group met at Bache's home, and he became the first president of the National Academy of Sciences on April 22, 1863, serving until his death, 1867, when he was succeeded by Joseph Henry, who had been previously vice-president. Odgers, *Bache*, pp. 169-170.

114. For the report of the investigating committee, see *Report of the National Academy of Sciences for the year 1863*, published Washington, D.C. 1864, pp. 98-112. For the vote against MFM's works, see *Annual of the National Academy of Sciences for 1863-1864*, published Cambridge, Mass., 1865, p. 60.

115. The bitterness felt by the Bache-Henry coterie toward MFM for having been appointed superintendent of the U.S. Naval Observatory (instead of their candidate, James Melville Gilliss) is revealed in the Gilliss Memoir. There is this description, "Lieut. Matthew F. Maury, a young officer without scientific education or experience, and with small scientific pretensions." Benjamin Apthorp Gould, the author of the memoir, spoke of men

continuing work at the Naval Observatory under Maury "that they might save the national institution, which it was partially in their power to protect, from becoming a source of national disgrace." Gould, former director of the Dudley Observatory, stated that when Maury left the Naval Observatory "charlatanism" was "no longer predominant" and Gilliss could take command with pride. See "Memoir of James Melville Gilliss, 1811-1865" by Benjamin Apthorp Gould, read before the National Academy, Jan. 26, 1866. See also "Memoir of Joseph Stillman Hubbard, 1823-1863," by Benjamin Apthorp Gould, read before the National Academy, Aug. 5, 1864, *Annual of the National Academy of Sciences for 1866*, pp. 77, 107; *Annual . . . for 1863-1864*, pp. 80-82.

116. MFM, *Address at the Fair of the Agricultural and Mechanical Society of Memphis, Oct. 17, 1871.*
117. MFM to his daughter Tots (Mary) Maury, May 5, 1872, MP, Vol. XL, LC.
118. MFM, Address to the National Agricultural Association, St. Louis, Mo., May 29, 1872, 30-page MS, MP, Vol. LI, LC.
119. Ibid.
120. The information about the resolution and the printing of copies is added to the original MS of the address (cited in Note 118) that MFM had sent Gen. W. H. Jackson, of Nashville, when it was thought that Jackson would read the speech. This original copy of the speech with added note is in Harding Collection, VUL.
121. MFM to Marin H. Jansen, July 14, 1872, MP, Vol. XL, LC.
122. By mid-December, 1871, MFM could report that his geographies were used in 5,000 Southern schools, but some schools were so small that the yearly average of sales was 40 geographies to a school; MFM to the Rev. Francis W. Tremlett, Dec. 10, 1871; for the geographies having cleared $30,000 in past year, see MFM to Tots (Mary) Maury, March 10, 1872, both in MP, Vols. XXXVIII, XXXIX, LC.
123. Indenture between MFM and Charles B. Richardson, Jan. 1, 1872, MP, Vol. XXXVIII, Folios 7594-7595, LC.
124. MFM, "What We Owe to Science," 12-page lecture delivered to the cadets, reprinted in V.M.I. student publication, *The Cadet*, Vol. II (January, 1872). See also MFM, "Astronomy for the Young Folk, the Moon with the Naked Eye," a 6-page, popular style article that MFM may have given as a talk to beginning physics students at V.M.I., *The Cadet*, Vol. I (July, 1871).
125. MFM first laid his proposal for establishment of a polytechnic college before the Virginia Educational Association in July, 1870. "It should be a general Polytechnic, adapted to the wants of the whole South, free to all her sons, and endowed by the joint contributions of her States and people." He urged that a school of scientific agriculture be included; "Introductory Address by Commodore M. F. Maury" before the Virginia Education Association, *Educational Journal of Virginia*, Vol. I, No. 10 (August, 1870), pp. 304-313; the quotation is from p. 306.

In 1871 MFM drafted for V.M.I. a 43-page MS memorial that embodied his proposal; see Memorial of the Academic Board of the Virginia Military Institute to the Legislature of Virginia in connection with assigning a portion of the Federal land grant scrip to V.M.I., signed by F. H. Smith for and in behalf of the Board, done at V.M.I., Dec. 18, 1871, MP, Vol. L, Folios 10084-10126, LC.

126. "Virginia, taking advantage of the Morrill Land Grant Act, opened in 1872 an agricultural and mechanical college at Blacksburg, the present Virginia Polytechnic Institute. When the Board of Visitors of the newly-established college were looking over the State for presidential timber for the school, a member of the board approached Maury and suggested to the great scientist that he (the board member) should present Maury's name to the board as a candidate for president. Maury, however, refused to have his name considered in this connection." Ralph Minthorne Brown, librarian, Virginia Polytechnic Institute, biographical sketch of MFM in *Bibliography of Commander Matthew Fontaine Maury, Bulletin of the Virginia Polytechnic Institute,* Vol. XXXVII, No. 12 (October, 1944), p. 13.

127. Letter of MFM to Tots (Mary) Maury cited in Note 117.

128. MFM to Marin H. Jansen, July 14, 1872, MP, Vol. XL, LC.

129. Ibid.; letters to MFM from William M. Burwell, July 17, 1872; from Dr. Thomas Nicholson, July 27, 1872, both in MP, Vol. XL, LC.

130. William M. F. Rowland, associate editor of the Boston *Daily Globe,* to MFM, June 5, 1872; the quotation is from MFM to the Rev. Francis W. Tremlett, Apr. 17, 1872, both in MP, Vol. XL, LC.

131. MFM to the Rev. Francis W. Tremlett, July 29, 1872, MP, Vol. XL, LC.

132. Rutson Maury to Mrs. Ann Herndon Maury, Sept. 17, 1872, MP, Vol. XLI, LC.

133. Mrs. Ann Herndon Maury to her husband, MFM, Oct. 3, 1872; Elie (Eliza) Maury to her mother, written from St. Louis, Oct. 9, 1872, both in MP, Vol. XLI, LC; Rutson Maury to Marin H. Jansen, March 25, 1873, MP, Vol. XLIV, LC. MFM's address was reported in the St. Louis *Democrat,* Oct. 10, 1872; for full text, see MS in MP, Vol. LI, Folios 10143-10172, LC.

134. MFM's address was read in his absence at the First Annual Fair of the Seaboard Agricultural Society at Norfolk, Va., Oct. 23, 1872. For account of MFM's last journey, see letter of Rutson Maury to Marin H. Jansen, March 25, 1873, cited in Note 133.

135. Corbin, *Maury,* p. 284.

136. Virginia Military Institute—*In Memoriam—Matthew Fontaine Maury, LL.D.,* pp. 23-24; Corbin, *Maury,* p. 286.

137. "Dick is a workin' I tell you. Dick, Dick, bright Dick, there's nobody praised by the Lexington folk like Dick. Sue too is a great favorite and making herself agreeable to everybody. She manages most admirably. Tuesday is their regular day with us besides odd times. 'T is pleasant to have one's young stepping in and out." MFM to B. Franklin Minor, Jan. 28, 1870, MC, UVAL. For rewriting of MFM's will, see recollections of her father's last days written by Eliza H. Maury immediately after MFM's death; Mary H. Maury to Marin H. Jansen, Apr. 9, 1873; for Dick's being at MFM's sickbed, see recollections of the last words of Commodore M. F. Maury to S. Wellford Corbin, Jan. 24 to Feb. 1, 1873, all in MP, Vol. XLII, Folios 8324, 8309, 8348, LC.

138. Recollections of . . . Eliza H. Maury, cited in Note 137, back of Folio 8325.

139. Recollections of one of his daughters quoted in Corbin, *Maury,* p. 284.

140. On January 30, after saying portion of his daily prayer "Pardon my sins and teach me the errors of my way," MFM added, as if speaking to himself, "And I thank my gracious maker He has done so." Letter of Mary H. Maury to Marin H. Jansen cited in Note 137; Recollections of . . . S. Wellford Corbin, cited in Note 137, Folio 8348.

141. S. Wellford Corbin to Marin H. Jansen, March 22, 1873, MP, Vol. XLIV, LC.

142. Letter of Mary H. Maury to Marin H. Jansen, Apr. 9, 1873, cited in Note 137, Folio 8308.

143. Ibid., Folios 8309-8310. Another prayer that had been used daily in MFM's last years was given me by his granddaughter, Mrs. N. Montgomery Osborne.

"O God, Our Heavenly Father, whose gift is strength of days, help us to make the noblest use of minds and bodies in our advancing years. Teach us to bear our infirmities with cheerful patience. Keep us from narrow pride in outgrown ways; from blind eyes that see not the good of changes. Give patient judgment of the methods and experience of others. Let Thy peace rule our spirits through all the trials of our waning powers. Take from us all fear of death and all despair or undue love of life; that with glad hearts at rest in Thee we may await Thy will concerning us, through Jesus Christ our Lord, Amen."

144. Letter of Mary H. Maury to Marin H. Jansen cited in Note 137, Folio 8310.

145. Recollections of one of MFM's daughters quoted in Corbin, *Maury*, p. 285.

146. Ibid.; recollections of Lucy M. Maury, MP, Vol. XLII, Folio 8258, LC. See also recollections by another of MFM's children, MP, Vol. XLIII, Folios 8426-8438.

147. Account of MFM's death as related by Diana and S. Wellford Corbin, MP, Vol. XLII, Folios 8348-8355, Vol. XLII, Folio 8402; Corbin, *Maury*, p. 285.

148. Gen. Francis H. Smith being in Petersburg, Va., the acting superintendent directed F. H. Smith, Jr., to send the telegrams. Note of F. H. Smith, Jr., adjutant, V.M.I., to Col. Richard L. Maury, Feb. 1, 1873, MP, Vol. XLII, LC; General Order No. 5, issued by Col. J. T. L. Preston, acting superintendent, F. H. Smith, Jr., adjutant, V.M.I., Feb. 1, 1873, MP, Vol. XLII, Folios 8234-8235, LC; Corbin, *Maury*, p. 288.

149. New York *Herald*, Feb. 3, 1873, p. 6.

150. Richmond *Daily Dispatch*, Feb. 6, 1873, p. 1.

151. Letter of S. Wellford Corbin to Marin H. Jansen cited in Note 141.

152. Eliza H. Maury to Marin H. Jansen, Oct. 9, 1873, MP, Vol. XLIV, LC.

153. M. F. Maury, Jr., to Marin H. Jansen, Sept. 21, 1873; Eliza H. Maury to Marin H. Jansen, Oct. 9, 1873, both in MP, Vol. XLIV, LC.

154. General Orders No. 41, Sept. 26, 1873, Virginia Military Institute, V.M.I. Archives; letter of Eliza H. Maury to Marin H. Jansen cited in Note 152, Folio 8713.

155. Ibid., back of Folio 8714; Corbin, *Maury*, p. 319.

156. Gen. Francis H. Smith to Gen. W. H. Richardson, Adjutant General of Virginia, Sept. 29, 1873, V.M.I. Archives.

157. Richmond *Daily Whig*, Sept. 29, 1873, p. 1.

Bibliography

SECTION I. MANUSCRIPT SOURCES

MAJOR COLLECTIONS OF MAURY MATERIAL

Library of Congress
  Manuscript Division
    Papers of Alexander Dallas Bache
      Especially Letter Books Vols. I and X
    Papers of Jefferson Davis
      Letter Books, 1855-1860; Miscellaneous File for 1860
    Papers of Matthew Fontaine Maury
      Personal Papers of Maury
        Account Books
        Addresses
        Certificates of membership in learned societies and other honors
        Commission as commander, U.S.N., commander, Virginia Navy
        Diaries
        Letters Received
        Letters Sent
        Miscellany Book, 1870
        Small book detailing scientific experiments on electric torpedoes, Dec. 17, 1864, to May 6, 1865
      Letters of Maury's wife, Ann Herndon Maury
      Short diary of Maury's son, John Herndon Maury
      Two-volume manuscript diary of Maury's daughter, Betty Maury (Mrs. William A. Maury)
      Miscellaneous collection of newspaper and magazine clippings, published pamphlets, and other Maury items
      Notes and papers about Maury by C. Alphonso Smith, then head of English Department, U.S. Naval Academy, Annapolis
      Unpublished (typescript) biography of Maury by Catherine Cate Coblentz
  Map Division
    Early maps, charts, and sailing directions

National Archives
  Navy Records, Navy and Military Service Branch
    Record Group 45:
      Acceptance, 1809-1861
      Applications for Appointments, 1808-1861
      Appointments, Orders, and Resignations, 1809-1861
      Captains' Letters, 1822-1861

Thomas A. Dornin, Lieut. U.S.N.—Journal kept on board U.S.S. *Brandy-wine,* 1826-1830

William Bolton Finch, Lieut. Commanding, U.S.S. *Vincennes,* reports and letters (facsimile) to U.S. Navy Department

Isaac Hull, 1773-1843, defendant. Minutes of proceedings of the court of inquiry into official conduct of Capt. Isaac Hull at U.S. Navy Yard, Charlestown, in State of Massachusetts, Aug. 12, 1822; also same for Capt. James Biddle, Oct. 7, 1822

Miscellaneous Records—Correspondence relating chiefly to Lieut. M. F. Maury, U.S.N., and the Plucking Board, 1855, 1 vol., No. 54. Press copies unarranged

Record of Officers, 1825-1861, Bureau of Navigation

Record Group 37:

Records of the Bureau of Ordnance and Hydrography, 1842-1861
Letters Sent; Letters Received
Hydrographic Surveys, 1854-1861

Record Group 125:

Records of the Office of the Judge Advocate General (Navy)
"The case of Lieut. M. F. Maury, Naval Court of Inquiry, No. 1,"
Courts of Inquiry, Act of Jan. 16, 1857, Vol. XXI, 68 pages

Record Group 78:

Records of the U.S. Naval Observatory
Abstract Logs Received, 1848-1861, in bound volumes and index thereto (meteorological and oceanic data collected by ships, evaluated by M. F. Maury at Observatory)
Meteorological Observations made at Observatory
Naval Observatory Letters Received, 1842-1861
Naval Observatory Letters Sent, 1842-1861
Various Records of Magnetic Observations

Record Group 45:

Secretary of the Navy: Executive Letter Books
Correspondence with Executive Group
Correspondence with Officers
Letters to Heads of Bureaus, Nos. 1-3
Letters to Navy Agents, No. 8
Letters to Officers, Ships of War, 1809-1839
Records of the Office of the Secretary of Navy, Personnel Records, 1809-1861

Record Group 24:

Ships' Records—Journals, Logbooks, Muster Rolls, Pay Rolls of
U.S.S. *Brandywine,* 1825-1827
U.S.S. *Dolphin,* 1833
U.S.S. *Falmouth,* 1831-1833
U.S.S. *Macedonian,* 1825-1826
U.S.S. *Potomac,* 1833-1834
U.S.S. *Vincennes,* 1827-1830

Weather Records of Other Government Departments or Establishments

Record Group 27:

Department of Commerce, Weather Bureau Records
Records of the Meteorological Division of the Smithsonian Institution
Records of the Surgeon-General's Office, 1819-1911

Bibliography

University of Virginia, Alderman Library
  Maury Collection: Letters from Matthew Fontaine Maury to Anne Fontaine
    Maury (Mrs. William Lewis Maury); to Ann, Matthew, and Rutson Maury;
    to Sarah Mytton Maury (Mrs. William Maury), on loan by Mrs. Anne Fon-
    taine Maury Herschfeld
  The Rev. James Maury—the Rev. John Camm Letterbook
  Vestry Minute Books of St. George's Parish (Spotsylvania County), 1726-1817

Virginia State Library and Archives
  County Records: Court orders, Deeds, Inventories, Marriages of Caroline,
    Louisa, and Spotsylvania counties, and Fredericksburg, Virginia, on micro-
    film or in bound books
  Map of Spotsylvania County c. 1820
  Map of Virginia . . . 1807, prepared by James Madison, D.D., President of
    William and Mary College
  Proceedings of the Advisory Council of Virginia, 1861, in 2 vols., one con-
    taining incomplete minutes, not signed by members, pay record of mem-
    bers at back. Other volume contains minutes, signed by each member in
    attendance, for each meeting of the council from April 21 through June
    19, 1861
  Records of Virginia Militia of Caroline and Spotsylvania counties
  Tentative bibliographies of Matthew Fontaine Maury by Adelaide R. Hasse,
    1917, and by Mary Beverley Ruffin, 1928
  Vestry Minute Books of Fredericksville Parish, Louisa County (later Albe-
    marle), Virginia, 2 vols., photostat

OTHER COLLECTIONS

Public Record Office, London
  Foreign Office
    5/762, folio 250 et seq., folios 395-444
    5/763, folio 230 et seq.
    5/1267 (no folios) Correspondence about Matthew and Rutson Maury be-
      ginning with entry for Nov. 18, 1861

City of Fredericksburg, Va.
  Court File No. 93, Sarah Ellis *v.* William Ellis, 1841
  Record Books of Deeds, Marriage Records, Wills

Confederate Museum, Richmond, Va.
  Matthew Fontaine Maury letters

George Washington University
  Vote to grant Maury honorary degree. Minutes of the meeting of the Board
    of Trustees, Columbian College (now George Washington University),
    Washington, D.C., July 13, 1853, in archives of the university

Harvard University
  Letter of Lieut. Charles Henry Davis, U.S.N., on duty with Office of the
    Coast Survey, to the Hon. Horace Mann, member of Congress, May 4,
    1848, in manuscript division of library

Mariners Museum Library, Newport News, Va.
  Old prints and engravings of early Navy ships and harbor scenes

Missouri Historical Society, St. Louis
   (Noah Miller) Ludlow—Smith Collection of letters and manuscripts

New York Public Library
   Maury Collection, especially letters of Maury to F. R. Hassler, Coast Survey,
      Washington, Feb. 11 and Aug. 12, 1839
   Early prints of ships and harbor scenes in Print Room and Picture Collec-
      tion

Peabody Institute, Baltimore
   Letter collection of John Pendleton Kennedy, Secretary of Navy, 1852-1853

Smithsonian Institution Archives
   Letters Sent and Letters Received: Joseph Henry, Secretary of the Smith-
      sonian Institution
   Journals of Joseph Henry
   Mary Henry's Abstracts (from her father's letters and journals)

Tennessee State Library and Archives
   Tennessee Historical Society Collection
      Letters or statements from Mrs. Mary Maury Werth, daughter of Matthew
         Fontaine Maury, and of her daughter, Mrs. Elie Werth Fitzgerald, to
         Charles Lee Lewis, 1921-1922
      Letters of R. H. Crockett of Franklin, Tenn., to Charles Lee Lewis, 1921-
         1922
      Letter of Thomas J. Wilson, Jr., Registrar, University of North Carolina,
         to Charles Lee Lewis, February, 1922, stating facts of awarding of two
         honorary degrees to Maury by the University of North Carolina
   Faw, Judge Walter W. "Boyhood Home of Matthew Fontaine Maury" and
      "Historical Sketch of Harpeth Academy," both typescripts
   Early maps and records of Tennessee counties

University of the South, Sewanee
   Diary of the Rt. Rev. Charles Todd Quintard, Bishop of Tennessee, Vice-
      Chancellor of the University of the South, entries for August, 1867-May,
      1868
   Letters of the Rt. Rev. Charles T. Quintard to Maj. George Rainsford Fair-
      banks, Dec. 26, 1867, Feb. 26 and March 12, 1868; to the Rt. Rev. J. P. B.
      Wilmer, Jan. 6, 1868
   Letters of Matthew Fontaine Maury to the Rt. Rev. Charles Todd Quintard,
      Jan. 4, 1868; to the Rt. Rev. W. M. Greene (Green), Bishop of Mississippi,
      Chancellor of the University of the South, April 21, 1868
   Minutes of the Executive Committee of the University of the South for meet-
      ings held April 4 and May 28, 1868
   Minutes of the Board of Trustees of the University of the South for meeting
      held Aug. 13, 1868

Vanderbilt University
   Collection of letters from Matthew Fontaine Maury to Gen. William Giles
      Harding of Nashville, Tenn., and other Maury papers, on loan by Mrs.
      Mary Harding Ragland

Virginia Historical Society
  Matthew Fontaine Maury papers
  Letter of Col. Richard L. Maury to Beverley B. Munford, June 1, 1907

Virginia Military Institute
  Letters, papers, and lectures of Matthew Fontaine Maury, Professor of Physics, V.M.I.
  Letters and papers of Gen. Francis H. Smith, Superintendent, V.M.I.
  V.M.I. General Orders No. 41, Sept. 26, 1873

Williamson County, Tennessee, Court Records
  Books of Deeds, Wills, and Inventories, courthouse, Franklin, Tenn.

Yale University
  Collection of letters of Matthew Fontaine Maury, especially letter to Professor Denison Olmsted, Oct. 24, 1837

A letter owned by an individual is cited in Notes.

SECTION II. PRINTED SOURCES: OFFICIAL DOCUMENTS

UNITED STATES CONGRESS

Report on the Rules for the Naval Service, 29 December, 1819, Secretary Smith Thompson, Senate Doc. No. 15, Ser. 26, Vol. I, 16th Cong., 1st Sess.

Rules and Regulations of the Naval Service, Secretary Smith Thompson, 11 January 1821, Senate Doc. No. 65, Ser. 43, Vol. II, 16th Cong., 2d Sess.

Presidential Message and Reports of Departments, House Doc. No. 2, p. 39, Ser. 195, 21st Cong., 1st Sess.

Rules and Regulations, Prepared by the Board of Revision for the Government of the Navy, 23 December, 1833. House Exec. Doc. Nos. 20 and 375, Ser. 254, 258, 23d Cong., 1st Sess.

Report on Exploring Expedition (1838) House Exec. Doc. No. 147, Ser. 327, 25th Cong., 2d Sess.

Secretary of Navy Abel P. Upshur's Report on Advisability of Steam for Navy Ships, Senate Doc. No. 1, p. 386, Ser. 395, 27th Cong., 2d Sess.

Report recommending construction of naval observatory, House Rep. No. 449, Ser. 408, 27th Cong., 2d Sess.

United States Committee on Claims (Cowens), n.t.p., 1842, House Rep. No. 496, Ser. 408, 27th Cong., 2d Sess.

General Regulations for Navy and Marine Corps. House Doc. No. 148. *Prepared in obedience to joint resolution of Congress of 24 May, 1842.* Ser. 421, 27th Cong., 2d Sess.

Extract from treatise by Lieut. Maury on maritime interests of South and West, House Doc. No. 33, Ser. 441, Vol. III, pp. 20-48, 28th Cong., 1st Sess.

Navy Yard and Depot at City of Memphis. *Report from House Committee on Naval Affairs, Jan. 31, 1844,* House Rep. No. 120, Ser. 488, 28th Cong., 1st Sess.

Report of Joseph Henry, Secretary of the Smithsonian Institution, to the Board of Regents, Dec. 8, 1847, Senate Misc. Doc. No. 23, Ser. 511, 30th Cong., 1st Sess.

Letter from Lieut. Maury to Secretary of Navy requesting regular employment of vessels to carry out his investigations of winds and currents. Reports of Secretaries of Navy and Interior. Senate Exec. Doc. No. 1, pp. 60-61, Part 2, Ser. 612, 32d Cong., 1st Sess.

Letter of Lieut. M. F. Maury to Secretary of War Charles M. Conrad sent at request of Secretary of Navy, on subject of land defenses and fortifications, 1851. House Exec. Doc. No. 5, pp. 160-193, Ser. 637, 32d Cong., 1st Sess.

Memorial of Lieut. Maury for a mail steamship line from Norfolk to Charleston to Para, Brazil, to connect with a line running thence to Rio de Janeiro, May 3, 1852. Senate Misc. Doc. No. 83, Ser. 629, Vol. 1, 32d Cong., 1st Sess.

Report on Naval Observatory, investigations of winds and currents of sea and other phenomena affecting commerce and navigation, Oct. 12, 1852. Senate Exec. Doc. No. 1, Ser. 659, Vol. II, pp. 341-342, 32d Cong., 2d Sess.

HERNDON, WILLIAM LEWIS. *Exploration of the Valley of the Amazon*, Vol. 1, Senate Exec. Doc. No. 36, Ser. 663, 664, 32d Cong., 2d Sess.

Memorial of Lieut. Maury in favor of free navigation of the Amazon, February, 1854. House Misc. Doc. No. 22, Ser. 741, Vol. 1, 33d Cong., 1st Sess.

GIBBON, LARDNER. *Exploration of the Valley of the Amazon, Vol. II,* House Exec. Doc. No. 53, Ser. 722, 33d Cong., 1st Sess.

GILLISS, JAMES MELVILLE. *U.S. Naval Astronomical Expedition,* House Ex. Doc. 121, Ser. 728, 33d Cong., 1st Sess.

M. F. Maury statement on telegraphic plateau. Senate Doc. No. 59, p. 2, Ser. 705, 33d Cong., 1st Sess.

Report of Senate Naval Affairs Committee to Accompany S657 recommending an appropriation of $25,000 for Lieut. M. F. Maury in appreciation for his oceanic investigations, presented in Senate, Jan. 29, 1855, by Senator Stephen R. Mallory, Senate Rep. No. 443, Ser. 775, Vol. 1, 33rd Cong., 2d Sess.

Report by Representative Ingersoll, in favor of Lieut. M. F. Maury's Memorial for the free navigation of the Amazon, Feb. 23, 1855. House Rep. No. 95, Ser. 808, Vol. 1, 33d Cong., 2d Sess.

1856 Debate on Naval Retiring Board, *Congressional Globe,* pp. 203, 343, 344, 346, 367, 388, 400-405, 407, 409, 487, 34th Cong., 1st Sess.

1856 Debate on Naval Retiring Board, *Congressional Globe Appendix,* pp. 170-173, 244, 245, 248, 250, 266-270, 310-325, 333-336, 487, 510, 572-574, 577, 584-587, 589, 34th Cong., 1st Sess.

1856 Debate on Naval Retiring Board and vote on S113, *Congressional Globe, Part II,* pp. 1594, 1638, 1795-1796, 2159-2160, 34th Cong., 1st Sess.

Final debate and vote on S113 in House, *Congressional Globe,* pp. 301-302, 34th Cong., 3d Sess.

Journal of the Executive Proceedings of the Senate of the United States of America from December 3, 1855, to June 16, 1858, Vol. X, pp. 268, 277, 285, 291

Report of Senate Committee on Agriculture in support of S481 to extend to the land the system of observations carried on at the National Observatory, presented by Senator James Harlan, Dec. 18, 1856, Senate Rep. No. 292, Ser. 891, Vol. I, 34th Cong., 3d Sess.

Congressional Globe, Part 1, p. 487 (Jan. 21, 1861), 36th Cong., 2d Sess.

Reconstruction House Report No. 30, Part II, Ser. 1273, 39th Cong., 1st Sess., Washington, 1866

RICHARDSON, JAMES D. (compiler). *A Compilation of the Messages and Papers of the Presidents, 1789-1897* (by authority of Congress). House Misc. Doc. No. 210, Ser. 3265, 53d Cong., 2d Sess., Washington, 1897

Biographical Directory of the American Congress 1774-1949. House Doc. No. 607, Ser. 11414, 81st Cong., 2d Sess. Washington, 1950

Authorization of vessels to further oceanic investigations of Lieut. M. F. Maury. Sec. II of an act to provide funds for the Navy. U.S. Statutes at Large, Vol. IX, pp. 374-379

"An Act to Promote the Efficiency of the Navy" (32d-33d Cong., 1851-1855), U.S. Statutes at Large, Vol. X, pp. 616-617

"An Act to Establish and Equalize the Grade of Line Officers of the United States Navy," U.S. Statutes at Large, Vol. XII, pp. 329-330

Establishment of Examining Boards of Naval Officers. *Annual Report of Secretary of Navy, 1862,* pp. 40-41, and also U.S. Statutes at Large, Vol. XIII, pp. 53-54, 420

HOMANS, BENJAMIN (compiler), *Laws of the United States in Relation to the Navy and the Marine Corps to the close of the second Session of the 26th Congress.* Pub. by authority of the Navy Department. Washington, 1841

UNITED STATES NAVY

Financial Regulations for Naval Officers, 1838. Washington, 1838

LYNCH, WILLIAM FRANCIS, U.S.N., Lieut. Commanding, *Official Report of the U.S. Expedition to Explore the Dead Sea and the River Jordan.* Publ. by U.S. Naval Observatory, Washington, 1852

Navy Department, Office of Research and Inventions. *Report on the Theory and Application of Pressure Pattern Flight.* Washington, 1945

Navy Rules, Regulations and Instructions for the Naval Service of the United States, 1818

Regulations, Circulars, Orders and Decisions for Guide of Officers of Navy, 1851. Washington, 1851

Regulations for the Government of the Navy of the United States. Naval Courts and Boards (1917)

Report on the Work of the Naval Observatory from July 1, 1846, to Jan. 1, 1850. Washington, 1851

Retirement Rules of December 21, 1861, of U.S. Navy

The Rules of the Navy Department Regulating the Civil Administration of the Navy. Washington, 1832

U.S. Hydrographic Office, under authority of the Secretary of Navy. *The Origin and Mission of the Hydrographic Office,* reprint of Hydrographic Information from the Pilot Charts and *Hydrographic Bulletin,* No. 9, Washington, Jan. 1, 1910

U.S. Navy Department, Regulations for Uniform and Dress, 1841.

U.S. Navy Register for years 1824-1861

U.S. Secretary of Navy's Annual Report for years 1824-1865

MISCELLANEOUS

Annual Reports of the Board of Regents of the Smithsonian Institution to Congress (Smithsonian Reports) for the years 1846-1879

Check List of U.S. Public Documents, 1789-1909. Washington, 1911

Guide to the Material in the National Archives, U.S. National Archives Publication No. *14.* Washington, 1940

HANSARD, THOMAS CURSON (ed.). *Great Britain House of Lords Parliamentary Debates* (authorized edition). Third Series. Vol. CXXVI, April 19, 1853-May 9, 1853, pp. 521-544. London, 1853

McLEAN, JOHN (ed.). *U.S. Circuit Court Reports 1829-1855,* Vol. II. Cincinnati, Ohio, 1840-1856

Range Map of Middle Tennessee, issued by "The Tennessee Government" c. 1810

"Records of the Weather Bureau." *Guide to the Records in the National Archives.* Washington, 1948

Report of the Joint Committee on Reconstruction at the First Session, Thirty-Ninth Congress. Washington, 1866

RHEES, WILLIAM J. (compiler and ed.). *The Smithsonian Institution, Journal of the Board of Regents, Reports of Committees, Statistics.* . . . Washington, 1879

—— (comp. and ed.). *Smithsonian Institution, Documents Relative to its Origin and History, 1835-1899.* 12 vols. See Vol. I. Washington, 1901

U.S. Census, for Spotsylvania County, Virginia, 1810; for Williamson County, Tennessee, 1820, for Fredericksburg, Va., 1840

U.S. Coast Survey Annual Reports for years 1846-1861

VIRGINIA

Acts of the Virginia General Assembly of 1857-58, p. 287

Calendar of Virginia State Papers and Other Manuscripts. Preserved in the Capitol at Richmond. Ed. H. W. Flournoy. Vol. XI. Richmond, 1893

Code of Virginia, 1873, p. 26

The Constitution of Virginia, framed by the convention that met in Richmond on Tuesday, Dec. 3, 1867. Passed April 17, 1868, Richmond. Printed at the office of the *New Nation,* 1868

CROZIER, WILLIAM ARMSTRONG (ed.). *Spotsylvania County Records, 1721-1800, Being Transcriptions from the Original Files at the County Court House of Wills, Deeds, Administrator and Guardians' bonds, Marriage licenses, and lists of revolutionary pensioners.* New York, 1905

Executive Journals of the Council of Colonial Virginia. Ed. H. R. McIlwaine and W. L. Hall. 5 vols. Richmond, 1925-1945

Journal of the Acts and Proceedings of a General Convention of the State of Virginia, 1861, and Documents I, XVII. Richmond, 1861

Journal of the Committee of the Whole, Virginia Convention, pp. 31-33

Journal of the Congress of the Confederate States of America, 1861-1865 (especially Vols. I, II). Washington, 1904-05

Journal of the House of Delegates of the State of Virginia for the Extra Session, 1861, pp. 10, 25, 65-67

HENING, WILLIAM WALLER (ed.). *The Statutes at Large: Being a Collection of all the Laws of Virginia, from the First Session of the Legislature in the year 1619.* Publ. pursuant to an Act of the General Assembly Passed on the

Fifth day of February, 1808. Vols. I, II, New York, 1823; Vol. III, Philadelphia, 1823; Vols. IV-XIII, Richmond, 1819-1827; 2d ed. of Vols. I-IV, Richmond, 1835-1836

Resolution of the General Assembly, April 8, 1858, urging promotion of Lieut. M. F. Maury, *Virginia Acts of 1857-58,* p. 287

WAR 1861-1865

Atlas to Accompany the Official Records of the Union and Confederate Armies, Washington, 1891-1895; new ed. issued as *The Official Atlas of the Civil War,* with introduction by Henry Steele Commager. New York and London, 1958

Confederate Navy Regulations, Richmond, 1862; repr. New Hope, Penn., 1952

Journal of the Convention of the People of South Carolina, Held in 1860-61. Charleston, 1861, pp. 46-47, 53

Map of the Country between Richmond and Petersburg. Drawn from Surveys made by Order of Maj. Gen. J. F. Gilmer, Chief Engineer, C.S.A., n.d. (but between 1861 and 1865)

Map of *Environs of Richmond* for use by Adjutant General's Office on May 6-7, 1944, from *Campaigns of Stuart's Cavalry,* by Maj. H. B. McClellan, A.A.G. and Chief of Staff

Map of Vicinity of Richmond and Part of the Peninsula. From Surveys Made under the Direction of A. H. Campbell, Capt. P.E., C.S.A., in charge of Topographical Dept. D.N.V., 1864

Official Records of the Union and Confederate Navies in the War of the Rebellion. 30 vols. Washington, 1894-1922

The War of the Rebellion: A Compilation of the Official Records of the Union and Confederate Armies. 70 vols. in 128 parts. Washington, 1880-1901. And atlas

SECTION III. NEWSPAPERS

Alexandria (Va.) *Gazette*
Baltimore *American*
Boston *Atlas*
Boston *Daily Evening Traveller*
Boston *Transcript*
Buffalo *Commercial Advertiser*
Charleston (S.C.) *Daily Courier*
Charleston (S.C.) *Mercury*
Chicago *Press and Tribune*
Cleveland *Plain Dealer*
Detroit *Daily Advertiser*
Edinburgh (Scotland) *Courant*
Franklin (Tenn.) *Review-Appeal*
Fredericksburg (Va.) *Free Lance-Star*
Fredericksburg (Va.) *Herald*
Fredricksburg (Va.) *Political Arena*

Galveston *Texas Daily News*
Knoxville (Tenn.) *Gazette*
(London) *Times*
Lynchburg (Va.) *News*
Lynchburg (Va.) *Virginian*
(Mexico City) *Diario del Imperio*
Montgomery (Ala.) *Advance*
Nashville (Tenn.) *Clarion and Tennessee Gazette*
Nashville (Tenn.) *Examiner*
Nashville (Tenn.) *Impartial Review*
Nashville (Tenn.) *Whig*
National Intelligencer (Washington, D.C.)
New Orleans *Picayune*
New York *Courier*
New York *Herald*
New York *Journal of Commerce*
New York *Times*
(Paris) *Messager de Paris*
Philadelphia *Public Ledger*
Richmond (Va.) *Daily Times*
Richmond (Va.) *Daily Whig*
Richmond (Va.) *Dispatch*
Richmond (Va.) *Enquirer and Examiner*
Richmond (Va.) *News Leader*
Richmond (Va.) *Semi-Weekly Whig*
Richmond (Va.) *Times Dispatch*
Richmond (Va.) *Whig and Public Advertiser*
St. Louis (Mo.) *Democrat*
(Washington, D.C.) *Army-Navy Chronicle and Scientific Repository*
Washington (D.C.) *Star*
Washington (D.C.) *Union*

SECTION IV. BOOKS, PAMPHLETS, AND PERIODICALS

ABBÉ, CLEVELAND. "The Meteorological Work of the U.S. Signal Service," *Weather Bureau Bulletin* XI, Part II, pp. 232-285. Washington, 1894.
ABERNETHY, THOMAS PERKINS. *From Frontier to Plantation in Tennessee.* Chapel Hill, N.C., 1932.
———. "The First Transmontane Advance," in James S. Wilson et al. *Humanistic Studies in Honor of John Calvin Metcalf. University of Virginia Studies,* Vol. I, pp. 120-138. Charlottesville, 1941.
———. "Thomas Walker," *Dictionary of American Biography,* Vol. XIX, pp. 360-361.
Account of Testimonial Dinner to Matthew Fontaine Maury, Willis' Rooms, London, June 5, 1866, *Illustrated London News,* June 23, 1866.
ADAMS, CHARLES FRANCIS. *Charles Francis Adams, by His Son.* Boston, 1900.
ADAMS, JAMES TRUSLOW. *The Living Jefferson.* New York, 1936.

668

Bibliography

ADAMS, JOHN QUINCY. *Memoirs of John Quincy Adams.* 12 vols. See Vols. X, XI, XII, especially XII, pp. 219, 763-801. Philadelphia, 1876-1877.

"Address of Earl of Harrowby, Liverpool, 1854." *Proceedings of the British Association [for the Advancement of Science], Fall Meeting, 1854.*

"Admiral Jansen. Obituary," *Geographical Journal* (London), ed. Clements R. Markham, secretary of the Royal Geographical Society, publisher of the *Journal,* Vol. II, No. 5 (November, 1893), pp. 465-468.

ALLEN, EDGAR JOHNSON (ed.). *Science of the Sea.* 2d ed. Oxford, 1928.

Almanach de Gotha Annuaire Diplomatique et Statistique. Pour l'année 1855 (also for 1859, 1861, 1863). Justus Perthes, Gotha, Germany.

American Annual Cyclopaedia and Register of Important Events of the year 1861 (known as *Appleton's Annual Cyclopaedia*). New York, 1866.

American Association for the Advancement of Science Proceedings and Reports, 1848-1851. Washington, 1852.

American Journal of Science and Arts. Founded in New Haven, Conn., 1818, by Benjamin Silliman, who was succeeded as editor by his son, Benjamin Silliman, Jr. Issues from 1834 through 1873.

The American Navy, Its Organization, Ships, Armament and Recent Experiences, reprinted as pamphlet from "Report of meeting, June 1, 1868," *Journal of the Royal United Service Institution* (London), Vol. XIII.

"The American Savant—Cmdr Maury," *Le Messager de Paris,* March 21, 1872.

AMMEN, DANIEL (Rear-Admiral U.S.N.). *The Atlantic Coast: The Navy in the Civil War.* New York, 1905.

———. *The Old Navy and the New. Personal Reminiscences.* Philadelphia, 1891.

ANDERSON, JOSEPH R. JR. *The Virginia Military Institute and Her Sons—In the Past.* Lexington, Va., 1904.

ANDREWS, MATTHEW PAGE. *Women of the South in War Times.* Baltimore, 1920.

ANGELIS, PEDRO DE. *De la Navegación del Amazonas. Respuesta a una memoria de M. Maury.* Caracas, Reimpreso 1857.

ARTHURS, ROBERT. *History of Fort Monroe.* Fort Monroe, Va., 1930.

Astronomische Nachrichten. Ed. Heinrich C. Schumacher (August, 1847), Art. No. 605, pp. 66-79, in compilation of 1847 issues bound as Vol. XXVI. Altona, Germany, 1848.

The Atlantic Telegraph. A history of preliminary experimental proceedings and a descriptive account of the present state and prospects of the undertaking. Published by order of the directors of the Atlantic Telegraph Company, Ltd. London, July, 1857.

[AYER, N. W., AND SON]. *Matthew Fontaine Maury: A Benefactor of the Race.* 11-page pamphlet. Philadelphia, 1912.

BACHE, ALEXANDER DALLAS. *Address of Professor Alexander Dallas Bache, President of the American Association [for the Advancement of Science] for the year 1851 on Retiring from the Duties of President.* Repr. from the *American Association for the Advancement of Science Proceedings. 6th meeting held at Albany, N.Y., August, 1851,* pp. xli-lx. Washington, 1852.

——— (Lieut. U.S.N.). "Report on the Gulf Stream," *Annual Report.* Coast Survey, 1846.

BALDWIN, HANSON. "The End of the Wine Mess," *U.S. Naval Institute Proceedings,* Vol. LXXXIV, No. 8, Whole No. 666 (August, 1958), pp. 82-91.

BALL, BENJAMIN LINCOLN, M.D. *Rambles in Eastern Asia, including China and Manilla, during several years' residence.* Boston, 1856.

BANCROFT, GEORGE. *History of the United States,* Vol. IV of 6-vol. rev. ed. Boston, 1876.

BARINGER, WILLIAM E. *A House Dividing; Lincoln as President Elect.* Springfield, 1945.

BARNES, J. S. (Lieut. Comdr. U.S.N.). *Submarine Warfare, Offensive and Defensive.* New York, 1869.

BASLER, ROY. *The Collected Works of Abraham Lincoln.* Vol. IV. New Brunswick, N.J., 1953.

BASSETT, JOHN SPENCER. *The Life of Andrew Jackson.* 2 vols. in one, new ed. New York, 1916.

—— (ed.). "A Progress to the Mines in the Year 1732," in *The Writings of Colonel William Byrd of Westover in Virginia, Esquire.* New York, 1901.

BEALE, H. K. *What Historians Have Said about the Causes of the Civil War, Theory and Practice in Historical Study.* New York, 1946.

BEARD, CHARLES A., and MARY R. BEARD. *The Rise of American Civilization.* 2 vols. New York, 1947.

BEEHLER, W. H. (Lieut. U.S.N.). "Origin and Work of the Division of Marine Meteorology, Hydrographic Office," *Report of the International Meteorological Congress held at Chicago, Illinois, Aug. 21-24, 1893* . . . (ed. Oliver L. Fassig); also publ. in *U.S. Naval Institute Proceedings,* Vol. XIX, No. 3, Whole No. 67, pp. 267-281; also repr. Annapolis, 1893.

BEERS, HENRY P. "Survey of Federal Archives, Bibliography of the Navy Department and the Naval Shore Establishments, The National Archives" (17-page typescript bound as book, LC).

BELL, JOHN, U.S. Senator. *Lieut. M. F. Maury. Speech of Hon. John Bell, of Tennessee, on the Naval Retiring Board,* delivered in the Senate of the United States, April 28 and 29, 1856. 13-page pamphlet. Washington, 1856.

BELL, LANDON C. *The Old Free State; A Contribution to the History of Lunenburg County and Southside Virginia.* 2 vols. Richmond, 1927.

BENJAMIN, MARCUS. *The Early Presidents of the American Association.* Address delivered to American Association for the Advancement of Science, 48th Annual Meeting. Pamphlet. Easton, Pa., 1899.

BENTON, THOMAS HART. *Historical and Legal Examination of that part of the Decision of the Supreme Court of the United States in the Dred Scott Case, which declares the Unconstitutionality of the Missouri Compromise Act, and the Self-Extension of the Constitution to Territories, Carrying Slavery Along with it.* New York, 1857.

Berghaus' Atlas von Asia. Section and map describing Campo Santo, Pueblo de Paco, Manila, Philippines, 1812-1823.

BERNHARD, [KARL] Duke of Saxe-Weimar-Eisenach. *Reise durch Nord-Amerika in 1825-26.* Plan von der Stadt, New York. Map.

BILL, ALFRED HOYT. *The Beleaguered City; Richmond, 1861-1865.* New York, 1946.

Biographical Sketch, and Services of Commodore Charles Stewart, of the Navy of the United States. 50 pp. Philadelphia, 1838.

BLACKFORD, LAUNCELOT MINOR. *Mine Eyes Have Seen the Glory.* Cambridge, Mass., 1954.

BLAIR, MARIA. *Matthew Fontaine Maury.* A paper read at the annual meeting of the Matthew Fontaine Maury Association, Richmond, May 13, 1918. Richmond, Va., 1918.

BOHN, C. *Bohn's Hand-Book of Washington,* 1854. Rev. and enl., 1864.

———. *Bohn's Album and Autographs of the University of Virginia.* Washington, 1859.

BOWDITCH, NATHANIEL, LL.D. *The New American Practical Navigator, An Epitome of Navigation and Nautical Astronomy.* Newburyport, Mass., 1802.

BOWERS, CLAUDE G. *The Young Jefferson, 1743-1789.* Boston, 1945.

BOYD, THOMAS. *Light-Horse Harry Lee.* New York, 1931.

BOYD, WILLIAM H. *Boyd's Washington and Georgetown Directory, 1860. Containing a Business Directory of Washington, Georgetown and Alexandria.* Washington, 1860.

BOYNTON, CHARLES B. *The History of the Navy During the Rebellion.* 2 vols. New York, 1867.

Bradford's *Tennessee Almanac.* Nashville, 1811, 1812, 1813.

BRADY, WILLIAM N. (Sailing Master U.S.N.). *The Kedge-Anchor; or Young Sailors' Assistant.* New York, 1848.

BRENT, JOHN CARROLL (ed.). *Letters on the National Institute, Smithsonian Legacy and the Fine Arts.* Washington, 1844.

BRIERLY, J. ERNEST. *The Streets of Old New York.* New York, 1953.

BRIGGS, CHARLES F., and AUGUSTUS MAVERICK. *The Story of the Telegraph and a History of the Great Atlantic Cable.* New York, 1858.

BROCK, ROBERT ALONZO. *Documents, chiefly unpublished, relating to the Huguenot emigration to Virginia . . . with an appendix of genealogies presenting data of the Fontaine, Maury . . . and other families.* Richmond, 1886.

———. *Virginia and Virginians.* Especially "Matthew Fontaine Maury—philosopher of the seas," in vol. I, pp. 268-270. 2 vols. Richmond and Toledo, 1888.

BROWN, ALEXANDER. *The Cabells and Their Kin.* 2d ed. Richmond, 1939.

BROWN, ALEXANDER CROSBY. *Lake Maury in Virginia, and A Biographical Sketch of Matthew Fontaine Maury.* Newport News, Va., 1936.

BROWN, GLENN. *History of the U.S. Capitol.* 2 vols. Washington, 1900-1903.

BROWN, RALPH MINTHORNE. *Bibliography of Commander Matthew Fontaine Maury. Bulletin of the Virginia Polytechnic Institute,* Vol. XXXVII, No. 12 (October, 1944). 46-page pamphlet.

———. "Commander Matthew Fontaine Maury and Agriculture," *Southern Literary Messenger, New Series.* Vol. II, No. 3 (March, 1940), pp. 147-148.

BRUCE, KATHLEEN, Ph.D. *Virginia Iron Manufacture in the Slave Era.* New York and London, 1931.

BRYAN, WILHELMUS BOGART. *A History of the National Capital from its Foundation through the period of the adoption of the organic act.* 2 vols. New York, 1914-1916.

BRYDON, GEORGE MacLAREN. *Virginia's Mother Church and the Political Conditions Under Which It Grew.* Philadelphia, 1952.

BUCHANAN, JAMES. *Mr. Buchanan's Administration on the Eve of the Rebellion.* London, 1865.

BULLOCH, JAMES DUNWODY, Naval Representative of the Confederate States in Europe during the Civil War. *The Secret Service of the Confederate States in Europe, or How the Confederate Cruisers were Equipped.* 2 vols. New York, 1884. New ed. with introduction by Philip Van Doren Stern, New York, 1959.

BULLOCK, HELEN D. "A Dissertation on Education in the Form of a Letter from

James Maury to Robert Jackson. July 17, 1762," *Albemarle County Historical Society Papers,* Vol. II (1941-42), pp. 36-60.

BURGESS, JOHN W., PhD., LL.D. *Reconstruction and the Constitution, 1866-1876.* American History Series. New York, 1907.

BURNHAM, W. D. *Presidential Ballots, 1836-1892.* Baltimore, 1955.

BURR, HENRY LESLIE. *Education in the Early Navy.* Dissertation, Temple University. Philadelphia, 1939.

BYERS, MARY LYTLE. *From Larochelle to Louisville.* Louisville, Ky., 1900.

BYRD, WILLIAM. *William Byrd's Histories of the Dividing Line Betwixt Virginia and North Carolina.* Ed. William K. Boyd. Raleigh, N.C., 1929.

———. *William Byrd's Natural History of Virginia, or the Newly Discovered Eden.* Ed. Richard Croom Beatty and William J. Mulloy. Richmond, 1940.

CALLAHAN, EDWARD WILLIAM (ed.). *List of Officers of the Navy of the United States and of the Marine Corps, 1775-1900* . . . compiled from Official Records of the Navy Department. New York: L. R. Hamersly and Company, 1901.

CAMPBELL, CHARLES. *History of the Colony and Ancient Dominion of Virginia.* Philadelphia, 1860.

CAMPBELL, JOHN ARCHIBALD. *The Administration and the Confederate States —letters and correspondence between the Hon. John A. Campbell and the Hon. Wm. H. Seward, all of which was laid before the Provisional Congress on Saturday by President Davis.* n.p. 1861.

———. "Papers of Hon. John A. Campbell, 1861-1865," *Southern Historical Society Papers,* New Ser., Vol. IV, Whole No. XLII (October, 1917), pp. 31-37.

CAMPBELL, THOMAS E. *Colonial Caroline; A History of Caroline County, Virginia.* Richmond, 1954.

CANFIELD, N. L., National Weather Records Center, Asheville, N.C. *Weather and the Navigation of the Sea.* Repr. from *Weekly Weather and Crop Bulletin, National Summary of Jan. 9, 1956.* Washington, D.C.

"Captain Maury," *Temple Bar* (London), Vol. XXXVIII (April, 1873), pp. 58-65.

CARR, JOHN. *Early Times in Middle Tennessee by a Pioneer of the West.* Nashville, 1857.

CARTER, HODDING. *The Angry Scar, The Story of Reconstruction.* Mainstream of America Series. New York, 1959.

CASKIE, JAQUELIN AMBLER. *Life and Letters of Matthew Fontaine Maury.* Richmond, 1928.

CATTON, BRUCE. *A Stillness at Appomattox.* Garden City, N.Y., 1953.

———. *The Coming Fury. The Centennial History of the Civil War.* Vol. I, New York, 1959.

The Celebration of the Centennial Anniversary of the Founding of the Albany Academy. May, 1913. Albany, 1914.

CHADWICK, FRENCH ENSOR. *Causes of the Civil War, 1859-1861.* New York, 1906.

CHAMBERS, WILLIAM NISBET. *Old Bullion Benton. Senator from the New West. Thomas Hart Benton, 1782-1858.* Boston-Toronto, 1956.

CHAPELLE, HOWARD IRVING. *The History of American Sailing Ships.* New York, 1935.

———. *The History of the American Sailing Navy, The Ships and Their Development.* New York, 1949.

Bibliography

"Charleston Under Arms," *Atlantic Monthly*, Vol. VII, No. 42 (April, 1861), pp. 488-505.

CHASTELLUX, F. J., MARQUIS DE. *Travels in North America*. New York, 1827.

CHESTER, C. M. (Rear-Admiral U.S.N.). "The Work of the Naval Observatory," *U.S. Naval Institute Proceedings*, Vol. XXX, No. 2, Whole No. 110 (June, 1904), pp. 265-268.

CHESTNUT, MARY BOYKIN. *A Diary from Dixie*. New York, 1905.

CHITTY, ARTHUR BENJAMIN. *Reconstruction at Sewanee; the founding of the University of the South and its first Administration, 1857-1872*. Sewanee, Tenn., 1954.

CHRISTIAN, W. ASBURY, D.D. *Richmond, Her Past and Present*. Richmond, 1912.

City Intelligence or Strangers Guide, Confederate States Directory. By V & C. Richmond, 1862.

City of Richmond, Business Directory and City Guide. Mills and Starke. 1866.

CLARKE, ARTHUR C. *Voice Across the Sea*. New York, 1958.

[CLOPTON, MRS. CLAY.] *A Belle of the Fifties. Memoirs of Mrs. Clay of Alabama covering Social and Political Life in Washington and the South, 1853-66*. Ed. Ada Sterling. New York, 1904.

[CLAYTON, JOHN M.] Speech of Hon. John M. Clayton of Delaware, in the U.S. Senate, March 31 and April 1, 1856, in reply to Senator Houston of Texas, and in defense of the Naval Board. 22-page pamphlet. Washington, 1856.

COFFIN, JAMES HENRY. "Winds of the Northern Hemisphere," *Smithsonian Institution Contributions to Knowledge*, Vol. VI, Art. 6. Washington, 1853.

COHN, DAVID L. *The Life and Times of King Cotton*. New York, 1956.

———. "Pathfinder of the Seas," *Reader's Digest*, Vol. XXXVII, No. 219 (July, 1940), pp. 61-64.

COKER, ROBERT ERVIN. *This Great and Wide Sea*. Chapel Hill, N.C. Rev. ed., 1949.

COLBERT, LEE OTIS (Rear-Admiral U.S.N.). "Alexander Dallas Bache as Superintendent of U.S. Coast Survey 1843-67," *American Philosophical Society Proceedings*, Vol. LXXXIV, No. 2, pp. 173-180. Philadelphia, February, 1941.

Columbia Encyclopedia. 1 vol. New York, 1935.

Columbia Lippincott Gazetteer of the World. New York, 1952.

"Commodore Matthew Fontaine Maury (obituary)," *Educational Journal of Virginia*, Vol. IV (March, 1873), pp. 189-190.

"Commodore Matthew Fontaine Maury, LL.D. (obituary)," *Report of the U.S. Commissioner of Education, 1873*, pp. 403-404. Washington, 1874.

"Commodore Maury and Immigration (obituary)," *Southern Planter and Farmer*, March, 1873, p. 113.

COMSTOCK, GEORGE C. "Benjamin Apthorp Gould," *National Academy of Sciences, Memoirs*. Seventh Memoir. Washington, January, 1859.

CONKLIN, EDWIN G. "Alexander Dallas Bache and His Connection with the American Philosophical Society," *American Philosophical Journal Proceedings*, Vol. LXXXIV, No. 2 (Feb. 14-15, 1941), pp. 125-144.

CONSTANTINE, Grand Admiral of Russia. Letter to Matthew F. Maury, July 27, 1861. *Southern Historical Society Papers*, Vol. II (July, 1876), p. 51.

Constitution of the National Institution [Institute] for the Promotion of Science. Washington, 1841.

COOKE, MARY LEWIS, and CHARLES LEE LEWIS. *An American Naval Officer in the Mediterranean, 1802-7,* repr. from *U.S. Naval Institute Proceedings,* Vol. LXVII, No. 11, Whole No. 465 (November, 1941), pp. 1534-1540.

CORBIN, DIANA FONTAINE MAURY. *A Life of Matthew Fontaine Maury, U.S.N. and C.S.N.,* compiled by his daughter. London, 1888.

CORTI, COUNT EGON CAESAR. *Maximilian and Charlotte of Mexico.* Trans. from the German by Catherine Alison Phillips. 2 vols. New York, 1928.

COULSON, THOMAS. *Joseph Henry, His Life and Work.* Princeton, 1950.

COUPER, WILLIAM. *One Hundred Years at V.M.I.,* with a foreword by Gen. George C. Marshall. Richmond, 1939.

COWEN, ROBERT C. *Frontiers of the Sea: The Story of Oceanographic Exploration.* Introduction by Roger R. Revelle. New York, 1960.

CRAVEN, AVERY ODELL. *The Coming of the Civil War.* Rev. 2d ed. New York, 1957.

———. *The Growth of Southern Nationalism, 1848-1861.* Baton Rouge, 1953.

———. *The Repressible Conflict, 1830-1861.* University, La., 1939.

———. "Slavery and the Civil War," *Southern Review.* Vol. IV (1938-39).

———. *Soil Exhaustion as a Factor in the Agricultural History of Virginia and Maryland, 1606-1860.* Vol. XIII, No. 1, *University of Illinois Studies in the Social Sciences.* Urbana, Ill., 1926.

CRAWFORD, SAMUEL WYLIE. *The Genesis of the Civil War; the Story of Sumter, 1860-61.* New York, 1887.

CROSS, ARTHUR L. *The Anglican Episcopate and the American Colonies.* New York, 1902.

DABNEY, REV. R. L. "Memoir of a Narrative Received of Col. John R. Baldwin of Staunton, Touching the Origin of the War," in *Southern Historical Society Papers,* Vol. I, No. 6, pp. 443-455.

DARTER, LEWIS J. JR. "The Federal Archives Relating to Matthew Fontaine Maury," *American Neptune* (quarterly journal of maritime history), Salem, Mass., Vol. I (April, 1941), pp. 149-158.

DAVIDSON, ARTHUR D. *Knights of the Golden Horseshoe.* Roanoke, Va.: Virginia Conservation Commission, 1934.

DAVIDSON, HUNTER. "Electrical Torpedoes as a System of Defence," *Southern Historical Society Papers,* Vol. II (1876), pp. 1-6.

DAVIS, CHARLES HENRY (Capt. U.S.N.). *Life of Charles Henry Davis, Rear-Admiral, 1807-1877; by his son.* Boston and New York, 1899.

DAVIS, CHARLES HENRY (Lieut. U.S.N.). "Report upon the Nautical Almanac." June 21, 1852. Cambridge, Mass., 1852.

DAVIS, JEFFERSON. *The Rise and Fall of the Confederate Government.* . . . 2 vols. New York, 1881.

DAVIS, JOHN. *Travels of Four Years and a Half in the United States of America during 1798, 1799, 1800, 1801 and 1802.* . . . Bristol, England, 1803.

DAVIS, LOTTIE WRIGHT. *Records of Lewis, Meriwether and Kindred Families.* Columbia, Mo., 1951.

[DAVIS, VARINA HOWELL.] *Jefferson Davis, Ex-President of the Confederate States of America. A Memoir by His Wife.* 2 vols. New York, 1890.

DELANO, JUDAH. *The Washington Directory.* Washington, D.C., 1820, 1822.

DE LEON, T. C. *Belles, Beaux and Brains of the 60's.* New York, 1909.

———. *Four Years in Rebel Capitals. An inside view of Life in the Southern Confederacy from Birth to Death.* Mobile, Ala., 1890.

DE MEISSNER, SOPHIE RADFORD. *Old Naval Days—Sketches from the Life of Rear Admiral William Radford, U.S.N.* New York, 1920.

DENZA, P. FRANCISCO. "Il Commodore M. F. Maury e la corrispondenza delle Alpi e degli Appenni ni Italiani," *Osservatorio di Moncalieri*. Torino, Italy, 1875.

DE ROOS, FREDERICK FITZGERALD. *Personal Narrative of Travels in the United States with remarks on Present State of American Navy. . . .* London, 1827.

DE VOTO, BERNARD. *The Year of Decision: 1846.* Boston, 1943.

Dictionary of American Biography. Ed. Allen Johnson, Dumas Malone, et al. 22 vols. and index vol. for I-XX. New York, 1928, 1943.

Dictionary of American History. Ed. James Truslow Adams. 6 vols. New York, 1940-1942.

Dictionary of National Biography. Ed. Leslie Stephen and Sidney Lee. London, 1885-1900, and supplementary vols., 1901 ff.

Die Chinesiche Küste von Macao. Gestochen von H. Herzberg. Map. Berlin, 1834.

DILL, REV. JACOB S. "American Scientist Who Charted the Oceans—Pathfinder of the Seas. Life Story of Commander Matthew Fontaine Maury . . . ," *Jour. of American History*, Vol. IV, No. 3, 1910.

DODD, WILLIAM E. *Jefferson Davis.* Philadelphia, 1907.

DODSON, LEONIDAS. *Alexander Spotswood, Governor of Colonial Virginia, 1710-1722.* Philadelphia, 1932.

DOGGETT's *New York City Directories*, 1849-1850, 1851.

DOMENECH, EMMANUEL. *Histoire du Mexique, Juarez et Maximilian.* 3 vols. Paris, 1868.

DOUBLEDAY, ABNER. *Reminiscences of Forts Sumter and Moultrie in 1860-61.* New York, 1876.

DOUGLAS, REV. WILLIAM. *The Douglas Register, being a detailed record of births, marriages and deaths . . . from 1750 to 1797.* Transcr. and ed. by W. Mac. Jones. Richmond, 1928.

DOWDEY, CLIFFORD. *Experiment in Rebellion.* New York, 1956.

DOZER, D. M. "Matthew Fontaine Maury's Letter of Instruction to William Lewis Herndon," *Hispanic Am. Historical Rev.*, Vol. 28 (1929), pp. 212-228.

DRAPER, JOHN WILLIAM. *History of the American Civil War . . .* 3 vols. New York, 1867-1870.

DRIVER, CARL S. *John Sevier, Pioneer of the Old Southwest.* Chapel Hill, N.C., 1932.

DUDLEY OBSERVATORY. *Statement of the Trustees.* Albany, N.Y., 1859.

DULLES, FOSTER R. *The Old China Trade.* Boston, 1930.

DUMOND, DWIGHT L. *The Secession Movement, 1860-1861.* New York, 1931.

DUNDONALD, EARL. *Autobiography of a Seaman.* London, 1860.

DUNNING, WILLIAM A. *Reconstruction, Political and Economic, 1865-1877.* New York, 1907.

Du Pont de Nemours and Company. "Matthew Fontaine Maury, The Pathfinder of the Seas." Script prepared and radio program produced Oct. 16, 1940, by Batten, Barton, Durstine, and Osborne, starring Karl Swenson.

DU PONT, HENRY. *Rear Admiral Samuel Francis Du Pont, U.S.N.* New York, 1926.

675

DUPRÉE, A. HUNTER. *Science in the Federal Government, A History of Policies and Activities to 1940.* Cambridge, Mass., 1957.

DURKIN, EDWIN. Obituary notice on Matthew Fontaine Maury. *Royal Astronomical Society Monthly Notices,* Vol. XXXIV, No. 4 (February, 1874), pp. 155-158.

DURKIN, JOSEPH THOMAS, S.J. *Stephen Russell Mallory, Confederate Navy Chief.* Chapel Hill, N.C., 1954.

ECKENRODE, HAMILTON JAMES. *Political History of Virginia During Reconstruction. Johns Hopkins University Studies in Historical and Political Science.* . . . Baltimore, 1904.

———. *Separation of Church and State in Virginia.* Richmond, 1910.

Eclectic Magazine of Foreign Literature, Science and Art, New Ser., Vol. XVIII, No. 1 (July, 1873), pp. 115-119.

Educational Association of Virginia, Minutes of the Fourth Annual Session, Held in Lexington, Va., July 13-15, 1869. Lynchburg, Va., 1870.

Educational Association of Virginia, Minutes of the Fifth Annual Session, Held in Warrenton, Va., July 12-15, 1870, pp. 3-6. Lynchburg, Va., 1871.

EGGLESTON, GEORGE CARY. *A Rebel's Recollections.* Introduction by David Donald. A reprint of the 4th ed., 1905. Bloomington, Ind., 1959.

ELLIOTT, S. A. *Washington Directory.* 1827, 1830.

ELLIOTT, WILLIAM. *The Washington Guide.* Washington, D.C., 1822 and 1826 eds.

ELLIS, HENRY THOMAS. *Hong Kong to Manilla . . . 1856.* London, 1859.

EMMONS, GEORGE FOSTER (Lieut. U.S.N.). *The Navy of the United States from the commencement, 1775 to 1853; with a brief history of each vessel's service and fate.* . . . Washington, 1853.

Encyclopaedia Britannica. 22 vols. Chicago, 1957 ed.

Encyclopedia Americana. 30 vols. New York, 1962.

Encyclopedia of Virginia Biography. Ed. Lyon Gardiner Tyler. New York, 1915.

Exploring Expedition, Correspondence between John N. Reynolds and Hon. Mahlon Dickerson. . . . New York, 1838.

FAGAN, GEORGE V. "Alexander Dallas Bache, Educator," *Barnwell Bulletin,* Vol. XVIII, No. 75 (April, 1941). Philadelphia.

FARRAGUT, LOYALL. *The Life of David Glasgow Farragut, first Admiral of the United States Navy, embodying his journals and letters.* New York, 1879.

FASANO, LAWRENCE (U.S.N.). *Naval Rank: Its Inception and Development.* New York, 1936.

FERGUSON, JAMES. Letter of former assistant in the Coast Survey to Freeman Hunt, editor. *Hunt's Merchants' Magazine,* Vol. XX, No. 6 (June, 1849), p. 595.

Ferslew's Directory for the City of Richmond, 1860.

FIELD, HENRY MARTYN. *The Story of the Atlantic Telegraph.* 1st ed. New York, 1892.

FONTAINE, REV. JAMES (JACQUES). *A Tale of the Huguenots, or Memoirs of a French Refugee Family.* New York, 1838.

———. *Memoirs of a Huguenot Family.* New York, 1853. (See Ann Maury.)

FOOTE, REV. WILLIAM HENRY. *Sketches of Virginia, Historical and Biographical.* 1st and 2d ser. Philadelphia, 1850-1856.

FORCE, PETER. *A Directory for the Public Offices.* Washington, 1820.

Bibliography

FORRESTER, IZOLA. *This One Mad Act . . . The Unknown Story of John Wilkes Booth and His Family.* Boston, 1937.

FOWLER, G. HERBERT, C.B.E., Ph.D., F.L.S. *Charts: Their Use and Meaning.* Prepared for The Challenger Society for the Promotion of the Study of Oceanography of England. London, 1931.

———— (ed.). *Science of the Sea: An Elementary Handbook of Practical Oceanography.* Prepared for The Challenger Society. Oxford, 1912.

FREEMAN, DOUGLAS SOUTHALL. *A Calendar of Confederate Papers. . . .* Richmond, 1908.

————. *George Washington. A Biography.* 6 vols. New York, 1948-1957.

————. *Lee's Lieutenants, A Study in Command.* 3 vols. New York, 1942-1944.

————. *R. E. Lee. A Biography.* 4 vols. Pulitzer Prize edition. New York and London, 1936.

FRY, JOSHUA, and PETER JEFFERSON. *The Fry and Jefferson Map of Virginia and Maryland.* Introduction by Dumas Malone. Princeton, 1950.

Funk and Wagnalls New Standard Dictionary of the English Language. New York and London, 1940.

Garden Study Club of Nashville (compiler). *History of Homes and Gardens of Tennessee.* Nashville, 1936.

Genealogical Chart of Fontaine and Maury Families (from Jean de la Fontaine through generation of children of Matthew Fontaine Maury). Begun by Ann Maury of New York c. 1850. New York, n.d.

GOODE, GEORGE BROWN. *The Smithsonian Institution, 1846-1896. The History of its First Half Century.* Washington, 1897.

GOODWIN, REV. EDWARD L. *The Colonial Church in Virginia, with biographical sketches of the first six bishops of the diocese of Virginia, and other historical papers, together with brief biographical sketches of the colonial clergy of Virginia.* Milwaukee, 1927.

————. *Parish Lines in the Diocese of Virginia.* Rev. and enl. by G. MacLaren Brydon. Richmond, 1927.

GOOLRICK, C. O'CONOR. "A Brief History of Fredericksburg, Virginia," *New Approved Guidebook of Fredericksburg, Virginia.* Fredericksburg, 1957.

GOOLRICK, JOHN TACKETT. *Historic Fredericksburg; the Story of an Old Town.* Richmond, 1922.

GOULD, BENJAMIN APTHORP JR. "Gilliss Memoir," *National Academy of Sciences Annual, 1866.*

————. *Reply to the Statement of the Trustees, Dudley Observatory.* Albany, N.Y., 1858.

GRAHAM, GERALD S. *Sea Power and British North America, 1783-1820.* Cambridge, Mass., 1941.

Great Virginians, Matthew Fontaine Maury. Ceremonies at the unveiling of the bust of Matthew Fontaine Maury, the old hall of the House of Delegates, State Capitol, Richmond, Nov. 15, 1932. Richmond, 1932.

GUYOT, ARNOLD. *A Collection of Meteorological Tables.* Washington, 1852.

————. *Directions for Meteorological Observations.* Washington, 1850.

GUYOT, ARNOLD, and JOSEPH HENRY. *Circular of Instructions to Meteorological Observers.* Washington, 1850.

GWATHMEY, JOHN HASTINGS. *Historical Register of Virginians in the Revolution . . .* Richmond, 1938.

GWATHMEY, JOHN HASTINGS. *Twelve Virginia Counties, Where the Western Migration Began.* Richmond, 1937.

HAMERSLY, LEWIS R. *The Records of Living Officers of the U.S. Navy and Marine Corps. . . .* Philadelphia, 1870.

———. *A Naval Encyclopedia.* Especially article, "Deep Sea Sounding," by George E. Belknap, U.S.N. Philadelphia, 1881.

HAMMOND, M. B. *The Cotton Industry. An Essay in American Economic History.* New York, 1897.

HANNA, A. J. "The Role of Matthew Fontaine Maury in the Mexican Empire," *Virginia Magazine of History and Biography.* Vol. LV, No. 2 (April, 1947), pp. 105-125.

HANSARD, THOMAS CURSON. *Great Britain, House of Lords, Parliamentary Debates.* Authorized edition. Second Series. Vol. CXXVI (April 19, 1853-May 9, 1853), pp. 521-544. London, 1853.

HARMON, GEORGE D. "Confederate Migration to Mexico," *Hispanic American Historical Review,* Vol. XVII (November, 1937), pp. 458-487.

HARRIS, MALCOLM H. *History of Louisa County, Virginia.* Richmond, 1936.

HARRISON, CONSTANCE CARY (MRS. BURTON). *Recollections Grave and Gay.* Richmond, 1911.

HARRISON, FAIRFAX. *Landmarks of Old Prince William.* 2 vols. Richmond, 1924.

HASKELL, DANIEL C. *The U.S. Exploring Expedition, 1838-42, and its publications, 1844-47; A Bibliography.* With an entry note by Harry Miller Lydenberg. New York Public Library, 1942.

HAWTHORNE, HILDEGARDE. *Matthew Fontaine Maury, Trail Maker of the Seas.* New York and Toronto, 1943.

HAYDEN, HORACE EDWIN. *Virginia Genealogies.* Wilkes-Barre, Pa., 1891.

HAYWOOD, JOHN. *Civil and Political History of Tennessee, from its earliest settlements up to the year 1796, including the boundaries of the state.* Knoxville, Tenn., 1823.

HECK, JOHANN GEORG. *Iconographic Encyclopaedia of Science, Literature and Art.* Vol. III. New York, 1851.

HEFLIN, L. (Lieut. U.S.N.). "Comments and Notes," *U.S. Naval Institute Proceedings,* Vol. LXXIV, No. 6, Whole No. 544 (June, 1948), pp. 759-760.

HEITMAN, FRANCIS B. *Historical Register and Dictionary of the U.S. Army, from its organization Sept. 29, 1789, to March 2, 1903.* Washington, 1903.

———. *Historical Register of Officers of the Continental Army during the War of the Revolution, April, 1775, to December, 1783.* Washington, 1914.

HELLWEG, J. F. (Capt. U.S.N.). *Memorial Windows in the Washington Cathedral to Lieutenant Matthew Fontaine Maury . . .* Address delivered in Washington, 1935, when Superintendent of Naval Observatory. Washington, 1940.

HELPER, HINTON ROWAN. *The Impending Crisis of the South; How to Meet It.* New York, 1857.

HEMPHILL, W. EDWIN. "His [James Monroe's] Course Fixed for Life?" *Virginia Cavalcade,* Vol. VII, No. 4 (Spring issue, 1958), pp. 40-48.

HENDERSON, ARCHIBALD. *Dr. Thomas Walker and the Loyal Company of Virginia.* Repr. from *American Antiquarian Society Proceedings.* Worcester, Mass., April, 1931.

———. *The Campus of the First State University.* Chapel Hill, N.C., 1949.

HENDRICK, BURTON J. *The Lees of Virginia.* Boston, 1935.

HENRY, JOSEPH. "The Coast Survey," *Princeton Review*, April, 1845, pp. 321-344.

——. "Meteorology in Its Connection with Agriculture," *Scientific Writings of Joseph Henry*. 2 vols. bound as one. See Vol. II, pp. 6-402, in *Smithsonian Miscellaneous Collections*, Vol. XXX. Washington, 1886.

——. "Report to Commissioner of Patents," 1856, *Scientific Writings of Joseph Henry*, 2 vols. bound as one. See Vol. II, pp. 455-492, in *Smithsonian Miscellaneous Collections*, Vol. XXX. Washington, 1886.

HENRY, ROBERT SELPH. *The Story of the Confederacy*. Indianapolis, 1931.

HENRY, WILLIAM WIRT. *Patrick Henry. Life, Correspondence and Speeches.* 3 vols. New York, 1891.

HERDMAN, WILLIAM A. *Founders of Oceanography and Their Work*. London, 1923.

HERNDON, BRODIE STRACHAN. "Professional View of the Death of Commodore M. F. Maury," *Atlanta Medical and Surgical Journal*, 1872-73.

HERNDON, JOHN GOODWIN. *The Herndons of the American Revolution. Part Two: Edward Herndon of Spotsylvania Co., Va., and His Descendants.* Lancaster, Pa., 1951.

HERNDON, WILLIAM LEWIS, and LARDNER GIBBON. *Exploration of the Valley of the Amazon, made under direction of the Navy Department.* 2 vols. Washington (Vol. I, Herndon) 1853, (Vol. II, Gibbon) 1854.

HERNDON, WILLIAM LEWIS. *Explorations of the Valley of the Amazon.* Vol. I, an abridgment of the original 1853 text, edited and with introduction by Hamilton Basso. New York, 1952.

J.F.W.H. [JOHN F. W. HERSCHEL]. "Physical Geography," *Encyclopaedia Britannica*, 8th ed., 1859, Vol. VII, pp. 569-642.

HESSELTINE, W. B. *The South in American History*. New York, 1951.

HILL, LAWRENCE F. "The Confederate Exodus to Latin America," *Southwestern Historical Quarterly*, Vol. XXXIX (October, 1935), pp. 98-134, and (January, 1936), pp. 161-199.

HODGSON, TELFAIR, D.D., Vice-Chancellor (ed.). *Reprints of the Documents and Proceedings of the Board of Trustees of the University of the South, University of the South Papers.* Series A, No. 1, pp. 63-68. Sewanee, Tenn., 1888.

HOOKER, WILLIAM. *Map of New York, 1830.* New York, 1830, 1831.

HOPLEY, CATHERINE C. *Life in the South; From the Commencement of the War, by Blockaded British Subject.* 2 vols. London, 1863.

HOUSTON, DAVID FRANKLIN. *A Critical Study of Nullification in South Carolina.* Cambridge, Mass., 1896.

HOWARTH, OSBERT JOHN RADCLIFF. *The British Association: A Retrospect, 1831-1921.* London, 1922.

HOWE, OCTAVIUS T., and FREDERICK C. MATTHEWS. *American Clipper Ships, 1833-1858.* 2 vols. Salem, Mass., 1926-27.

HUDDY, WILLIAM M., and PETER S. DUVAL. *The Huddy and Duval Prints; being hand-colored facsimiles of the uniform plates representing the volunteers of the U.S.A., together with the Army and Navy* . . . New York, 1955.

HUGHES, W. S. (Lieut. U.S.N.). *Founding and Development of the U.S. Hydrographic Office. Prepared by direction of Commdr. J. R. Bartlett, U.S.N. Hydrographer.* Washington, 1887.

HUGHES, W. S. (Lieut. U.S.N.). "Memoir on the Founding and Progress of the U.S. Naval Observatory," *Washington Observations*. Appendix 4. Washington, 1871.

HUMBOLDT, ALEXANDER VON. *Cosmos: a sketch of a physical description of the universe*. Trans. from the German by E. C. Otté. 5 vols. London, 1849-1858.

HUMPHREY, WILLIAM J. *Ways of the Weather*. Lancaster, Pa., 1942.

HUNTLEY, ELIZABETH VALENTINE. *Peninsula Pilgrimage*. Richmond, 1941.

Hunt's Merchants' Magazine and Commercial Review, Vol. XX, No. 2 (February, 1849), No. 6 (June, 1849).

In Memoriam—Matthew Fontaine Maury. Publ. by Virginia Military Institute. Lexington, Va., 1873.

ISELIN, COLUMBUS O'DONNELL. *Matthew Fontaine Maury (1806-1873), Pathfinder of the Seas, The Development of Oceanography*. An address delivered before the Newcomen Society in North America at Falmouth, Mass., June 6, 1957. New York, San Francisco, Montreal, 1957.

JAFFE, BERNARD. *Men of Science in America; The Role of Science in the Growth of our Country*. New York, 1944.

JAHNS, PATRICIA. *Matthew Fontaine Maury and Joseph Henry: Scientists of the Civil War*. New York, 1960.

JAMES, MARQUIS. *The Raven; A Biography of Sam Houston*. Indianapolis, 1929.

JANSEN, MARIN H. Het Leven Van een blooshouder Gedenk Schriften van M. H. Jansen, door S.P.L'Honoré Naber, *Historisch Genootschap te Utrecht*, Derde Serie, No. 49 (memoirs of M. H. Jansen—an original manuscript annotated by S. P. L'Honoré Naber, Professor of History, University of Utrecht, Holland). Over den Dom te Utrecht: Kemmink and Zoon, 1925.

(JANSEN, MARIN H.) "Obituary. Admiral Jansen." *Geographical Journal* (London), Vol. II, No. 5 (November, 1893), pp. 465-468.

JANSEN, MARIN H. "The Gulf Stream," *Ocean Highways: The Geographical Review* (London), ed. Clements R. Markham, C.B., New Ser., Vol. I, No. 3 (June, 1873), pp. 98-101.

JENKINS, STEPHEN. *The Greatest Street in the World: The Story of Broadway Old and New*. New York and London, 1911.

JOHNSON, ROBERT UNDERWOOD, and C. C. BUEL (eds.). *Battles and Leaders of the Civil War*. 4 vols. New York, 1887.

JOHNSTON, JOSEPH E. *Narrative of Military Operations during the late War Between the States . . .* New York, 1872.

JONES, CHARLES C. JR. *The Life and Services of Commodore Josiah Tattnall*. Savannah, Ga., 1878.

JONES, GEORGE. *Sketches of Naval Life with Notices of Men, Manners and Scenery on the Shores of the Mediterranean in a Series of Letters from the Brandywine and Constitution Frigates*. 2 vols. New Haven, 1829.

JONES, HUGH. *The Present State of Virginia*. Ed. Richard L. Morton. Chapel Hill, N.C., 1956. Original ed., London, 1724.

JONES, JOHN BEAUCHAMP. *A Rebel War Clerk's Diary at the Confederate States Capital*. 2 vols. Philadelphia, 1866.

JONES, J. WILLIAM, D.D., formerly Chaplain Army of Northern Virginia and of Washington College, Virginia. *Personal Reminiscences, Anecdotes, and Letters of General Robert E. Lee*. Publ. by authority of the Lee family and of the Faculty of Washington and Lee University. New York, 1874.

Bibliography

JONES, NEWMAN, and J. S. EWBANK. *Illuminated Pictorial Directory of New York*. New York, 1848.

JUDSON, ISABELLA FIELD. *Cyrus W. Field, His Life and Work*. New York, 1896.

KANE, ELISHA KENT, M.D., U.S.N. *Arctic Explorations, the Second Grinnell Expedition in Search of Sir John Franklin in 1853, '54, '55*. 2 vols. See Vol. I. Philadelphia, 1856.

———. *The U.S. Grinnell Expedition in Search of Sir John Franklin, A Personal Narrative*. New York, 1853.

KANE, JOSEPH NATHAN. *The American Counties*. New York, 1960.

KEAN, ROBERT GARLICK HILL. *Inside the Confederate Government: The Diary of Robert Garlick Hill Kean*. Ed. Edward Younger. New York, 1957.

Keim's Illustrated Handbook. Old Washington City, for the Compiler, 1844.

KLAPP, ORRIN E. (Lieut. U.S.N.). "Matthew Fontaine Maury, Naval Scientist," *U.S. Naval Institute Proceedings*, Vol. LXXI, No. 11, Whole No. 513 (November, 1945), pp. 1315-1325. Pamphlet repr. by U.S. Naval Institute, Annapolis, Md.

KULL, IRVING S., and NELL M. KULL. *A Short Chronology of American History, 1492-1950*. New Brunswick, N.J., 1952.

LANDSTRÖM, BJÖRN. *The Ship, An Illustrated History*. New York, 1961.

LANGLEY, S. P. "The Meteorological Work of the Smithsonian Institution," *Bulletin No. 11 of the U.S. Weather Bureau*. Washington, 1894.

LAROUSSE, PIERRE. *Larousse du xxe Siècle*. 6 Tomes. Paris, 1958.

LATHAM, JEAN LEE. *Matthew Fontaine Maury—Trail Blazer of the Sea*. Boston, 1956.

LAWTON, EBA ANDERSON. *Major Robert Anderson and Fort Sumter, 1861*. New York, 1911.

LESLEY, J. PETER. *The Iron Manufacturer's Guide to the furnaces, forges and rolling mills of the United States*. New York and London, 1859.

LETCHER, GOVERNOR JOHN. "Official Correspondence," *Southern Historical Society Papers*, Vol. I (June, 1876), pp. 455-462.

LEVASSEUR, AUGUSTE. *Lafayette in America in 1824 and 1825; or a Journal of a Voyage to the U.S.* Trans. John D. Godman. 2 vols. Philadelphia, 1829.

LEWIS, CHARLES LEE. *Admiral Franklin Buchanan, Fearless Man of Action*. Baltimore, 1929.

———. *David Glasgow Farragut, Admiral in the Making*. 2 vols. Vol. I. Annapolis, 1941-43.

———. "Matthew Fontaine Maury, An International Figure," *Southern Magazine*, Vol. I, No. 9 (January, 1935), pp. 9-11, 43.

———. *Matthew Fontaine Maury, The Pathfinder of the Seas*. Annapolis, 1927.

———. "Maury and the Messenger," *Southern Literary Messenger*, New Ser., Vol. I, No. 3 (March, 1939), pp. 165-171.

———. *Our Navy in the Pacific and Far East Long Ago*. Repr. as pamphlet from *U.S. Naval Institute Proceedings*, Vol. LXIX, No. 6, Whole No. 484 (June, 1943), pp. 857-864.

Lippincott's Gazetteer of the World. New ed. Philadelphia, 1880.

Lippincott's Pronouncing Gazetteer of the World. Philadelphia, 1906.

Longworth's *New York City Directories*, 1830-1840.

LOSSING, BENJAMIN J. *The Pictorial Field Book of War of 1812*. New York, 1868 and 1896.

LOVETTE, LELAND P. (Lieut. Comdr. U.S.N.). *Naval Customs, Traditions, and Usage*. Annapolis, 1939.

Lowenstrom, C. *New York Pictorial Business Directory of Wall Street, 1849.* New York, 1850.

Ludlow, Noah Miller (actor and manager for thirty-eight years). *Dramatic Life as I Have Found It.* St. Louis, Mo., 1880.

———. *A Genealogical History of the Ludlow Family.* St. Louis, Mo., 1884.

Lyman, John (Lieut. Comdr. U.S.N. Inactive). "The Centennial of Pressure Pattern Navigation," *U.S. Naval Institute Proceedings,* Vol. LXXIV, No. 3, Whole No. 541 (March, 1948), pp. 309-314.

Lynch, William Francis (Lieut. Commanding). *Narrative of the U.S. Expedition to the River Jordan and the Dead Sea.* Philadelphia, 1849.

———. *Naval Life or Observations Afloat and on Shore. The Midshipman.* New York, 1851.

Mabee, Carleton. *The American Leonardo, the Life of Samuel F. B. Morse.* New York, 1943.

Magruder, Allan B. "A Piece of Secret History; President Lincoln and the Virginia Convention of 1861," *Atlantic Monthly,* Vol. XXXV, No. CCX (April, 1875), pp. 438-445.

Mahan, Alfred Thayer (U.S.N.). *From Sail to Steam; Recollections of Naval Life.* New York, 1907.

———. *Sea Power in Its Relation to the War of 1812.* Boston, 1905.

Malone, Dumas. *Jefferson, the Virginian.* Boston, 1948.

Marcou, Jules. *Louis Agassiz.* 2 vols. New York, 1896.

"The Marine Meteorological Service of the United States," *Weather Bureau Bulletin No. 678.* U.S. Department of Agriculture, Weather Bureau, C. F. Marvin, Chief. Washington, 1919.

H.A.M. [Harry A. Marmer]. "Matthew Fontaine Maury," *Dictionary of American Biography,* 1933. Vol. XII, pp. 428-431.

Marshall, Edward Chauncy. *Historical Sketch of the U.S. Naval Academy.* New York, 1862.

Martin, Joseph. *A New and Comprehensive Gazetteer of Virginia and the District of Columbia, 1836.* Charlottesville, Va., 1836.

Martin, Percy Alvin. *The Influence of the United States on the opening of the Amazon to the World's Commerce,* repr. from *Hispanic American Historical Review,* Vol. I, No. 2 (May, 1918).

Martin, Pete. "Century Plant" (The Tredegar Iron Works, Richmond, Va.), *Saturday Evening Post,* Vol. CCXVI, No. 4 (July 24, 1943), pp. 26-27.

"Matthew Fontaine Maury." Address given on the occasion of the unveiling of his bust at the Hall of Fame of New York University, May 14, 1931, *Science,* New Ser., Vol. LXXIII (June 12, 1931), pp. 632-634.

"Matthew Fontaine Maury," in S. A. Allibone, *A Critical Dictionary of English Literature,* 1882, Vol. II, pp. 1249-1250.

"Matthew Fontaine Maury—An Appreciation," by Algernon B. Chandler Jr.; "Maury and the Confederate Navy," by E. Lee Trinkle, Governor of Virginia; addresses delivered June 22, 1922, *Bulletin State Normal School for Women,* Vol. VIII, No. 5 (January, 1923), pp. 3-7, 9-12.

"Matthew Fontaine Maury," *Appleton's New Practical Cyclopaedia,* Vol. IV (n.p.). New York, 1915.

"Matthew Fontaine Maury," *Ballou's Pictorial Magazine,* Vol. XIII, No. 13, Whole No. 327 (Sept. 26, 1857), p. 193.

"Matthew Fontaine Maury," *Leisure Hour,* Vol. XV (1866), p. 679.

Bibliography

"Matthew Fontaine Maury," *National Cyclopedia of American Biography,* Vol. VI, pp. 35-36. New York, 1892.

"Matthew Fontaine Maury—Pathfinder of the Seas" (an article about Maury and unveiling of monument to him in Goshen Pass, Va., June 9, 1923), New York *Times* Book Review and Magazine Section, July 15, 1923.

"Matthew Fontaine Maury—A Sketch," *Popular Science Monthly,* Vol. XXXVII, No. 3 (July, 1890), pp. 400-407.

"Matthew Fontaine Maury—A Sketch," *Southern Magazine,* Vol. XII (1872), p. 385.

MAURY, ANN (translator and compiler). *Memoirs of a Huguenot Family: translated and compiled from the original autobiography of the Rev. James Fontaine, and other family manuscripts; comprising an original journal of travels* [of John Fontaine] *in Va., N.Y., etc. in 1715 and 1716.* New York, 1853; 2d ed., 1872.

MAURY, ANNE FONTAINE. *Intimate Virginiana, A Century of Maury Travels by Land and Sea.* Richmond, 1941.

MAURY, GEN. DABNEY HERNDON. *Address at the Reunion of Confederate Veterans, Maury Camp, No. 2, Fredericksburg, Va., Aug. 23, 1883.* Fredericksburg, n.d.

———. "How the Confederacy Changed Naval Warfare," *Southern Historical Society Papers,* Vol. XXII (1894), pp. 75-81.

———. *Recollections of a Virginian in the Mexican, Indian and Civil Wars* . . . New York, 1894.

MAURY, M. F. (obituary notice). *Am. Jour. of Science,* Vol. V (1873), p. 242.

"Maury on South America," *Southern Quarterly Review.* Vol. VIII (1853), pp. 412-449.

"Maury, Pathfinder of the Seas," *Mentor,* Vol. XIV (October, 1926), p. 40.

MAURY, RICHARD LAUNCELOT. *The Battle of Williamsburg and the charge of the 24th Virginia of Early's brigade.* Written for the Southern Historical Society, publ. in its *Papers* for 1880. 20-page reprint. Richmond, 1880.

———. *A Brief Sketch of the Work of Matthew Fontaine Maury During the War, 1861-65.* Richmond, 1915.

———. "The First Marine Torpedoes," *Southern Historical Society Papers,* Vol. XXXI (1903), pp. 326-333.

———. *The Huguenots in Virginia.* Publ. by the Southern Historical Society. Richmond, n.d.

MAURY, SARAH MYTTON. *The Statesmen of America in 1846.* London and Philadelphia, 1847.

MAURY, WILLIAM ARDEN. *John Walker Maury, His Lineage and Life.* Washington, 1916.

McCORDOCK, ROBERT STANLEY. *The Yankee Cheese Box.* Philadelphia, 1938.

McCORKLE, WILLIAM ALEXANDER. *The White Sulphur Springs, West Virginia; the Tradition, History, Social Life.* New York, 1916.

McCORMAC, EUGENE IRVING, Ph.D. *James K. Polk, A Political Biography.* Berkeley, Calif., 1922.

McDONALD, PHILIP B. *A Saga of the Sea.* New York, 1937.

McGREGOR, JAMES C. *The Disruption of Virginia.* New York, 1922.

McKAY, RICHARD C. *South Street, A Maritime History of New York.* New York, 1934.

McMaster, John Bach. *A History of the People of the United States from the Revolution to the Civil War.* 8 vols. New York, 1900.

McPherson, Edward. *A Political History of the U.S. During Reconstruction.* Washington, 1875.

Meade, Robert Douthat. *Judah P. Benjamin.* New York, 1943.

———. *Patrick Henry, Patriot in the Making.* Philadelphia and New York, 1957.

Meade, Bishop William. *Old Churches, Ministers and Families of Virginia.* 2 vols. Philadelphia, 1861.

Mellen, Kathleen Dickinson. *The Gods Depart, A Saga of the Hawaiian Kingdom, 1832-1873.* New York, 1936.

Memorial Windows in the Washington Cathedral to Lieut. Matthew Fontaine Maury, the Hon. Myron T. Herrick, James Parmelee. Addresses on the occassion of the dedication of those windows in 1935, especially the speech of Capt. J. F. Hellweg, U.S.N., then Superintendent U.S. Naval Observatory, in tribute to Maury. Privately published, Washington, 1940.

Michaux, François André, M.D. *Travels to the Westward of the Allegany Mountains in . . . Tennessee, in the year 1802 . . .* Trans. from the French. London, 1805.

Miers, Earl Schenck. *The Great Rebellion.* Cleveland, 1958.

Miller, Eric R. "The Evolution of Meteorological Institutions in the United States," *Monthly Weather Review,* Vol. LIX, No. 1 (January, 1931).

Miller, Francis T. *The Photographic History of the Civil War.* 10 vols. New York, 1911.

Milton, George Fort. *The Eve of Conflict; Stephen A. Douglas and the Needless War.* Boston, 1934.

B.B.M. [Benjamin Blake Minor]. "Stars and Streamers," *Southern Literary Messenger,* Vol. XIV, No. 6 (June, 1848), pp. 344-349.

Minor, John B. *The Minor Family of Virginia.* Lynchburg, Va., 1923.

Moore, Frank. *The Rebellion Record; A Diary of American Events.* Vol. I. New York, 1861.

Morgan, George. *Life of James Monroe.* Boston, 1921.

Morgan, James Morris. *Recollections of a Rebel Reefer.* Boston and New York, 1917.

Morison, Samuel Eliot. *John Paul Jones, A Sailor's Biography.* Boston and Toronto, 1959.

Morris, Charles (U.S.N.). *The Autobiography of Commodore Charles Morris, U.S. Navy,* with portrait and explanatory notes. Boston, 1880.

Morris, Richard B. (ed.). *Encyclopedia of American History.* 1 vol., rev. and enl. New York, 1961.

Morse, Edward L. *Samuel F. B. Morse; his letters and journals.* Boston and New York, 1914.

Morton, Richard L. *Colonial Virginia.* 2 vols. Chapel Hill, N.C., 1960.

Mullaly, John. *The Laying of the Cable or The Ocean Telegraph, Being a Complete and Authentic Narrative of the Attempt to Lay the Cable . . .* New York, 1858.

Munford, Beverley B. *Virginia's Attitude Toward Slavery and Secession.* New York, London, Bombay and Calcutta, 1909.

Murray, Sir John, and Dr. Johan Hjort. *The Depths of the Ocean. A general account of the Modern Science of Oceanography . . .* London, 1912.

MUSSER, JOHN. *The Establishment of Maximilian's Empire in Mexico.* Menasha, Wis., 1918.

NABUCO, JOAQUIM. *Um Estadista do Imperio. Nabucio De Aranjo* (by his son). Vol. III. Paris, 1897.

National Academy of Sciences. *Annual of the National Academy of Sciences for 1863-1864,* pp. 60, 79-82. Cambridge, Mass., 1865.

———. *Annual of the National Academy of Sciences for 1866,* pp. 77, 107. Cambridge, Mass., 1867.

———. *Biographical Memoirs of the National Academy of Sciences,* Vol. I, Washington, 1877.

———. *Report of the National Academy of Sciences for the year 1863,* pp. 98-112. Washington, 1864.

National Agricultural Association Congress, May 27-30, 1872, Proceedings, pp. 40-54. Indianapolis, 1872.

National Institute for the Promotion of Science, Washington, D.C. *Papers relative to the National Institute, collected and arranged by Francis Markoe Jr., corresponding secretary* [Washington, D.C., 18—]. 15 pamphlets in 1 vol.

National Institute for the Promotion of Science, Proceedings. Washington, 1855-57.

"Nautical Intelligence," review of Maury's *Sailing Directions and Charts, South Atlantic Ocean,* repr. from the *British Army Despatch,* London. *Hunt's Merchants' Magazine,* Vol. XXVI (March, 1852), p. 239.

NEESER, ROBERT WILDEN. *Statistical and Chronological History of the U.S. Navy, 1775-1907.* New York, 1909.

NEVINS, ALLAN. *The War for the Union, The Improvised War 1861-1862.* New York, 1959.

New Pronouncing Dictionary of the Spanish and English Languages. Ed. Mariano Velázquez de la Cadena. New York, 1904.

NEWTON, VIRGINIUS. "The Confederate Navy." *Southern Historical Society Papers.* Vol. XXII (1894), p. 90.

NICHOLS, ROY. *Franklin Pierce, Young Hickory of the Granite Hills.* Philadelphia, 1931.

NICOLAY, JOHN GEORGE. *The Outbreak of Rebellion.* New York, 1881.

NOEL, JOHN VAVASOUR JR. (Comdr. U.S.N.). *Naval Terms Dictionary.* New York, 1952.

NOLL, REV. ARTHUR HOWARD (ed.). *Doctor Quintard, Chaplain C.S.A. and Second Bishop of Tennessee* . . . Sewanee, Tenn., 1905.

NORDENSKIÖLD, NILS ERIK. *Periplus; an Essay on the Early History of Charts and Sailing Directions.* Trans. from the Swedish by Francis A. Bather. Stockholm, 1897.

ODGERS, MERLE MIDDLETON. *Alexander Dallas Bache: Scientist and Educator, 1806-1867.* Philadelphia, 1947.

OWEN, THOMAS McADORY (ed.). *John Owen's Journal of His Removal from Virginia to Alabama in 1818.* Baltimore, 1897.

PAGE, THOMAS JEFFERSON. "Autobiographical Sketch of Thomas Jefferson Page," submitted by Commander R. S. Crenshaw, *U.S. Naval Institute Proceedings,* Vol. XLIX, No. 10, Whole No. 248 (October, 1923), pp. 1672, 1687-1690.

———. *La Plata: The Argentine Confederation and Paraguay, being a narrative of the exploration of the tributaries of the River La Plata during the years 1853, '54, '55 and '56, under orders of the U.S. Government.* New York, 1859.

PARKER, WILLIAM HARWAR (Capt. U.S.N.). *Recollections of a Naval Officer, 1841-65.* New York, 1883.

PATRICK, REMBERT WALLACE. *The Fall of Richmond.* Baton Rouge, La., 1960.

PAULLIN, CHARLES OSCAR. *Diplomatic Negotiations of American Naval Officers, 1778-1883.* Baltimore, 1912.

——. "Early Movements for a National Observatory," *Columbian Historical Society Records,* Vol. XXV (1923). Washington, D.C.

——. *Early Voyages of American Naval Vessels to the Orient,* repr. from *U.S. Naval Institute Proceedings,* Vol. XXXVI, No. 2, Whole No. 134 (June, 1910), pp. 429-463.

——. "A Half Century of Naval Administration in America, 1861-1911," *U.S. Naval Institute Proceedings,* Vol. XXXVIII, No. 4, Whole No. 144 (1912), pp. 1309-1336; Vol. XXXIX, No. 5, Whole No. 145, pp. 165, 735, 1217, 1469.

——. *Naval Administration under the Navy Commissioners, 1815-1842.* Repr. from *U.S. Naval Institute Proceedings,* Vol. XXXIII, No. 2, Whole No. 122, pp. 597-641. Annapolis, 1907.

——. "Washington City and the Old Navy," *Columbian Historical Society Records,* Vols. XXXIII-XXXIV (combined vols.). Washington, 1932.

PERRY, WILLIAM STEVENS (ed.). *Historical Collections Relating to the American Colonial Church.* Vol. I, *Virginia.* Hartford, Conn., 1870.

——. *The History of the American Episcopal Church, 1587-1883 . . .* 2 vols. Boston, 1885.

Philippine Islands, Campo Santo de Manila, Pueblo de Paco. Manila, 1823. (Map and description, in Division of Maps, Library of Congress.)

PHILLIPS, ULRICH BONNELL. *American Negro Slavery.* New York, 1918.

——. *The Course of the South to Secession.* New York, 1939.

——. *The Life of Robert Toombs.* New York, 1913.

—— (ed.). *The Correspondence of Robert Toombs, Alexander H. Stephens, and Howell Cobb.* Washington, 1913.

[JOEL POINSETT] "The Exploring Expedition," *North American Review,* Vol. LVI (1843), pp. 259-264.

POLLARD, EDWARD A. *Jefferson Davis, with a Secret History of the Confederacy.* Philadelphia, 1869.

PORTER, ARCHIBALD DOUGLAS. *Commodore David Porter, 1843-1870.* New York and London, 1929.

PORTER, ADMIRAL DAVID DIXON. *The Naval History of the Civil War.* New York, 1886.

PORTER, DAVID (Capt. U.S.N.). *Journal of a Cruise made to the Pacific Ocean in U.S. Frigate Essex 1812, '13 and '14.* Vol. II. New York, 1822.

Post Office Directory Map, London, 1866.

POWELL, EDWARD PAYSON. *Nullification and Secession in the United States; a History of the Six Attempts During the First Century of the Republic.* New York, 1897.

POWELL, MRS. MARY G. *The History of Old Alexandria, Virginia, from July 13, 1749, to May 24, 1861.* Richmond, 1928.

Bibliography

Bibliography

PRATT, FLETCHER. *The Navy, A History; the Story of a Service in Action.* Garden City, N.Y., 1941.

PREBLE, GEORGE HENRY (Capt. U.S.N.). *The First Cruise of the U.S. Frigate Essex.* Salem, 1870.

———. "Naval Uniforms," *United Service,* Vol. II (1880), pp. 741-753.

PRESSLY, THOMAS JAMES. *Americans Interpret Their Civil War.* Princeton, N.J., 1954.

PRIESTLEY, HERBERT INGRAM. *The Mexican Nation.* New York, 1923.

The Pro-Slavery Argument; as Maintained by the Most Distinguished Writers of the Southern States, containing the several essays on the subject, of Chancellor Harper, Governor Hammond, Dr. Simms, and Professor Dew. Charleston, 1852.

PRYOR, SALLY A. (MRS. ROGER ATKINSON). *Reminiscences of Peace and War.* New York, 1904.

PUTNAM, ALBIGENCE WALDO. *History of Middle Tennessee or the Life and Times of General James Robertson.* Nashville, 1859.

PUTNAM, MRS. SALLIE ANN (BROCK). *Richmond During the War; Four Years of Personal Observation.* New York, 1867.

QUETELET, ADOLPHE. "Matthew Fontaine Maury," *Les Mondes,* March 27, 1873.

———. "Notice sur le Capitaine M. F. Maury, Associé de l'Académie Royale de Belgique," *Annuaire de l'Observatoire Royale de Belgique, 1873,* pp. 147-204. Repr. as 55-page pamphlet. Brussells, 1874.

QUINN, SILVANUS JACKSON. *The History of the City of Fredericksburg, Virginia.* Richmond, 1908.

RAINS, GABRIEL JAMES. "Torpedoes," *Southern Historical Society Papers,* Vol. III, Nos. 5 and 6 (May and June, 1877), pp. 255-260.

RAMSDELL, CHARLES WILLIAM. "The Confederate Government and the Railroads," *American Historical Review,* Vol. XXII, No. 4 (July, 1917).

RAMSEY, JAMES GETTYS McGREGOR. *The Annals of Tennessee to the End of the Eighteenth Century . . .* Philadelphia, 1853.

RANDALL, HENRY STEPHENS. *The Life of Thomas Jefferson.* 3 vols. Philadelphia, 1871.

RANDALL, JAMES GARFIELD. *Civil War and Reconstruction.* Boston, 1937.

RANDOLPH, SARAH N. *Domestic Life of Thomas Jefferson.* Cambridge, Mass., 1939.

RATHBUN, RICHARD. *The Columbian Institute for the Promotion of Arts and Sciences 1816-1838. U.S. National Museum, Smithsonian Institution Bulletin 101.* Washington, 1917.

RAWLINGS, MARY. *Ante-bellum Albemarle.* Charlottesville, Va., 1935.

REID, WHITELAW. *After the War: A Southern Tour.* Cincinnati, Ohio, 1866.

REINFELD, FRED. *The Story of Civil War Money.* New York, 1959.

RENIERS, PERCIVAL. *The Springs of Virginia.* Chapel Hill, N.C., 1941.

Report of Commissioner of Patents, 1856, pp. 455-492. 2 vols. combined in one. Smithsonian Institution. Washington, 1886.

Report of the Organization Committee of the Smithsonian Institution. Washington, 1847.

Revue des Deux Mondes, Paris, 1855.

REYNOLDS, FRANCIS JOSEPH. *The U.S. Navy from Revolution to Date.* New York, 1918.

REYNOLDS, JEREMIAH N. *Voyage of the U.S. Frigate Potomac under the Command of Commodore John Downes during the Circumnavigation of the Globe in 1831-34.* New York, 1835.

Reynolds' Map of London, 1860. London, 1860.

RHEA, MATTHEW. *Statistical Table and Map, Tennessee.* 1832.

RHODES, JAMES FORD. *History of the United States from the Compromise of 1850 to the Final Restoration of Home Rule in the South in 1877.* 7 vols. New York, 1892-1906.

RICHARDSON, LEM B. and ANDREW J. SCARLETT. *General College Chemistry.* 4th edition. New York, 1947.

RICHARDSON, RALPH. "The Choice of Jefferson Davis as Confederate President," *Journal of Mississippi History,* Vol. XVII, No. 3, July, 1955.

RIETSTAP, JOHANNES BAPTIST (ed.). *Armorial Général, Réédition originale sous le patronage de l'Académie Internationale d'Héraldique.* Published by Société de Sauvegarde Historique. Vol. II. Lyon, France, 1950.

RILEY, FRANKLIN LAFAYETTE. *General Robert E. Lee After Appomattox.* New York, 1922.

RIPPY, J. FRED. *The United States and Mexico.* New York, 1931.

RIVES, WILLIAM CABELL. *History of the Life and Times of James Madison.* 3 vols. Boston, 1859-1868.

RIZ, RAMÓN EDUARDO (ed.). *An American in Maximilian's Mexico—the Diaries of William Marshall Anderson.* San Marino, Calif., 1959.

ROBERT, JOSEPH CLARKE. *Story of Tobacco in America.* New York, 1949.

ROBINSON, WILLIAM MORRISON JR. *The Confederate Privateers.* New Haven, Conn., 1928.

ROOSEVELT, THEODORE. *The Naval War of 1812.* 2 vols. New York, 1882.

——. *The Winning of the West.* 4 vols. Vol. I (James Robertson and John Sevier). New York, 1889-1896.

ROSCOE, THEODORE, and FRED FREEMAN. *A Picture History of the U.S. Navy.* New York, 1956.

ROWLAND, DUNBAR (ed.). *Jefferson Davis, Constitutionalist, His Letters, Papers and Speeches.* 10 vols. Vols. II and IV. Jackson, Miss., 1923.

Royal Astronomical Society. *History of the Royal Astronomical Society, 1820-1920.* London, 1923.

RUFFIN, EDMUND. "Extracts from the Diary of Edmund Ruffin," *William and Mary Quarterly,* Ser. I, Vol. XXIII, No. 4 (April, 1915), pp. 253-254.

RUSSELL, SIR WILLIAM HOWARD. *The Atlantic Telegraph.* London, 1866.

SANDBURG, CARL. *Abraham Lincoln; The War Years.* 4 vols. New York, 1939.

SANDS, BENJAMIN F. (U.S.N.). *From Reefer to Rear Admiral—Reminiscences and Journal Jottings of Nearly Half a Century of Naval Life.* New York, 1899.

——. *Astronomical and Meteorological Observations Made During the Year 1871 at the U.S. Naval Observatory.* Errata sheet. Washington, 1873.

SCHARF, JOHN THOMAS. *History of the Confederate States Navy From Its Organization to the Surrender of Its Last Vessel.* New York, 1887.

SCHMUCKER (SMUCKER), SAMUEL MOSHEIM. *The Life of Dr. Elisha Kent Kane and of Other Distinguished American Explorers . . .* Philadelphia, 1859.

SCHOFIELD, JOHN McALLISTER. *Forty-Six Years in the Army.* New York, 1897.

SCHOONMAKER, W. M. "Naval Uniforms—Origin and Development," *U.S. Naval Institute Proceedings,* Vol. LVIII, Whole No. 350, No. 4 (April, 1932), p. 519.

Bibliography

SCHWAB, JOHN CHRISTOPHER. *The Confederate States of America 1861-1864; A Financial and Industrial History of the South During the Civil War*. New York, 1901.

SCOTT, W. W. "Reminiscences of Matthew Fontaine Maury," *Southern Magazine*, Vol. V (1894), p. 179.

SECCHI, P. ANGELO. "Un omaggio alla memoria del Commodore Maury," *Bolletino Meteorologico del Collegio Romana*. Vol. XII (1873), pp. 41-42; *Revista Scientifico Industriali en Firenze*, Vol. V (1873), pp. 80-81.

SEMMES, RAPHAEL. *Service Afloat and Ashore During the Mexican War*. Cincinnati, 1851.

———. *Service Afloat; or the Remarkable Career of the Confederate Cruisers Sumter and Alabama During the War Between the States*. Baltimore, 1887.

SEWARD, WILLIAM HENRY. *The Irrepressible Conflict*. Speech at Rochester, N.Y., 1858. New York, 1858.

SEYMOUR, CHARLES C. B. *Self-Made Men*. Article on Lieut. Matthew F. Maury, pp. 51-58. New York, 1858.

SHAW, SIR WILLIAM NAPIER. *Manual of Meteorology*. 4 vols. Cambridge, England, 1926-1931.

SHERMAN, WILLIAM TECUMSEH. *Memoirs of General William T. Sherman*. Vol. I. New York, 1875.

SHOEMAKER, MICHAEL MEYERS. *Quaint Corners of Ancient Empires*. New York, 1899.

SILLIMAN, BENJAMIN. "Remarks on Some of the Gold Mines and on Parts of the Gold Region of Virginia, Founded on Personal Observations Made in the Months of August and September, 1836," *Am. Jour. of Science and Arts*, Vol. XXXII, No. 1, Art. X (1837), pp. 98-130. "U.S. Gold Mine near Fredericksburg, Va.," pp. 183-184.

SKINNER, A. H. "The U.S. Naval Observatory from 1830-1889," *Science*, Vol. IX (1899), pp. 1-16.

SLAUGHTER, PHILIP, D.D. *History of St. George's Parish* (Spotsylvania). Ed. R. A. Brock. Richmond, 1890.

SMITH, CHARLES ALPHONSO. *Matthew Fontaine Maury*. 10-page pamphlet repr. from the *Alumni Bulletin of the University of Virginia*, January, 1924.

———. "Matthew Fontaine Maury," *Southern Literary Studies*, pp. 168-181. Chapel Hill, N.C., 1927.

SMITH, FRANCIS HENNEY. "Matthew Fontaine Maury," *Library of Southern Literature*, ed. by Edwin A. Alderman, Vol. VIII, pp. 3435-3457. Atlanta, 1907.

———. *The Virginia Military Institute, Its Building and Rebuilding*. Lynchburg, 1912.

SMITH, H. D. "Naval Uniforms," *United Service*, New Ser., Vol. II (October, 1889), p. 377.

Smithsonian Miscellaneous Collections, Vol. II (1862), pp. 7-38.

SOLEY, JAMES RUSSELL. "Early Operations on the Potomac River," *Battles and Leaders of the Civil War*, Vol. II, p. 143. New York, 1887.

———. *Historical Sketch of the U.S. Naval Academy*. Washington, 1876.

———. *The Navy in the Civil War: The Blockades and the Cruisers*. New York, 1890.

Southern Historical Society Papers. 47 vols. Richmond, 1876-1930. (Index through Vol. XXXVIII in July-October, 1913, issue of *Virginia State Library Bulletin*.) New Series begins with Whole No. 39, 1914.

Southern Literary Messenger. Richmond, Va., 1834-1864. (General Index compiled by David K. Jackson: *The Contributors and Contributions to the Southern Literary Messenger [1834-1864]*, 1936.)

SPOTSWOOD, ALEXANDER. *The Official Letters of Alexander Spotswood, Lieutenant-Governor of the Colony of Virginia, 1710-1722, Now First Printed from the Collections of the Virginia Historical Society*. Ed. R. A. Brock. 2 vols. Richmond, 1882-1885.

SPROSTON, JOHN GLENDY (U.S.N.). *Private Journal*. Tokyo, 1940.

STANARD, MARY NEWTON. *Colonial Virginia, Its People and Customs*. Philadelphia and London, 1917.

——. *The Story of Virginia's First Century*. Philadelphia and London, 1928.

STEPHENS, ALEXANDER HAMILTON. *A Constitutional View of the Late War between the States: Its Causes, Character, Conduct and Results*. 2 vols. Philadelphia, 1868 and 1870.

STEPHENS, WILLIAM O., and CHARLES ALPHONSO SMITH. *Two Early Proposals for Naval Education*. Reprinted from *U.S. Naval Institute Proceedings*, Vol. XXXIX, No. 1, Whole No. 145 (March, 1913), p. 127 et seq.

STERN, PHILIP VAN DOREN. *Secret Missions of the Civil War*. Chicago, 1959.

STEWART (CHAPLAIN), CHARLES SAMUEL. *A Visit to the South Seas in the U.S. Ship Vincennes during the Years 1829-1830*. 2 vols. New York, 1831.

Stewart's Naval Magazine for 1836.

STILES, ROBERT. *Reconstruction in Virginia*. Baltimore, 1890.

STOKES, ISAAC NEWTON PHELPS. *New York Past and Present; Its History and Landmarks 1524-1939*. New York, 1939.

STRODE, HUDSON. *Jefferson Davis, American Patriot, 1808-1861*. New York, 1955.

——. *Jefferson Davis: Confederate President*. New York, 1959.

SWEM, EARL GREGG. *Maps Relating to Virginia*. Richmond, 1914. (*Virginia State Library Bulletin* VII)

——. *Virginia Historical Index*. 2 vols. Roanoke, 1934, 1936.

SYDNOR, CHARLES SACKETT. *The Development of Southern Sectionalism, 1819-1848*. Baton Rouge, 1948.

TALMAN, CHARLES FITZHUGH. "Maury's Work Goes On," *Nature Magazine*, Vol. XXVI, No. 3 (September, 1935), pp. 149-150.

TAYLOR, RICHARD. *Destruction and Reconstruction. Personal Experiences of the Late War*. New York, 1879.

TAYLOR, WILLIAM B. "The Scientific Work of Joseph Henry," *Bulletin of the Philosophical Society of Washington, 1878*, Vol. II, pp. 230-238.

"They Fought For Freedom. Matthew Fontaine Maury—Pathfinder of the Seas." Picture biography. *Scholastic*, Vol. XLIV, No. 2 (Feb. 14-19, 1944), p. 9.

THORNTON, DR. H. G., F.R.S., D.Sc., "The Invisible College that became the Royal Society," *English-Speaking World* (March, 1960), Vol. XLII, No. 2, pp. 10-15.

TODD, RICHARD CECIL. *Confederate Finance*. Athens, Ga., 1954.

TORELLI, LUIGI. *Matteo Fontaine Maury e La Meteorologia Applicata All'Agricoltura*. Venezia, 1872.

——. *Commemorazione di Matteo Fontaine Maury*. Venezia, 1874.

TROWBRIDGE, PROF. W. P. (Asst. Supt., U.S. Coast Survey). Report "On Deep Sea Soundings," *Am. Jour. of Science and Arts*, 2d Ser., Vol. XXVI, No. 77 (September, 1858), Art. XVII, pp. 157-176.

Bibliography

TURNBULL, ARCHIBALD DOUGLAS. *Commodore David Porter, 1780-1843*. New York and London, 1929.

Twentieth Century Biographical Dictionary of Notable Americans. Editor-in-Chief Rossiter Johnson. Boston, Mass., 1904.

TYLER, LYON GARDINER. *The Cradle of the Republic: Jamestown and James River*. 2d ed. Richmond, 1906.

Tyler's Quarterly Magazine.

United Service, Vol. II (June, 1880).

U.S. Agricultural Society Journal for 1856, Part I, Vol. III, Journal of 4th Annual Meeting, January, 1856. Boston, 1856.

Virginia Historical Register. Ed. William Maxwell. 6 vols. Richmond, 1848-1853.

Virginia Magazine of History and Biography. Publ. by the Virginia Historical Society. Richmond, Va., 1893.

Virginia State Agricultural Society Resolution, Oct. 29, 1855 (approving Maury's meteorological plan), *Southern Planter and Farmer*, Vol. XV, No. 12 (December, 1855), pp. 353-355.

VYLE, PHILLIP. "Maury's Lanes Across the Atlantic," *Running Tide* (publication of the Cunard Steamship Co.), March, 1930. Repr. in *Neptune Log*, April, 1930, pp. 5-6.

WARRINER, FRANCIS. *Cruise of the United States Frigate Potomac 'round the World, during the years 1831-34; Embracing the attack on Quallah-Battoo*. Boston, 1835.

Washington City and Georgetown Directories. Ten Eyck, Homans, et al., 1827, 1842, 1855.

Washington Directory and Governmental Register, 1843, by John T. Towers. Washington, 1843.

WAYLAND, JOHN WALTER. Address delivered at ceremonies held by Washington-Lewis Chapter, D.A.R., to dedicate grave marker of Revolutionary soldier Edward Herndon, at Laurel Hill. Fredericksburg (Va.) *Free Lance Star*, July 3, 1931.

———. *Historic Homes of Northern Virginia and the Eastern Panhandle of West Virginia*. Staunton, Va., 1937.

———. *The Pathfinder of the Seas. The Life of Matthew Fontaine Maury*. Richmond, 1930.

"Weather Bureau," *Dictionary of American History*, Vol. V (pp. 430-431), Vol. VI (pp. 300-301).

WEBER, GUSTAVUS ADOLPHUS. *The Coast and Geodetic Survey, Its History, Activities and Organization*. Service Monograph of the U.S. Government No. 16, Institute for Government Research. Baltimore, 1923.

———. *The Hydrographic Office, Its History, Activities and Organization*. Service Monograph of the U.S. Government No. 42, Institute for Government Research. Baltimore, 1926.

———. *The Naval Observatory, Its History, Activities and Organization*. Service Monograph of the U.S. Government No. 39, Institute for Government Research. Baltimore, 1926.

———. *The Weather Bureau, Its History, Activities and Organization*. New York, 1922.

WELD, ISAAC. *Travel Through the States of North America . . . during the Years 1795, 1796, and 1797*. 2 vols. London, 1799.

Matthew Fontaine Maury

West and Johnston Map of the State of Virginia, with illustrations. Richmond, 1862.

Whitbread's New Plan of London, 1869.

WICKHAM, JULIA P. "Matthew Fontaine Maury," *Richmond Magazine,* Vol. XV, Nos. 7-10 (January-April), 1929.

WILKES, CHARLES. *Narrative of the U.S. Exploring Expedition, 1838-1842.* 5 vols. Washington, 1844.

WILKINS, THURMAN. *Clarence King, A Biography.* New York, 1958.

William and Mary Quarterly Magazine of History. 1st, 2d, and 3d Ser., 1892—.

WILLIAMS, FRANCES LEIGH. *They Faced the Future, A Saga of Growth.* Richmond, 1951.

WINES, ENOCH COBB. *Two Years and a Half in the Navy; or Journal of a Cruise in the Mediterranean and Levant, on Board the U.S. Frigate Constellation in the years 1829, 1830 and 1831.* 2 vols. Philadelphia, 1832.

WIRT, WILLIAM. *Sketches of the Life and Character of Patrick Henry.* Philadelphia, 1818.

WISE, JENNINGS C. *The Military History of the Virginia Military Institute from 1839 to 1865.* Lynchburg, Va., 1915.

WOODS, REV. EDGAR. *Albemarle County in Virginia.* Charlottesville, Va., 1901.

WORCESTER, JOSEPH E. *Geographical Dictionary or Universal Gazetteer.* Vol. II. Andover, Mass., 1817.

Works Progress Administration in Maryland (compiler). *A Guide to the U.S. Naval Academy* (American Guide Series). Service Academy Series, Sponsored by the U.S.N.A. New York, 1941.

Writers' Program, Virginia. *Roanoke, Story of County and City.* Compiled by workers of the Writers' Program of the Work Projects Administration in the State of Virginia . . . Roanoke, Va., 1942.

YOUMANS, WILLIAM J., M.D. *Pioneers of Science in America,* pp. 464-474. New York, 1896.

ZOGBAUM, RUFUS FAIRCHILD. *All Hands, pictures of life in U.S. Navy.* New York, 1897.

Bibliography of the Published Works of Matthew Fontaine Maury

(Divisions are by subjects covered; order is chronological within divisions)

NAVIGATION AND OCEANOGRAPHY
(see also Meteorology of Sea and Land)

"On the Navigation of Cape Horn," *American Journal of Science and Arts,* Vol.
XXVI (July, 1834), pp. 54-63.

"Plan of an Instrument for Finding the True Lunar Distance," *Am. Jour. Science,* Vol. XXVI (July, 1834), pp. 63-65.

*A New Theoretical and Practical Treatise on Navigation; together with a new
and easy plan for finding diff. lat., course and distance, in which the auxiliary branches of mathematics and astronomy, comprised of algebra, geometry, variation of the compass, etc. are treated. Also the theory and most
simple method of finding time, latitude and longitude.* Philadelphia: Key
and Biddle, 1836.

Elementary, Practical and Theoretical Treatise on Navigation (rev. ed. of above
text). Philadelphia: E. C. and J. Biddle, 2d ed., 1843; rev. and enl. 3d ed.,
1845. Maury used these titles for his textbook; others called it "Maury's
Navigation."

"Blank Charts on Board Public Cruisers," Paper urging scientific observations
be made and records kept, read before the National Institute, Washington,
July 4, 1843. *Southern Literary Messenger,* Vol. IX, No. 8 (August, 1843),
pp. 458-461.

"The Gulf Stream and Currents of the Sea," Paper read before National Institute Annual Meeting, Apr. 2, 1844. *SLM,* Vol. X, No. 7 (July, 1844), pp.
393-409; repr. Richmond, 1844, as 16-page pamphlet; repr. in *Am. Jour.
Science,* Vol. XLVII (1844), pp. 161-181.

"Steam Navigation to China," *Western Jour. and Civilian,* Vol. I (1848), p. 259;
SLM, Vol. XIV, No. 4 (April, 1848), pp. 246-254. *Circular Address to the
People of the United States.* Memphis, Tenn.: Twyman and Tannehill,
1849.

WIND AND CURRENT CHARTS (U.S. Hydrographic Office)

Wind and Current Charts, Series A. Track Charts. 35.3″ x 24.1″
Atlantic Ocean, North
  Sheet 1: 1847; 1848; 1850; 3d ed., 1852
  Sheet 2: n.d.; n.d.; 3d ed., 1852

Sheet 3: n.d.; n.d.; 3d ed., 1852
Sheet 4: n.d.; n.d.; 3d ed., 1849
Sheet 5: n.d.; n.d.; 3d ed., 1849
Sheet 6: n.d.; n.d.; 3d ed., 1849
Sheet 7: n.d.; n.d.; 3d ed., 1849
Sheet 8: n.d.; n.d.; 3d ed., 1849
Atlantic Ocean, South
  Sheet 1: n.d.; 2d ed., 1853
  Sheets 2, 3: n.d.; 2d ed., n.d.
  Sheet 4: n.d.
  Sheets 5 and 6: not issued although base charts printed in 1850
Indian Ocean
  Sheets 1, 2, and 3: not issued
  Sheets 4 and 5: 1854
  Sheets 6, 7, and 8: 1856
  Sheet 9: n.d.
  Sheet 10: n.d.; 2d ed., 1856
  Sheet 11: 1856
Pacific Ocean, North
  Sheet 1: not issued although base chart printed in 1853
  Sheet 2: 1851
  Sheet 3: 1850
  Sheet 4: n.d.
  Sheet 5: 1849
  Sheets 6, 7, 8, and 9: n.d.
  Sheet 10: 1852
  Sheet 11: 1852
Pacific Ocean, South
  Sheets 1, 2, 3, and 4: not issued
  Sheet 5: 1852
  Sheets 6 and 7: not issued
  Sheet 8: n.d.
  Sheet 9: n.d., 2d ed., 1856
  Sheet 10: n.d.

Wind and Current Charts, Series B. Trade Wind Charts
Atlantic Ocean, 35.3" x 24.1". 1851, repr. 1858.
Indian Ocean, Monsoon and Trade Wind Chart. 17.3" x 35.4". 1859.

Wind and Current Charts, Series C. Pilot Charts. 35.3" x 24.1"
Atlantic Ocean, North
  Sheet 1: 1849; 2d ed., 1853; 2d ed., enl. and impr., 1857
Atlantic Ocean, South
  Sheet 1: 1850; 2d ed., 1853; 2d ed., enl. and impr., 1857
  Sheet 2: 1850; 2d ed., 1853; 2d ed., enl. and impr., 1857
Brazil
  Sheet 1: 1849; 1852; 1854
Cape Horn
  Sheets 1 and 2: 1852

Indian Ocean, North
    Sheets 1 and 2: 1853; 1855. These superseded Sheets 1 and 2 of North Pacific Ocean, were printed as one chart in 1855.
Indian Ocean, South
    Sheets 1 and 2: 1853. These were the same as Sheets 1 and 2 of South Pacific Pilot Charts of 1853.
    Sheet 3: 1859
Pacific Ocean, North
    Sheets 1 and 2: same as North Indian Ocean Sheets 1 and 2, 1853
    Sheet 3: 1853
    Sheets 4, 5, and 6: 1852
Pacific Ocean, South
    Sheets 1 and 2: 1853. These were the same as South Indian Ocean Pilot Charts of 1853.
    Sheet 1: 1854
    Sheet 3: 2d ed., 1856. See Explanation below.
    Area 4: 1859; First issued in 1859 as Sheet 1
    Sheet 5: 1855; issued in 1856 as Sheet 2
    Sheet 6: 1851; reissued as 2d ed. 1856 but renumbered Sheet 3
Explanation of the system Maury used to number his Pilot Charts of the South Pacific: Originally, this series was to consist of 6 sheets, Sheets 1, 2, and 3 to cover the South Indian Ocean and Sheets 4, 5, and 6 to cover the South Pacific Ocean. However, when Sheets 1 and 2 of the South Pacific were printed in 1853, they were also reprinted as Sheets 1 and 2 of the South Indian Ocean. Sheet 3, covering the third area, was not printed until 1859, and then in the South Indian Ocean Series only. A Pilot Chart covering what was to have been the fifth area was first issued about 1855 as Sheet 5 of the South Pacific Series, then again in 1856 as Sheet 2. A Pilot Chart for the sixth area was originally issued as Sheet 6 in 1851, but when reissued in 1856, as a second edition, it was renumbered Sheet 3 of the South Pacific Series.

Although Sheets 1 and 2 of the Pilot Charts of the North Pacific were superseded in 1855 by Sheets 1 and 2 of the North Indian Ocean Series, the remaining North Pacific sheets were not renumbered.

Wind and Current Charts, Series D. Thermal Sheets. 35.3" x 24.1"
Atlantic Ocean, North
    Sheet 1: 1850; 1852
    Sheets 2 to 8: n.d.
Atlantic Ocean, South
    Sheet 1: 1852
    Sheets 2 to 4: n.d. (1854)
    Sheets 5 and 6: not issued

Wind and Current Charts, Series E. Storm and Rain Charts. 35.3" x 24.1"
Atlantic Ocean, North   1853
Atlantic Ocean, South   1854
Pacific Ocean, North   1860 24.1" x 28.5"
Pacific Ocean, South   not issued

Matthew Fontaine Maury

MISCELLANEOUS CHARTS AND MAPS

Whale Chart of the World, Series F (of Wind and Current Charts). 24.1" x 35.8"
  Sheet 1: 1852
  Sheets 2, 3, and 4: n.d.

Chart showing favorite resort of sperm and right whale, by M. F. Maury, constructed from Maury's *Whale Chart of the World* by Robert H. Wyman.
  23.4" x 36.6". 1853(?); 2d ed., 1853; re-engraved 1859.

Orographic Map of the North Atlantic Ocean, 1852, in *Sailing Directions,* 5th
  ed., 1853. Gives a profile of the bottom of the ocean between America and
  Europe near the parallel of 39° north latitude. This map was in conjunction with the Bathymetrical Chart below.

*Chart of cruise of American Expedition in search of Sir John Franklin in 1850
  and 1851,* fitted out by Henry Grinnell, commanded by E. J. De Haven,
  brig *Advance,* Lt. De Haven, schooner *Rescue,* S. P. Griffin. Compiled by
  George P. Welsh under direction of M. F. Maury from materials in Bureau of Ordnance and Hydrography. 23.6" x 25". c. 1853.

*Bathymetrical Map of the North Atlantic Basin with Contour Lines drawn in
  at 1,000, 2,000, 3,000, and 4,000 fathoms.* This map, the first of this type
  published was originally drawn in 1852, first published in 5th ed. of *Sailing
  Directions,* 1853. Improved version published in Maury's *Physical Geography of the Sea,* 1855.

Chart showing two steamer lanes each twenty miles wide, North Atlantic. Publ.
  at expense of New York Board of Underwriters, New York, 1855.

Orographic profiles showing telegraphic plateau along Maury's proposed route.
  In Maury's *Sailing Directions,* 8th ed., 1858, Vol. I, Chap. XIII.

*Chart of the Winds; Thermal and Tidal Chart; Map of the Currents of the Sea
  and Drainage of the Land; Hyetographic or Rain Chart; Isothermal Lines
  Chart,* all published c. 1873 but not by U.S. Navy Hydrographic Office.

See Geography section for other maps and charts.

Abstract Log for the Use of American Navigators. (Interpreted *Wind and Current Chart* publ. 1847.) Washington: C. Alexander, 1848; 2d ed., 1848, repr.
  1849.

"Observations Accompanying Wind and Current Charts of the North Atlantic,"
  British Association for Advancement of Science Reports, Part 2, London,
  1848, pp. 34-36.

"Contributions of the Navy to Science and Commerce," Address delivered to
  Association of American Geologists and Naturalists Annual Meeting, Boston, July (?), 1847, *De Bow's Review,* Vol. V, No. 1 (January, 1848), pp.
  64-68.

"On the Winds and Currents of the Ocean," *American Association for the Advancement of Science Proceedings,* 1848, pp. 64-68; also *Am. Jour. Science,*
  2d Ser., Vol. VI, No. 19 (November, 1848), pp. 399-401.

"On the Currents of the Atlantic Ocean," *AAAS Proceedings,* Charleston, S.C.,
  1850, pp. 74-80.

Notice to Mariners (considered 1st ed. of *Explanations and Sailing Directions
  to Accompany the Wind and Current Charts*). Washington, D.C.: C. Alexander, 1850, 18 pp.; 2d ed., 1850, 51 pp. (considered 2d ed. of *Explanations and Sailing Directions*). See *Check List of U.S. Public Documents,
  1789-1909,* Vol. I, p. 778.

"On the Influence Arising from the Discovery of the Gulf Stream on the Commerce of Charleston," *AAAS Proceedings,* Charleston, S.C., March 12, 1850, pp. 17-20; *Explanations and Sailing Directions,* 3d ed., 1851, pp. 25-37; 4th ed., 1852, pp. 43-46.

"Southern Commerce as Influenced by the Gulf Stream," *De Bow's Review,* Vol. IX, No. 4 (October, 1850), pp. 439-449.

"On the Currents of the Atlantic and the Existence of the North-West Passage," *New Philosophical Journal,* Edinburgh, Vol. LI (April-October, 1851), pp. 51-55.

"The Cruise of the Taney—deep sea soundings," *Explanations and Sailing Directions,* 3d ed., 1851, pp. 57-70; 4th ed., 1852, pp. 125-139.

"On the Habits of the Whale," (given by title only) *AAAS Proceedings,* Albany, N.Y., 1851, p. 312; "Important Notice to Whalemen" (dated April 16, 1851), *Hunt's Merchants' Magazine,* Vol. XXIV, No. 6 (June, 1851), pp. 773-777.

Explanations and Sailing Directions to Accompany the Wind and Current Charts (cited hereafter as *Sailing Directions*). For 1st and 2d ed., see *Notice to Mariners* (above). 3d ed., 1851; 4th ed., 1852; 5th ed., 1853, all published by C. Alexander, Washington. 6th ed. published by E. C. and J. Biddle, Philadelphia, 1854. 7th ed., 1855, and Vol. I of 8th ed. published by William A. Harris, Washington, 1858. Vol. II of 8th ed. published by Cornelius Wendell, Washington, 1859. In above see especially re charts: Wind and Current, 1851, pp. 3-25; Currents of the Sea, 1851, pp. 38-42, and 1852, pp. 46-51; Storm and Wind, 1851, pp. 91-93, and 1852, pp. 191-193; Pilot, 1851, pp. 112-116, and 1852, pp. 193-198; Thermal, 1851, pp. 116-135, and 1852, pp. 198-217; Track, 1851, pp. 135-136, and 1852, pp. 217-218; Trade Wind, 1851, pp. 136-142, and 1852, pp. 218-230; Whale, 1851, pp. 177-212, and 1852, pp. 234-273. See also: Routes to and from Europe (letter to Secretary of Navy, Jan. 1, 1850), 1852, pp. 270-285; On the Saltness of the Sea, 1852, pp. 51-62.

Investigations of the Winds and Currents of the Sea. Repr. from *Appendix to Washington Astronomical Observations for 1846* (pp. 41-164). Washington: C. Alexander, 1851.

Report on the Harbor of Charleston, S.C. Prof. A. D. Bache, Lieuts. C. H. Davis, J. N. Maffitt, M. F. Maury, U.S.N., S. D. Kurtz, U.S.E. Charleston, S.C.: Councell and Daggett, 1852.

"The Sea and the Circulation of Its Waters," *Hunt's Merchants' Magazine,* Vol. XXVIII, No. 4 (April, 1853), pp. 412-419.

Letter stressing advantages of his Wind and Current Charts to vessels sailing from Atlantic to Pacific and requesting regular employment of vessels to carry out his investigations. Senate Exec. Doc. No. 1, pp. 60-61, 32d Cong., 1st Sess.; *Hunt's Merchants' Magazine,* Vol. XXIII, No. 1 (July, 1850), pp. 114-115.

Report on Naval Observatory, Oct. 12, 1852, regarding investigations of winds and currents of the sea and other phenomena affecting commerce and navigation. Senate Exec. Doc., No. 1, Vol. II, pp. 341-342, Series 659, 32d Cong., 2d Sess.

Letter to Capt. L. McKay, July 28, 1852, offering new charts and sailing directions from the equator to San Francisco and predicting a 103-day voyage for *Sovereign of the Seas* from New York to San Francisco if used. *Hunt's Merchants' Magazine,* Vol. XXVIII, No. 2 (February, 1853), p. 246.

Abstract Log for the Merchant Service, Wind and Current Charts. Philadelphia: E. C. and J. Biddle, 1854.

Abstract Log for Men of War. Philadelphia: E. C. and J. Biddle, 1855.

Sailing Directions from the Sea to Sandy Hook. Publ. separately by authority of the Hon. J. C. Dobbin, Secretary of Navy. Philadelphia: E. C. and J. Biddle, May, 1855.

Lanes for the Steamers Crossing the Atlantic, compiled by Maury, publ. by Board of Underwriters, New York, 1855. 12-page booklet with map, chart.

Physical Geography of the Sea

American Editions

Physical Geography of the Sea. New York: Harper and Brothers, 1st ed., 1855; 2d, 3d, 4th and 5th eds. (actually reprints), all 1855; rev. and enl., 1856; enl., 1857; 1858; rev. and enl., 1859; rev. and enl., 1861; rev. and enl., 1871. Cambridge, Mass.: Harvard Univ. Press, 1963 (re-issue of 1861 ed.).

British Editions

Physical Geography of the Sea and Its Meteorology (fuller title used in England). 1st ed., 1855; 2d (enl.) ed., 1855; rev. 3d ed., 1858; rev. and enl., 1859; 1860; 1861; 1864; 1869; 1872; (1883), all published by Sampson Low, Son and Co., London. Rev., enl. ed. with rev. charts also published in London by T. Nelson and Sons, 1859. (Some editions not found but the 1883 ed. bore the imprint "19th edition.")

Dutch Edition

Natuurkundige Beschrijving der Zeen. Vertaald door M. H. Jansen. Dordrecht: P. K. Braat, 1855.

German Editions

Die Physische Geographie des Meeres. Deutsch bearbeitet von Dr. C. Boettger. Leipzig: G. Mayer, 1856; 2d ed., 1859.

French Editions

Géographie Physique de la Mer. Traduit par P. A. Terquem. Paris: J. Correard, 1858; rev. et completée 2d ed., 1861.

Géographie Physique de la Mer. Traduit par P. F. Zurcher et Elie Margollé. Paris: Hetzel, 1865; 2d ed., 1868.

Extrait de la Géographie Physique (de la mer). Traduit par M. E. Tricault. Paris: Paul Dupont, 1858.

Italian Edition

Geografia Fisica del Mare e sua Meteorologia di M. F. Maury. Versione Italiana dalla 14 ed. inglese, autorizzata dell'autore, del luogotenente Luigi Gatta. Roma: E. Loescher, 1872.

Report of the voyage of the U.S. Ship Arctic in 1856 across the Atlantic Ocean between St. John's, Newfoundland, and the coast of Ireland for the purpose of ascertaining the practicability of laying telegraphic cable between America and Europe to Sec. of the Navy. Washington, 1856. Contains report of Lieut. O. H. Berryman, Commanding the *Arctic,* to the Secretary of Navy and the report of Lieut. Maury on examination of specimens obtained from the bed of the Atlantic by Lieut. Berryman.

Observations sur les Navigations des Paquebots qui Traversent l'Atlantique. Routes à suivre pour éviter les abordages du mer. Paris: Leydoque, 1856. Repr. from *Annales Hydrographiques.*

"On the Gulf Streams and Currents of the Sea," *Nautical Magazine,* London, Vol. XXVIII (October, 1859), pp. 514-524.

Steam Lanes Across the Atlantic. U.S. Hydrographic Office, Publication No. 40. Government Printing Office, Washington, 1872; repr. from data on subject in *Sailing Directions,* 7th ed., Philadelphia, 1855, and 8th ed., Vol. II, Washington, 1859.

METEOROLOGY OF SEA AND LAND

"The Currents of the Sea as Connected with Meteorology," *Association of American Geologists and Naturalists Proceedings,* Washington, May 14, 1844.

"Influence of Winds on Plants," *Western Jour. and Civilian* (1850), Vol. IV, No. 5 (August, 1850), pp. 315-324.

"On the General Circulation of the Atmosphere," *AAAS Proceedings,* Charleston, S.C., 1850, pp. 126-147; *Sailing Directions,* 3d ed., 1851, pp. 42-57; 4th ed., 1852, pp. 62-78.

"Circulation of the Atmosphere," *Western Jour. and Civilian,* Vol. VI (April, 1851), pp. 16-33. *Sailing Directions,* 3d ed., 1851, pp. 143-172.

"On the Probable Relation Between Magnetism and the Circulation of the Atmosphere, Especially the Trade Winds," *New Phil. Jour.,* Vol. LI (1851), pp. 271-292.

"On the Probable Relation Between Magnetism and the Circulation of the Atmosphere." Letter to the Hon. William A. Graham, Secretary of Navy, Jan. 30, 1851. *Appendix Washington Astronomical Observations for 1846-1851,* pp. 74-88; repr. by C. Alexander, Washington, 1851; *Sailing Directions,* 3d ed., 1851, pp. 157-172; 4th ed., 1852, pp. 90-104.

"Red Fogs and Sea Dust," *Sailing Directions,* 3d ed., 1851, pp. 149-157; 4th ed., 1852, pp. 78-90.

"On the Geological Agency of the Winds," *AAAS Proceedings,* Albany, N.Y., 1851, pp. 277-296; *Sailing Directions,* 4th ed., 1852, pp. 111-125.

"On the Clouds and the Equatorial Cloud Ring," *AAAS Proceedings,* Albany, N.Y., 1851, pp. 160-167; *New Phil Jour.,* Vol. LIII (1852), pp. 92-94; *Annual of Scientific Discovery,* Boston, 1852, pp. 387-389; *Sailing Directions,* 3d ed., 1851, pp. 172-177; 4th ed., 1852, pp. 105-111; 8th ed., 1858, Vol. I, Chap. VI, "Equatorial Cloud Ring," pp. 53-59.

On the Establishment of a Universal System of Meteorological Observations by Sea and Land. Correspondence of Maury and others. Compiled by Maury. Washington: C. Alexander, 1851.

"Observations on Atmospheric Pressure," *Am. Jour. Science,* Vol. XVI, No. 47 (September, 1853), pp. 294-296.

"Sur la Dépression Barométrique Observée à la Hauteur du Cap Horn," *Bulletin Academie Royale . . . de Belgique,* Brussels, Vol. XXI (1854), pp. 72-73.

"Barometric Anomalies about the Andes," *Am. Jour. Science,* Vol. XIX, No. 57 (May, 1855), pp. 385-391.

"Cartas de vientos y corrientes de F. Maury [sic], recopilado y traducido por Cesareo Fernandez," *Cron. Naval de España,* Vol. II (1855), pp. 84-105.

"An Appeal to the Agricultural Interests of Virginia" (to support Maury's plan for meteorology for farmers), *Southern Planter and Farmer,* Vol. XV, No. 6 (June, 1855), pp. 161-163.

"Meteorology for the Farmers," *American Farmer,* Vol. XI, No. 2 (August, 1855), pp. 33-35.

"Agricultural Meteorology." Address to U.S. Agricultural Society, Washington, Jan. 10, 1856. Substance reported in *Annual Report, U.S. Agricultural Society, 1856.*

Report of the Committee on Agriculture, Senator James Harlan, Ind. In favor of S481 to extend to the land the system of observations carried on at the National Observatory. Presented Dec. 18, 1856. 10 pp. Inspired by and largely written by Maury. Senate Rep. No. 292, Series 891, Vol. I, 34th Cong., 3d Sess.

"The Great Snow Storm of January, 1857," *Southern Planter and Farmer,* Vol. XVII, No. 3 (March, 1857), pp. 136-139.

Gales in the Atlantic: Wind and Current Charts. Washington: National Observatory, May, 1857.

Lettre à M. Ch. Sainte-Claire Deville, sur quelques causes particulières qui peuvent influencer la température des eaux à la surface de la mer. *Comptes Rendus des Séances de l'Académie des Sciences,* Paris, Vol. XLVII (1858), pp. 72-74.

Service Hydrographique. Instructions nautiques destinées à accompagner les cartes de vents et de courants. Par. M. F. Maury. Traduit par Ed. Vaneechout, L. de Vaisseau. Paris, 1859.

De la nécessité d'un Système Générale d'Observations Nautiques et Météorologiques. Lettre de M. F. Maury à M. Ad. Quetelet. *Extrait des Bulletins de l'Académie Royale de Belgique,* 2nd Sér., Tome IX, No. 5. 20-page pamphlet. Brussels: M. Hayez, 1860.

"On the Climates of the Antarctic Regions as indicated by observations upon the height of the barometer and direction of the winds at sea," *Brit. AAS Reports,* Part 2 (1860), pp. 46-48.

Projet de conférence internationale, pour étendre sur le globe entier le système des observations météorologiques adopté pour la mer dans la conférence de 1853. Brussels: *Acad. Science Bulletin,* Vol. IX (1860), pp. 415-435.

Letter dated April 10 (?), 1861, from Comdr. Maury of the United States, urging the importance of an expedition to the antarctic for meteorological and other scientific purposes, *Brit. AAS Reports,* Part 2 (1861), pp. 65-72.

Lettre de M. F. Maury à M. Mercier, Ambassadeur de France aux États-Unis datée du 10 Avril, 1861, et traitant principalement la question du climat au pôle sud, *Annales Hydrographiques,* 1862, p. 150. (See also: "Une Page d'Histoire et d'Actualité," incl. selections from letter of Maury.) *Extrait du Bulletin de la Société Belge d'Astronomie,* No. 12 (1903).

Nautical Monographs

No. 1. *The Winds at Sea: their mean direction and annual average duration from each of the four quarters.* Washington, 1859.

No. 2. *The Barometer at Sea.* Washington, March, 1861.

No. 3. *The Southeast Trade Winds of the Atlantic.* Washington, 1861.

"The Organization of a Telegraphic Meteorological Bureau." Paper by Maury read for him by a European scientific colleague before the International Congress for the Advancement of Geographical Knowledge, St. Petersburg, Russia, Summer, 1872. See *Proceedings* thereof.

Météorologique Nautique. Vents et Courants, Routes Générales, Extrait des Sailing Directions de Maury, et des travaux les plus récents, par M. Charles Ploix, Ministère de la Marine et des Colonies, France. Paris: Didot Frères, 1863.

Address Urging Establishment of a Telegraphic Meteorological Bureau, given before the fair of the Agricultural and Mechanical Society of Memphis, Tenn., Oct. 17, 1871 (10-page pamphlet). Memphis: *Appeal* Job Office, 1871. See Chap. XXIII and Notes of this biography for location of newspaper reports and MS copies of Maury's other addresses on this subject.

"Resolutions drawn by Commodore Maury and lately adopted by the Agricultural and Mechanical Society of Memphis, approved and adopted by the National Agricultural Society, Aug. 3, 1871, looking to an international conference for devising a uniform and general system of meteorological observations and crop reports." *Southern Planter and Farmer*, Vol. XXXII, No. 11 (November, 1871), pp. 653-654.

Letter to Capt. Henry Toynbee (head of Meteorological Dept., Board of Trade, London) describing a meteorographic model, dated June 21, 1871. *Quarterly Jour. of Royal Meteorological Society*, Vol. III (1877), pp. 299-302.

Address on crop and weather forecasts at St. Louis Agricultural and Mechanical Association Fair, Oct. 9, 1872. St. Louis *Democrat*, Oct. 10, 1872; also in *Twelfth Annual Report of St. Louis Agricultural and Mechanical Association*, Jefferson City, Mo., 1873.

Mémoires Originaux sur la Circulation Générale de l'Atmosphere. Par Hadley, Halley, Maury, Ferrell, W. Siemens, Möller, Oberbeck, von Helmholtz. Annotés et commentés par M. Brillouin. Paris: Carré et Naud, 1900.

NAVY REFORM AND NEED FOR NAVAL ACADEMY
(The magazine articles were written by Maury under pseudonyms)

Harry Bluff—nine articles, Richmond, *Whig and Public Advertiser*, Aug. 10, 13, 14, 17, 18, 25, 27, 28, Sept. 4, 1838, all on either p. 1 or 2.

Letters from Will Watch to his old messmate Harry Bluff, Richmond *Whig and Public Advertiser*, Dec. 21, 25, 28, 1838.

"Scraps from the Lucky Bag," by Harry Bluff. No. 1, *SLM*, Vol. VI, No. 4 (April, 1840), pp. 233-240; No. 2, *SLM*, Vol. VI, No. 5 (May, 1840), pp. 306-320; No. 3, *SLM*, Vol. VI, No. 12 (December, 1840), pp. 786-800, No. 4, *SLM*, Vol. VII, No. 1 (January, 1841), pp. 3-25; "Supplement to Scraps from the Lucky Bag," *SLM*, Vol. VII, No. 2 (February, 1841), pp. 169-170; "More Scraps from the Lucky Bag," *SLM*, Vol. VII, Nos. 5 and 6 (May and June, 1841), pp. 345-379.

"Letters to Mr. Clay," by Union Jack, *SLM*, Vol. VII, No. 10 (October, 1841), pp. 724-729.

"The Navy and the West," *SLM*, Vol. IX, No. 1 (January, 1843), pp. 1-5.

Extract from treatise by Lieut. Maury on maritime interests of South and West. House Doc. No. 33, Series 441, Vol. III, pp. 20-48, 28th Cong., 1st Sess.

Navy Yard and Depot at the city of Memphis. Report from the House Committee on Naval Affairs, presented in the House by Representative Peyton of Tennessee, Jan. 31, 1844. Report, written by Maury, included much of his earlier material on scheme for rebuilding Southern commerce, included one chart by him. House Rep. No. 120, Ser. 488, 28th Cong., 1st Sess.

"Another Scrap from the Lucky Bag—Lake Defences and Western Interests," *SLM*, Vol. XI, No. 2 (February, 1845), pp. 83-91.

"To the Memphis Convention," *SLM*, Vol. XI, No. 10 (October, 1845), pp. 577-602. An article written under the pen name Harry Bluff in which Maury sought to call the attention of the Memphis economic convention to the following subjects: a ship canal between the Mississippi and the Great Lakes, bread for the Navy, a school for ship engineers, mail and snag-boats, river marks, the New Orleans bar, lighthouses on the Florida and Gulf coast, the warehousing system and direct trade with the South, a monthly mail to Oregon.

ASTRONOMY

Astronomical Observations made during the year 1845 at the National Observatory, Washington, under the direction of M. F. Maury, A.M., Lt. U.S.N., superintendent, Vol. I. Washington: J. and G. S. Gideon, 1846.

Astronomical Observations made under the direction of M. F. Maury, Lt. U.S.N., at the U.S. Naval Observatory, Washington. Vol. I. Washington: J. and G. S. Gideon, 1846.

Astronomical Observations made during the year 1846 at the National Observatory, Washington. Under the direction of M. F. Maury, Lt. U.S.N., superintendent. Vol. II. Washington: C. Alexander, 1851.

Astronomical Observations made during the year 1847 at the National Observatory, Washington, under the direction of M. F. Maury, LL.D., Lt. U.S.N., superintendent. Vol. III. Washington: C. Alexander, 1853.

Astronomical Observations made during the year 1848 at the U.S.N. Observatory, Washington, under the direction of M. F. Maury, LL.D., Lt. U.S.N., superintendent. Vol. IV. Washington: A. O. P. Nicholson, 1856.

Astronomical Observations made during the years 1849 and 1850 at the U.S. Naval Observatory, Washington . . . by M. F. Maury, LL.D., U.S.N., superintendent of U.S. Observatory and Hydrographical Office. Vol. V. Washington: Cornelius Wendel, 1859.

"Duplicity of Biela's Comet," *Royal Astronomical Society Monthly Notices* (cited hereafter as *Roy. Astr. Soc. Mon. Not.*), London, Vol. VII (1845-1847), pp. 90-91.

"Observations of the June Comet, of Encke's and Biela," Maury and Sears C. Walker, *Astronomische Nachrichten* (cited hereafter as *Astr. Nachr.*), Vol. XXIV (1846), cols. 133-146.

Refraction and Other Tables, prepared for the reduction of observations at the National Observatory, Washington, Lt. M. F. Maury, U.S.N., superintendent. Washington: J. and G. S. Gideon, 1846.

"Observations on Neptune," *Astr. Nachr.*, Vol. XXV (1847), cols. 397-400.

"Observations of Hebe," *Roy. Astr. Soc. Mon. Not.*, Vol. VIII (1847-1848), pp. 40-41.

"National Observatory," letter to John Quincy Adams, *SLM*, Vol. XIV, No. 1 (January, 1848), pp. 4-10.

"The U.S. Naval Observatory at Washington," *American Almanac*, 1848, pp. 67-71.

Circular prepared by the direction of the Hon. William Ballard Preston, Sec. of Navy, in relation to the Astronomical Expedition to Chile, by Lt. M. F. Maury, U.S.N., superintendent of the National Observatory, Washington. Washington: C. Alexander, 1849. (*Astronomical Pamphlets*, Vol. III, No. 14.)

"National Observatory," *SLM*, Vol. XV, No. 5 (May, 1849), pp. 304-308. Address to the Virginia Historical Society, Dec. 14, 1848, repr. from *Virginia Historical Register* (1849), Vol. II, pp. 85-96.

"Petersen's Third Comet," *Roy. Astr. Soc. Mon. Not.*, Vol. X (1849-1850), pp. 164-167.

"Observations of Petersen's Comet of 1850," *Astr. Nachr.*, Vol. XXXI (1851), cols. 257-262.

Report on the Work of the Naval Observatory from July 1, 1846-Jan. 1, 1850. Washington, 1851.

"On the Variable Light of Clio," *Astronomical Jour.*, Cambridge, Mass., Vol. I (1851), p. 188.

"Mittlere Öerter für 1850, o von Vergleichsternen zu den Washingtoner Beobachtungen des Enckeschen Cometen," Nr. 805 der A. N., *Astr. Nachr.*, Vol. XXXIV (1852), cols. 277-278.

"Observations of Irene," *Astr. Jour.*, Vol. II (1852), p. 23.

"On a Supposed Missing Star," *Astr. Jour.*, Vol. II (1852), p. 53.

"On the Missing Star of October, 1850," *Astr. Jour.*, Vol. II (1852), p. 91.

"Solar Eclipse of 28th of July, 1851," *Astr. Jour.*, Vol. II (1852), pp. 49-53.

Tables for facilitating the reduction of the apparent right ascensions and declinations of the fixed stars to their mean places, together with a general table for annual precessions. From *Appendix to the Washington Astronomical Observations for 1847*, pp. 33-116. Washington: C. Alexander, 1853.

"Über einen neuentdecketen Planeten," *Wien. Sitzungsberichte*, Akademie der Wissenschaften, Vol. XIV (1854), pp. 292-293.

"Apparent right-ascension of the moon's limb and of moon culminating stars, observed with transit instrument of the observatory, Washington," *Astr. Nachr.*, Vol. LII (1860), cols. 197-202; Vol. LIII (1860), cols. 103-108.

"Entdeckung eines neuen Planeten," *Astr. Nachr.*, Vol. LIV (1860), cols. 95-96.

"Observations of Leda, Polyhymnia, Mnemosyne, and Pandora," *Astr. Nachr.*, Vol. LII (1860), cols. 233-234.

Zones of Stars Observed at the National Observatory, Washington . . . by Commander M. F. Maury, LL.D., superintendent. Vol. I, Part 1 (containing the zones observed with the meridian circle in 1846). Washington: George W. Bowman, 1860.

"Apparent right-ascensions of the moon's limb and of moon-culminating stars," *Astr. Jour.*, Vol. VI (1861), pp. 84, 98-99.

ATLANTIC CABLE

Explanations and Sailing Directions to Accompany the Wind and Current Charts, 4th ed., 1852, pp. 125-190; 6th ed., 1854, chapter on "Physical Geography of Sea"; 8th ed., 1858, Vol. I, pp. 113-166, 167-179, 180-199; 8th ed., 1859, Vol. II, pp. 151-155.

"Submarine Telegraph Across the Atlantic," *De Bow's Review*, Vol. XVI, No. 6 (June, 1854), pp. 626-628.

"On the Construction of a Submarine Transatlantic Telegraph," *Annual of Scientific Discovery, 1855,* pp. 161-162.

Introduction and Chap. XII of *Physical Geography of the Sea.* 1st ed., New York, 1855.

The Annual Address delivered before the Maryland Institute for the Promotion of the Mechanic Arts, Maryland Agricultural Society, Oct. 25, 1855. Pamphlet. Baltimore, 1856.

Nautical Directions for Sailing from Valentia to Newfoundland. Letter to Cyrus W. Field advising on weather and route for cable, dated March 28, 1857. London, 1857.

"Das Telegraphen-Plateau des Nord-Amerikan Atlantischen Ozeans," *Petermann's Mittheilungen,* December, 1857, pp. 507-508.

"The Atlantic Telegraph-Cable," *Jour. of the Royal Society of Dublin,* Vol. II (1858-1859), pp. 221-229.

Letter to John Locke, Esquire, December 29, 1858, read before the Royal Dublin Society, Friday, January 28, 1859. Rogers' electric cord and deep sea telegraph line. . . . 16-page pamphlet. Washington, 1859.

"Deep-sea Telegraphic Cord." Letter to Cromwell F. Vartery, Electrician, etc., London, dated Sept. 8, 1869, *Educational Jour. of Virginia,* Vol. I (1869-1870), pp. 16-19.

See text and Notes, Chap. XII, for unprinted material on Atlantic cable.

GEOGRAPHY

"Geography of Commerce," *De Bow's Review,* Vol. XV, No. 4 (October, 1853), pp. 385-400.

"Progress of Geographical Science." Address delivered at annual meeting, 1854, of American Geographical and Statistical Society (cited hereafter as Am. Geog. and Statis. Soc.). *Am. Geog. and Statis. Soc. Bull.,* Vol. I, Part 3 (1854), pp. 1-31; *De Bow's Review,* Vol. XVII, No. 6 (December, 1854), pp. 569-593.

Physical Geography for Schools and General Readers. Longmans and Co., London: 1864.

First Lessons in Geography. Richardson and Co., New York: 1868; 2d ed., New York: University Publishing Co., 1871.

The World We Live In. New York: Richardson and Co., 1868; 2d ed., University Publishing Co., 1871.

Manual of Geography. A Complete treatise on Mathematical, Physical & Political Geography. New York: University Publishing Co., 1870, rev. eds., 1880, 1887, 1891, 1893, 1895, 1899, 1906; American Book Co., 1925.

See also *Physical Geography of the Sea* under "Navigation and Oceanography" of this bibliography, Orographic Views of Central Asia, Central Europe, United States c. 1870. Maps: Africa, Europe, North America, Asia, South America, United States and part of Canada, the World; Political, Physical and Commercial Map of the World. All publ. by University Publishing Co., New York, c. 1872.

Map of the Principal Vegetable Growths; Map Showing Lines of Equal Magnetic Declination; Chart of Volcanoes; Chart Showing the Distribution of the Races; Map Showing the Geographical Distribution of Certain Minerals; Map of the Mountains and Rivers of the United States; Map of the World on the Globular Projection; Chart of the Principal Industrial Pur-

suits; *Map Showing the Geographical Distribution of Beasts, Birds and Fishes;* all published by University Publishing Co., New York, c. 1873.

Physical Geography. Rev. by Mytton Maury (different from above 1864 version). New York and Baltimore: University Publishing Co., 1873, 1883, 1888, 1891, 1903.

Le Monde ou Nous Vivons. Traduit de l'anglais par P. F. Zurcher et Elie Margollé. Paris, 1877.

Geography of Virginia, 1878 and 1882; *Geography of North Carolina,* 1882; *Special Geography of South Carolina,* 1884; *Geography of New York,* 1885; *Geography of Alabama,* 1888 (all supplements to above *Manual of Geography*). Publ. by University Publishing Co., New York.

Elementary Geography of M. F. Maury, LL.D. Rev. and abr. from *First Lessons* and *World We Live In.* New York: University Publishing Co., 1881.

Maury's Revised Elementary Geography. Rev. and abr. from *First Lessons* and *World We Live In.* New York: University Publishing Co., 1900; 2d ed., American Book Company, 1913, rev. eds., 1915, 1921, 1924.

New Complete Geography. New York and Boston: University Publishing Co., 1906; rev., American Book Co., 1909.

New Elements of Geography for Primary and Intermediate Classes. New York: American Book Company, 1907, 1908, 1911; rev. ed., 1921, 1922, 1925.

Maury-Simonds Physical Geography. M. F. Maury's text rev. and largely rewritten by Frederic W. Simonds, Ph.D., professor of geology, University of Texas. New York: American Book Co., 1908.

EDUCATION

Navy education, see "Scraps from the Lucky Bag" (by Maury, signed "Harry Bluff"), *SLM,* Vol. VI, No. 5 (May, 1840), pp. 306-320; Vol. VI, No. 12 (December, 1840), pp. 786-800. "Letters to Mr. Clay" (by Maury signed "Union Jack"), *SLM,* Vol. VII, No. 10 (October, 1841), letter 2, pp. 724-729.

Address before the Philodemic Society, Georgetown College, Washington, Aug. 28, 1846, at commencement. 16-page pamphlet. Washington: J. and G. S. Gideon, 1846.

["Rules of Conduct"] *Address delivered before the Literary Societies of the University of Virginia on the 28th June, 1855.* Richmond: H. K. Ellyson's Steam Presses, 1855. Extracts from same in Diana Maury Corbin, *Life of Matthew Fontaine Maury, U.S.N. and C.S.N.,* pp. 142-146. London, 1888.

"Address on the Study of Physical Geography," at the laying of the cornerstone of the University of the South, Sewanee, Tenn., Oct. 10, 1860, in *Documents and Proceedings . . . University of the South Prior to 1860,* ed. by the Rev. Telfair Hodgson, Ser. A, No. 1, Sewanee, Tenn., 1888, pp. 63-68.

Annual Address to the Graduating Class of the Virginia Military Institute, July 2, 1869. Lexington, Va., 1869.

Introductory Address before the Educational Association of Virginia, July 13, 1870, urging establishment of state polytechnic school for teaching all life sciences in complete manner, tuition to be free to any Southerner. *Educational Jour. of Virginia,* Vol. I, No. 10 (August, 1870), pp. 303-313.

"Astronomy for the Young Folk, the Moon with the Naked Eye," *The Cadet,* V.M.I., Vol. I (July, 1871).

What We Owe to Science. Lecture given at V.M.I., 1872. *The Cadet*, V.M.I., Vol. II (January, 1872).

EXPLORATION AND TRANSPORTATION DEVELOPMENT

"A Scheme for Rebuilding Southern Commerce. Direct Trade with the South" (by Maury but unsigned), *SLM*, Vol. V, No. 1 (January, 1839), pp. 3-12.

"Maritime Interests of the South and West" (by Maury but unsigned), *Southern Quarterly Review*, Vol. IV, No. 8 (October, 1849), pp. 309-346. Partially reprinted in *SLM*, Vol. XI, No. 11 (November, 1845), pp. 651-661.

"Lake Defences and Western Interests" (by Maury, signed "Harry Bluff"), *SLM*, Vol. XI (February, 1845), pp. 83-91. Reprinted in *Illinois Reports to Senate and House*, 1845, pp. 251-266.

"To the Memphis Convention," by Maury, signed "Harry Bluff," *SLM*, Vol. XI, No. 11 (November, 1845), pp. 577-602 in part. Sections are on The Ship Canal Between the Mississippi and the Lakes, Mail and Snag-Boats, River Marks, The New Orleans Bar, The Warehousing System and Direct Trade with the South, A Monthly Mail to Oregon.

"A Railroad from the Atlantic to the Pacific," *Hunt's Merchants' Magazine*, Vol. XVIII, No. 6 (June, 1848), pp. 592-601.

"Letter to the Hon. John C. Calhoun, March 29, 1848, on the best route across the country, for reaching by railroad, the Pacific Coast of U.S.," *De Bow's Review*, Vol. VI, No. 3 (September, 1848), pp. 205-214.

"Steam Navigation to China." See under "Navigation and Oceanography," this bibliography.

"The Dead Sea Expedition. Lieut. Lynch's circumnavigation of sea," *SLM*, Vol. XIV, No. 9 (September, 1848), pp. 547-553.

"The Isthmus Line to the Pacific," *SLM*, Vol. XV, No. 5 (May, 1849), pp. 259-266. Publ. as 7-page pamphlet by the National Observatory, Washington, 1849.

Letter of Maury opposing the Tehuantepec Railroad, Mexico, read to 1849 session of Congress, *De Bow's Review*, Vol. VII, No. 1 (July, 1849), pp. 16-17.

"Panama Railway and the Gulf of Mexico. Great Commercial Advantages of the Gulf of Mexico," *SLM*, Vol. XV, No. 8 (August, 1849), pp. 441-457.

"Address delivered as president before Pacific Railroad Convention, Memphis, Tenn., Oct. 23, 1849," *Minutes and Proceedings of Memphis Convention, October, 1849*, pp. 55-61; *Daily National Intelligencer*, Nov. 10, 1849.

"Communication with the Pacific" (advocating building of a ship canal and railroad across the Isthmus of Panama), Washington *Daily National Intelligencer*, Nov. 4, 1849.

Letter on the Post Road from Fort Smith to San Diego, April (n.d.), 1850, to accompany H.R. No. 492, March 3, 1851. House Rep. No. 95, pp. 1-5, 31st Cong., 2d Sess.

"Channel of the Mississippi River," *Western Jour. and Civilian*, 1851, Vol. VI, p. 368.

"The Commercial Prospects of the South." *Proceedings of the Virginia Mercantile Convention . . . Sept. 10, 11, 1851*. Richmond, Va., 1851. Repr. in *SLM*, Vol. XVII, Nos. 10-11 (October-November, 1851), pp. 686-698.

"Direct Foreign Trade of the South, Commercial Conventions," *De Bow's Review*, Vol. XII, No. 2 (February, 1852), pp. 126-148.

"On Extending the Commerce of the South and West by Sea." A letter dated Dec. 16, 1851, to Glendy Burke, committee, Southwestern Railroad Convention to be held in New Orleans in January, 1852, *De Bow's Review*, Vol. XII, No. 4 (April, 1852), pp. 381-399.

Letter to Henry Grinnell, president, American Geographical and Statistical Society, requesting suggestions relative to Ringgold Expedition to Bering Straits, *Am. Geog. and Statis. Soc. Bull.*, 1852, Vol. I (1852), pp. 82-83.

Memorial by Maury praying the establishment of a line of mail steamships from Norfolk to Charleston to Para, Brazil, to connect with a line running thence to Rio de Janeiro, May 3, 1852. Senate Misc. Doc. No. 83, Series 629, Vol. I, 32d Cong., 1st Sess.

The Amazon and the Atlantic Slopes of South America (on the cover the title is *The Valley of the Amazon*). A series of letters originally published in Washington *National Intelligencer*, Nov. 17 to Dec. 3, 1852, under signature of "Inca" (Maury's pseudonym). Rev. and cor. by author. Washington: Franck Taylor, 1853.

Letter to Daniel W. Fiske, general secretary, Am. Geog. and Statis. Soc., New York, on the Polar Exploring Expedition, *Am. Geog. and Statis. Soc. Papers, 1853-1868*, pp. 7-8.

"Shall the Valleys of the Amazon and the Mississippi Reciprocate Trade?" by Maury, signed "Inca," *De Bow's Review*, Vol. XIV, No. 2 (February, 1853), pp. 136-145.

El Rio Amazonas y las Comarcas que Forman su Hoya Vertientes Hacia el Atlantica. By Maury, signed "Manco-Capac." Lima, Peru: J. M. Monterola, 1853.

"Valley of the Amazon," No. I, *De Bow's Review*, Vol. XIV, No. 5 (May, 1853), pp. 449-460.

"Valley of the Amazon," No. II, *De Bow's Review*, Vol. XIV, No. 6 (June, 1853), pp. 556-567.

"Valley of the Amazon," No. III, *De Bow's Review*, Vol. XV, No. 1 (July, 1853), pp. 36-43.

Memorial on the Navigation of the Amazon, by Maury, February, 1854, in favor of free navigation of the Amazon River. House Misc. Doc., No. 22, Series 741, Vol. I, 33d Cong., 1st Sess.

"On the Remission of the Duties on Railroad Iron: Commercial Convention of the South," *De Bow's Review*, Vol. XVII, No. 3 (September, 1854), pp. 258-260.

El Rio Amazonas, las Regiones que Forman su Hoya y las Vertientes Atlanticas de Sud-America . . . , y tran. al castellano por Rafael Butillo. La Paz, Bolivia: E. Alarcón, 1854.

Abstract of letter enclosing tracing of U.S.S. *Vincennes* track to North Pacific Ocean, North Pacific Exploring Expedition, *Am. Geog. and Statis. Soc. Proceedings, 1855-57*, Vol. I, p. 16.

"Letter on the Southern Steamship Lines," *De Bow's Review*, Vol. XXII, No. 5 (May, 1857), pp. 513-514.

"On Antarctic Expeditions," *Brit. AAS Reports*, 1860, Part 2, pp. 44-46.

"On the physical geography of the sea, in connection with the antarctic regions," *Am. Geog. and Statis. Soc. Proceedings*, 1861, Vol. V, pp. 22-26.

"Report to Richmond and York River Railroad Company concerning the harbor of West Point, Virginia," extracts therefrom in *Prospectus of the Terminal Improvement Company of West Point, Va.* (n.p., n.d.), pp. 5-10.

Letter to Thomas P. Atkinson, M.D., Danville, Va., dated Nov. 17, 1869, concerning policy of land contributions, need and benefits of co-operation of all Virginia interests for certain great works with special reference to port of Norfolk in comparison to British ports. *Norfolk and Great Western R.R. Co. Proceedings, 3d Ann. Meet. Stockholders,* Dec. 2, 1869, pp. 24-29. Richmond: Evening News Steam Presses, 1870.

Letter to Capt. Bradford Pim, R.N., M.P., relating to link with Pacific across Panama or Nicaragua, July (n.d.), 1866. Senate Doc. No. 83, 58th Cong., 2d Sess.; also in *Am. Geog. and Statis. Soc. Jour.,* Vol. XI (1879), pp. 201-205; also in Van Nostrand's *Engineering Magazine,* Vol. XXII (January-June, 1880).

CIVIL WAR

Captain Maury's Letter on American Affairs. Letter to Rear Admiral Robert Fitzroy, R.N., London, August, 1861. 16-page pamphlet. Richmond, 1861.

Series of articles written under pseudonym "Ben Bow" urging Confederate government to build a navy without delay, especially a fleet of small steam launches armed with big guns, Richmond *Enquirer,* Sept. 27, Oct. 3, 1861, and subsequent issues.

Letter on conditions in the Confederate States and hopefulness of the Southern cause, *Times* (London), Dec. 22, 1862.

"A Vindication of Virginia and the South," *Southern Historical Society Papers,* Vol. I, No. 2 (February, 1876), pp. 49-61; reprinted under title "A Vindication of the South and of Virginia," Diana Corbin Maury, *Life of Matthew Fontaine Maury, U.S.N. and C.S.N.* (Appendix C), pp. 302-314.

Letter to Grand Duke Constantine, St. Petersburg, refusing invitation to pursue scientific career in Russia, Nov. 1, 1861, *Southern Historical Society Papers,* Vol. II (July, 1876), pp. 51-53.

Reports and letters—see *Official Records of the Union and Confederate Navies in the War of the Rebellion* citations in Chap. XIX-XX Notes of this biography.

MEXICO

Decrees for the Encouragement of Immigration and Colonization (drafted originally by Maury). Printed by order of M. F. Maury, Office of Colonization, Mexico, November, 1865. Mexico City, 1865. 16-page pamphlet.

Letter in response to inquiries about Mexico from prospective ex-Confederate immigrants. *De Bow's Review,* Vol. XXXII, No. 6 (June, 1866), pp. 624-630.

"Biografia de Monseñor Labastida," dirigida á si Majestad el Emperadoe por M. F. Maury in *Los Traidores Pintados por si Mismos.* Prologo y notas por Angel Pola. Biblioteca Reformista, Vol. I. Mexico: E. Publin, 1900.

VIRGINIA MILITARY INSTITUTE

Address at his installation as professor of physics, V.M.I., Sept. 10, 1868, including a commentary on the importance of science and a plea for co-operation on making physical survey of Virginia, *Southern Planter and Farmer,* Vol. XXVIII, No. 10 (October, 1868), pp. 633-638.

"An Appeal to the Public for Information on Virginia, Physical Survey of the State, Sept. 10, 1868," Richmond *Whig*, Sept. 28, 1868, pp. 2 and 3.

"The Augusta County Fair and Speech of Com. M. F. Maury," *Southern Planter and Farmer*, Vol. XXXVIII, No. 11 (November, 1868), pp. 698-704.

Physical Survey of Virginia. Geographical position of; its commercial advantages and national importance. December, 1868. Preliminary Report No. 1. Richmond: W. A. R. Nye, December, 1868. 2nd ed. New York: D. Van Nostrand, March, 1869.

An appeal to the county courts of Virginia to encourage immigration, letter written by Maury, signed by John Letcher, Board of Visitors, Virginia Military Institute, Lexington, 1869.

Physical Survey of Virginia. Her resources, climate and productions. Preliminary Report No. 2 . . . with notes and additions by his son, Richard L. Maury, July 1, 1877. Richmond: N. V. Randolph, 1878.

Lectures at V.M.I. See under "Education," this bibliography.

MISCELLANEOUS

"Notice of the Gold Veins of the United States Mine near Fredericksburg" (Virginia), *Am. Jour. Science*, Vol. XXXII (July, 1837), pp. 325-330.

"Description of an Alembic for Distilling Amalgam of Gold contrived by M. F. Maury, U.S.N.," *Am. Jour. Science*, Vol. XXXIII (January, 1838), pp. 66-70.

"The Right of Search" (by Maury, signed "Harry Bluff"), *SLM*, Vol. VIII, No. 4 (April, 1842), pp. 289-301.

"Our Relations with England," *SLM*, Vol. VIII, No. 6 (June, 1842), pp. 381-396.

A treatise on the subject of a Western depot and armory and touching generally the maritime interests of the South and West. 1843. House Doc. No. 33, Series 441, Vol. III, pp. 20-48, 28th Cong., 1st Sess.

"Right of Search" (not signed, possibly by another author), *Foreign Quarterly Review*, 1844, Vol. XXXV, pp. 211-252.

Logarithms of Sines, Cosines, Tangents . . . (to six places . . . and tables of proportional logarithms), repr. from Maury's *Navigation*. 60 pp. Philadelphia, 1845.

Letter to Secretary of War Charles M. Conrad on Land Defenses and Fortifications, written at request of Secretary of the Navy to be referred to House Committee on Military Affairs, 1851. House Exec. Doc. No. 5, Series 637, pp. 160-193, 32d Cong., 1st Sess.

"The Bible and Science," *Southern Churchman*, Jan. 22, 1855.

The Petition of Matthew Fontaine Maury to the Senate and House of Representatives in Congress Assembled. Washington, January, 1856 (17 pp. text, 18 pp. of appendices).

Memorial of Washington National Monument Society. Signed by J. B. H. Smith and M. F. Maury, in *Virginia Annual Reports for 1859*.

Letter from Maury read at Humboldt Commemoration, June 2, 1859, *Am. Geog. and Statis. Soc. Jour.*, Vol. I (1859), pp. 226-227.

A Description of the Elizabeth Furnace Iron Property, Augusta County, Virginia . . . with maps and a report by Commodore M. F. Maury, LL.D. Oxon (should have been Cambridge). Washington, 1869. The *Description* was written by Jedediah Hotchkiss.

Mesūkē 'eres . . . trans. from the English and supplemented with notes by Nahum Sokolov. Warsaw, 1878. 96 pp.

Matthew Fontaine Maury

Report of Lt. Matthew F. Maury on the loss of the U.S. Mail Steamer Central America *under the command of Commander William Lewis Herndon* (written Oct. 19, 1857). Washington, 1884.

See also Section II (Published Documents) of bibliography of this book for material in which Maury had a share of the writing or drafting.

Index

Index